CONCISE CATALOGUE

OF THE

TATE GALLERY COLLECTION

Tate Gallery

ISBN 1 85437 082 0

Published by order of the Trustees 1991

First published 1967
Second edition 1969
Third edition 1971
Fourth edition 1973
Fifth edition 1975
Sixth edition 1977
Seventh edition 1980
Eighth edition 1984
Ninth edition 1991

Published by Tate Gallery Publications and Documentation
and IT, Tate Gallery, Millbank, London SW1P 4RG
Typeset by Documentation and IT, Tate Gallery
Printed and bound in Great Britain by the Hillingdon Press,
Uxbridge, Middlesex, on Fineblade Smooth 130 gsm

Contents

Foreword   v

Introduction   vii

Explanations   viii

Concise Catalogue   1

Loans to the Tate Gallery   448

Works of art forming part of the fabric of the
Tate Gallery's Millbank building   453

Mixed groups: contributing artists   454

Concordance of former National Gallery
numbers to Tate Gallery numbers   456

Sources of reference for the Collection   458

Borrowing from the Collection –
conditions for loan   459

FOREWORD

The Tate Gallery is responsible for maintaining and developing the national collections of British Painting and of Twentieth-Century Painting and Sculpture. This catalogue provides a complete but compact reference to the Collection.

This edition gives details of all the works which were in the Collection on 31 March 1990. At that time the Collection contained 16,798 works, an increase of 3,837 on those listed in the last edition which was published in 1984.

The long interval between editions has been one of considerable endeavour for those members of our staff who are involved with the recording and documentation of the Collection. During the seven year period the Tate Gallery has moved from a manual, paper-based documentation practice to an automated, computer-based one. The exercise has provided a number of opportunities to review and add consistency to our core documentation. The review process has inevitably highlighted shortcomings in the information provided and the task of providing much of the improved or missing information has fallen to the curatorial and conservation staff, almost all of whom have contributed.

The conversion from manual to automated documentation practice and the amassing of corrections and additions to the data and the production of the copy for this ninth edition have been managed, at various stages and times, by Peter Wilson (Head of Gallery Services), Jonathan Mason (Registrar until 1988), Susan Liddell (Registrar from 1988), and by Graham Peters (Documentation Officer and IT Manager) who has designed and developed the collection database information systems and standards, and desktop publishing applications used for production of the copy.

The format and content of this edition reflects the thorough review of the information it contains and we present it not as a definitive catalogue but as an authoritative guide to the current state of documentation of our Collection. Full details of the changes incorporated and a guide to use follow in the Introduction and Explanations.

Our new procedures will enable further editions to follow at intervals of approximately two years. In the meantime, we hope that users will find this to be a helpful and thorough guide to the riches of the Tate Gallery Collection.

Nicholas Serota
Director

INTRODUCTION

The first complete listing of the Collection was published in 1967 as *The Collections of the Tate Gallery*. Within the Tate Gallery it and its successors have always been known as the 'Concise Catalogue' after the opening words of the foreword of that edition. The first edition pioneered the use of camera-ready copy - then typescript - and many of the conventions and abbreviations employed in that edition were designed to reduce each item entry to a single line. That method of production was abandoned several editions ago in favour of computer typeset text, new editions being produced from a single much-amended copy of the previous edition of the Concise Catalogue held in the Registrar's Office.

Since the last edition was published in 1984 the documentation of the Gallery's collection has undergone a radical change. The basis of this change has been the introduction of information technology (IT). The authoritative source of core collection documentation is now a series of data files held on the Gallery's computer network. The information held in this database computer is used throughout the Gallery for collections management, display labels and many other purposes. This edition represents a 'snapshot' of the state of the information held at 3 May 1991 for works of art acquired up to and including 31 March 1990. The production method has come full circle and this edition has once again been produced from camera-ready copy. Now, however, the source of the copy is constantly-updated information from the collection databases output and typeset in-house.

The new method of production, no longer constrained by the single line format, has allowed us to dispense with many of the abbreviation conventions of previous editions. The recording conventions are as close as possible to those employed in the Gallery's fuller catalogues. The sole exception is the encoded description of object type. We have decided to retain the system for this edition, having removed a few glaring inconsistencies and anomalies.

It has also been possible to expand the range of information provided in each entry. For example, group titles are recorded consistently for series of works and, where the Gallery's working titles or group titles are translations from a foreign language, the original language title is also given.

The introduction of IT has enabled us to improve the consistency of the information recorded - this is particularly noticeable in the 'credit line' which identifies the source of bequests, transfers and gifts.

EXPLANATIONS

The Concise Catalogue is ordered alphabetically by artists' surnames. Additional entries introduced for cross-referencing purposes should eliminate any difficulty for the user.

Accession number

Each artist's works appear in order of accession, with the exception of modern prints which appear in a separate sequence following other works. In general this means that works of art identified by N-prefixed accession numbers (for works acquired prior to the separation of the Tate Gallery from the National Gallery in 1954) are followed by those with T-prefixed accession numbers (works accessioned since 1954) and finally by modern prints with P-prefixed accession numbers. Finally, in exception to the above rules, come works of art identified by A-prefixed accession numbers: occasionally, in the past, groups of works were accessioned under one number, the individual items being identified by a subsequent letter or roman numeral. The numbering of these works has been rationalised to provide each with a unique number in a new sequence prefixed A. An appendix lists these changes in numbering.

British Collection and Modern Collection

Users of previous editions of the *Concise Catalogue* will note that the former practice of dividing the works into two sequences, British Collection and Modern Collection, has been abandoned. The collection to which the artist's works are assigned is now noted immediately after the artist's name and life dates.

Tate Gallery Archive

The appearance of the line 'Tate Gallery Archive holds material concerning this artist' has replaced the asterisk which preceded the artist's surname in previous editions.

Super group title

Very occasionally works of art form part of a 'super group': a group of groups of works of art (see below).

Group title

Works of art, particularly prints, are sometimes produced or known under a **group title.** The group title, group date (rarely applied) and accession numbers of works in the group (when in the collection) are given. When considered relevant, a statement of whether the Tate Gallery holding represents the complete group is also made. If the group was executed by more than one artist then it is recorded as a **mixed group**. An appendix lists contributing artists for each mixed group.

Title

When the original title was in a foreign language Tate Gallery practice is to use a translation as the primary title, unless the artist deliberately chose a foreign title (e.g. T03053 'Lieder ohne Worte' by Frederic, Lord Leighton). The foreign title is also recorded.

Works without titles or without known titles are indicated as '[no title]' or '[title not known]' to avoid confusion with works deliberately named 'Untitled' by their makers (e.g. T01347 'Untitled' by David Annesley).

Physical description of the work of art

It has not been practicable, in time for this edition, to arrive at a satisfactory method of dealing with physical description which does not involve abbreviations. Therefore, we have continued the previous convention of describing the physical nature of the work of art in encoded form. A key to the coding appears below. Complete descriptions in plain English are to be found in *Tate Gallery Biennial Reports* or *Illustrated Catalogues of Acquisitions*.

Key to physical description codes

A number before a letter indicates that the works comprises that number of parts, e.g. 20F = 20 photographs.

Medium or process

A   Acrylic or other modern synthetic resin-based paint or medium

B   Block or plate engraved for printing

D   Drawing in pen and ink, chalk, or pencil

E   Enamel or similar

F   Photograph

G   Gouache or bodycolour, distemper

H   Hand-applied colour other than watercolour, oil paint, or synthetic resin-based paints (e.g. felt-tip pen inks, crayons, dyestuffs and inks)

I   Intaglio print (etching, drypoint, aquatint)

J   Relief print (woodcut, linocut)

K   Kinetic - mobile or moving

L   Lithograph (including collotype)

M   Monoprint

N   Screenprint

O   Oil or oleoresin-based paint or medium

P   Pastel

R   Relief

S   Sculpture

T   Tempera, casein, wax or similar

V   Various, mixed or assembled

W   Watercolour, wash

X   Video

π Paper

Material or support

a   acrylic, plastic, synthetic resin or similar

b   board (cardboard, millboard etc.)

c   canvas (linen, cotton duck etc.)

f   fabric other than canvas (e.g. silk)

g   glass

i   ivory

m   metal (except bronze)

p   plaster or other cast or moulded material (including ceramic)

s   stone (including marble)

v   various

w   wood or cork

z   bronze

π paper

A support indicated in brackets, followed by a different support, means that the paint-surface and primary support has been transferred from the first to the second, e.g. O(c)w, indicating that an oil painting on canvas has been transferred to panel.

Size

Dimensions are expressed in millimetres throughout, and in the order: height, width, depth. The sizes given represent **image area or painted area** for canvases, panels and prints, **support size** for unique works on paper, **installed size** of installations or assembled works (these are variable in some cases), and **individual dimensions** for each part of some multi-part works (e.g. the sizes for each panel of a triptych). The user should note that, in many cases, the metric dimensions have been derived from imperial measurements by automatic conversion. No attempt has been made to accommodate a consideration of limits of accuracy for larger dimensions: dimensions are simply quoted to the nearest millimetre, as measured or converted.

Signed

The former practice of indicating that works of art are signed by the use of the 'X' symbols has been abandoned in favour of the appearance of the word 'signed' in the entry after the dimensions.

The credit line

This information records the manner and date of acquisition. The information now follows standard Gallery cataloguing practice and abbreviations are no longer used. The date appearing at the end of of the line indicates the year the works entered the collection of the Tate Gallery, or entered the national collections when that date pre-dated the separate existence of the Tate Gallery. There are several instances when works of art were originally acquired by the National Gallery, the Victoria and Albert Museum or the British Museum and subsequently transferred to the Tate Gallery.

CONCISE CATALOGUE

ABBEY, Edwin Austin 1852-1911
British Collection
Tate Gallery Archive holds material concerning this artist

N03987 Illustration to 'She Stoops to Conquer' (circa 1882-7)
Dπ:251x295:signed:Presented by a group of admirers
through John Singer Sargent 1924

N03988 Illustration to 'She Stoops to Conquer' (1885)
Dπ:267x413:signed:Presented by a group of admirers
through John Singer Sargent 1924

N03989 The Letter (1890)
Dπ:305x267:signed:Presented by a group of admirers
through John Singer Sargent 1924

N03990 Illustration to 'The Leather Bottel' (1887)
Dπ:260x286:signed:Presented by a group of admirers
through John Singer Sargent 1924

N03991 Illustration to 'Sally in our Alley' (1886)
Dπ:394x254:signed:Presented by a group of admirers
through John Singer Sargent 1924

N03992 Illustration to 'Judith Shakespeare' (1883)
Dπ:305x419:signed:Presented by a group of admirers
through John Singer Sargent 1924

ABBOTT, Lemuel Francis 1760-1803
British Collection

N01198 Henry Byne, of Carshalton
Oc:737x610:Presented by Miss C.C. Lippincott 1885

T01067 Portrait of the Engraver Francesco Bartolozzi
Oc:756x676:Presented by Mrs M. Bernard 1968

ABRAHAMS, Ivor born 1935
Modern Collection
Tate Gallery Archive holds material concerning this artist

T02330 Winter Sundial (1975)
MAπ:702x838:Presented by Mme Andrée Stassart 1979

T03369 Lady in Niche (1973)
Sv:2095x1575x762:Purchased 1982

For John Constable (P03149-P03157, P03159-P03161,
P03180-P03185; complete group; mixed group)
P03149 [no title] (1976)
CNπ:445x594:Presented by Bernard Jacobson Gallery
1976

The Garden Suite (P04001-P04005; complete group)
P04001 Garden Suite I (1970)
CNπ:329x534:Presented by Rose and Chris Prater
through the Institute of Contemporary Prints 1975

P04002 Garden Suite II (1970)
CNπ:295x526:Presented by Rose and Chris Prater
through the Institute of Contemporary Prints 1975

P04003 Garden Suite III (1970)
CNπ:372x508:Presented by Rose and Chris Prater
through the Institute of Contemporary Prints 1975

P04004 Garden Suite IV (1970)
CNπ:452x471:Presented by Rose and Chris Prater
through the Institute of Contemporary Prints 1975

P04005 Garden Suite V (1970)
CNπ:372x529:Presented by Rose and Chris Prater
through the Institute of Contemporary Prints 1975

P07384 Sundial I (Summer) (1975)
CNVπ:1016x1197:Purchased 1980

P08150 Untitled [from the book 'Oxford Gardens: a Sketchbook'
by Ivor Abrahams] (1977)
CNπ:197x130:Transferred from the Library 1979

Garden Emblems (P11099-P11100; incomplete group)
P11099 Garden Emblems I (1967)
CNπ:766x565:Presented by Evelyne Abrahams 1986
P11100 Garden Emblems II (1967)
CNπ:766x565:Presented by Evelyne Abrahams 1986

Privacy Plots (P11101-P11105; complete group)
P11101 Privacy Plots I (1970)
CNπ:518x482:Presented by Evelyne Abrahams 1986
P11102 Privacy Plots II (1970)
CNπ:388x611:Presented by Evelyne Abrahams 1986
P11103 Privacy Plots III (1970)
CNπ:410x580:Presented by Evelyne Abrahams 1986
P11104 Privacy Plots IV (1970)
CNπ:355x603:Presented by Evelyne Abrahams 1986
P11105 Privacy Plots V (1970)
CNπ:400x595:Presented by Evelyne Abrahams 1986

Arches (P11106-P11109; complete group)
P11106 Arches I (1971)
CLπ:600x792:Presented by Evelyne Abrahams 1986
P11107 Arches II (1971)
MLπ:596x796:Presented by Evelyne Abrahams 1986
P11108 Arches III (1971)
MLπ:596x794:Presented by Evelyne Abrahams 1986
P11109 Arches IV (1971)
MLπ:596x795:Presented by Evelyne Abrahams 1986

P11110 Suburban Shrub I (1972)
CLπ:828x620:Presented by Evelyne Abrahams 1986
P11111 Suburban Shrub II (1972)
CLπ:831x630:Presented by Evelyne Abrahams 1986

Schemes for Summer Borders (P11112-P11115;
complete group)
P11112 Sunflowers (1972)
CNπ:565x610:Presented by Evelyne Abrahams 1986
P11113 Hydrangeas (1972)
CNπ:344x455:Presented by Evelyne Abrahams 1986
P11114 Hollyhocks (1972)
CNπ:246x410:Presented by Evelyne Abrahams 1986
P11115 Rose Trees (1972)
CNπ:372x540:Presented by Evelyne Abrahams 1986

P11116 Double Shrub I (1973)
CLπ:647x820:Presented by Evelyne Abrahams 1986
P11117 Double Shrub II (1973)
CLπ:647x821:Presented by Evelyne Abrahams 1986
P11118 Sundial II (Winter) (1975)
CNπ:1016x1195:Presented by Evelyne Abrahams 1986
P11119 Stone Bench (1975)
CLπ:555x515:Presented by Evelyne Abrahams 1986

Pathways (P11120-P11125; complete group)
P11120 Pathways I (1975)
CLπ:340x430:Presented by Evelyne Abrahams 1986
P11121 Pathways II (1975)
CLπ:460x350:Presented by Evelyne Abrahams 1986
P11122 Pathways III (1975)
CLπ:318x445:Presented by Evelyne Abrahams 1986
P11123 Pathways IV (1975)
CLπ:300x485:Presented by Evelyne Abrahams 1986
P11124 Pathways V (1975)
CLπ:345x440:Presented by Evelyne Abrahams 1986
P11125 Pathways VI (1975)
CLπ:423x335:Presented by Evelyne Abrahams 1986

Works Past (P11126-P11130; complete group)

P11126 Works Past I (1976)
MIπ:274x200:Presented by Evelyne Abrahams 1986

P11127 Works Past II (1976)
MIπ:274x200:Presented by Evelyne Abrahams 1986

P11128 Works Past III (1976)
MIπ:248x175:Presented by Evelyne Abrahams 1986

P11129 Works Past IV (1976)
MIπ:247x199:Presented by Evelyne Abrahams 1986

P11130 Works Past V (1976)
MIπ:247x199:Presented by Evelyne Abrahams 1986

P11131 Stage Proof for Works Past I (1976)
MIπ:276x202:Presented by Evelyne Abrahams 1986

P11132 Stage Proof for Works Past I (1976)
MIπ:276x202:Presented by Evelyne Abrahams 1986

P11133 Stage Proof for Works Past I (1976)
Iπ:276x202:Presented by Evelyne Abrahams 1986

P11134 Stage Proof for Works Past I (1976)
Iπ:276x202:Presented by Evelyne Abrahams 1986

Edgar Allan Poe (P11135-P11154; complete group)

P11135 The Domain of Arnheim (1976)
CNπ:226x166:Presented by Evelyne Abrahams 1986

P11136 Alone (1976)
CNπ:189x182:Presented by Evelyne Abrahams 1986

P11137 The Valley of Unrest (1976)
CNπ:246x200:Presented by Evelyne Abrahams 1986

P11138 The Man that was Used Up (1976)
CNπ:161x188:Presented by Evelyne Abrahams 1986

P11139 A Predicament (1976)
CNπ:232x175:Presented by Evelyne Abrahams 1986

P11140 Philosophy of Furniture (1976)
CNπ:250x162:Presented by Evelyne Abrahams 1986

P11141 A Dream Within a Dream (1976)
CNπ:220x180:Presented by Evelyne Abrahams 1986

P11142 The Haunted Palace (1976)
CNπ:153x183:Presented by Evelyne Abrahams 1986

P11143 Lenore (1976)
CNπ:152x200:Presented by Evelyne Abrahams 1986

P11144 The Conqueror Worm (1976)
CNπ:257x175:Presented by Evelyne Abrahams 1986

P11145 The Premature Burial (1976)
CNπ:129x174:Presented by Evelyne Abrahams 1986

P11146 The Pit and the Pendulum (1976)
CNπ:250x160:Presented by Evelyne Abrahams 1986

P11147 The Raven (1976)
CNπ:196x140:Presented by Evelyne Abrahams 1986

P11148 The Sleeper (1976)
CNπ:142x190:Presented by Evelyne Abrahams 1986

P11149 The Masque of the Red Death (1976)
CNπ:275x198:Presented by Evelyne Abrahams 1986

P11150 Xing a Paragraph (1976)
CNπ:235x165:Presented by Evelyne Abrahams 1986

P11151 Ligeia (1976)
CNπ:137x134:Presented by Evelyne Abrahams 1986

P11152 Morella (1976)
CNπ:210x160:Presented by Evelyne Abrahams 1986

P11153 Silence - A Parable (1976)
CNπ:227x163:Presented by Evelyne Abrahams 1986

P11154 The Sphinx (1976)
CNπ:143x205:Presented by Evelyne Abrahams 1986

P11155 Hedges I (1977)
CNπ:1408x1026:Presented by Evelyne Abrahams 1986

P11156 Hedges II (1977)
CNπ:1407x1024:Presented by Evelyne Abrahams 1986

Oxford Gardens Suite (P11157-P11166; complete group)

P11157 Oxford Gardens I (1977)
CNπ:239x184:Presented by Evelyne Abrahams 1986

P11158 Oxford Gardens II (1977)
CNπ:247x160:Presented by Evelyne Abrahams 1986

P11159 Oxford Gardens III (1977)
CNπ:205x152:Presented by Evelyne Abrahams 1986

P11160 Oxford Gardens IV (1977)
CNπ:165x242:Presented by Evelyne Abrahams 1986

P11161 Oxford Gardens V (1977)
CNπ:190x241:Presented by Evelyne Abrahams 1986

P11162 Oxford Gardens VI (1977)
CNπ:155x240:Presented by Evelyne Abrahams 1986

P11163 Oxford Gardens VII (1977)
CNπ:159x235:Presented by Evelyne Abrahams 1986

P11164 Oxford Gardens VIII (1977)
CNπ:153x246:Presented by Evelyne Abrahams 1986

P11165 Oxford Gardens IX (1977)
CNπ:165x287:Presented by Evelyne Abrahams 1986

P11166 Oxford Gardens X (1977)
CNπ:155x242:Presented by Evelyne Abrahams 1986

Monuments (P11167-P11169; complete group)

P11167 Urn (1978)
CNπ:685x455:Presented by Evelyne Abrahams 1986

P11168 Sphinx (1978)
CNπ:637x465:Presented by Evelyne Abrahams 1986

P11169 Tombs (1978)
CNπ:650x471:Presented by Evelyne Abrahams 1986

P11170 Femme du Midi I (1979)
CIπ:360x235:Presented by Evelyne Abrahams 1986

P11171 Femme du Midi II (1979)
CIπ:362x280:Presented by Evelyne Abrahams 1986

P11172 Femme du Midi III (1979)
CIπ:323x220:Presented by Evelyne Abrahams 1986

P11173 Femme du Midi IV (1979)
CIπ:367x293:Presented by Evelyne Abrahams 1986

P11174 Femme du Midi V (1979)
CIπ:375x195:Presented by Evelyne Abrahams 1986

P11175 Femme du Midi VI (1979)
CIπ:360x210:Presented by Evelyne Abrahams 1986

Edmund Burke Series (P11176-P11190; complete group)

P11176 [no title] (1979)
CLπ:430x252:Presented by Evelyne Abrahams 1986

P11177 [no title] (1979)
CLπ:365x272:Presented by Evelyne Abrahams 1986

P11178 [no title] (1979)
CLπ:290x370:Presented by Evelyne Abrahams 1986

P11179 [no title] (1979)
CLπ:390x320:Presented by Evelyne Abrahams 1986

P11180 [no title] (1979)
CLπ:335x300:Presented by Evelyne Abrahams 1986

P11181 [no title] (1979)
CLπ:430x375:Presented by Evelyne Abrahams 1986

P11182 [no title] (1979)
CLπ:288x345:Presented by Evelyne Abrahams 1986

P11183 [no title] (1979)
CLπ:365x350:Presented by Evelyne Abrahams 1986

P11184 [no title] (1979)
CLπ:260x400:Presented by Evelyne Abrahams 1986

P11185 [no title] (1979)
CLπ:415x315:Presented by Evelyne Abrahams 1986

P11186 [no title] (1979)
CLπ:365x280:Presented by Evelyne Abrahams 1986

P11187 [no title] (1979)
CLπ:350x320:Presented by Evelyne Abrahams 1986

P11188 [no title] (1979)
CLπ:390x350:Presented by Evelyne Abrahams 1986

P11189 [no title] (1979)
CLπ:397x310:Presented by Evelyne Abrahams 1986

P11190 [no title] (1979)
CLπ:330x330:Presented by Evelyne Abrahams 1986

P11191 Diptych (1981)
CLπ:829x1232:Presented by Evelyne Abrahams 1986

P11192 Baigneuses (1983)
CLπ:648x500:Presented by Evelyne Abrahams 1986

P11193 Vahine I (1984)
CNπ:1070x802:Presented by Evelyne Abrahams 1986

P11194 Vahine II (1984)
CNπ:1074x804:Presented by Evelyne Abrahams 1986

P11195 Nereids I (1986)
CNπ:754x960:Presented by Evelyne Abrahams 1986

P11196 Nereids II (1986)
CNπ:1008x750:Presented by Evelyne Abrahams 1986

ACCONCI, Vito born 1940
Modern Collection
Tate Gallery Archive holds material concerning this artist

P07639 3 Flags for 1 Space and 6 Regions (1979-81)
6 CLπ:2430x1860:Purchased 1982

ACKLING, Roger born 1947
Modern Collection

T03562 Five Sunsets in One Hour (1978)
Vb:559x368:Presented by the Contemporary Art Society 1983

ACKROYD, Norman born 1938
Modern Collection
Tate Gallery Archive holds material concerning this artist

P07131 1st Millbank Print (1972)
CLπ:505x454:Purchased 1975

P07132 Millbank, Black Version (1972)
MIπ:505x457:Purchased 1975

P07133 Gentle Rainstorm (1974)
CLπ:216x190:Purchased 1975

P08210 The Avenue at Avington (1982)
MIπ:95x114:signed:Transferred from the Library 1983

ADAMS, Harry William 1868-1947
British Collection

N01838 Winter's Sleep (1900)
Oc:1226x1841:Presented by the Trustees of the Chantrey Bequest 1900

ADAMS, Norman born 1927
Modern Collection
Tate Gallery Archive holds material concerning this artist

T00923 The Whole (The Dream I) (1964)
Oc:864x914:Presented by the Trustees of the Chantrey Bequest 1967

T01127 Rainbow Painting (I) (1966)
Oc:1270x1270:Presented by the Trustees of the Chantrey Bequest 1969

ADAMS, Robert 1917-1984
Modern Collection
Tate Gallery Archive holds material concerning this artist

T00555 Large Screen Form No. 2 (1962)
Sm:1924x749x89:Purchased 1962

T00906 Maquette for Architectural Screen (1956)
Sz:229x749x89:Presented by the Trustees of the Chantrey Bequest 1967

T03866 Figure (1949)
Sw:1000x230x230:Purchased 1984

IAA Portfolio (P03096-P03104, P03107; complete group; mixed group)

P03096 Untitled (1975)
CLπ:489x349:Presented by the International Association of Art 1975

P06001 Untitled (1961)
CLπ:686x540:Presented by Curwen Studio through the Institute of Contemporary Prints 1975

P06002 Screen I (1962-3)
CLπ:570x325:Presented by Curwen Studio through the Institute of Contemporary Prints 1975

P06003 Screen II (1962-3)
CLπ:630x504:Presented by Curwen Studio through the Institute of Contemporary Prints 1975

P06004 Screen III (1962-3)
CLπ:676x472:Presented by Curwen Studio through the Institute of Contemporary Prints 1975

Penwith Portfolio (P01416, P06005, P06108, P06130, P06241, P06324, P06346, P06359, P06399, P06519, P06700; complete group; mixed group)

P06005 Screen Form (1973)
CLπ:562x292:Presented by Curwen Studio through the Institute of Contemporary Prints 1975

P77147 [title not known] (1949)
MLπ:461x345:Purchased 1986

P77148 [title not known] (1949)
CLπ:375x288:Purchased 1986

P77149 [title not known] (1950)
CLπ:405x285:Purchased 1986

P77150 [title not known] (1957)
MJπ:507x382:Purchased 1986

P77151 [title not known] (1971)
MIπ:184x322:Purchased 1986

P77152 [title not known]
CJπ:407x252:Purchased 1986

P77153 [title not known]
CJπ:230x250:Purchased 1986

ADENEY, Bernard 1878-1966
British Collection
Tate Gallery Archive holds material concerning this artist

N04568 Toy Sailing Boats, the Round Pond (1911)
Tc:2267x3048:Purchased 1931

ADLER, Jankel 1895-1949
Modern Collection
Tate Gallery Archive holds material concerning this artist

N06202 No Man's Land (1943)
Oc:860x1108:signed:Presented by C.R. Churchill 1953

T00299 Woman with Hat (1940)
Ob:311x251:signed:Presented by Mr and Mrs Alexander Margulies 1959

T00372 The Mutilated (1942-3)
Oc:864x1118:signed:Presented by Robert Strauss 1960

ADZAK, Roy 1927-1987
Modern Collection
Tate Gallery Archive holds material concerning this artist

T00875 Cut Bottle Relief (1966)
RAv:330x406x73:signed:Presented by Miss Iris Clert 1966

AFRO (Afro Basaldella) 1912-1976
Modern Collection

T00017 The Struggle (1951)
La sopraffazione
TDπ:267x210:signed:Purchased 1955

AGAR, Eileen born 1899
Modern Collection
Tate Gallery Archive holds material concerning this artist

T00492 Head of Dylan Thomas (1960)
OAb:600x435:signed:Purchased 1962

T00707 Three Symbols (1930)
Oc:1003x559:signed:Purchased 1964

T02064 The Reaper (1938)
GVπ:210x279:signed:Purchased 1976

T03809 Angel of Anarchy (1936-40)
Sfpv:520x317x336:Presented by the Friends of the Tate Gallery 1983

T05024 The Autobiography of an Embryo (1933-4)
Ob:2130x9914:signed:Purchased 1987

AGASSE, Jacques Laurent 1767-1849
British Collection

T02350 Two Hunters with a Groom (circa 1805)
Oc:638x759:Presented by Paul Mellon through the British Sporting Art Trust 1979

T02351 Lord Rivers's Groom Leading a Chestnut Hunter towards a Coursing Party in Hampshire (1807)
Oc:660x625:signed:Presented by Paul Mellon through the British Sporting Art Trust 1979

AITCHISON, Craigie born 1926
Modern Collection

T00712 Model Standing against Blue Wall (1962)
Oc:660x559:Purchased 1964

T04942 Crucifixion (1986-7)
Oc:2147x1830:Presented by the Trustees of the Chantrey Bequest 1987

P04006 Africa (1969)
CNπ:1003x692:signed:Presented by Rose and Chris Prater through the Institute of Contemporary Prints 1975

P04007 Get Well Soon (1969)
CNπ:810x457:signed:Presented by Rose and Chris Prater through the Institute of Contemporary Prints 1975

AJMONE, Giuseppe born 1923
Modern Collection

T00379 Autumn (1959)
Autumno
Oc:997x648:signed:Presented by Professor Gino Ghiringhelli 1960

AKEN, Joseph van - see VAN AKEN, Joseph

ALBERS, Josef 1888-1976
Modern Collection

T00783 Study for Homage to the Square: Departing in Yellow (1964)
Ob:762x762:signed:Purchased 1965

T02310 Study for Homage to the Square: Beaming (1963)
Oab:762x762:signed:Presented by Mrs Anni Albers, the artist's widow and the Josef Albers Foundation 1978

T02311 Study for Homage to the Square (1963)
Oab:762x762:signed:Presented by Mrs Anni Albers, the artist's widow and the Josef Albers Foundation 1978

T02312 Study for Homage to the Square (1964)
Oab:762x762:signed:Presented by Mrs Anni Albers, the artist's widow and the Josef Albers Foundation 1978

P01786 White Line Square IV (1966)
CLπ:400x400:signed:Presented by the Museum of Modern Art, New York 1976

ALBRIGHT, Ivan 1897-1983
Modern Collection

T02316 Josephine Medill Paterson Albright (1954)
Sz:346x225x270:Presented by Mr and Mrs Michael Croydon through the American Federation of Arts 1978

ALDRIDGE, John 1905-1983
Modern Collection
Tate Gallery Archive holds material concerning this artist

T00449 Aberayron, Evening (1954)
Oc:508x762:signed:Presented by the Trustees of the Chantrey Bequest 1961

ALECHINSKY, Pierre born 1927
Modern Collection
Tate Gallery Archive holds material concerning this artist

For Jorn (P03241-P03255; complete group; mixed group)
Pour Jorn
P03241 [no title] (1975-6)
CLπ:691x510:signed:Presented by the Asger Jorn Foundation 1978

P03242 [no title] (1975-6)
CLπ:724x520:signed:Presented by the Asger Jorn Foundation 1978

P07520 In the Process of Vanishing (1978)
En voie de disparition
CLπ:540x740:signed:Purchased 1981

P07521 Starving Fireman (1979)
Clπ:346x210:signed:Purchased 1981

P07522 Jumbled Ephemerides (1980)
Ephémérides brouillées
Clπ:1680x899:signed:Purchased 1981

P77240 The Hairdresser (1948)
Le Coiffeur
Iπ:140x97:signed:Purchased 1987

P77241 Something of a World (1952)
Quelque chose d'un monde
Iπ:247x349:signed:Purchased 1987

P77242 The Night (1952)
La Nuit
Iπ:234x307:signed:Purchased 1987

ALEXANDER, Edwin 1870-1926
British Collection

N01965 Peacock and Python (1905)
Wπ:1018x1780:signed:Presented by the Trustees of the
Chantrey Bequest 1905

after
ALEXANDER, William 1767-1816
British Collection

Picturesque Views on the Southern Coast of England
(T05218-T05463; complete group; mixed group)

T05314 Carisbrook Castle (1814)
Iπ:142x218:Purchased 1988

T05315 Carisbrook Castle (1814)
Iπ:143x220:Purchased 1988

ALKEN, Henry Thomas 1785-1851
British Collection

T02352 The Belvoir Hunt: The Meet (circa 1830-40)
Oc:451x648:signed:Presented by Paul Mellon through the
British Sporting Art Trust 1979

T02353 The Belvoir Hunt: Jumping into and out of a Lane (circa
1830-40)
Oc:451x648:signed:Presented by Paul Mellon through the
British Sporting Art Trust 1979

T02354 The Belvoir Hunt: Full Cry (circa 1830-40)
Oc:451x648:signed:Presented by Paul Mellon through the
British Sporting Art Trust 1979

T02355 The Belvoir Hunt: The Death (circa 1830-40)
Oc:451x648:signed:Presented by Paul Mellon through the
British Sporting Art Trust 1979

ALLAN, Julian Phelps born 1892
Modern Collection

N04479 Marjorie (1928)
Sz:368x203x229:signed:Presented by the Trustees of the
Chantrey Bequest 1929

ALLAN, Sir William 1782-1850
British Collection

N00373 Tartar Robbers Dividing Spoil (1817)
Ow:641x521:signed:Presented by Robert Vernon 1847

ALLEN, Joseph William 1803-1852
British Collection

N01904 A Landscape
Oc:787x1206:Presented by T.W. Bacon 1902

ALLEY, Anthea born 1927
Modern Collection
Tate Gallery Archive holds material concerning this artist

T00655 Spatial Form (1962-3)
Sm:337x279x298:Purchased 1964

ALLINGTON, Edward born 1951
Modern Collection

T04910 Seated in Darkness (1987)
Dπc:1830x2440:Presented by Weltkunst Foundation 1987

T05214 Ideal Standard Forms (1980)
Sp:475x3000x2280:Purchased 1988

ALLINSON, Adrian 1890-1959
Modern Collection
Tate Gallery Archive holds material concerning this artist

T01864 Ibizan Waterfront (1933)
Oc:664x813:signed:Presented by Miss Mary
Mitchell-Smith 1974

ALMA-TADEMA, Sir Lawrence 1836-1912
British Collection
Tate Gallery Archive holds material concerning this artist

N01523 A Silent Greeting (1889)
Ow:305x229:signed:Presented by Sir Henry Tate 1894

N02675 A Favourite Custom (1909)
Ow:660x451:signed:Presented by the Trustees of the
Chantrey Bequest 1909

N03513 A Foregone Conclusion (1885)
Ow:311x229:signed:Bequeathed by Amy, Lady Tate 1920

N03527 Sunday Morning (?1871)
Ow:400x330:signed:Bequeathed by R.H. Prance 1920

N04949 A Priestess of Apollo (?circa 1888)
Oc:349x298:signed:Bequeathed by R.H. Williamson 1938

ALTOON, John 1925-1969
Modern Collection

T03266 Black and White 55 (1963)
ADπ:762x1016:Presented by the artist's widow 1981

AMICONI, Giacomo 1682-1752
British Collection

T01299 Mercury About to Slay Argus (1730-2)
Oc:655x645:Purchased 1971

AMIET, Cuno 1868-1961
Modern Collection

T00393 View from the Studio (1921)
Atelierausblick
Wπ:213x152:signed:Presented by Mrs Leila Pirani 1960

T00394 Landscape from the Jura Mountains (1924)
Landschaft mit Jura
Wπ:251x298:signed:Presented by Mrs Leila Pirani 1960

AMUCHASTEGUI, Axel born 1921
Modern Collection

P06006   Ocelot Head (1968)
CLπ:518x406:signed:Presented by Curwen Studio through the Institute of Contemporary Prints 1975

ANDERTON, Henry circa 1630-1665
British Collection

T03543   Mountain Landscape with Dancing Shepherd (circa 1650-60)
Oc:457x597:signed:Bequeathed by Hugh Paget 1983

ANDRE, Carl born 1935
Modern Collection
Tate Gallery Archive holds material concerning this artist

T01533   Last Ladder (1959)
Sw:2140x156x156:Purchased 1972

T01534   Equivalent VIII (1966)
S:127x686x2292:Purchased 1972

T01767   144 Magnesium Square (1969)
Sm:10x3658x3658:Purchased 1973

T02135   Diagram of 'Reef' (1967)
Dπ:222x276:signed:Presented by David Novros through the American Federation of Arts 1977

T02136   Drawing for 'The Perfect Painting' (1967)
Dπ:216x279:Presented by David Novros through the American Federation of Arts 1977

T02137   Rotor Reflector Review (1967)
Dπ:273x210:signed:Presented by David Novros through the American Federation of Arts 1977

T02138   Diagram for Installation of Magnet Pieces 1966, at Tibor de Nagy Gallery, New York (1966)
Dπ:257x419:Presented by David Novros through the American Federation of Arts 1977

ANDREW, John - see FINLAY, Ian Hamilton and ANDREW, John

ANDREWS, Michael born 1928
Modern Collection

T00169   A Man who Suddenly Fell Over (1952)
Ob:1206x1727:Purchased 1958

T01897   The Deer Park (1962)
Ow:2140x2445:signed:Purchased 1974

T02334   Melanie and Me Swimming (1978-9)
Ac:1829x1829:Purchased 1979

ANGELLIS, Peter 1685-1734
British Collection

T00789   Conversation Piece (circa 1715-20)
Oc:937x797:signed:Presented by the Friends of the Tate Gallery 1965

ANNESLEY, David born 1936
Modern Collection
Tate Gallery Archive holds material concerning this artist

T00828   Orinoco (1965)
ASm:1289x2032x1740:Purchased 1966

T01339   X-Act (1964)
SAm:876x2134x533:Presented by Alistair McAlpine (later Lord McAlpine of West Green) 1970

T01340   Swing Low (1964)
SAm:1283x1759x368:Presented by Alistair McAlpine (later Lord McAlpine of West Green) 1970

T01341   Jump (1965)
SAm:1140x1575x279:Presented by Alistair McAlpine (later Lord McAlpine of West Green) 1970

T01342   Loquat (1965)
SAm:1003x2070x737:Presented by Alistair McAlpine (later Lord McAlpine of West Green) 1970

T01343   Godroon (1966)
SAm:1441x1441x508:Presented by Alistair McAlpine (later Lord McAlpine of West Green) 1970

T01344   Big Ring (1965)
SAm:1822x2683x457:Presented by Alistair McAlpine (later Lord McAlpine of West Green) 1970

T01345   Big Yellow Circle (1966)
SAm:1924x2000x508:Presented by Alistair McAlpine (later Lord McAlpine of West Green) 1970

T01346   Narrow Blue Circle (1966)
SAm:2089x2292x686:Presented by Alistair McAlpine (later Lord McAlpine of West Green) 1970

T01347   Untitled (1968)
SAm:2115x1937x610:Presented by Alistair McAlpine (later Lord McAlpine of West Green) 1970

T01348   Untitled (1968-9)
SAm:2222x2470x610:Presented by Alistair McAlpine (later Lord McAlpine of West Green) 1970

P04008   Mauve, Orange, Yellow, Turquoise on Pale Blue (1970)
CNπ:556x765:signed:Presented by Rose and Chris Prater through the Institute of Contemporary Prints 1975

P04009   Red, Yellow, Blue and Turquoise (1970)
CNπ:581x765:signed:Presented by Rose and Chris Prater through the Institute of Contemporary Prints 1975

ANQUETIN, Louis 1861-1932
Modern Collection

N03690   Girl Reading a Newspaper (1890)
Jeune Femme lisant un Journal
Pπ:540x432:signed:Presented by Francis Howard 1922

N05074   The Finish of the Horse Race (circa 1898-9)
Wb:260x530:Bequeathed by Frank Hindley Smith 1940

N05252   Two Studies for 'The Three Graces' (circa 1899)
Oc:616x768:Purchased 1941

ANREP, Boris 1883-1969
Modern Collection

T01181   Varvara Theodossieva (1906)
Dπ:743x502:Bequeathed by the artist 1969

T03538   Nude and Ruins (1944)
Gb:604x370:signed:Bequeathed by Mrs M.J.A. Russell 1982

ANSDELL, Richard 1815-1885
British Collection

N04798   A Ploughing Match
Oc:781x1346:Purchased 1935

ANUSKIEWICZ, Richard born 1930
Modern Collection

P01787   Untitled (1965)
CNπ:619x619:signed:Presented by the Museum of Modern Art, New York 1976

APPEL, Karel born 1921
Modern Collection
Tate Gallery Archive holds material concerning this artist

T00212 Amorous Dance (1955)
Danse amoureuse
Oc:1140x1460:Purchased 1958

T04158 Questioning Children (1949)
Vragende kinderen
GRw:873x598x158:signed:Presented by the artist 1986

T04163 People, Birds and Sun (1954)
Mensen, vogels, zonnen
Oc:1730x2428:signed:Purchased 1986

T05077 Hip, Hip, Hoorah (1949)
Hiep, hiep, hoera!
Oc:817x1270:signed:Purchased 1988

P01788 Heads in a Colourful Landscape (1965)
CLπ:575x762:signed:Presented by the Museum of
Modern Art, New York 1976

For Jorn (P03241-P03255; complete group; mixed group)
Pour Jorn

P03243 [no title] (1975-6)
CLπ:692x483:signed:Presented by the Asger Jorn
Foundation 1978

P08225 Untitled (1960)
Lπ:299x296:Transferred from the Library 1989

APPELBEE, Leonard born 1914
Modern Collection
Tate Gallery Archive holds material concerning this artist

N05151 The King Crab (1938)
Oc:362x470:signed:Purchased 1940

N05342 Landscape, Meadle (1939)
Oc:457x660:signed:Presented by the Trustees of the
Chantrey Bequest 1940

P06007 Carp (1970-71)
CLπ:448x594:Presented by Curwen Studio through the
Institute of Contemporary Prints 1975

P06008 Red Bream (1971)
CLπ:451x606:Presented by Curwen Studio through the
Institute of Contemporary Prints 1975

APPLEYARD, Fred 1874-1963
British Collection

N03029 A Secret (1914-5)
Oc:914x1232:signed:Presented by the Trustees of the
Chantrey Bequest 1915

ARAKAWA, Shusaku born 1936
Modern Collection
Tate Gallery Archive holds material concerning this artist

P07523 A Forgettance (Exhaustion Exhumed) (1974-5)
CNLVπ:794x1953:Purchased 1981

ARCANGELO, Allan d' - see
D'ARCANGELO, Allan

ARCHIPENKO, Alexander 1887-1964
Modern Collection

T00335 Woman Combing her Hair (1915)
Sz:356x86x83:signed:Purchased 1960

ARDIZZONE, Edward 1900-1979
Modern Collection
Tate Gallery Archive holds material concerning this artist

N04940 Airing the Children (circa 1930-1)
WDπ:197x267:signed:Presented by Miss Lillian Browse
1938

N05671 Priest Begging a Lift in Louvain, May 1940 (1940)
WDπ:241x308:signed:Presented by the War Artists'
Advisory Committee 1946

N05672 On a Fortified Island, the Night Watch (1941)
WDπ:273x349:Presented by the War Artists' Advisory
Committee 1946

N05673 Soldiers Holding Up Rosaries to be Blessed at a Papal
Audience (1944)
WDπ:181x187:signed:Presented by the War Artists'
Advisory Committee 1946

N05674 Scout Cars of a Regiment of Hussars Liberating a Stalag
(1945)
WDπ:578x781:Presented by the War Artists' Advisory
Committee 1946

T01066 View from the Window of My Studio in Kent (1967)
Wπ:264x406:signed:Presented by the Trustees of the
Chantrey Bequest 1968

P06009 The Last Stand of the Spoons (1959)
MLπ:356x530:Presented by Curwen Studio through the
Institute of Contemporary Prints 1975

P06010 Life Class (1960)
MLπ:251x359:Presented by Curwen Studio through the
Institute of Contemporary Prints 1975

P06011 Lovers by the Sea (1960)
MLπ:210x352:Presented by Curwen Studio through the
Institute of Contemporary Prints 1975

P06012 Boating Pond (1961)
CLπ:340x483:signed:Presented by Curwen Studio
through the Institute of Contemporary Prints 1975

P06013 Boys Playing (1961)
MLπ:244x352:Presented by Curwen Studio through the
Institute of Contemporary Prints 1975

The Rake's Progress (A01029-A01033; complete group)
A01029 At the Brasserie (1931)
WDπ:152x222:signed:Purchased 1940
A01030 The Meeting (1931)
WDπ:190x159:signed:Purchased 1940
A01031 The Arrival (1931)
WDπ:152x184:signed:Purchased 1940
A01032 The Bedroom (1931)
WDπ:171x229:Purchased 1940
A01033 The Departure (1931)
WDπ:171x210:Purchased 1940

ARDON, Mordecai born 1896
Modern Collection

T00608 Missa Dura: The Knight, Crystal Night, House No. 5
(1958-60)
Missa Dura: Ritter, Kristallnacht, Haus nr. 5
Oc:195x520:signed:Presented by the Miriam Sacher
Charitable Trust through the Friends of the Tate Gallery
1963

ARIKHA, Avigdor born 1929
Modern Collection

T04939 Tubes of Paint in their Drawer (1985)
Pπ:499x329:signed:Presented by the Friends of the Tate Gallery 1987

P02945 R.B. Kitaj (1982, published 1983)
CLπ:258x340:signed:Presented by the artist 1987

ARMAN (Armand Fernandez) born 1928
Modern Collection
Tate Gallery Archive holds material concerning this artist

T03380 Bluebeard's Wife (1969)
Sav:835x290x320:Purchased 1982

T03381 Condition of Woman I (1960)
Condition de la femme I
SVw:1920x462x320:signed:Purchased 1982

ARMFIELD, Maxwell Ashby 1881-1972
Modern Collection
Tate Gallery Archive holds material concerning this artist

T01902 Oh! Willo! Willo! Willo! (1902)
Oc:445x289:signed:Purchased 1974

T01975 This England: Portrait of an Owner (1943)
Tπ:394x397:signed:Purchased 1975

ARMITAGE, Edward 1817-1896
British Collection
Tate Gallery Archive holds material concerning this artist

N00759 The Remorse of Judas (1866)
Oc:1276x2013:signed:Presented by the artist 1866

ARMITAGE, Kenneth born 1916
Modern Collection
Tate Gallery Archive holds material concerning this artist

T00186 Square Figure Relief (1954)
Rz:1067x686x146:Purchased 1958

T00366 People in a Wind (1950)
Sz:648x400x343:Purchased 1960

T00518 Sibyl III (1961)
Sz:1029x622x311:signed:Purchased 1962

T01268 Diarchy (1957)
Sz:1708x1086x1003:signed:Purchased 1971

T03708 Seated Woman with Square Head (Version B) (1955)
Sz:600x251x311:Transferred from the Victoria & Albert Museum 1983

P01802 Scurrying Figures (1974)
MIπ:203x254:signed:Presented by Taranman Gallery 1976

P06014 Seated Group (1960)
CLπ:410x584:signed:Presented by Curwen Studio through the Institute of Contemporary Prints 1975

P06015 Balanced Figure (1960-61)
CLπ:581x406:Presented by Curwen Studio through the Institute of Contemporary Prints 1975

ARMSTEAD, Henry Hugh 1828-1905
British Collection

N01929 Remorse (1903)
Ss:1029x889x489:Presented by the Trustees of the Chantrey Bequest 1903

N02054 Hero and Leander (circa 1875)
Rs:1257x1829:Bequeathed by the artist 1906

ARMSTRONG, John 1893-1973
Modern Collection
Tate Gallery Archive holds material concerning this artist

N04934 Dreaming Head (1938)
Tw:464x781:signed:Purchased 1938

N05257 Icarus (1940)
Tb:533x375:signed:Purchased 1941

N05675 Coggeshall Church, Essex (1940)
Tw:571x381:signed:Presented by the War Artists' Advisory Committee 1946

T01061 Tocsin III (1967)
Oc:711x914:signed:Presented by the Trustees of the Chantrey Bequest 1968

ARNALD, George 1763-1841
British Collection

N01156 View on the Ouse at York (?exhibited 1803)
Oc:1118x1410:signed:Purchased 1884

ARNATT, Keith born 1930
Modern Collection
Tate Gallery Archive holds material concerning this artist

T01747 Self-Burial (Television Interference Project) (1969)
Fπ:467x467:Presented by Westdeutsches Fernsehen 1973

ARP, Jean (Hans Arp) 1888-1966
Modern Collection
Tate Gallery Archive holds material concerning this artist

N06025 Pagoda Fruit (1949)
Fruit de pagode
Sz:889x679x762:Purchased 1951

T00242 Constellation According to the Laws of Chance (circa 1930)
Constellation selon les lois du hasard
ROw:549x698:Bequeathed by E.C. Gregory 1959

T01219 Torn-Up Woodcut (1920/54)
Bois déchiré
Mb:213x165:signed:Presented by Mr and Mrs Robert Lewin through the Friends of the Tate Gallery 1970

T02007 Winged Being (1961)
Entité ailée
Sp:1400x350x300:Presented by Mme Marguerite Arp-Hagenbach, the artist's widow 1975

T04854 To be Lost in the Forest (1932)
Etre perdu dans la forêt
3 Sz:90x222x154, 60x120x100, 65x55x93:Accepted by the Commissioners of Inland Revenue in lieu of tax and allocated 1986

T05005 According to the Laws of Chance (1933)
Selon les lois du hasard
Hπb:159x173:signed:Presented by Mr and Mrs Robert Lewin through the Friends of the Tate Gallery 1987

T05006 Goblin Fruit (1943)
Fruit de lutin
Rw:298x210x28:signed:Presented by Mr and Mrs Robert Lewin through the Friends of the Tate Gallery 1987

T05007 Head, Danger of Death (1954)
Tête, danger de mort
Dπ:322x257:signed:Presented by Mr and Mrs Robert Lewin through the Friends of the Tate Gallery 1987

T05504 Moustaches (circa 1925)
ROb:307x227x5:signed:Presented by Mr and Mrs Robert Lewin through the Friends of the Tate Gallery 1988

ART & LANGUAGE (ATKINSON, Terry and BALDWIN, Michael) born 1942, born 1945
Modern Collection
Tate Gallery Archive holds material concerning these artists

P01356 Map of Thirty-Six Square Mile Surface Area of Pacific Ocean West of Oahu (1967)
MJπ:597x505:signed:Presented by the Institute of Contemporary Prints 1975

P01357 Map Not to Indicate (1967)
MJπ:508x629:signed:Presented by the Institute of Contemporary Prints 1975

P08005 Ten Postcards (1977)
CLπ:203x765:Transferred from the Library 1977

ART & LANGUAGE (BALDWIN, Michael and RAMSDEN, Mel) born 1945, born 1944
Modern Collection

T03453 Gustave Courbet's 'Burial at Ornans'; Expressing a Sensuous Affection . . ./Expressing a Vibrant Erotic Vision . . ./Expressing States of Mind that are Vivid and Compelling (1981)
3 DHπc:3240x6990:Purchased 1982

T03800 Index: The Studio at 3 Wesley Place, in the Dark (VI), Showing the Position of 'Embarrassments' in (IV) (1982)
FDVπa:797x1680:Presented by Art & Language and Lisson Gallery 1983

T03801 Index: The Studio at 3 Wesley Place, in the Dark (IV), and Illuminated by an Explosion nearby (VI) (1982)
FVπ:784x1627:Presented by Art & Language and Lisson Gallery 1983

T03802 Index: The Studio at 3 Wesley Place, Executed by Mouth (II) (1982)
Vπ:975x2100:Presented by Art & Language and Lisson Gallery 1983

T03803 Index: The Studio at 3 Wesley Place (VI), Illuminated by an Explosion nearby (1982)
FVπ:1067x1603:Presented by Art & Language and Lisson Gallery 1983

T03804 Index: The Studio at 3 Wesley Place (1981-2)
DFVv:762x1623:Purchased 1983

ARTSCHWAGER, Richard born 1923
Modern Collection

T03793 Table and Chair (1963-4)
SVw:755x1320x952, 1143x438x533:Purchased 1983

P77154 Interior I (1977)
Iπ:227x250:signed:Purchased 1986

P77155 Interior II (1977)
Iπ:250x302:signed:Purchased 1986

ASKEW, Victor born 1909
Modern Collection

N05861 The Studio, St John's Wood (1948)
Oc:787x698:signed:Presented by the Trustees of the Chantrey Bequest 1948

ATKINS, Samuel active 1787-1808
British Collection

T00964 Shakespeare's Cliff, Dover
Wπ:340x479:signed:Presented by the National Art Collections Fund (Herbert Powell Bequest) 1967

ATKINSON, Conrad born 1940
Modern Collection
Tate Gallery Archive holds material concerning this artist

T03229 For Wordsworth; for West Cumbria (1980)
16 FAVb:521x622:Purchased 1981

P02949 Thanx Jackson (1988)
CNπ:1127x764:signed:Presented by the artist, Peacock Printmakers, Aberdeen and the Ronald Feldman Gallery 1988

P02950 Thanx Andy (1987)
CNπ:1133x765:signed:Presented by the artist, Peacock Printmakers, Aberdeen and the Ronald Feldman Gallery 1988

P02951 Thanx Picasso (1988)
CNπ:1123x768:signed:Presented by the artist, Peacock Printmakers, Aberdeen and the Ronald Feldman Gallery 1988

P07322 Strike (1972)
CNπ:765x562:Purchased 1979

P07323 For Chile (1973)
CNπ:1006x768:Purchased 1979

P07324 Northern Ireland (1973)
CNπ:1010x768:Purchased 1979

P77261 Thanx Joseph (1988)
CNπ:1115x760:signed:Purchased 1988

ATKINSON, Lawrence 1873-1931
British Collection

T00717 The Lake (circa 1915-20)
DWπ:254x368:Purchased 1965

T03692 Composition No. 10 (1914-15)
Wπ:495x330:Purchased 1983

ATKINSON, Terry - see ART & LANGUAGE (ATKINSON, Terry and BALDWIN, Michael)

ATLAN, Jean-Michel 1913-1960
Modern Collection

T00300 Baal the Warrior (1953)
Baal Guerrier
Oc:1626x1295:signed:Presented by Mr and Mrs Alexander Margulies 1959

ATWOOD, Clare 1866-1962
British Collection

N04881 John Gielgud's Room (1933)
Oc:629x762:signed:Presented by Mrs E.L. Shute 1937

AUERBACH, Arnold 1898-1978
Modern Collection

T04111 Mechanised Head (1928)
Sz:420x181x230:signed:Presented by Galerie Huber und Reichard and Mrs Jean M. Auerbach, the artist's widow 1985

T04112 Torso Form (1928)
Sz:815x195x146:signed:Presented by Galerie Huber und Reichard and Mrs Jean M. Auerbach, the artist's widow 1985

AUERBACH, Frank born 1931
Modern Collection
Tate Gallery Archive holds material concerning this artist

T00312 Small Head of E.O.W. (1957-8)
Ob:305x216:Purchased 1959

T00313 E.O.W. Nude (1953-4)
Oc:508x768:Purchased 1959

T00418 Oxford Street Building Site I (1959-60)
Ob:1981x1537:Purchased 1961

T01270 Primrose Hill (1967-8)
Ob:1219x1467:Purchased 1971

T01271 Working Drawing for 'Primrose Hill' (1968)
Dπ:251x311:Purchased 1971

T01272 Working Drawing for 'Primrose Hill' (1968)
Dπ:267x318:Purchased 1971

T01273 Working Drawing for 'Primrose Hill' (1968)
Dπ:251x305:Purchased 1971

T01274 Working Drawing for 'Primrose Hill' (1968)
Dπ:225x267:Purchased 1971

T01275 Working Drawing for 'Primrose Hill' (1968)
Dπ:225x260:Purchased 1971

T02100 Head of E.O.W. (1959-60)
DWVπ:787x581:signed:Purchased 1976

T03247 To the Studios (1979-80)
Oc:1232x1026:signed:Purchased 1981

T03319 J.Y.M. Seated No. 1 (1981)
Ob:711x610:Purchased 1981

T03933 The Sitting Room (1964)
Ob:1282x1277:Presented by the Friends of the Tate Gallery 1984

P03138 Tretire I (1975)
MNIπ:298x298:signed:Presented by Marlborough Graphics 1976

P03262 Tretire II (1976)
MNIπ:298x298:signed:Presented by Marlborough Graphics 1978

Heads and Figures (P04010, P04012-P04015; incomplete group)

P04010 Head of G.B. (1967)
CNπ:800x584:signed:Presented by Rose and Chris Prater through the Institute of Contemporary Prints 1975

P04012 Reclining Figure II (1966)
CNπ:580x806:signed:Presented by Rose and Chris Prater through the Institute of Contemporary Prints 1975

P04013 Reclining Figure I (1966)
CNπ:574x810:signed:Presented by Rose and Chris Prater through the Institute of Contemporary Prints 1975

P04014 Seated Figure (1966)
CNπ:787x577:signed:Presented by Rose and Chris Prater through the Institute of Contemporary Prints 1975

P04015 Playing Card - Two Heads J.Y.M. (1969)
CNπ:824x609:signed:Presented by Rose and Chris Prater through the Institute of Contemporary Prints 1975

Four Studies for 'Oxford Street Building Site I' (A01034-A01037; complete group)

A01034 [title not known] (1959)
Dπ::Presented by the artist 1961

A01035 [title not known] (1959)
Dπ::Presented by the artist 1961

A01036 [title not known] (1959)
Dπ::Presented by the artist 1961

A01037 [title not known] (1959)
Dπ::Presented by the artist 1961

AUMONIER, James 1832-1911
British Collection

N01619 Sheep-Washing in Sussex (exhibited 1889)
Oc:959x1657:signed:Presented by the Trustees of the Chantrey Bequest 1889

N01962 The Black Mountains (exhibited 1905)
Oc:1219x1829:signed:Presented by the Trustees of the Chantrey Bequest 1905

AUSTIN, Robert 1895-1973
Modern Collection

N04179 Palaces, Grand Canal, Venice (1925)
Dπ:362x495:signed:Purchased 1926

N04547 The Foot Bath (exhibited 1930)
Wπ:482x381:signed:Presented by the Trustees of the Chantrey Bequest 1930

N05676 Sewing Worn Parts on Cradle Legs (1941)
Dπ:540x660:signed:Presented by the War Artists' Advisory Committee 1946

P07001 Woman Milking Goat (1925)
MIπ:114x117:signed:Purchased 1926

AVERY, Milton 1893-1965
Modern Collection

T00575 Yellow Sky (1958)
Oc:1562x1841:Presented by Mr and Mrs Philip G. Cavanaugh through the American Federation of Arts 1963

P77109 Dawn (1952, published 1953)
MJπ:180x230:signed:Purchased 1985

AVILINE, François Antoine - see HOGARTH, William and AVILINE, François Antoine

AYOT, Pierre born 1943
Modern Collection
Tate Gallery Archive holds material concerning this artist

Homage to Albert Dumouchel (P03166-P03178; complete group; mixed group)
Hommage à Albert Dumouchel

P03166 ... and Chewing Gum (1971)
... et Boule de gomme
CLπ:705x483:Presented by the University of Quebec 1976

AYRES, Gillian born 1930
Modern Collection
Tate Gallery Archive holds material concerning this artist

T01714 Distillation (1959)
Ow:2134x1524:signed:Purchased 1973

T01715 Break-off (1961)
Oc:1524x3048:signed:Purchased 1973

T03458 Antony and Cleopatra (1982)
Oc:2893x2872:signed:Purchased 1982

The Institute of Contemporary Arts Portfolio (P04016, P04038, P04053, P04076, P04115, P04125, P04166, P04248, P04256, P04315-P04316, P04334, P04378-P04380, P04419, P04635, P04752, P04938, P05138, P05155, P05248; complete group; mixed group)

P04016   Untitled (1964)
CNπ:584x914:signed:Presented by Rose and Chris Prater through the Institute of Contemporary Prints 1975

P04017   Crivelli's Room I (1967)
CNπ:521x670:signed:Presented by Rose and Chris Prater through the Institute of Contemporary Prints 1975

P04018   Crivelli's Room II (1967)
CNπ:772x575:signed:Presented by Rose and Chris Prater through the Institute of Contemporary Prints 1975

P04019   Damask (1967)
CNπ:645x483:signed:Presented by Rose and Chris Prater through the Institute of Contemporary Prints 1975

P04020   Khuds (1967)
CNπ:695x400:signed:Presented by Rose and Chris Prater through the Institute of Contemporary Prints 1975

P04021   Lorenzo the Magnificent and Niccolo the Gear (1967)
CNπ:686x492:signed:Presented by Rose and Chris Prater through the Institute of Contemporary Prints 1975

P77156   Tachiste 1 (1956)
Lπ:546x376:signed:Purchased 1986

AYRTON, Michael 1921-1975

Modern Collection
Tate Gallery Archive holds material concerning this artist

T00460   Icarus Transformed I (1961)
Sz:203x584x305:Presented by Benjamin Sonnenberg 1961

T02104   Study for 'Greek Landscape II' (1960)
Wπ:210x276:Presented by the Institute of Contemporary Prints 1976

T03611   The Temptation of St Anthony (1942-3)
Ow:581x752:signed:Purchased 1983

P06016   Greek Landscape I (1960-61)
CLπ:406x560:Presented by Curwen Studio through the Institute of Contemporary Prints 1975

P06017   Greek Landscape II (1960-61)
CLπ:435x590:Presented by Curwen Studio through the Institute of Contemporary Prints 1975

P06018   Greek Landscape III (1960-61)
CLπ:380x567:Presented by Curwen Studio through the Institute of Contemporary Prints 1975

P08211   Bearded Head (1939)
Iπ:139x117:signed:Transferred from the Archive 1986

P08212   Clown (1939)
Iπ:69x88:signed:Transferred from the Archive 1986

P08213   Au Cirque (1939)
Iπ:178x127:signed:Transferred from the Archive 1986

BACON, Francis born 1909
Modern Collection
Tate Gallery Archive holds material concerning this artist

N05941 Figure in a Landscape (1945)
Oc:1448x1283:Purchased 1950

N06131 Study of a Dog (1952)
Oc:1981x1372:signed:Presented by Eric Hall 1952

N06171 Three Studies for Figures at the Base of a Crucifixion (circa 1944)
Ob:940x737, 940x737, 940x737:Presented by Eric Hall 1953

T00226 Study for a Portrait of Van Gogh IV (1957)
Oc:1524x1168:Presented by the Contemporary Art Society 1958

T00453 Reclining Woman (1961)
OVc:1988x1416:Purchased 1961

T00459 Seated Figure (1961)
Oc:1651x1422:Presented by J. Sainsbury Ltd 1961

T00604 Study for Portrait on Folding Bed (1963)
Oc:1981x1473:Purchased 1963

T00879 Portrait of Isabel Rawsthorne (1966)
Oc:813x686:Purchased 1966

T02112 Three Figures and Portrait (1975)
OPc:1981x1473:signed:Purchased 1977

T02414 Study for Portrait II (after the Life Mask of William Blake) (1955)
Oc:610x508:Purchased 1979

T03073 Triptych - August 1972 (1972)
Oc:1981x1473, 1981x1473:signed:Purchased 1980

BACON, John Henry F. 1868-1915
British Collection

T01450 Michael Lewis Myers (1906)
Oc:702x832:signed:Presented by Mrs Beatrice Benson 1971

BAER, Jo born 1929
Modern Collection

T03110 Stations of the Spectrum (Primary) (1967-9)
OAc:1835x1829, 1835x1829, 1835x1829:signed:Purchased 1980

BAERTLING, Olle 1911-1981
Modern Collection

T00747 Ardek (1963)
Oc:1949x968:signed:Presented by Dr Teddy Brunius 1965

T00880 Kero (1957)
Sm:2603x476x432:Presented by Mrs Birgit Silfverhjelm 1966

BAILY, Edward Hodges 1788-1867
British Collection

N02236 Bust of the Duke of Wellington (after Nollekens) (circa 1830)
Ss:787x635x381:Presented by Robert Vernon 1847

N02247 Bust of George Canning (after Nollekens) (circa 1830)
Ss:724x508x279:Presented by Robert Vernon 1847

BAJ, Enrico born 1924
Modern Collection
Tate Gallery Archive holds material concerning this artist

T01777 Fire! Fire! (1963-4)
Al fuoco, al fuoco
OVf:1286x972:signed:Presented by Avvocato Paride Accetti 1973

For Jorn (P03241-P03255; complete group; mixed group)
Pour Jorn
P03244 [no title] (1975-6)
CLπ:752x549:signed:Presented by the Asger Jorn Foundation 1978

BALDACCINI, César - see CÉSAR

BALDESSARI, John born 1931
Modern Collection
Tate Gallery Archive holds material concerning this artist

Black Dice (P07808-P07816, P07853; complete group)
P07808 [no title] (1982)
CIπ:162x203:signed:Purchased 1983

P07809 [no title] (1982)
CIπ:162x203:signed:Purchased 1983

P07810 [no title] (1982)
CIπ:162x203:signed:Purchased 1983

P07811 [no title] (1982)
CIπ:162x203:signed:Purchased 1983

P07812 [no title] (1982)
CIπ:162x203:signed:Purchased 1983

P07813 [no title] (1982)
CIπ:162x203:signed:Purchased 1983

P07814 [no title] (1982)
CIπ:162x203:signed:Purchased 1983

P07815 [no title] (1982)
CIπ:162x203:signed:Purchased 1983

P07816 [no title] (1982)
CIπ:162x203:signed:Purchased 1983

P07853 [no title] (1982)
MFπ:178x222:signed:Purchased 1983

BALDWIN, Michael - see ART & LANGUAGE (ATKINSON, Terry and BALDWIN, Michael) and ART & LANGUAGE (BALDWIN, Michael and RAMSDEN, Mel)

BALLA, Giacomo 1871-1958
Modern Collection

T01222 Abstract Speed - The Car has Passed (1913)
Velocità astratta - l'auto è passata
Oc:502x654:signed:Presented by the Friends of the Tate Gallery 1970

BALTHUS (Balthasar Klossowski de Rola) born 1908
Modern Collection

T00297 Sleeping Girl (1943)
Dormeuse
Ob:797x984:signed:Presented by the Friends of the Tate Gallery 1959

BANC, Jef born 1930
Modern Collection

T00357 Pair-Bearing Matrix (1956)
Matrice gémellipare
Oc:730x600:signed:Presented by Mr and Mrs Charles
Damiano 1960

BANTING, John 1902-1971
Modern Collection
Tate Gallery Archive holds material concerning this artist

T01470 Conversation Piece (1935)
Tπ:524x460:Purchased 1971

P07002 Snake in the Grass, Alas (1931)
CJπ:229x276:signed:Purchased 1972

P07003 Explosion (1931)
CJπ:83x127:signed:Purchased 1972

P07004 Siamese Triplets (1932)
CJπ:273x222:signed:Purchased 1972

P07005 One Man Band (1934)
CJπ:197x327:signed:Purchased 1972

P07006 Abstract (1935)
MJπ:229x273:signed:Purchased 1972

P07007 Negro Guitarist (1935)
MJπ:235x276:signed:Purchased 1972

BARAN, Stefan born 1922
Modern Collection

P04024 Royal Family (1972)
CNπ:616x435:Presented by Rose and Chris Prater
through the Institute of Contemporary Prints 1975

P04025 Ted Heath (1972)
CNπ:613x441:Presented by Rose and Chris Prater
through the Institute of Contemporary Prints 1975

BARENGER, James 1780-1831
British Collection

T02356 Jonathan Griffin, Huntsman to the Earl of Derby's
Staghounds (1813)
Oc:1016x1270:signed:Presented by Paul Mellon through
the British Sporting Art Trust 1979

BARKER, Clive born 1940
Modern Collection
Tate Gallery Archive holds material concerning this artist

T01211 Splash (1967)
Sm:864x356x356:Purchased 1970

P01803 Homage to Magritte (1969)
CNπ:762x508:signed:Presented by Gordon House 1976

P04022 Zip I (1965)
CNπ:762x495:signed:Presented by Rose and Chris Prater
through the Institute of Contemporary Prints 1975

P04023 Zip II (1965)
CNπ:762x470:signed:Presented by Rose and Chris Prater
through the Institute of Contemporary Prints 1975

BARKER, Margaret born 1907
Modern Collection

N04474 Any Morning (exhibited 1929)
Oc:622x914:Presented by the Trustees of the Chantrey
Bequest 1929

BARKER, Thomas, of Bath 1767-1847
British Collection

N00792 The Woodman and his Dog in a Storm (circa 1787)
Oc:2362x1486:Presented by R.E. Lofft 1868

N01039 Getting in Clover: Noon (1807)
Oc:660x991:signed:Purchased 1878

N01306 Landscape with Figures and Sheep (circa 1815)
Oc:813x1130:Purchased 1890

N02987 Landscape (circa 1800)
Oc:762x610:Bequeathed by Richard and Catherine
Garnons 1854

N04196 Landscape, near Bath (circa 1798)
Oc:813x1067:Presented by Lord Duveen 1926

N05044 Self-Portrait (circa 1796)
Oc:756x629:Presented by the National Art Collections
Fund 1939

BARLACH, Ernst 1870-1938
Modern Collection

T00951 The Avenger (1914, later cast)
Der Rächer
Sz:438x578x203:signed:Purchased 1967

BARLOW, Francis 1626 or 7 - 1704
British Collection

T01402 A Roller, Two Peregrine Falcons and a Long-Eared Owl
with her Young
Oc:1060x1372:Purchased 1971

T05572 Monkeys and Spaniels Playing (1661)
Oc:1055x1320:Purchased with assistance from the
Friends of the Tate Gallery 1989

BARNI, Roberto born 1939
Modern Collection

P77024 Knights of the Daily Round (1982)
Cavaliere del quotidiano
MIπ:584x787:signed:Purchased 1984

P77025 Fatherhood (1982)
Paternità
CIπ:237x473:signed:Purchased 1984

BARNS-GRAHAM, Wilhelmina born 1912
Modern Collection
Tate Gallery Archive holds material concerning this artist

T00708 Glacier Crystal, Grindelwald (1950)
Oc:514x609:signed:Presented by the Contemporary Art
Society 1964

T02237 Composition I (1954)
ODb:178x254:signed:Bequeathed by Miss E.M.
Hodgkins 1977

T02238 Red Form (1954)
Ob:340x419:signed:Bequeathed by Miss E.M. Hodgkins
1977

BARRET, George, Senior 1728 or 32 - 1784
British Collection

T01881 River Scene with Watermill, Figures and Cows
Oc:997x1248:Bequeathed by Alan Evans 1974

BARRET, George, Junior 1767-1842
British Collection

T01860 Landscape with a Bridge
WDπ:498x670:Purchased 1974

BARRON, Hugh 1747-1791
British Collection

T01882 The Children of George Bond of Ditchleys (1768)
Oc:1060x1397:signed:Bequeathed by Alan Evans 1974

BARRY, James 1741-1806
British Collection

T00556 King Lear Weeping over the Dead Body of Cordelia
(1786-8)
Oc:2692x3670:signed:Purchased 1962

T03784 A Grecian Harvest Home (first published 1792)
Iπ:470x625:signed:Purchased 1983

T03785 The Thames, or the Triumph of Navigation (first
published 1792)
Iπ:457x562:signed:Purchased 1983

T03786 The Distribution of Premiums in the Society of Arts
(first published 1792)
Iπ:430x528:signed:Purchased 1983

T03787 Elysium and Tartarus (first published 1792)
Iπ:524x925:signed:Purchased 1983

T03788 Detail of the Diagorides Victors (first published 1795)
Iπ:770x508:signed:Purchased 1983

BARTLETT, Jennifer born 1941
Modern Collection
Tate Gallery Archive holds material concerning this artist

P07443 At Sea Japan (1980)
CJNπ:571x2545:signed:Purchased 1981

BAS, Edward le - see LE BAS, Edward

BASALDELLA, Afro - see AFRO

BASELITZ, Georg born 1938
Modern Collection
Tate Gallery Archive holds material concerning this artist

T03442 Rebel (1965)
Rebell
Oc:1627x1302:signed:Purchased 1982

T03672 Adieu (1982)
Adieu
Oc:2052x3004:signed:Purchased 1983

T03945 Study for Woodcut (1967)
Vorzeichnung für Holzschnitt
Dπ:611x430:signed:Purchased 1984

P07737 Rebel (1965)
Rebell
MIπ:320x235:signed:Purchased 1982

P07738 Untitled (1965)
Ohne Titel
MIπ:310x245:signed:Purchased 1982

P07739 Untitled (with Dog and Axe) (1967)
Ohne Titel (Mit Hund und Axt)
MIπ:334x245:signed:Purchased 1982

P07779 Eagle (1981)
Adler
MJπ:647x497, 858x609:signed:Purchased 1982

P07780 Head (1982)
Kopf
CJπ:651x502:signed:Purchased 1982

P07998 Drummer (1982)
Trommler
MJ:2010x1508:signed:Purchased 1984

P77011 Female Nude on a Kitchen Chair (1977-9)
Weiblicher Akt auf Küchenstuhl
MJc:2021x1370:signed:Purchased 1984

P77263 Large Head (1966)
Grosser Kopf
Jπ:438x405:Purchased 1988

P77266 Man on the Beach (1982)
Mann am Strand
Jπ:853x634:Purchased 1988

P77268 From the Front (1985)
Von Vorne
Jπ:650x490:Purchased 1985

BASKIN, Leonard born 1922
Modern Collection
Tate Gallery Archive holds material concerning this artist

P01789 The Anatomist (1952)
CJπ:502x279:signed:Presented by the Museum of
Modern Art, New York 1976

BATEMAN, James 1815-1849
British Collection

T03210 Highland Scene (1844)
Ow:203x254:signed:Presented anonymously in memory of
Mrs M. Bernard 1981

BATEMAN, James 1893-1959
Modern Collection

N04471 Pastoral (1928)
Oc:991x1829:signed:Presented by the Trustees of the
Chantrey Bequest 1929

N04834 Commotion in the Cattle Ring (1935)
Oc:1016x1270:signed:Presented by the Trustees of the
Chantrey Bequest 1936

N04958 Cattle Market (1937)
Oc:914x1118:signed:Presented by the Trustees of the
Chantrey Bequest 1938

BATES, Harry 1850-1899
British Collection

N01750 Pandora (exhibited 1891)
Ssiz:940x508x737:signed:Presented by the Trustees of the
Chantrey Bequest 1891

N01767 Hounds in Leash (1888-9)
Sp:1067x2210x1067:signed:Presented by Lord Wemyss
1899

N01783 Sketch for War (1887)
Rp:546x267x89:signed:Presented by C.J. Knowles 1900

BATES, Maxwell born 1906
Modern Collection

Centennial Suite (P03217-P03225, P03228-P03229;
complete group; mixed group)
P03217 Interior (1968)
CNπ:508x384:signed:Presented by Simon Fraser
University, British Columbia 1977

BAUCHANT, André 1873-1958
Modern Collection

N05319 Greek Dance in a Landscape (1937)
Danse grecque dans un paysage
Om:302x1460:signed:Purchased 1942

T00466 The Funeral Procession of Alexander the Great (1940)
Les Funérailles d'Alexandre-le-Grand
Oc:1140x1949:signed:Bequeathed by Arthur Jeffress 1961

BAUER, Marius 1867-1932
Modern Collection

N04588 Strasbourg Cathedral (circa 1891)
Wπ:689x521:signed:Presented by Sir Michael Sadler
through the National Art Collections Fund in memory of
Lady Sadler 1931

BAUMEISTER, Willi 1889-1955
Modern Collection

P08214 Untitled (1953)
Ohne Titel
MLπ:260x208:signed:Transferred from the Library 1987

BAUMGARTEN, Lothar born 1944
Modern Collection

P77183 Fish (1985)
CNπ:680x999:signed:Purchased 1987
P77284 Shaprai Bow (1985)
Nπ:685x1001:Purchased 1989
P77285 Equator (1985)
Aquator
Nπ:610x898:Purchased 1989
P77286 Metals (1985)
Metalle
Nπ:597x851:Purchased 1989
P77293 Yanomami (1987)
NHπ:907x1280:signed:Purchased 1989

BAWDEN, Edward 1903-1989
Modern Collection
Tate Gallery Archive holds material concerning this artist

N05156 The Bell Inn (1939)
Wπ:457x546:signed:Purchased 1940
N05677 Cairo, the Citadel: Mohammed Ali Mosque (circa 1941)
WDπ:470x597:signed:Presented by the War Artists'
Advisory Committee 1946
N05678 Cairo, the Citadel: On the Roof of the Officers' Mess
(circa 1941)
WDπ:464x591:signed:Presented by the War Artists'
Advisory Committee 1946
N05679 Gallabat: Guns Firing on Metemma (1940)
Wπ:394x514:signed:Presented by the War Artists'
Advisory Committee 1946

N05680 Gubba: Panorama of the Town (1941)
WDπ:381x978:signed:Presented by the War Artists'
Advisory Committee 1946
N05681 Burnt Tukl at Gubba (1941)
WDπ:394x521:signed:Presented by the War Artists'
Advisory Committee 1946
N05682 View from the Enemy H.Q. at Gubba (1941)
WDπ:394x514:signed:Presented by the War Artists'
Advisory Committee 1946
N05683 The Catholic Church, Addis Ababa (1941)
WDπ:457x578:signed:Presented by the War Artists'
Advisory Committee 1946
N05684 Tobruk: The Harbour (1942)
WDπ:451x1156:signed:Presented by the War Artists'
Advisory Committee 1946
N05685 Zghorta, Syria: Panorama of the Camp of the 8th, 10th
and 12th Indian Mule Corps; in the Distance Lebanon
(1942)
WDπ:457x1206:signed:Presented by the War Artists'
Advisory Committee 1946
N06012 The Canmore Mountain Range (1950)
GDπ:565x718:signed:Purchased 1951
T00036 The Church Wall (1954)
WDπ:451x571:signed:Purchased 1955
T00206 Houses at Ironbridge (1956, 1957)
WDπ:470x581:signed:Purchased 1958
T00281 Caradon (1958)
Wπ:464x578:signed:Purchased 1959
T04919 Roses and Rue (1986)
WDπ:504x654:signed:Purchased 1987
T04920 Emma Nelson by the Fire (1987)
DWπ:498x645:signed:Purchased 1987
P01358 Audley End House (1973)
CJπ:508x635:signed:Presented by Christie's
Contemporary Art through the Institute of
Contemporary Prints 1975

Six London Markets (P06019-P06024; complete group)
P06019 Billingsgate Market (1967)
CLπ:463x613:signed:Presented by Curwen Studio
through the Institute of Contemporary Prints 1975
P06020 Borough Market (1967)
CLπ:460x612:signed:Presented by Curwen Studio
through the Institute of Contemporary Prints 1975
P06021 Covent Garden Flower Market (1967)
CLπ:464x611:signed:Presented by Curwen Studio
through the Institute of Contemporary Prints 1975
P06022 Covent Garden Fruit Market (1967)
CLπ:460x612:signed:Presented by Curwen Studio
through the Institute of Contemporary Prints 1975
P06023 Leadenhall Market (1967)
CLπ:462x616:signed:Presented by Curwen Studio
through the Institute of Contemporary Prints 1975
P06024 Smithfield Market (1967)
CLπ:462x618:signed:Presented by Curwen Studio
through the Institute of Contemporary Prints 1975

BAWDEN, Richard born 1936
Modern Collection

Follies (P06025, P06028-P06029, P06315-P06316,
P06518, P06588-P06589; complete group; mixed group)
P06025 Sezincote (1971)
CLπ:473x613:signed:Presented by Curwen Studio
through the Institute of Contemporary Prints 1975

P06721 Telford's Bridge, Conway (1965)
CLπ:597x457:signed:Presented by Curwen Studio 1977

BAXTER, Glen born 1944
Modern Collection

[no title, portfolio of six letter press prints]
(P07604-P07609; complete group)
P07604 It was Henderson's Sixth Attempt at Lasagne (1978)
MJπ:100x125:signed:Purchased 1982
P07605 Seth's Snood was the Envy of the Boys in the Bunkhouse
(1978)
MJπ:107x160:signed:Purchased 1982
P07606 The Twins Devoted an Hour Each Day to the Walnut
(1978)
MJπ:111x150:signed:Purchased 1982
P07607 The Twins Introduced the Imposter (1978)
MJπ:117x125:signed:Purchased 1982
P07608 'To me the window is still a symbolically loaded motif'
Drawled Cody (1978)
MJπ:120x112:signed:Purchased 1982
P07609 'To my mind there's no finer sight than kale moving at
speed' Opined Millward (1978)
MJπ:120x147:signed:Purchased 1982

BAXTER, Iain born 1936
Modern Collection

Centennial Suite (P03217-P03225, P03228-P03229;
complete group; mixed group)
P03218 Bagged Day-Glo Oranges (1967-8)
CNπ:508x381:signed:Presented by Simon Fraser
University, British Columbia 1977

BAYER, Herbert born 1900
Modern Collection

P04026 The Four Seasons (1969)
Die Vier Jahreszeiten
CNπ:445x448:signed:Presented by Rose and Chris Prater
through the Institute of Contemporary Prints 1975
P04027 Four Yellow Corners (1969)
Vier Gelbe Ecken
CNπ:457x457:signed:Presented by Rose and Chris Prater
through the Institute of Contemporary Prints 1975
P04028 Building a House (1969)
Ein Haus bauen
CNπ:781x575:signed:Presented by Rose and Chris Prater
through the Institute of Contemporary Prints 1975
P04029 One Reversed (1969)
Eins umgekehrt
CNπ:432x432:signed:Presented by Rose and Chris Prater
through the Institute of Contemporary Prints 1975

A Series of Eight Screenprints (P04030-P04037;
complete group)
P04030 Birthday Picture I (1970)
Geburtstagsbild I
CNπ:750x750:signed:Presented by Rose and Chris Prater
through the Institute of Contemporary Prints 1975
P04031 Birthday Picture II (1970)
Geburtstagsbild II
CNπ:750x750:signed:Presented by Rose and Chris Prater
through the Institute of Contemporary Prints 1975

P04032 Chromatic Intersection (1970)
Chromatisch durchkreuzt
CNπ:750x752:signed:Presented by Rose and Chris Prater
through the Institute of Contemporary Prints 1975
P04033 Chromatic Triangulation II (1970)
Chromatische Triangulierung II
CNπ:750x750:signed:Presented by Rose and Chris Prater
through the Institute of Contemporary Prints 1975
P04034 Chromatic Twist (1970)
Chromatische Drehung
CNπ:752x752:signed:Presented by Rose and Chris Prater
through the Institute of Contemporary Prints 1975
P04035 Complementary with Gold (1970)
Komplimentär mit Gold
CNπ:753x753:signed:Presented by Rose and Chris Prater
through the Institute of Contemporary Prints 1975
P04036 Four Segmented Circles (1970)
Vier Kreisabschnitte
CNπ:755x755:signed:Presented by Rose and Chris Prater
through the Institute of Contemporary Prints 1975
P04037 Yellow Centre (1970)
Gelbes Zentrum
CNπ:755x755:signed:Presented by Rose and Chris Prater
through the Institute of Contemporary Prints 1975

BAYES, Gilbert 1872-1953
British Collection
Tate Gallery Archive holds material concerning this artist
N02739 Sigurd (exhibited 1910)
Szsv:886x483x286:Presented by the Trustees of the
Chantrey Bequest 1910

BAYES, Walter 1869-1956
British Collection

N04388 The Ford (circa 1917-20)
Oc:1022x1448:signed:Purchased 1928
N04738 Under the Candles: Mr Charles Ginner Presiding (1933)
GDπ:724x1168:signed:Presented by the friends
associated with the artist during his Headmastership of
Westminster School 1934

BAZIOTES, William 1912-1963
Modern Collection

T01693 Mammoth (1957)
Oc:1219x1524:signed:Presented by Mr and Mrs Leonard
S. Field 1972

BEACH, Thomas 1738-1806
British Collection

T01883 Portrait of a Gentleman in a Green Robe (1773)
Oc:759x641:signed:Bequeathed by Alan Evans 1974

attributed to
BEALE, Mary 1633-1699
British Collection

N03546 Portrait of a Man
Oc:749x629:Presented by Alfred A. de Pass 1920

BEAMENT, Tib born 1941
Modern Collection

Homage to Albert Dumouchel (P03166-P03178;
complete group; mixed group)
Hommage à Albert Dumouchel
P03167   [no title] (1971-2)
MIπ:505x403:signed:Presented by the University of
Quebec 1976

BEARDSLEY, Aubrey 1872-1898
British Collection
Tate Gallery Archive holds material concerning this artist

N03815   Caprice. Verso: Masked Woman with a White Mouse
(circa 1894)
Oc:762x635, 641x514:Purchased 1923
N04171   Cover Design for the 'Yellow Book' (1894)
DWπ:260x216:signed:Bequeathed by John Lane 1926
N04172   Design for the Frontispiece to John Davidson's Plays
(1894)
DWπ:286x187:signed:Bequeathed by John Lane 1926
N04235   Professor Fred Brown (1892)
Dπ:254x254:signed:Presented by Mrs Helen Thorp 1927
N04423   Messalina and her Companion (1895)
DWπ:279x178:Presented by A.L. Assheton 1928
N04608   La Dame aux Camelias (1894)
DWπ:279x181:Presented by Colonel James Lister Melvill
at the request of his brother, Harry Edward Melvill 1931
N04609   The Fat Woman (1894)
DWπ:178x162:signed:Presented by Colonel James Lister
Melvill at the request of his brother, Harry Edward
Melvill 1931

BEARE, George active 1743-1749
British Collection

T00201   Portrait of a Gentleman, possibly Hugh Marriott (1746)
Oc:759x632:Purchased 1958

BEATTIE, Basil born 1935
Modern Collection

P77110   Circus (1984)
CLπ:573x775:signed:Purchased 1985

BEAUMONT, Sir George Howland, Bt
1753-1827
British Collection

N00119   Landscape, with Jacques and the Wounded Stag (?1819)
Oc:756x1016:Presented by the Dowager Lady Beaumont
1828
T01148   Landscape
Oπ:133x159:Purchased 1969
T01221   Waterfall at Keswick (1803)
DWπ:311x279:Purchased 1970
T01231   The River Stour at Dedham (1790)
DWπ:165x225:Purchased 1970

BECHER, Bernhard and BECHER, Hilla
born 1931, born 1934
Modern Collection
Tate Gallery Archive holds material concerning these
artists

T01922   Pitheads (1974)
Fb:1133x1318:Purchased 1974
T01923   Coal Bunkers (1974)
Fb:1495x1003:Purchased 1974

BECKER, Harald born 1940
Modern Collection

P01359   Man and Dog (1973)
CNπ:629x502:signed:Presented by Editions Alecto
through the Institute of Contemporary Prints 1975

BECKMANN, Max 1884-1950
Modern Collection

T02395   Prunier (1944)
Oc:1003x768:Purchased 1979
T03294   Carnival (1920)
Fastnacht
Oc:1864x918:signed:Purchased with assistance from the
National Art Collections Fund and Friends of the Tate
Gallery and Mercedes-Benz (U.K.) Ltd 1981

BEECHEY, Sir William 1753-1839
British Collection

N00120   Joseph Nollekens (exhibited 1812)
Oc:762x635:Purchased with assistance from the Rev.
R.E. Kerrich 1835
N01670   James P. Johnstone
Oc:749x619:Bequeathed by Maj.-Gen. John Julius
Johnstone 1898
N01671   Alexander P. Johnstone (circa 1790-95)
Oc:762x635:Bequeathed by Maj.-Gen. John Julius
Johnstone 1898
N04688   Thomas Law Hodges (?exhibited 1795)
Oc:765x635:Bequeathed by Sir Edward Stern 1933

BEER, Richard born 1928
Modern Collection
Tate Gallery Archive holds material concerning this artist

P01360   Magdalen Bridge (1973)
CLπ:597x467:signed:Presented by Christie's
Contemporary Art through the Institute of
Contemporary Prints 1975
P01361   Oxford Spires (1974)
CLπ:591x438:signed:Presented by Christie's
Contemporary Art through the Institute of
Contemporary Prints 1975
P06026   Nash Terrace (1970)
CLπ:581x451:signed:Presented by Curwen Studio
through the Institute of Contemporary Prints 1975
P06027   Ca Rezzonico (1971)
CLπ:768x419:signed:Presented by Curwen Studio
through the Institute of Contemporary Prints 1975

Follies (P06025, P06028-P06029, P06315-P06316,
P06518, P06588-P06589; complete group; mixed group)
P06028   Conolly's Obelisk (1971)
CLπ:651x467:signed:Presented by Curwen Studio
through the Institute of Contemporary Prints 1975

P06029 Rushton Triangular Lodge (1971)
CLπ:664x435:signed:Presented by Curwen Studio through the Institute of Contemporary Prints 1975

P06030 Greenlands (1972)
CLπ:613x464:signed:Presented by Curwen Studio through the Institute of Contemporary Prints 1975

BEERBOHM, Sir Max 1872-1956
British Collection
Tate Gallery Archive holds material concerning this artist

N03199 John S. Sargent. Verso: Studies of Heads (circa 1910)
WDπ:406x206:Presented by Sir William Rothenstein in memory of Gerard Chowne 1917

N04165 A Quiet Morning in the Tate Gallery (1907)
WDπ:368x318:signed:Purchased 1926

N04332 Annual Banquet: A Suggestion to the New English Art Club (1913)
WDπ:305x406:signed:Bequeathed by J.R. Holliday 1927

N06043 Bravura: Sir William Orpen (1914)
WDπ:394x283:signed:Presented by Simon Nowell Smith 1952

N06075 The New English Art Club (1907)
WDπ:343x419:signed:Purchased 1952

Rossetti and his Friends (A01038-A01060; complete group)

A01038 D.G. Rossetti Precociously Manifesting . . . that Queer Indifference to Politics . . . (1916-17)
DWπ:273x419:signed:Bequeathed by Sir Hugh Walpole 1941

A01039 British Stock and Alien Inspiration, 1849 (1917)
DWπ:298x419:signed:Bequeathed by Sir Hugh Walpole 1941

A01040 Rossetti's Courtship (1916)
DWπ:324x210:signed:Bequeathed by Sir Hugh Walpole 1941

A01041 The Sole Remark Likely to Have Been Made by Benjamin Jowett about the Mural Paintings at the Oxford Union (1916)
DWπ:451x298:signed:Bequeathed by Sir Hugh Walpole 1941

A01042 Miss Cornforth: 'Oh, very pleased to meet Mr Ruskin, I'm sure' (1916)
DWπ:330x248:signed:Bequeathed by Sir Hugh Walpole 1941

A01043 Ford Madox Brown being Patronized by Holman Hunt (1916)
DWπ:362x397:signed:Bequeathed by Sir Hugh Walpole 1941

A01044 A Momentary Vision that Once Befell Young Millais (1916)
DWπ:324x432:signed:Bequeathed by Sir Hugh Walpole 1941

A01045 Spring Cottage, Hampstead, 1860 (1917)
DWπ:324x432:signed:Bequeathed by Sir Hugh Walpole 1941

A01046 Woolner at Farringford, 1857 (1917)
DWπ:330x260:signed:Bequeathed by Sir Hugh Walpole 1941

A01047 Blue China (1916)
DWπ:337x273:signed:Bequeathed by Sir Hugh Walpole 1941

A01048 The Small Hours in the 'Sixties at 16 Cheyne Walk (1916)
DWπ:225x349:signed:Bequeathed by Sir Hugh Walpole 1941

A01049 Topsy and Ned Jones Settled on the Settle in Red Lion Square (1916)
DWπ:311x387:signed:Bequeathed by Sir Hugh Walpole 1941

A01050 Rossetti, having just had a fresh consignment of 'stunning' fabrics . . . tries hard to prevail on his younger sister to accept . . . one (1917)
DWπ:343x286:signed:Bequeathed by Sir Hugh Walpole 1941

A01051 Rossetti in his Worldlier Days Leaving the Arundel Club with George Augustus Sala (1916)
DWπ:375x257:signed:Bequeathed by Sir Hugh Walpole 1941

A01052 Rossetti Insistently Exhorted by George Meredith to Come Forth into the Glorious Sun and Wind for a Walk to Hendon and Beyond (1916)
DWπ:330x419:signed:Bequeathed by Sir Hugh Walpole 1941

A01053 Mr Morley . . . introduces Mr John Stuart Mill (1917)
DWπ:406x298:signed:Bequeathed by Sir Hugh Walpole 1941

A01054 Riverside Scene. Algernon Swinburne Takes his Great New Friend Gosse to See Gabriel Rossetti (1916)
DWπ:305x298:signed:Bequeathed by Sir Hugh Walpole 1941

A01055 Mr Browning Brings a Lady of Rank and Fashion to See Mr Rossetti (1916)
DWπ:286x419:signed:Bequeathed by Sir Hugh Walpole 1941

A01056 Mr William Bell Scott Wondering What It is Those Fellows Seem to See in Gabriel (1916)
DWπ:292x394:signed:Bequeathed by Sir Hugh Walpole 1941

A01057 The Man from Hymettus. Mr Frederick Leighton (1916)
DWπ:438x318:signed:Bequeathed by Sir Hugh Walpole 1941

A01058 Quis Custodiet Ipsum Custodem (1916)
DWπ:349x286:signed:Bequeathed by Sir Hugh Walpole 1941

A01059 Mr - and Miss - Nervously Perpetuating the Touch of a Vanished Hand (1917)
DWπ:318x387:signed:Bequeathed by Sir Hugh Walpole 1941

A01060 The Name of Dante Gabriel Rossetti is Heard for the First Time in the Western States of America (1916)
DWπ:400x368:signed:Bequeathed by Sir Hugh Walpole 1941

BEETON, Alan 1880-1942
Modern Collection

N04668 Decomposing (circa 1929)
Oc:343x394:Presented by the Trustees of the Chantrey Bequest 1931

BEGGS, Guy born 1947
Modern Collection

P06031 In the Shade (1973)
CLπ:232x229:Presented by Curwen Studio through the Institute of Contemporary Prints 1975

BEHNES, William 1795-1864
British Collection

N02237 Robert Vernon (1849)
Ss:787x565x279:signed:Presented by Queen Victoria, the Prince Consort and other subscribers in acknowledgment of his gift to the nation in 1847 of his collection of British paintings and sculptures 1850

BELCHER, George 1875-1947
British Collection

N04327 'Alablaster Busks, lidy, 2d. each' (1909-11)
DWπ:295x215:signed:Bequeathed by J.R. Holliday 1927

N04328 'I've sent for you to mend a piece of wood in the conservatory . . .' (1908-9)
Dπ:356x261:signed:Bequeathed by J.R. Holliday 1927

BELL, Graham 1910-1943
Modern Collection
Tate Gallery Archive holds material concerning this artist

N05461 Miss Anne Popham (1937-8)
Oc:762x635:signed:Purchased 1944

T00905 Dover Front (1938)
Oc:635x762:signed:Presented by the Trustees of the Chantrey Bequest 1967

BELL, John Zephaniah 1794-1883
British Collection

N01392 Cardinal Bourchier Urges the Widow of Edward IV to Let her Son out of Sanctuary (exhibited 1868)
Oc:1321x1765:Presented by the artist's widow 1893

BELL, Larry born 1939
Modern Collection
Tate Gallery Archive holds material concerning this artist

T01473 Untitled (1971)
Sgv:1880x5490x2440:Purchased 1971

T01695 Untitled (1962)
Sgw:349x324x222:Purchased 1972

T01696 Untitled (1964)
Smg:222x222x222:Purchased 1972

T01697 Untitled (1967)
Smg:362x362x362:Purchased 1972

T02411 Vapour Drawing LDIF 4 (1979)
DMπ:1524x924:signed:Purchased 1979

T02412 Vapour Drawing LNVF XI (1979)
DMπ:1527x1076:signed:Purchased 1979

BELL, Laura Anning 1867-1950
British Collection

N04563 Miss Annie Horniman (?circa 1910)
Pπ:502x400:signed:Presented by the artist 1931

BELL, Robert Anning 1863-1933
British Collection

N02073 The Listeners (1906)
WGπ:495x749:signed:Presented by the Trustees of the Chantrey Bequest 1906

N02478 Music by the Water (1900)
WGπ:387x540:signed:Bequeathed by Major-General Sir Mathew Gossett KCB 1909

N03335 Mary in the House of Elizabeth (1917)
Oc:1422x762:signed:Presented by the Trustees of the Chantrey Bequest 1918

N04753 Her Son (?circa 1933)
WGπ:552x781:Presented by the Trustees of the Chantrey Bequest 1934

BELL, Trevor born 1930
Modern Collection
Tate Gallery Archive holds material concerning this artist

T00479 Overcast (1961)
Oc:610x610:signed:Purchased 1962

P06032 Five Stages (1961)
CLπ:810x575:Presented by Curwen Studio through the Institute of Contemporary Prints 1975

BELL, Vanessa 1879-1961
British Collection

N03836 Chrysanthemums (1920)
Oc:610x457:signed:Presented by the Contemporary Art Society 1924

N05077 Nude (circa 1922-3)
Oc:813x654:Bequeathed by Frank Hindley Smith 1940

N05078 Interior with a Table (1921)
Oc:540x641:signed:Bequeathed by Frank Hindley Smith 1940

N05749 Pheasants (1931)
Oc:908x730:signed:Presented by Sir Kenneth Clark (later Lord Clark of Saltwood) through the Contemporary Art Society 1946

T01123 Helen Dudley (circa 1915)
Oc:724x610:Presented by the Trustees of the Chantrey Bequest 1969

T01133 Still Life on Corner of a Mantelpiece (1914)
Oc:559x457:Purchased 1969

T01277 Frederick and Jessie Etchells Painting (1912)
Ob:511x530:signed:Purchased 1971

T01768 Mrs St John Hutchinson (1915)
Ob:737x578:signed:Purchased 1973

T01935 Abstract Painting (circa 1914)
Gc:441x387:Purchased 1974

T02010 The Tub (1917)
Vc:1803x1664:Purchased 1975

T02080 Studland Beach. Verso: Group of Male Nudes by Duncan Grant (circa 1912)
Oc:762x1016:Purchased 1976

BELLANY, John born 1942
Modern Collection

T02333 Celtic Marriage (1978)
Oc:2540x1270:Purchased 1979

T02336 Star of Bethlehem (1968)
Ob:1841x2454:Presented by the Contemporary Art Society 1979

T05734 Self Portrait (1988)
Wπ:774x568:Purchased 1990

T05735 Self Portrait (1988)
Wπ:570x386:Purchased 1990

P07901 Death Knell for John Knox (1972)
MIπ:473x500:signed:Purchased 1983

P07902 Janus (1982)
CNπ:915x685:signed:Purchased 1983

The Old Man and the Sea (P77201-P77203; incomplete group)

P77201 [no title] (1987)
Lπ:530x425:signed:Purchased 1987

P77202 [no title] (1987)
Lπ:479x324:signed:Purchased 1987

P77203 [no title] (1987)
Lπ:756x568:signed:Purchased 1987

BELLEGARDE, Claude born 1927
Modern Collection

T00301 Bird I (1957)
L'Oiseau I
OVc:549x1003:signed:Presented by Mr and Mrs
Alexander Margulies 1959

BELLEROCHE, Count Albert de - see DE BELLEROCHE, Count Albert

BELLINGHAM-SMITH, Elinor 1906-1988
Modern Collection

N05873 Dragon-Flies (1947-8)
Oc:610x914:signed:Purchased 1948

BELLMER, Hans 1902-1975
Modern Collection

T00713 Peg-Top (circa 1937-52)
La Toupie
Oc:648x648:signed:Purchased 1964

T01157 The Doll (1936/1965)
La Poupée
SOm:464x260x229:signed:Purchased 1969

T02305 The Doll (circa 1937-8)
La Poupée
FDπ:184x648:signed:Presented anonymously through the
Friends of the Tate Gallery 1978

T05008 Portrait of Jean Arp (1954)
Portrait de Jean Arp
Dπ:482x320:signed:Presented by Mr and Mrs Robert
Lewin through the Friends of the Tate Gallery 1987

BENJAMIN, Anthony born 1931
Modern Collection
Tate Gallery Archive holds material concerning this artist

Roxy Bias (P01362-P01367; complete group)

P01362 Butterfly Echo (1972)
CNπ:991x686:signed:Presented by Clarendon Graphics
through the Institute of Contemporary Prints 1975

P01363 Eraze function (1972)
CNπ:991x686:signed:Presented by Clarendon Graphics
through the Institute of Contemporary Prints 1975

P01364 Inverse Echo (1972)
CNπ:991x686:signed:Presented by Clarendon Graphics
through the Institute of Contemporary Prints 1975

P01365 Multi Mode Jitter (1972)
CNπ:991x686:signed:Presented by Clarendon Graphics
through the Institute of Contemporary Prints 1975

P01366 O Factor (1972)
CNπ:991x686:signed:Presented by Clarendon Graphics
through the Institute of Contemporary Prints 1975

P01367 Ringing Filter (1972)
CNπ:991x686:signed:Presented by Clarendon Graphics
through the Institute of Contemporary Prints 1975

P08026 Drifting Blue Edge (1968)
CNπ:1016x762:signed:Transferred from the Library 1978

BENNETT, William 1811-1871
British Collection

N01722 In Richmond Park (1852)
Wπ:368x546:signed:Presented by E. Homan 1899

BENOIS, Alexander 1870-1960
Modern Collection

T00652 Limburg on the Lahn (1894)
Limburg an der Lahn
Wπ:359x260:Transferred from the Library 1964

BENOIS, Nadia 1896-1975
Modern Collection
Tate Gallery Archive holds material concerning this artist

N04855 Near La Garde Freinet (1935)
Oc:635x762:signed:Presented by the Contemporary Art
Society 1936

BENRATH, Frederick born 1930
Modern Collection

P08222 Untitled (1956)
Lπ:428x293:Transferred from the Library 1989

BENSON, Abraham Harris 1878-1929
British Collection

N04648 Anemones (1929)
Wb:282x267:signed:Presented by Mrs A.H. Benson 1932

N04649 Newlands Corner (1928)
Wb:155x368:signed:Presented by Mrs A.H. Benson 1932

BÉRAUD, Jean 1849-1935
Modern Collection

N04867 After the Misdeed (circa 1885-90)
Après la Faute
Oc:381x460:Presented by Mlle Emilie Yznaga 1937

BERBER, Mersad born 1940
Modern Collection

P02547 Byzantium III (1973-80)
CNπ:1196x836:signed:Presented by the artist 1981

P07583 Byzantium I (1980)
CNπ:1200x800:signed:Purchased 1981

BERG, Adrian born 1929
Modern Collection

T03929 Gloucester Gate, Regent's Park, May 1982 (1982)
Oc:1775x1774:signed:Presented by the Trustees of the
Chantrey Bequest 1984

BERMAN, Eugène 1899-1972
Modern Collection

T00334 The Jug on the Window (1934)
La Cruche sur la fenêtre
Oc:810x600:signed:Presented by Arthur Jeffress 1960

BERNIK, Janez born 1933
Modern Collection

T00428 Evening in the Quarry (1960)
Kamnolom
OVc:1407x851:signed:Purchased 1961

P02548 Untitled 8 (1979)
CNJπ:505x665:signed:Presented by the artist 1981

P07584 Untitled (1978)
CNJπ:496x698:signed:Purchased 1981

BERRY, John born 1925
Modern Collection
Tate Gallery Archive holds material concerning this artist

P01759 Angel (1969)
CNπ:584x502:signed:Presented by the artist 1976

P01760 Helmetatec (1969-71)
CNπ:594x502:signed:Presented by the artist 1976

P01761 Helmetatec Hello (1969-71)
CNπ:571x495:signed:Presented by the artist 1976

P01762 Love Tower Number One (1969-71)
CNπ:467x454:signed:Presented by the artist 1976

P01763 Untitled (1969-71)
CNπ:597x495:Presented by the artist 1976

BERTHOT, Jake born 1939
Modern Collection

P11208 [no title] (1987)
Jπ:615x458:Presented by Garner H. Tullis and Pamela
Auchincloss 1989

P11209 [no title] (1987)
Jπ:602x450:Presented by Garner H. Tullis and Pamela
Auchincloss 1989

BETTES, John active 1531-1576
British Collection

N01496 A Man in a Black Cap (1545)
Ow:470x410:Purchased 1897

BEUYS, Joseph 1921-1986
Modern Collection
Tate Gallery Archive holds material concerning this artist

T01542 Bed (1950)
Bett
Sz:200x524x248:Purchased 1972

T03323 Felt Suit (1970)
Filzanzug
RF:1880x762x216:Purchased 1981

T03594 Four Blackboards (1972)
Ohne Titel
4 Db:1216x914x18:Transferred from the Archive 1983

T03825 Untitled (Vitrine) (1983)
Ohne Titel (Vitrine)
SVv:2060x2200x500:Purchased 1984

T03826 Untitled (Vitrine) (1983)
Ohne Titel (Vitrine)
SV:2060x2200x500:Purchased 1984

T03919 Fat Battery (1963)
Fettbatterie
Sv:132x373x248:Presented by E.J. Power through the
Friends of the Tate Gallery 1984

T03920 Bathtub for a Heroine (1950, cast 1984)
Badewanne für eine Heldin
3 SV:155x410x248:Presented by the artist 1984

T03921 Animal Woman (1949, cast 1984)
Tierfrau
Sz:315x79x85:Presented by the artist 1984

P07594 Airmail (1971)
Luftpost
CLJπ:292x163:signed:Purchased 1982

P07595 The Revolution is Us (1972)
La Rivoluzione siamo noi
CNπ:1915x1003:signed:Purchased 1982

P07596 We Can't Do it without the Rose (1972)
Ohne die Rose tun wir's nicht . . .
CLπ:804x568:signed:Purchased 1982

P07597 Iphigenia (1973)
CNa:413x559:signed:Purchased 1982

P07598 From the Eurasien Staff (1973)
Aus dem Eurasienstab
MNπ:800x530:signed:Purchased 1982

P07599 Cosmos and Damien Polished (1975)
Cosmos und Damien gebohnert
CLHπ:330x230:signed:Purchased 1982

P07600 Halved Felt Cross over Cologne (1977)
Halbiertes Filzkreuz über Köln
HCLπ:230x330:signed:Purchased 1982

P07601 Chinese Hare Sugar (1979)
Chinesischer Hasenzucker
CNπ:210x296:signed:Purchased 1982

P08001 Untitled [from the book 'Madrid Codex'] (1975)
Ohne Titel [from the book 'Codices Madrid']
MLπ:216x162:signed:Transferred from the Library 1977

BEVAN, Robert 1865-1925
British Collection
Tate Gallery Archive holds material concerning this artist

N04750 Horse Sale at the Barbican (1912)
Oc:787x1219:signed:Presented by the Trustees of the
Chantrey Bequest 1934

N05911 The Cab Horse (exhibited 1910)
Oc:635x762:Presented by the Trustees of the Duveen
Paintings Fund 1949

T00250 Ploughing in Brittany. Verso: Study of a Woman (circa
1893-4)
WDπ:254x349:Purchased 1959

T00282 Haze over the Valley (circa 1913)
Oc:432x533:Presented by the Trustees of the Chantrey
Bequest 1959

T01121 Morning over the Ploughed Fields (circa 1901 or 1903)
Oc:219x264:Purchased 1969

BEWICK, Thomas 1753-1828
British Collection
Tate Gallery Archive holds material concerning this artist

N03970 Zebra, Illustration to 'General History of Quadrupeds'
(published 1790)
Jπ:102x114:Purchased 1924

BICAT, Andre born 1909
Modern Collection
Tate Gallery Archive holds material concerning this artist

P01368 Berkshire Downs (1974)
CJπ:337x454:signed:Presented by Christie's
Contemporary Art through the Institute of
Contemporary Prints 1975

P01369 The Thames at Goring (1974)
CJπ:340x454:signed:Presented by Christie's
Contemporary Art through the Institute of
Contemporary Prints 1975

BIEDERMAN, Charles born 1906
Modern Collection
Tate Gallery Archive holds material concerning this artist

T00882 Structurist Relief, Red Wing No. 20 (1954-65)
ROm:1048x914x149:signed:Purchased 1966

BIGGE, John (Sir John Amherst Selby-Bigge, Bt) 1892-1973
Modern Collection
Tate Gallery Archive holds material concerning this artist

T03056 Dieppe (1931)
Ob:448x606:signed:Purchased 1980

T03057 Abstract Composition (1933)
Ob:575x768:signed:Purchased 1980

BINNING, Bertram born 1909
Modern Collection

Centennial Suite (P03217-P03225, P03228-P03229; complete group; mixed group)
P03219 Merging Sides (1967-68)
CNπ:356x495:signed:Presented by Simon Fraser
University, British Columbia 1977

BIONDA, Mario born 1913
Modern Collection

T00378 Forms on a White Background (1958)
Immagine su fondo bianco
ODAc:727x918:signed:Presented by Professor Gino
Ghiringhelli 1960

BIRCH, S.J. Lamorna 1869-1955
British Collection
Tate Gallery Archive holds material concerning this artist

N04959 St Ives, Cornwall (1938)
Oc:508x635:signed:Presented by the Trustees of the
Chantrey Bequest 1938

BIRD, Edward 1762-1819
British Collection

N00323 The Raffle for the Watch
Ow:445x610:Presented by Robert Vernon 1847

BIRD, John born 1945
Modern Collection
Tate Gallery Archive holds material concerning this artist

Jam Press Phase One (P08006-P08014; complete group; mixed group)
P08006 I.I. (1973-4)
MLπ:559x441:Transferred from the Library 1977

BISHOP, Henry 1868-1939
British Collection

N04225 A Street in Carrara (exhibited 1926)
Oc:381x457:signed:Purchased 1927

N04698 Shakespeare's Cliff, Dover (exhibited 1933)
Oc:641x768:signed:Presented by the Trustees of the
Chantrey Bequest 1933

N05006 Sirocco, Tetuan (circa 1907-8)
Oc:305x356:signed:Presented by Cecil French in memory
of the artist 1940

BISSIER, Julius 1893-1965
Modern Collection

T00362 20 Jan. 59 Zurich (1959)
Tf:200x235:signed:Purchased 1960

BISSIERE, Roger 1888-1964
Modern Collection

P77113 Untitled (1955)
CIπ:394x318:signed:Purchased 1985

BISSILL, George 1896-1973
Modern Collection

N05341 Landscape, Layton (1935)
Ob:635x756:signed:Presented by the Trustees of the
Chantrey Bequest 1940

BLACK, Sheila
Modern Collection
Tate Gallery Archive holds material concerning this artist

P03090 Broad Street Line (1967-8)
CNπ:3048x1829:Presented by the Welsh Arts Council
1975

BLACKADDER, Elizabeth born 1931
Modern Collection
Tate Gallery Archive holds material concerning this artist

T00859 Still Life with Pomegranates (1963)
Oc:864x1118:signed:Presented by the Trustees of the
Chantrey Bequest 1966

P06033 Italian Landscape (1960)
CLπ:479x667:signed:Presented by Curwen Studio
through the Institute of Contemporary Prints 1975

P06034 Fifeshire Farm (1960)
CLπ:476x676:signed:Presented by Curwen Studio
through the Institute of Contemporary Prints 1975

P06035 Staithes (1962)
CLπ:521x787:Presented by Curwen Studio through the
Institute of Contemporary Prints 1975

P06036 Roman Wall I (1960)
CLπ:537x711:Presented by Curwen Studio through the
Institute of Contemporary Prints 1975

P06037 Dark Hill, Fifeshire (1960)
CLπ:479x667:Presented by Curwen Studio through the
Institute of Contemporary Prints 1975

P06038 Roman Wall II - Walltown (1960)
CLπ:489x721:Presented by Curwen Studio through the
Institute of Contemporary Prints 1975

BLACKER, Kate born 1955
Modern Collection

T04911 Made in '84 (1984)
SOm:2870x1525x580:Presented by the Patrons of New Art through the Friends of the Tate Gallery 1987

BLAIS, Jean-Charles born 1956
Modern Collection

P11223 Blue Sky (1987)
Jπ:755x575:signed:Presented by Garner H. Tullis and Pamela Auchincloss 1989

BLAKE, Benjamin circa 1790 - circa 1830
British Collection

N02946 Still Life (?1829)
Ow:254x200:Bequeathed by Sir Henry Layard 1913

BLAKE, John born 1945
Modern Collection
Tate Gallery Archive holds material concerning this artist

Jam Press Phase One (P08006-P08014; complete group; mixed group)
P08007 1. 2 & 1. 3 (1973-4)
MLπ:559x441:Transferred from the Library 1977

P77117 Six Hundred Eyes for Krzysztofory (1981)
NFπ:993x1257:signed:Purchased 1985

BLAKE, Peter born 1932
Modern Collection
Tate Gallery Archive holds material concerning this artist

T00566 On the Balcony (1955-7)
Oc:1213x908:signed:Presented by the Contemporary Art Society 1963

T01174 The Fine Art Bit (1959)
EVb:914x610x25:Purchased 1970

T01175 The Toy Shop (1962)
Rv:1568x1940x340:signed:Purchased 1970

T01877 The Masked Zebra Kid (1965)
AVw:552x267x38:signed:Purchased 1974

T01934 Tuesday (1961)
OVb:476x267x38:Presented by E.J. Power through the Friends of the Tate Gallery 1974

T02406 Self-Portrait with Badges (1961)
Ob:1743x1219:signed:Presented by the Moores Family Charitable Foundation to celebrate the John Moores Liverpool Exhibition 1979

T03419 The First Real Target (1961)
Ecb:537x493:signed:Purchased 1982

T03790 'The Meeting' or 'Have a Nice Day, Mr Hockney' (1981-3)
Oc:992x1244:Presented by the Friends of the Tate Gallery out of funds bequeathed by Miss Helen Arbuthnot 1983

Six French Postcards (P01072-P01077; complete group)
P01072 J.A. (1969)
CNπ:430x272:signed:Presented by Waddington Galleries through the Institute of Contemporary Prints 1975

P01073 Leo 79 (1969)
CNπ:273x426:signed:Presented by Waddington Galleries through the Institute of Contemporary Prints 1975

P01074 Leo 139 (1969)
CNπ:431x275:signed:Presented by Waddington Galleries through the Institute of Contemporary Prints 1975

P01075 Leo 153 (1969)
CNπ:432x280:signed:Presented by Waddington Galleries through the Institute of Contemporary Prints 1975

P01076 Serie 83 (1969)
CNπ:431x276:signed:Presented by Waddington Galleries through the Institute of Contemporary Prints 1975

P01077 3765 (1969)
CNπ:425x272:signed:Presented by Waddington Galleries through the Institute of Contemporary Prints 1975

P01078 Girl in a Poppy Field (1974)
CNπ:413x273:signed:Presented by Waddington Galleries through the Institute of Contemporary Prints 1975

P01729 Studio Tack-Board (1972)
CNπ:972x1368:Presented by Robert Simon 1975

For John Constable (P03149-P03157, P03159-P03161, P03180-P03185; complete group; mixed group)
P03180 Liberty as a 'Suffolk Child by John Constable R.A.' (1976)
CIVπ:664x498:signed:Presented by Bernard Jacobson Gallery 1976

The Institute of Contemporary Arts Portfolio (P04016, P04038, P04053, P04076, P04115, P04125, P04166, P04248, P04256, P04315-P04316, P04334, P04378-P04380, P04419, P04635, P04752, P04938, P05138, P05155, P05248; complete group; mixed group)
P04038 Beach Boys (1964)
CNπ:530x308:signed:Presented by Rose and Chris Prater through the Institute of Contemporary Prints 1975

Illustrations to Through the Looking-Glass (P04039-P04046; complete group)
P04039 'and to show you I'm not proud, you may shake hands with me!' (1970)
CNπ:242x180:signed:Presented by Rose and Chris Prater through the Institute of Contemporary Prints 1975

P04040 'and the two knights sat and looked at each other without speaking' (1970)
CNπ:243x181:signed:Presented by Rose and Chris Prater through the Institute of Contemporary Prints 1975

P04041 'But isn't it old!' Tweedledum cried (1970)
CNπ:244x181:signed:Presented by Rose and Chris Prater through the Institute of Contemporary Prints 1975

P04042 'It isn't manners for us to begin, you know', said the Rose (1970)
CNπ:241x178:signed:Presented by Rose and Chris Prater through the Institute of Contemporary Prints 1975

P04043 'For instance now, now there's the King's messenger' (1970)
CNπ:241x178:signed:Presented by Rose and Chris Prater through the Institute of Contemporary Prints 1975

P04044 Just at this moment, somehow or other, they began to run (1970)
CNπ:243x180:signed:Presented by Rose and Chris Prater through the Institute of Contemporary Prints 1975

P04045 So Alice picked him up very gently (1970)
CNπ:245x181:signed:Presented by Rose and Chris Prater through the Institute of Contemporary Prints 1975

P04046 'Well, this is grand!' said Alice (1970)
CNπ:242x179:signed:Presented by Rose and Chris Prater through the Institute of Contemporary Prints 1975

P04047   Costume Life Drawing (1971)
CNπ:432x225:signed:Presented by Rose and Chris Prater
through the Institute of Contemporary Prints 1975

The Wrestlers (P04048-P04052; complete group)
P04048   Ebony Tarzan (1972)
CNπ:298x120:signed:Presented by Rose and Chris Prater
through the Institute of Contemporary Prints 1975

P04049   Penny Black (1972)
CNπ:233x114:signed:Presented by Rose and Chris Prater
through the Institute of Contemporary Prints 1975

P04050   Pretty Boy Michaelangelo (1972)
CNπ:208x109:signed:Presented by Rose and Chris Prater
through the Institute of Contemporary Prints 1975

P04051   Red Power (1972)
CNπ:204x83:signed:Presented by Rose and Chris Prater
through the Institute of Contemporary Prints 1975

P04052   The Tuareg (1972)
CNπ:258x134:signed:Presented by Rose and Chris Prater
through the Institute of Contemporary Prints 1975

P11031   Illustration to the cover of 'Face Dances' (1981)
CLπ:225x253:signed:Presented by Simon Wilson 1981

BLAKE, Robert 1767-1787
British Collection

A00001   A Figure Bowing before a Seated Old Man with his Arm
Outstretched in Benediction. Verso: Indecipherable
Sketch
WDπ:394x419:Presented by Mrs John Richmond 1922

A00002   Two Drawings of Frightened Figures, Probably for 'The
Approach of Doom'
Dπ:311x213:Presented by Mrs John Richmond 1922

A00003   The Preaching of Warning. Verso: An Old Man
Enthroned between Two Groups of Figures
Dπ:343x467:Presented by Mrs John Richmond 1922

A00004   Six Drawings of Figures with Outstretched Arms
Dπ:318x394:Presented by Mrs John Richmond 1922

BLAKE, William 1757-1827
British Collection
Tate Gallery Archive holds material concerning this artist

N01110   The Spiritual Form of Pitt Guiding Behemoth (?1805)
TVc:740x627:signed:Purchased 1882

N01164   The Body of Christ Borne to the Tomb (circa 1799-1800)
Tc:267x378:signed:Presented by Francis T. Palgrave 1884

N02230   David Delivered out of Many Waters (circa 1805)
WDπ:415x348:signed:Presented by George Thomas Saul
1878

N02231   Epitome of James Hervey's 'Meditations among the
Tombs' (circa 1820-5)
WDπ:431x292:signed:Presented by George Thomas Saul
1878

N02686   Oberon, Titania and Puck with Fairies Dancing (circa
1785)
WDπ:475x675:Presented by Alfred A. de Pass in memory
of his wife Ethel 1910

N03006   The Spiritual Form of Nelson Guiding Leviathan (circa
1805-9)
Tc:762x625:Purchased 1914

N03007   Bathsheba at the Bath (circa 1799-1800)
Tc:263x376:signed:Presented by the National Art
Collections Fund 1914

N03340   Satan Smiting Job with Sore Boils (circa 1826)
DTw:326x432:signed:Presented by Miss Mary H. Dodge
through the National Art Collections Fund 1918

Illustrations to Dante's 'Divine Comedy'
(N03351-N03370, T01950-T01956, A00005-A00011;
complete group)
N03351   Dante and Virgil Penetrating the Forest (1824-7)
WDπ:371x527:Purchased with the assistance of a special
grant from the National Gallery and donations from the
National Art Collections Fund, Lord Duveen and others,
and presented through the National Art Collections Fund
1919

N03352   The Inscription over the Gate (1824-7)
WDπ:527x374:signed:Purchased with the assistance of a
special grant from the National Gallery and donations
from the National Art Collections Fund, Lord Duveen
and others, and presented through the National Art
Collections Fund 1919

N03353   Homer and the Ancient Poets (1824-7)
WDπ:371x528:Purchased with the assistance of a special
grant from the National Gallery and donations from the
National Art Collections Fund, Lord Duveen and others,
and presented through the National Art Collections Fund
1919

N03354   Cerberus (1824-7)
WDπ:372x528:Purchased with the assistance of a special
grant from the National Gallery and donations from the
National Art Collections Fund, Lord Duveen and others,
and presented through the National Art Collections Fund
1919

N03355   Plutus (1824-7)
WDπ:527x371:Purchased with the assistance of a special
grant from the National Gallery and donations from the
National Art Collections Fund, Lord Duveen and others,
and presented through the National Art Collections Fund
1919

N03356   The Wood of the Self-Murderers: The Harpies and the
Suicides (1824-7)
WDπ:372x527:Purchased with the assistance of a special
grant from the National Gallery and donations from the
National Art Collections Fund, Lord Duveen and others,
and presented through the National Art Collections Fund
1919

N03357   The Simoniac Pope (1824-7)
WDπ:527x368:signed:Purchased with the assistance of a
special grant from the National Gallery and donations
from the National Art Collections Fund, Lord Duveen
and others, and presented through the National Art
Collections Fund 1919

N03358   The Devils, with Dante and Virgil by the Side of the Pool
(1824-7)
WDπ:372x527:Purchased with the assistance of a special
grant from the National Gallery and donations from the
National Art Collections Fund, Lord Duveen and others,
and presented through the National Art Collections Fund
1919

N03359   The Hypocrites with Caiaphas. Verso: Sketch of a
Stooping Figure (1824-7)
WDπ:373x527:Purchased with the assistance of a special
grant from the National Gallery and donations from the
National Art Collections Fund, Lord Duveen and others,
and presented through the National Art Collections Fund
1919

N03360 The Laborious Passage along the Rocks (1824-7)
WDπ:373x527:Purchased with the assistance of a special grant from the National Gallery and donations from the National Art Collections Fund, Lord Duveen and others, and presented through the National Art Collections Fund 1919

N03361 The Serpent Attacking Buoso Donati. Verso: A Man with a Transparent Hood (?) over his Head (1824-7)
WDπ:372x527:Purchased with the assistance of a special grant from the National Gallery and donations from the National Art Collections Fund, Lord Duveen and others, and presented through the National Art Collections Fund 1919

N03362 The Pit of Disease: The Falsifiers (1824-7)
WDπ:372x527:signed:Purchased with the assistance of a special grant from the National Gallery and donations from the National Art Collections Fund, Lord Duveen and others, and presented through the National Art Collections Fund 1919

N03363 The Primaeval Giants Sunk in the Soil (1824-7)
WDπ:372x527:Purchased with the assistance of a special grant from the National Gallery and donations from the National Art Collections Fund, Lord Duveen and others, and presented through the National Art Collections Fund 1919

N03364 The Punishment of the Thieves (1824-7)
WDπ:372x527:Purchased with the assistance of a special grant from the National Gallery and donations from the National Art Collections Fund, Lord Duveen and others, and presented through the National Art Collections Fund 1919

N03365 Virgil Girding Dante's Brow with a Rush (1824-7)
WDπ:527x371:Purchased with the assistance of a special grant from the National Gallery and donations from the National Art Collections Fund, Lord Duveen and others, and presented through the National Art Collections Fund 1919

N03366 The Ascent of the Mountain of Purgatory (1824-7)
WDπ:528x372:Purchased with the assistance of a special grant from the National Gallery and donations from the National Art Collections Fund, Lord Duveen and others, and presented through the National Art Collections Fund 1919

N03367 Dante and Virgil Approaching the Angel Who Guards the Entrance of Purgatory (1824-7)
WDπ:527x373:Purchased with the assistance of a special grant from the National Gallery and donations from the National Art Collections Fund, Lord Duveen and others, and presented through the National Art Collections Fund 1919

N03368 The Rock Sculptured with the Recovery of the Ark and the Annunciation (1824-7)
WDπ:528x374:Purchased with the assistance of a special grant from the National Gallery and donations from the National Art Collections Fund, Lord Duveen and others, and presented through the National Art Collections Fund 1919

N03369 Beatrice Addressing Dante from the Car (1824-7)
WDπ:372x527:Purchased with the assistance of a special grant from the National Gallery and donations from the National Art Collections Fund, Lord Duveen and others, and presented through the National Art Collections Fund 1919

N03370 Dante in the Empyrean, Drinking at the River of Light (1824-7)
WDπ:528x371:Purchased with the assistance of a special grant from the National Gallery and donations from the National Art Collections Fund, Lord Duveen and others, and presented through the National Art Collections Fund 1919

N03373 Frontispiece to 'Visions of the Daughters of Albion' (circa 1795)
CWπ:170x120:Purchased with the assistance of a special grant from the National Gallery and donations from the National Art Collections Fund, Lord Duveen and others, and presented through the National Art Collections Fund 1919

N03374 Plate 4 of 'Visions of the Daughters of Albion' (circa 1795)
CWπ:75x115:Purchased with the assistance of a special grant from the National Gallery and donations from the National Art Collections Fund, Lord Duveen and others, and presented through the National Art Collections Fund 1919

N03551 The Bard, from Gray (?1809)
TVc:600x441:signed:Purchased 1920

Urizen (N03696, N05190; complete group)
N03696 Plate 2 of 'Urizen': 'Teach these Souls to Fly' (?1796)
CWπ:109x102:Purchased 1922

N05055 Elohim Creating Adam (1795/circa 1805)
CWπ:431x536:signed:Presented by W. Graham Robertson 1939

N05056 Hecate (?) (circa 1795)
CWπ:439x581:signed:Presented by W. Graham Robertson 1939

N05057 The Good and Evil Angels (1795/?circa 1805)
CWπ:445x594:signed:Presented by W. Graham Robertson 1939

N05058 Newton (1795/circa 1805)
CWπ:460x600:signed:Presented by W. Graham Robertson 1939

N05059 Nebuchadnezzar (1795/circa 1805)
CWπ:446x620:signed:Presented by W. Graham Robertson 1939

N05060 The House of Death (1795/circa 1805)
CWπ:485x610:signed:Presented by W. Graham Robertson 1939

N05061 Lamech and his Two Wives (1795)
CWπ:431x608:signed:Presented by W. Graham Robertson 1939

N05062 Pity (circa 1795)
CWπ:425x539:signed:Presented by W. Graham Robertson 1939

N05063 God Judging Adam (1795)
CWπ:432x535:signed:Presented by W. Graham Robertson 1939

N05183 Age Teaching Youth (circa 1785-90)
Wπ:108x80:Bequeathed by Miss Alice G.E. Carthew 1940

N05184 The Head of the Ghost of a Flea. Verso: A Profile and a Reduced Drawing of Milton's First Wife (circa 1819)
Dπ:189x153:Bequeathed by Miss Alice G.E. Carthew 1940

N05188 Catherine Blake. Verso: A Man's Head and Other Drawings (circa 1805)
Dπ:286x221:Bequeathed by Miss Alice G.E. Carthew 1940

N05189 Lear and Cordelia in Prison (circa 1779)
WDπ:123x175:Bequeathed by Miss Alice G.E. Carthew
1940

N05192 The House of Death (circa 1790)
WDπ:318x451:Bequeathed by Miss Alice G.E. Carthew
1940

N05195 The Blasphemer (circa 1800)
WDπ:384x340:signed:Bequeathed by Miss Alice G.E.
Carthew 1940

N05198 The Good Farmer, probably the Parable of the Wheat
and the Tares. Verso: Rough Sketch of Two or Three
Figures in a Landscape (circa 1780-5)
DWπ:267x375:Bequeathed by Miss Alice G.E. Carthew
1940

N05200 Job, his Wife and his Friends: The Complaint of Job.
Verso: Job's Wife and other Sketches (circa 1785)
DWπ:311x451:Bequeathed by Miss Alice G.E. Carthew
1940

N05300 The Soul Hovering over the Body Reluctantly Parting
with Life (circa 1805)
Dπ:272x456:Bequeathed by Sir Hugh Walpole 1941

N05875 Christ Appearing to the Apostles after the Resurrection
(circa 1795)
CWπ:406x499:Bequeathed by W. Graham Robertson
1948

N05887 The River of Life (circa 1805)
WDπ:305x336:signed:Bequeathed by W. Graham
Robertson 1949

N05888 The Body of Abel Found by Adam and Eve (circa 1826)
TVw:325x433:signed:Bequeathed by W. Graham
Robertson 1949

N05889 The Ghost of a Flea (circa 1819-20)
TVw:214x162:signed:Bequeathed by W. Graham
Robertson 1949

N05892 Satan in his Original Glory: 'Thou wast Perfect till
Iniquity was Found in Thee' (circa 1805)
WDπ:429x339:signed:Presented by the executors of W.
Graham Robertson through the National Art Collections
Fund 1949

N05893 Christ Blessing the Little Children (1799)
Tc:260x375:signed:Presented by the executors of W.
Graham Robertson through the National Art Collections
Fund 1949

N05894 The Agony in the Garden (circa 1799-1800)
Tm:270x380:signed:Presented by the executors of W.
Graham Robertson through the National Art Collections
Fund 1949

N05895 The Crucifixion: 'Behold Thy Mother' (circa 1805)
WDπ:413x300:signed:Presented by the executors of W.
Graham Robertson through the National Art Collections
Fund 1949

N05896 The Entombment (circa 1805)
WDπ:417x310:signed:Presented by the executors of W.
Graham Robertson through the National Art Collections
Fund 1949

N05897 The Four and Twenty Elders Casting their Crowns before
the Divine Throne (circa 1803-5)
Wπ:354x293:signed:Presented by the executors of W.
Graham Robertson through the National Art Collections
Fund 1949

N05898 The Penance of Jane Shore in St Paul's Church (circa
1793)
WDπ:245x295:signed:Presented by the executors of W.
Graham Robertson through the National Art Collections
Fund 1949

N05899 The Death of the Virgin (1803)
Wπ:378x371:signed:Presented by the executors of W.
Graham Robertson through the National Art Collections
Fund 1949

T00547 Los and Orc (circa 1792-3)
WDπ:217x295:Presented by Mrs Jane Samuel in memory
of her husband 1962

T01128 An Allegory of the Bible. Verso: Part Drawing of a Nude
Male Figure (?): Two Shins (circa 1780-5)
DWπ:615x349:Bequeathed by Miss Rachel M. Dyer 1969

Pages from the Small Blake-Varley Sketchbook
(T01334-T01335; complete group)

T01334 A Figure Standing in a Gothic Apse, perhaps the
Empress Maud. Verso: Detailed Drawings for 'The
Empress Maud in Bed' (circa 1819)
Dπ:155x205:Purchased 1971

T01335 Detailed Drawings for 'A Figure Standing in a Gothic
Apse' (1819)
Dπ:155x205:Purchased 1971

Illustrations to Dante's 'Divine Comedy'
(N03351-N03370, T01950-T01956, A00005-A00011;
complete group)

T01950 The Circle of the Lustful: Francesca da Rimini ('The
Whirlwind of Lovers') (1826-7, reprinted 1968)
Iπ:243x335:Presented by Lessing J. Rosenwald 1975

T01951 Ciampolo the Barrator Tormented by the Devils (1826-7,
reprinted 1968)
Iπ:238x335:Presented by Lessing J. Rosenwald 1975

T01952 The Baffled Devils Fighting (1826-7, reprinted 1968)
Iπ:241x332:Presented by Lessing J. Rosenwald 1975

T01953 The Six-Footed Serpent Attacking Agnolo Brunelleschi
(1826-7, reprinted 1968)
Iπ:245x337:Presented by Lessing J. Rosenwald 1975

T01954 The Serpent Attacking Buoso Donati (1826-7, reprinted
1968)
Iπ:241x335:Presented by Lessing J. Rosenwald 1975

T01955 The Pit of Disease: The Falsifiers (1826-7, reprinted
1968)
Iπ:240x335:Presented by Lessing J. Rosenwald 1975

T01956 Dante Striking Against Bocca degli Abati (1826-7,
reprinted 1968)
Iπ:235x337:Presented by Lessing J. Rosenwald 1975

Illustrations to Robert John Thornton, 'The Pastorals of
Virgil' (T02115-T02131; complete group)

T02115 Thenot and Colinet (1821, reprinted 1977)
Jπ:61x83:Presented by British Museum Publications Ltd
1977

T02116 Thenot Remonstrates with Colinet (1821, reprinted
1977)
Jπ:38x74:Presented by British Museum Publications Ltd
1977

T02117 Thenot and Colinet Converse Seated between Two Trees
(1821, reprinted 1977)
Jπ:33x75:Presented by British Museum Publications Ltd
1977

T02118 Thenot Remonstrates with Colinet: Lightfoot in the
Distance (1821/1977)
Jπ:33x73:Presented by British Museum Publications Ltd
1977

T02119 Thenot, with Colinet Waving his Arms in Sorrow (1821,
reprinted 1977)
Jπ:36x73:Presented by British Museum Publications Ltd
1977

T02120 The Blighted Corn (1821, reprinted 1977)
Jπ:34x73:Presented by British Museum Publications Ltd 1977

T02121 'Nor Fox, nor Wolf, nor Rat among our Sheep' (1821, reprinted 1977)
Jπ:35x73:Presented by British Museum Publications Ltd 1977

T02122 Sabrina's Silvery Flood (1821, reprinted 1977)
Jπ:33x73:Presented by British Museum Publications Ltd 1977

T02123 Colinet's Fond Desire Strange Lands to Know (1821, reprinted 1977)
Jπ:36x73:Presented by British Museum Publications Ltd 1977

T02124 'A Rolling Stone is ever Bare of Moss' (1821, reprinted 1977)
Jπ:32x76:Presented by British Museum Publications Ltd 1977

T02125 Colinet Rests by a Stream at Night (1821, reprinted 1977)
Jπ:32x75:Presented by British Museum Publications Ltd 1977

T02126 Colinet with his Shepherd's Pipe, Mocked by Two Boys (1821, reprinted 1977)
Jπ:36x77:Presented by British Museum Publications Ltd 1977

T02127 'For him Our Yearly Wakes and Feasts We Hold' (1821, reprinted 1977)
Jπ:35x75:Presented by British Museum Publications Ltd 1977

T02128 Thenot and Colinet Folding their Flocks together at Sunset (1821, reprinted 1977)
Jπ:36x76:Presented by British Museum Publications Ltd 1977

T02129 Thenot and Colinet at Supper (1821, reprinted 1977)
Jπ:35x76:Presented by British Museum Publications Ltd 1977

T02130 'With Songs the Jovial Hinds Return from Plow' (1821, reprinted 1977)
Jπ:33x77:Presented by British Museum Publications Ltd 1977

T02131 'And Unyok'd Heifers, Loitering Homewards, Low' (1821, reprinted 1977)
Jπ:33x77:Presented by British Museum Publications Ltd 1977

T02387 Winter (circa 1820-5)
Tw:902x297:Purchased 1979

T03233 Every Man also Gave him a Piece of Money. Verso: God the Father with Attendant Angels (circa 1821-3)
DWπ:228x178:Presented by the Friends of the Tate Gallery 1981

T04134 Moses Indignant at the Golden Calf (circa 1799-1800)
Tc:380x266:Bequeathed by Ian L. Phillips 1986

T05716 A Vision: The Inspiration of the Poet (circa 1819-20?)
DWπ:244x211:Purchased with assistance from Mr Edwin C. Cohen and the Echoing Green Foundation 1989

Illustrations to 'The Book of Job' (A00012-A00032, T05845; complete group)

T05845 Title-Page of 'The Book of Job' (1825, reprinted 1874)
Lπ:191x147:Purchased with the assistance of a special grant from the National Gallery and donations from the National Art Collections Fund, Lord Duveen and others, and presented through the National Art Collections Fund 1919

Illustrations to Dante's 'Divine Comedy' (N03351-N03370, T01950-T01956, A00005-A00011; complete group)

A00005 The Circle of the Lustful: Francesca da Rimini ('The Whirlwind of Lovers') (1826-7, reprinted 1892)
Lπ:243x335:Purchased with the assistance of a special grant from the National Gallery and donations from the National Art Collections Fund, Lord Duveen and others, and presented through the National Art Collections Fund 1919

A00006 Ciampolo the Barrator Tormented by the Devils (1826-7, reprinted 1892)
Lπ:240x338:Purchased with the assistance of a special grant from the National Gallery and donations from the National Art Collections Fund, Lord Duveen and others, and presented through the National Art Collections Fund 1919

A00007 The Baffled Devils Fighting (1826-7, reprinted 1892)
Lπ:242x334:Purchased with the assistance of a special grant from the National Gallery and donations from the National Art Collections Fund, Lord Duveen and others, and presented through the National Art Collections Fund 1919

A00008 The Six-Footed Serpent Attacking Agnolo Brunelleschi (1826-7, reprinted 1892)
Lπ:246x340:Purchased with the assistance of a special grant from the National Gallery and donations from the National Art Collections Fund, Lord Duveen and others, and presented through the National Art Collections Fund 1919

A00009 The Serpent Attacking Buoso Donati (1826-7, reprinted 1892)
Lπ:241x335:Purchased with the assistance of a special grant from the National Gallery and donations from the National Art Collections Fund, Lord Duveen and others, and presented through the National Art Collections Fund 1919

A00010 The Pit of Disease: The Falsifiers (1826-7, reprinted 1892)
Lπ:243x340:Purchased with the assistance of a special grant from the National Gallery and donations from the National Art Collections Fund, Lord Duveen and others, and presented through the National Art Collections Fund 1919

A00011 Dante Striking against Bocca Degli Abati (1826-7, reprinted 1892)
Lπ:236x340:Purchased with the assistance of a special grant from the National Gallery and donations from the National Art Collections Fund, Lord Duveen and others, and presented through the National Art Collections Fund 1919

Illustrations to 'The Book of Job' (A00012-A00032, T05845; complete group)

A00012 Job and his Family (1828, reprinted 1874)
Lπ:184x150:Purchased with the assistance of a special grant from the National Gallery and donations from the National Art Collections Fund, Lord Duveen and others, and presented through the National Art Collections Fund 1919

A00013 Satan before the Throne of God (1825, reprinted 1874)
Lπ:197x151:Purchased with the assistance of a special grant from the National Gallery and donations from the National Art Collections Fund, Lord Duveen and others, and presented through the National Art Collections Fund 1919

A00014 Job's Sons and Daughters Overwhelmed by Satan (1825, reprinted 1874)
Lπ:197x153:Purchased with the assistance of a special grant from the National Gallery and donations from the National Art Collections Fund, Lord Duveen and others, and presented through the National Art Collections Fund 1919

A00015 The Messengers tell Job of his Misfortunes (1825, reprinted 1874)
Lπ:200x152:Purchased with the assistance of a special grant from the National Gallery and donations from the National Art Collections Fund, Lord Duveen and others, and presented through the National Art Collections Fund 1919

A00016 Satan Going Forth from the Presence of the Lord, and Job's Charity (1825, reprinted 1874)
Lπ:198x152:Purchased with the assistance of a special grant from the National Gallery and donations from the National Art Collections Fund, Lord Duveen and others, and presented through the National Art Collections Fund 1919

A00017 Satan Smiting Job with Sore Boils (1825, reprinted 1874)
Lπ:198x153:Purchased with the assistance of a special grant from the National Gallery and donations from the National Art Collections Fund, Lord Duveen and others, and presented through the National Art Collections Fund 1919

A00018 Job's Comforters (1825, reprinted 1874)
Lπ:198x153:Purchased with the assistance of a special grant from the National Gallery and donations from the National Art Collections Fund, Lord Duveen and others, and presented through the National Art Collections Fund 1919

A00019 Job's Despair (1825, reprinted 1874)
Lπ:199x150:Purchased with the assistance of a special grant from the National Gallery and donations from the National Art Collections Fund, Lord Duveen and others, and presented through the National Art Collections Fund 1919

A00020 The Vision of Eliphaz (1825, reprinted 1874)
Lπ:198x152:Purchased with the assistance of a special grant from the National Gallery and donations from the National Art Collections Fund, Lord Duveen and others, and presented through the National Art Collections Fund 1919

A00021 Job Rebuked by his Friends (1825, reprinted 1874)
Lπ:198x152:Purchased with the assistance of a special grant from the National Gallery and donations from the National Art Collections Fund, Lord Duveen and others, and presented through the National Art Collections Fund 1919

A00022 Job's Evil Dreams (1825, reprinted 1874)
Lπ:197x152:Purchased with the assistance of a special grant from the National Gallery and donations from the National Art Collections Fund, Lord Duveen and others, and presented through the National Art Collections Fund 1919

A00023 The Wrath of Elihu (1825, reprinted 1874)
Lπ:200x151:Purchased with the assistance of a special grant from the National Gallery and donations from the National Art Collections Fund, Lord Duveen and others, and presented through the National Art Collections Fund 1919

A00024 The Lord Answering Job out of the Whirlwind (1825, reprinted 1874)
Lπ:198x151:Purchased with the assistance of a special grant from the National Gallery and donations from the National Art Collections Fund, Lord Duveen and others, and presented through the National Art Collections Fund 1919

A00025 When the Morning Stars Sang Together (1825, reprinted 1874)
Lπ:191x150:Purchased with the assistance of a special grant from the National Gallery and donations from the National Art Collections Fund, Lord Duveen and others, and presented through the National Art Collections Fund 1919

A00026 Behemoth and Leviathan (1825, reprinted 1874)
Lπ:200x151:Purchased with the assistance of a special grant from the National Gallery and donations from the National Art Collections Fund, Lord Duveen and others, and presented through the National Art Collections Fund 1919

A00027 The Fall of Satan (1825, reprinted 1874)
Lπ:186x150:Purchased with the assistance of a special grant from the National Gallery and donations from the National Art Collections Fund, Lord Duveen and others, and presented through the National Art Collections Fund 1919

A00028 The Vision of Christ (1825, reprinted 1874)
Lπ:200x151:Purchased with the assistance of a special grant from the National Gallery and donations from the National Art Collections Fund, Lord Duveen and others, and presented through the National Art Collections Fund 1919

A00029 Job's Sacrifice (1825, reprinted 1874)
Lπ:198x150:Purchased with the assistance of a special grant from the National Gallery and donations from the National Art Collections Fund, Lord Duveen and others, and presented through the National Art Collections Fund 1919

A00030 Every Man also Gave him a Piece of Money (1825, reprinted 1874)
Lπ:197x150:Purchased with the assistance of a special grant from the National Gallery and donations from the National Art Collections Fund, Lord Duveen and others, and presented through the National Art Collections Fund 1919

A00031 Job and his Daughters (1825, reprinted 1874)
Lπ:199x151:Purchased with the assistance of a special grant from the National Gallery and donations from the National Art Collections Fund, Lord Duveen and others, and presented through the National Art Collections Fund 1919

A00032 Job and his Family Restored to Prosperity (1825, reprinted 1874)
Lπ:196x149:Purchased with the assistance of a special grant from the National Gallery and donations from the National Art Collections Fund, Lord Duveen and others, and presented through the National Art Collections Fund 1919

A00033 Sketch for 'The Four and Twenty Elders Casting their Crowns before the Divine Throne'. Verso: Standing Figure with Arms at his Side (circa 1803, circa 1805-10)
Dπ:488x389:Presented by Mrs John Richmond 1922

A00034 'Europe': Fragment of Pages 3 and 4 (1794/circa 1830-5)
JWπ:92x166:Presented by Mrs John Richmond 1922

Songs of Innocence and of Experience (A00034-A00039; complete group)

A00035 'Songs of Innocence and of Experience': 'Infant Sorrow' (1794, reprinted 1831 or later)
Jπ:112x97:Presented by Mrs John Richmond 1922

A00036 'Songs of Innocence and of Experience': 'Infant Sorrow' (1794, reprinted 1831 or later)
Jπ:112x97:Presented by Mrs John Richmond 1922

A00037 'Songs of Innocence and of Experience': 'Spring' (1794, reprinted 1831 or later)
Jπ:115x79:Presented by Mrs John Richmond 1922

A00038 'Songs of Innocence': Title-Page (1789, reprinted 1831 or later)
Jπ:120x64:Presented by Mrs John Richmond 1922

A00039 'Songs of Innocence': Title-Page (1789, reprinted 1831 or later)
Jπ:120x64:Presented by Mrs John Richmond 1922

A00040 Sketches for 'Tiriel Supporting the Dying Myratana' (circa 1789)
Dπ:291x450:Presented by Mrs John Richmond 1922

A00041 Landscape near Felpham (circa 1800)
WDπ:237x343:Presented by Mrs John Richmond 1922

A00042 Two Figures in a Decorative Border (circa 1790)
Dπ:122x203:Presented by Mrs John Richmond 1922

A00043 Preliminary Sketch for 'Christ Girding Himself with Strength'. Verso: Standing Figure with One Arm Raised (circa 1805, circa 1805-10)
Dπ:505x425:Presented by Mrs John Richmond 1922

A00044 Lower Half of a Woman Playing a Harp. Verso: Seraphim and Other Drawings (circa 1785, circa ?1807)
Dπ:268x450:Presented by Mrs John Richmond 1922

A00045 Charon, Copy from the Antique? Verso: Part of a Face, Copy from the Antique? (?circa 1779-80)
Dπ:435x338:Presented by Mrs John Richmond 1922

A00046 The Crucifixion (circa 1825-7)
Dπ:432x276:Presented by Mrs John Richmond 1922

A00047 Composition Sketch, Possibly a Subject from Dante. Verso: A Man Standing over a Figure Reclining on a Bed (?1824-7, ?circa 1800-10)
Dπ:454x339:Presented by Mrs John Richmond 1922

A00048 Composition Sketch. Verso: Standing Figure Holding a Spear (?circa 1805-10)
Dπ:508x370:Presented by Mrs John Richmond 1922

A00049 Composition Sketch for 'The Fall of the Rebel Angels'? Verso: Standing Figure with Flaming Hair (?circa 1805-10)
Dπ:502x425:Presented by Mrs John Richmond 1922

Illustrations to Thornton's 'Pastorals of Virgil' (A00111-A00127; complete group)

A00111 Frontispiece: Thenot and Colinet (1821/circa 1830)
Jπ:62x84:Presented by Herbert Linnell 1924

A00112 Thenot Remonstrates with Colinet (1821/circa 1830)
Jπ:38x74:Presented by Herbert Linnell 1924

A00113 Thenot and Colinet Converse Seated between Two Trees (1821/circa 1830)
Jπ:33x75:Presented by Herbert Linnell 1924

A00114 Thenot Remonstrates with Colinet; Lightfoot in the Distance (1821/circa 1830)
Jπ:33x73:Presented by Herbert Linnell 1924

A00115 Thenot, with Colinet Waving his Arms in Sorrow (1821/circa 1830)
Jπ:36x73:Presented by Herbert Linnell 1924

A00116 The Blighted Corn (1821/circa 1830)
Jπ:34x73:Presented by Herbert Linnell 1924

A00117 'Nor Fox, nor Wolf, nor Rat among our Sheep' (1821/circa 1830)
Jπ:35x73:Presented by Herbert Linnell 1924

A00118 Sabrina's Silvery Flood (1821/circa 1830)
Jπ:33x72:Presented by Herbert Linnell 1924

A00119 Colinet's 'Fond Desire Strange Lands to Know' (1821/circa 1830)
Jπ:37x74:Presented by Herbert Linnell 1924

A00120 'A Rolling Stone is ever Bare of Moss' (1821/circa 1830)
Jπ:33x77:Presented by Herbert Linnell 1924

A00121 Colinet Rests by a Stream at Night (1821/circa 1830)
Jπ:33x75:Presented by Herbert Linnell 1924

A00122 Colinet with his Shepherd's Pipe, Mocked by Two Boys (1821/circa 1830)
Jπ:36x77:Presented by Herbert Linnell 1924

A00123 'For him Our Yearly Wakes and Feasts We Hold' (1821/circa 1830)
Jπ:35x75:Presented by Herbert Linnell 1924

A00124 Thenot and Colinet Folding their Flocks together at Sunset (1821/circa 1830)
Jπ:36x76:Presented by Herbert Linnell 1924

A00125 Thenot and Colinet at Supper (1821/circa 1830)
Jπ:35x76:Presented by Herbert Linnell 1924

A00126 'With Songs the Jovial Hinds Return from Plow' (1821/circa 1830)
Jπ:35x75:Presented by Herbert Linnell 1924

A00127 'And Unyok'd Heifers, Loitering Homeward, Low' (1821/circa 1830)
Jπ:33x77:Presented by Herbert Linnell 1924
after

BLAKE, William 1757-1827
British Collection

N05187 The Man Who Taught Blake Painting in his Dreams (counterproof)
Dπ:296x235:Bequeathed by Miss Alice G.E. Carthew 1940

Urizen (N03696, N05190; complete group)
N05190 Plate 3 of 'Urizen': Oh! Flames of Furious Desires'
Wπ:60x98:Bequeathed by Miss Alice G.E. Carthew 1940

N05193 Christ in the Carpenter's Shop: The Humility of the Saviour
WDπ:330x349:Bequeathed by Miss Alice G.E. Carthew 1940

N05196 The Parable of the Wise and Foolish Virgins
Wπ:400x333:Bequeathed by Miss Alice G.E. Carthew 1940

N05197 David Delivered out of Many Waters
WDπ:422x356:Bequeathed by Miss Alice G.E. Carthew 1940

N05199 The Raising of Lazarus
WDπ:432x321:Bequeathed by Miss Alice G.E. Carthew 1940

BLAMEY, Norman born 1914
Modern Collection

T04116 Decoy Duck and Self-Portrait (1984-5)
Oc:1220x1220:signed:Presented by the Trustees of the Chantrey Bequest 1985

BLANCHE, Jacques-Emile 1861-1942
Modern Collection
Tate Gallery Archive holds material concerning this artist

N03580 Thomas Hardy (1906)
Oc:918x730:signed:Purchased with assistance from subscribers 1921

N04862 Arthur Symons (1895)
Oc:810x651:signed:Bequeathed by Mrs Rhoda Symons 1937

N04907 Portraits of Charles Shannon and Charles Ricketts (1904)
Oc:921x730:signed:Bequeathed by Charles Shannon 1937

N04995 Francis Poictevin (1887)
Oc:267x165:signed:Presented by Miss Hilda Trevelyan 1939

N05427 On the Pier at Dieppe (circa 1938)
Oc:502x610:Presented by Sir John Rothenstein 1943

N05754 Charles Conder (1904)
Oc:1108x864:signed:Presented by Georges A. Mevil-Blanche 1947

N05755 Ludgate Circus: Entrance to the City (November, Midday) (circa 1910)
Ludgate Circus: Entrée de la City (Novembre, midi)
Ob:1048x816:signed:Presented by Georges A. Mevil-Blanche 1947

N05756 August Morning, Dieppe Beach (circa 1934)
Matinée d'août, plage de Dieppe
Oc:730x603:signed:Presented by Georges A. Mevil-Blanche 1947

BLAND, Beatrice 1864-1951
British Collection

N04475 Striped Camellias (1927)
Oc:457x349:signed:Presented by the Trustees of the Chantrey Bequest 1929

N04964 Yachts at Lymington (exhibited 1938)
Oc:508x610:signed:Presented by the Trustees of the Chantrey Bequest 1938

BLAYMIRES, Charles Henry 1908 - circa 1970s
Modern Collection

T03709 Inscription: 'To be afraid' (circa 1925)
Rs:380x670x90:Transferred from the Victoria & Albert Museum 1983

BLISS, Douglas Percy 1900-1984
Modern Collection

T03203 Gunhills, Windley (1946-52)
Oc:762x1016:signed:Purchased 1981

BLOCH, Martin 1883-1954
Modern Collection
Tate Gallery Archive holds material concerning this artist

N06235 The Mississippi at Minneapolis (1948-50)
Oc:711x921:signed:Purchased 1954

T00435 Casa Rigo, Lake Garda II (1925)
Oc:914x737:signed:Purchased 1961

T00455 Sleeping Nude - Torso (1937)
Dπ:498x571:signed:Presented by Cyril Frankel 1961

T00883 Afternoon in Bangor (1952-4)
Oc:1270x914:signed:Presented by Mrs C. Bloch, the artist's widow 1966

after
BLORE, Edward 1789-1879
British Collection

Picturesque Views on the Southern Coast of England (T05218-T05463; complete group; mixed group)
T05240 St Margaret's, at Cliff, near Dover, Kent
Lπ:178x253:Purchased 1988

T05241 St Margaret's at Cliff, near Dover, Kent
Lπ:178x254:Purchased 1988

BLOW, Sandra born 1925
Modern Collection
Tate Gallery Archive holds material concerning this artist

T00355 Space and Matter (1959)
Ob:1518x1226:signed:Purchased 1960

IAA Portfolio (P03096-P03104, P03107; complete group; mixed group)
P03097 Untitled (1975)
CNπ:445x422:signed:Presented by the International Association of Art 1975

BOCCIONI, Umberto 1882-1916
Modern Collection

T01589 Unique Forms of Continuity in Space (1913, cast 1972)
Forme uniche della continuità nello spazio
Sz:1175x876x368:Purchased 1972

BOCHNER, Mel born 1940
Modern Collection
Tate Gallery Archive holds material concerning this artist

T01858 Four Times Three (1973)
Dπ:965x1270:Purchased 1974

BOCK, Théophile de 1851-1904
Modern Collection

N02873 Woudrichem (?1890s)
Ow:330x438:signed:Presented by J.C.J. Drucker to the National Gallery 1912

BODEN, Neville born 1929
Modern Collection
Tate Gallery Archive holds material concerning this artist

T01209 Blow in her Ear (1969)
SAm:1822x737x991:Purchased 1970

BOEHM, Sir Joseph Edgar 1834-1890
British Collection

N02243 Mr Wynn Ellis
Ss:660x483x305:Presented by S.W. Graystone 1906

N02244 Mrs Wynn Ellis
Ss:648x457x267:Presented by S.W. Graystone 1906

BOISVERT, Gilles born 1940
Modern Collection

Homage to Albert Dumouchel (P03166-P03178; complete group; mixed group)
Hommage à Albert Dumouchel
P03168 Silver Bird over the Rue St Laurent (1971)
L'Oiseau d'Argent au dessus de la rue St Laurent
CNπ:613x410:Presented by the University of Quebec 1976

after
BOITARD, Louis Philippe active 1734-1760
British Collection

N05853 An Exact Representation of the Game of Cricket (circa 1760)
Oc:489x591:Purchased 1948

BOLUS, Michael born 1934
Modern Collection

T00738 Nenuphar (1963)
ASm:349x1219x1219:Purchased 1965

T01045 No. 3 (1968)
OSm:406x2743x3962:Purchased 1968

T01349 1st Sculpture (1963)
SAm:1105x1105x483:Presented by Alistair McAlpine (later Lord McAlpine of West Green) 1970

T01350 5th Sculpture (1963)
SAm:606x816x410:Presented by Alistair McAlpine (later Lord McAlpine of West Green) 1970

T01351 8th Sculpture (1963)
SAm:1029x1035x311:Presented by Alistair McAlpine (later Lord McAlpine of West Green) 1970

T01352 11th Sculpture (1963)
SAm:921x1734x708:Presented by Alistair McAlpine (later Lord McAlpine of West Green) 1970

T01353 7th Sculpture (1965)
SAm:768x1835x1206:Presented by Alistair McAlpine (later Lord McAlpine of West Green) 1970

T01354 1st Sculpture (1966)
SAm:610x914x610:Presented by Alistair McAlpine (later Lord McAlpine of West Green) 1970

T01355 4th Sculpture (1966)
SAm:5409x2159x2445:Presented by Alistair McAlpine (later Lord McAlpine of West Green) 1970

T01356 5th Sculpture (1966)
SAm:559x2680x2502:Presented by Alistair McAlpine (later Lord McAlpine of West Green) 1970

T01357 1st Sculpture (1967-8)
SAm:1841x4362x2508:Presented by Alistair McAlpine (later Lord McAlpine of West Green) 1970

T01358 1st Sculpture (1970)
SAm:1743x3277x2419:Presented by Alistair McAlpine (later Lord McAlpine of West Green) 1970

T01359 Untitled (1971)
SAm:1702x6852x1016:Presented by Alistair McAlpine (later Lord McAlpine of West Green) 1970

BOMBERG, David 1890-1957
Modern Collection
Tate Gallery Archive holds material concerning this artist

N03722 Sleeping Men (1911)
Wπ:222x902:signed:Purchased 1923

N03723 Study for Canadian War Painting (circa 1918-19)
DWπ:394x318:Purchased 1923

N06133 Flowers (1943)
Oc:914x718:signed:Presented by the artist's wife and family 1952

T00318 Lilian (1932)
Oc:762x559:signed:Purchased 1959

T00319 Study for 'Sappers at Work: A Canadian Tunnelling Company, Hill 60, St Eloi' (circa 1918-19)
Oc:3042x2438:Purchased 1959

T00585 Ju-Jitsu (circa 1913)
Ob:619x619:signed:Presented by the Trustees of the Chantrey Bequest 1963

T00610 Barges (1919)
Oc:597x775:signed:Purchased 1963

T00656 The Mud Bath (1914)
Oc:1524x2242:signed:Purchased 1964

T00910 Tregor and Tregoff, Cornwall (1947)
Oc:870x1073:signed:Presented by Mrs Rosemary Peto 1967

T00913 In the Hold (circa 1913-4)
Oc:1962x2311:Presented by the Friends of the Tate Gallery 1967

T00914 Study for 'In the Hold' (circa 1914)
Dw:556x660:signed:Presented by the Friends of the Tate Gallery 1967

T01055 Bathing Scene (circa 1912-13)
Ow:559x686:Purchased 1968

T01086 Vigilante (1955)
Ob:718x600:signed:Purchased 1968

T01197 Vision of Ezekiel (1912)
Oc:1143x1372:signed:Purchased with assistance from the Morton Bequest through the Contemporary Art Society 1970

T01681 Study for 'The Vision of Ezekiel' (1912)
Dπ:565x686:Presented by the executors of Mrs Helen Bentwich 1972

T01683 Jerusalem, Looking to Mount Scopus (1925)
Oc:565x752:signed:Purchased 1972

T01961 Sketches for 'The Dancer' (circa 1913-14)
Dπ:381x279:Presented by Mrs Lilian Bomberg 1975

T01962 Imaginative Composition - 'The Tent' (circa 1920-3)
Oπ:352x502:signed:Presented by Mrs Lilian Bomberg 1975

T01963 Study for 'The Mud Bath' (1914)
WDπ:286x349:Purchased 1975

T01964 St Paul's and River (1945)
Dπ:508x638:Purchased 1975

T02074 Players (1919)
Dπ:260x197:signed:Presented by Mrs Lilian Bomberg 1976

T03260 Raie, the Artist's Sister (circa 1910)
Dπ:610x476:Presented in memory of the artist by Mr and Mrs J. Newmark through the Contemporary Art Society 1981

T03261 Study for Two Figures in a Composition (circa 1919-20)
DGπ:311x203:Presented in memory of the artist by Mr and Mrs J. Newmark through the Contemporary Art Society 1981

T03262 Study for a Figure in a Composition (circa 1919-21)
DGπ:311x203:Presented in memory of the artist by Mr and Mrs J. Newmark through the Contemporary Art Society 1981

T03263 Kitty (1929)
Dπ:629x476:signed:Presented in memory of the artist by Mr and Mrs J. Newmark through the Contemporary Art Society 1981

T03264 San Justo and Toledo Hills (1929)
Oc:333x438:signed:Presented in memory of the artist by Mr and Mrs J. Newmark through the Contemporary Art Society 1981

T03265 Self-Portrait (1932)
Oc:606x511:signed:Presented in memory of the artist by Mr and Mrs J. Newmark through the Contemporary Art Society 1981

T03338 Lilian Painting David (Painting Lilian) (1929)
Oc:660x514:signed:Presented by Lilian Bomberg, the artist's second wife 1982

T03353 The Baby Diana (1937)
Oc:502x403:Presented by Mrs Dinora Davies-Rees, the artist's step-daughter 1982

T04165 The Artist's Wife and Baby (1937)
Oc:766x562:Presented by Mrs Dinora Davies-Rees, the artist's step-daughter 1986

T04166 Nude (1943)
Oc:915x715:signed:Presented by Julie Lamont, the artist's step grand-daughter 1986

T04890 The City on the Rock, Evening, Ronda, Spain (1935)
Dπ:470x610:signed:Presented by Mrs Dinora Davies-Rees, the artist's step-daughter, and Juliet Lamont, her daughter, through the Contemporary Art Society 1987

T04891 Picos de Europa, Asturias, Spain (1935)
Dπ:468x633:signed:Presented by Mrs Dinora Davies-Rees, the artist's step-daughter, and Juliet Lamont, her daughter, through the Contemporary Art Society 1987

Russian Ballet (P07008-P07013; complete group)
P07008 i (circa 1914-19)
CLπ:102x98:signed:Purchased 1970

P07009 ii (circa 1914-19)
CLπ:78x53:signed:Purchased 1970

P07010 iii (circa 1914-19)
CLπ:76x159:signed:Purchased 1970

P07011 iv (circa 1914-19)
CLπ:76x159:signed:Purchased 1970

P07012 v (circa 1914-19)
CLπ:50x67:signed:Purchased 1970

P07013 vi (circa 1914-19)
CLπ:77x68:signed:Purchased 1970

BOMBERG, David and MICHELMORE, Richard 1890-1957, born 1928
Modern Collection

T03600 Recto: Messiah. Verso: Messiah (1953)
Ob:715x1080:signed:Presented by Richard Michelmore 1983

BONE, Sir Muirhead 1876-1953
British Collection
Tate Gallery Archive holds material concerning this artist

N02300 Study for 'The Great Gantry, Charing Cross Station' (1906)
Dπ:262x378:signed:Presented by Miss Evelyn de Ponsonby McGhee 1908

N03166 Snowy Morning, Queen Margaret's College, Glasgow (1900-1)
Oc:630x765:signed:Presented by the Contemporary Art Society 1917

N03433 A Church in the Citadel at Arras (1916)
Dπ:305x236:signed:Presented by the artist 1919

N03434 A View in Flanders behind the Lines, Showing Locre and the Tops of Dug-Outs on the Scherpenber (1916)
DWπ:267x413:signed:Presented by the artist 1919

N03435 Waiting for the Wounded at a Collecting Station in the Field on the Somme at Montauban (1916)
DWπ:330x495:signed:Presented by the artist 1919

N03436 A Ruined Village in France: Bécordel-Bécourt (1916)
DWπ:308x478:signed:Presented by the artist 1919

N03437 A French Chateau Occupied by the 3rd Coldstream Guards, October 1916 (1916)
DWπ:356x279:signed:Presented by the artist 1919

N03438 On the Somme near Mametz (1916)
DWπ:243x358:signed:Presented by the artist 1919

N03439 Heavy Artillery Officers' Mess, Vlamertinghe Chateau, August 1916 (1916)
DWπ:252x358:signed:Presented by the artist 1919

N03440 Ruins of the Church at Péronne, April 1917 (1917)
DWπ:228x324:signed:Presented by the artist 1919

N03441 Church at Bapâume (1917)
DWπ:539x361:signed:Presented by the artist 1919

N03442 A Soldiers' Cemetery at Lihons, May 1917 (1917)
Dπ:382x565:signed:Presented by the artist 1919

N03443 An Officers Billet at G.H.Q., June 1917 (1917)
DWπ:401x295:signed:Presented by the artist 1919

N03444 In the War Zone (1916)
DWπ:254x396:signed:Presented by the artist 1919

N03445 From the After Deck of a Battleship (HMS Tiger from HMS Repulse) (1917)
DWπ:209x285:signed:Presented by the artist 1919

N03446 From the Bridge of a Battleship (1917)
Dπ:293x230:signed:Presented by the artist 1919

N04558 The Mountain Background, Gerona (?1926)
WDπ:235x355:signed:Purchased 1930

N04577 Ballantrae School House (circa 1905-7)
Ob:251x356:signed:Bequeathed by Hans Velten 1931

N04587 The British Museum Reading Room, May 1907 (1907)
Dπ:780x768:signed:Presented by Sir Michael Sadler through the National Art Collections Fund 1931

N05686 Torpedoed Oil Tanker (1940)
DWπ:592x915:signed:Presented by the War Artists' Advisory Committee 1946

P01001 Demolition of St James's Hall (Exterior) (1907)
MIπ:298x278:signed:Presented by Edward Marsh 1909

The Great War: Britain's Efforts and Ideals (P03001-P03007, P03011-P03023, P03031-P03036, P03039-P03044; incomplete group; mixed group)
Building Ships (P03001-P03007; complete group)
P03001 Ready for Sea (circa 1917)
MLπ:460x353:signed:Presented by the Ministry of Information 1918

P03002 A Shipyard (circa 1917)
MLπ:464x363:Presented by the Ministry of Information 1918

P03003 On the Stocks (circa 1917)
MLπ:355x455:Presented by the Ministry of Information 1918

P03004 A Shipyard Seen from a Big Crane (circa 1917)
MLπ:460x352:Presented by the Ministry of Information 1918

P03005 A Workshop (circa 1917)
MLπ:370x475:Presented by the Ministry of Information 1918

P03006 A Fitting Out Basin (circa 1917)
MLπ:457x355:Presented by the Ministry of Information 1918

P03007 Somerset House (1905)
MIπ:305x286:Presented by the Ministry of Information 1918

BONE, Stephen 1904-1958
Modern Collection
Tate Gallery Archive holds material concerning this artist

N04618 Charles Aitken (exhibited 1932)
Oc:610x508:signed:Presented by Sir Robert and Lady
Witt through the National Art Collections Fund 1932

BONECHI, Lorenzo born 1955
Modern Collection

P77026 Gorgiti (1983)
MIπ:292x226:signed:Purchased 1984

P77027 Small Book (1983)
Libretto
MIπ:637x485:signed:Purchased 1984

P77028 Little Temple (1983)
Tempietto
MIπ:225x244:signed:Purchased 1984

P77133 The House of the Angel (1984)
La casa dell 'angelo
MIπ:606x485:signed:Purchased 1986

P77134 The Deer Hunt (1985)
La caccia al cervo
MIπ:829x987:signed:Purchased 1986

BONINGTON, Richard Parkes 1802-1828
British Collection
Tate Gallery Archive holds material concerning this artist

N00374 The Column of St Mark, Venice (exhibited 1828)
Oc:457x375:signed:Presented by Robert Vernon 1847

N02664 Near Boulogne (1823-4)
Oc:314x438:Bequeathed by George Salting 1910

N05789 Venice: Ducal Palace with a Religious Procession
(exhibited 1828)
Oc:1143x1626:signed:Presented by Frederick John
Nettlefold 1947

N06326 The Pont des Arts, Paris (circa 1826)
Ob:356x451:Bequeathed by P. Ralli 1961

T00965 The Grand Canal, Venice (1826)
DWπ:206x289:Presented by the National Art Collections
Fund (Herbert Powell Bequest) 1967

T03857 A Scene on the French Coast (circa 1825)
WDπ:213x342:signed:Purchased 1984

after
BONINGTON, Richard Parkes 1802-1828
British Collection

N04377 On the French Coast
Oc:381x533:Presented in memory of Frank Lloyd by his
daughter Mrs Garwood 1927

manner of
BONINGTON, Richard Parkes 1802-1828
British Collection

N04254 Mountain Landscape
Oπ:267x343:Presented by Lord Ivor Spencer Churchill
1927

N05790 Landscape in Normandy
Oc:387x549:Presented by Frederick John Nettlefold 1947

BONNARD, Pierre 1867-1947
Modern Collection
Tate Gallery Archive holds material concerning this artist

N04134 The Table (1925)
La Table
Oc:1029x743:signed:Presented by the Courtauld Fund
Trustees 1926

N04494 The Window (1925)
La Fenêtre
Oc:1086x886:signed:Presented by Lord Ivor Spencer
Churchill through the Contemporary Art Society 1930

N04495 The Bath (1925)
Baignoire (Le Bain)
Oc:860x1206:Presented by Lord Ivor Spencer Churchill
through the Contemporary Art Society 1930

N05414 Coffee (1915)
Le Café
Oc:730x1064:signed:Presented by Sir Michael Sadler
through the National Art Collections Fund 1941

N05462 Pont de la Concorde (1913/15)
Oc:600x832:signed:Presented by the Earl of Sandwich
1944

T00936 The Bowl of Milk (circa 1919)
Le Bol de lait
Oc:1162x1210:signed:Bequeathed by Edward Le Bas
1967

T01076 Nude Bending Down (1923)
Femme nue se baissant
Oc:571x527:signed:Bequeathed by the Hon. Mrs A.E.
Pleydell-Bouverie through the Friends of the Tate Gallery
1968

T01077 Bathing Woman, Seen from the Back (circa 1919)
Baigneuse, de dos
Oc:441x346:signed:Bequeathed by the Hon. Mrs A.E.
Pleydell-Bouverie through the Friends of the Tate Gallery
1968

BONTECOU, Lee born 1931
Modern Collection

T00506 Drawing (1961)
Dπ:686x997:signed:Presented by Leo Castelli 1962

BORNFRIEND, Jacob 1904-1976
Modern Collection
Tate Gallery Archive holds material concerning this artist

T00462 Grey and Blue Still Life (1960)
Oc:711x914:signed:Presented by Dr Henry Roland 1961

BOROFSKY, Jonathan born 1942
Modern Collection
Tate Gallery Archive holds material concerning this artist

T03908 Untitled at 2,660,260 (1980)
Dπ:106x241:signed:Purchased 1984

T03909 Head with Light Bulb at 2,607,008 (circa 1979-80)
Dπ:242x153:signed:Purchased 1984

T03910 Man with Briefcase at 2,756,805 (1980)
Hπ:298x210:signed:Purchased 1984

T03911 Untitled at 2,545,878 (1978)
Hπ:216x140:signed:Purchased 1984

T03912 Untitled at 2,600,588 (1979)
Dπ:163x98:Purchased 1984

T03913 Untitled at 2,598,228 (1979)
Dπ:230x305:Purchased 1984

T03914 Untitled at 2,711,922 (1981)
Dπ:253x204:signed:Purchased 1984

T03915 Self-Portrait at 2,485,479 (circa 1977)
Dπ:355x279:signed:Purchased 1984

T03916 I Dreamed I Could Fly at 2,518,124 (circa 1977-8)
Dπ:271x210:signed:Purchased 1984

T03917 Untitled at 2,436,185 (circa 1977-8)
Dπ:355x307:signed:Purchased 1984

2740475 (P07817-P07829; complete group)

P07817 [no title] (1982)
MNπ:705x202:signed:Purchased 1983

P07818 [no title] (1982)
MIπ:95x127:signed:Purchased 1983

P07819 [no title] (1982)
MNπ:558x344:signed:Purchased 1983

P07820 [no title] (1982)
MIπ:58x45:signed:Purchased 1983

P07821 [no title] (1982)
MNπ:451x521:signed:Purchased 1983

P07822 [no title] (1982)
MIπ:64x54:signed:Purchased 1983

P07823 [no title] (1982)
MNπ:235x286:signed:Purchased 1983

P07824 [no title] (1982)
MIπ:165x70:signed:Purchased 1983

P07825 [no title] (1982)
MNπ:749x406:signed:Purchased 1983

P07826 [no title] (1982)
MIπ:70x38:signed:Purchased 1983

P07827 [no title] (1982)
MNπ::signed:Purchased 1983

P07828 [no title] (1982)
MIπ:70x52:signed:Purchased 1983

P07829 [no title] (1982)
MNπ:686x204:signed:Purchased 1983

BORSELLER, Peter active 1664-1687
British Collection

N06175 Portrait of a Lady
Oc:914x711:Bequeathed by Sir Edward Marsh through the National Art Collections Fund 1953

BOSHIER, Derek born 1937
Modern Collection
Tate Gallery Archive holds material concerning this artist

T01287 The Identi-Kit Man (1962)
Oc:1829x1829:signed:Purchased 1971

P01370 Plan 1 (1972)
CLNπ:549x803:signed:Presented by the artist through the Institute of Contemporary Prints 1975

P01371 Plan II (1972)
CLNπ:549x803:signed:Presented by the artist through the Institute of Contemporary Prints 1975

P01372 F.E. (1973)
MJπ:495x375:signed:Presented by the artist through the Institute of Contemporary Prints 1975

P01373 Untitled (1973)
CLVπ:489x702:signed:Presented by the artist through the Institute of Contemporary Prints 1975

The Institute of Contemporary Arts Portfolio (P04016, P04038, P04053, P04076, P04115, P04125, P04166, P04248, P04256, P04315-P04316, P04334, P04378-P04380, P04419, P04635, P04752, P04938, P05138, P05155, P05248; complete group; mixed group)

P04053 Untitled (1964)
CNπ:533x746:signed:Presented by Rose and Chris Prater through the Institute of Contemporary Prints 1975

P04054 Output (1966)
CNπ:467x816:signed:Presented by Rose and Chris Prater through the Institute of Contemporary Prints 1975

BOSMAN, Richard born 1944
Modern Collection

P77135 Falling Man (published 1984)
MJπ:1448x1068:signed:Purchased 1986

BOSWELL, James 1906-1971
Modern Collection
Tate Gallery Archive holds material concerning this artist

T02253 Street Scene (circa 1946)
DGVπ:343x486:Presented by Ruth Boswell, the artist's widow 1977

T02254 Man in an Interior (1949)
DWπ:441x298:signed:Presented by Ruth Boswell, the artist's widow 1977

T02255 Camp 17, Iraq (1943)
DWπ:352x505:signed:Presented by Ruth Boswell, the artist's widow 1977

T03459 Le Sphinx (1937)
Dπ:320x460:Presented by Ruth Boswell, the artist's widow 1982

T03460 Le Sphinx (1937)
Dπ:342x506:Presented by Ruth Boswell, the artist's widow 1982

T03461 Le Sphinx, 4 a.m. Verso: Three figure drawings (1937)
Dπ:341x505:Presented by Ruth Boswell, the artist's widow 1982

T03462 Punch and Judy (circa 1945)
DGπ:170x277:Presented by Ruth Boswell, the artist's widow 1982

T03463 Café, Kentish Town (1947)
DGπ:396x530:Presented by Ruth Boswell, the artist's widow 1982

P01819 Leicester Square (1934)
MLπ:213x213:signed:Presented by Ruth Boswell, the artist's widow 1977

P01820 The Means Test (1934)
MLπ:171x133:signed:Presented by Ruth Boswell, the artist's widow 1977

P01821 The Means Test 2 (1934)
MLπ:200x168:Presented by Ruth Boswell, the artist's widow 1977

P01822 Soldier, Soldier (1934)
CLπ:295x264:Presented by Ruth Boswell, the artist's widow 1977

P01823 Empire Builders (1935)
MLπ:251x219:signed:Presented by Ruth Boswell, the artist's widow 1977

P01824 Quiet Evening (1940)
MLπ:305x254:signed:Presented by Ruth Boswell, the artist's widow 1977

BOUGH, Samuel 1822-1878
British Collection
Tate Gallery Archive holds material concerning this artist

N01936 Holmwood, Dorking (1856)
Oc:292x457:signed:Presented by the Earl of Carlisle 1904

BOUGHTON, George Henry 1833-1905
British Collection

N01539 Weeding the Pavement (1882)
Oc:895x1505:signed:Presented by Sir Henry Tate 1894

BOUMANS, Bart born 1940
Modern Collection
Tate Gallery Archive holds material concerning this artist

P01374 Dutch Landscape (1973)
Hollands Landschap
CLπ:422x492:signed:Presented by de Jong and Co.
through the Institute of Contemporary Prints 1975

BOURDELLE, Antoine 1861-1929
Modern Collection
Tate Gallery Archive holds material concerning this artist

N04115 Sir James George Frazer (1922)
Sp:692x311x400:signed:Presented by Lady Frazer 1925

BOUVIER de CACHARD, Comte Regis de born 1929
Modern Collection

P06039 Solitude (1972)
CLπ:775x575:signed:Presented by Curwen Studio
through the Institute of Contemporary Prints 1975

P06040 Epitase (1972-3)
CLπ:486x613:signed:Presented by Curwen Studio
through the Institute of Contemporary Prints 1975

P06041 Epitase III (1972-3)
CLπ:486x616:signed:Presented by Curwen Studio
through the Institute of Contemporary Prints 1975

P06042 Tower of London (1972-3)
CLπ:486x654:signed:Presented by Curwen Studio
through the Institute of Contemporary Prints 1975

BOWER, Edward active 1629 - circa 1667
British Collection

T00500 Sir John Drake (1646)
Oc:1270x1026:signed:Purchased 1962

BOWEY, Olwyn born 1936
Modern Collection

T00662 Portrait Sketch of L.S. Lowry (1963-64)
Oc:914x711:signed:Presented by the Trustees of the
Chantrey Bequest 1964

BOWLER, Henry Alexander 1824-1903
British Collection

N03592 The Doubt: 'Can these Dry Bones Live?' (exhibited
1855)
Oc:610x508:Presented by H. Archer Bowler 1921

BOWLING, Frank born 1936
Modern Collection

T04889 Spreadout Ron Kitaj (1986)
Ac:2285x2860:signed:Purchased 1987

BOX, E. 1919-1988
Modern Collection

T02219 The Expulsion (1951)
OAc:502x362:Presented by Professor Marston Fleming
1977

BOXALL, Sir William 1800-1879
British Collection

N00601 Geraldine (exhibited 1850)
Oc:1156x838:Presented by James Booth at the wish of
the late John Kenyon 1858

BOYCE, George Price 1826-1897
British Collection
Tate Gallery Archive holds material concerning this artist

N05000 Night Sketch of the Thames near Hungerford Bridge
(?circa 1866)
Wπ:222x337:Bequeathed by Miss May Morris 1939

N05250 Landscape at Wotton, Surrey: Autumn (1864-5)
Wπ:248x349:signed:Bequeathed by Mrs Lawder-Eaton
through the National Art Collections Fund 1940

T01587 A Girl by a Beech Tree in a Landscape (1857)
Ob:298x479:signed:Purchased 1972

T04943 On the West Lyn, North Devon (1858)
WGπ:278x393:signed:Presented by John Watson 1987

T05011 Blackfriars Bridge: Moonlight Sketch (1863)
Wπ:161x224:signed:Presented by Mrs John Gere 1987

T05018 A Girl's Portrait (?circa 1868)
WDπ:249x182:Purchased with assistance from the
Abbott Fund 1987

BOYCE, Sonia born 1962
Modern Collection
Tate Gallery Archive holds material concerning this artist

T05020 Missionary Position II (1985)
WPHπ:1238x1830:signed:Purchased 1987

T05021 From Tarzan to Rambo: English Born 'Native' Considers
her Relationship to the Constructed/Self Image and her
Roots in Reconstruction (1987)
ADHFπ:1240x3590:signed:Purchased 1987

BOYD, Arthur born 1920
Modern Collection

P06043 Hammock Lovers (1970)
CLπ:406x457:signed:Presented by Curwen Studio
through the Institute of Contemporary Prints 1975

P06044 Bullfrog Head (1970)
CLπ:425x533:signed:Presented by Curwen Studio
through the Institute of Contemporary Prints 1975

P06045 Romeo and Juliet (1970)
CLπ:406x502:signed:Presented by Curwen Studio
through the Institute of Contemporary Prints 1975

P06046 St Francis Preaching Naked (1970)
CLπ:489x610:signed:Presented by Curwen Studio
through the Institute of Contemporary Prints 1975

P06047 Butterfly Man (Maroon) (1970)
CLπ:591x781:signed:Presented by Curwen Studio through the Institute of Contemporary Prints 1975

P06048 Butterfly Man (Red) (1970)
CLπ:597x781:signed:Presented by Curwen Studio through the Institute of Contemporary Prints 1975

P06049 St Francis Taking the Rosary (1970)
CLπ:489x613:signed:Presented by Curwen Studio through the Institute of Contemporary Prints 1975

P06050 Nebuchadnezzar (1972-4)
CLπ:448x537:signed:Presented by Curwen Studio through the Institute of Contemporary Prints 1975

P06760 Juiker on Sandbank (1978)
CLπ:467x527:signed:Presented by Curwen Studio 1978

BOYD and EVANS (Fionnuala Boyd and Leslie Evans) born 1944, born 1945
Modern Collection
Tate Gallery Archive holds material concerning these artists

T04909 The Wall (1986)
Ac:914x1372:signed:Presented by Philip and Psyche Hughes through the Angela Flowers Gallery and the Friends of the Tate Gallery 1987

BOYD, Fionnuala - see BOYD and EVANS

BOYD HARTE, Glynn born 1948
Modern Collection

Metroland (P06785-P06786; complete group)
P06785 [no title] (1977)
CLπ:775x575:Presented by Curwen Studio 1978

P06786 [no title] (1977)
CLπ:775x575:Presented by Curwen Studio 1978

BOYLE, Mark born 1934
Modern Collection
Tate Gallery Archive holds material concerning this artist

T01145 Holland Park Avenue Study (1967)
Ra:2388x2388x114:Purchased 1969

T02413 The Rock and Scree Series (Triptych) (1977)
3 RVa:1848x1841x318, 1829x1829x419, 1829x1841x298:Presented anonymously 1979

BOYS, Thomas Shotter 1803-1874
British Collection

T00966 The Seine and Palace of the Tuileries
Wπ:200x295:signed:Presented by the National Art Collections Fund (Herbert Powell Bequest) 1967

BRABAZON, Hercules Brabazon 1821-1906
British Collection

N02109 Houses at Tivoli (circa 1860)
WGDπ:254x368:signed:Presented by Mrs Harvey Combe 1907

N02110 Roses (circa 1887)
Gπ:343x241:signed:Presented by Mrs Harvey Combe 1907

N02111 Murcia
Gπ:152x216:signed:Presented by Mrs Harvey Combe 1907

N02112 Tivoli (circa 1868)
WGπ:140x305:Presented by Mrs Harvey Combe 1907

N02113 The Pink Palace (exhibited 1892)
Gπ:241x349:Presented by the Ethel Parker Memorial Fund 1907

N02114 The Grand Canal, Venice (circa 1890)
Gπ:146x260:signed:Presented by the Ethel Parker Memorial Fund 1907

N02115 Les Rochers Rouges
Gπ:165x241:signed:Presented by John Singer Sargent 1907

N03043 Souvenir of de Hoogh
WGπ:216x171:Presented by J. Bowyer Nichols through the National Art Collections Fund 1915

N03561 Fondamenta della Salute, Venice
Gπ:244x349:signed:Presented by Lord Duveen 1920

N03651 Sunset: Mountain and Lake
Gπ:216x248:signed:Presented by a friend in memory of the Hon. Mr Justice Peterson 1922

N03652 Como
Pπ:146x210:signed:Presented by a friend in memory of the Hon. Mr Justice Peterson 1922

N03653 Monaco
Gπ:229x337:signed:Presented by a friend in memory of the Hon. Mr Justice Peterson 1922

N03654 Side Canal, Venice
Wπ:292x286:signed:Presented by a friend in memory of the Hon. Mr Justice Peterson 1922

N03655 A Grey Day, Venice
Gb:210x318:Presented by a friend in memory of the Hon. Mr Justice Peterson 1922

N03656 Sunset (after Turner)
Gπ:121x175:signed:Presented by a friend in memory of the Hon. Mr Justice Peterson 1922

N04768 Canal in Venice
WGπ:216x146:signed:Bequeathed by Miss Fanny Davies 1934

N04769 The Bay
WGπ:244x349:signed:Bequeathed by Miss Fanny Davies 1934

N04770 Landscape in the Campagna (?)
WGDπ:222x292:signed:Bequeathed by Miss Fanny Davies 1934

N04771 Canal in Venice
WDπ:190x273:signed:Bequeathed by Miss Fanny Davies 1934

N04772 Venice: the Salute, Campanile and Doge's Palace from the Giudecca
WGDπ:178x235:Bequeathed by Miss Fanny Davies 1934

N04773 Lake Scene
Dπ:171x222:signed:Bequeathed by Miss Fanny Davies 1934

N04774 Mountain Scene
Dπ:171x222:signed:Bequeathed by Miss Fanny Davies 1934

N04775 Scene in Venice
WGπ:152x216:Bequeathed by Miss Fanny Davies 1934

N06252 Akaba
WGπ:254x330:signed:Bequeathed by Sir Victor A.A.H. Wellesley Bt 1954

BRADLEY, Martin born 1931
Modern Collection
Tate Gallery Archive holds material concerning this artist

P06051   Untitled (1961)
CLπ:556x540:Presented by Curwen Studio through the Institute of Contemporary Prints 1975

P06052   Untitled (1961)
CLπ:686x546:Presented by Curwen Studio through the Institute of Contemporary Prints 1975

BRAMLEY, Frank 1857-1915
British Collection

N01627   A Hopeless Dawn (1888)
Oc:1226x1676:signed:Presented by the Trustees of the Chantrey Bequest 1888

T03962   Primrose Day (1885)
Oc:502x351:signed:Presented by Arthur Grogan 1985

BRAMMER, Leonard born 1906
Modern Collection

N05549   The Two Ovens (1931)
DWGπ:216x235:signed:Presented by the Contemporary Art Society 1944

BRANCUSI, Constantin 1876-1957
Modern Collection
Tate Gallery Archive holds material concerning this artist

T00296   Danaide (circa 1918)
Sz:279x171x210:signed:Presented by Sir Charles Clore 1959

T01751   Maiastra (1911)
Szs:905x171x178:Purchased 1973

T03066   Head (circa 1919-23)
Sw:292x194x210:Purchased 1980

BRANDT, Bill 1904-1983
Modern Collection

For John Constable (P03149-P03157, P03159-P03161, P03180-P03185; complete group; mixed group)
P03150   [no title] (1976)
MFπ:283x314:signed:Presented by Bernard Jacobson Gallery 1976

BRANGWYN, Sir Frank 1867-1956
British Collection
Tate Gallery Archive holds material concerning this artist

N03151   The Poulterer's Shop (exhibited 1916)
Oc:1575x2515:signed:Presented by the Trustees of the Chantrey Bequest 1916

The Great War: Britain's Efforts and Ideals (P03001-P03007, P03011-P03023, P03031-P03036, P03039-P03044; incomplete group; mixed group)
Making Sailors (P03011-P03016; complete group)
P03011   Youthful Ambition (circa 1917)
MLπ:455x360:Presented by the Ministry of Information 1918

P03012   The Lookout (circa 1917)
MLπ:458x355:Presented by the Ministry of Information 1918

P03013   Going Abroad (circa 1917)
MLπ:470x355:Presented by the Ministry of Information 1918

P03014   The Gun (circa 1917)
MLπ:550x383:Presented by the Ministry of Information 1918

P03015   'Duff' (circa 1917)
MLπ::Presented by the Ministry of Information 1918

P03016   Boatdrill (circa 1917)
MLπ:463x363:Presented by the Ministry of Information 1918

BRANWHITE, Nathan 1813-1894
British Collection

N02388   Miniature Portrait of W.J. Müller
DWi:60x48:Presented by Lady Weston as part of the Sir Joseph Weston Gift 1908

BRAQUE, Georges 1882-1963
Modern Collection
Tate Gallery Archive holds material concerning this artist

N04166   Glass and Plate of Apples (1925)
Verre et plat de pommes
Ob:400x600:signed:Presented by Paul Rosenberg 1926

N04416   Guitar and Jug (1927)
Guitare et pichet
Oc:810x1165:signed:Presented by C. Frank Stoop 1928

N04722   Bather (1925)
Baigneuse
Ob:670x543:signed:Bequeathed by C. Frank Stoop 1933

T00445   Bottle and Fishes (circa 1910-2)
Bouteille et poissons
Oc:616x749:signed:Purchased 1961

T00833   Mandora (1909-10)
La Mandore
Oc:711x559:signed:Purchased 1966

T02318   Clarinet and Bottle of Rum on a Mantelpiece (1911)
Clarinette et bouteille de rhum sur une cheminée
Oc:810x600:signed:Purchased with assistance from a special government grant and with assistance from the National Art Collections Fund 1978

T05028   The Glass (1910)
Le Verre
Oc:331x372:signed:Bequeathed by Sir Anthony Hornby through the Friends of the Tate Gallery 1988

School Prints (P01698-P01727; complete group; mixed group)
P01698   The Bird (1946-9)
CLπ:498x762:signed:Presented by Patrick Seale Prints 1975

P77198   Profile with Palette (1953)
Profil à la palette
CLπ:520x712:signed:Purchased 1987

P77264   Black Chariot (1958)
Char Noir
Iπ:236x295:signed:Purchased 1988

BRATBY, Jean born 1927
Modern Collection
Tate Gallery Archive holds material concerning this artist

T00278   Self-Portrait (1958)
Oc:1149x838:signed:Presented by the Trustees of the Chantrey Bequest 1959

BRATBY, John born 1928
Modern Collection
Tate Gallery Archive holds material concerning this artist

T00104 Still Life with Chip Frier (1954)
Ob:1314x921:Presented by the Contemporary Art Society 1956

T00122 Elm Park Gardens (1955)
Oc:1016x1270:Purchased 1957

T00153 Window, Self-Portrait, Jean and Hands (1957)
Ob:1219x3658:signed:Purchased 1957

T00154 Susan Ballam (1956)
Dπ:1321x495:Presented by Sir Edward and Lady Hulton 1957

T00347 Dartmouth Row Studio: Autumn 1956 (1956)
Dπ:1689x3467:Presented by the artist 1960

BREAKWELL, Ian born 1943
Modern Collection
Tate Gallery Archive holds material concerning this artist

T03936 Keep Things as They Are: In Mysterious Ways (1981)
DVπ:1513x1295:signed:Purchased 1984

T03937 Keep Things as They Are: In the Same Vein (1981)
DVπ:1525x1377:signed:Purchased 1984

T03938 Keep Things as They Are: In Silken Chains (1981)
DVπ:1516x1395:signed:Purchased 1984

Repertory (P04055-P04059; complete group)

P04055 [no title] (1974)
MNπ:814x557:signed:Presented by Rose and Chris Prater through the Institute of Contemporary Prints 1975

P04056 [no title] (1974)
MNπ:816x556:signed:Presented by Rose and Chris Prater through the Institute of Contemporary Prints 1975

P04057 [no title] (1974)
MNπ:817x555:signed:Presented by Rose and Chris Prater through the Institute of Contemporary Prints 1975

P04058 [no title] (1974)
MNπ:816x555:signed:Presented by Rose and Chris Prater through the Institute of Contemporary Prints 1975

P04059 [no title] (1974)
MNπ:815x555:signed:Presented by Rose and Chris Prater through the Institute of Contemporary Prints 1975

10 Diary Pages 1968-82 (P77032-P77041; complete group)

P77032 [no title] (1983)
CNπ:302x210:Purchased 1984

P77033 [no title] (1983)
CNπ:302x210:Purchased 1984

P77034 [no title] (1983)
CNπ:302x210:Purchased 1984

P77035 [no title] (1983)
CNπ:302x210:Purchased 1984

P77036 [no title] (1983)
CNπ:302x210:Purchased 1984

P77037 [no title] (1983)
CNπ:302x210:Purchased 1984

P77038 [no title] (1983)
CNπ:302x210:Purchased 1984

P77039 [no title] (1983)
CNπ:302x210:Purchased 1984

P77040 [no title] (1983)
CNπ:302x210:Purchased 1984

P77041 [no title] (1983)
CNπ:302x210:Purchased 1984

BREE, Rev. William 1754-1822
British Collection

T05471 A Much-Repaired Gate (1804)
Wπ:114x187:Presented by Miss Marjorie Ball 1988

BREEZE, Claude born 1938
Modern Collection

Centennial Suite (P03217-P03225, P03228-P03229; complete group; mixed group)

P03220 Untitled (1967)
CNπ:498x371:signed:Presented by Simon Fraser University, British Columbia 1977

BRETON, André 1896-1966
Modern Collection
Tate Gallery Archive holds material concerning this artist

T03807 I Saluted at Six Paces Commander Lefebvre des Noëttes (poem object) (1942)
J'ai salué à six pas le Commandant Lefebvre des Noëttes (Poème objet)
DVπ:340x250:Purchased 1983

BRETT, Bernard born 1925
Modern Collection

P06053 The Royal Pavilion, Brighton (1974)
CLπ:492x705:signed:Presented by Curwen Studio through the Institute of Contemporary Prints 1975

P06054 The Palace Pier, Brighton (1974)
CLπ:502x702:signed:Presented by Curwen Studio through the Institute of Contemporary Prints 1975

BRETT, The Hon. Dorothy 1883-1977
Modern Collection

T00284 Ceremonial Indian Dance: The Matachinas (1948)
Oc:1270x1016:signed:Presented by the artist 1959

T00285 Massacre in the Canyon of Death: Vision of the Sun God (1958)
OVb:883x679:signed:Presented by the artist 1959

BRETT, John 1831-1902
British Collection
Tate Gallery Archive holds material concerning this artist

N01617 Britannia's Realm (1880)
Oc:1054x2121:signed:Presented by the Trustees of the Chantrey Bequest 1880

N01902 The British Channel Seen from the Dorsetshire Cliffs (1871)
Oc:1060x2127:signed:Presented by Mrs Brett 1902

N03393 Lady with a Dove: Madame Loeser (1864)
Oc:610x457:signed:Presented by Lady Holroyd in accordance with the wishes of the late Sir Charles Holroyd 1919

N05643 Glacier of Rosenlaui (1856)
Oc:445x419:signed:Purchased 1946

T01560 Florence from Bellosguardo (1863)
Oc:600x1013:signed:Presented by Thomas Stainton in memory of Charles and Lavinia Handley-Read 1972

BRIDELL, Frederick Lee 1831-1863
British Collection

N01205 The Woods of Sweet Chestnut above Varenna, Lake Como (1860)
Oc:559x1505:signed:Presented by Mrs Bridell-Fox 1886

BRIDGEWATER, Alan 1903-1962
Modern Collection

T03710 Inscription 'Remember Jane Snowfield' (1927)
Rs:270x540x70:Transferred from the Victoria & Albert Museum 1983

BRIGGS, Ernest 1866-1913
British Collection

N02936 A Flood on the Ken at Earlstoun Linn (exhibited 1913)
Wπ:787x1143:signed:Presented by the Trustees of the Chantrey Bequest 1913

BRIGGS, Henry Perronet 1793-1844
British Collection

N00375 The First Interview Between the Spaniards and the Peruvians (exhibited 1826)
Oc:1448x1956:Presented by Robert Vernon 1847

N00376 Juliet and the Nurse (exhibited 1827)
Oc:889x698:Presented by Robert Vernon 1847

BRILL, Frederick 1920-1984
Modern Collection

T04857 Quarry Face, Worth Matravers (1956)
Oc:915x1220:signed:Presented by Mr and Mrs John Gere 1986

BRISLEY, Stuart born 1933
Modern Collection
Tate Gallery Archive holds material concerning this artist

T03315 Beneath Dignity Bregenz (1977)
Fπ:425x546:Purchased 1981

T03316 ZL636595c Gallery House London (1972)
Fπ:546x422:Purchased 1981

T03317 Moments of Decision/Indecision, Warsaw (1975)
Fπ:546x425:Purchased 1981

T05002 Nul Comma Nul (1984 and 1986)
SV:2450x1850x6200:Purchased 1987

BRITISH SCHOOL 16th century
British Collection

N04811 Portrait of a Lady (1576)
Ow:743x464:Presented by Mrs Willingham-Rawnsley 1935

T00400 A Young Lady Aged 21, Possibly Helena Snakenborg, Later Marchioness of Northampton (1569)
Ow:629x483:Presented by the Friends of the Tate Gallery 1961

T00402 Sir Henry Unton (1586)
Ow:578x451:Bequeathed by E. Peter Jones 1961

T05729 An Allegory of Man (circa 1570)
Ow:570x514:Presented by the Patrons of British Art 1990

BRITISH SCHOOL 17th century
British Collection

N02878 A Lady of the Horton Family (circa 1655)
Oc:749x622:Purchased 1912

T00069 The Cholmondeley Sisters (circa 1600-10)
Ow:889x1727:Presented anonymously 1955

T02308 William Style of Langley (1636)
Oc:2051x1359:Purchased 1978

T03029 Sir Thomas Pope, Later 3rd Earl of Downe (circa 1635)
Oc:2026x1194:Purchased with assistance from the Friends of the Tate Gallery, the National Art Collections Fund and the Pilgrim Trust 1980

T03031 A Lady in a Masque Dress, Called Elizabeth, Lady Tanfield (1615)
Oc:2222x1365:Purchased with assistance from the Friends of the Tate Gallery, the National Art Collections Fund and the Pilgrim Trust 1980

BRITISH SCHOOL 17th or 18th century
British Collection

T03032 George Talbot, 6th Earl of Shrewsbury
Oc:2286x1460:Purchased with assistance from the Friends of the Tate Gallery, the National Art Collections Fund and the Pilgrim Trust 1980

BRITISH SCHOOL 18th century
British Collection

N01254 Hyde Park Corner (circa 1790)
Oc:546x889:Presented by Miss Emily J. Wood 1888

N01706 Self-Portrait of an Unknown Artist at the Age of Twenty-two (?circa 1740)
Oc:749x619:Purchased 1879

N02220 Study of a Human Skull (?circa 1750)
Dπ:178x199:Presented by the Rev. John Gibson 1892

N02221 Study of a Man's Head (?circa 1765)
Dπ:82x71:Presented by the Rev. John Gibson 1892

N02716 Castle by a Lake (late 18th C)
Ow:197x260:Presented by A.E. Anderson 1910

N02917 Dr Henry Hepburn
Oc:635x508:Presented by Miss Dudgeon 1912

N02981 The Tummel (late 18th C)
Ow:219x267:Bequeathed by Richard and Catherine Garnons 1854

N02982 Classical Landscape with Mountains (circa 1720-40)
Oc:356x457:Bequeathed by Richard and Catherine Garnons 1854

N02985 Landscape with a Dark Tree (late 18th C)
Oc:660x775:Bequeathed by Richard and Catherine Garnons 1854

N03728 Mrs Cadoux (circa 1770)
Oc:2127x1359:Bequeathed by Miss Mary Burgess Hudson 1931

N04764 Greenwich Hospital (after 1750)
Oc:337x900:Presented by the Hon. Mrs Phillimore 1934

N04765 Chelsea Hospital (after 1751)
Oc:337x898:Presented by the Hon. Mrs Phillimore 1934

N05049 A Family Group in a Landscape (circa 1750)
Oc:698x902:Presented by Mrs H.A. Wilder 1939

N05397 Lady Catherine Henry in Turkish Dress (circa 1760-4)
Oc:743x616:Presented by T.A.G. Strickland 1942

T01896 A Family Group in a Garden (circa 1754)
WGπ:392x357:Bequeathed by Alan Evans 1974

Portrait Miniatures (A00051-A00056; complete group)
A00051 [title not known]
Wπ::Bequeathed by Miss Julia Emily Gordon 1896
A00052 [title not known]
Wπ::Bequeathed by Miss Julia Emily Gordon 1896
A00053 [title not known]
Wπ::Bequeathed by Miss Julia Emily Gordon 1896
A00054 [title not known]
Wπ::Bequeathed by Miss Julia Emily Gordon 1896
A00055 [title not known]
Wπ::Bequeathed by Miss Julia Emily Gordon 1896
A00056 [title not known]
Wπ::Bequeathed by Miss Julia Emily Gordon 1896

BRITISH (?) SCHOOL 18th century
British Collection

N05566 Claudian Landscape
Ow:267x267:Presented by Miss M.H. Turner 1944

BRITISH SCHOOL 19th century
British Collection

N01719 Cheyne Walk (circa 1840)
Wπ:114x178:Presented by E. Homan 1899
N02730 Silhouette Portrait of J.M.W. Turner
WVb:111x76:Presented by James Lahee 1860
N05386 A Black Model (circa 1830-40)
Oc:1283x1016:Purchased 1942
T00031 Country Girl with Downcast Eyes
Wπ:292x235:Purchased 1955

BRITISH (?) SCHOOL 19th century
British Collection

N01071 River with Rocky Banks
Ow:152x216:Purchased 1879
N04483 A Painter's Self-Portrait
Oc:597x495:Bequeathed by Lady Haversham 1929

BROCK, Sir Thomas 1847-1922
British Collection

N01747 A Moment of Peril (1880)
Sz:1905x2464x1270:signed:Presented by the Trustees of
the Chantrey Bequest 1881
N01765 Sir Henry Tate (exhibited 1898)
Sz:533x584x356:signed:Presented by subscribers 1898
N01784 Eve (1900)
Ss:1740x502x406:signed:Presented by Sir Henry Tate 1900
N02074 Thomas Gainsborough, R.A. (1906)
Ss:2102x864x749:signed:Commissioned under the will of
Henry Vaughan 1906

BROCQUY, Louis le - see LE BROCQUY, Louis

BRODZKY, Horace 1885-1969
Modern Collection
Tate Gallery Archive holds material concerning this artist

T01786 Interior of Gaudier-Brzeska's Studio, Putney (1915)
Dπ:178x260:signed:Purchased 1973
T01787 Exterior of Gaudier-Brzeska's Studio, Putney (1915)
Dπ:178x260:signed:Purchased 1973

BROODTHAERS, Marcel 1924-1976
Modern Collection
Tate Gallery Archive holds material concerning this artist

T01976 Casserole and Closed Mussels (1964)
Casserole et moules fermées
Smv:305x279x248:Purchased 1975
T01977 Mademoiselle Rivière and Monsieur Bertin (1975)
Fb:841x733:Purchased 1975
T03089 I Return to Matter, I Rediscover the Tradition of the
Primitives, Painting with Egg, Painting with Egg (1966)
Je retourne à la matière, je retrouve la tradition des
primitifs, peinture à l'oeuf, peinture à l'oeuf
Swv:257x257x76:signed:Purchased 1980
T03696 Paintings (1973)
Peintures
9 Oc:800x1003:Purchased 1983
P01810 Tractatus Logico Catalogicus - Art or the Art of Selling
(1972)
Tractatus Logico-Catalogicus - L'Art ou l'art de vendre
MNπ:606x1464:Presented by Alexander Tate Gilmour
1977
P07208 Dear Little Sister (1972)
Chère Petite Soeur
MLπ:156x210:signed:Purchased 1977
P07209 A Railway Robbery (1972)
Ein Eisenbahnüberfall
MLπ:841x559:Purchased 1977
P07210 Rebus (1973)
Rébus
CLπ:702x502:signed:Purchased 1977
P07211 Citron-Citroën (1974)
Citron-Citröen
CLNπ:1048x664:signed:Purchased 1977
P07212 Comedy (1974)
Comédie
CLπ:635x457:signed:Purchased 1977
P07213 Atlas (1975)
MJπ:489x635:signed:Purchased 1977
P07214 Daguerre's Soup (1975)
La Soupe de Daguerre
CNFVπ:530x514:signed:Purchased 1977
P07385 The Farm Animals (1974)
Les Animaux de la ferme
2 CLπ:819x603:signed:Purchased 1980

BROOK, Peter born 1927
Modern Collection

P06055 Snowline (1973)
CLπ:714x502:signed:Presented by Curwen Studio
through the Institute of Contemporary Prints 1975
P06056 Pennine Way (1974)
CLπ:505x762:signed:Presented by Curwen Studio
through the Institute of Contemporary Prints 1975
P06631 Misty Morning (1975)
CLπ:508x711:signed:Presented by Curwen Studio 1976

Twelve Months of the Year (P06632-P06633, P06722,
P06761-P06769; complete group)
P06632 JANUARY Pennine Valley (1976-7)
CLπ:511x712:signed:Presented by Curwen Studio 1978
P06633 FEBRUARY Fill-Dyke in Wigan (1976-7)
CLπ:510x711:signed:Presented by Curwen Studio 1978
P06722 MARCH Melting Snow (1976-7)
CLπ:511x711:signed:Presented by Curwen Studio 1978

P06761 APRIL Showers (1976-7)
CLπ:505x715:signed:Presented by Curwen Studio 1978

P06762 MAY Misty Morning (1976-7)
CLπ:510x710:signed:Presented by Curwen Studio 1978

P06763 JUNE Canal (1976-7)
CLπ:510x710:signed:Presented by Curwen Studio 1978

P06764 JULY After the Gala (1976-7)
CLπ:510x710:signed:Presented by Curwen Studio 1978

P06765 AUGUST Cottage in Anglesey (1976-7)
CLπ:510x710:signed:Presented by Curwen Studio 1978

P06766 SEPTEMBER Cornfield - Sheep on the Wrong Side of the Gate (1976-7)
CLπ:511x711:signed:Presented by Curwen Studio 1978

P06767 OCTOBER Pennine Road (1976-7)
CLπ:510x710:signed:Presented by Curwen Studio 1978

P06768 NOVEMBER Late Afternoon (1976-7)
CLπ:510x710:signed:Presented by Curwen Studio 1978

P06769 DECEMBER Sheep Coming In (1976-7)
CLπ:511x711:signed:Presented by Curwen Studio 1978

BROOKE, William Henry 1772-1860
British Collection

T03300 Lanherne Bay near the Nunnery, Cornwall (1819)
Wπ:146x190:signed:Purchased 1981

BROOKER, William 1918-1983
Modern Collection
Tate Gallery Archive holds material concerning this artist

T01983 Still Life, New Studio (1974)
Oc:914x914:signed:Purchased 1975

BROOKING, Charles circa 1723-1759
British Collection

N01475 Fishing Smacks Becalmed near a Shore
Oc:273x838:Bequeathed by Rev. Richard G. Maul 1896

N04003 A Flagship before the Wind with other Vessels
Oc:368x1016:Presented by Miss Florence Le Marchant Tupper in memory of Lt-Gen. Sir Gaspard Le Marchant Tupper 1924

T00115 A British Man of War Firing a Salute (circa 1750-9)
Oc:1022x1480:Purchased 1956

BROOKS, James born 1906
Modern Collection

T00253 Boon (1957)
Oc:1803x1730:signed:Presented by the Friends of the Tate Gallery 1959

BROUGH, Robert 1872-1905
British Collection

N01956 Fantasie en Folie (1897)
Oc:1022x1257:Bequeathed by the artist 1905

BROUGH, Romey born 1944
Modern Collection

P06723 Sunflowers (1972)
CLπ:451x698:signed:Presented by Curwen Studio 1976

BROWN, Sir Arnesby 1866-1955
British Collection

N01898 Morning (exhibited 1901)
Oc:1283x1841:signed:Presented by the Trustees of the Chantrey Bequest 1901

N02738 Silver Morning (exhibited 1910)
Oc:1600x1835:signed:Presented by the Trustees of the Chantrey Bequest 1910

N03448 The Line of the Plough (exhibited 1919)
Oc:635x762:signed:Presented by the Trustees of the Chantrey Bequest 1919

BROWN, Frederick 1851-1941
British Collection
Tate Gallery Archive holds material concerning this artist

N03282 Landscape, the Storm (1914)
WDπ:241x356:signed:Presented by subscribers through the National Art Collections Fund 1918

N04702 Portrait of the Painter (1932)
Oc:921x654:signed:Presented by the Trustees of the Chantrey Bequest 1940

N05104 The Ivy Arch (?circa 1933-7)
Oc:457x610:signed:Presented by the Trustees of the Chantrey Bequest 1940

BROWN, Ford Madox 1821-1893
British Collection
Tate Gallery Archive holds material concerning this artist

N01356 Cathy Madox Brown at the Age of Three (1853)
Dπ:171x146:signed:Purchased 1923

N01394 Jesus Washing Peter's Feet (1852-6)
Oc:1168x1333:signed:Presented by subscribers 1893

N02063 Chaucer at the Court of Edward III (1856-68)
Oc:1232x991:signed:Purchased 1906

N02409 King René's Honeymoon
Dπ:260x168:Presented by Edmund Houghton 1898

N02410 Sheepshearing (circa 1887)
Dπ:241x279:Presented by Edmund Houghton 1898

N02411 Studies for 'Work' (1855)
Dπ:124x175:signed:Presented by Edmund Houghton 1898

N02412 Design for Badge for Gillum's Homes
Dπ:114x178:signed:Presented by Edmund Houghton 1898

N02413 Arkwright's Mill (1878)
Dπ:140x229:signed:Presented by Edmund Houghton 1898

N02414 Study for 'John Kay' (1889)
Dπ:178x254:signed:Presented by Edmund Houghton 1898

N02415 Study for 'Southend'
Dπ:140x229:Presented by Edmund Houghton 1898

N02416 'Where are you going, my pretty maid?'
Dπ:222x178:Presented by Edmund Houghton 1898

N02417 Section of the Bridgewater Canal (1890)
Dπ:111x178:Presented by Edmund Houghton 1898

N02418 A Barge on the Bridgewater Canal (1890)
Dπ:95x171:Presented by Edmund Houghton 1898

N02419 Study of the Tow-Path on the Bridgewater Canal (1890)
Dπ:95x171:Presented by Edmund Houghton 1898

N02684 Our Lady of Good Children (1847-61)
WPπ:781x591:signed:Presented by Alfred A. de Pass 1910

N02791 Arkwright's Mill (1881)
Dπ:133x216:Presented by Edmund Houghton 1898

N02792 The Bridgewater Canal (1890)
Dπ:114x178:Presented by Edmund Houghton 1898

N02793 The Bridgewater Canal
Dπ:114x178:Presented by Edmund Houghton 1898

N03064 The Last of England (1864-6)
Wπ:356x330:Purchased 1916

N03065 Lear and Cordelia (1849-54)
Oc:711x991:signed:Purchased with assistance from the National Art Collections Fund and subscribers 1916

N03228 Mauvais Sujet (1863)
Wπ:232x210:signed:Purchased 1917

N03229 King René's Honeymoon (1864)
Wπ:260x171:signed:Purchased 1917

N03472 Study of a Man Painting (1839)
Dπ:279x229:signed:Purchased 1919

N03528 The Brent at Hendon (1854-5)
Ob:203x248:signed:Presented by F. Hindley Smith 1920

N04014 Elijah and the Widow's Son, engraved by the Dalziel Brothers (published 1881)
Mπ:229x149:Presented by Gilbert Dalziel 1924

N04280 Study for the Dean in the 'Execution of Mary Queen of Scots' (circa 1840)
Oπ:470x394:Bequeathed by J.R. Holliday 1927

N04281 Sketch for 'Jesus Washing Peter's Feet' (1852)
Dπ:171x200:signed:Bequeathed by J.R. Holliday 1927

N04282 Sketch for 'Cromwell on his Farm' (circa 1853)
Dπ:146x98:Bequeathed by J.R. Holliday 1927

N04429 'Take your Son, Sir' (?1851-92)
Oc:705x381:signed:Presented by Miss Emily Sargent and Mrs Ormond in memory of their brother, John S. Sargent 1929

N04584 The Coat of Many Colours (1867)
Wπ:305x305:signed:Bequeathed by J.R. Holliday 1931

N04625 Stages of Cruelty
Wπ:143x121:Bequeathed by H.F. Stephens 1932

N04735 Carrying Corn (1854-5)
Ow:197x276:signed:Purchased 1934

N04803 Head of a Girl
Oπ:514x356:signed:Purchased 1935

N04866 Portrait of Dykes Barry as a Child (1853)
Ob:152x127:Bequeathed by Miss A.B. Marshall 1937

N05301 Jesus Washing Peter's Feet (1857-1858)
Wπ:394x448:signed:Bequeathed by Sir Hugh Walpole 1941

N05383 Platt Lane (1884)
Oc:394x260:signed:Presented by the National Art Collections Fund 1942

T00571 Verso: A Head Crowned with Laurels (1852)
Dπ:292x343:signed:Purchased 1963

T01035 Sketch for 'Jesus Washing Peter's Feet' (circa 1851)
Dπ:73x89:Purchased 1968

T01920 The Hayfield (1855-6)
Ow:241x333:signed:Purchased 1974

BROWN, Kellock 1856-1934
British Collection

N03960 Ju-Jitsu (1923)
Sz:356x635x305:signed:Presented by the Trustees of the Chantrey Bequest 1924

BROWN, Mortimer 1874-1966
British Collection

N02896 Shepherd Boy (1911)
Sz:1580x530x536:signed:Presented by the Trustees of the Chantrey Bequest 1912

BROWN, Ralph born 1928
Modern Collection
Tate Gallery Archive holds material concerning this artist

T00374 Swimming (1959-60)
Sz:603x787x318:Purchased 1960

BROWNE, Henriette 1829-1901
Modern Collection

N01969 A Greek Captive (1863)
Oc:921x730:Bequeathed by C. Fraser 1868

BRUN, Christopher le. - see LE BRUN, Christopher

BRUNDRIT, Reginald 1883-1960
Modern Collection

N05327 Fresh Air Stubbs (circa 1938)
Oc:965x889:signed:Presented by the Trustees of the Chantrey Bequest 1938

N05340 Nutwith Common, Masham (exhibited 1940)
Oc:457x610:signed:Presented by the Trustees of the Chantrey Bequest 1940

BRUNSDON, John born 1933
Modern Collection

P01375 Pass near Conniston (1973)
CLπ:594x445:signed:Presented by Christie's Contemporary Art through the Institute of Contemporary Prints 1975

P01376 Windermere (1973)
CLπ:594x445:signed:Presented by Christie's Contemporary Art through the Institute of Contemporary Prints 1975

P01861 Welsh Scene: Harlech (1978)
CLπ:356x448:Presented by Christie's Contemporary Art 1979

BRUS, Günter born 1938
Modern Collection

T03695 Run-through of an Action (1966)
Ablauf einer Aktion
17 Dπ::signed:Purchased 1983

T03861 Crystals of Standstill (1983)
Kristalle des Stillstands
DVπ:1228x840:signed:Purchased 1984

T04927 Untitled (1960)
Ohne Titel
Dπ:1257x900:signed:Purchased 1987

Great Fear of the Earth (P07991-P07993; complete group)
Grosse Erdangst

P07991 Great Fear of the Earth I (1982)
Grosse Erdangst I
MLπ:604x908:signed:Purchased 1984

P07992 Great Fear of the Earth II (1982)
Grosse Erdangst II
MIπ:604x908:signed:Purchased 1984

P07993 Great Fear of the Earth III (1982)
Grosse Erdangst III
MIπ:604x908:signed:Purchased 1984

Night Quartet (P77001-P77008; complete group)
Nachtquartett

P77001 [no title] (1982)
MIπ:238x167:signed:Purchased 1983

P77002 [no title] (1982)
MIπ:238x167:signed:Purchased 1983

P77003 [no title] (1982)
MIπ:238x167:signed:Purchased 1983

P77004 [no title] (1982)
MIπ:238x167:signed:Purchased 1983

P77005 [no title] (1982)
MIπ:238x167:signed:Purchased 1983

P77006 [no title] (1982)
MIπ:238x167:signed:Purchased 1983

P77007 [no title] (1982)
MIπ:238x167:signed:Purchased 1983

P77008 [no title] (1982)
MIπ:238x167:signed:Purchased 1983

BRUS, Günter and RAINER, Arnulf born 1938, born 1929
Modern Collection

T05212 No, Daphne, No! (1984)
Nein, Daphne, Nein!
Dπ:577x402:Purchased 1988

T05213 Charm - Flower - Ring (1984)
Reizblütenreigen
Dπ:577x402:Purchased 1988

Deepening through Clouding (P77235-P77239; complete group)
Vertiefung durch Bewölkung

P77235 [no title] (1985)
Iπ:469x295:signed:Purchased 1987

P77236 [no title] (1985)
Iπ:429x296:signed:Purchased 1987

P77237 [no title] (1985)
Iπ:430x295:signed:Purchased 1987

P77238 [no title] (1985)
Iπ:445x309:signed:Purchased 1987

P77239 [no title] (1985)
Iπ:435x305:Purchased 1987

BUCKLEY, Stephen born 1944
Modern Collection
Tate Gallery Archive holds material concerning this artist

T01684 Nice (1972)
Racw:810x902x51:signed:Purchased 1972

T01685 Trullisatio (1972)
AVcw:1156x997x19:signed:Purchased 1972

T02024 Triptych (1974)
Oc:1524x1829x70:signed:Purchased 1976

T03070 Java (1980)
ROwcb:2007x1981:signed:Purchased 1980

The September Suite (P07325-P07335; complete group)

P07325 [no title] (1977)
CIπ:650x500:signed:Purchased 1979

P07326 [no title] (1977)
CIπ:700x492:signed:Purchased 1979

P07327 [no title] (1977)
CIπ:400x545:signed:Purchased 1979

P07328 [no title] (1977)
CIπ:695x495:signed:Purchased 1979

P07329 [no title] (1977)
CIπ:647x495:signed:Purchased 1979

P07330 [no title] (1977)
CIπ:635x495:signed:Purchased 1979

P07331 [no title] (1977)
CIπ:495x697:signed:Purchased 1979

P07332 [no title] (1977)
CIπ:697x495:signed:Purchased 1979

P07333 [no title] (1977)
CIπ:700x495:signed:Purchased 1979

P07334 [no title] (1977)
CIπ:495x375:signed:Purchased 1979

P07335 [no title] (1977)
CIπ:420x520:signed:Purchased 1979

Ten Colour Etchings (P07367-P07376; complete group)

P07367 [no title] (1979-80)
CIπ:185x197:signed:Purchased 1980

P07368 [no title] (1979-80)
CIπ:133x178:signed:Purchased 1980

P07369 [no title] (1979-80)
CIπ:120x76:signed:Purchased 1980

P07370 [no title] (1979-80)
CIπ:90x95:signed:Purchased 1980

P07371 [no title] (1979-80)
CIπ:73x73:signed:Purchased 1980

P07372 [no title] (1979-80)
CIπ:140x140:signed:Purchased 1980

P07373 [no title] (1979-80)
CIπ:74x74:signed:Purchased 1980

P07374 [no title] (1979-80)
CIπ:160x64:signed:Purchased 1980

P07375 [no title] (1979-80)
CIπ:185x162:signed:Purchased 1980

P07376 [no title] (1979-80)
CIπ:140x133:signed:Purchased 1980

P07754 Les Flons Flons (1981-2)
CNπ:772x1018:signed:Purchased 1982

BUFFET, Bernard born 1928
Modern Collection
Tate Gallery Archive holds material concerning this artist

T00004 Portrait of the Artist (1954)
Portrait de l'Artiste
Oc:1464x1140:signed:Presented by J. Spreiregen 1955

P77136 Holy Face (1953)
Sainte-Face
MIπ:509x647:signed:Purchased 1985

BUHLER, Robert 1916-1989
Modern Collection
Tate Gallery Archive holds material concerning this artist

N05862 Carlyle Square, Chelsea (1946-7)
Ob:914x1219:signed:Presented by the Trustees of the Chantrey Bequest 1948

T00032 Barnett Freedman (circa 1947)
Oc:762x635:Purchased 1955

BUNDY, Edgar 1862-1922
British Collection

N01960 The Morning of Sedgemoor (1905)
Oc:1524x1264:signed:Presented by the Trustees of the Chantrey Bequest 1905

BURCHFIELD, Charles 1893-1967
Modern Collection

N04833 Freight Cars in March (1933)
Wb:610x864:signed:Presented by Samuel Courtauld 1936

BUREN, Daniel born 1938
Modern Collection
Tate Gallery Archive holds material concerning this artist

P07386 Framed/Exploded/Defaced (1978-9)
25 Clπ:210x206:Purchased 1980

BURGIN, Victor born 1941
Modern Collection
Tate Gallery Archive holds material concerning this artist

P07230 Room (1970)
MJπ:298x210:signed:Purchased 1973

P07231 Lei-feng (1973-4)
MFπ:406x508:signed:Purchased 1974

BURKERT, Robert born 1930
Modern Collection
Tate Gallery Archive holds material concerning this artist

P06057 Spanish Landscape (1968)
CLπ:479x692:Presented by Curwen Studio through the Institute of Contemporary Prints 1975

P06058 Moonlit Tree (1968)
MLπ:698x537:Presented by Curwen Studio through the Institute of Contemporary Prints 1975

P06059 English Garden (1968)
CLπ:457x679:Presented by Curwen Studio through the Institute of Contemporary Prints 1975

P06060 Pollard Tree (1968)
CLπ:511x445:Presented by Curwen Studio through the Institute of Contemporary Prints 1975

P06701 Three Trees (circa 1968)
MLπ:508x724:Presented by Curwen Studio through the Institute of Contemporary Prints 1976

BURN, Rodney J. 1899-1984
Modern Collection
Tate Gallery Archive holds material concerning this artist

N03721 Study of a Girl (exhibited 1922)
DWπ:432x330:signed:Purchased 1923

N04242 The Pick-a-Back (circa 1925)
DWπ:495x279:signed:Purchased 1927

N06178 Bembridge (1952)
Oc:813x1016:signed:Presented by the Trustees of the Chantrey Bequest 1953

T00860 Seascape near Crinan, Argyll (1965)
Oc:457x610:Presented by the Trustees of the Chantrey Bequest 1966

T03214 By the Lake (1922)
Oc:917x1222:signed:Presented by the Trustees of the Chantrey Bequest 1981

BURNE-JONES, Lady - see MACDONALD, Georgina

BURNE-JONES, Sir Edward Coley, Bt 1833-1898
British Collection
Tate Gallery Archive holds material concerning this artist

N01771 King Cophetua and the Beggar Maid (1884)
Oc:2934x1359:signed:Presented by subscribers 1900

N02760 Desiderium (1873)
Dπ:210x133:signed:Presented by Sir Philip Burne-Jones Bt 1910

N03141 Sisyphus
Dπ:216x216:Bequeathed by A.N. MacNicholl 1916

N03142 Tantalus
Dπ:216x216:Bequeathed by A.N. MacNicholl 1916

N03145 Study of a Girl's Head
Dπ:190x178:Bequeathed by A.N. MacNicholl 1916

N03425 Study of a Woman
Dπ:1575x584:Purchased 1919

N03426 St Luke (1872)
Dπ:1219x521:Purchased 1919

N03427 A Sibyl (1873)
Dπ:1257x508:Purchased 1919

N03428 Fountain of Youth (1873-81)
GOπ:622x1016:Purchased 1919

N03452 The Temple of Love
Oc:2134x927:Presented by the Trustees of the Chantrey Bequest 1919

N03453 The Passing of Venus (1881)
Gπ:1067x2438:Presented by the Trustees of the Chantrey Bequest 1919

N03454 King Cophetua and the Beggar Maid (1862)
Oc:762x635:Presented by the Trustees of the Chantrey Bequest 1919

N03455 The Magic Circle (circa 1880)
Wπ:356x330:signed:Presented by the Trustees of the Chantrey Bequest 1919

Designs for 'The Story of Perseus' (N03456-N03458; complete group)

N03456 The Arming of Perseus, Perseus and the Graiae, Perseus and the Nereids (1875-6)
WDπ:406x1067:Presented by the Trustees of the Chantrey Bequest 1919

N03457 The Finding of Medusa, the Birth of Pegasus and Chrysaor and the Death of Medusa (1875-6)
WDπ:406x1321:Presented by the Trustees of the Chantrey Bequest 1919

N03458 Atlas, the Rock of Doom, the Doom Fulfilled - the Court of Phineas, the Baleful Head (1875-6)
WDπ:368x1486:Presented by the Trustees of the Chantrey Bequest 1919

N03719 Ezekiel and the Boiling Pot
Db:260x152:signed:Purchased 1923

N03822 Fair Rosamund and Queen Eleanor (1862)
Wπ:260x267:signed:Presented by J.R. Holliday through
the National Art Collections Fund 1923

N03872 Woman in an Interior (?circa 1861)
Gπ:225x318:Purchased 1924

N03975 Female Head
Dπ:190x165:Presented by Lord Duveen 1924

N03976 Head of Miss M. Benson
Dπ:238x178:Presented by Lord Duveen 1924

N03977 Head
Dπ:197x165:Presented by Lord Duveen 1924

N03978 Medusa
Dπ:273x178:Presented by Lord Duveen 1924

N03979 The Pilgrim
Dπ:368x225:Presented by Lord Duveen 1924

N03980 Andromeda
Dπ:381x279:Presented by Lord Duveen 1924

N03981 Study of Dancing Woman for 'The Mill'
Dπ:356x254:Presented by Lord Duveen 1924

N03982 Figures for 'The Mirror of Venus'
Dπ:254x178:Presented by Lord Duveen 1924

N03983 Figure of Medusa for 'The Death of Medusa'
Dπ:264x171:Presented by Lord Duveen 1924

N03984 Studies for 'Love Leading the Pilgrim'
Dπ:229x324:Presented by Lord Duveen 1924

N03986 Drapery Study. Verso: Man with Sword
Dπ:254x140:Presented by Lord Duveen 1924

N04005 The Golden Stairs (1880)
Oc:2692x1168:signed:Bequeathed by Lord Battersea 1924

N04015 Parable of the Burning Pot, engraved by the Dalziel
Brothers (published 1881)
Jπ:178x133:Bequeathed by Lord Battersea 1924

N04046 Sigurd the Crusader, engraved by the Dalziel Brothers
(published 1862)
Jπ:156x114:Purchased 1925

N04047 Summer Snow, engraved by the Dalziel Brothers
(published 1863)
Jπ:146x108:Presented by Harold Hartley 1925

N04048 Parable of the Burning Pot, engraved by the Dalziel
Brothers (published 1881)
Jπ:178x133:Presented by Harold Hartley 1925

N04110 Madonna and Child for 'The Star of Bethlehem'
Dπ:270x152:Presented by Lord Duveen 1925

N04111 Figure Study for 'The Calling of Perseus' (?1877)
Dπ:254x165:Presented by Lord Duveen 1925

N04113 Figure of Demophoön for 'Phyllis and Demophoön'
(circa 1870)
Dπ:248x133:Presented by Lord Duveen 1925

N04114 Figure of Image for 'The Godhead Fires' in the
Pygmalion Series
Dπ:264x143:Presented by Lord Duveen 1925

N04337 St Agnes
Dπ:1194x457:Bequeathed by J.R. Holliday 1927

N04342 Figure Study. Verso: Study for an Annunciation?
Dπ:279x178:signed:Bequeathed by J.R. Holliday 1927

N04343 Figure of the Virgin for an Annunciation
Dπ:343x368:Bequeathed by J.R. Holliday 1927

N04344 Study for 'Cinderella' (circa 1863)
Dπ:337x197:signed:Bequeathed by J.R. Holliday 1927

N04350 Study for 'The Mirror of Venus'
Dπ:283x238:Bequeathed by J.R. Holliday 1927

N04390 Clerk Saunders (1861)
Wπ:686x419:signed:Presented by Mrs Winifred Hadley
through the National Art Collections Fund 1927

N04637 Head and Hand
Dπ:225x165:Bequeathed by H.F. Stephens 1932

N04638 Head and Shoulders, Back View
Dπ:143x133:Bequeathed by H.F. Stephens 1932

N04639 Head and Shoulders, Front View
Dπ:203x143:Bequeathed by H.F. Stephens 1932

N04743 The Annunciation and the Adoration of the Magi (1861)
3 Oc:1086x737, 1086x1562, 1086x737:Presented by G.H.
Bodley in memory of George Frederick Bodley 1934

N04888 The Morning of the Resurrection (1886)
Ow:845x1511:signed:Bequeathed by Mrs S.G. Potter 1937

N05119 Frieze of Eight Women Gathering Apples (1876)
Ow:737x1829:signed:Bequeathed by Lady Horner in
memory of her father, William Graham 1940

N05175 A Zither Player (1896)
Dπ:349x200:signed:Bequeathed by Miss Maud
Beddington 1940

N05176 Vespertina Quies (1893)
Oc:1079x622:signed:Bequeathed by Miss Maud
Beddington 1940

N05177 Study of the Maid for 'King Cophetua and the Beggar
Maid' (1883-4)
ODπ:1206x622:signed:Bequeathed by Miss Maud
Beddington 1940

N05178 Orpheus and Eurydice (1870)
Gπ::signed:Bequeathed by Miss Maud Beddington 1940

N05180 Studies of Female Figures
Dπ:254x375:Bequeathed by Miss Maud Beddington 1940

N05181 Study of Drapery for 'King Cophetua and the Beggar
Maid' (N01771)
Dπ:194x181:Bequeathed by Miss Maud Beddington 1940

N05182 Study of Hands for 'King Cophetua and the Beggar Maid'
(N01771)
Dπ:194x181:Bequeathed by Miss Maud Beddington 1940

N05381 Love and the Pilgrim (1896-7)
Oc:1575x3048:signed:Presented by the National Art
Collections Fund 1942

N05877 Sidonia von Borke 1560 (1860)
Wπ:330x171:signed:Bequeathed by W. Graham
Robertson 1948

N05878 Clara von Borke 1560 (1860)
Wπ:337x178:signed:Bequeathed by W. Graham
Robertson 1948

T00457 The Mermaid (1882)
WGb:311x235:signed:Bequeathed by Miss Katharine
Elizabeth Lewis 1961

T00565 Study of the Maid for 'King Cophetua and the Beggar
Maid' (N01771) (1883)
Dπ:352x248:signed:Purchased 1963

T03313 Decorative Design: Sun Ripening Corn (circa 1892-8)
WGb:248x178:Purchased with assistance from the
Abbott Fund 1981

A00057 Study of a Woman's Head (1870)
Dπ:203x184:signed:Bequeathed by A.N. MacNicholl 1916

A00058 Study of a Woman's Head (1866)
Dπ:286x216:Bequeathed by A.N. MacNicholl 1916

A00059 Study of a Man's Head (1866)
Dπ:222x171:Bequeathed by A.N. MacNicholl 1916

A00060 Study of a Girl's Head (1866)
Dπ:260x216:Bequeathed by A.N. MacNicholl 1916

A00061 Study of a Standing Woman for 'The Passing of Venus' (1877)
DWπ:260x152:signed:Bequeathed by A.N. MacNicholl 1916

A00062 Study of a Seated Woman for 'The Passing of Venus' (?1877, 1887)
DWπ:241x210:signed:Bequeathed by A.N. MacNicholl 1916

A00063 Study of Seated Figure for 'The Garden Court' (Briar Rose Series)
Dπ:121x171:signed:Bequeathed by A.N. MacNicholl 1916

A00064 Study of Seated Figure for 'The Garden Court' (Briar Rose Series)
Dπ:121x165:signed:Bequeathed by A.N. MacNicholl 1916

A00065 Verso: Study of a Head for 'The Council Chamber' (Briar Rose Series)
Dπ:213x235:Bequeathed by A.N. MacNicholl 1916

A00066 Studies for 'The Council Chamber' (Briar Rose Series)
Dπ:321x222:Bequeathed by A.N. MacNicholl 1916

A00067 Studies of a Sleeve
Dπ:244x152:Bequeathed by A.N. MacNicholl 1916

A00068 Kneeling Woman
Dπ:152x165:Presented by Lord Duveen 1924

A00069 Stooping Woman
Dπ:152x165:Presented by Lord Duveen 1924

A00070 Female Head
Dπ:146x149:Presented by Lord Duveen 1925

A00071 Female Head
Dπ:146x149:Presented by Lord Duveen 1925

A00072 Ruth and Boaz
Dπ:648x521:Bequeathed by J.R. Holliday 1927

A00073 The Finding of Moses
Dπ:648x521:Bequeathed by J.R. Holliday 1927

Designs for windows at St Mary Virgin, Speldhurst, Kent (A00074-A00077; complete group)

A00074 St Alban (1875)
Dπ:730x400:Bequeathed by J.R. Holliday 1927

A00075 St Aidan (1875)
Dπ:730x400:Bequeathed by J.R. Holliday 1927

A00076 St Oswald (1875)
Dπ:730x400:Bequeathed by J.R. Holliday 1927

A00077 St Boniface (1875)
Dπ:730x400:Bequeathed by J.R. Holliday 1927

A00078 Head of Tristram for 'The Madness of Sir Tristram'
Dπ:102x130:signed:Bequeathed by J.R. Holliday 1927

A00079 Figure of Tristram for 'The Madness of Sir Tristram' (circa 1862)
Dπ:210x241:signed:Bequeathed by J.R. Holliday 1927

A00080 Roundel with the Head of a Man
Dπ::Bequeathed by J.R. Holliday 1927

A00081 Roundel with the Head of a Woman
Dπ::Bequeathed by J.R. Holliday 1927

A00082 Roundel with the Head of a Woman
Dπ::Bequeathed by J.R. Holliday 1927

A00083 Composition Study for 'The Merciful Knight'. Verso: Study for a Nativity (circa 1863)
Dπ:254x152:signed:Bequeathed by J.R. Holliday 1927

A00085 Composition Study for 'The Merciful Knight' (circa 1863)
Dπ:222x159:signed:Bequeathed by J.R. Holliday 1927

A00086 Nude Study of Knight for 'The Merciful Knight' (circa 1863)
Dπ:298x133:signed:Bequeathed by J.R. Holliday 1927

A00087 Nude Study of Knight for 'The Merciful Knight' (circa 1863)
Dπ:330x140:signed:Bequeathed by J.R. Holliday 1927

A00088 Study of Knight for 'The Merciful Knight' (circa 1863)
Dπ:248x175:signed:Bequeathed by J.R. Holliday 1927

A00089 Nude Study of Knight for 'The Merciful Knight' (circa 1863)
Dπ:203x190:signed:Bequeathed by J.R. Holliday 1927

A00090 Nude Study for the Briar Rose Series?
Dπ:168x130:signed:Bequeathed by J.R. Holliday 1927

A00091 Nude Studies for the Briar Rose Series?
Dπ:181x337:signed:Bequeathed by J.R. Holliday 1927

A00092 Study for 'Blind Love'
Dπ:302x140:signed:Bequeathed by J.R. Holliday 1927

A00093 Study for 'Blind Love'
Dπ:311x133:signed:Bequeathed by J.R. Holliday 1927

A00094 Study for 'Clerk Saunders' (?1861)
Dπ:298x149:Bequeathed by J.R. Holliday 1927

A00095 Study of a Seated Woman
Dπ:483x264:Bequeathed by J.R. Holliday 1927

A00096 Study of a Reclining Figure
Dπ:105x152:Bequeathed by J.R. Holliday 1927

A00097 Head of a Girl
Dπ:187x140:Bequeathed by J.R. Holliday 1927

A00098 Two Studies for the Head of the King in 'King Cophetua and the Beggar Maid' (circa 1880)
Dπ:152x162:Bequeathed by J.R. Holliday 1927

A00099 Head of a Woman
Dπ:140x168:signed:Bequeathed by J.R. Holliday 1927

A00101 Head of a Girl
Dπ:159x117:Bequeathed by J.R. Holliday 1927

A00102 Figure Study
Dπ:114x149:signed:Bequeathed by J.R. Holliday 1927

A00103 Study of Head for 'The Adoration of the Magi' (circa 1861)
Dπ:156x146:Bequeathed by J.R. Holliday 1927

A00105 Study for 'Clerk Saunders' (?1861)
Dπ:403x184:Bequeathed by J.R. Holliday 1927

A00106 Head of a Man
Dπ:114x130:Bequeathed by J.R. Holliday 1927

A00108 Study for 'The Story of Orpheus': The House of Pluto
Dπ:229x305:Bequeathed by J.R. Holliday 1927

A00109 'Chant d'Amour'
Dπ:190x305:signed:Bequeathed by J.R. Holliday 1927

A00110 Backgammon Players (circa 1862)
Dπ:210x225:signed:Bequeathed by J.R. Holliday 1927

A00128 Studies for a Nativity
Dπ:137x98:signed:Bequeathed by J.R. Holliday 1927

A00129 Design for a Window: Ethelbert
DWπ:343x216:Bequeathed by J.R. Holliday 1927

A00130 Design for a Window: St James the Greater
DWπ:311x235:Bequeathed by J.R. Holliday 1927

A01160 The Nativity
Dπ:229x318:Bequeathed by J.R. Holliday 1927

A01161 Study for 'Buondelmonte's Wedding' (circa 1859)
Dπ:235x311:signed:Bequeathed by J.R. Holliday 1927

A01162 Study for 'Buondelmonte's Wedding' (circa 1859)
Dπ:235x270:signed:Bequeathed by J.R. Holliday 1927

A01163 Composition Study for 'Ezekiel and the Boiling Pot' (circa 1860)
Dπ:181x133:signed:Bequeathed by J.R. Holliday 1927

A01164 Composition Study for 'Ezekiel and the Boiling Pot'
(circa 1860)
Dπ:178x133:signed:Bequeathed by J.R. Holliday 1927

A01165 Study of Ezekiel's Hand for 'Ezekiel and the Boiling Pot'
(circa 1860)
Dπ:44x117:signed:Bequeathed by J.R. Holliday 1927

A01166 Study of Ezekiel's Arm and Hand for 'Ezekiel and the
Boiling Pot' (circa 1860)
Dπ:35x57:signed:Bequeathed by J.R. Holliday 1927

A01167 King René's Honeymoon
Dπ:124x105:signed:Bequeathed by J.R. Holliday 1927

A01168 Orpheus and Eurydice
Dπ:117x92:signed:Bequeathed by J.R. Holliday 1927

A01169 Lovers in a Garden (?1863)
DWπ:216x362:Bequeathed by J.R. Holliday 1927

A01170 Figure of a Queen (1861)
WDf:254x130:Bequeathed by J.R. Holliday 1927

A01171 Thisbe (1861)
DWf:254x133:Bequeathed by J.R. Holliday 1927

A01172 Dido (1861)
DWf:254x127:Bequeathed by J.R. Holliday 1927

A01173 Dido (tracing of A01172)
Dπ:124x105:Bequeathed by J.R. Holliday 1927

A01174 Design for a Window: Two Male Saints
DWπ:203x133:Bequeathed by J.R. Holliday 1927

A01175 The Nativity
Dπ:114x63:signed:Bequeathed by J.R. Holliday 1927

A01176 The Nativity
Dπ:105x73:signed:Bequeathed by J.R. Holliday 1927

BURNET, James 1788-1816
British Collection

N02947 View on the Thames (?exhibited 1816)
Ow:362x495:signed:Bequeathed by Sir Henry Layard
1913

BURRA, Edward 1905-1976
Modern Collection
Tate Gallery Archive holds material concerning this artist

N05004 Harlem (1934)
Gπ:794x571:signed:Purchased 1939

N05005 Dancing Skeletons (1934)
Gπ:787x559:signed:Purchased 1939

Wake (N05165-N05166; complete group)

N05165 [title not known] (1940)
GWπ:1022x698:signed:Purchased 1940

N05166 [title not known] (1940)
GWπ:1022x698:signed:Purchased 1940

N05167 Mexican Church (circa 1938)
GWπ:1321x1035:Purchased 1940

N05377 Soldiers at Rye (1941)
GWπ:1022x2070:signed:Presented by Studio 1942

T00013 Skeleton Party (circa 1952-4)
Wπ:718x1041:signed:Purchased 1955

T01471 Keep your Head (1930)
Dv:597x543:Purchased 1971

T01543 Coffee Stall. Verso: Scenes with Figures (circa 1930)
Dπ:552x749:Purchased 1972

T01756 Valley and River, Northumberland (1972)
WDπ:1016x686:signed:Presented by the Friends of the
Tate Gallery 1973

T03051 The Snack Bar (1930)
Oc:762x559:signed:Purchased 1980

P01002 Balcony (circa 1928-29)
MJπ:152x102:signed:Presented by Redfern Gallery 1971

P01003 Café (circa 1928-29)
MJπ:102x152:signed:Presented by Redfern Gallery 1971

P01004 Cupbearer (1929)
MJπ:152x102:signed:Presented by Redfern Gallery 1971

P01005 Fleet's in (circa 1928-29)
MJπ:152x102:signed:Presented by Redfern Gallery 1971

P03008 Mrs Pott (1971)
MIπ:251x273:signed:Presented by Alexander Postan 1973

P03009 Wednesday Night (1972)
MIπ:302x251:signed:Presented by Alexander Postan 1973

P03010 Drag Queen (1972)
MIπ:298x251:signed:Presented by Alexander Postan 1973

BURRI, Alberto born 1915
Modern Collection
Tate Gallery Archive holds material concerning this artist

T00787 Sacking and Red (1954)
Sacco e rosso
AVc:864x1003:signed:Purchased 1965

BURT, Laurence born 1925
Modern Collection

T00639 Helmet I (1962)
Sm:692x394x470:Purchased 1964

BURTON, Scott 1939-1989
Modern Collection

T04136 Asymmetrical Settee (1982)
Ss:920x1650x850:Presented by Jacqueline and Gilbert de
Botton 1986

BURTON, William Shakespeare 1824-1916
British Collection

N03389 Detail of Two Figures from 'The Wounded Cavalier'
(1871)
Oc:419x305:signed:Presented by Capt. H.L.P. Hulbert
1919

BURY, Pol born 1922
Modern Collection

T00918 3069 White Dots on an Oval Background (1966)
3069 Points blancs sur un fond oval
KRmw:673x1206x254:signed:Purchased 1967

T00919 16 Balls, 16 Cubes in 8 Rows (1966)
16 Boules, 16 cubes sur 8 rangées
KRw:800x400x200:signed:Purchased 1967

BUSH, Jack 1909-1977
Modern Collection

T00900 Colour Column on Suede (1965)
Oc:2267x1372:signed:Purchased 1967

P04060 Green Loop (1971)
CNπ:575x768:Presented by Rose and Chris Prater
through the Institute of Contemporary Prints 1975

P04061 Low Sun (1971)
CNπ:772x575:Presented by Rose and Chris Prater
through the Institute of Contemporary Prints 1975

P04062 Red M (1971)
CNπ:575x765:Presented by Rose and Chris Prater through the Institute of Contemporary Prints 1975

P04063 Three and Blue Loop (1971)
CNπ:565x772:Presented by Rose and Chris Prater through the Institute of Contemporary Prints 1975

P04064 Yellow Mark (1971)
CNπ:772x556:Presented by Rose and Chris Prater through the Institute of Contemporary Prints 1975

P04065 Cross Over (1974)
CNπ:708x530:signed:Presented by Rose and Chris Prater through the Institute of Contemporary Prints 1975

P04066 Low Spread (1974)
CNπ:562x749:signed:Presented by Rose and Chris Prater through the Institute of Contemporary Prints 1975

P04067 Pink Moon (1974)
CNπ:740x537:signed:Presented by Rose and Chris Prater through the Institute of Contemporary Prints 1975

P04068 Purple Thrust (1974)
CNπ:733x549:signed:Presented by Rose and Chris Prater through the Institute of Contemporary Prints 1975

P04069 White Flip (1974)
CNπ:746x521:signed:Presented by Rose and Chris Prater through the Institute of Contemporary Prints 1975

BUSSY, Simon 1870-1954
Modern Collection
Tate Gallery Archive holds material concerning this artist

N04246 Landscape (circa 1902-3)
Pπ:184x184:signed:Presented by Julian Lousada 1927

N05662 Lady Strachey (circa 1905)
Oc:892x743:Presented by Miss Philipa Strachey and Miss Joan Pernel Strachey 1946

N06015 Lady Ottoline Morrell (circa 1920)
Oc:318x292:signed:Presented by Clive Bell and Duncan Grant 1951

BUTLER, Elizabeth (Lady Butler) 1846-1933
British Collection

N01553 The Remnants of an Army (1879)
Oc:1321x2337:signed:Presented by Sir Henry Tate 1897

BUTLER, Mildred Anne 1858-1941
British Collection

N01708 Morning Bath (exhibited 1896)
Wπ:711x521:signed:Presented by the Trustees of the Chantrey Bequest 1896

BUTLER, Reg 1913-1981
Modern Collection
Tate Gallery Archive holds material concerning this artist

N05942 Woman (1949)
Sm:2210x711x483:Purchased 1950

N06223 Girl (1953-4)
Sz:1778x406x241:Purchased 1950

T00262 Ophelia (1955)
Sz:521x114x102:Purchased 1959

T00263 Study for Woman Resting (1950)
Sz:127x349x127:Purchased 1959

T02332 Working Model for 'The Unknown Political Prisoner' (1955-6)
Smzp:2238x879x854:Presented by Cortina and Creon Butler 1979

T03392 Woman (1949)
Smp:335x109x107:Purchased 1982

T03703 Musée Imaginaire (1961-3)
Szw:800x1213x120:signed:Purchased 1983

T03711 Crouching Woman (1948)
Sm:189x86x63:Transferred from the Victoria & Albert Museum 1983

T03867 Circe Head (1952-3)
Sz:430x235x215:signed:Purchased with assistance from the Gytha Trust 1984

P06061 Figure in Space (1962-3)
MLπ:606x457:signed:Presented by Curwen Studio through the Institute of Contemporary Prints 1975

P06062 Italian Girl (1962-3)
CLπ:343x492:signed:Presented by Curwen Studio through the Institute of Contemporary Prints 1975

P06063 Girl (1968-9)
CLπ:537x759:Presented by Curwen Studio through the Institute of Contemporary Prints 1975

P06064 Tower (1968-9)
CLπ:651x467:Presented by Curwen Studio through the Institute of Contemporary Prints 1975

A01061 Study for Head of Watcher (1951-2)
DWπ:264x203:signed:Presented by the Contemporary Art Society 1957

A01062 Study for Head of Watcher (1951-2)
DWπ:267x197:signed:Presented by the Contemporary Art Society 1957

A01063 Study for Head of Watcher (1951-2)
DWπ:273x203:signed:Presented by the Contemporary Art Society 1957

BUTLER, Samuel 1835-1902
British Collection

N02761 Mr Heatherley's Holiday: An Incident in Studio Life (1874)
Oc:921x708:signed:Presented by representatives of Jason Smith 1911

attributed to
BUTTS, John circa 1728-1764
British Collection

T01815 Poachers: View in the Dargle
Oc:686x899:Purchased 1973

BUVELOT, Louis 1814-1888
British Collection

N06017 The Pool (1878)
Wπ:178x254:signed:Presented by Mrs M.W. Moody in memory of her two sons who were killed in the war, 1939-45 1951

CACHARD, Regis Bouvier de - see
BOUVIER de CACHARD, Regis

CAGE, John born 1912
Modern Collection
Tate Gallery Archive holds material concerning this artist

T05516 Where R=Ryoanji (1984)
Dπ:259x488:Purchased 1988

P07903 Déreau No. 33 (1982)
CIπ:463x629:signed:Purchased 1983

CAHN, Miriam born 1949
Modern Collection

T04921 City (1985)
Stadt
Dπ:2722x3757:Purchased 1987

T04922 Hills (1985)
Berge
Dπ:2721x3384:Purchased 1987

CAIN, Neville 1855-1935
Modern Collection

N03993 John S. Sargent (circa 1875)
Oc:410x330:signed:Presented by A. Heseltine 1924

CAISERMAN-ROTH, Ghitta born 1923
Modern Collection

Homage to Albert Dumouchel (P03166-P03178;
complete group; mixed group)
Hommage à Albert Dumouchel
P03169 Sunflower 3 (1971-2)
CIπ:568x762:signed:Presented by the University of
Quebec 1976

CALDECOTT, Randolph 1846-1886
British Collection

N04049 Good-bye, Baby Bunting, engraved by Edmund Evans
Jπ:159x184:Presented by Harold Hartley 1925

N04325 Scene in a Churchyard
Wπ:216x305:signed:Bequeathed by J.R. Holliday 1927

N04326 Tug of War (1877)
Dπ:175x260:signed:Bequeathed by J.R. Holliday 1927

CALDER, Alexander 1898-1976
Modern Collection
Tate Gallery Archive holds material concerning this artist

T00541 Antennae with Red and Blue Dots (1960)
KSm:1111x1283x1283:Purchased 1962

T01090 Black Sun (1953)
Gπ:737x1079:signed:Presented by Mr and Mrs Robert
Lewin through the Friends of the Tate Gallery 1968

T01142 T and Swallow (circa 1936)
Swm:7620x324x286:signed:Purchased 1969

CALDERON, Philip Hermogenes 1833-1898
British Collection

N01573 Renunciation (1891)
Oc:1530x2134:signed:Presented by the Trustees of the
Chantrey Bequest 1891

N03677 By the Waters of Babylon (1852)
Oc:718x514:signed:Presented by Mrs George Calderon
1922

N04211 Half Hours with the Best Authors ('The Siesta') (1866)
WGπ:178x279:signed:Presented by Mrs George
Calderon 1922

N05780 Broken Vows (1856)
Oc:914x679:signed:Purchased 1947

CALLCOTT, Sir Augustus Wall 1779-1844
British Collection

N00340 Dutch Peasants Returning from Market (exhibited 1834)
Oc:1092x1448:Presented by Robert Vernon 1847

N00341 Dutch Coast Scene, Waiting for the Boats (?exhibited
1832)
Oc:686x914:Presented by Robert Vernon 1847

N00342 Dutch Landscape with Cattle (circa 1830-40)
Ow:162x337:Presented by Robert Vernon 1847

N00343 Wooden Bridge (circa 1835)
Oc:229x298:Presented by Robert Vernon 1847

N00344 Sketch for 'The Benighted Traveller' (circa 1832)
Oπ:159x133:Presented by Robert Vernon 1847

N00345 The Old Pier at Littlehampton (exhibited 1812)
Oc:1067x1410:Presented by Robert Vernon 1847

N00346 Entrance to Pisa from Leghorn (exhibited 1833)
Oc:1067x1626:Presented by Robert Vernon 1847

N00347 Peasants Waiting the Return of the Passage Boat
(exhibited 1834)
Oc:648x959:Presented by Robert Vernon 1847

N00348 The Coast of Scheveningen (after Adriaen van de Velde)
(circa 1830-5)
Ow:152x241:Presented by Robert Vernon 1847

N00813 Sheerness and the Isle of Sheppey (after J.M.W. Turner)
(circa 1807-8)
Oc:698x895:Bequeathed by John Meeson Parsons 1870

N01841 Fishing on the Mere (circa 1807)
Oc:333x438:Bequeathed by Henry Vaughan 1900

T05470 A Road Leading to a Village (circa 1812)
Ow:197x260:Presented by Miss Marjorie Ball 1988

CALLIYANNIS, Manolis born 1923
Modern Collection

T00089 The Mountain Opposite II (1955-6)
La Montagne en face II
TOc:597x806:signed:Purchased 1956

CALLOW, William 1812-1908
British Collection

N02435 Richmond Castle, Yorkshire (1843)
WDπ:337x514:Presented by the artist's widow 1909

N02436 The Grand Canal Venice (1880)
WDπ:222x298:signed:Presented by the artist's widow
1909

A00131 Frankfurt (1840)
Dπ:264x365:Purchased 1912

A00132 Frauenkirche, Nuremberg (1846)
Dπ:264x365:Purchased 1912

A00133 Giessen (1871)
Dπ:248x346:Purchased 1912

A00134 Prague (1874)
Dπ:248x346:Purchased 1912

A00135 Frauenkirche, Prague (1874)
Dπ:248x349:Purchased 1912

A00136 Cochem (1860)
Dπ:264x365:Purchased 1912

A00137 Maximilianstrasse, Augsburg
Dπ:264x365:Purchased 1912

A00138 Haupt Markt and St Sebald, Nuremberg (1846)
Dπ:264x365:Purchased 1912

A00139 Markt, Coburg (1863)
Dπ:248x349:Purchased 1912

A00140 Coburg (1863)
Dπ:254x349:Purchased 1912

A00141 Frankfurt (1846)
Dπ:264x365:Purchased 1912

A00142 Rathaus, Hanover (1852)
Dπ:254x337:Purchased 1912

A00143 Unidentified Market Place, ? Lubeck or Leipzig (1852)
Dπ:254x349:Purchased 1912

A00144 Royal Palace, Dresden (1852)
Dπ:254x349:Purchased 1912

A00145 Rathaus, Gotha (1852)
Dπ:254x349:Purchased 1912

A00146 Rathaus, Eisenach (1852)
Dπ:254x349:Purchased 1912

A00147 Quai on the Moselle (1860)
Dπ:264x365:Purchased 1912

A00148 Place St Pharailde, Ghent (1850)
Dπ:264x365:Purchased 1912

A00149 Vegetable Market, Ghent
Dπ:264x365:Purchased 1912

A00150 Rotterdam (1845)
Dπ:264x362:Purchased 1912

A00151 Namur (1844)
Dπ:254x362:Purchased 1912

A00152 St Paul, Antwerp (1844)
Dπ:254x362:Purchased 1912

A00153 Old Palais de Justice, Malines (1850)
Dπ:264x365:Purchased 1912

A00154 St Michael and Belfry, Ghent (1844)
Dπ:254x362:Purchased 1912

A00155 Botzen (1846)
Dπ:264x365:Purchased 1912

A00156 Innsbruck (1846)
Dπ:264x365:Purchased 1912

CALTHROP, Claude 1845-1893
British Collection

N01921 Meeting of Scottish Jacobites (exhibited 1878)
Oc:889x1270:signed:Presented by Mrs C. Calthrop 1903

CALVERT, Edward 1799-1883
British Collection

N02883 Elemental Life
Ob:168x276:Presented by S. Calvert 1912

N02884 Mary Calvert, the Artist's Wife (circa 1825-30)
Dπ:251x181:Presented by S. Calvert 1912

N03693 The Bride (1828)
Lπ:76x127:Presented by Mrs John Richmond 1922

N05398 Nude Study (circa 1830-50)
Oc:514x378:Presented by the National Art Collections Fund 1942

N05924 A Migration of Nomads: Arcadian Shepherds Moving Their Flocks by Dawn (circa 1860-80)
Oc:375x991:Bequeathed by Mrs Hilda Fothergill Medlicott 1950

A00157 The Bride (1828)
Lπ:76x127:Presented by S. Calvert 1912

A00158 The Sheep of his Pasture (circa 1828)
Lπ:41x76:Presented by S. Calvert 1912

A00159 The Ploughman (1827)
Jπ:83x130:Presented by S. Calvert 1912

A00160 The Brook (1829)
Jπ:51x89:Presented by S. Calvert 1912

A00161 The Chamber Idyll (1831)
Jπ:41x76:Presented by S. Calvert 1912

A00162 The Cyder Feast (1828)
Jπ:76x127:Presented by S. Calvert 1912

A00163 The Lady and the Rooks (1829)
Jπ:41x76:Presented by S. Calvert 1912

A00164 The Return Home (1830)
Jπ:41x76:Presented by S. Calvert 1912

A00165 The Bacchante, engraved by Welby Sherman (circa 1825)
Jπ:89x51:Presented by S. Calvert 1912

A00166 The Flood (1829)
Lπ:41x76:Presented by S. Calvert 1912

A00167 Ideal Pastoral Life (1829)
Lπ:41x76:Presented by S. Calvert 1912

CAMARGO, Sergio de born 1930
Modern Collection

T00797 Large Split White Relief No. 34/74 (1964-5)
Grand relief fendu No. 34/4/74
Rw:2153x921x273:signed:Purchased 1965

CAMERON, Sir David 1865-1945
British Collection

N03209 Ben Ledi (1914)
Oc:1308x1156:signed:Presented by the Contemporary Art Society 1917

N03324 Stirling Castle (?circa 1914)
Oc:451x705:signed:Presented by Viscount Bearsted through the National Art Collections Fund 1918

N03813 Rue du Bourg, Chartres (1917)
Oc:610x406:signed:Presented by the National Art Collections Fund 1923

P01006 The Admiralty (1889)
MLπ:194x137:signed:Presented by Ernest Marsh 1909

P01007 Turkish Fort (1909)
MLπ:140x267:signed:Presented by J. McLehose 1924

CAMERON, Katherine 1874-1965
British Collection

N04513 The Mountain Fern (1923)
WDπ:510x285:signed:Presented by Arthur Kay, the artist's husband, through the National Art Collections Fund 1930

P02947 The Mountain Fern
Lπ:429x191:signed:Presented by the artist 1959, accessioned 1987

CAMP, Jeffery born 1923
Modern Collection
Tate Gallery Archive holds material concerning this artist

T03215 Beachy Head: Brink (1975)
Oc:2432x1502:Presented by the Trustees of the Chantrey Bequest 1981

CAMPBELL, Steven born 1954
Modern Collection
Tate Gallery Archive holds material concerning this artist

T04137 The Dangerous Early and Late Life of Lytton Strachey (1985)
Oc:2618x2745:Presented by the Patrons of New Art through the Friends of the Tate Gallery 1986

CAMPION, George B. 1796-1870
British Collection

N02406 Guards (circa 1825-30)
Mπ:137x248:Presented by Edmund Houghton 1898

CANIN, Martin born 1927
Modern Collection

P04070 Untitled (1969)
CNπ:435x559:signed:Presented by Rose and Chris Prater through the Institute of Contemporary Prints 1975

P04071 Untitled (1969)
CNπ:432x559:signed:Presented by Rose and Chris Prater through the Institute of Contemporary Prints 1975

P04072 Untitled (1969)
CNπ:432x559:signed:Presented by Rose and Chris Prater through the Institute of Contemporary Prints 1975

P04073 Untitled (1969)
CNπ:432x559:signed:Presented by Rose and Chris Prater through the Institute of Contemporary Prints 1975

P04074 Untitled (1972)
CNπ:610x914:signed:Presented by Rose and Chris Prater through the Institute of Contemporary Prints 1975

P04075 Untitled (1972)
CNπ:610x914:signed:Presented by Rose and Chris Prater through the Institute of Contemporary Prints 1975

CAPELAIN, Jean le - see LE CAPELAIN, Jean

CAPEL-DORAY, Audrey born 1931
Modern Collection

Centennial Suite (P03217-P03225, P03228-P03229; complete group; mixed group)
P03221 Diamond (1967-8)
CNπ:381x508:signed:Presented by Simon Fraser University, British Columbia 1977

CARDER, Malcolm born 1936
Modern Collection

T00824 Construction No. 21/64 (1964)
Sv:483x457x273:Purchased 1966

CARDONA, Jaume Rocamora i born 1946
Modern Collection

P08179 [title not known] (1980)
CNπ:343x257:Transferred from the Library 1981

CARDOSO, José, Junior 1861-1947
Modern Collection

N05580 They Amuse Themselves (circa 1935-40)
Elas se divertem
Oc:540x689:signed:Presented by Lord Bossom 1945

CARLINE, George 1855-1920
British Collection

T02262 The Gleaners (1887)
Gπ:289x565:signed:Presented by Richard Carline 1978

T02263 Under a Midsummer Sun (1889)
Oc:257x362:Presented by Richard Carline 1978

CARLINE, Hilda 1889-1950
Modern Collection
Tate Gallery Archive holds material concerning this artist

T01998 Self-Portrait (1923)
Oc:749x578:Presented by Miss Shirin Spencer and Miss Unity Spencer, the artist's daughters, and Richard Carline the artist's brother 1975

CARLINE, Nancy born 1909
Modern Collection
Tate Gallery Archive holds material concerning this artist

T04117 Supper on the Terrace (1946)
Oc:610x765:signed:Presented by the artist 1985

CARLINE, Richard 1896-1980
Modern Collection
Tate Gallery Archive holds material concerning this artist

T01914 Studio Interior, Hampstead (1918)
Oc:714x511:Purchased 1974

T02028 Portrait of Hilda Carline (1918)
Oc:762x635:signed:Presented by the artist 1976

T03597 Sea Shore (1920)
Oc:940x562:signed:Presented by Mrs Nancy Carline, the artist's widow 1983

CARLINE, Sydney 1888-1929
Modern Collection
Tate Gallery Archive holds material concerning this artist

N04440 St John's, Downshire Hill, Hampstead (1927-8)
Oc:648x540:Purchased with assistance from Sir George Clausen and Sir Edward Marsh 1929

T01997 Bank Holiday on Hampstead Heath (1915)
Oc:838x816:Presented by Mrs Gwendolyn Carline, the artist's widow, and Richard Carline the artist's brother 1975

CARLISLE, George Howard, Ninth Earl of 1843-1911
British Collection

N05460 View from the Front of St John Lateran, Rome (circa 1870)
Wπ:533x737:Bequeathed by Mrs A.M. Armstrong 1944

CARLO, Michael born 1945
Modern Collection
Tate Gallery Archive holds material concerning this artist

P01862   Evening (1978)
CNπ:381x254:signed:Presented by Christie's
Contemporary Art 1979

CARO, Sir Anthony born 1924
Modern Collection
Tate Gallery Archive holds material concerning this artist

T00264   Woman Waking Up (1955)
Sz:267x679x349:Purchased 1959

T00799   Yellow Swing (1965)
ASm:1791x1981x3975:Purchased 1965

T00805   Early One Morning (1962)
ASm:2896x6198x3353:Presented by the Contemporary
Art Society 1965

T01151   Piece LXXXII (1969)
SOm:445x1206x1460:Purchased 1969

T01454   Quartet (1971)
SOm:1524x2845x3531:Purchased 1971

T01987   Twenty Four Hours (1960)
SOm:1384x2235x838:Purchased 1975

T03455   Emma Dipper (1977)
Sm:2130x1700x3200:Presented by the artist 1982

T03457   Tundra (1975)
Sm:2720x5790x1320:Purchased 1982

P77272   Figure (1956)
Jπ:594x457:Purchased 1989

CARR, Thomas born 1909
Modern Collection
Tate Gallery Archive holds material concerning this artist

School Prints (P01698-P01727; complete group; mixed
group)
P01699   Fireside (1946-9)
CLπ:495x762:signed:Presented by Patrick Seale Prints
1975

CARRIERE, Eugène 1849-1906
Modern Collection

N04261   Winding Wool (1887)
Les Dévideuses
Oc:597x733:signed:Presented by Mrs R.M. Dunlop 1927

T00364   Nelly Carrière (circa 1903)
Oc:60x81:signed:Presented by Mrs Georgette Seligman
1960

T03638   Head of a Child (Jean-René Carrière?) (circa 1891)
Ob:48x71:signed:Presented anonymously in memory of
Sir Terence Rattigan 1983

CARRINGTON, Dora 1893-1932
Modern Collection
Tate Gallery Archive holds material concerning this artist

T04945   Farm at Watendlath (1921)
Oc:611x669:Presented by Noel Carrington 1987

CARTER, B.A.R. born 1909
Modern Collection
Tate Gallery Archive holds material concerning this artist

T00443   Nude Model (1960)
Ob:641x559:Presented by the Trustees of the Chantrey
Bequest 1961

CARTER, Hugh 1837-1903
British Collection

N01955   The Last Ray (circa 1878)
Oc:622x737:signed:Presented by Mrs Carter 1905

CARTER, Samuel John 1835-1892
British Collection

N01559   Morning with the Wild Red Deer (1876)
Oc:1473x2400:signed:Presented by Sir Henry Tate 1894

CARTER, William 1863-1939
British Collection

N04896   The Refectory Table (1936)
Oc:635x762:signed:Presented by the Trustees of the
Chantrey Bequest 1937

CASAS - see VILACASAS, Joan

CAST, Jesse Dale 1900-1976
Modern Collection
Tate Gallery Archive holds material concerning this artist

T03598   'The Windmill', Clapham Common (1934)
Oc:432x546:signed:Presented by David Cast, the artist's
son 1983

T03599   Self-Portrait (1934)
Pπ:400x290:signed:Presented by David Cast, the artist's
son 1983

T04878   Miss Beatrice M. Dale Cast (1950 and circa 1964)
Oc:562x406:signed:Presented by David Cast, the artist's
son, through the National Art Collections Fund 1987

CATTERMOLE, George 1800-1868
British Collection

N01721   A Castle Entrance (1844)
Wπ:495x368:signed:Presented by E. Homan 1899

N01730   Landscape Study
Dπ:337x489:Presented by John Henderson 1879

N01731   A Scene of Monastic Life with a Figure at a Pulpit
Dπ:330x445:Presented by John Henderson 1879

N01732   A Scene of Monastic Life with a Figure Enthroned
Dπ:311x432:Presented by John Henderson 1879

N01733   Landscape Study with Castle
Dπ:337x432:Presented by John Henderson 1879

N03500   View in Venice (1852)
Wπ:229x333:signed:Presented by John Henderson 1879

N03501   Ancient Monastic Life
Wπ:254x597:signed:Presented by John Henderson 1879

N03502   Ancient Monastic Life
Wπ:302x422:Presented by John Henderson 1879

N03503   Craigmillar Castle
Wπ:438x311:Presented by John Henderson 1879

N03504   Ancient Monastic Life (1850)
Wπ:318x454:signed:Presented by John Henderson 1879

N03505   Stream and Water Mill
Wπ:295x397:signed:Presented by John Henderson 1879

CAULFIELD, Patrick born 1936
Modern Collection
Tate Gallery Archive holds material concerning this artist

T00949   Battlements (1967)
Oc:1524x2743:signed:Purchased 1967

T01134   Pottery (1969)
Oc:2134x1524:signed:Presented by Mrs H.K. Morton
through the Contemporary Art Society 1969

T02031   Vases of Flowers (1962)
Ob:1219x1219:Purchased with assistance from the Tate
Gallery Publications Department and the Trustees of the
Tate Gallery Trust Fund 1976

T02032   Still Life with Dagger (1963)
Ob:1216x1219:Purchased 1976

T02033   After Lunch (1975)
Ac:2489x2134:signed:Purchased 1976

T03101   Greece Expiring on the Ruins of Missolonghi (after
Delacroix) (1963)
Ob:1524x1219:signed:Purchased 1980

For John Constable (P03149-P03157, P03159-P03161,
P03180-P03185; complete group; mixed group)

P03151   [no title] (1976)
CNπ:1026x775:signed:Presented by Bernard Jacobson
Gallery 1976

The Institute of Contemporary Arts Portfolio (P04016,
P04038, P04053, P04076, P04115, P04125, P04166,
P04248, P04256, P04315-P04316, P04334,
P04378-P04380, P04419, P04635, P04752, P04938,
P05138, P05155, P05248; complete group; mixed group)

P04076   Ruins (1964)
CNπ:508x762:signed:Presented by Rose and Chris Prater
through the Institute of Contemporary Prints 1975

P04077   Coloured Still Life (1967)
CNπ:559x914:signed:Presented by Rose and Chris Prater
through the Institute of Contemporary Prints 1975

P04078   Earthenware (1967)
CNπ:559x914:signed:Presented by Rose and Chris Prater
through the Institute of Contemporary Prints 1975

P04079   The Hermit (1967)
CNπ:559x838:signed:Presented by Rose and Chris Prater
through the Institute of Contemporary Prints 1975

P04080   The Letter (1967)
CNπ:483x762:signed:Presented by Rose and Chris Prater
through the Institute of Contemporary Prints 1975

P04081   Sweet Bowl (1967)
CNπ:559x914:signed:Presented by Rose and Chris Prater
through the Institute of Contemporary Prints 1975

P04082   Weekend Cabin (1967)
CNπ:559x914:signed:Presented by Rose and Chris Prater
through the Institute of Contemporary Prints 1975

P04083   Bathroom Mirror (1968)
CNπ:711x937:signed:Presented by Rose and Chris Prater
through the Institute of Contemporary Prints 1975

P04084   Cafe Sign (1968)
CNπ:711x924:signed:Presented by Rose and Chris Prater
through the Institute of Contemporary Prints 1975

P04085   Cross (1968)
CNπ:711x937:signed:Presented by Rose and Chris Prater
through the Institute of Contemporary Prints 1975

P04086   Found Objects (1968)
CNπ:711x937:signed:Presented by Rose and Chris Prater
through the Institute of Contemporary Prints 1975

P04087   Loudspeaker (1968)
CNπ:711x937:signed:Presented by Rose and Chris Prater
through the Institute of Contemporary Prints 1975

P04088   Coal Fire (1969)
CNπ:359x308:signed:Presented by Rose and Chris Prater
through the Institute of Contemporary Prints 1975

P04089   Lampshade (1969)
CNπ:359x308:signed:Presented by Rose and Chris Prater
through the Institute of Contemporary Prints 1975

P04090   Small Window (1969)
CNπ:356x308:signed:Presented by Rose and Chris Prater
through the Institute of Contemporary Prints 1975

P04091   Two Jugs (1969)
CNπ:359x308:signed:Presented by Rose and Chris Prater
through the Institute of Contemporary Prints 1975

P04092   Wine Glasses (1969)
CNπ:359x308:signed:Presented by Rose and Chris Prater
through the Institute of Contemporary Prints 1975

P04093   Interior: Evening (1970-1)
CNπ:710x585:signed:Presented by Rose and Chris Prater
through the Institute of Contemporary Prints 1975

P04094   Interior: Noon (1970-1)
CNπ:710x585:signed:Presented by Rose and Chris Prater
through the Institute of Contemporary Prints 1975

P04095   Interior: Morning (1970-1)
CNπ:710x585:signed:Presented by Rose and Chris Prater
through the Institute of Contemporary Prints 1975

P04096   Interior: Night (1970-1)
CNπ:710x585:signed:Presented by Rose and Chris Prater
through the Institute of Contemporary Prints 1975

P04097   Portrait of a Frenchman (1971)
CNπ:635x537:signed:Presented by Rose and Chris Prater
through the Institute of Contemporary Prints 1975

P04098   Vase on Display (1970-1)
CNπ:660x562:signed:Presented by Rose and Chris Prater
through the Institute of Contemporary Prints 1975

P04099   Fig Branch (1972)
CNπ:868x664:signed:Presented by Rose and Chris Prater
through the Institute of Contemporary Prints 1975

P04100   Napkin and Onions (1972)
CNπ:870x664:signed:Presented by Rose and Chris Prater
through the Institute of Contemporary Prints 1975

P04101   Occasional Table (1972)
CNπ:584x714:signed:Presented by Rose and Chris Prater
through the Institute of Contemporary Prints 1975

P04102   Pipe (1972)
CNπ:870x664:signed:Presented by Rose and Chris Prater
through the Institute of Contemporary Prints 1975

P04103   Window at Night (1972)
CNπ:867x664:signed:Presented by Rose and Chris Prater
through the Institute of Contemporary Prints 1975

P04104   Black and White Cafe (1972-3)
CNπ:714x600:signed:Presented by Rose and Chris Prater
through the Institute of Contemporary Prints 1975

P04105   Coat Stand (1973)
MNπ:559x787:signed:Presented by Rose and Chris
Prater through the Institute of Contemporary Prints 1975

P04106   Curtain and Bottle (1973)
MNπ:559x787:signed:Presented by Rose and Chris
Prater through the Institute of Contemporary Prints 1975

P04107 Paris Separates (1973)
MNπ:559x787:signed:Presented by Rose and Chris
Prater through the Institute of Contemporary Prints 1975

P04108 Pipe and Jug (1973)
MNπ:559x787:signed:Presented by Rose and Chris
Prater through the Institute of Contemporary Prints 1975

P04109 Spider Plant (1973)
MNπ:559x787:signed:Presented by Rose and Chris
Prater through the Institute of Contemporary Prints 1975

P04110 Tulips (1973)
MNπ:559x787:signed:Presented by Rose and Chris
Prater through the Institute of Contemporary Prints 1975

P04111 Jar (1974)
CNπ:651x546:signed:Presented by Rose and Chris Prater
through the Institute of Contemporary Prints 1975

P04112 Jug (1974)
CNπ:651x549:signed:Presented by Rose and Chris Prater
through the Institute of Contemporary Prints 1975

P05360 Evening Menu (1975)
CNπ:775x1029:signed:Presented by Rose and Chris
Prater 1976

P05361 Garden with Pines (1975)
CNπ:775x1029:signed:Presented by Rose and Chris
Prater 1976

P05362 Lamp and Pines (1975)
CNπ:775x1029:Presented by Rose and Chris Prater 1976

P05363 Rosé Bottle (1975)
CNπ:775x1029:signed:Presented by Rose and Chris
Prater 1976

P05364 Signature Pots (1975)
CNπ:775x1029:Presented by Rose and Chris Prater 1976

P05365 Terracotta Vase (1975)
CNπ:775x1029:signed:Presented by Rose and Chris
Prater 1976

P05411 Glazed Earthenware (1976)
CNπ:543x765:signed:Presented by Rose and Chris Prater
1978

P05412 Pipe in Bowl (1976)
CNπ:406x410:signed:Presented by Rose and Chris Prater
1978

P05413 Still Life Ingredients (1976)
CNπ:533x537:signed:Presented by Rose and Chris Prater
1978

P05414 White Pot (1976)
CNπ:857x775:signed:Presented by Rose and Chris Prater
1978

P05415 Bananas and Leaves (1977)
CNπ:746x911:signed:Presented by Rose and Chris Prater
1978

P05416 Big Sausage (1978)
CNπ:730x581:signed:Presented by Rose and Chris Prater
1978

P05417 Cigar (1978)
CNπ:448x483:signed:Presented by Rose and Chris Prater
1978

P05418 Picnic Set (1978)
CNπ:933x876:signed:Presented by Rose and Chris Prater
1978

P05419 Sausage (1978)
CNπ:746x914:signed:Presented by Rose and Chris Prater
1978

P05420 Three Sausages (1978)
CNπ:533x711:signed:Presented by Rose and Chris Prater
1978

P05499 Bowl and Fruit (1979)
CNπ:838x597:signed:Presented by Rose and Chris Prater
1979

P05500 Cream Glazed Pot (1979)
CNπ:838x597:signed:Presented by Rose and Chris Prater
1979

P05501 Plant Pot (1979)
CNπ:838x597:signed:Presented by Rose and Chris Prater
1979

P05545 Fern Pot (1980)
CNπ:840x597:signed:Presented by Rose and Chris Prater
1980

P05546 Ridged Jar (1980)
CNπ:840x594:signed:Presented by Rose and Chris Prater
1980

P05560 Dressed Lobster (1980)
CNπ:600x750:signed:Presented by Rose and Chris Prater
1980

Some Poems of Jules Laforgue (P07152-P07173;
complete group)

P07152 1. Ah! This life is so everyday (1973)
CNπ:410x359:signed:Purchased 1976

P07153 2. Watch me eat, without appetite, à la carte (1973)
CNπ:410x359:signed:Purchased 1976

P07154 3. She fled along the avenue (1973)
CNπ:410x359:signed:Purchased 1976

P07155 4. Her handkerchief swept me along the Rhine (1973)
CNπ:410x359:signed:Purchased 1976

P07156 5. I'll take my life monotonous (1973)
CNπ:410x359:signed:Purchased 1976

P07157 6. You'll be sick if you spend all your time indoors (1973)
CNπ:410x359:signed:Purchased 1976

P07158 7. Crying to the walls: My God! My God! Will she relent?
(1973)
CNπ:410x359:signed:Purchased 1976

P07159 8. All these confessions . . . (1973)
CNπ:410x359:signed:Purchased 1976

P07160 9. Making circles on park lagoons (1973)
CNπ:410x359:signed:Purchased 1976

P07161 10. Oh! If one of them, some fine evening, would try
(1973)
CNπ:410x359:signed:Purchased 1976

P07162 11. Thus, she would come, escaped, half-dead to my door
(1973)
CNπ:410x359:signed:Purchased 1976

P07163 12. And with my eyes bolting toward the unconscious
(1973)
CNπ:410x359:signed:Purchased 1976

P07164 13. We wanted to bleed the silence (1973)
CNπ:410x359:signed:Purchased 1976

P07165 14. Along a twilighted sky (1973)
CNπ:410x359:signed:Purchased 1976

P07166 15. Oh Helen, I roam my room (1973)
CNπ:410x359:signed:Purchased 1976

P07167 16. I've only the friendship of hotel rooms (1973)
CNπ:410x359:signed:Purchased 1976

P07168 17. She'll have forgotten her scarf (1973)
CNπ:410x359:signed:Purchased 1976

P07169 18. And I am alone in my house (1973)
CNπ:410x359:signed:Purchased 1976

P07170 19. All the benches are wet, the woods are so rusty (1973)
CNπ:410x359:signed:Purchased 1976

P07171 20. Ah! Storm clouds rushed from the Channel coasts (1973)
CNπ:410x359:signed:Purchased 1976

P07172 21. Curtains drawn back from balconies of shores (1973)
CNπ:410x359:signed:Purchased 1976

P07173 22. My Life inspires so many desires (1973)
CNπ:410x359:signed:Purchased 1976

P07755 Brown Jug (1982)
CNπ:1000x776:signed:Purchased 1982

CAZIN, Jean-Charles 1841-1901
Modern Collection

N04365 Ulysses after the Shipwreck (circa 1890)
Oc:733x597:signed:Presented by Arthur R. Anderson 1927

CAZIN, Marie 1844-1924
Modern Collection

N05571 Evening (?circa 1884-8)
Oc:327x460:signed:Bequeathed by Mrs Mary James Mathews in memory of her husband Frank Claughton Mathews 1944

CELIC, Stojan born 1925
Modern Collection

P07585 Region (1979)
CLπ:572x400:signed:Purchased 1981

CELICE, Pierre born 1932
Modern Collection

P01079 White Landscape (1968-9)
Paysage blanc
CLπ:387x546:signed:Presented by Waddington Galleries through the Institute of Contemporary Prints 1975

P01080 Les Savis de L'Atelier (1968-9)
Les Savis de l'atelier
CLπ:403x514:signed:Presented by Waddington Galleries through the Institute of Contemporary Prints 1975

P01081 Red Studio (1969-70)
Atelier rouge
CLπ:460x641:signed:Presented by Waddington Galleries through the Institute of Contemporary Prints 1975

P01082 Grey Landscape (1969)
Paysage gris
CLπ:416x641:signed:Presented by Waddington Galleries through the Institute of Contemporary Prints 1975

P01083 Studio 5 (1971)
Atelier 5
CLπ:546x791:signed:Presented by Waddington Galleries through the Institute of Contemporary Prints 1975

P01084 Studio 6 (1971)
Atelier 6
CLπ:527x745:signed:Presented by Waddington Galleries through the Institute of Contemporary Prints 1975

P01085 Studio 7 (1971)
Atelier 7
CLπ:507x655:signed:Presented by Waddington Galleries through the Institute of Contemporary Prints 1975

P01086 Marine (1971)
CLπ:546x743:signed:Presented by Waddington Galleries through the Institute of Contemporary Prints 1975

P01087 Marine IV (1971)
CLπ:524x743:signed:Presented by Waddington Galleries through the Institute of Contemporary Prints 1975

P01088 Untitled - Blue (1972)
CLπ:508x664:signed:Presented by Waddington Galleries through the Institute of Contemporary Prints 1975

P01089 Untitled - Orange (1972)
CLπ:508x657:signed:Presented by Waddington Galleries through the Institute of Contemporary Prints 1975

CÉSAR (César Baldaccini) born 1921
Modern Collection
Tate Gallery Archive holds material concerning this artist

T00183 The Man of Saint-Denis (1958)
L'Homme de Saint-Denis
Sm:508x1118x292:Purchased 1958

T00337 Large Panel (1958)
Grand panneau
Sm:2489x1746x552:signed:Presented by J. Sainsbury Ltd 1960

T00409 Drawing (circa 1960)
Dπ:727x568:signed:Presented by the artist 1961

T00472 Torn-Away Paper (1961)
Papier arraché
Dπ:1651x1248:Presented by J. Sainsbury Ltd 1962

T00819 Thumb (1965)
Le Pouce
Sa:406x140x203:signed:Presented by the artist 1966

T01052 Three Compressions (1968)
Sm:622x1702x622:signed:Presented by the artist 1968

T01204 Portrait of Patrick Waldberg (1961-2)
Portrait de Patrick Waldberg
Rm:1994x2203x264:signed:Presented by Kate Maremont Foundation on behalf of Mr and Mrs Arnold H. Maremont 1970

CÉZANNE, Paul 1839-1906
Modern Collection

N04724 The Gardener Vallier (circa 1906)
Le Jardinier Vallier
Oc:654x549:Bequeathed by C. Frank Stoop 1933

N04725 Still Life with Water Jug (circa 1892-3)
Nature morte à la cruche
Oc:530x711:Bequeathed by C. Frank Stoop 1933

N05303 Montagne Sainte Victoire (1905-6)
La Montagne Sainte-Victoire
Wπ:362x549:Bequeathed by Sir Hugh Walpole 1941

T01074 The Avenue at the Jas de Bouffan (circa 1874-5)
L'Allée au Jas de Bouffan
Oc:381x460:Bequeathed by the Hon. Mrs A.E. Pleydell-Bouverie through the Friends of the Tate Gallery 1968

P01008 The Large Bathers (circa 1898)
Les Grands Baigneurs
CLπ:403x492:Presented by Lord Duveen 1927

CHADWICK, Helen born 1953
Modern Collection

P11269 Anatoli (1989)
Iπ:795x574:signed:Presented by the King Edward's Hospital Fund 1989

CHADWICK, Lynn born 1914
Modern Collection
Tate Gallery Archive holds material concerning this artist

N06035 Dragonfly (1951)
KSm:2770x1060x260:Presented by the Contemporary Art Society 1951

T00416 Winged Figures (1955)
Sz:559x432x356:signed:Purchased 1961

T01149 Twister I (1962)
Sm:635x305x130:Presented by Alistair McAlpine (later Lord McAlpine of West Green) 1969

T01226 Inner Eye (Maquette III) (1952)
KSma:286x152x102:Purchased 1970

T03712 Conjunction (1953)
Sm:420x300x200:Transferred from the Victoria & Albert Museum 1983

Moon Series (P01377-P01382; complete group)

P01377 Moon Series A (1965-6)
CLπ:504x654:signed:Presented by Marlborough Graphics through the Institute of Contemporary Prints 1975

P01378 Moon Series B (1965-6)
CLπ:504x654:signed:Presented by Marlborough Graphics through the Institute of Contemporary Prints 1975

P01379 Moon Series C (1965-6)
CLπ:505x658:signed:Presented by Marlborough Graphics through the Institute of Contemporary Prints 1975

P01380 Moon Series D (1965-6)
CLπ:509x654:signed:Presented by Marlborough Graphics through the Institute of Contemporary Prints 1975

P01381 Moon Series E (1965-6)
CLπ:506x654:signed:Presented by Marlborough Graphics through the Institute of Contemporary Prints 1975

P01382 Moon Series F (1965-6)
CLπ:506x654:signed:Presented by Marlborough Graphics through the Institute of Contemporary Prints 1975

P01383 Standing Figure (1969)
CNπ:619x184:signed:Presented by Marlborough Graphics through the Institute of Contemporary Prints 1975

P06065 Untitled (1962-3)
CLπ:657x502:signed:Presented by Curwen Studio through the Institute of Contemporary Prints 1975

P06066 Moon in Alabama (1963)
CLπ:657x508:Presented by Curwen Studio through the Institute of Contemporary Prints 1975

P06067 Figure I (1966)
CLπ:816x597:Presented by Curwen Studio through the Institute of Contemporary Prints 1975

P06068 Figure II (1966)
CLπ:816x597:Presented by Curwen Studio through the Institute of Contemporary Prints 1975

P06069 Figure III (1966)
CLπ:816x597:Presented by Curwen Studio through the Institute of Contemporary Prints 1975

P06070 Figure IV (1966)
CLπ:816x597:Presented by Curwen Studio through the Institute of Contemporary Prints 1975

P06071 Two Winged Figures (1968-71)
CLπ:333x248:signed:Presented by Curwen Studio through the Institute of Contemporary Prints 1975

P06072 Seated Figure (1969)
CLπ:594x8198:signed:Presented by Curwen Studio through the Institute of Contemporary Prints 1975

P06702 Figure I (trial proof) (1966)
CLπ:819x594:Presented by Curwen Studio 1976

P06703 Moon in Alabama (colour variant) (1963)
CLπ:657x508:Presented by Curwen Studio 1976

P06704 Moon in Alabama (colour variant) (1963)
CLπ:657x508:Presented by Curwen Studio 1976

CHAGALL, Marc 1887-1985
Modern Collection
Tate Gallery Archive holds material concerning this artist

N05390 The Poet Reclining (1915)
Le Poète allongé
Ob:772x775:signed:Purchased 1942

N05757 The Vision (1924-5/circa 1937)
L'Apparition
PGMIπ:368x267:signed:Presented by Lady Clerk 1947

N05758 The Green Donkey (1911)
L'Ane vert
Gb:324x413:signed:Presented by Lady Clerk 1947

N05759 The Cat Transformed into a Woman (circa 1928-31/1947)
La Chatte métamorphosée en Femme
OMIπ:295x241:signed:Presented by Lady Clerk 1947

N05804 Bouquet with Flying Lovers (circa 1934-37)
Bouquet aux Amoureux volants
Oc:1305x975:signed:Purchased 1948

N06135 The Dance and the Circus (1950)
La Danse et le Cirque
Oc:349x267:signed:Presented by the artist 1953

N06136 The Blue Circus (1950)
Le Cirque bleu
Oc:349x267:signed:Presented by the artist 1953

CHAIMOWICZ, Marc Camille born 1947
Modern Collection
Tate Gallery Archive holds material concerning this artist

T03384 Le Désert . . . (1981)
13 RVv::signed:Purchased 1982

CHALLENGER, Michael born 1942
Modern Collection

P03108 Green Jay (1975)
CNπ:302x225:signed:Presented by Challenger Clegg Editions 1975

P03109 Mrs Jones has Fallen Over (1975)
CNπ:324x486:signed:Presented by Challenger Clegg Editions 1975

P03110 Rememory (1975)
CNπ:330x210:signed:Presented by Challenger Clegg Editions 1975

CHALON, Henry Bernard 1770-1849
British Collection

T02357 A Representation of the Persians in the Costume of their Country, Attending at Carlton Palace (?1819)
Oc:1010x1441:Presented by Paul Mellon through the British Sporting Art Trust 1979

CHAMBERLAIN, Christopher 1918-1984
Modern Collection

N06220 The Dangerous Corner (1954)
Ob:1003x1486:signed:Presented by the Trustees of the
Chantrey Bequest 1954

CHAMBERLAIN, John born 1927
Modern Collection

T01089 Koko-Nor II (1967)
Sv:991x1270x1219:Presented by Alan P. Power 1968

T01094 Kora (1963)
SOm:870x1410x1054:Presented by Mrs Martha Jackson
through the American Federation of Arts 1968

CHAMBERS, George 1803-1840
British Collection
Tate Gallery Archive holds material concerning this artist

N01966 Dutch East Indiamen Weighing their Anchors (circa
1830-40)
Oc:952x1365:Purchased 1905

T00967 The Hay-Barge
Wπ:156x244:Presented by the National Art Collections
Fund (Herbert Powell Bequest) 1967

attributed to
CHANDLER, J.W. circa 1770-1804/5
British Collection

N01208 William Godwin (1798)
Oc:749x622:Purchased 1886

CHANDRA, Avinash born 1931
Modern Collection
Tate Gallery Archive holds material concerning this artist

T00724 Hills of Gold (1964)
Oc:1016x2413:signed:Presented by Dr Gerhard and
Hella Adler 1965

CHANEY, Israel
Modern Collection

P04113 Untitled (1968)
CNπ:521x521:signed:Presented by Rose and Chris Prater
through the Institute of Contemporary Prints 1975

CHANTREY, Sir Francis Legatt 1781-1841
British Collection
Tate Gallery Archive holds material concerning this artist

N01591 Self-Portrait (circa 1810)
Oc:787x641:Presented by the Trustees of the Chantrey
Bequest 1894

N01950 A Reclining Nymph
Sp:133x267x114:Presented by Miss Tye 1904

CHAPLIN, Bob born 1947
Modern Collection
Tate Gallery Archive holds material concerning this artist

P07256 Pathway above Oxteddle Bottom (1976)
CLπ:629x305:signed:Purchased 1979

P07257 Seven Sisters a.m./p.m. (1978)
CINπ:413x695:signed:Purchased 1979

CHAPPELL, William born 1907
Modern Collection

T03654 Young Man Playing a Guitar (1926)
Oπ:285x215x18:signed:Presented anonymously in
memory of Sir Terence Rattigan 1983

CHARBONNEAU, Monique born 1928
Modern Collection

Homage to Albert Dumouchel (P03166-P03178;
complete group; mixed group)
Hommage à Albert Dumouchel
P03170 The Tribulations of Little Antoine (1971)
Les Tribulations du petit Antoine
MLπ:670x498:signed:Presented by the University of
Quebec 1976

CHARLES, James 1851-1906
British Collection

N02119 Will It Rain? (1887)
Oc:457x356:signed:Presented by John Maddocks 1907

N02122 Studies of Sheep (1863)
Dπ:241x298:signed:Presented by Prof. F. Brown 1907

N02123 In the Hayfield: Two Studies (1876)
Dπ:241x305:signed:Presented by Prof. F. Brown 1907

N02124 Heads: Children and a Family Group (circa 1900)
Dπ:241x292:signed:Presented by the artist's widow 1907

N02125 Studies of Landscapes and Figures (circa 1902)
Dπ:241x292:signed:Presented by the artist's widow 1907

N02126 A Country Road
Dπ:76x229:signed:Presented by the artist's widow 1907

N03394 Threatening Weather
Oc:445x787:signed:Presented by Lady Holroyd in
accordance with the wishes of the late Sir Charles
Holroyd 1919

CHARLESWORTH, Sarah - see
INTERNATIONAL LOCAL

CHARLTON, Alan born 1948
Modern Collection

T03894 Channel Painting No. 6 (1975)
Ac:2220x1990:signed:Purchased 1984

CHARLTON, George 1899-1979
Modern Collection
Tate Gallery Archive holds material concerning this artist

N04008 Elephants (1924)
PDπ:190x533:Purchased 1924

CHARNAY, Armand 1844-1916
Modern Collection

N02290 The Park of Sansac (Indre-et-Loire) (1885)
Le Parc de Sansac (Indre-et-Loire)
Oc:295x394:signed:Presented by the artist 1908

CHAROUX, Siegfried 1896-1967
Modern Collection
Tate Gallery Archive holds material concerning this artist

N05863 Youth (exhibited 1948)
Sp:2134x1105x762:signed:Presented by the Trustees of
the Chantrey Bequest 1948

T00597 Civilization: The Judge (1962)
Sz:495x330x273:signed:Presented by the Trustees of the Chantrey Bequest 1963

CHATELAIN, Jean Baptiste Claude
1710-1771
British Collection

T05472 Pastoral Landscape, with a River
DWπ:85x137:Presented by Miss Marjorie Ball 1988

CHEESE, Bernard born 1925
Modern Collection
Tate Gallery Archive holds material concerning this artist

P06705 A Fisherman's Story (1956)
CLπ:483x733:Presented by Curwen Studio 1976

CHEESE, Chloe born 1952
Modern Collection

P06770 Pink Carnations (1978)
CLπ:559x406:signed:Presented by Curwen Studio 1978

CHÉRON, Louis 1660-1725
British Collection

T00578 Vulcan Catching Mars and Venus in his Net (circa 1695)
Oπ:495x391:Purchased 1963

CHESTON, Charles 1882-1960
Modern Collection
Tate Gallery Archive holds material concerning this artist

N04441 Ramsgate (1928)
Wπ:273x378:signed:Purchased 1929

P01009 Across the Marshes (1912)
MIπ:133x406:signed:Presented by D. MacColl 1918

CHESTON, Evelyn 1875-1929
British Collection

N03905 Betchworth Lane, October (1917)
Wπ:250x370:Purchased 1924

CHIA, Sandro born 1946
Modern Collection
Tate Gallery Archive holds material concerning this artist

T03469 Water Bearer (1981)
OPc:2065x1700:signed:Purchased 1982

April Manual (P07632-P07636; complete group)
Manuale d'aprile
P07632 The Artifice (1981)
L'artificio
CIπ:295x312:signed:Purchased 1982

P07633 To the Tower (1981)
Alla torre
CIπ:282x300:signed:Purchased 1982

P07634 About the Unseizable (1981)
Circa l'imprendibile
CIπ:315x292:signed:Purchased 1982

P07635 A Good Soul (1981)
Anima buona
CIπ:292x310:signed:Purchased 1982

P07636 And the Heroes at the Window (1981)
E gli eroi alla finestra
CIπ:292x310:signed:Purchased 1982

P07637 Running Boy with Strange Fingers (1981)
MIπ:650x400:signed:Purchased 1982

P07638 The Butcher (1981)
MIπ:645x490:signed:Purchased 1982

CHIGHINE, Alfredo born 1914
Modern Collection

T00377 Composition with Palm Trees (1960)
Composizione con palma
Oc:648x813:signed:Presented by Professor Gino Ghiringhelli 1960

CHILLIDA, Eduardo born 1924
Modern Collection
Tate Gallery Archive holds material concerning this artist

T00750 Modulation of Space I (1963)
Sm:546x698x400:Purchased 1965

CHINNERY, George 1774-1852
British Collection

N05369 How Qua, Senior Hong Merchant at Canton, China
Oc:622x483:Presented by the National Art Collections Fund 1942

T01910 Colonel Woodburn of the Bengal Artillery (circa 1803)
Oc:476x375:Bequeathed by Alan Evans 1974

CHIRICO, Giorgio de - see DE CHIRICO, **Giorgio**

CHOWNE, Gerard 1875-1917
British Collection
Tate Gallery Archive holds material concerning this artist

N05433 Spanish Landscape (circa 1913)
Wπ:241x375:Presented by Michel Salaman 1943

CHRISTIE, John born 1945
Modern Collection
Tate Gallery Archive holds material concerning this artist

P02558 Frankfurt Circle (1981)
CNπ:230x230:signed:Presented by the artist 1982

P07524 Exchange (1976)
GCFπ:252x203:Purchased 1981

P07525 For Dora Maurer (1976)
CNFπ:343x290:Purchased 1981

P07526 Sounds Barely Heard . . . (1979)
WCNπ:394x292:Purchased 1981

P07527 Banners No. I (1980)
CNπ:403x252:Purchased 1981

P07528 Check-Out Music (1980)
CNπ:228x371:Purchased 1981

P07529 Dancers No. I (1980)
CNπ:205x155:Purchased 1981

P07530 Lemonade Music (1980)
CNπ:220x140:Purchased 1981

P07603 Homage to Ursonate (1981)
CNπ:245x466:Purchased 1981

CHRISTO (Christo Javacheff) born 1935
Modern Collection
Tate Gallery Archive holds material concerning this artist

T01581   Valley Curtain (Project for Colorado) Rifle, Grand Hogback (1971)
DVπ:711x559:signed:Purchased 1971

T03290   Inventories (1960)
Inventaires
SV:120x105:signed:Purchased 1981

P07640   Der Spiegel (1963)
CLAVπ:305x115:signed:Purchased 1982

CHRYSSA, Varda born 1933
Modern Collection
Tate Gallery Archive holds material concerning this artist

T01088   Study for Gates No. 4 (1967)
Sav:1092x883x702:Presented by S. Herbert Meller through the American Federation of Arts 1968

CHURCHILL, Sir Winston 1874-1965
British Collection
Tate Gallery Archive holds material concerning this artist

T00039   The Loup River, Alpes Maritimes (1930)
Oc:511x610:Presented by the artist 1955

CHURCHYARD, Thomas 1798-1865
British Collection

T01682   View on the Deben
Ob:219x311:signed:Purchased 1972

T03618   Windmills
Ow:164x122:Presented anonymously in memory of Sir Terence Rattigan 1983

T03619   A House by a River
Ow:143x200:signed:Presented anonymously in memory of Sir Terence Rattigan 1983

T03620   The Garden Tent
Ow:180x164:signed:Presented anonymously in memory of Sir Terence Rattigan 1983

T03621   Aldeburgh Beach
Ob:120x154:Presented anonymously in memory of Sir Terence Rattigan 1983

CIARDI, Emma 1879-1933
Modern Collection

N04427   Diaphanous Day (1924)
Oc:603x787:signed:Presented by Sir Edmund Davis through the National Art Collections Fund 1928

CIUHA, Joze born 1924
Modern Collection

P02549   Icon IX (1980)
Ikone IX
CNVπ:940x670:signed:Presented by the artist 1981

P07586   The Legend of the Third (1976)
CNVπ:558x446, 707x502:signed:Purchased 1981

CLARK, Joseph 1834-1926
British Collection

N01593   Mother's Darling (1884)
Oc:508x400:signed:Presented by the Trustees of the Chantrey Bequest 1885

N01610   Early Promise (1877)
Oc:762x610:signed:Presented by the Trustees of the Chantrey Bequest 1877

CLARK, Judy born 1949
Modern Collection

T01826   Catalogue ♀ 3 Skin (1973)
Da:387x464:Purchased 1973

T01827   Catalogue ♂ Skin (1973)
Da:387x464:Purchased 1973

CLARKE, Brian born 1953
Modern Collection
Tate Gallery Archive holds material concerning this artist

The Two Cultures (P11062-P11069; complete group)

P11062   [no title] (1981)
CNπ:1016x635:signed:Presented by Paul Beldock 1983

P11063   [no title] (1981)
CNπ:1120x685:signed:Presented by Paul Beldock 1983

P11064   [no title] (1981)
CNπ:755x504:signed:Presented by Paul Beldock 1983

P11065   [no title] (1981)
CNπ:1003x700:signed:Presented by Paul Beldock 1983

P11066   [no title] (1981)
CNπ:1005x698:signed:Presented by Paul Beldock 1983

P11067   [no title] (1981)
CNπ:1007x695:signed:Presented by Paul Beldock 1983

P11068   [no title] (1981)
CNπ:1115x688:signed:Presented by Paul Beldock 1983

P11069   [no title] (1981)
CNπ:1120x686:signed:Presented by Paul Beldock 1983

CLARKE, Geoffrey born 1924
Modern Collection
Tate Gallery Archive holds material concerning this artist

T00736   Block with Eight Pieces (1964)
Sm:508x616x889:Purchased 1965

T02060   Woman (1953)
Sm:327x241x168:signed:Purchased 1976

T03713   Head (1952)
Sm:180x90x110:Transferred from the Victoria & Albert Museum 1983

P01010   Woman and Child (1953)
CLπ:352x279:signed:Presented anonymously 1974

P01011   Crucifixion (1954)
MLπ:410x295:signed:Presented anonymously 1974

P01012   Head (1956)
CLπ:575x394:signed:Presented anonymously 1974

P03162   The Family (1950)
MLπ:352x200:signed:Presented by Taranman Gallery 1976

P03163   Birth of a Flower (1951)
CLπ:216x451:signed:Presented by Taranman Gallery 1976

CLARKE, Graham born 1941
Modern Collection
Tate Gallery Archive holds material concerning this artist

P01863   Mullion Cove (1976)
CLπ:286x406:signed:Presented by Christie's Contemporary Art 1979

CLARKE HALL, Lady Edna 1879-1979
British Collection
Tate Gallery Archive holds material concerning this artist

N04228   Girl Leaning on a Gate (1915)
WDπ:311x241:signed:Purchased 1927

N05131   Catherine Earnshaw Walking (1924)
Dπ:578x394:signed:Presented by the Contemporary Art Society 1940

N05273   Catherine Earnshaw and Heathcliff at Wuthering Heights (circa 1910-11)
Dπ:559x749:Purchased 1941

N05274   Justin Reading (1932)
Wπ:340x505:signed:Purchased 1941

N05418   Heathcliff Supporting Catherine (circa 1924)
DWπ:394x286:signed:Presented by Mrs F. Samuel, Mrs E. Bishop and Michel H. Salaman through the Contemporary Art Society 1941

N05419   Heathcliff and Catherine in a Loft (1924)
DWπ:400x571:signed:Presented by Mrs F. Samuel, Mrs E. Bishop and Michel H. Salaman through the Contemporary Art Society 1941

N05420   Fireside with Woman and Dog (circa 1899)
DWπ:397x279:signed:Presented anonymously through the Contemporary Art Society 1941

N05421   The Earnshaw Family by the Fireside (circa 1899)
DWGπ:356x254:signed:Presented by Mrs F. Samuel, Mrs E. Bishop and Michel H. Salaman through the Contemporary Art Society 1941

N05422   Heathcliff Supporting Catherine on a Couch
DWGπ:381x279:signed:Presented by Mrs F. Samuel, Mrs E. Bishop and Michel H. Salaman through the Contemporary Art Society 1941

N05423   Seated Woman
DWπ:295x229:signed:Presented by Mrs F. Samuel, Mrs E. Bishop and Michel H. Salaman through the Contemporary Art Society 1941

N05424   Fireside Scene
WGπ:394x286:signed:Presented by Mrs F. Samuel, Mrs E. Bishop and Michel H. Salaman through the Contemporary Art Society 1941

Miscellaneous Drawings, mostly for Wuthering Heights (A01064-A01073)

A01064   Catherine Leaning on a Wall (circa 1900-5)
DWπ:279x216:signed:Presented by Mrs F. Samuel, Mrs E. Bishop and Michel H. Salaman through the Contemporary Art Society 1941

A01065   Catherine and Heathcliffe as Children. Verso: Fragmentary Figure
DWπ:13x394:signed:Presented by Mrs F. Samuel, Mrs E. Bishop and Michel H. Salaman through the Contemporary Art Society 1941

A01066   Catherine and Heathcliff Walking
DWπ:286x400:signed:Presented by Mrs F. Samuel, Mrs E. Bishop and Michel H. Salaman through the Contemporary Art Society 1941

A01067   Seated Woman (circa 1899)
DWπ:356x254:signed:Presented by Mrs F. Samuel, Mrs E. Bishop and Michel H. Salaman through the Contemporary Art Society 1941

A01068   Catherine Linton Seated at a Window During her Last Illness. Verso: Four Figures at Table
DWπ:273x197:signed:Presented by Mrs F. Samuel, Mrs E. Bishop and Michel H. Salaman through the Contemporary Art Society 1941

A01069   Four Figures and a Cat. Verso: study of Hareton
Dπ:279x216:signed:Presented by Mrs F. Samuel, Mrs E. Bishop and Michel H. Salaman through the Contemporary Art Society 1941

A01070   Nelly with Baby Hareton and Catherine Earnshaw. Verso: similar composition
DWπ:229x184:signed:Presented by Mrs F. Samuel, Mrs E. Bishop and Michel H. Salaman through the Contemporary Art Society 1941

A01071   Catherine the Younger and Hareton. Verso: study of cows
DWπ:229x175:signed:Presented by Mrs F. Samuel, Mrs E. Bishop and Michel H. Salaman through the Contemporary Art Society 1941

A01072   Study for Catherine. Verso: Upminster Common (1902)
DWπ:178x229:signed:Presented by Mrs F. Samuel, Mrs E. Bishop and Michel H. Salaman through the Contemporary Art Society 1941

A01073   Catherine and Heathcliff Sitting in a Field
DWπ:149x229:signed:Presented by Mrs F. Samuel, Mrs E. Bishop and Michel H. Salaman through the Contemporary Art Society 1941

CLATWORTHY, Robert born 1928
Modern Collection

T00265   Bull (1956)
Sz:324x432x451:Purchased 1959

T03714   Bull (1956)
Sz:180x380x150:Transferred from the Victoria & Albert Museum 1983

CLAUSEN, Sir George 1852-1944
British Collection
Tate Gallery Archive holds material concerning this artist

N01612   The Girl at the Gate (1889)
Oc:1714x1384:signed:Presented by the Trustees of the Chantrey Bequest 1890

N02259   The Gleaners Returning (1908)
Oc:838x660:signed:Presented by the Trustees of the Chantrey Bequest 1908

N03824   The Road, Winter Morning (exhibited 1923)
Oc:508x610:signed:Presented by the Trustees of the Chantrey Bequest 1923

N04472   A Dancer (exhibited 1929)
Oc:457x356:signed:Presented by the Trustees of the Chantrey Bequest 1929

N04484   Brown Eyes (1891)
Oc:559x413:signed:Presented by C.N. Luxmoore 1929

N04485   A Frosty March Morning (1904)
Oc:635x762:signed:Presented by C.N. Luxmoore 1929

N04486   Gleaners Coming Home (1904)
Oc:927x1226:signed:Presented by C.N. Luxmoore 1929

N05335   My Back Garden (exhibited 1940)
Oc:508x610:signed:Presented by the Trustees of the Chantrey Bequest 1940

T03666   Winter Work (1883-4)
Oc:775x921:signed:Purchased with assistance from the Friends of the Tate Gallery 1983

The Great War: Britain's Efforts and Ideals (P03001-P03007, P03011-P03023, P03031-P03036, P03039-P03044; incomplete group; mixed group)
Making Guns (P03017-P03023; complete group)

P03017   Where the Guns are Made (1917)
Lπ:352x457:signed:Presented by the Ministry of Information 1918

P03018 The Furnace (1917)
Lπ:460x347:signed:Presented by the Ministry of
Information 1918

P03019 The Great Hammer (1917)
Lπ:347x455:signed:Presented by the Ministry of
Information 1918

P03020 Turning a Big Gun (1917)
Lπ:385x510:signed:Presented by the Ministry of
Information 1918

P03021 The Radial Crane (1917)
Lπ:357x457:signed:Presented by the Ministry of
Information 1918

P03022 Lifting an Inner Tube (1917)
Lπ:460x346:signed:Presented by the Ministry of
Information 1918

P03023 Reconstruction of Belgium (1917)
Lπ:680x435:signed:Presented by the Ministry of
Information 1918

CLAVÉ, Antoni born 1913
Modern Collection

T00302 Child with a Water-Melon (circa 1947-8)
Enfant à la pastèque
Oc:549x457:signed:Presented by Mr and Mrs Alexander
Margulies 1959

CLEMENTE, Francesco born 1952
Modern Collection
Tate Gallery Archive holds material concerning this artist

T03551 Midnight Sun II (1982)
Oc:2010x2507:Purchased 1983

T05566 Eternity's Smell (1989)
Pπ:666x1017:Purchased 1989

T05567 Confused Recollection (1989)
Pπ:667x1017:Purchased 1989

High Fever (P07830-P07838, P07848; complete group)
Febbre alta

P07830 [no title] (1982)
MJπ:514x422:signed:Purchased 1983

P07831 [no title] (1982)
MJπ:476x356:signed:Purchased 1983

P07832 [no title] (1982)
MJπ:536x410:signed:Purchased 1983

P07833 [no title] (1982)
MJπ:543x356:signed:Purchased 1983

P07834 [no title] (1982)
MJπ:540x410:signed:Purchased 1983

P07835 [no title] (1982)
MJπ:356x362:signed:Purchased 1983

P07836 [no title] (1982)
MJπ:553x353:signed:Purchased 1983

P07837 [no title] (1982)
MJπ:438x521:signed:Purchased 1983

P07838 [no title] (1982)
MJπ:330x343:Purchased 1983

P07848 [no title] (1982)
MJπ:368x127:Purchased 1983

P07904 Seascape (1981)
MIπ:619x470:signed:Purchased 1983

P07905 Self-Portrait No. 6 (Stoplight) (1981)
MIπ:235x337:signed:Purchased 1983

P11276 Semen (1987)
Iπ:1035x1690:signed:Presented by Mr and Mrs Edward
Lee 1990

P77180 Untitled B (1986)
MLπ:659x2010:signed:Purchased 1987

CLEMENTE, Jack 1926-1974
Modern Collection

T00235 Mineral Efflorescence (1958)
Floraison minerale
Oc:1457x1137:Purchased 1959

T00236 Volcanic City (1957)
Cité volcanique
Oc:1457x889:Purchased 1959

after
CLENNELL, Luke 1781-1840
British Collection

Picturesque Views on the Southern Coast of England
(T05218-T05463; complete group; mixed group)

T05244 St Mary's Church, Dover (1814)
Iπ:111x156:Purchased 1988

T05245 St Mary's Church, Dover (1814)
Iπ:120x157:Purchased 1988

T05255 Folkestone (1814)
Iπ:72x173:Purchased 1988

T05256 Folkestone (1814)
Iπ:76x183:Purchased 1988

T05265 Hythe (1814)
Iπ:80x178, 140x210:Purchased 1988

T05266 Hythe (1814)
Iπ:88x182:Purchased 1988

T05269 Saltwood Castle, Kent (1816)
Iπ:101x158:Purchased 1988

T05278 The Beach at Hastings, Looking East (1815)
Iπ:79x163:Purchased 1988

T05279 The Beach at Hastings, Looking East (1815)
Iπ:82x168:Purchased 1988

T05296 Church at New Shoreham, Sussex (1815)
Iπ:83x156:Purchased 1988

T05297 Church at New Shoreham, Sussex (1815)
Iπ:101x161:Purchased 1988

T05309 Ventnor Cove, Isle of Wight
Iπ:102x158:Purchased 1988

T05316 Carisbrook Castle from the Calbourn Road (1814)
Iπ:111x167:Purchased 1988

T05317 Carisbrook Castle from the Calbourn Road (1814)
Iπ:115x176:Purchased 1988

T05374 Dawlish (1820)
Iπ:100x155:Purchased 1988

T05375 Dawlish (1820)
Iπ:106x159:Purchased 1988

CLINT, Alfred 1807-1883
British Collection

N04809 Hampstead from the South-East (circa 1852-5)
Oc:610x914:Purchased 1935

CLINT, George 1770-1854
British Collection

N00377 Falstaff and Mistress Ford (exhibited 1831)
Oc:768x641:signed:Presented by Robert Vernon 1847

CLINTON, Margery
Modern Collection

P06073 Charlotte Square, Edinburgh (1961)
CLπ:508x762:signed:Presented by Curwen Studio
through the Institute of Contemporary Prints 1975

CLOSE, Chuck born 1940
Modern Collection

P07387 Self-Portrait Etching (1977)
MIπ:1131x902:signed:Purchased 1980

CLOUGH, Prunella born 1919
Modern Collection
Tate Gallery Archive holds material concerning this artist

T00376 Cooling Tower II (1958)
Oc:965x914:Purchased 1960

T00691 Rockery, 1963 (1962-3)
Oc:660x508:signed:Purchased 1964

T02093 By the Canal (1976)
Oc:1829x1422:signed:Purchased 1976

T03450 Yellow Mesh (1981)
Oc:1227x1912:signed:Purchased 1982

T03451 Wire and Demolition (1982)
Oc:1520x1670:signed:Purchased 1982

T03810 The White Root (1946)
Ob:505x395:signed:Purchased 1982

P06074 Electrical Area (1961)
MLπ:486x448:Presented by Curwen Studio through the
Institute of Contemporary Prints 1975

P06075 Tideline (1961-2)
CLπ:530x457:signed:Presented by Curwen Studio
through the Institute of Contemporary Prints 1975

P06076 Wall and Scrap (1961-2)
CLπ:502x464:Presented by Curwen Studio through the
Institute of Contemporary Prints 1975

P07906 Geological Landscape (1949)
CLπ:149x201:Purchased 1984

P07907 Can and Basket (1950)
CLπ:167x162:Purchased 1984

P07908 Jelly Fish (1950)
CLπ:254x323:Purchased 1984

P07909 Float (1950)
MLπ:168x114:Purchased 1984

P07910 Cranes (1952)
CLπ:430x368:signed:Purchased 1984

P07911 Kippers (1954)
MIπ:100x149:Purchased 1984

P07912 Marsh Plants (1954)
MIπ:150x100:Purchased 1984

P07913 Pimentoes (1954)
MIπ:75x102:Purchased 1984

P07914 Skull and Pomegranate (1954)
MIπ:85x125:Purchased 1984

P07915 Corrugated Fence (1955)
MIπ:87x123:Purchased 1984

P07916 Off the Tracks (1977)
MIπ:254x220:signed:Purchased 1984

P07917 Fence/Climbing Plant (1978)
WNπ:241x293:Purchased 1984

P07918 Gate Detail (1980)
WNπ:484x573:Purchased 1984

P07919 Gate (1981)
HWCNπ:190x225:Purchased 1984

P07920 Untitled (1981)
MJπ:274x308:Purchased 1984

P77157 Untitled Monotype No. 3 (1983)
Jπ:1190x810:signed:Purchased 1986

COATES, George 1869-1930
British Collection

N04928 The Children's Orchestra (1903-5)
Oc:813x908:signed:Presented by the artist's widow 1938

COCKRAM, George 1861-1950
British Collection

N01707 Solitude (exhibited 1892)
Wπ:660x1295:signed:Presented by the Trustees of the
Chantrey Bequest 1892

COHEN, Bernard born 1933
Modern Collection
Tate Gallery Archive holds material concerning this artist

T00481 Phoenix (1961)
ODc:1016x1270:signed:Purchased 1962

T00510 Early Mutation Green No. II (1960)
OAc:1835x2134:signed:Presented by E.J. Power through
the Friends of the Tate Gallery 1962

T00800 In That Moment (1965)
OTc:2438x2438:Purchased 1965

T01162 Floris (1964)
OTc:1829x1829:signed:Presented by the Friends of the
Tate Gallery 1969

T01535 Matter of Identity I (1963)
OETc:2438x2438:signed:Purchased 1972

T01536 Fall (1964)
OTc:2438x3048:signed:Purchased 1972

T01537 Blue Spot (1966)
Ac:2438x3353:Purchased 1972

T01538 Painting with Three Spots, One Blue and Two Yellow
(1970)
Ac:1524x3962:Purchased 1972

T01867 Zany Balances (1973-4)
Ac:2743x1368:signed:Purchased 1974

T03284 Matter of Identity III - the Trace (1979)
Ac:1835x1835:signed:Presented by the Friends of the
Tate Gallery 1981

White Ink Suite 1-6 (P01090-P01095; complete group)
P01090 Untitled (1973)
CLπ:370x377:signed:Presented by Waddington Galleries
through the Institute of Contemporary Prints 1975

P01091 Untitled (1973)
CLπ:277x350:signed:Presented by Waddington Galleries
through the Institute of Contemporary Prints 1975

P01092 Untitled (1973)
CLπ:436x436:signed:Presented by Waddington Galleries
through the Institute of Contemporary Prints 1975

P01093 Untitled (1973)
CLπ:335x335:signed:Presented by Waddington Galleries through the Institute of Contemporary Prints 1975

P01094 Untitled (1973)
CLπ:335x333:signed:Presented by Waddington Galleries through the Institute of Contemporary Prints 1975

P01095 Untitled (1973)
CLπ:340x335:signed:Presented by Waddington Galleries through the Institute of Contemporary Prints 1975

P01384 November +1 (1970)
CLπ:716x921:Presented by the Institute of Contemporary Prints 1975

P01385 November +2 (1970)
CLπ:717x920:Presented by the Institute of Contemporary Prints 1975

P01386 November +3 (1970)
CLπ:713x920:Presented by the Institute of Contemporary Prints 1975

Tamarind Institute (P02270-P02272; incomplete group)
P02270 New Mexico I (1969)
CLπ:629x918:signed:Presented by the artist 1976

P02271 New Mexico 2 (1970)
CLπ:629x918:signed:Presented by the artist 1976

P02272 New Mexico 4 (1969-70)
CLπ:613x616:signed:Presented by the artist 1976

6 Untitled Lithographs (P03024-P03029; complete group)
P03024 No. 1 (1971)
CLπ:718x908:signed:Presented by Waddington Galleries 1972

P03025 No. 2 (1971)
CLπ:720x902:signed:Presented by Waddington Galleries 1972

P03026 No. 3 (1971)
CLπ:723x911:signed:Presented by Waddington Galleries 1972

P03027 No. 4 (1971)
CLπ:724x902:signed:Presented by Waddington Galleries 1972

P03028 No. 5 (1971)
CLπ:725x903:signed:Presented by Waddington Galleries 1972

P03029 No. 6 (1971)
CLπ:723x905:signed:Presented by Waddington Galleries 1972

Six Images for J (P03186-P03191; complete group)
P03186 First Image for J (1976)
CLπ:460x920:signed:Presented by Waddington Galleries 1972

P03187 Second Image for J (1976)
CLπ:460x920:signed:Presented by Waddington Galleries 1972

P03188 Third Image for J (1976)
CLπ:460x917:signed:Presented by Waddington Galleries 1972

P03189 Fourth Image for J (1976)
CLπ:490x926:signed:Presented by Waddington Galleries 1972

P03190 Fifth Image for J (1976)
CLπ:460x920:signed:Presented by Waddington Galleries 1972

P03191 Sixth Image for J (1976)
CLπ:460x920:signed:Presented by Waddington Galleries 1972

P04114 Silver (1964)
CNπ:476x749:signed:Presented by Rose and Chris Prater through the Institute of Contemporary Prints 1975

The Institute of Contemporary Arts Portfolio (P04016, P04038, P04053, P04076, P04115, P04125, P04166, P04248, P04256, P04315-P04316, P04334, P04378-P04380, P04419, P04635, P04752, P04938, P05138, P05155, P05248; complete group; mixed group)

P04115 Taper (1964)
CNπ:486x629:signed:Presented by Rose and Chris Prater through the Institute of Contemporary Prints 1975

Group M. Nine (P04116-P04124; complete group)
P04116 Print 1 (1967)
CNπ:686x686:signed:Presented by Rose and Chris Prater through the Institute of Contemporary Prints 1975

P04117 Print 2 (1967)
CNπ:686x686:signed:Presented by Rose and Chris Prater through the Institute of Contemporary Prints 1975

P04118 Print 3 (1967)
CNπ:686x686:signed:Presented by Rose and Chris Prater through the Institute of Contemporary Prints 1975

P04119 Print 4 (1967)
CNπ:686x686:signed:Presented by Rose and Chris Prater through the Institute of Contemporary Prints 1975

P04120 Print 5 (1967)
CNπ:686x686:signed:Presented by Rose and Chris Prater through the Institute of Contemporary Prints 1975

P04121 Print 6 (1967)
CNπ:686x686:signed:Presented by Rose and Chris Prater through the Institute of Contemporary Prints 1975

P04122 Print 7 (1967)
CNπ:686x686:signed:Presented by Rose and Chris Prater through the Institute of Contemporary Prints 1975

P04123 Print 8 (1967)
CNπ:686x686:signed:Presented by Rose and Chris Prater through the Institute of Contemporary Prints 1975

P04124 Print 9 (1967)
CNπ:686x686:signed:Presented by Rose and Chris Prater through the Institute of Contemporary Prints 1975

P05547 Concerning the Meal (1980)
CLπ:686x545:signed:Presented by Rose and Chris Prater 1980

P07756 Imitations (1981)
CLπ:686x541:signed:Purchased 1982

COHEN, Harold born 1928
Modern Collection
Tate Gallery Archive holds material concerning this artist

T00470 Benedictus (1961)
Oc:838x2337:signed:Purchased 1962

T00549 Tribune (1962)
Oc:2140x2438:signed:Purchased 1962

T04167 Untitled Computer Drawing (1982)
DHπ:575x765:signed:Presented by Michael Compton 1986

T04856 Before the Event (1963)
TOc:2490x2930:signed:Purchased 1986

The Homecoming (P02283-P02291; complete group)
P02283 [no title] (1968)
CLπ:440x700:signed:Presented by the artist 1976

P02284 [no title] (1968)
CLπ:440x698:signed:Presented by the artist 1976

P02285 [no title] (1968)
CLπ:440x347:signed:Presented by the artist 1976

P02286 [no title] (1968)
CLπ:440x347:signed:Presented by the artist 1976

P02287 [no title] (1968)
CLπ:442x348:signed:Presented by the artist 1976

P02288 [no title] (1968)
CLπ:440x347:signed:Presented by the artist 1976

P02289 [no title] (1968)
CLπ:440x347:signed:Presented by the artist 1976

P02290 [no title] (1968)
CLπ:440x348:signed:Presented by the artist 1976

P02291 [no title] (1968)
CLπ:440x347:signed:Presented by the artist 1976

P02292 Untitled (1971)
CNπ:318x394:signed:Presented by the artist 1976

P02293 Untitled (1971)
CNπ:194x286:signed:Presented by the artist 1976

P02294 Untitled (1971)
CNπ:664x800:signed:Presented by the artist 1976

P02295 Untitled (1972)
CNπ:397x581:signed:Presented by the artist 1976

The Institute of Contemporary Arts Portfolio (P04016, P04038, P04053, P04076, P04115, P04125, P04166, P04248, P04256, P04315-P04316, P04334, P04378-P04380, P04419, P04635, P04752, P04938, P05138, P05155, P05248; complete group; mixed group)

P04125 Untitled (1964)
CNπ:511x740:signed:Presented by Rose and Chris Prater through the Institute of Contemporary Prints 1975

First Folio (P04126-P04132; complete group)

P04126 First Folio A (1965)
CNπ:490x485:signed:Presented by Rose and Chris Prater through the Institute of Contemporary Prints 1975

P04127 First Folio B (1965)
CNπ:484x449:signed:Presented by Rose and Chris Prater through the Institute of Contemporary Prints 1975

P04128 First Folio C (1965)
CNπ:540x536:signed:Presented by Rose and Chris Prater through the Institute of Contemporary Prints 1975

P04129 First Folio D (1965)
CNπ::signed:Presented by Rose and Chris Prater through the Institute of Contemporary Prints 1975

P04130 First Folio E (1965)
CNπ:485x495:signed:Presented by Rose and Chris Prater through the Institute of Contemporary Prints 1975

P04131 First Folio F (1965)
CNπ::signed:Presented by Rose and Chris Prater through the Institute of Contemporary Prints 1975

P04132 First Folio G (1965)
CNπ::signed:Presented by Rose and Chris Prater through the Institute of Contemporary Prints 1975

Derrynan [including 4 artist's proofs for Derrynan III and 3 artist's proofs for Derrynan IV] (P04133-P04142; complete group)

P04133 Derrynan I (1967)
CNπ:665x664:signed:Presented by Rose and Chris Prater through the Institute of Contemporary Prints 1975

P04134 Derrynan II (1967)
CNπ:664x664:signed:Presented by Rose and Chris Prater through the Institute of Contemporary Prints 1975

P04135 Derrynan III (1967)
CNπ:643x642:signed:Presented by Rose and Chris Prater through the Institute of Contemporary Prints 1975

P04136 Derrynan III (1967)
CNπ:642x640:signed:Presented by Rose and Chris Prater through the Institute of Contemporary Prints 1975

P04137 Derrynan III (1967)
CNπ:644x642:signed:Presented by Rose and Chris Prater through the Institute of Contemporary Prints 1975

P04138 Derrynan III (1967)
CNπ:643x641:signed:Presented by Rose and Chris Prater through the Institute of Contemporary Prints 1975

P04139 Derrynan IV (1967)
CNπ:637x638:signed:Presented by Rose and Chris Prater through the Institute of Contemporary Prints 1975

P04140 Derrynan IV (1967)
CNπ:638x638:signed:Presented by Rose and Chris Prater through the Institute of Contemporary Prints 1975

P04141 Derrynan IV (1967)
CNπ:638x638:signed:Presented by Rose and Chris Prater through the Institute of Contemporary Prints 1975

P04142 Derrynan V (1967)
CNπ:637x636:signed:Presented by Rose and Chris Prater through the Institute of Contemporary Prints 1975

Richard Hamilton (P04143-P04150; complete group)

P04143 Richard H (1967)
CNπ:653x735:signed:Presented by Rose and Chris Prater through the Institute of Contemporary Prints 1975

P04144 Richard I (1967)
CNπ:649x737:signed:Presented by Rose and Chris Prater through the Institute of Contemporary Prints 1975

P04145 Richard II (1967)
CNπ:651x735:signed:Presented by Rose and Chris Prater through the Institute of Contemporary Prints 1975

P04146 Richard III (1967)
CNπ:652x735:signed:Presented by Rose and Chris Prater through the Institute of Contemporary Prints 1975

P04147 Richard IV (1967)
CNπ:651x736:signed:Presented by Rose and Chris Prater through the Institute of Contemporary Prints 1975

P04148 Richard V (1967)
CNπ:652x735:signed:Presented by Rose and Chris Prater through the Institute of Contemporary Prints 1975

P04149 Richard VI (1967)
CNπ:653x735:signed:Presented by Rose and Chris Prater through the Institute of Contemporary Prints 1975

P04150 Richard VII (1967)
CNπ:653x735:signed:Presented by Rose and Chris Prater through the Institute of Contemporary Prints 1975

P04151 Untitled (1970)
CNπ:686x686:signed:Presented by Rose and Chris Prater through the Institute of Contemporary Prints 1975

P04152 Untitled (1970)
CNπ:686x686:signed:Presented by Rose and Chris Prater through the Institute of Contemporary Prints 1975

P06077 Close-Up I (1966)
CLπ:843x843:Presented by Curwen Studio 1975

P06078 Close-Up II (1966)
CLπ:844x844:Presented by Curwen Studio 1975

P06079 Close-Up III (1966)
CLπ:595x595:Presented by Curwen Studio 1975

P06080 Close-Up IV (1966)
CLπ:597x595:Presented by Curwen Studio 1975

P06081 Close-Up V (1966)
CLπ:595x594:Presented by Curwen Studio 1975

P06082 Close-Up VI (1966)
CLπ:842x843:Presented by Curwen Studio 1975

COKER, Peter born 1926
Modern Collection
Tate Gallery Archive holds material concerning this artist

T03216 Man Carrying Pig (1955)
Ob:1829x838:signed:Presented by the Trustees of the Chantrey Bequest 1981

T03302 Table and Chair (1955)
OVb:1524x1219:signed:Purchased 1981

T03307 Hanging Hare (1955)
Dπ:768x562:signed:Presented by the artist 1981

T03308 Two Studies for Skinned Hare (1955)
Dπ:559x381:Presented by the artist 1981

T03309 Sheep's Head (1955)
DWPπ:384x543:Presented by the artist 1981

T03310 Nicholas, Two Studies for Table and Chair (1955)
2 Dπ:384x279, 229x130:signed:Presented by the artist 1981

T03311 Sheep's Head on Newspaper (1955)
Dπ:416x552:signed:Presented by the artist 1981

T04113 The Gorse Bush (1957)
Ob:1452x1213:signed:Presented by the artist in memory of his son Nicholas Coker 1985

T05027 Butcher's Shop (1955)
Dπ:428x282:signed:Presented by the artist 1987

COLDSTREAM, Sir William 1908-1987
Modern Collection
Tate Gallery Archive holds material concerning this artist

N05108 Man with a Beard (1939)
Oc:610x406:Presented by the Trustees of the Chantrey Bequest 1940

N05687 Havildar Ajmer Singh (Sikh) (1943)
Oc:787x565:Presented by the War Artists' Advisory Committee 1946

N05883 Mrs Inez Spender (1937-8)
Oc:762x1010:Presented by the Contemporary Art Society 1949

T00074 Dr Bell, Bishop of Chichester (1954)
Oc:908x711:Presented by Dr Bell 1956

T00339 Mrs Winifred Burger (1936-7)
Oc:781x546:Presented by the Trustees of the Chantrey Bequest 1960

T00537 Studio Interior (1932-3)
Oc:1372x914:Purchased 1962

T01107 Casualty Reception Station, Capua (1944)
Oc:730x927:Presented by the British Council 1969

T02079 Reclining Nude (1974-6)
Oc:1016x1270:Purchased 1976

T03068 On the Map (1937)
Oc:508x508:Purchased 1980

T03704 Seated Nude (1951-2)
Oc:1067x707:signed:Purchased 1983

COLE, George Vicat 1833-1893
British Collection

N01599 The Pool of London (1888)
Oc:1892x3048:signed:Presented by the Trustees of the Chantrey Bequest 1888

COLEMAN, Samuel - see COLMAN, Samuel

COLESCOTT, Warrington born 1921
Modern Collection
Tate Gallery Archive holds material concerning this artist

A Wild West (P06083-P06088; complete group)

P06083 2. Wagon Train (1968)
CLπ:595x788:signed:Presented by Curwen Studio through the Institute of Contemporary Prints 1975

P06084 4. Cowboys and Indians (1968)
CLπ:605x435:signed:Presented by Curwen Studio through the Institute of Contemporary Prints 1975

P06085 6. Custard's Last Stand (1968)
CLπ:647x510:signed:Presented by Curwen Studio through the Institute of Contemporary Prints 1975

P06086 3. Dodge City (1968)
CLπ:604x446:signed:Presented by Curwen Studio through the Institute of Contemporary Prints 1975

P06087 1. High Noon for Hoot Gibson (1968)
CLπ:590x793:signed:Presented by Curwen Studio through the Institute of Contemporary Prints 1975

P06088 5. Home on the Range (1968)
CLπ:791x588:signed:Presented by Curwen Studio through the Institute of Contemporary Prints 1975

COLLA, Ettore 1896-1968
Modern Collection
Tate Gallery Archive holds material concerning this artist

P01013 Screenprint (1953)
Serie serigrafica
MNπ:244x343:signed:Presented by Mariolina Colla 1972

P01014 Screenprint (Development) (1953)
Svolgimento
CNπ:162x229:signed:Presented by Mariolina Colla 1972

P01015 Screenprint (circa 1954)
Serie serigrafica
CNπ:276x346:Presented by Mariolina Colla 1972

P01016 Screenprint (Angles in Unity) (circa 1953)
Angoli in una Unità
MNπ:352x502:signed:Presented by Mariolina Colla 1972

P01017 Screenprint (circa 1953)
Serie serigrafica
MNπ:352x502:Presented by Mariolina Colla 1972

COLLIER, Edward active 1662-1706
British Collection

N05856 Still Life (1698)
Oc:762x635:signed:Purchased 1948

N05916 Still Life with a Volume of Wither's 'Emblems' (1696)
Oc:838x1079:signed:Purchased 1949

T03853 A Trompe l'Oeil of Newspapers, Letters and Writing Implements on a Wooden Board (circa 1699)
Oc:588x462:signed:Purchased 1984

COLLIER, The Hon. John 1850-1934
British Collection

N01616 The Last Voyage of Henry Hudson (exhibited 1881)
Oc:2140x1835:Presented by the Trustees of the Chantrey Bequest 1881

N04378 Mrs Huxley (circa 1927-8)
Oc:610x508:signed:Presented by Prof. H. Tonks and Col. W.E. Armstrong 1928

COLLIER, Thomas 1840-1891
British Collection

N03577 Cromer
Wπ:241x349:signed:Purchased 1921

COLLINS, Cecil 1908-1989
Modern Collection
Tate Gallery Archive holds material concerning this artist

N06036 The Sleeping Fool (1943)
Oc:298x400:signed:Presented by the Contemporary Art
Society 1951

T00431 The Golden Wheel (1958)
Ob:914x1219:signed:Purchased 1961

T00437 Hymn (1953)
Ob:1226x1530:signed:Presented by the Friends of the
Tate Gallery 1961

T01478 The Cells of Night (1934)
Oc:762x635:signed:Purchased 1971

T01692 The Promise (1936)
Ow:508x610:signed:Purchased 1972

T01905 Landscape with Heads (1940)
WDπ:387x559:signed:Purchased 1974

T03322 The Divine Land (1979)
WGDπ:406x584:signed:Purchased 1981

T03971 The Angel of the Flowing Light (1968)
Ob:1220x1060:signed:Purchased with assistance from the
Carroll Donner Bequest 1985

P01895 The Fool with a Fish (1944)
MJπ:210x140:signed:Presented by Elisabeth and Cecil
Collins 1979

P01896 The Voice of the Fool (1944)
MJπ:219x171:signed:Presented by Elisabeth and Cecil
Collins 1979

P01897 Head (1944)
MJπ:286x200:signed:Presented by Elisabeth and Cecil
Collins 1979

P01898 Island (1944)
MJπ:203x295:signed:Presented by Elisabeth and Cecil
Collins 1979

P01899 The Joy of the Fool (1944)
MJπ:308x206:signed:Presented by Elisabeth and Cecil
Collins 1979

P01900 The Pilgrim (1944)
MJπ:171x127:signed:Presented by Elisabeth and Cecil
Collins 1979

P01901 Tree & Hills (1944)
MJπ:206x244:signed:Presented by Elisabeth and Cecil
Collins 1979

P01902 Figure (1958)
MLπ:476x337:signed:Presented by Elisabeth and Cecil
Collins 1979

P01903 Angels (1960)
MLπ:241x384:signed:Presented by Elisabeth and Cecil
Collins 1979

P01904 Head (1960)
MLπ:302x254:signed:Presented by Elisabeth and Cecil
Collins 1979

P01905 A Song (1960)
MLπ:556x400:signed:Presented by Elisabeth and Cecil
Collins 1979

P01906 Sun Head (1960)
MLπ:254x305:signed:Presented by Elisabeth and Cecil
Collins 1979

P01907 A Joy Beast (1962)
MLπ:229x254:signed:Presented by Elisabeth and Cecil
Collins 1979

P01908 Spanish Lady (1962)
MLπ:298x248:signed:Presented by Elisabeth and Cecil
Collins 1979

P01909 A Sweet Song (1962)
MLπ:298x244:signed:Presented by Elisabeth and Cecil
Collins 1979

P01910 The Great Happiness (1965)
MLπ:476x251:signed:Presented by Elisabeth and Cecil
Collins 1979

P01911 Head (1974)
MLπ:403x327:signed:Presented by Elisabeth and Cecil
Collins 1979

P01912 Angel (1977)
MLπ:213x121:signed:Presented by Elisabeth and Cecil
Collins 1979

P01913 Head (1977)
MLπ:124x98:signed:Presented by Elisabeth and Cecil
Collins 1979

P01914 Kneeling Fool (1977)
MLπ:200x133:signed:Presented by Elisabeth and Cecil
Collins 1979

P01915 Fool and Bird (1978)
MLπ:251x178:signed:Presented by Elisabeth and Cecil
Collins 1979

P01916 Bird Smoking a Pipe (1939)
Mlπ:95x73:signed:Presented by Elisabeth and Cecil
Collins 1979

P01917 Landscape (1939)
Mlπ:140x108:signed:Presented by Elisabeth and Cecil
Collins 1979

P01918 Landscape (1939)
Mlπ:79x121:signed:Presented by Elisabeth and Cecil
Collins 1979

P11016 Head (1939)
Mlπ:86x74:signed:Presented by Elisabeth and Cecil
Collins 1981

P11017 The Artist's Wife Seated in a Tree (1944)
MJπ:222x178:signed:Presented by Elisabeth and Cecil
Collins 1981

P11018 The Fool (1944)
MJπ:305x133:signed:Presented by Elisabeth and Cecil
Collins 1981

P11019 Self-Portrait (1944)
MJπ:229x203:signed:Presented by Elisabeth and Cecil
Collins 1981

P11020 Fool with a Bird (1960)
MLπ:260x232:signed:Presented by Elisabeth and Cecil
Collins 1981

P11021 Temple of the Sun (1960)
MLπ:390x512:signed:Presented by Elisabeth and Cecil
Collins 1981

P11022 The Eternal Sun (1961)
MLπ:568x407:signed:Presented by Elisabeth and Cecil
Collins 1981

P11023 The Fruit of the Sun (1961)
MLπ:358x248:signed:Presented by Elisabeth and Cecil
Collins 1981

P11024 Sunrise (1961)
MLπ:482x355:signed:Presented by Elisabeth and Cecil
Collins 1981

P11025 Angel and Woman (1962)
MLπ:540x381:signed:Presented by Elisabeth and Cecil Collins 1981

P11026 Dance Landscape (1962)
MLπ:407x561:signed:Presented by Elisabeth and Cecil Collins 1981

P11027 Fool and Woman (1963)
MLπ:380x305:signed:Presented by Elisabeth and Cecil Collins 1981

P11028 Head (1963)
MLπ:305x255:signed:Presented by Elisabeth and Cecil Collins 1981

P11029 Head of a Woman (1963)
MLπ:380x321:signed:Presented by Elisabeth and Cecil Collins 1981

COLLINS, Charles circa 1680-1744
British Collection

T03301 Lobster on a Delft Dish (1738)
Oc:705x910:signed:Purchased 1981

COLLINS, Charles Allston 1828-1873
British Collection
Tate Gallery Archive holds material concerning this artist

N03520 The Convent Garden (1853)
Dπ:330x197:signed:Bequeathed by Mrs Louise d'Este Oliver 1920

N03521 The Devout Childhood of St Elizabeth of Hungary (1852)
Dπ:273x175:signed:Bequeathed by Mrs Louise d'Este Oliver 1920

T03025 May, in the Regent's Park (1851)
Ow:445x692:signed:Purchased 1980

COLLINS, William 1788-1847
British Collection

N00351 As Happy as a King (circa 1836)
Oc:711x914:Presented by Robert Vernon 1847

N00352 The Prawn Catchers (1828)
Ow:435x584:signed:Presented by Robert Vernon 1847

N01910 Cromer Sands (1846)
Oc:978x1270:signed:Bequeathed by Lord Cheylesmore 1902

N01912 Sunday Morning (?exhibited 1836)
Oc:813x1067:Bequeathed by Charles Gassiot 1902

after
COLLINS, William 1788-1847
British Collection

T04867 Eton on the Thames, for 'The Rivers of England' engraved by Thomas Lupton (1823)
Iπ:150x213:signed:Purchased 1987

Picturesque Views on the Southern Coast of England (T05218-T05463; complete group; mixed group)

T05238 Walmer Castle (1824)
Iπ:97x145:Purchased 1988

T05239 Walmer Castle (1824)
Iπ:97x145:Purchased 1988

T05371 Salcombe, Devonshire (1824)
Iπ:102x138, 153x227:Purchased 1988

T05372 Sidmouth, Devon (1821)
Iπ:90x135:Purchased 1988

T05373 Sidmouth, Devon (1821)
Iπ:91x134:Purchased 1988

T05394 Hall Sands, Devon (1821)
Iπ:102x171:Purchased 1988

T05395 Hall Sands, Devon (1821)
Iπ:108x172:Purchased 1988

T05450 Lynmouth (1824)
Iπ:107x129:Purchased 1988

T05451 Lynmouth (1824)
Iπ:110x131:Purchased 1988

T05452 Porlock, Devon (1824)
Iπ:109x139:Purchased 1988

COLLINSON, James 1825-1881
British Collection

N02421 The Child Jesus (1850)
Mπ:102x175:Presented by Edmund Houghton 1898

N03201 The Empty Purse (replica of 'For Sale') (?circa 1857)
Oc:610x492:Presented anonymously 1917

T04105 Home Again (1856)
Oc:827x1155:signed:Purchased 1985

COLMAN, Samuel (or Coleman) 1780-1845
British Collection

N06038 The Temple of Flora
Oc:457x610:signed:Purchased 1952

T01980 The Destruction of the Temple (circa 1830-40)
Oc:1356x1965:Purchased 1975

T02109 The Death of Amelia (?1804)
Oc:629x756:Purchased 1977

COLQUHOUN, Ithell 1906-1988
Modern Collection
Tate Gallery Archive holds material concerning this artist

T02140 Scylla (1938)
Ob:914x610:signed:Purchased 1977

COLQUHOUN, Robert 1914-1962
Modern Collection
Tate Gallery Archive holds material concerning this artist

N06211 Woman with Leaping Cat (1945)
Oc:762x610:signed:Purchased 1954

T00184 Woman with Still Life (1958)
Oc:1422x762:signed:Purchased 1958

T00185 Two Sisters (1945)
WDπ:565x381:signed:Purchased 1958

T02076 The Fortune Teller (1946)
Oc:1264x806:signed:Presented by Sir Colin and Lady Anderson through the Contemporary Art Society 1976

P06089 Mysterious Figures (1960)
CLπ:403x540:Presented by Curwen Studio through the Institute of Contemporary Prints 1975

P06090 Two Horsemen (1960)
MLπ:387x254:Presented by Curwen Studio through the Institute of Contemporary Prints 1975

P06091 Woman (1960)
MLπ:676x470:Presented by Curwen Studio through the Institute of Contemporary Prints 1975

P06342 Head of Alsatian (1960)
CLπ:543x419:Presented by Curwen Studio through the Institute of Contemporary Prints 1975

COLTON, William Robert 1867-1921
British Collection

N01766   The Girdle (1898)
Sz:1289x940x737:Presented by the Trustees of the
Chantrey Bequest 1899

N01928   The Springtide of Life (1903)
Ss:1359x635x610:signed:Presented by the Trustees of the
Chantrey Bequest 1903

COLVERSON, Ian born 1940
Modern Collection
Tate Gallery Archive holds material concerning this artist

P02225   Project Print (1973)
CNπ:762x502:Presented by the artist 1975

COLVERSON, Ian and MASI, Denis born 1940, born 1942
Modern Collection
Tate Gallery Archive holds material concerning these artists

P02224   For Otiose Sailors and Girl Guides Only . . . (1973)
CLπ:3048x2032:Presented by the artist 1975

CONDER, Charles 1868-1909
British Collection
Tate Gallery Archive holds material concerning this artist

N03194   Fan: The Romantic Excursion (1899)
Wf:203x425:signed:Presented by Sir Edmund Davis 1917

N03195   Gossip (?exhibited 1904)
Wf:610x470:Presented by Lady Davis 1917

N03196   Masked Woman
Dπ:254x209:Presented by Sir William Rothenstein in
memory of Gerard Chowne 1917

N03423   The Plum Tree (1891)
Oc:800x451:signed:Bequeathed by Arthur Studd 1919

N03645   Windy Day at Brighton (circa 1904-5)
Oc:635x914:Purchased 1922

N03837   A Summer Afternoon: The Green Apple (1894)
Oc:610x737:signed:Presented by the Contemporary Art
Society 1924

N04221   Springtime (1892)
Oc:730x603:signed:Purchased 1926

N04243   The New Moon Fan (1896)
Wf:216x451:signed:Bequeathed by Mrs John Lane 1927

N04407   Swanage (circa 1901)
Oc:229x305:signed:Presented by Mrs Jessop in memory
of W.H. Jessop 1928

N04411   Swanage Bay (circa 1901)
Oc:457x610:signed:Presented by Mrs Jessop in memory
of W.H. Jessop 1928

N04412   By the Sea: Swanage (circa 1901)
Oc:229x305:signed:Presented by Mrs Jessop in memory
of W.H. Jessop 1928

N04497   Verso: Study of a Man in Bed and a Nurse Holding a
Lamp (circa 1901-6)
Ob:432x311:Purchased 1930

N04498   Portrait Study (circa 1901-6)
Ob:432x318:Purchased 1930

N04499   A Fan (circa 1893-8)
WVb:133x438:signed:Purchased 1930

N04578   Spring by the Sea (circa 1905)
Oc:508x914:Bequeathed by Hans Velten 1931

N04939   Gibraltar from Algeciras (1905)
Oc:749x940:signed:Presented by Mrs A. Cecil Lawson
1938

N05365   In the Blue Country or Colloque Sentimentale (circa
1895)
Wf:248x400:Purchased 1942

N05547   Trees in a Meadow (circa 1895)
Oc:724x597:signed:Presented by Dr Robert Steele 1944

P01018   Spanish Set (1905)
MLπ:295x451:signed:Presented by Mr and Mrs F. Gibson
1917

CONNARD, Philip 1875-1958
British Collection
Tate Gallery Archive holds material concerning this artist

N02998   Jane, Evelyn, James and Helen (1913)
Oc:508x610:Presented by Francis Howard through the
National Loans Exhibition Committee 1914

N03673   Summer (exhibited 1922)
Oc:711x914:signed:Presented by the Trustees of the
Chantrey Bequest 1922

N04244   Le Petit Journal (circa 1926)
WDπ:267x343:signed:Purchased 1927

N04414   Woman on a Balcony (1909)
Oc:610x508:Purchased 1928

N04699   A New Arrival at the Zoo (exhibited 1933)
TCπ:1270x1016:signed:Presented by the Trustees of the
Chantrey Bequest 1933

N05326   Winter at Richmond (1938)
Oc:508x686:signed:Presented by the Trustees of the
Chantrey Bequest 1938

N05333   Pelican Ponds (exhibited 1930)
Tc:762x1010:signed:Presented by the Trustees of the
Chantrey Bequest 1940

CONSAGRA, Pietro born 1920
Modern Collection

N06166   The Unknown Political Prisoner (1952)
Prigioniero politico ignoto
Sz:502x267x286:signed:Purchased 1953

CONSTABLE, George 1792-1878
British Collection

T03236   Landscape with Cottage and Figures
Ob:133x200:Purchased 1981

CONSTABLE, John 1776-1837
British Collection
Tate Gallery Archive holds material concerning this artist

N00327   The Valley Farm (1835)
Oc:1473x1251:signed:Presented by Robert Vernon 1847

N01235   East Bergholt House (circa 1809)
Oc:225x686:Presented by Miss Isabel Constable 1887

N01236   Hampstead Heath, with the House Called 'The Salt Box'
(circa 1820)
Oc:384x670:Presented by Miss Isabel Constable 1887

N01237   Hampstead Heath, with Harrow in the Distance (circa
1820-2)
Oπ:171x314:Presented by Miss Isabel Constable 1887

N01244   Gillingham Bridge, Dorset (1823)
Oc:321x514:Presented by Miss Isabel Constable 1888

N01245   The Church Porch, East Bergholt (exhibited 1810)
Oc:445x359:Presented by Miss Isabel Constable 1888

N01246 The Grove, Hampstead (circa 1821-2)
Oc:356x302:Presented by Miss Isabel Constable 1888

N01273 Flatford Mill ('Scene on a Navigable River') (1816-17)
Oc:1016x1270:signed:Bequeathed by Miss Isabel Constable as the gift of Maria Louisa, Isabel and Lionel Bicknell Constable 1888

N01274 The Glebe Farm (circa 1830)
Oc:648x956:Bequeathed by Miss Isabel Constable as the gift of Maria Louisa, Isabel and Lionel Bicknell Constable 1888

N01275 Hampstead Heath with a Rainbow (1836)
Oc:508x762:Bequeathed by Miss Isabel Constable as the gift of Maria Louisa, Isabel and Lionel Bicknell Constable 1888

N01276 Harwich Lighthouse (?exhibited 1820)
Oc:327x502:Presented by Miss Isabel Constable as the gift of Maria Louisa, Isabel and Lionel Bicknell Constable 1888

N01813 Branch Hill Pond, Hampstead Heath, with a Boy Sitting on a Bank (circa 1825)
Oc:333x502:Bequeathed by Henry Vaughan 1900

N01814 Salisbury Cathedral from the Meadows (circa 1830)
Oc:365x511:Bequeathed by Henry Vaughan 1900

N01816 The Mill Stream. Verso: Night Scene with Bridge (circa 1810)
Ob:210x292:Bequeathed by Henry Vaughan 1900

N01817 The Gleaners, Brighton (1824)
Oπ:159x302:Bequeathed by Henry Vaughan 1900

N01818 View at Epsom (1809)
Ob:298x359:Bequeathed by Henry Vaughan 1900

N01819 Stoke-by-Nayland (circa 1810-11)
Oc:181x264:Bequeathed by Henry Vaughan 1900

N01820 Dedham Lock (1820s)
Oπ:165x254:Bequeathed by Henry Vaughan 1900

N01821 A Lane near Flatford (circa 1810-11)
Oπ:203x305:Bequeathed by Henry Vaughan 1900

N01822 Dedham from near Gun Hill, Langham (circa 1810)
Oπ:251x305:Bequeathed by Henry Vaughan 1900

N01823 The Glebe Farm (circa 1830)
Oc:597x781:Bequeathed by Henry Vaughan 1900

N01824 Harnham Ridge, Salisbury (1820 or 1829)
Oπ:114x238:Bequeathed by Henry Vaughan 1900

N02650 Yarmouth Jetty (after 1823)
Oc:324x505:Bequeathed by George Salting 1910

N02653 Malvern Hall, Warwickshire (1809)
Oc:514x768:Bequeathed by George Salting 1910

N02654 Dedham from Langham (?1813)
Oc:137x190:Bequeathed by George Salting 1910

N02655 Maria Bicknell, Mrs John Constable (1816)
Oc:305x251:Bequeathed by George Salting 1910

N02656 The Sea near Brighton (1826)
Oπ:175x238:Bequeathed by George Salting 1910

N02657 A Windmill near Brighton (1824)
Oc:203x251:Bequeathed by George Salting 1910

N02658 A Bank on Hampstead Heath (circa 1820-2)
Oc:206x254:Bequeathed by George Salting 1910

N02659 Trees at Hampstead (1829)
Oc:924x740:signed:Bequeathed by George Salting 1910

N02661 Dedham Lock and Mill (?1817)
Oc:546x765:Bequeathed by George Salting 1910

N03155 View towards Stratford St Mary Church (circa 1805)
Wπ:219x152:Presented by the National Art Collections Fund 1916

N04237 Branch Hill Pond, Hampstead Heath, with a Cart and Carters (circa 1825)
Oc:537x768:Bequeathed by Miss Susan Field 1927

N04810 Sketch for 'Hadleigh Castle' (circa 1828-9)
Oc:1226x1673:Purchased 1935

N05957 Chain Pier, Brighton (1826-7, exhibited 1827)
Oc:1270x1829:Purchased 1950

N05965 The Revd Dr James Andrew (1818)
Oc:775x645:Purchased 1950

N05966 Mrs James Andrew (1818)
Oc:775x645:Purchased 1950

N06065 Cloud Study (1822)
Oπ:476x575:Presented anonymously 1952

N06130 The Bridges Family (1804)
Oc:1359x1838:Presented by Mrs Walter Bogue Bridges 1952

T01141 Susannah Lloyd (1806)
Oc:600x502:Bequeathed by Miss Edith Dorothy Engstrom 1969

T01147 Netley Abbey by Moonlight (circa 1833)
Wπ:146x200:Purchased 1969

T01497 Wooded Landscape with a Church Tower
Dπ:175x219:signed:Purchased 1971

T01940 Cloud Study with Verses from Bloomfield (1830s)
Dπ:337x213:Purchased 1974

T03121 Brightwell Church and Village (1815)
Ow:155x228:Purchased with assistance from the Friends of the Tate Gallery, the National Art Collections Fund, the Wolfson Trust and National Westminster Bank 1980

T03607 Study of a Girl in a Cloak and Bonnet (1810)
Ob:316x175:Purchased 1983

T03899 Self-Portrait (1806)
Dπ:190x145:Purchased 1984

T03900 Maria Bicknell (circa 1805-9)
Dπ:488x348:Purchased 1984

T03901 Golding Constable (1815)
Oc:759x632:Purchased 1984

T03902 Ann Constable (circa 1800-05 or ?circa 1815)
Oc:765x639:Purchased 1984

T03903 Maria Constable with Two of her Children. Verso: Copy after Teniers (circa 1820)
Ow:166x221:Purchased 1984

T04135 Beaching a Boat, Brighton (1824)
Oπc:248x294:Presented by Mrs P.M. Rainsford 1986

T04904 The Opening of Waterloo Bridge ('Whitehall Stairs, June 18th, 1817') (exhibited 1832)
Oc:1308x2180:Purchased with assistance from the National Heritage Memorial Fund, the Clore Foundation, the National Art Collections Fund, the Friends of the Tate Gallery and others 1987

T05493 Study for 'Flatford Mill' (circa 1816)
Dπ:255x312:Purchased 1988

doubtfully attributed to
CONSTABLE, John 1776-1837
British Collection

N01815 'Summer, Afternoon - After a Shower'
Oc:346x435:Bequeathed by Henry Vaughan 1900

formerly attributed to
CONSTABLE, John 1776-1837
British Collection

N01065 A Cornfield with Figures
Oc:248x403:Purchased 1879

N01066 'Barnes Common'
Oc:251x352:Purchased 1879

N02660 Trunk and Lower Branches of a Tree
Oc:635x759:Bequeathed by George Salting 1910

N02663 Dedham Vale with the House Called 'Dedham Valley'
Oπ:238x387:Bequeathed by George Salting 1910

T00968 The Downs
Dπ:203x270:Presented by the National Art Collections
Fund (Herbert Powell Bequest) 1967

T01146 Hadleigh Castle
Dπ:127x184:Purchased 1969

T01240 The Leaping Horse
Ow:175x229:Bequeathed by E.J. Blaiberg 1970

CONSTABLE, John and LUCAS, David
1776-1837, 1802-1881
British Collection

Mezzotints from 'Various Subjects of Landscape,
Characteristic of English Scenery' ('English Landscape')
(T03983-T04063; complete group)

T03983 Frontispiece: East Bergholt, Suffolk (published 1832)
Lπ:140x187:signed:Purchased 1985

T03984 Frontispiece: East Bergholt, Suffolk (published 1832)
Lπ:139x185:signed:Purchased 1985

T03985 Frontispiece: East Bergholt, Suffolk
Lπ:139x187:signed:Purchased 1985

T03986 Spring (published 1830)
Lπ:127x245:signed:Purchased 1985

T03987 Spring
Lπ:127x245:signed:Purchased 1985

T03988 Spring
Lπ:127x245:signed:Purchased 1985

T03989 Spring
Lπ:127x243:signed:Purchased 1985

T03990 Autumnal Sun Set (published 1832)
Lπ:129x240:signed:Purchased 1985

T03991 Autumnal Sun Set
Lπ:130x242:signed:Purchased 1985

T03992 Autumnal Sun Set
Lπ:129x240:signed:Purchased 1985

T03993 Noon (published 1831)
Lπ:139x219:signed:Purchased 1985

T03994 Noon
Lπ:139x219:signed:Purchased 1985

T03995 Noon
Lπ:139x219:signed:Purchased 1985

T03996 River Stour, Suffolk (published 1831)
Lπ:145x222:signed:Purchased 1985

T03997 River Stour, Suffolk
Lπ:144x222:signed:Purchased 1985

T03998 River Stour, Suffolk
Lπ:143x223:signed:Purchased 1985

T03999 River Stour, Suffolk
Lπ:145x223:signed:Purchased 1985

T04000 River Stour, Suffolk
Lπ:144x222:signed:Purchased 1985

T04001 Summer Morning (published 1831)
Lπ:141x218:signed:Purchased 1985

T04002 Summer Morning
Lπ:142x219:signed:Purchased 1985

T04003 Summer Morning
Lπ:141x217:signed:Purchased 1985

T04004 Summer Morning
Lπ:142x219:signed:Purchased 1985

T04005 Summer Evening (published 1831)
Lπ:142x218:signed:Purchased 1985

T04006 Summer Evening
Lπ:140x216:signed:Purchased 1985

T04007 Summer Evening
Lπ:141x218:signed:Purchased 1985

T04008 A Dell, Helmingham Park, Suffolk (published 1830)
Lπ:146x185:signed:Purchased 1985

T04009 A Dell, Helmingham Park, Suffolk (published 1830)
Lπ:146x185:signed:Purchased 1985

T04010 A Dell, Helmingham Park, Suffolk
Lπ:145x185:signed:Purchased 1985

T04011 A Dell, Helmingham Park, Suffolk
Lπ:146x185:signed:Purchased 1985

T04012 A Dell, Helmingham Park, Suffolk
Lπ:146x185:signed:Purchased 1985

T04013 A Heath (published 1831)
Lπ:141x190:signed:Purchased 1985

T04014 A Heath (published 1831)
Lπ:142x190:signed:Purchased 1985

T04015 A Heath
Lπ:143x190:signed:Purchased 1985

T04016 A Heath
Lπ:142x189:signed:Purchased 1985

T04017 A Heath
Lπ:141x190:signed:Purchased 1985

T04018 Yarmouth, Norfolk (published 1832)
Lπ:140x220:signed:Purchased 1985

T04019 Yarmouth, Norfolk
Lπ:140x220:signed:Purchased 1985

T04020 Yarmouth, Norfolk
Lπ:140x220:signed:Purchased 1985

T04021 A Seabeach (published 1830)
Lπ:142x220:signed:Purchased 1985

T04022 A Seabeach (published 1830)
Lπ:142x221:signed:Purchased 1985

T04023 A Seabeach
Lπ:142x220:signed:Purchased 1985

T04024 A Seabeach
Lπ:142x220:signed:Purchased 1985

T04025 Mill Stream (published 1831)
Lπ:141x190:signed:Purchased 1985

T04026 Mill Stream
Lπ:141x290:signed:Purchased 1985

T04027 Mill Stream
Lπ:141x190:signed:Purchased 1985

T04028 Mill Stream
Lπ:141x189:signed:Purchased 1985

T04029 A Lock on the Stour, Suffolk (published 1831)
Lπ:145x180:signed:Purchased 1985

T04030 A Lock on the Stour, Suffolk
Lπ:145x179:signed:Purchased 1985

T04031 A Lock on the Stour, Suffolk
Lπ:145x180:signed:Purchased 1985

T04032 A Lock on the Stour, Suffolk
Lπ:145x179:signed:Purchased 1985

T04033 Old Sarum (first plate) (published 1830)
Lπ:141x215:signed:Purchased 1985

T04034 Old Sarum (first plate)
Lπ:140x215:signed:Purchased 1985

T04035 Old Sarum (second plate) (published 1833)
Lπ:150x223:signed:Purchased 1985

T04036 Old Sarum (second plate)
Lπ:150x224:signed:Purchased 1985

T04037 A Summerland (published 1831)
Lπ:151x227:signed:Purchased 1985

T04038 A Summerland
Lπ:151x227:signed:Purchased 1985

T04039 A Summerland
Lπ:150x226:signed:Purchased 1985

T04040 Stoke by Neyland, Suffolk (published 1830)
Lπ:145x219:signed:Purchased 1985

T04041 Stoke by Neyland, Suffolk
Lπ:144x220:signed:Purchased 1985

T04042 Stoke by Neyland, Suffolk
Lπ:145x219:signed:Purchased 1985

T04043 A Mill (published 1830)
Lπ:143x215:signed:Purchased 1985

T04044 A Mill
Lπ:143x215:signed:Purchased 1985

T04045 A Mill
Lπ:143x215:signed:Purchased 1985

T04046 A Mill
Lπ:143x215:signed:Purchased 1985

T04047 A Mill (published 1833)
Lπ:142x216:signed:Purchased 1985

T04048 Weymouth Bay, Dorsetshire (published 1830)
Lπ:144x182:signed:Purchased 1985

T04049 Weymouth Bay, Dorsetshire
Lπ:144x182:signed:Purchased 1985

T04050 Weymouth Bay, Dorsetshire
Lπ:144x183:signed:Purchased 1985

T04051 Weymouth Bay, Dorsetshire
Lπ:144x182:signed:Purchased 1985

T04052 Summer, Afternoon - After a Shower (published 1831)
Lπ:143x190:signed:Purchased 1985

T04053 Summer, Afternoon - After a Shower
Lπ:142x189:signed:Purchased 1985

T04054 Summer, Afternoon - After a Shower
Lπ:143x188:signed:Purchased 1985

T04055 The Glebe Farm (published 1832)
Lπ:146x224:signed:Purchased 1985

T04056 The Glebe Farm
Lπ:147x225:signed:Purchased 1985

T04057 The Glebe Farm
Lπ:147x225:signed:Purchased 1985

T04058 Hadleigh Castle near the Nore (published 1832)
Lπ:152x229:signed:Purchased 1985

T04059 Hadleigh Castle near the Nore
Lπ:153x230:signed:Purchased 1985

T04060 Hadleigh Castle near the Nore
Lπ:152x230:signed:Purchased 1985

T04061 Vignette: Hampstead Heath, Middlesex (1831 or 2)
Lπ:92x154:signed:Purchased 1985

T04062 Vignette: Hampstead Heath, Middlesex (published 1832)
Lπ:91x153:signed:Purchased 1985

T04063 Vignette: Hampstead Heath, Middlesex (published 1845)
Lπ:91x154:signed:Purchased 1985

English Landscape Scenery, ed. H.G. Bohn
(T04064-T04013; complete group)

T04064 Frontispiece: East Bergholt, Suffolk (published 1855)
Lπ:139x187:signed:Purchased 1985

T04065 Spring (published 1855)
Lπ:127x245:signed:Purchased 1985

T04066 A Dell, Helmingham Park, Suffolk (published 1855)
Lπ:145x185:signed:Purchased 1985

T04067 Flatford Mill (published 1855)
Lπ:141x180:signed:Purchased 1985

T04068 Porch of the Church at East Bergholt, Suffolk (published 1855)
Lπ:189x155:signed:Purchased 1985

T04069 Willy Lott's House (published 1855)
Lπ:172x153:signed:Purchased 1985

T04070 Mill Stream (published 1855)
Lπ:140x190:signed:Purchased 1985

T04071 Hadleigh Castle near the Nore (published 1855)
Lπ:151x230:signed:Purchased 1985

T04072 Cornfields near Brighton (published 1855)
Lπ:130x198:signed:Purchased 1985

T04073 Hampstead Heath, Harrow in the Distance (published 1855)
Lπ:141x180:signed:Purchased 1985

T04074 A Mill near Brighton (published 1855)
Lπ:146x115:signed:Purchased 1985

T04075 View on the River Stour (published 1855)
Lπ:139x188:signed:Purchased 1985

T04076 Hampstead Heath (published 1855)
Lπ:140x182:signed:Purchased 1985

T04077 River Stour, Suffolk (published 1855)
Lπ:143x224:signed:Purchased 1985

T04078 Salisbury Cathedral from the Meadows (published 1855)
Lπ:139x215:signed:Purchased 1985

T04079 Yarmouth, Norfolk (published 1855)
Lπ:140x221:signed:Purchased 1985

T04080 Opening of Waterloo Bridge (published 1855)
Lπ:136x221:signed:Purchased 1985

T04081 A Lock on the Stour, Suffolk (published 1855)
Lπ:144x180:signed:Purchased 1985

T04082 Summer, Afternoon - After a Shower (published 1855)
Lπ:141x189:signed:Purchased 1985

T04083 The Glebe Farm (published 1855)
Lπ:146x225:signed:Purchased 1985

T04084 Gillingham Mill, Dorsetshire (published 1855)
Lπ:186x154:signed:Purchased 1985

T04085 A Heath (published 1855)
Lπ:140x190:signed:Purchased 1985

T04086 A Mill (published 1855)
Lπ:142x215:signed:Purchased 1985

T04087 Autumnal Sun Set (published 1855)
Lπ:130x243:signed:Purchased 1985

T04088 Summer Evening (published 1855)
Lπ:140x217:signed:Purchased 1985

T04089 A Summerland (published 1855)
Lπ:150x227:signed:Purchased 1985

T04090 Jaques and the Wounded Stag (published 1855)
Lπ:132x189:signed:Purchased 1985

T04091 View on the Orwell near Ipswich (published 1855)
Lπ:142x182:signed:Purchased 1985

T04092 Old Sarum (second plate) (published 1855)
Iπ:149x223:signed:Purchased 1985

T04093 Sir Richard Steele's Cottage, Hampstead Road
(published 1855)
Iπ:132x187:signed:Purchased 1985

T04094 Castle Acre Priory (published 1855)
Iπ:145x227:signed:Purchased 1985

T04095 Summer Morning (published 1855)
Iπ:140x219:signed:Purchased 1985

T04096 A Cottage in a Cornfield (published 1855)
Iπ:190x156:signed:Purchased 1985

T04097 Mill near Colchester (published 1855)
Iπ:134x187:signed:Purchased 1985

T04098 Weymouth Bay, Dorsetshire (published 1855)
Iπ:143x183:signed:Purchased 1985

T04099 Noon (published 1855)
Iπ:139x221:signed:Purchased 1985

T04100 Stonehenge (published 1855)
Iπ:131x198:signed:Purchased 1985

T04101 A Seabeach (published 1855)
Iπ:140x220:signed:Purchased 1985

T04102 Arundel Mill and Castle (published 1855)
Iπ:132x189:signed:Purchased 1985

T04103 Stoke by Neyland, Suffolk (published 1855)
Iπ:143x220:signed:Purchased 1985

CONSTABLE, Lionel Bicknell 1828-1887
British Collection

N02649 Near Stoke-by-Nayland (circa 1850)
Oc:356x445:Bequeathed by George Salting 1910

N02662 Leathes Water (Thirlmere) (circa 1850)
Oπ:244x394:Bequeathed by George Salting 1910

T01258 Near Stoke-by-Nayland (circa 1850)
Dπ:117x175:Purchased 1970

CONSTANT (Constant A. Nieuwenhuys) born 1920
Modern Collection
Tate Gallery Archive holds material concerning this artist

T03705 After Us, Liberty (1949)
Après Nous La Liberté
Oc:395x66:signed:Purchased 1983

For Jorn (P03241-P03255; complete group; mixed group)
Pour Jorn

P03245 [no title] (1975-6)
CLπ:645x502:signed:Presented by the Asger Jorn
Foundation 1978

COOK, Barrie born 1929
Modern Collection
Tate Gallery Archive holds material concerning this artist

T01576 Painting (1970)
ADc:2438x3042:Presented by E.J. Power through the
Friends of the Tate Gallery 1972

COOK, Thomas - see HOGARTH, William, prints after

COOKE, Edward William 1811-1880
British Collection

N00447 Dutch Boats in a Calm (1843)
Ow:422x686:signed:Presented by Robert Vernon 1847

N00448 Undercliff Cave, Ventnor (exhibited 1836)
Oc:419x521:Presented by Robert Vernon 1847

N01780 Canal of the Giudecca, Venice (1867)
Oc:902x1397:signed:Bequeathed by H.S. Ashbee 1900

N01802 Wier's Paper Mill, near Oxford (1835-42)
Ow:241x343:Bequeathed by Henry Vaughan 1900

N01968 Boat, near Venice (1858)
Oc:279x400:Bequeathed by C. Fraser 1905

COOPER, Abraham 1787-1868
British Collection

N05977 Draught Horses (1828)
Oc:705x908:signed:Presented by Mr and Mrs G.F.
Jerdein 1951

T03422 The Day Family (1838)
Oc:968x1273:signed:Bequeathed by Mrs F. Ambrose
Clark through the British Sporting Art Trust 1982

COOPER, Austin 1890-1964
Modern Collection

T00572 Abstraction 199/62 (1951-62)
WVb:419x483:signed:Presented by the Calouste
Gulbenkian Foundation 1963

T00573 Abstraction 200/62 (1957-62)
WVb:400x473:signed:Presented by the Calouste
Gulbenkian Foundation 1963

T00574 Congeries B/4/7 (1958)
WVb:248x318:signed:Presented by the Calouste
Gulbenkian Foundation 1963

COOPER, Gerald 1899-1971
Modern Collection
Tate Gallery Archive holds material concerning this artist

School Prints (P01698-P01727; complete group; mixed
group)

P01700 Striped Lily (1946)
CLπ:762x498:signed:Presented by Patrick Seale Prints
1975

COOPER, Thomas Sidney 1803-1902
British Collection

N00435 Farm Yard, Milking Time (exhibited 1834)
Oc:965x1333:signed:Presented by Robert Vernon 1847

N00436 Among Cumberland Mountains - Mist Clearing (1847)
Oc:597x889:signed:Presented by Robert Vernon 1847

N01800 Landscape and Cattle (1854)
Ow:292x406:signed:Bequeathed by Henry Vaughan 1900

N01976 A Cow and Two Sheep (1860)
Wπ:216x298:signed:Bequeathed by C. Fraser 1905

COOPER, Thomas Sidney and LEE, Frederick Richard - see LEE, Frederick Richard and COOPER, Thomas Sidney

COPLEY, John Singleton 1738-1815
British Collection
Tate Gallery Archive holds material concerning this artist

N00100 The Collapse of the Earl of Chatham in the House of
Lords, 7 July 1778 (1779-80)
Oc:2286x3073:Presented by the Earl of Liverpool 1830

N00733 The Death of Major Peirson, 6 January 1781 (1783)
Oc:2515x3658:Purchased 1864

N00787 The Siege and Relief of Gibraltar, 13 September 1782;
?replica (circa 1783)
Oc:1346x1899:Purchased 1868

N01072 Study for 'The Collapse of the Earl of Chatham' (circa
1779)
Oc:635x768:Purchased 1879

N01073 Study for 'The Collapse of the Earl of Chatham' (circa
1779)
Oc:711x1029:Purchased 1879

N04984 Study for 'The Death of Major Peirson' (circa 1783)
Dπ:356x575:Purchased 1939

T02386 Portrait of Mrs Gill (circa 1770-1)
Oc:1280x1022:Presented by Mr and Mrs H.J. Heinz II
1979

COPLEY, William N. born 1919
Modern Collection

T00442 Place de l'Opéra (1956)
Oc:1159x810:Presented by Sir Roland Penrose 1961

CORBET, Matthew Ridley 1850-1902
British Collection

N01592 Morning Glory (1893-4)
Oc:1245x2032:signed:Presented by the Trustees of the
Chantrey Bequest 1894

N01899 Val d'Arno: Evening (exhibited 1901)
Oc:908x2089:signed:Presented by the Trustees of the
Chantrey Bequest 1901

CORBUSIER - see LE CORBUSIER

CORDERY, Don born 1942
Modern Collection

P06092 Spectacled Owl (1973)
CLπ:613x454:signed:Presented by Curwen Studio
through the Institute of Contemporary Prints 1975

P06093 Two Owls (1974-5)
CLπ:508x635:signed:Presented by Curwen Studio
through the Institute of Contemporary Prints 1975

P06771 Goshawk (1977)
CLπ:502x394:signed:Presented by Curwen Studio 1978

CORINTH, Lovis 1858-1925
Modern Collection

N04831 The Temptation of St Anthony after Gustave Flaubert
(1908)
Die Versuchung des heil. Antonius nach Gustave Flaubert
Oc:1353x2003:signed:Presented by Erich Goeritz 1936

CORKER, Douglas born 1939
Modern Collection

P05502 Untitled (1979)
MNπ:648x483:signed:Presented by Rose and Chris
Prater 1979

CORNEILLE, Guillaume born 1922
Modern Collection

For Jorn (P03241-P03255; complete group; mixed group)
Pour Jorn
P03246 [no title] (1975-6)
CLπ:756x546:signed:Presented by the Asger Jorn
Foundation 1978

CORNELL, Joseph 1903-1972
Modern Collection

T01846 Giuditta Pasta (Dedicace) (1950)
Sgwv:305x457x102:signed:Purchased 1974

attributed to
COSWAY, Richard 1742-1821
British Collection

T04114 A Lady (? Harriet Mellon) as a Sibyl (circa 1805)
Ow:764x624:Purchased 1985

COTES, Francis 1726-1770
British Collection

N01281 Mrs Brocas (?)
Oc:743x622:Presented by George Holt 1889

N01943 Paul Sandby (1761)
Oc:1251x1003:signed:Bequeathed by W.A. Sandby 1904

N04387 A Gentleman with a Cane (1765 or 69)
Oc:908x705:signed:Presented by the National Art
Collections Fund 1928

N04689 Portrait of a Lady (1768)
Oc:1267x1016:signed:Bequeathed by Sir Edward Stern
1933

T03251 Anna Maria Astley, Aged Seven, and her Brother
Edward, Aged Five and a Half (1767)
Oc:2000x1603:signed:Purchased 1981

COTMAN, John Sell 1782-1842
British Collection
Tate Gallery Archive holds material concerning this artist

N03327 West View of the Castle at Falaise (1818)
WDπ:222x356:Presented by Sir Jeremiah Colman Bt
through the National Art Collections Fund 1918

N03328 Château Gaillard (1818-19)
WDπ:260x419:signed:Presented by Sir Jeremiah Colman
Bt through the National Art Collections Fund 1918

N03329 North-West View of the Castle at Falaise (1818)
WDπ:194x387:signed:Presented by Sir Jeremiah Colman
Bt through the National Art Collections Fund 1918

N03330 Crypt in the Church of St Gervais, Rouen (1819)
WDπ:184x276:signed:Presented by Sir Jeremiah Colman
Bt through the National Art Collections Fund 1918

N03331 North-West View of the Tower of the Church of Gravelle,
Near Havre de Grace (1818)
WDπ:225x171:signed:Presented by Sir Jeremiah Colman
Bt through the National Art Collections Fund 1918

N03332 Sculpture in the Church of St Peter, Caen (1821)
WDπ:238x178:signed:Presented by Sir Jeremiah Colman
Bt through the National Art Collections Fund 1918

N03572 Duncombe Park (circa 1806-8)
Oπ:416x279:Purchased 1921

N03632 The Drop Gate (circa 1826)
Oc:349x260:Presented by Sir William Lancaster 1922

N03633 Distant View of Greta Bridge from Mortham Wood
(circa 1805)
Wπ:260x394:Presented by Leonard Bolingbroke 1922

N03634 Durham (circa 1805)
WDπ:235x254:Presented by Mrs Helen Hawksley 1922

N03635 On the Greta (circa 1805)
WDπ:330x260:Presented by Mrs Helen Hawksley 1922

N03667 Crowland Abbey (circa 1804)
Wπ:216x159:Purchased 1922

N04218 Mountain Lake (circa 1804)
Wπ:162x283:Presented by Wyndham Tryon 1926

N04785 Seashore with Boats (circa 1808)
Ob:283x410:Purchased 1935

N05636 Norwich Market-Place (circa 1806)
Wπ:406x648:signed:Presented by Francis E. Halsey 1945

T00969 Harlech Castle (circa 1800-2)
Wπ:267x429:signed:Presented by the National Art
Collections Fund (Herbert Powell Bequest) 1967

T00970 Llanthony Abbey (1801)
Wπ:438x330:signed:Presented by the National Art
Collections Fund (Herbert Powell Bequest) 1967

T00971 Ruins and Houses, North Wales (circa 1800-2)
Wπ:251x356:Presented by the National Art Collections
Fund (Herbert Powell Bequest) 1967

T00972 The Ramparts, Domfront (circa 1820)
DWπ:222x321:Presented by the National Art Collections
Fund (Herbert Powell Bequest) 1967

T00973 Rievaulx Abbey (1803)
Dπ:371x270:signed:Presented by the National Art
Collections Fund (Herbert Powell Bequest) 1967

attributed to
COTMAN, John Sell 1782-1842
British Collection

N01111 Wherries on Breydon (circa 1808)
Oc:546x787:Purchased 1882

manner of
COTMAN, John Sell 1782-1842
British Collection

N01458 A Galiot in a Gale
Oc:1092x1384:Purchased 1895

COTTINGHAM, Robert born 1935
Modern Collection

Landfall Set (P07641-P07643; complete group)
P07641 Carl's (1977)
CLπ:257x261:signed:Purchased 1982

P07642 Black Girl (1980)
CLπ:266x266:signed:Purchased 1982

P07643 Frankfurters (1980)
CLπ:265x267:signed:Purchased 1982

COUDERC, G. born 1900
Modern Collection

School Prints (P01698-P01727; complete group; mixed
group)
P01701 Cargo Ship in Sete (1946-9)
CLπ:438x692:signed:Presented by Patrick Seale Prints
1975

COWIE, James 1886-1956
Modern Collection

T03549 An Outdoor School of Painting (1938-41)
Oc:864x1651:signed:Purchased 1983

COWPER, Frank Cadogan 1877-1958
British Collection

N01961 St Agnes in Prison Receiving from Heaven the 'Shining
White Garment' (1905)
Oc:743x451:signed:Presented by the Trustees of the
Chantrey Bequest 1905

N02973 Lucretia Borgia Reigns in the Vatican in the Absence of
Pope Alexander VI (1908-14)
Oc:2210x1537:Presented by the Trustees of the Chantrey
Bequest 1914

COX, David 1783-1859
British Collection

N01734 Harlech Castle, Wales (?)
Wπ:178x279:Presented by Miss Julia Emily Gordon 1888

N01735 A Harbour
Wπ:76x229:Presented by Miss Julia Emily Gordon 1888

N01736 Beckenham Church, Kent (circa 1842)
Wπ:229x279:Bequeathed by Miss Julia Emily Gordon
1896

N02665 Moorland Road (1851)
Oc:273x356:signed:Bequeathed by George Salting 1910

N02666 A Windy Day (1850)
Oc:267x359:signed:Bequeathed by George Salting 1910

N02667 The Road across the Common (1853)
Oc:190x241:signed:Bequeathed by George Salting 1910

N02668 River Scene with Boys Fishing
Ow:190x248:Bequeathed by George Salting 1910

N04301 Calais: Street Scene with Lighthouse
WDπ:162x254:Bequeathed by J.R. Holliday 1927

N04302 Near the Pont d'Arcole, Paris (1829)
WDπ:244x368:Bequeathed by J.R. Holliday 1927

N04303 Calais: Hôtel de Guise (1829 or 1832)
WDπ:162x216:Bequeathed by J.R. Holliday 1927

N04304 Westminster from Battersea
Wb:133x241:Bequeathed by J.R. Holliday 1927

N04305 Caernarvon Castle with Boats
Wπ:149x298:Bequeathed by J.R. Holliday 1927

N04306 Buildings on the Banks of the Thames
Wπ:143x305:Bequeathed by J.R. Holliday 1927

N04307 Still Life
Wπ:171x210:Bequeathed by J.R. Holliday 1927

N04308 Windmill
Wb:225x159:Bequeathed by J.R. Holliday 1927

N04310 Houses at Dulwich
Wπ:178x152:Bequeathed by J.R. Holliday 1927

N04311 Landscape with Salmon Traps
DWπ:330x530:Bequeathed by J.R. Holliday 1927

N04312 Coast Scene. Verso: Coast Scene
WDπ:273x387:Bequeathed by J.R. Holliday 1927

N04313 A Ship. Verso: Open Landscape
Wπ:152x200:Bequeathed by J.R. Holliday 1927

N04844 A Welsh Funeral, Bettws-y-Coed (circa 1845-50)
Oπ:540x749:signed:Purchased 1936

N05616 Boy Opening Gate for Sheep
Wπ:267x362:Bequeathed by Travers Buxton 1945

N05617 Waiting for the Ferry Boat (circa 1835)
Wπ:197x292:Bequeathed by Travers Buxton 1945

T00974 A Mountain Landscape
Wπ:356x524:signed:Presented by the National Art
Collections Fund (Herbert Powell Bequest) 1967

T00975 A River Scene
Wπ:175x165:Presented by the National Art Collections
Fund (Herbert Powell Bequest) 1967

T00976 A Country Scene
Wπ:251x197:Presented by the National Art Collections
Fund (Herbert Powell Bequest) 1967

T00977 Tour d'Horloge, Rouen (1829)
WDπ:343x257:Presented by the National Art Collections
Fund (Herbert Powell Bequest) 1967

T04130 Rhyl Sands (circa 1854)
Oc:454x630:Purchased with assistance from the Friends
of the Tate Gallery 1985

A00168 Windmill. Verso: Foliage (?)
Wπ:102x178:Bequeathed by J.R. Holliday 1927

A00169 Horse and Barge. Verso: tracing of horse from recto
WDπ:102x140:Bequeathed by J.R. Holliday 1927

A00170 Horse's Head
WDπ:149x83:Bequeathed by J.R. Holliday 1927

A00171 Head and Shoulders of a Horse
Wπ:152x73:Bequeathed by J.R. Holliday 1927

A00172 Two Naval Pensioners with Shipping Behind
Wπ:124x79:Bequeathed by J.R. Holliday 1927

A00173 Seated Naval Pensioner. Verso: indecipherable sketch
Wπ:83x67:Bequeathed by J.R. Holliday 1927

A00174 Two Naval Pensioners. Verso: traces of pencil drawing
Dπ:83x79:Bequeathed by J.R. Holliday 1927

A00175 Naval Pensioner
WDπ:86x48:Bequeathed by J.R. Holliday 1927

A00176 Bridge and Castle
Wπ:76x114:Bequeathed by J.R. Holliday 1927

A00177 Caernarvon Castle
Wπ:86x222:Bequeathed by J.R. Holliday 1927

A00178 Landscape
Wπ:105x143:Bequeathed by J.R. Holliday 1927

A00179 Landscape with Flock of Sheep
Wπ:108x162:Bequeathed by J.R. Holliday 1927

A00180 Open Landscape
Wπ:137x184:Bequeathed by J.R. Holliday 1927

A00181 A Bridge
Wπ:102x152:Bequeathed by J.R. Holliday 1927

A00182 Landscape with Windmill and Man Ploughing
Wπ:105x165:Bequeathed by J.R. Holliday 1927

A00183 Landscape with Windmill
Wπ:108x156:Bequeathed by J.R. Holliday 1927

A00184 Landscape
WDπ:63x92:Bequeathed by J.R. Holliday 1927

A00185 Sketch for 'Crossing Lancaster Sands'
DWπ:63x95:Bequeathed by J.R. Holliday 1927

A00186 Costume Study: Peasant Woman
WDπ:133x54:Bequeathed by J.R. Holliday 1927

A00187 Costume Study: Woman with Umbrella. Verso: erased
figure study
Wπ:194x137:Bequeathed by J.R. Holliday 1927

A00188 Studies of Farm Hands and a Coat on a Fence. Verso:
tracing of farm boy from recto
Wπ:98x190:Bequeathed by J.R. Holliday 1927

A00189 Four Figure Studies. Verso: Landscape with Water
WDπ:146x171:Bequeathed by J.R. Holliday 1927

COX, Stephen born 1946
Modern Collection
Tate Gallery Archive holds material concerning this artist

T03356 Tondo: We Must Always Turn South (1981)
Rs:667x70:Purchased 1982

T03794 Gethsemane (1982)
Rs:2297x5994x90:Purchased 1983

T05506 Study for Etruscan (1985)
Dπ:615x420, 757x1013, 615x420:signed:Presented by
Weltkunst Foundation 1988

T05507 Study for Etruscan (1985)
Dπ:585x440, 757x1013, 585x440:signed:Presented by
Weltkunst Foundation 1988

T05508 Study for Ganepathi and Devi (1988)
DPπ:384x557:signed:Presented by Weltkunst Foundation
1988

T05509 Torso Untitled (1987)
Pπ:1510x1070:signed:Presented by Weltkunst
Foundation 1988

T05510 Crowned Torso (1988)
DPπ:1945x1077:signed:Presented by Weltkunst
Foundation 1988

T05511 Untitled (1977)
Wπ:1010x620:signed:Presented by the artist 1988

T05512 Untitled (1977)
Wπ:1010x620:signed:Presented by the artist 1988

T05513 Untitled (1977)
Wπ:1010x620:signed:Presented by the artist 1988

T05514 Untitled (1977)
Wπ:1010x620:signed:Presented by the artist 1988

T05720 Drawing for 'Gethsemane' (1981-2)
20 Pπ:3000x6000:signed:Purchased 1989

COXON, Raymond born 1896
Modern Collection
Tate Gallery Archive holds material concerning this artist

N04968 Mountain Landscape (1938)
Oc:914x1524:signed:Presented by Mrs Hazel McKinley
1938

T01062 Blue Bird (1968)
Oc:1521x1013:signed:Presented by the Trustees of the
Chantrey Bequest 1968

COZENS, Alexander 1717-1786
British Collection
Tate Gallery Archive holds material concerning this artist

N01359 Landscape with Fir Trees
WDπ:133x171:signed:Presented by E.H. Coles 1923

N04535 Classical Landscape
WDπ:489x660:Presented by A.E. Anderson 1930

T00978 A Hilly Country
Wπ:219x302:Presented by the National Art Collections
Fund (Herbert Powell Bequest) 1967

T00979 The Rhône
Wπ:229x394:Presented by the National Art Collections
Fund (Herbert Powell Bequest) 1967

T00980 A Lake (1763)
DWπ:133x175:signed:Presented by the National Art
Collections Fund (Herbert Powell Bequest) 1967

T00981 Landscape (1763)
DWπ:133x175:signed:Presented by the National Art
Collections Fund (Herbert Powell Bequest) 1967

T01949 Before Storm (circa 1770)
Oπ:241x314:Purchased 1975

Plates 1-16 ('blot' landscapes) for 'A New Method of Assisting the Invention in Drawing Original Compositions of Landscape' (T03169-T03184; complete group)

T03169 Plate 1 (circa 1785)
Iπ:240x314:Purchased 1980

T03170 Plate 2 (circa 1785)
Iπ:240x314:Purchased 1980

T03171 Plate 3 (circa 1785)
Iπ:240x314:Purchased 1980

T03172 Plate 4 (circa 1785)
Iπ:239x312:Purchased 1980

T03173 Plate 5 (circa 1785)
Iπ:239x313:Purchased 1980

T03174 Plate 6 (circa 1785)
Iπ:240x315:Purchased 1980

T03175 Plate 7 (circa 1785)
Iπ:240x314:Purchased 1980

T03176 Plate 8 (circa 1785)
Iπ:240x314:Purchased 1980

T03177 Plate 9 (circa 1785)
Iπ:240x315:Purchased 1980

T03178 Plate 10 (circa 1785)
Iπ:240x312:Purchased 1980

T03179 Plate 11 (circa 1785)
Iπ:240x316:Purchased 1980

T03180 Plate 12 (circa 1785)
Iπ:240x314:Purchased 1980

T03181 Plate 13 (circa 1785)
Iπ:240x315:Purchased 1980

T03182 Plate 14 (circa 1785)
Iπ:240x314:Purchased 1980

T03183 Plate 15 (circa 1785)
Iπ:237x311:Purchased 1980

T03184 Plate 16 (circa 1785)
Iπ:240x313:Purchased 1980

COZENS, John Robert 1752-1797
British Collection
Tate Gallery Archive holds material concerning this artist

N04408 Lake of Albano and Castel Gandolfo (circa 1783-8)
Wπ:489x679:signed:Presented by A.E. Anderson in memory of his brother Frank through the National Art Collections Fund 1928

N05807 Lake Nemi (circa 1783-8)
Wπ:445x632:Presented by Miss Evelyn Brooke 1947

T00982 Lake Nemi
Wπ:254x365:Presented by the National Art Collections Fund (Herbert Powell Bequest) 1967

T00983 Padua (after 1782)
Wπ:260x371:Presented by the National Art Collections Fund (Herbert Powell Bequest) 1967

T00984 The Gulf of Salerno (circa 1790)
Wπ:371x537:signed:Presented by the National Art Collections Fund (Herbert Powell Bequest) 1967

T00985 The Lake of Geneva (?) (?1776)
DWπ:229x359:Presented by the National Art Collections Fund (Herbert Powell Bequest) 1967

CRAGG, Tony born 1949
Modern Collection
Tate Gallery Archive holds material concerning this artist

T03347 Britain Seen from the North (1981)
RV:3696x6985, 1702x584:Purchased 1982

T03791 Axehead (1982)
Swv:1092x3931x4902:Purchased 1983

T04866 Mineral Vein (1986)
SV:2110x1195x815:Purchased 1986

T04903 Raleigh (1986)
Sms:1938x3264x3417:Purchased 1987

T05519 On the Savannah (1988)
Sz:2250x4000x3000:Purchased 1988

P77288 Six Bottles Large, State 1 (1988)
Iπ:371x612:signed:Purchased 1989

P77289 Laboratory Still Life 1, State 1 (1988)
Iπ:300x347:signed:Purchased 1989

P77290 Laboratory Still Life 2, State 1 (1988)
Iπ:292x904:signed:Purchased 1989

P77291 Laboratory Still Life 3 (1988)
Iπ:301x351:signed:Purchased 1989

P77292 Laboratory Still Life 4 (1988)
Iπ:461x485:signed:Purchased 1989

CRAIG, Frank 1874-1918
British Collection

N02071 The Heretic (1906)
Oc:813x1473:signed:Presented by the Trustees of the Chantrey Bequest 1906

CRAIG-MARTIN, Michael born 1941
Modern Collection
Tate Gallery Archive holds material concerning this artist

T01153 4 Identical Boxes with Lids Reversed (1969)
SAw:610x2438x914:Purchased 1969

T01158 Drawings of '4 Identical Boxes with Lids Reversed' (1969)
Aπ:521x635:signed:Purchased 1969

T01495 4 Complete Clipboard Sets: 1. Clipboard 2. Sheet of Paper 3. Pencil 4. Written Title 5. Eraser (1971)
Dv:768x2556:Purchased 1971

T01764 Conviction (1973)
Rga:533x4115:Purchased 1973

T03102 Reading with Globe (1980)
DA, DAa::Purchased 1980

CRANCH, John 1751-1821
British Collection

T01048 Monks Merrymaking (circa 1804)
Ow:162x210:signed:Purchased 1968

CRANE, Walter 1845-1915
British Collection
Tate Gallery Archive holds material concerning this artist

N02920 The Renaissance of Venus (1877)
Tc:1384x1841:signed:Presented by Mrs Watts by the wish of the late George Frederic Watts 1913

CRAWFORD, Susan born 1941
Modern Collection

P06094 Horse and Rider (1973)
CLπ:578x781:signed:Presented by Curwen Studio through the Institute of Contemporary Prints 1975

CRAWHALL, Joseph 1861-1913
British Collection
Tate Gallery Archive holds material concerning this artist

N03680 The Dove (circa 1895)
Gf:241x305:signed:Purchased 1982

CRAXTON, John born 1922
Modern Collection
Tate Gallery Archive holds material concerning this artist

T00117 Hotel by the Sea (1946)
Oc:495x610:signed:Purchased 1957

T03836 Dreamer in Landscape (1942)
Dπb:548x762:signed:Purchased 1984

T03837 Dark Landscape (1944-5)
Ob:546x705:signed:Purchased 1984

T03838 Pastoral for P.W. (1948)
Oc:2045x2626:signed:Purchased 1984

CREE, Janet born 1910
Modern Collection
Tate Gallery Archive holds material concerning this artist

N04707 The Oriental Portrait (1932)
Tc:305x225:Presented by the Trustees of the Chantrey Bequest 1933

CRESWICK, Thomas 1811-1869
British Collection

N00429 The Stile (1839)
Ow:610x495:signed:Presented by Robert Vernon 1847

N01785 The Ford
Oc:521x698:signed:Bequeathed by Henry Vaughan 1900

CRIPPA, Roberto 1921-1972
Modern Collection

T00087 Aurora Borealis (1952)
Aurora Boreale
Oc:600x702:Purchased 1956

CRISTALL, Joshua 1767-1847
British Collection

T01851 Beach Scene, Hastings (circa 1808)
Wπ:184x302:signed:Purchased 1974

T01852 Arcadian Landscape (1830)
WDπ:254x219:signed:Purchased 1974

after
CRISTALL, Joshua 1767-1847
British Collection

Picturesque Views on the Southern Coast of England
(T05218-T05463; complete group; mixed group)
T05305 Bonchurch, Isle of Wight, Hampshire (1816)
Iπ:131x232:Purchased 1988

T05306 Bonchurch, Isle of Wight, Hampshire (1816)
Iπ:131x233:Purchased 1988

CRITCHLOW, Keith born 1933
Modern Collection

P06773 Nasr (Victory) (1976)
CLπ:635x508:Presented by Curwen Studio 1978

CROME, John 1768-1821
British Collection
Tate Gallery Archive holds material concerning this artist

N00689 Mousehold Heath, Norwich (circa 1818-20)
Oc:1099x1810:Purchased 1863

N00897 A View of Chapel-Fields, Norwich
Oc:737x1041:Bequeathed by H.F. Chorley 1872

N00926 A Windmill near Norwich (circa 1816)
Ow:1111x914:Purchased 1875

N01037 Slate Quarries (circa 1802-5)
Oc:1238x1587:Purchased 1878

N02645 Moonrise on the Yare (?) (circa 1811-16)
Oc:711x1111:Bequeathed by George Salting 1910

N02674 The Poringland Oak (circa 1818-20)
Oc:1251x1003:Purchased 1910

N03211 Yarmouth Jetty
Wπ:89x210:Bequeathed by Miss Harriet Higginson 1917

N05361 Yarmouth Harbour - Evening (circa 1817)
Oc:406x660:Bequeathed by S. Arthur Peto 1942

after
CROME, John 1768-1821
British Collection

N01504 Hingham Lane Scene, Norfolk
Oc:622x819:Presented by Sir Henry Tate 1894

manner of
CROME, John 1768-1821
British Collection

N01831 Brathay Bridge, Westmorland (?)
Oc:470x667:Bequeathed by Henry Vaughan 1900

N02644 Heath Scene
Ow:546x724:Bequeathed by George Salting 1910

N05791 View on the Maas
Oc:533x902:Presented by Frederick John Nettlefold 1947

CROME, John Berney 1794-1842
British Collection

N02643 Moonlight
Oc:254x330:Bequeathed by George Salting 1910

CROTTI, Jean 1878-1958
Modern Collection

T02315 Portrait of Edison (1920)
Portrait d'Edison
DGWπ:489x645:signed:Purchased 1978

CRUIKSHANK, George 1792-1878
British Collection

N00795 The Worship of Bacchus (1860-2)
Oc:2375x4039:Presented by R.E. Lofft and friends 1869

CRUIKSHANK, George and MOTTRAM, Charles 1792-1878, 1807-1876
British Collection

T02268   Worship of Bacchus (published 1864)
Lπ:648x1051:Purchased 1978

CRUTCHFIELD, William born 1932
Modern Collection

P04153   Alphabet Spire II (1972)
CNπ:616x921:signed:Presented by Rose and Chris Prater
through the Institute of Contemporary Prints 1975

P04154   Beached City (1972)
CNπ:651x972:signed:Presented by Rose and Chris Prater
through the Institute of Contemporary Prints 1975

P04155   Help II (1972)
CNπ:765x651:signed:Presented by Rose and Chris Prater
through the Institute of Contemporary Prints 1975

P04156   Third City of Troy (1972)
CNπ:943x635:signed:Presented by Rose and Chris Prater
through the Institute of Contemporary Prints 1975

CRUZ-DIEZ, Carlos born 1923
Modern Collection

T02094   Physichromie No. 123 (1963)
ARm:400x230x40:signed:Presented by the artist 1976

T03715   Physichromie No. 123 (1964)
RVb:400x232x41:Transferred from the Victoria & Albert
Museum 1983

CUCCHI, Enzo born 1949
Modern Collection

P77332   A Dark Image (1982)
Un immagine oscura
INπ:870x1380:Purchased 1989

CUIXART, Modestos born 1925
Modern Collection

P08004   Untitled (1977)
CLπ:222x241:signed:Transferred from the Library 1977

CUMBERLAND, George 1754-1849
British Collection

T02304   Inside the Peak Cavern, Castleton, Derbyshire (circa
1820)
Wπ:146x219:Presented by William Drummond 1978

CUNDALL, Charles 1890-1971
Modern Collection
Tate Gallery Archive holds material concerning this artist

N04700   Bank Holiday, Brighton (1933)
Oc:864x1118:signed:Presented by the Trustees of the
Chantrey Bequest 1933

N04963   Building in Berkeley Square (1938)
Oc:806x648:signed:Presented by the Trustees of the
Chantrey Bequest 1938

CUNDELL, Nora L.M. 1889-1948
Modern Collection

N03718   Smiling Woman (1922)
Ob:156x127:Purchased 1923

CURRIE, John S. circa 1884-1914
Modern Collection

N04090   Head of a Woman (1913)
Ow:454x349:signed:Presented by Mr and Mrs Julian
Lousada through the National Art Collections Fund 1925

CUTTS, Simon born 1944
Modern Collection
Tate Gallery Archive holds material concerning this artist

P08181   Winter Fruit (1980)
CJπ:60x90:Transferred from the Library 1982

DADD, Frank 1851-1929
British Collection

N02264 Gold Lace has a Charm for the Fair (1908)
Wπ:330x470:signed:Presented by the Trustees of the
Chantrey Bequest 1908

DADD, Richard 1817-1886
British Collection
Tate Gallery Archive holds material concerning this artist

N03023 A Turk (1863)
Wb:63x63:signed:Presented in memory of H.B. Hagreen
by his children 1915

N04502 Pilot Boats (1858-9)
WDπ:283x451:Purchased 1930

N05767 The Flight out of Egypt (1849-50)
Oc:1010x1264:signed:Purchased 1947

N06251 The Child's Problem (1857)
WDπ:171x254:signed:Presented by Dr R.C. Neville 1954

T00598 The Fairy Feller's Master-Stroke (1855-64)
Oc:540x394:signed:Presented by Siegfried Sassoon in
memory of his friend and fellow officer Julian Dadd, a
great-nephew of the artist, and of his two brothers who
gave their lives in the First World War 1963

DAGLISH, Peter born 1930
Modern Collection

Homage to Albert Dumouchel (P03166-P03178;
complete group; mixed group)
Hommage à Albert Dumouchel

P03171 Thoze Parker House Daze (1971-2)
MLπ:524x438:signed:Presented by the University of
Quebec 1976

P06095 Area/Aria (1969)
CLπ:508x664:signed:Presented by Curwen Studio
through the Institute of Contemporary Prints 1975

P06096 To Paris (1969)
CLπ:505x660:Presented by Curwen Studio through the
Institute of Contemporary Prints 1975

DALI, Salvador 1904-1989
Modern Collection
Tate Gallery Archive holds material concerning this artist

T01078 Forgotten Horizon (1936)
Ow:222x267:signed:Bequeathed by the Hon. Mrs A.E.
Pleydell-Bouverie through the Friends of the Tate Gallery
1968

T01978 Autumnal Cannibalism (1936)
Oc:651x651:Purchased 1975

T01979 Mountain Lake (1938)
Oc:730x921:signed:Purchased 1975

T02343 Metamorphosis of Narcissus (1937)
Métamorphose de Narcisse
Oc:511x781:Purchased 1979

T03257 Lobster Telephone (1936)
Télèphone - Homard
SV:178x330x178:Purchased 1981

P01864 King of Aragon (1973)
CLπ:483x356:signed:Presented by Christie's
Contemporary Art 1979

DALL, Nicholas Thomas active 1748-1776
British Collection

N01779 River Scene with Ruins (circa 1756-65)
Oc:857x1254:Bequeathed by H.S. Ashbee 1900

DALLAS, Angela born 1946
Modern Collection

P03091 First Out of the Box (1967-8)
CNπ:3048x1829:Presented by the Welsh Arts Council
1975

DALOU, Jules 1838-1902
Modern Collection

T00825 Seated Nude Taking off her Stocking (circa 1875-80, cast
1965)
Femme nue assise dans un fauteuil et retirant son bas
Sz:184x156x190:signed:Presented by Miss Nadia Nerina
through the Friends of the Tate Gallery 1966

DALWOOD, Hubert 1924-1976
Modern Collection
Tate Gallery Archive holds material concerning this artist

T00266 Standing Draped Figure (1954)
Sm:511x235x184:Purchased 1959

T00323 Large Object (1959)
Sm:762x889x889:Purchased 1960

T03474 Maquette for 'Arbor' (1971)
Swp:356x483x457:Purchased 1982

T03475 O.A.S. Assassins (1962)
Smv:765x510x340:Purchased 1982

T03716 Lucca (1958)
Sm:660x620x240:Transferred from the Victoria & Albert
Museum 1983

DALZIEL, Edward 1817-1905
British Collection
Tate Gallery Archive holds material concerning this artist

N04128 The Battlefield (published 1854)
Jπ:137x102:Presented by Gilbert Dalziel 1925

DALZIEL, Edward Gurden 1849-1888
British Collection

N04129 Market Day at Old Maran Hall (published 1871)
Jπ:114x175:Presented by Gilbert Dalziel 1925

N04130 Spring Flowers (published 1869)
Jπ:175x121:Presented by Gilbert Dalziel 1925

DALZIEL, Thomas 1823-1906
British Collection
Tate Gallery Archive holds material concerning this artist

N04131 The Alarm (published 1864)
Jπ:171x130:Presented by Gilbert Dalziel 1925

DANBY, Francis 1793-1861
British Collection

N06134 The Deluge (?circa 1840)
Oc:711x1092:Purchased 1953

T01132 The Wood Nymph's Hymn to the Rising Sun (1845)
Oc:1073x1524:signed:Presented by the Friends of the
Tate Gallery 1969

T01337 The Deluge (exhibited 1840)
Oc:2845x4521:Presented by the Friends of the Tate Gallery 1971

T03667 Children by a Brook (circa 1822)
Oc:345x460:Purchased 1983

T04104 Liensfiord, Norway: Calm (circa 1835)
Ow:411x542:signed:Purchased 1985

DANCE, Nathaniel - see
DANCE-HOLLAND, Sir Nathaniel

DANCE-HOLLAND, Sir Nathaniel
1735-1811
British Collection

T00053 Thomas Nuthall with a Dog and Gun
Oc:2242x1460:Bequeathed by Ernest E. Cook through the National Art Collections Fund 1955

DANIELL, Thomas 1749-1840
British Collection

N00899 Bridge near Rajmahal, Bihar (1827)
Oc:978x1372:signed:Bequeathed by Mrs William Mansfield 1872

T01403 Sher Shah's Mausoleum, Sasaram (1810)
Oc:972x1359:signed:Purchased 1971

T01404 Idgah at Amroha (1810)
Oc:981x1359:signed:Purchased 1971

DANIELL, William 1769-1837
British Collection

A Voyage Round Great Britain (first published 1814-25, reprinted 1978-9; T02415-T02720 (plates), T02721-T03024, T03239, T03240 (prints); complete group)

T02415 The Lands End, Cornwall
B:229x305:Presented by Tate Gallery Publications 1979

T02416 The Long-ships Light-house, off the Lands End, Cornwall
B:229x305:Presented by Tate Gallery Publications 1979

T02417 The Entrance to Portreath, Cornwall
B:229x305:Presented by Tate Gallery Publications 1979

T02418 Boscastle Pier on the Coast of Cornwall
B:229x305:Presented by Tate Gallery Publications 1979

T02419 Hartland Pier, North Devon
B:229x305:Presented by Tate Gallery Publications 1979

T02420 Clovelly, on the Coast of North Devon
B:229x305:Presented by Tate Gallery Publications 1979

T02421 Ilfracombe, on the Coast of North Devon
B:229x305:Presented by Tate Gallery Publications 1979

T02422 View of Ilfracombe, from Hilsborough
B:229x305:Presented by Tate Gallery Publications 1979

T02423 Near Combmartin, on the Coast of North Devon
B:229x305:Presented by Tate Gallery Publications 1979

T02424 Lynmouth, on the Coast of North Devon
B:229x305:Presented by Tate Gallery Publications 1979

T02425 St Donats, Glamorganshire
B:229x305:Presented by Tate Gallery Publications 1979

T02426 Britton Ferry, Glamorganshire
B:229x305:Presented by Tate Gallery Publications 1979

T02427 The Mumbles Light-house, in Swansea Bay
B:229x305:Presented by Tate Gallery Publications 1979

T02428 The Worms-head, in Tenby Bay
B:229x305:Presented by Tate Gallery Publications 1979

T02429 Tenby, Pembrokeshire
B:229x305:Presented by Tate Gallery Publications 1979

T02430 The Eligug-Stack, near St Gowans-head, Pembrokeshire
B:229x305:Presented by Tate Gallery Publications 1979

T02431 Solva, near St David's, Pembrokeshire
B:229x305:Presented by Tate Gallery Publications 1979

T02432 View of the Entrance to Fishguard, from Goodwych Sands
B:229x305:Presented by Tate Gallery Publications 1979

T02433 Goodwych Pier, near Fishguard, Pembrokeshire
B:229x305:Presented by Tate Gallery Publications 1979

T02434 View near Aberystwith, Cardiganshire
B:229x305:Presented by Tate Gallery Publications 1979

T02435 Barmouth, Merionethshire
B:229x305:Presented by Tate Gallery Publications 1979

T02436 View of Caernarvon Castle, from Anglesea
B:229x305:Presented by Tate Gallery Publications 1979

T02437 The Harbour Light-house, Holyhead
B:229x305:Presented by Tate Gallery Publications 1979

T02438 Light-house on the South Stack, Holyhead
B:229x305:Presented by Tate Gallery Publications 1979

T02439 Part of the South Stack, Holyhead
B:229x305:Presented by Tate Gallery Publications 1979

T02440 The Rope Bridge, near the Light-house, Holyhead
B:229x305:Presented by Tate Gallery Publications 1979

T02441 Black Marble Quarry, near Red Wharf Bay, Anglesea
B:229x305:Presented by Tate Gallery Publications 1979

T02442 The Entrance to Amlwych Harbour, Anglesea
B:229x305:Presented by Tate Gallery Publications 1979

T02443 Red Wharf Bay, Anglesea
B:229x305:Presented by Tate Gallery Publications 1979

T02444 Beaumaris Castle, Anglesea
B:229x305:Presented by Tate Gallery Publications 1979

T02445 View on Puffin Island, near Anglesea
B:229x305:Presented by Tate Gallery Publications 1979

T02446 The Bath, built by Lord Penryn, near Bangor, N. Wales
B:229x305:Presented by Tate Gallery Publications 1979

T02447 Penman-maur, taken from near Aber, N. Wales
B:229x305:Presented by Tate Gallery Publications 1979

T02448 View of Conway Castle, Caernarvonshire
B:229x305:Presented by Tate Gallery Publications 1979

T02449 The Light-house on Point of Air, Flintshire
B:229x305:Presented by Tate Gallery Publications 1979

T02450 View near Hoyle-lake, Cheshire
B:229x305:Presented by Tate Gallery Publications 1979

T02451 The Towns-end Mill, Liverpool
B:229x305:Presented by Tate Gallery Publications 1979

T02452 Seacombe Ferry, Liverpool
B:229x305:Presented by Tate Gallery Publications 1979

T02453 Liverpool, taken from Opposite Side of the River
B:229x305:Presented by Tate Gallery Publications 1979

T02454 Lancaster Castle
B:229x305:Presented by Tate Gallery Publications 1979

T02455 View near Lower Heysham, Lancashire
B:229x305:Presented by Tate Gallery Publications 1979

T02456 Distant View of Whitbarrow Scar, Westmoreland
B:229x305:Presented by Tate Gallery Publications 1979

T02457 Castle-head, Westmoreland
B:229x305:Presented by Tate Gallery Publications 1979

T02458 Peel Castle, Lancashire
B:229x305:Presented by Tate Gallery Publications 1979

T02459 Whitehaven, Cumberland
B:229x305:Presented by Tate Gallery Publications 1979

T02460 Harrington near Whitehaven, Cumberland
B:229x305:Presented by Tate Gallery Publications 1979

T02461 Mary Port, Cumberland
B:229x305:Presented by Tate Gallery Publications 1979

T02462 Carlaverock Castle, Dumfrieshire
B:229x305:Presented by Tate Gallery Publications 1979

T02463 Kirkcudbright
B:229x305:Presented by Tate Gallery Publications 1979

T02464 The Mull of Galloway, Wigtonshire
B:229x305:Presented by Tate Gallery Publications 1979

T02465 Port Patrick, Wigtonshire
B:229x305:Presented by Tate Gallery Publications 1979

T02466 Cardness Castle, near Gatehouse, Kirkcudbrightshire
B:229x305:Presented by Tate Gallery Publications 1979

T02467 Near Carsleith, Galloway
B:229x305:Presented by Tate Gallery Publications 1979

T02468 Wigton, Galloway
B:229x305:Presented by Tate Gallery Publications 1979

T02469 Cree-town, Kirkcudbrightshire
B:229x305:Presented by Tate Gallery Publications 1979

T02470 The Crag of Ailsa
B:229x305:Presented by Tate Gallery Publications 1979

T02471 Culzean Castle, Ayrshire
B:229x305:Presented by Tate Gallery Publications 1979

T02472 Distant View of Ayr
B:229x305:Presented by Tate Gallery Publications 1979

T02473 Pier at Ardrossan, Ayrshire
B:229x305:Presented by Tate Gallery Publications 1979

T02474 The Isle of Arran, taken near Ardrossan
B:229x305:Presented by Tate Gallery Publications 1979

T02475 Ardgowan, Renfrewshire
B:229x305:Presented by Tate Gallery Publications 1979

T02476 Greenock, on the Clyde
B:229x305:Presented by Tate Gallery Publications 1979

T02477 Steam Boat on the Clyde near Dumbarton
B:229x305:Presented by Tate Gallery Publications 1979

T02478 Mount Stuart, Isle of Bute
B:229x305:Presented by Tate Gallery Publications 1979

T02479 Loch Ranza - Isle of Arran
B:229x305:Presented by Tate Gallery Publications 1979

T02480 Duntrune Castle, Loch Crenan, Argyllshire
B:229x305:Presented by Tate Gallery Publications 1979

T02481 Loch Swene, Argyllshire
B:229x305:Presented by Tate Gallery Publications 1979

T02482 Rassella near Kilmartin, Loch Crenan, Argyllshire
B:229x305:Presented by Tate Gallery Publications 1979

T02483 On the Isle of Jura
B:229x305:Presented by Tate Gallery Publications 1979

T02484 Inverary Castle, Argyllshire
B:229x305:Presented by Tate Gallery Publications 1979

T02485 Dunolly Castle, near Oban, Argyllshire
B:229x305:Presented by Tate Gallery Publications 1979

T02486 Dunstaffnage Castle, Argyllshire
B:229x305:Presented by Tate Gallery Publications 1979

T02487 Clam-shell Cave, Staffa, Iona in the Distance
B:229x305:Presented by Tate Gallery Publications 1979

T02488 Exterior of Fingal's Cave, Staffa
B:229x305:Presented by Tate Gallery Publications 1979

T02489 Entrance to Fingal's Cave, Staffa
B:229x305:Presented by Tate Gallery Publications 1979

T02490 In Fingal's Cave, Staffa
B:229x305:Presented by Tate Gallery Publications 1979

T02491 Staffa near Fingal's Cave
B:229x305:Presented by Tate Gallery Publications 1979

T02492 The Cormorants Cave, Staffa
B:229x305:Presented by Tate Gallery Publications 1979

T02493 View from the Island of Staffa
B:229x305:Presented by Tate Gallery Publications 1979

T02494 The Island of Staffa from the East
B:229x305:Presented by Tate Gallery Publications 1979

T02495 The Island of Staffa, from the South West
B:229x305:Presented by Tate Gallery Publications 1979

T02496 View of Iona, from the N. East
B:229x305:Presented by Tate Gallery Publications 1979

T02497 The Cathedral at Iona
B:229x305:Presented by Tate Gallery Publications 1979

T02498 View of Ben-more, from near Ulva House
B:229x305:Presented by Tate Gallery Publications 1979

T02499 Remains of the Chapel &c. on Inch Kenneth
B:229x305:Presented by Tate Gallery Publications 1979

T02500 Gribune-head in Mull
B:229x305:Presented by Tate Gallery Publications 1979

T02501 Loch-na-Gael, near Knock on Mull
B:229x305:Presented by Tate Gallery Publications 1979

T02502 Distant View of Cruachan-ben, taken near Arros Bridge, Isle of Mull
B:229x305:Presented by Tate Gallery Publications 1979

T02503 Arros Castle, Isle of Mull
B:229x305:Presented by Tate Gallery Publications 1979

T02504 Tobermory, on the Isle of Mull
B:229x305:Presented by Tate Gallery Publications 1979

T02505 Mingarry Castle, Argyllshire
B:229x305:Presented by Tate Gallery Publications 1979

T02506 Ardnamurchan Point, Argyllshire
B:229x305:Presented by Tate Gallery Publications 1979

T02507 Scoor Eig, on the Isle of Eig
B:229x305:Presented by Tate Gallery Publications 1979

T02508 Part of the Isle of Rum
B:229x305:Presented by Tate Gallery Publications 1979

T02509 Armidal, the Seat of Lord Macdonald of Skye
B:229x305:Presented by Tate Gallery Publications 1979

T02510 Iloransay, Isle of Skye
B:229x305:Presented by Tate Gallery Publications 1979

T02511 Balmacarro-house, Loch-alsh, Rosshire
B:229x305:Presented by Tate Gallery Publications 1979

T02512 Castle Ellen-donan
B:229x305:Presented by Tate Gallery Publications 1979

T02513 Loch-duich, Ross-shire
B:229x305:Presented by Tate Gallery Publications 1979

T02514 Ilan-dreoch-Glenbeg, Invernesshire
B:229x305:Presented by Tate Gallery Publications 1979

T02515 The Bay of Barrisdale, in Loch Hourne
B:229x305:Presented by Tate Gallery Publications 1979

T02516 Loch Hourne Head
B:229x305:Presented by Tate Gallery Publications 1979

T02517 Glen-coe Taken near Ballachulish
B:229x305:Presented by Tate Gallery Publications 1979

T02518 Near Kylakin, Skye
B:229x305:Presented by Tate Gallery Publications 1979

T02519 Liveras, near Boradford, Skye
B:229x305:Presented by Tate Gallery Publications 1979

T02520 Portree on the Isle of Skye
B:229x305:Presented by Tate Gallery Publications 1979

T02521 Glenvargle Bridge, near Portree, Skye
B:229x305:Presented by Tate Gallery Publications 1979

T02522 Duntulm, Isle of Skye
B:229x305:Presented by Tate Gallery Publications 1979

T02523 Dunvegan Castle, Isle of Skye
B:229x305:Presented by Tate Gallery Publications 1979

T02524 Dunvegan Castle
B:229x305:Presented by Tate Gallery Publications 1979

T02525 Little Brieshmeal, near Talisker, Skye
B:229x305:Presented by Tate Gallery Publications 1979

T02526 Loch Scavig, Skye
B:229x305:Presented by Tate Gallery Publications 1979

T02527 Loch Coruisg near Loch Scavig
B:229x305:Presented by Tate Gallery Publications 1979

T02528 The Coolin, taken from Loch Slapin
B:229x305:Presented by Tate Gallery Publications 1979

T02529 From the Isle of Rasay, Looking Westward
B:229x305:Presented by Tate Gallery Publications 1979

T02530 Castle Broichin on the Isle of Raasay
B:229x305:Presented by Tate Gallery Publications 1979

T02531 Rowadill in Harris
B:229x305:Presented by Tate Gallery Publications 1979

T02532 Light House on the Isle of Scalpa, Harris
B:229x305:Presented by Tate Gallery Publications 1979

T02533 Part of the Northern Face of One of the Shiant Isles
B:229x305:Presented by Tate Gallery Publications 1979

T02534 Near View of One of the Shiant Isles
B:229x305:Presented by Tate Gallery Publications 1979

T02535 Stornoway, on the Isle of Lewis
B:229x305:Presented by Tate Gallery Publications 1979

T02536 Remains of a Temple at Galston, Isle of Lewis
B:229x305:Presented by Tate Gallery Publications 1979

T02537 Druidical Stone at Strather, near Barvas, Isle of Lewis
B:229x305:Presented by Tate Gallery Publications 1979

T02538 The Gair-loch, Ross-shire
B:229x305:Presented by Tate Gallery Publications 1979

T02539 Gair-loch Head, Ross-shire
B:229x305:Presented by Tate Gallery Publications 1979

T02540 Creen Stone Rock, Loch Broom
B:229x305:Presented by Tate Gallery Publications 1979

T02541 Pier at Tanera, Loch Broom
B:229x305:Presented by Tate Gallery Publications 1979

T02542 Ben Sulvhein, from Loch-Inver
B:229x305:Presented by Tate Gallery Publications 1979

T02543 View of Cuniag, from Loch Inver
B:229x305:Presented by Tate Gallery Publications 1979

T02544 Unapool in Kyles-cu Assynt
B:229x305:Presented by Tate Gallery Publications 1979

T02545 Rispand, Durness
B:229x305:Presented by Tate Gallery Publications 1979

T02546 Entrance to the Cave of Smowe
B:229x305:Presented by Tate Gallery Publications 1979

T02547 Whiten-head, Loch Eribol
B:229x305:Presented by Tate Gallery Publications 1979

T02548 Bay of Tongue
B:229x305:Presented by Tate Gallery Publications 1979

T02549 Strath-naver, Sutherlandshire
B:229x305:Presented by Tate Gallery Publications 1979

T02550 The Clett-rock, Holborn-head
B:229x305:Presented by Tate Gallery Publications 1979

T02551 Thurso, from near Holborn Head
B:229x305:Presented by Tate Gallery Publications 1979

T02552 Castle Sinclair, Thurso
B:229x305:Presented by Tate Gallery Publications 1979

T02553 Castle Hill near Thurso
B:229x305:Presented by Tate Gallery Publications 1979

T02554 Mey Castle, Caithness
B:229x305:Presented by Tate Gallery Publications 1979

T02555 The Ferry at Scarskerry, Caithness
B:229x305:Presented by Tate Gallery Publications 1979

T02556 Near Berry-head, Hoy, Orkney
B:229x305:Presented by Tate Gallery Publications 1979

T02557 The Snook, Hoy, Orkney
B:229x305:Presented by Tate Gallery Publications 1979

T02558 The Old Man of Hoy
B:229x305:Presented by Tate Gallery Publications 1979

T02559 Stromness, Orkney
B:229x305:Presented by Tate Gallery Publications 1979

T02560 Stones of Stennis, Orkney
B:229x305:Presented by Tate Gallery Publications 1979

T02561 The Cathedral of St Magnus, Kirkwall, Orkney
B:229x305:Presented by Tate Gallery Publications 1979

T02562 S.E. View of the Cathedral & Palace, at Kirkwall, Orkney
B:229x305:Presented by Tate Gallery Publications 1979

T02563 Kirkwall, Orkney, from the Bay
B:229x305:Presented by Tate Gallery Publications 1979

T02564 N. West View of the Cathedral, Kirkwall
B:229x305:Presented by Tate Gallery Publications 1979

T02565 Tower of the Bishops Palace, Kirkwall
B:229x305:Presented by Tate Gallery Publications 1979

T02566 Remains of the Earls Palace, Kirkwall
B:229x305:Presented by Tate Gallery Publications 1979

T02567 Light House on the Start, Isle of Sandy, Orkney
B:229x305:Presented by Tate Gallery Publications 1979

T02568 John O'Groats, Caithness
B:229x305:Presented by Tate Gallery Publications 1979

T02569 Duncansby Stacks, Caithness
B:229x305:Presented by Tate Gallery Publications 1979

T02570 Keis Castle, Caithness
B:229x305:Presented by Tate Gallery Publications 1979

T02571 Ackergill Tower, Caithnesshire
B:229x305:Presented by Tate Gallery Publications 1979

T02572 Castles Sinclair & Girnigo, Caithness
B:229x305:Presented by Tate Gallery Publications 1979

T02573 Wick, Caithness
B:229x305:Presented by Tate Gallery Publications 1979

T02574 Old Wick Castle, Caithness
B:229x305:Presented by Tate Gallery Publications 1979

T02575 The Stack of Hempriggs, Caithness
B:229x305:Presented by Tate Gallery Publications 1979

T02576 Scene at Hempriggs, Caithness
B:229x305:Presented by Tate Gallery Publications 1979

T02577 Forse Castle, Sutherland
B:229x305:Presented by Tate Gallery Publications 1979

T02578 Dunbeath Castle, Caithness
B:229x305:Presented by Tate Gallery Publications 1979

T02579 Berrydale, Caithness
B:229x305:Presented by Tate Gallery Publications 1979

T02580 Castle of Berrydale
B:229x305:Presented by Tate Gallery Publications 1979

T02581 Helmsdale, Sutherlandshire
B:229x305:Presented by Tate Gallery Publications 1979

T02582 Dunrobin Castle, Sutherlandshire
B:229x305:Presented by Tate Gallery Publications 1979

T02583 Dunrobin Castle, from the N.E., Sutherlandshire
B:229x305:Presented by Tate Gallery Publications 1979

T02584 Dornoch, Sutherlandshire
B:229x305:Presented by Tate Gallery Publications 1979

T02585 Bonar Bridge
B:229x305:Presented by Tate Gallery Publications 1979

T02586 Cromarty
B:229x305:Presented by Tate Gallery Publications 1979

T02587 Pier at Fortrose, Ross-shire
B:229x305:Presented by Tate Gallery Publications 1979

T02588 Inverness
B:229x305:Presented by Tate Gallery Publications 1979

T02589 Nairn
B:229x305:Presented by Tate Gallery Publications 1979

T02590 Obelisk at Forres
B:229x305:Presented by Tate Gallery Publications 1979

T02591 Nelson's Tower, Forres
B:229x305:Presented by Tate Gallery Publications 1979

T02592 Brugh-head, Murrayshire
B:229x305:Presented by Tate Gallery Publications 1979

T02593 Coxtown Tower, near Elgin
B:229x305:Presented by Tate Gallery Publications 1979

T02594 Finlater Castle, Banffshire
B:229x305:Presented by Tate Gallery Publications 1979

T02595 Boyne-Castle, Banffshire
B:229x305:Presented by Tate Gallery Publications 1979

T02596 Duff-house, Banff
B:229x305:Presented by Tate Gallery Publications 1979

T02597 Banff
B:229x305:Presented by Tate Gallery Publications 1979

T02598 Fraserburgh, Aberdeenshire
B:229x305:Presented by Tate Gallery Publications 1979

T02599 Kinnaird Head, Aberdeenshire
B:229x305:Presented by Tate Gallery Publications 1979

T02600 Peterhead, Aberdeenshire
B:229x305:Presented by Tate Gallery Publications 1979

T02601 Slanes Castle, Aberdeenshire
B:229x305:Presented by Tate Gallery Publications 1979

T02602 Bridge of Don, Old Aberdeen
B:229x305:Presented by Tate Gallery Publications 1979

T02603 Aberdeen
B:229x305:Presented by Tate Gallery Publications 1979

T02604 Dunotter Castle, Kincardineshire
B:229x305:Presented by Tate Gallery Publications 1979

T02605 Montrose, Forfarshire
B:229x305:Presented by Tate Gallery Publications 1979

T02606 Inverbernie Bridge
B:229x305:Presented by Tate Gallery Publications 1979

T02607 Broughty Castle, Forfarshire
B:229x305:Presented by Tate Gallery Publications 1979

T02608 Dundee, Forfarshire
B:229x305:Presented by Tate Gallery Publications 1979

T02609 St Andrews, Fifeshire
B:229x305:Presented by Tate Gallery Publications 1979

T02610 Wems Castle, Fifeshire
B:229x305:Presented by Tate Gallery Publications 1979

T02611 Distant View of Edinburgh, with Wemys Castle
B:229x305:Presented by Tate Gallery Publications 1979

T02612 Edinburgh, from the Castle
B:229x305:Presented by Tate Gallery Publications 1979

T02613 Edinburgh, with Part of the North Bridge & Castle
B:229x305:Presented by Tate Gallery Publications 1979

T02614 Edinburgh, from the Calton Hill
B:229x305:Presented by Tate Gallery Publications 1979

T02615 Leith
B:229x305:Presented by Tate Gallery Publications 1979

T02616 Tantallon Castle, Haddingtonshire
B:229x305:Presented by Tate Gallery Publications 1979

T02617 The Bass Rock
B:229x305:Presented by Tate Gallery Publications 1979

T02618 Dunbar, Haddingtonshire
B:229x305:Presented by Tate Gallery Publications 1979

T02619 Berwick upon Tweed
B:229x305:Presented by Tate Gallery Publications 1979

T02620 Castle on Holy Island, Northumberland
B:229x305:Presented by Tate Gallery Publications 1979

T02621 Bamborough Castle, Northumberland
B:229x305:Presented by Tate Gallery Publications 1979

T02622 North Shields, Northumberland
B:229x305:Presented by Tate Gallery Publications 1979

T02623 Tynemouth, Northumberland
B:229x305:Presented by Tate Gallery Publications 1979

T02624 Sunderland Pier, Durham
B:229x305:Presented by Tate Gallery Publications 1979

T02625 Whitby, Yorkshire
B:229x305:Presented by Tate Gallery Publications 1979

T02626 Whitby Abbey, Yorkshire
B:229x305:Presented by Tate Gallery Publications 1979

T02627 Scarborough, Yorkshire
B:229x305:Presented by Tate Gallery Publications 1979

T02628 Light-house on Flambro'-head, Yorkshire
B:229x305:Presented by Tate Gallery Publications 1979

T02629 Boston, Lincolnshire
B:229x305:Presented by Tate Gallery Publications 1979

T02630 Yarmouth from Gorleston
B:229x305:Presented by Tate Gallery Publications 1979

T02631 Lowestoft, Suffolk
B:229x305:Presented by Tate Gallery Publications 1979

T02632 Southwold, Suffolk
B:229x305:Presented by Tate Gallery Publications 1979

T02633 The Orford Ness Light Houses, Suffolk
B:229x305:Presented by Tate Gallery Publications 1979

T02634 Harwich, Essex
B:229x305:Presented by Tate Gallery Publications 1979

T02635 Mistley near Harwich, Essex
B:229x305:Presented by Tate Gallery Publications 1979

T02636 South End, Essex
B:229x305:Presented by Tate Gallery Publications 1979

T02637 Sheerness
B:229x305:Presented by Tate Gallery Publications 1979

T02638 The Reculvers
B:229x305:Presented by Tate Gallery Publications 1979

T02639 Pier at Margate
B:229x305:Presented by Tate Gallery Publications 1979

T02640 North Foreland Light House
B:229x305:Presented by Tate Gallery Publications 1979

T02641 Broadstairs
B:229x305:Presented by Tate Gallery Publications 1979

T02642 Ramsgate
B:229x305:Presented by Tate Gallery Publications 1979

T02643 Deal Castle
B:229x305:Presented by Tate Gallery Publications 1979

T02644 Walmer Castle
B:229x305:Presented by Tate Gallery Publications 1979

T02645 Dover Castle
B:229x305:Presented by Tate Gallery Publications 1979

T02646 Dover, from Shakespears Cliff
B:229x305:Presented by Tate Gallery Publications 1979

T02647 Shakespears Cliff
B:229x305:Presented by Tate Gallery Publications 1979

T02648 Folkestone, Kent
B:229x305:Presented by Tate Gallery Publications 1979

T02649 Hythe
B:229x305:Presented by Tate Gallery Publications 1979

T02650 Dungeness Light House
B:229x305:Presented by Tate Gallery Publications 1979

T02651 Rye, Sussex
B:229x305:Presented by Tate Gallery Publications 1979

T02652 Winchelsea
B:229x305:Presented by Tate Gallery Publications 1979

T02653 Hastings, from near the White Rock
B:229x305:Presented by Tate Gallery Publications 1979

T02654 Hastings, from the East Cliff
B:229x305:Presented by Tate Gallery Publications 1979

T02655 Near Beachy-head
B:229x305:Presented by Tate Gallery Publications 1979

T02656 Brighton
B:229x305:Presented by Tate Gallery Publications 1979

T02657 Near Regents Square, Brighton
B:229x305:Presented by Tate Gallery Publications 1979

T02658 Ovington near Brighton
B:229x305:Presented by Tate Gallery Publications 1979

T02659 Shoreham
B:229x305:Presented by Tate Gallery Publications 1979

T02660 Pier at Little Hampton
B:229x305:Presented by Tate Gallery Publications 1979

T02661 View from the Park, Arundel
B:229x305:Presented by Tate Gallery Publications 1979

T02662 Bognor
B:229x305:Presented by Tate Gallery Publications 1979

T02663 View from Portsdown Hill
B:229x305:Presented by Tate Gallery Publications 1979

T02664 West Cowes
B:229x305:Presented by Tate Gallery Publications 1979

T02665 Lord Henry Seymours Castle
B:229x305:Presented by Tate Gallery Publications 1979

T02666 Mr Nash's Castle
B:229x305:Presented by Tate Gallery Publications 1979

T02667 Ryde
B:229x305:Presented by Tate Gallery Publications 1979

T02668 Brading Harbour
B:229x305:Presented by Tate Gallery Publications 1979

T02669 Shanklin Chine
B:229x305:Presented by Tate Gallery Publications 1979

T02670 Freshwater Bay, Isle of Wight
B:229x305:Presented by Tate Gallery Publications 1979

T02671 Needles Cliff & Needles, Isle of Wight
B:229x305:Presented by Tate Gallery Publications 1979

T02672 Distant View of the Needles & Hurst Castle
B:229x305:Presented by Tate Gallery Publications 1979

T02673 Christchurch
B:229x305:Presented by Tate Gallery Publications 1979

T02674 Poole, Dorsetshire
B:229x305:Presented by Tate Gallery Publications 1979

T02675 Corfe Castle
B:229x305:Presented by Tate Gallery Publications 1979

T02676 Swanage
B:229x305:Presented by Tate Gallery Publications 1979

T02677 Lulworth Cove
B:229x305:Presented by Tate Gallery Publications 1979

T02678 Weymouth
B:229x305:Presented by Tate Gallery Publications 1979

T02679 Light-house, Isle of Portland
B:229x305:Presented by Tate Gallery Publications 1979

T02680 St Catherine's Chapel, Dorset
B:229x305:Presented by Tate Gallery Publications 1979

T02681 Bridport Harbour, Dorset
B:229x305:Presented by Tate Gallery Publications 1979

T02682 Lyme Regis, from Charmouth, Dorset
B:229x305:Presented by Tate Gallery Publications 1979

T02683 Sidmouth, Devon
B:229x305:Presented by Tate Gallery Publications 1979

T02684 Exmouth, Devon
B:229x305:Presented by Tate Gallery Publications 1979

T02685 Teignmouth, Devon
B:229x305:Presented by Tate Gallery Publications 1979

T02686 Babbacombe, Devon
B:229x305:Presented by Tate Gallery Publications 1979

T02687 Torbay, Devon
B:229x305:Presented by Tate Gallery Publications 1979

T02688 Tor-abbey, Devon
B:229x305:Presented by Tate Gallery Publications 1979

T02689 Tor-quay, Devon
B:229x305:Presented by Tate Gallery Publications 1979

T02690 Brixham, Torbay, Devon
B:229x305:Presented by Tate Gallery Publications 1979

T02691 Entrance to Dartmouth, Devon
B:229x305:Presented by Tate Gallery Publications 1979

T02692 The Junction of the Dart with the Sea
B:229x305:Presented by Tate Gallery Publications 1979

T02693 Near Kingswear, on the Dart, Devon
B:229x305:Presented by Tate Gallery Publications 1979

T02694 Kingswear, Devon
B:229x305:Presented by Tate Gallery Publications 1979

T02695 Salcombe, Devon
B:229x305:Presented by Tate Gallery Publications 1979

T02696 Bovisand, near Plymouth
B:229x305:Presented by Tate Gallery Publications 1979

T02697 Quay at Straddon Point, near Plymouth
B:229x305:Presented by Tate Gallery Publications 1979

T02698 The Citadel, Plymouth
B:229x305:Presented by Tate Gallery Publications 1979

T02699 Catwater, Plymouth, from the Citadel
B:229x305:Presented by Tate Gallery Publications 1979

T02700 Mount Edgecumbe, from the Citadel, Plymouth
B:229x305:Presented by Tate Gallery Publications 1979

T02701 View from Mount Edgecumbe
B:229x305:Presented by Tate Gallery Publications 1979

T02702 Hamoaze, from Mount Edgecumbe
B:229x305:Presented by Tate Gallery Publications 1979

T02703 Port Wrinkle, Cornwall
B:229x305:Presented by Tate Gallery Publications 1979

T02704 East Looe, Cornwall
B:229x305:Presented by Tate Gallery Publications 1979

T02705 Polperro, Cornwall
B:229x305:Presented by Tate Gallery Publications 1979

T02706 Fowey, from Bodenick, Cornwall
B:229x305:Presented by Tate Gallery Publications 1979

T02707 Fowey Castle, Cornwall
B:229x305:Presented by Tate Gallery Publications 1979

T02708 Polkerris, Cornwall
B:229x305:Presented by Tate Gallery Publications 1979

T02709 Mevagissey, Cornwall
B:229x305:Presented by Tate Gallery Publications 1979

T02710 Mevagissey, Cornwall
B:229x305:Presented by Tate Gallery Publications 1979

T02711 Gorran Haven, Cornwall
B:229x305:Presented by Tate Gallery Publications 1979

T02712 Port-looe, Cornwall
B:229x305:Presented by Tate Gallery Publications 1979

T02713 Falmouth, Cornwall
B:229x305:Presented by Tate Gallery Publications 1979

T02714 The Lizard Light-houses, Cornwall
B:229x305:Presented by Tate Gallery Publications 1979

T02715 Mullyan Cover, Cornwall
B:229x305:Presented by Tate Gallery Publications 1979

T02716 Near Mullyan Cover, Cornwall
B:229x305:Presented by Tate Gallery Publications 1979

T02717 St Michaels Mount, Cornwall
B:229x305:Presented by Tate Gallery Publications 1979

T02718 St Michaels Mount, Cornwall
B:229x305:Presented by Tate Gallery Publications 1979

T02719 Penzance, Cornwall
B:229x305:Presented by Tate Gallery Publications 1979

T02720 The Land's End, Cornwall
B:229x305:Presented by Tate Gallery Publications 1979

T02721 The Lands-end, Cornwall
Mπ:162x241:Presented by Tate Gallery Publications 1979

T02722 The Long-ships Light House, off the Lands End, Cornwall
Mπ:162x241:Presented by Tate Gallery Publications 1979

T02723 The Entrance to Portreath, Cornwall
Mπ:162x241:Presented by Tate Gallery Publications 1979

T02724 Boscastle Pier on the Coast of Cornwall
Mπ:162x241:Presented by Tate Gallery Publications 1979

T02725 Hartland Pier, North Devon
Mπ:162x241:Presented by Tate Gallery Publications 1979

T02726 Colvelly, on the Coast of North Devon
Mπ:162x241:Presented by Tate Gallery Publications 1979

T02727 Ilfracombe, on the Coast of North Devon
Mπ:162x241:Presented by Tate Gallery Publications 1979

T02728 View of Ilfracombe, from Hilsborough
Mπ:162x241:Presented by Tate Gallery Publications 1979

T02729 Near Combmartin, on the Coast of North Devon
Mπ:162x241:Presented by Tate Gallery Publications 1979

T02730 Lynmouth, on the Coast of North Devon
Mπ:162x241:Presented by Tate Gallery Publications 1979

T02731 St Donats, Glamorganshire
Mπ:162x241:Presented by Tate Gallery Publications 1979

T02732 Britton Ferry, Glamorganshire
Mπ:162x241:Presented by Tate Gallery Publications 1979

T02733 The Mumbles Light-house, in Swansea Bay
Mπ:162x241:Presented by Tate Gallery Publications 1979

T02734 The Worms-head, in Tenby Bay
Mπ:162x241:Presented by Tate Gallery Publications 1979

T02735 Tenby, Pembrokeshire
Mπ:162x241:Presented by Tate Gallery Publications 1979

T02736 The Eligug-Stack, near St Gowans-head, Pembrokeshire
Mπ:162x241:Presented by Tate Gallery Publications 1979

T02737 Solva, near St Davids, Pembrokeshire
Mπ:162x241:Presented by Tate Gallery Publications 1979

T02738 View of the Entrance to Fishguard, from Goodwych Sands
Mπ:162x241:Presented by Tate Gallery Publications 1979

T02739 Goodwych Pier, near Fishguard, Pembrokeshire
Mπ:162x241:Presented by Tate Gallery Publications 1979

T02740 View near Aberystwith, Cardiganshire
Mπ:162x241:Presented by Tate Gallery Publications 1979

T02741 Barmouth, Merionethshire
Mπ:162x241:Presented by Tate Gallery Publications 1979

T02742 View of Caernarvon Castle, from Anglesea
Mπ:162x241:Presented by Tate Gallery Publications 1979

T02743 The Harbour Light-house, Holyhead
Mπ:162x241:Presented by Tate Gallery Publications 1979

T02744 Light-house on the South Stack, Holyhead
Mπ:162x241:Presented by Tate Gallery Publications 1979

T02745 Part of the South Stack, Holyhead
Mπ:162x241:Presented by Tate Gallery Publications 1979

T02746 The Rope Bridge, near the Light-house, Holyhead
Mπ:162x241:Presented by Tate Gallery Publications 1979

T02747 Black Marble Quarry, near Red Wharf Bay, Anglesea
Mπ:162x241:Presented by Tate Gallery Publications 1979

T02748 The Entrance to Almwych Harbour, Anglesea
Mπ:162x241:Presented by Tate Gallery Publications 1979

T02749 Red Wharf Bay, Anglesea
Mπ:162x241:Presented by Tate Gallery Publications 1979

T02750 Beaumaris Castle, Anglesea
Mπ:162x241:Presented by Tate Gallery Publications 1979

T02751 View on Puffin Island, near Anglesea
Mπ:162x241:Presented by Tate Gallery Publications 1979

T02752 The Bath, built by Lord Penryn, near Bangor, N. Wales
Mπ:162x241:Presented by Tate Gallery Publications 1979

T02753 Penman-maur, taken from near Aber, N. Wales
Mπ:162x241:Presented by Tate Gallery Publications 1979

T02754 View of Conway Castle, Caernarvonshire
Mπ:162x241:Presented by Tate Gallery Publications 1979

T02755 The Light-house on Point of Air, Flintshire
Mπ:162x241:Presented by Tate Gallery Publications 1979

T02756 View near Hoyle-lake, Cheshire
Mπ:162x241:Presented by Tate Gallery Publications 1979

T02757 The Towns-End Mill, Liverpool
Mπ:162x241:Presented by Tate Gallery Publications 1979

T02758 Seacombe Ferry, Liverpool
Mπ:162x241:Presented by Tate Gallery Publications 1979

T02759 Liverpool, taken from the Opposite Side of the River
Mπ:162x241:Presented by Tate Gallery Publications 1979

T02760 Lancaster Castle
Mπ:162x241:Presented by Tate Gallery Publications 1979

T02761 View near Lower Heysham, Lancashire
Mπ:162x241:Presented by Tate Gallery Publications 1979

T02762 Distant View of Whitbarrow Scar, Westmoreland
Mπ:162x241:Presented by Tate Gallery Publications 1979

T02763 Castle-head, Westmoreland
Mπ:162x241:Presented by Tate Gallery Publications 1979

T02764 Peel Castle, Lancashire
Mπ:162x241:Presented by Tate Gallery Publications 1979

T02765 Whitehaven, Cumberland
Mπ:162x241:Presented by Tate Gallery Publications 1979

T02766 Harrington near Whitehaven, Cumberland
Mπ:162x241:Presented by Tate Gallery Publications 1979

T02767 Mary Port, Cumberland
Mπ:162x241:Presented by Tate Gallery Publications 1979

T02768 Carlaverock Castle, Dumfrieshire
Mπ:162x241:Presented by Tate Gallery Publications 1979

T02769 Kirkcudbright
Mπ:162x241:Presented by Tate Gallery Publications 1979

T02770 The Mull of Galloway, Wigtonshire
Mπ:162x241:Presented by Tate Gallery Publications 1979

T02771 Port Patrick, Wigtonshire
Mπ:162x241:Presented by Tate Gallery Publications 1979

T02772 Cardness Castle, near Gatehouse, Kirkcudbrightshire
Mπ:162x241:Presented by Tate Gallery Publications 1979

T02773 Near Carsleith, Galloway
Mπ:162x241:Presented by Tate Gallery Publications 1979

T02774 Wigton, Galloway
Mπ:162x241:Presented by Tate Gallery Publications 1979

T02775 Cree-town, Kirkcudbrightshire
Mπ:162x241:Presented by Tate Gallery Publications 1979

T02776 The Crag of Ailsa
Mπ:162x241:Presented by Tate Gallery Publications 1979

T02777 Culzean Castle, Ayrshire
Mπ:162x241:Presented by Tate Gallery Publications 1979

T02778 Distant View of Ayr
Mπ:162x241:Presented by Tate Gallery Publications 1979

T02779 Pier at Ardrossan, Ayrshire
Mπ:162x241:Presented by Tate Gallery Publications 1979

T02780 The Isle of Arran, taken near Ardrossan
Mπ:162x241:Presented by Tate Gallery Publications 1979

T02781 Ardgowan, Renfrewshire
Mπ:162x241:Presented by Tate Gallery Publications 1979

T02782 Greenock, on the Clyde
Mπ:162x241:Presented by Tate Gallery Publications 1979

T02783 Stream Boat on the Clyde near Dumbarton
Mπ:162x241:Presented by Tate Gallery Publications 1979

T02784 Mount Stuart, Isle of Bute
Mπ:162x241:Presented by Tate Gallery Publications 1979

T02785 Loch-ranza Isle of Arran
Mπ:162x241:Presented by Tate Gallery Publications 1979

T02786 Duntrune Castle, Loch Crenan, Argyllshire
Mπ:162x241:Presented by Tate Gallery Publications 1979

T02787 Loch Swene, Argyllshire
Mπ:162x241:Presented by Tate Gallery Publications 1979

T02788 Rassella near Kilmartin Loch Crenan, Argyllshire
Mπ:162x241:Presented by Tate Gallery Publications 1979

T02789 On the Isle of Jura
Mπ:162x241:Presented by Tate Gallery Publications 1979

T02790 Inverary Castle, Argyllshire
Mπ:162x241:Presented by Tate Gallery Publications 1979

T02791 Dunolly Castle, near Oban, Argyllshire
Mπ:162x241:Presented by Tate Gallery Publications 1979

T02792 Dunstaffnage Castle, Argyllshire
Mπ:162x241:Presented by Tate Gallery Publications 1979

T02793 Clam-shell Cave, Staffa, Iona in the Distance
Mπ:162x241:Presented by Tate Gallery Publications 1979

T02794 Exterior of Fingal's Cave, Staffa
Mπ:162x241:Presented by Tate Gallery Publications 1979

T02795 Entrance to Fingal's Cave, Staffa
Mπ:162x241:Presented by Tate Gallery Publications 1979

T02796 In Fingals Cave Staafa
Mπ:162x241:Presented by Tate Gallery Publications 1979

T02797 Staffa near Fingal's Cave
Mπ:162x241:Presented by Tate Gallery Publications 1979

T02798 The Cormorants Cave, Staffa
Mπ:162x241:Presented by Tate Gallery Publications 1979

T02799 View from the Island of Staffa
Mπ:162x241:Presented by Tate Gallery Publications 1979

T02800 The Island of Staffa, from the East
Mπ:162x241:Presented by Tate Gallery Publications 1979

T02801 The Island of Staffa, from the South West
Mπ:162x241:Presented by Tate Gallery Publications 1979

T02802 View of Iona, from the N. East
Mπ:162x241:Presented by Tate Gallery Publications 1979

T02803 The Cathedral at Iona
Mπ:162x241:Presented by Tate Gallery Publications 1979

T02804 View of Ben-more, from near Ulva House
Mπ:162x241:Presented by Tate Gallery Publications 1979

T02805 Remains of the Chapel &c. on Inch Kenneth
Mπ:162x241:Presented by Tate Gallery Publications 1979

T02806 Gribune-head in Mull
Mπ:162x241:Presented by Tate Gallery Publications 1979

T02807 Loch-na-gael, near Knock on Mull
Mπ:162x241:Presented by Tate Gallery Publications 1979

T02808 Distant View of Cruachan-ben, taken near Arros Bridge, Isle of Mull
Mπ:162x241:Presented by Tate Gallery Publications 1979

T02809 Arros Castle, Isle of Mull
Mπ:162x241:Presented by Tate Gallery Publications 1979

T02810 Tobermory, on the Isle of Mull
Mπ:162x241:Presented by Tate Gallery Publications 1979

T02811 Mingarry Castle, Argyllshire
Mπ:162x241:Presented by Tate Gallery Publications 1979

T02812 Ardnamurchan Point, Argyllshire
Mπ:162x241:Presented by Tate Gallery Publications 1979

T02813 Scoor Eig, on the Isle of Eig
Mπ:162x241:Presented by Tate Gallery Publications 1979

T02814 Part of the Isle of Rum
Mπ:162x241:Presented by Tate Gallery Publications 1979

T02815 Armidal, the Seat of Lord Macdonald, Isle of Skye
Mπ:162x241:Presented by Tate Gallery Publications 1979

T02816 Iloransay, Isle of Skye
Mπ:162x241:Presented by Tate Gallery Publications 1979

T02817 Balmacarro-house, Loch-alsh, Rosshire
Mπ:162x241:Presented by Tate Gallery Publications 1979

T02818 Castle Ellen-donan
Mπ:162x241:Presented by Tate Gallery Publications 1979

T02819 Loch-duich, Ross-shire
Mπ:162x241:Presented by Tate Gallery Publications 1979

T02820 Ilan-dreoch-glenbeg, Invernesshire
Mπ:162x241:Presented by Tate Gallery Publications 1979

T02821 The Bay of Barrisdale, in Loch Hourne
Mπ:162x241:Presented by Tate Gallery Publications 1979

T02822 Loch Hourne Head
Mπ:162x241:Presented by Tate Gallery Publications 1979

T02823 Glen-coe Taken near Ballachulish
Mπ:162x241:Presented by Tate Gallery Publications 1979

T02824 Newar Kylakin, Skye
Mπ:162x241:Presented by Tate Gallery Publications 1979

T02825 Liveras, near Broadford, Skye
Mπ:162x241:Presented by Tate Gallery Publications 1979

T02826 Portree on the Isle of Skye
Mπ:162x241:Presented by Tate Gallery Publications 1979

T02827 Glenvargle Bridge, near Portree, Skye
Mπ:162x241:Presented by Tate Gallery Publications 1979

T02828 Duntulm, Isle of Skye
Mπ:162x241:Presented by Tate Gallery Publications 1979

T02829 Dunvegan Castle, Isle of Skye
Mπ:162x241:Presented by Tate Gallery Publications 1979

T02830 Dunvegan Castle
Mπ:162x241:Presented by Tate Gallery Publications 1979

T02831 Little Brieshmeal, near Talisker, Skye
Mπ:162x241:Presented by Tate Gallery Publications 1979

T02832 Loch Scavig, Skye
Mπ:162x241:Presented by Tate Gallery Publications 1979

T02833 Loch Coruisq near Loch Scavig
Mπ:162x241:Presented by Tate Gallery Publications 1979

T02834 The Coolin, taken from Loch Slapin
Mπ:162x241:Presented by Tate Gallery Publications 1979

T02835 From the Isle of Rasay, Looking Westward
Mπ:162x241:Presented by Tate Gallery Publications 1979

T02836 Castle Broichin on the Isle of Rasay
Mπ:162x241:Presented by Tate Gallery Publications 1979

T02837 Rowadill in Harris
Mπ:162x241:Presented by Tate Gallery Publications 1979

T02838 Light House on the Isle of Scalpa, Harris
Mπ:162x241:Presented by Tate Gallery Publications 1979

T02839 Part of the Northern Face of One of the Shiant Isles
Mπ:162x241:Presented by Tate Gallery Publications 1979

T02840 Near View of One of the Shiant Isles
Mπ:162x241:Presented by Tate Gallery Publications 1979

T02841 Stornaway, on the Isle of Lewis
Mπ:162x241:Presented by Tate Gallery Publications 1979

T02842 Remains of a Temple at Galston, Isle of Lewis
Mπ:162x241:Presented by Tate Gallery Publications 1979

T02843 Druidical Stone at Strather, near Barvas, Isle of Lewis
Mπ:162x241:Presented by Tate Gallery Publications 1979

T02844 The Gair-loch, Ross-shire
Mπ:162x241:Presented by Tate Gallery Publications 1979

T02845 Gair-loch Head, Ross-shire
Mπ:162x241:Presented by Tate Gallery Publications 1979

T02846 Green-stone Rock, Loch Broom
Mπ:162x241:Presented by Tate Gallery Publications 1979

T02847 Pier at Tanera, Loch Broom
Mπ:162x241:Presented by Tate Gallery Publications 1979

T02848 Ben Sulvhein, from Loch-inver
Mπ:162x241:Presented by Tate Gallery Publications 1979

T02849 View of Cuniag, from Loch Inver
Mπ:162x241:Presented by Tate Gallery Publications 1979

T02850 Unapool in Kyles-cu Assynt
Mπ:162x241:Presented by Tate Gallery Publications 1979

T02851 Rispand, Durness
Mπ:162x241:Presented by Tate Gallery Publications 1979

T02852 Entrance to the Cave of Smowe
Mπ:162x241:Presented by Tate Gallery Publications 1979

T02853 Whitten-head, Loch Eribol
Mπ:162x241:Presented by Tate Gallery Publications 1979

T02854 Bay of Tongue
Mπ:162x241:Presented by Tate Gallery Publications 1979

T02855 Strath-naver, Sutherlandshire
Mπ:162x241:Presented by Tate Gallery Publications 1979

T02856 The Clett-rock, Holborn-head
Mπ:162x241:Presented by Tate Gallery Publications 1979

T02857 Thurso, from near Holborn Head
Mπ:162x241:Presented by Tate Gallery Publications 1979

T02858 Castle Sinclair, Thurso
Mπ:162x241:Presented by Tate Gallery Publications 1979

T02859 Castle Hill, near Thurso
Mπ:162x241:Presented by Tate Gallery Publications 1979

T02860 Mey Castle, Caithness
Mπ:162x241:Presented by Tate Gallery Publications 1979

T02861 The Ferry at Scarskerry, Caithness
Mπ:162x241:Presented by Tate Gallery Publications 1979

T02862 Near the Berry-head, Hoy, Orkney
Mπ:162x241:Presented by Tate Gallery Publications 1979

T02863 The Snook, Hoy, Orkney
Mπ:162x241:Presented by Tate Gallery Publications 1979

T02864 The Old Man of Hoy
Mπ:162x241:Presented by Tate Gallery Publications 1979

T02865 Stromness, Orkney
Mπ:162x241:Presented by Tate Gallery Publications 1979

T02866 Stones of Stennis, Orkney
Mπ:162x241:Presented by Tate Gallery Publications 1979

T02867 The Cathedral of St Magnus, Kirkwall, Orkney
Mπ:162x241:Presented by Tate Gallery Publications 1979

T02868 S.E. View of the Cathedral & Palace, at Kirkwall, Orkney
Mπ:162x241:Presented by Tate Gallery Publications 1979

T02869 Kirkwall, Orkney, from the Bay
Mπ:162x241:Presented by Tate Gallery Publications 1979

T02870 N. West View of the Cathedral, Kirkwall
Mπ:162x241:Presented by Tate Gallery Publications 1979

T02871 Tower of the Bishops Palace, Kirkwall
Mπ:162x241:Presented by Tate Gallery Publications 1979

T02872 Remains of the Earls Palace, Kirkwall
Mπ:162x241:Presented by Tate Gallery Publications 1979

T02873 Light House on the Start, Isle of Sandy, Orkney
Mπ:162x241:Presented by Tate Gallery Publications 1979

T02874 John O'Groats, Caithness
Mπ:162x241:Presented by Tate Gallery Publications 1979

T02875 Duncansby Stacks, Caithness
Mπ:162x241:Presented by Tate Gallery Publications 1979

T02876 Keiss Castle, Caithness
Mπ:162x241:Presented by Tate Gallery Publications 1979

T02877 Ackergill Tower, Caithnesshire
Mπ:162x241:Presented by Tate Gallery Publications 1979

T02878 Castles Sinclair & Girnigo, Caithness
Mπ:162x241:Presented by Tate Gallery Publications 1979

T02879 Wick, Caithness
Mπ:162x241:Presented by Tate Gallery Publications 1979

T02880 Old Wick Castle, Caithness
Mπ:162x241:Presented by Tate Gallery Publications 1979

T02881 The Stack of Hempriggs, Caithness
Mπ:162x241:Presented by Tate Gallery Publications 1979

T02882 Scene at Hempriggs, Caithness
Mπ:162x241:Presented by Tate Gallery Publications 1979

T02883 Forse Castle, Sutherland
Mπ:162x241:Presented by Tate Gallery Publications 1979

T02884 Denbeath Castle, Caithness
Mπ:162x241:Presented by Tate Gallery Publications 1979

T02885 Berrydale, Caithness
Mπ:162x241:Presented by Tate Gallery Publications 1979

T02886 Castle of Berrydale
Mπ:162x241:Presented by Tate Gallery Publications 1979

T02887 Helmsdale, Sutherlandshire
Mπ:162x241:Presented by Tate Gallery Publications 1979

T02888 Dunrobin Castle, Sutherlandshire
Mπ:162x241:Presented by Tate Gallery Publications 1979

T02889 Dunrobin Castle, from the N.E., Sutherlandshire
Mπ:162x241:Presented by Tate Gallery Publications 1979

T02890 Dornoch, Sutherlandshire
Mπ:162x241:Presented by Tate Gallery Publications 1979

T02891 Bonar Bridge
Mπ:162x241:Presented by Tate Gallery Publications 1979

T02892 Cromarty
Mπ:162x241:Presented by Tate Gallery Publications 1979

T02893 Pier at Fortrose, Ross-shire
Mπ:162x241:Presented by Tate Gallery Publications 1979

T02894 Inverness
Mπ:162x241:Presented by Tate Gallery Publications 1979

T02895 Nairn
Mπ:162x251:Presented by Tate Gallery Publications 1979

T02896 Obelisk at Forres
Mπ:162x241:Presented by Tate Gallery Publications 1979

T02897 Nelson's Tower, Forres
Mπ:162x241:Presented by Tate Gallery Publications 1979

T02898 Brugh-head, Murrayshire
Mπ:162x241:Presented by Tate Gallery Publications 1979

T02899 Coxtown Tower, near Elgin
Mπ:162x241:Presented by Tate Gallery Publications 1979

T02900 Finlater Castle, Banffshire
Mπ:162x241:Presented by Tate Gallery Publications 1979

T02901 Boyne Castle, Banffshire
Mπ:162x241:Presented by Tate Gallery Publications 1979

T02902 Duff-house, Banff
Mπ:162x241:Presented by Tate Gallery Publications 1979

T02903 Banff
Mπ:162x241:Presented by Tate Gallery Publications 1979

T02904 Fraserburgh, Aberdeenshire
Mπ:162x241:Presented by Tate Gallery Publications 1979

T02905 Kinnaird Head, Aberdeenshire
Mπ:162x241:Presented by Tate Gallery Publications 1979

T02906 Peterhead, Aberdeenshire
Mπ:162x241:Presented by Tate Gallery Publications 1979

T02907 Slanes Castle, Aberdeenshire
Mπ:162x241:Presented by Tate Gallery Publications 1979

T02908 Bridge of Don, Old Aberdeen
Mπ:162x241:Presented by Tate Gallery Publications 1979

T02909 Aberdeen
Mπ:162x241:Presented by Tate Gallery Publications 1979

T02910 Dunotter Castle, Kincardineshire
Mπ:162x241:Presented by Tate Gallery Publications 1979

T02911 Montrose, Forfarshire
Mπ:162x241:Presented by Tate Gallery Publications 1979

T02912 Inverbernie Bridge
Mπ:162x241:Presented by Tate Gallery Publications 1979

T02913 Broughty Castle, Forfarshire
Mπ:162x241:Presented by Tate Gallery Publications 1979

T02914 Dundee, Forfarshire
Mπ:162x241:Presented by Tate Gallery Publications 1979

T02915 St Andrews, Fifeshire
Mπ:162x241:Presented by Tate Gallery Publications 1979

T02916 Wemys Castle, Fifeshire
Mπ:162x241:Presented by Tate Gallery Publications 1979

T02917 Distant View of Edinburgh, with Wemys Castle
Mπ:162x241:Presented by Tate Gallery Publications 1979

T02918 Edinburgh, from the Castle
Mπ:162x241:Presented by Tate Gallery Publications 1979

T02919 Edinburgh, with Part of the North Bridge & Castle
Mπ:162x241:Presented by Tate Gallery Publications 1979

T02920 Edinburgh, from the Calton Hill
Mπ:162x241:Presented by Tate Gallery Publications 1979

T02921 Leith
Mπ:162x241:Presented by Tate Gallery Publications 1979

T02922 Tantallon Castle, Haddingtonshire
Mπ:162x241:Presented by Tate Gallery Publications 1979

T02923 The Bass Rock
Mπ:162x241:Presented by Tate Gallery Publications 1979

T02924 Dunbar, Haddingtonshire
Mπ:162x241:Presented by Tate Gallery Publications 1979

T02925 Berwick Upon Tweed
Mπ:162x241:Presented by Tate Gallery Publications 1979

T02926 Castle on Holy Island, Northumberland
Mπ:162x241:Presented by Tate Gallery Publications 1979

T02927 Bamborough Castle, Northumberland
Mπ:162x241:Presented by Tate Gallery Publications 1979

T02928 North Shields, Northumberland
Mπ:162x241:Presented by Tate Gallery Publications 1979

T02929 Tynemouth, Northumberland
Mπ:162x241:Presented by Tate Gallery Publications 1979

T02930 Sunderland Pier, Durham
Mπ:162x241:Presented by Tate Gallery Publications 1979

T02931 Whitby, Yorkshire
Mπ:162x241:Presented by Tate Gallery Publications 1979

T02932 Whitby Abbey, Yorkshire
Mπ:162x241:Presented by Tate Gallery Publications 1979

T02933 Scarborough, Yorkshire
Mπ:162x241:Presented by Tate Gallery Publications 1979

T02934 Light-house on Flambro'-head, Yorkshire
Mπ:162x241:Presented by Tate Gallery Publications 1979

T02935 Boston, Lincolnshire
Mπ:162x241:Presented by Tate Gallery Publications 1979

T02936 Yarmouth from Gorleston
Mπ:162x241:Presented by Tate Gallery Publications 1979

T02937 Lowestoft, Suffolk
Mπ:162x241:Presented by Tate Gallery Publications 1979

T02938 Southwold, Suffolk
Mπ:162x241:Presented by Tate Gallery Publications 1979

T02939 The Orford Ness Light Houses, Suffolk
Mπ:162x241:Presented by Tate Gallery Publications 1979

T02940 Harwich, Essex
Mπ:162x241:Presented by Tate Gallery Publications 1979

T02941 Mistley near Harwich, Essex
Mπ:162x241:Presented by Tate Gallery Publications 1979

T02942 South End, Essex
Mπ:162x241:Presented by Tate Gallery Publications 1979

T02943 Sheerness
Mπ:162x241:Presented by Tate Gallery Publications 1979

T02944 The Reculvers
Mπ:162x241:Presented by Tate Gallery Publications 1979

T02945 Pier at Margate
Mπ:162x241:Presented by Tate Gallery Publications 1979

T02946 North Foreland Light House
Mπ:162x241:Presented by Tate Gallery Publications 1979

T02947 Broadstairs
Mπ:162x241:Presented by Tate Gallery Publications 1979

T02948 Ramsgate
Mπ:162x241:Presented by Tate Gallery Publications 1979

T02949 Deal Castle
Mπ:162x241:Presented by Tate Gallery Publications 1979

T02950 Walmer Castle
Mπ:162x241:Presented by Tate Gallery Publications 1979

T02951 Dover Castle
Mπ:162x241:Presented by Tate Gallery Publications 1979

T02952 Dover, from Shakespears Cliff
Mπ:162x241:Presented by Tate Gallery Publications 1979

T02953 Shakespears Cliff
Mπ:162x241:Presented by Tate Gallery Publications 1979

T02954 Folkestone, Kent
Mπ:162x241:Presented by Tate Gallery Publications 1979

T02955 Dungeness Light House
Mπ:162x241:Presented by Tate Gallery Publications 1979

T02956 Rye, Sussex
Mπ:162x241:Presented by Tate Gallery Publications 1979

T02957 Winchelsea
Mπ:162x241:Presented by Tate Gallery Publications 1979

T02958 Hastings, from the White Rock
Mπ:162x241:Presented by Tate Gallery Publications 1979

T02959 Hastings, from the East Cliff
Mπ:162x241:Presented by Tate Gallery Publications 1979

T02960 Near Beachy-head
Mπ:162x241:Presented by Tate Gallery Publications 1979

T02961 Near Regents Square, Brighton
Mπ:162x241:Presented by Tate Gallery Publications 1979

T02962 Ovington near Brighton
Mπ:162x241:Presented by Tate Gallery Publications 1979

T02963 Shoreham
Mπ:162x241:Presented by Tate Gallery Publications 1979

T02964 Pier at Little Hampton
Mπ:162x241:Presented by Tate Gallery Publications 1979

T02965 View from the Park, Arundel
Mπ:162x241:Presented by Tate Gallery Publications 1979

T02966 Bognor
Mπ:162x241:Presented by Tate Gallery Publications 1979

T02967 View from Portsdown Hill
Mπ:162x241:Presented by Tate Gallery Publications 1979

T02968 West Cowes
Mπ:162x241:Presented by Tate Gallery Publications 1979

T02969 Lord Henry Seymours Castle
Mπ:162x241:Presented by Tate Gallery Publications 1979

T02970 Mr Nash's Castle
Mπ:162x241:Presented by Tate Gallery Publications 1979

T02971 Ryde
Mπ:162x241:Presented by Tate Gallery Publications 1979

T02972 Brading Harbour
Mπ:162x241:Presented by Tate Gallery Publications 1979

T02973 Shanklin Chine
Mπ:162x241:Presented by Tate Gallery Publications 1979

T02974 Freshwater Bay, Isle of Wight
Mπ:162x241:Presented by Tate Gallery Publications 1979

T02975 Needles Cliff, & Needles, Isle of Wight
Mπ:162x241:Presented by Tate Gallery Publications 1979

T02976 Distant View of the Needles & Hurst Castle
Mπ:162x241:Presented by Tate Gallery Publications 1979

T02977 Christchurch
Mπ:162x241:Presented by Tate Gallery Publications 1979

T02978 Poole, Dorsetshire
Mπ:162x241:Presented by Tate Gallery Publications 1979

T02979 Corfe Castle
Mπ:162x241:Presented by Tate Gallery Publications 1979

T02980 Swanage
Mπ:162x241:Presented by Tate Gallery Publications 1979

T02981 Lulworth Cove
Mπ:162x241:Presented by Tate Gallery Publications 1979

T02982 Weymouth
Mπ:162x241:Presented by Tate Gallery Publications 1979

T02983 Light-house, Isle of Portland
Mπ:162x241:Presented by Tate Gallery Publications 1979

T02984 St Catherine's Chapel, Dorset
Mπ:162x241:Presented by Tate Gallery Publications 1979

T02985 Bridport Harbour, Dorset
Mπ:162x241:Presented by Tate Gallery Publications 1979

T02986 Lyme Regis, from Charmouth, Dorset
Mπ:162x241:Presented by Tate Gallery Publications 1979

T02987 Sidmouth, Devon
Mπ:162x241:Presented by Tate Gallery Publications 1979

T02988 Exmouth, Devon
Mπ:162x241:Presented by Tate Gallery Publications 1979

T02989 Teignmouth, Devon
Mπ:162x241:Presented by Tate Gallery Publications 1979

T02990 Babbacombe, Devon
Mπ:162x241:Presented by Tate Gallery Publications 1979

T02991 Torbay, Devon
Mπ:162x241:Presented by Tate Gallery Publications 1979

T02992 Tor-abbey, Devon
Mπ:162x241:Presented by Tate Gallery Publications 1979

T02993 Tor-quay, Devon
Mπ:162x241:Presented by Tate Gallery Publications 1979

T02994 Brixham, Torbay, Devon
Mπ:162x241:Presented by Tate Gallery Publications 1979

T02995 Entrance to Dartmouth, Devon
Mπ:162x241:Presented by Tate Gallery Publications 1979

T02996 The Junction of the Dart with the Sea
Mπ:162x241:Presented by Tate Gallery Publications 1979

T02997 Near Kingswear, on the Dart, Devon
Mπ:162x241:Presented by Tate Gallery Publications 1979

T02998 Kingswear, Devon
Mπ:162x241:Presented by Tate Gallery Publications 1979

T02999 Salcombe, Devon
Mπ:162x241:Presented by Tate Gallery Publications 1979

T03000 Bovisand, near Plymouth
Mπ:162x241:Presented by Tate Gallery Publications 1979

T03001 Quay at Straddon Point, near Plymouth
Mπ:162x241:Presented by Tate Gallery Publications 1979

T03002 The Citadel, Plymouth
Mπ:162x241:Presented by Tate Gallery Publications 1979

T03003 Catwater, Plymouth from the Citadel
Mπ:162x241:Presented by Tate Gallery Publications 1979

T03004 Mount Edgecumbe, from the Citadel, Plymouth
Mπ:162x241:Presented by Tate Gallery Publications 1979

T03005 View from Mount Edgecumbe
Mπ:162x241:Presented by Tate Gallery Publications 1979

T03006 Hamoaze, from Mount Edgecumbe
Mπ:162x241:Presented by Tate Gallery Publications 1979

T03007 Port Wrinkle, Cornwall
Mπ:162x241:Presented by Tate Gallery Publications 1979

T03008 East Looe, Cornwall
Mπ:162x241:Presented by Tate Gallery Publications 1979

T03009 Polperro, Cornwall
Mπ:162x241:Presented by Tate Gallery Publications 1979

T03010 Fowey, from Bodenick, Cornwall
Mπ:162x241:Presented by Tate Gallery Publications 1979

T03011 Fowey Castle, Cornwall
Mπ:162x241:Presented by Tate Gallery Publications 1979

T03012 Polkerris, Cornwall
Mπ:162x241:Presented by Tate Gallery Publications 1979

T03013 Mevagissey, Cornwall
Mπ:162x241:Presented by Tate Gallery Publications 1979

T03014 Mevagissey, Cornwall
Mπ:162x241:Presented by Tate Gallery Publications 1979

T03015 Gorran Haven, Cornwall
Mπ:162x241:Presented by Tate Gallery Publications 1979

T03016 Port-looe, Cornwall
Mπ:162x241:Presented by Tate Gallery Publications 1979

T03017 Falmouth, Cornwall
Mπ:162x241:Presented by Tate Gallery Publications 1979

T03018 The Lizard Light-houses, Cornwall
Mπ:162x241:Presented by Tate Gallery Publications 1979

T03019 Mullyan Cover, Cornwall
Mπ:162x241:Presented by Tate Gallery Publications 1979

T03020 Near Mullyan Cover, Cornwall
Mπ:162x241:Presented by Tate Gallery Publications 1979

T03021 St Michaels Mount, Cornwall
Mπ:162x241:Presented by Tate Gallery Publications 1979

T03022 St Michaels Mount, Cornwall
Mπ:162x241:Presented by Tate Gallery Publications 1979

T03023 Penzance, Cornwall
Mπ:162x241:Presented by Tate Gallery Publications 1979

T03024 The Land's End, Cornwall
Mπ:162x241:Presented by Tate Gallery Publications 1979

T03239 Hythe
Mπ:162x241:Presented by Tate Gallery Publications 1979

T03240 Brighton
Mπ:162x241:Presented by Tate Gallery Publications 1979

DANIELS, Harvey born 1936
Modern Collection

IAA Portfolio (P03096-P03104, P03107; complete group; mixed group)

P03098 Marc's Dogs (1975)
CLπ:622x349:signed:Presented by the International Association of Art 1975

DARBOVEN, Hanne born 1941
Modern Collection

T03410 Card Index: Filing Cabinet, Part 2 (1975)
10 VDπb:1880x2210:signed:Purchased 1982

D'ARCANGELO, Allan born 1930
Modern Collection

P04157 Constellation I (1971)
CNπ:661x661:signed:Presented by Rose and Chris Prater through the Institute of Contemporary Prints 1975

P04158 Constellation II (1971)
CNπ:662x661:signed:Presented by Rose and Chris Prater through the Institute of Contemporary Prints 1975

P04159 Constellation III (1971)
CNπ:661x660:signed:Presented by Rose and Chris Prater through the Institute of Contemporary Prints 1975

P04160 Constellation IV (1971)
CNπ:661x661:signed:Presented by Rose and Chris Prater through the Institute of Contemporary Prints 1975

DAVID, Allen born 1926
Modern Collection

P06097 The Sun and the Heralds (1967)
MLπ:610x457:signed:Presented by Curwen Studio through the Institute of Contemporary Prints 1975

P06098 Blue Fountain (1970)
CLπ:613x467:Presented by Curwen Studio through the Institute of Contemporary Prints 1975

P06099 Green Exploding Sun (1970)
CLπ:483x486:signed:Presented by Curwen Studio through the Institute of Contemporary Prints 1975

P06100 Red Fountain II (1970)
CLπ:610x464:Presented by Curwen Studio through the Institute of Contemporary Prints 1975

DAVIE, Alan born 1920
Modern Collection
Tate Gallery Archive holds material concerning this artist

T00203 Birth of Venus (1955)
Ob:1600x2438:signed:Purchased 1958

T00267 Head (circa 1955)
DWπ:244x910:signed:Purchased 1959

T00417 Entrance for a Red Temple No. 1 (1960)
Oc:2134x1727:signed:Purchased 1961

T00633 Sacrifice (1956)
Ob:2337x3200:Purchased 1964

T01526 Entrance to a Paradise (1949)
Ob:1518x1210:signed:Purchased 1972

T01584 Fairy Tree No. 5 (1971)
Oc:1727x2134:signed:Presented by the artist 1972

T01748 Image of the Fish God (1956)
Ow:1530x1219:Presented by E.J. Power through the Friends of the Tate Gallery 1973

T01749 Black Mirror (1952)
Ow:1219x1219:signed:Purchased 1973

T03815 Village Myths No. 36 (1983)
Oc:2135x1730:signed:Purchased 1983

P06101 Sleep My Angel (1961-2)
CLπ:578x813:Presented by Curwen Studio through the Institute of Contemporary Prints 1975

P06102 Bird Noises (1963)
CLπ:578x806:Presented by Curwen Studio through the Institute of Contemporary Prints 1975

P06103 Celtic Dreamboat I (1965)
CLπ:514x768:signed:Presented by Curwen Studio through the Institute of Contemporary Prints 1975

P06104 Celtic Dreamboat II (1965)
CLπ:514x768:signed:Presented by Curwen Studio through the Institute of Contemporary Prints 1975

P06105 Celtic Dreamboat III (1965)
CLπ:514x768:signed:Presented by Curwen Studio through the Institute of Contemporary Prints 1975

P06106 For the Hens (trial proof) (1968)
MLπ:514x772:Presented by Curwen Studio through the Institute of Contemporary Prints 1975

P06107 Italian Image (1973)
CLπ:333x613:Presented by Curwen Studio through the Institute of Contemporary Prints 1975

Penwith Portfolio (P01416, P06005, P06108, P06130, P06241, P06324, P06346, P06359, P06399, P06519, P06700; complete group; mixed group)

P06108 Bird Through Wall (1973)
CLπ:502x708:signed:Presented by Curwen Studio through the Institute of Contemporary Prints 1975

P06706 For the Hens (1968)
CLπ:514x768:signed:Presented by Curwen Studio 1976

P06774 Magic Picture No. 1 (1977)
CLπ:546x743:signed:Presented by Curwen Studio 1978

P77276 A Great Sound in the Heavens (1948)
Jπ:230x295:Purchased 1989

P77277 Night Sky on a Holiday (1948)
Jπ:482x335:Purchased 1989

P77278 Interested Sperm Around an Egg (1948)
Jπ:255x403:Purchased 1989

P77279 Spirit Over the Landscape (1948)
Jπ:255x403:Purchased 1989

P77280 Obscure Biological Function Surrounded by Nerve
Impulses (1948)
Jπ:254x401:Purchased 1989

DAVIES, John born 1946
Modern Collection
Tate Gallery Archive holds material concerning this artist

T01577 Dogman (1972)
Sv:279x178x267:Purchased 1972

T01578 William Jeffrey with Device (1972)
Sv:305x203x394:Purchased 1972

T02382 Young Man (1969-71)
Sva:1803x508x279:Presented by Mme Andrée Stassart
1979

T03907 Head with Blue Eyes (1983-84)
Sap:1046x635x671:signed:Purchased 1984

DAVIS, Lady (neé Mary Halford) 1866-1941
British Collection

N03004 Fan: Masques and Bergamasques
Wf:190x413:Presented by Francis Howard through the
National Loans Exhibition Committee 1914

DAVIS, Gene born 1920
Modern Collection

T01116 Quiet Firecracker (1968)
Ac:2210x537:signed:Presented by the artist through the
American Federation of Arts 1969

DAVIS, Henry William Banks 1833-1914
British Collection

N01528 Mother and Son (1881)
Oc:508x762:signed:Presented by Sir Henry Tate 1894

N01608 Returning to the Fold (1880)
Oc:686x1213:signed:Presented by the Trustees of the
Chantrey Bequest 1880

N01774 Approaching Night (1899)
Oc:559x914:signed:Presented by the Trustees of the
Chantrey Bequest 1899

DAVIS, John Scarlett 1804-1845
British Collection
Tate Gallery Archive holds material concerning this artist

N04794 Interior of Amiens Cathedral (?exhibited 1841)
Oc:737x1654:Presented by Percy Moore Turner 1935

attributed to
DAVIS, John Scarlett 1804-1845
British Collection

N05634 Man in a Top Hat (circa 1838)
Oc:635x527:Presented by Percy Moore Turner 1945

DAVIS, Ron born 1937
Modern Collection

T01068 Vector (1968)
Aa:1435x3454x54:Purchased 1968

DAVIS, William 1812-1873
British Collection

T04170 A Day's Sport at Bidston Hill (circa 1865)
Oc:301x401:signed:Purchased 1986

DAVISON, Francis 1919-1984
Modern Collection

T04865 Brilliant Black (1982)
Vb:1425x1460:signed:Purchased 1986

DAWE, George 1781-1829
British Collection

T00718 Imogen Found in the Cave of Belarius (exhibited 1809)
Oc:1003x1270:signed:Purchased 1965

DAWS, Lawrence born 1927
Modern Collection

P04161 Burning Train (1972)
CNπ:540x543:signed:Presented by Rose and Chris Prater
through the Institute of Contemporary Prints 1975

P04162 The Cage (1972)
CNπ:606x610:signed:Presented by Rose and Chris Prater
through the Institute of Contemporary Prints 1975

P04163 Omen Bird (1972)
CNπ:533x537:signed:Presented by Rose and Chris Prater
through the Institute of Contemporary Prints 1975

P04164 Pacific Eye (1972)
CNπ:610x613:signed:Presented by Rose and Chris Prater
through the Institute of Contemporary Prints 1975

DAYES, Edward 1763-1804
British Collection

T00986 West Gate, Winchester (1792)
Wπ:213x137:signed:Presented by the National Art
Collections Fund (Herbert Powell Bequest) 1967

T05210 The Fall of the Rebel Angels (1798)
WDπ:910x650:signed:Purchased 1988

DEACON, Richard born 1949
Modern Collection
Tate Gallery Archive holds material concerning this artist

T03958 For Those Who Have Ears, No. 2 (1983)
Swv:2730x4000x1100:Presented by the Patrons of New
Art through the Friends of the Tate Gallery 1985

T04859 It's Orpheus When There's Singing No. 7 (1979)
GPDπ:1117x1470:Presented by Weltkunst Foundation
1986

T05208 Untitled Drawing No. 1 (1980)
Dπ:460x645:Presented by Weltkunst Foundation 1988

T05209 Untitled Drawing (1981)
Dπ:740x1110:Presented by Weltkunst Foundation 1988

T05558 Struck Dumb (1988)
Sm:1580x3900x2500:Purchased 1989

Muzot (P77252-P77255; complete group)
P77252 1 (1987)
Lπ:644x641:signed:Purchased 1988

P77253   2 (1987)
         Iπ:644x644:signed:Purchased 1988
P77254   3 (1987)
         Ia:640x640:signed:Purchased 1988
P77255   4 (1987)
         Ia:640x640:signed:Purchased 1988

DEAN, Catherine 1905-1983
Modern Collection

N05123   Sheep's Skull and Ferns (1935)
         Oc:406x508:signed:Presented by Lady Matthews 1940

DE BELLEROCHE, Count Albert 1864-1944
British Collection
Tate Gallery Archive holds material concerning this artist

T00003   Olympia de la Fontaine (?exhibited 1904)
         Ow:146x114:Presented by Count William de Belleroche,
         the artist's son 1955

DE BOCK, Théophile - see BOCK, Théophile de

DE CACHARD, Comte Regis de Bouvier - see BOUVIER de CACHARD, Comte Regis de

DE CAMARGO, Sergio - see CAMARGO, Sergio de

DE CHIRICO, Giorgio 1888-1978
Modern Collection
Tate Gallery Archive holds material concerning this artist

N05976   The Painter's Family (1926)
         La Famille du peintre
         Oc:1464x1149:signed:Purchased 1951
T02309   The Melancholy of Departure (1916)
         Melanconia della partenza
         Oc:518x359:signed:Purchased 1978
T04109   The Uncertainty of the Poet (1913)
         L'Incertitude du poète
         Oc:1060x940:signed:Purchased with assistance from the
         National Art Collections Fund (Eugene Cremetti Fund),
         the Carroll Donner Bequest, the Friends of the Tate
         Gallery and members of the public 1985

DE FRANCIA, Peter born 1921
Modern Collection

T04140   Disparates (Omnia Vincit Amor) (1977)
         ODc:2127x1647:signed:Purchased 1986
T04141   Disparates (A Little Night Music) (1969)
         Dπ:775x571:signed:Purchased 1986
T04142   Disparates (Romulus and Remus) (1974)
         Dπ:775x571:signed:Purchased 1986
T04143   Prometheus Offering a Torch (1983)
         Dπ:559x736:signed:Purchased 1986
T04144   Prometheus Steals the Fire (1982)
         Dπ:559x762:signed:Purchased 1986

DEGAS, Edgar 1834-1917
Modern Collection
Tate Gallery Archive holds material concerning this artist

N03157   Carlo Pellegrini (circa 1876-7)
         Oπ:632x340:signed:Presented by the National Art
         Collections Fund 1916
N03390   Head of a Woman (circa 1874)
         Tête de femme
         Oc:321x267:signed:Presented by Viscount D'Abernon
         and Lord Duveen 1919
N03833   Head of a Woman (circa 1873)
         Tête de femme
         Oc:175x197:Presented by A.E. Anderson through the
         National Art Collections Fund 1924
N04710   Miss Lala at the Cirque Fernando (1879)
         Miss Lala au Cirque Fernando
         Pπ:610x476:signed:Presented by Samuel Courtauld 1933
N04711   Woman at her Toilet (circa 1894)
         Femme à sa toilette
         Pπ:956x1099:signed:Presented by C. Frank Stoop 1933
N04712   Bed-Time (circa 1880-5)
         Le Coucher
         PMπ:229x445:signed:Presented by C. Frank Stoop 1933
N05917   Grande Arabesque (circa 1885-90, posthumous cast)
         Sz:400x508x343:signed:Presented by the National Art
         Collections Fund 1951
N05918   Dancer Putting on her Stocking (circa 1900, posthumous
         cast)
         Danseuse mettant son bas
         Sz:470x222x267:signed:Presented by the National Art
         Collections Fund 1951
N05919   Dancer Looking at the Sole of her Right Foot (?1910-11,
         posthumous cast)
         Danseuse regardant la plante de son pied droit
         Sz:476x267x216:signed:Purchased 1949
N05920   Dancer at Rest, her Hands on her Hips, Right Leg
         Forward (circa 1890, cast 1919-20)
         Danseuse au repos, les mains sur les reins, la jambe
         droite en avant
         Sz:457x152x229:signed:Purchased 1949
N06072   Horse Clearing an Obstacle (circa 1887-8)
         Cheval s'enlevant sur l'obstacle
         Sz:305x387x241:signed:Presented by the National Art
         Collections Fund 1952
N06076   Little Dancer Aged Fourteen (1880-1, cast circa 1922)
         Petite danseuse de quatorze ans
         Szv:984x419x365:Purchased with assistance from the
         National Art Collections Fund 1952
T03563   Woman in a Tub (circa 1883)
         Femme au tub
         Pπ:700x700:signed:Bequeathed by Mrs A.F. Kessler 1983

DE GLEHN, Wilfred Gabriel 1870-1951
British Collection

N04805   Soir Antique (circa 1934)
         Tc:711x914:signed:Presented by the Trustees of the
         Chantrey Bequest 1934

DE GREY, Roger born 1918
Modern Collection
Tate Gallery Archive holds material concerning this artist

T00098   Wrotham Hill (1953)
         Oc:610x775:signed:Presented by the Trustees of the
         Chantrey Bequest 1956

T00661 Landscape from the Balcony (1963)
Oc:711x914:signed:Presented by the Trustees of the
Chantrey Bequest 1964

T03220 Interior: Exterior (1977)
Oc:1829x889:signed:Presented by the Trustees of the
Chantrey Bequest 1981

DEHN, Adolf born 1895
Modern Collection

School Prints (P01698-P01727; complete group; mixed
group)

P01702 Minnesota (1947)
CLπ:495x762:signed:Presented by Patrick Seale Prints
1975

DE KARLOWSKA, Stanislawa 1876-1952
British Collection
Tate Gallery Archive holds material concerning this artist

N04816 Berkeley Square (exhibited 1935)
Oc:610x508:signed:Presented anonymously 1935

N06238 Fried Fish Shop (circa 1907)
Oc:337x394:signed:Presented by the artist's family 1954

N06239 Swiss Cottage (exhibited 1914)
Oc:610x762:signed:Presented by the artist's family 1954

DEKKERS, Ad 1938-1974
Modern Collection

T01784 Wood Engraving No. 26 (1973)
Houtgrafiek No XXV1
Swa:1200x1200x19:signed:Purchased 1973

T01785 Wood Engraving No. 27 (1973)
Houtgrafiek No XXV11
Swa:1200x1200x19:signed:Purchased 1973

DE KOONING, Willem born 1904
Modern Collection
Tate Gallery Archive holds material concerning this artist

T01103 Untitled (1966-7)
Dπ:610x476:signed:Presented by the artist through the
American Federation of Arts 1969

T01104 Untitled (1966-7)
Dπ:476x610:signed:Presented by the artist through the
American Federation of Arts 1969

T01108 The Visit (1966-7)
Oc:1524x1219:signed:Purchased 1969

T01178 Women Singing II (1966)
Oπ:914x610:signed:Presented by the artist through the
American Federation of Arts 1970

T03162 Seated Figure on a Bench (1972)
Sz:965x940x829:signed:Purchased 1980

P77158 Landscape at Stanton Street (1971)
MLπ:650x485:signed:Purchased 1986

DELAMOTTE, William 1775-1863
British Collection

T01050 Waterperry, Oxfordshire (1803)
Ob:324x489:signed:Purchased 1968

DeLAP, Tony born 1927
Modern Collection

T00909 Modern Times II (1966)
Sa:362x610x318:signed:Presented anonymously through
the American Federation of Arts 1967

DELAUNAY, Robert 1885-1941
Modern Collection

T00217 Study for 'The City' (1909-10)
Study for 'La Ville'
Oc:883x1245:Purchased 1958

T00920 Windows Open Simultaneously (First Part, Third Motif)
(1912)
Fenêtres ouvertes simultanément (1ère partie 3ème
motif)
Oc:457x375:signed:Purchased 1967

T01233 Endless Rhythm (1934)
Rythme sans fin
Oc:1619x1302:Purchased 1970

DELAUNAY, Sonia 1885-1979
Modern Collection
Tate Gallery Archive holds material concerning this artist

T00817 Triptych (1963)
Triptyque
Oc:997x200:signed:Purchased 1966

P07355 Prose on the Trans-Siberian Railway and of Little
Jehanne of France (1913)
La Prose du Transsibérien et de la Petite Jehanne de
France
WCJπ:1956x356:Purchased 1980

DELL, Edwin la - see LA DELL, Edwin

DE LOMBOS, Philip Alexius Laszlo - see LASZLO de LOMBOS, Philip Alexius

DE LOUTHERBOURG, Philip James 1740-1812
British Collection

N00316 Lake Scene in Cumberland: Evening (1792)
Oc:425x603:signed:Presented by Robert Vernon 1847

N05389 A Distant Hail-Storm Coming On, and the March of
Soldiers with their Baggage (1799)
Oc:1092x1626:signed:Presented by the National Art
Collections Fund 1942

T00772 An Avalanche in the Alps (1803)
Oc:1099x1600:signed:Presented by the Friends of the
Tate Gallery 1965

T00921 Travellers Attacked by Banditti (1781)
Oc:673x1051:signed:Purchased 1967

T01138 The Vision of the White Horse (1798)
Oc:1222x991:signed:Purchased 1969

T01451 The Battle of Camperdown (1799)
Oc:1524x2140:signed:Purchased with assistance from the
Friends of the Tate Gallery 1971

T01452 The Battle of the Nile (1800)
Oc:1524x2140:signed:Purchased with assistance from the
Friends of the Tate Gallery 1971

DELVAUX, Paul born 1897
Modern Collection
Tate Gallery Archive holds material concerning this artist

T00134 Sleeping Venus (1944)
La Vénus endormie
Oc:1727x1991:signed:Presented by Baron Urvater 1957

T03361 Leda (1948)
Léda
Ob:1527x950:signed:Purchased 1982

DE MAISTRE, Roy 1894-1968
Modern Collection

N06201 Interior with Lamp (1953)
Ob:914x635:signed:Purchased 1953

N06225 Still Life: Fruit (1954)
Oc:775x546:signed:Presented by Eric Hall 1954

T00029 Pieta (1950)
Oc:1524x1143:signed:Presented by R.A. Butler (later
Lord Butler of Saffron Walden) 1955

T00137 Vegetable Still Life (1956)
Ob:787x610:Purchased 1957

T01092 Marriage (circa 1936)
Oc:1524x1143:signed:Presented by Sir John Rothenstein
through the Friends of the Tate Gallery 1968

DEMNIG, Gunther born 1947
Modern Collection

T03421 Blood Trail (Kassel/London) (1981)
Blutspur (Kassel/London)
SVm, Vc:800x500x2185, 5620x600:signed:Presented by
the artist 1982

DENNY, Robyn born 1930
Modern Collection
Tate Gallery Archive holds material concerning this artist

T00740 Life Line I (1963)
Oc:2134x1829:Purchased 1965

T01039 First Light (1965-6)
Oc:2438x1981:signed:Purchased 1968

T01040 Garden (1966-7)
Oc:2438x1981:Purchased 1968

T01523 Golem I (1957-8)
OVb:1518x2438:signed:Purchased 1972

T01729 Home from Home (1959)
Oc:2438x1981:signed:Purchased 1973

T01730 Baby is Three (1960)
Oc:2134x3658:Purchased 1973

T01830 Slats (1957)
Ovw:318x514:signed:Presented by the artist 1973

T01831 Collage 2 (The Rout of San Romano, Small Version No.
I) (1957)
VGb:559x1041:signed:Presented by the artist 1973

T01832 Manman (1957)
Dπ:162x232:signed:Presented by the artist 1973

T01833 Word Row (1957)
VGb:235x206:signed:Presented by the artist 1973

T01834 Abbey Wood No. I (1958-9)
VGπ:264x283:signed:Presented by the artist 1973

T01835 Collage (Austin Reed, Version I) (1959)
VGb:264x273:signed:Presented by the artist 1973

T01836 Painting (1959)
OGπ:756x552:signed:Presented by the artist 1973

T01837 Figure I (1960)
ODVπ:527x432:signed:Presented by the artist 1973

T01838 Figure II (1960)
DVπ:454x381:signed:Presented by the artist 1973

T01839 Painting (1962)
OGb:533x343:signed:Presented by the artist 1973

T01919 Glass I. From Here (1971)
Oc:2743x5182:Purchased 1974

For John Constable (P03149-P03157, P03159-P03161,
P03180-P03185; complete group; mixed group)

P03152 [no title] (1976)
CNVπ:622x1032:signed:Presented by Bernard Jacobson
Gallery 1976

P04165 Untitled / Müller Calendar Print (1963)
CNπ:337x340:signed:Presented by Rose and Chris Prater
through the Institute of Contemporary Prints 1975

The Institute of Contemporary Arts Portfolio (P04016,
P04038, P04053, P04076, P04115, P04125, P04166,
P04248, P04256, P04315-P04316, P04334,
P04378-P04380, P04419, P04635, P04752, P04938,
P05138, P05155, P05248; complete group; mixed group)

P04166 Untitled (1964)
CNπ:486x483:signed:Presented by Rose and Chris Prater
through the Institute of Contemporary Prints 1975

Suite 66 (P04167-P04176; complete group)

P04167 Suite 66 I (1966)
CNπ:495x762:signed:Presented by Rose and Chris Prater
through the Institute of Contemporary Prints 1975

P04168 Suite 66 II (1966)
CNπ:795x495:signed:Presented by Rose and Chris Prater
through the Institute of Contemporary Prints 1975

P04169 Suite 66 III (1966)
CNπ:762x495:signed:Presented by Rose and Chris Prater
through the Institute of Contemporary Prints 1975

P04170 Suite 66 IV (1966)
CNπ:758x496:signed:Presented by Rose and Chris Prater
through the Institute of Contemporary Prints 1975

P04171 Suite 66 V (1966)
CNπ:759x495:signed:Presented by Rose and Chris Prater
through the Institute of Contemporary Prints 1975

P04172 Suite 66 VI (1966)
CNπ:756x456:signed:Presented by Rose and Chris Prater
through the Institute of Contemporary Prints 1975

P04173 Suite 66 VII (1966)
CNπ:760x495:signed:Presented by Rose and Chris Prater
through the Institute of Contemporary Prints 1975

P04174 Suite 66 VIII (1966)
CNπ:760x495:signed:Presented by Rose and Chris Prater
through the Institute of Contemporary Prints 1975

P04175 Suite 66 IX (1966)
CNπ:758x495:signed:Presented by Rose and Chris Prater
through the Institute of Contemporary Prints 1975

P04176 Suite 66 X (1966)
CNπ:758x495:signed:Presented by Rose and Chris Prater
through the Institute of Contemporary Prints 1975

Waddington Suite (P04167-P04181; complete group)

P04177 [title not known] (1968-9)
CNπ:610x534:signed:Presented by Rose and Chris Prater
through the Institute of Contemporary Prints 1975

P04178 [title not known] (1968-9)
CNπ:609x534:signed:Presented by Rose and Chris Prater
through the Institute of Contemporary Prints 1975

P04179 [title not known] (1968-9)
CNπ:609x534:signed:Presented by Rose and Chris Prater through the Institute of Contemporary Prints 1975

P04180 [title not known] (1968-9)
CNπ:609x534:signed:Presented by Rose and Chris Prater through the Institute of Contemporary Prints 1975

P04181 [title not known] (1968-9)
CNπ:607x534:signed:Presented by Rose and Chris Prater through the Institute of Contemporary Prints 1975

The Paradise Suite (P04182-P04186; complete group)
P04182 [title not known] (1969)
CNπ:8454x656:signed:Presented by Rose and Chris Prater through the Institute of Contemporary Prints 1975

P04183 [title not known] (1969)
CNπ:844x655:signed:Presented by Rose and Chris Prater through the Institute of Contemporary Prints 1975

P04184 [title not known] (1969)
CNπ:845x655:signed:Presented by Rose and Chris Prater through the Institute of Contemporary Prints 1975

P04185 [title not known] (1969)
CNπ:844x655:signed:Presented by Rose and Chris Prater through the Institute of Contemporary Prints 1975

P04186 [title not known] (1969)
CNπ:844x656:signed:Presented by Rose and Chris Prater through the Institute of Contemporary Prints 1975

The Paramount Suite (P04187-P04189; complete group)
P04187 [no title] (1969)
CNπ:664x861:signed:Presented by Rose and Chris Prater through the Institute of Contemporary Prints 1975

P04188 [no title] (1969)
CNπ:664x860:signed:Presented by Rose and Chris Prater through the Institute of Contemporary Prints 1975

P04189 [no title] (1969)
CNπ:663x860:signed:Presented by Rose and Chris Prater through the Institute of Contemporary Prints 1975

All Through the Day (P04190-P04194; complete group)
P04190 [no title] (1970)
CNπ:724x761:signed:Presented by Rose and Chris Prater through the Institute of Contemporary Prints 1975

P04191 [no title] (1970)
CNπ:723x760:signed:Presented by Rose and Chris Prater through the Institute of Contemporary Prints 1975

P04192 [no title] (1970)
CNπ:723x762:signed:Presented by Rose and Chris Prater through the Institute of Contemporary Prints 1975

P04193 [no title] (1970)
CNπ:723x761:signed:Presented by Rose and Chris Prater through the Institute of Contemporary Prints 1975

P04194 [no title] (1970)
CNπ:724x762:signed:Presented by Rose and Chris Prater through the Institute of Contemporary Prints 1975

Light of the World Suite (P04195-P04204; complete group)
P04195 [no title] (1970)
CNπ:724x794:signed:Presented by Rose and Chris Prater through the Institute of Contemporary Prints 1975

P04196 [no title] (1970)
CNπ:723x794:signed:Presented by Rose and Chris Prater through the Institute of Contemporary Prints 1975

P04197 [no title] (1970)
CNπ:724x794:signed:Presented by Rose and Chris Prater through the Institute of Contemporary Prints 1975

P04198 [no title] (1970)
CNπ:723x794:signed:Presented by Rose and Chris Prater through the Institute of Contemporary Prints 1975

P04199 [no title] (1970)
CNπ:724x792:signed:Presented by Rose and Chris Prater through the Institute of Contemporary Prints 1975

P04200 [no title] (1970)
CNπ:724x793:signed:Presented by Rose and Chris Prater through the Institute of Contemporary Prints 1975

P04201 [no title] (1970)
CNπ:724x794:signed:Presented by Rose and Chris Prater through the Institute of Contemporary Prints 1975

P04202 [no title] (1970)
CNπ:724x794:signed:Presented by Rose and Chris Prater through the Institute of Contemporary Prints 1975

P04203 [no title] (1970)
CNπ:724x794:signed:Presented by Rose and Chris Prater through the Institute of Contemporary Prints 1975

P04204 [no title] (1970)
CNπ:724x794:signed:Presented by Rose and Chris Prater through the Institute of Contemporary Prints 1975

Heavenly Suite (P04205-P04209; complete group)
P04205 [title not known] (1971)
CNπ:794x724:signed:Presented by Rose and Chris Prater through the Institute of Contemporary Prints 1975

P04206 [title not known] (1971)
CNπ:794x724:signed:Presented by Rose and Chris Prater through the Institute of Contemporary Prints 1975

P04207 [title not known] (1971)
CNπ:794x724:signed:Presented by Rose and Chris Prater through the Institute of Contemporary Prints 1975

P04208 [title not known] (1971)
CNπ:794x724:signed:Presented by Rose and Chris Prater through the Institute of Contemporary Prints 1975

P04209 [title not known] (1971)
CNπ:794x724:signed:Presented by Rose and Chris Prater through the Institute of Contemporary Prints 1975

Night Suite (P04210-P04214; complete group)
P04210 [title not known] (1972)
CNπ:781x606:signed:Presented by Rose and Chris Prater through the Institute of Contemporary Prints 1975

P04211 [title not known] (1972)
CNπ:781x606:signed:Presented by Rose and Chris Prater through the Institute of Contemporary Prints 1975

P04212 [title not known] (1972)
CNπ:781x606:signed:Presented by Rose and Chris Prater through the Institute of Contemporary Prints 1975

P04213 [title not known] (1972)
CNπ:781x606:signed:Presented by Rose and Chris Prater through the Institute of Contemporary Prints 1975

P04214 [title not known] (1972)
CNπ:781x606:signed:Presented by Rose and Chris Prater through the Institute of Contemporary Prints 1975

P04215 From Life (1973)
CNπ:775x606:signed:Presented by Rose and Chris Prater through the Institute of Contemporary Prints 1975

Colour Boxes (P07215-P07219; complete group)
P07215 [no title] (1969)
CNπ:615x510:signed:Purchased 1976

P07216 [no title] (1969)
CNπ:615x510:signed:Purchased 1976

P07217 [no title] (1969)
CNπ:615x510:signed:Purchased 1976

P07218 [no title] (1969)
CNπ:615x510:signed:Purchased 1976

P07219 [no title] (1969)
CNπ:615x510:signed:Purchased 1976

Generations (P07388-P07393; incomplete group)

P07388 [no title] (1978)
CNπ:524x705:signed:Purchased 1980

P07389 [no title] (1978)
CNπ:524x705:signed:Purchased 1980

P07390 [no title] (1978)
CNπ:524x705:signed:Purchased 1980

P07391 [no title] (1978)
CNπ:524x705:signed:Purchased 1980

P07392 [no title] (1978)
CNπ:524x705:signed:Purchased 1980

P07393 [no title] (1978)
CNπ:524x705:signed:Purchased 1980

Autographs (P07610-P07614; complete group)

P07610 [no title] (1981)
CNπ:1051x752:signed:Purchased 1982

P07611 [no title] (1981)
CNπ:1051x752:signed:Purchased 1982

P07612 [no title] (1981)
CNπ:1051x752:signed:Purchased 1982

P07613 [no title] (1981)
CNπ:1051x752:signed:Purchased 1982

P07614 [no title] (1981)
CNπ:1051x752:signed:Purchased 1982

DENTITH, Henry (D. Henry) born 1931
Modern Collection

P06109 Still Life (1970)
CLπ:702x514:signed:Presented by Curwen Studio
through the Institute of Contemporary Prints 1975

DERAIN, André 1880-1954
Modern Collection
Tate Gallery Archive holds material concerning this artist

N04784 Landscape near Barbizon (circa 1922)
Oc:708x727:signed:Purchased 1935

N06030 The Pool of London (1906)
Oc:657x991:Presented by the Trustees of the Chantrey
Bequest 1951

T00127 Sketch for 'The Old Bridge at Cagnes' (1910)
DWπ:197x222:Purchased 1957

T00165 Henri Matisse (1905)
Oc:460x349:signed:Purchased 1958

T03368 Madame Derain in a White Shawl (circa 1919-20)
Madame Derain au châle blanc
Oc:1955x975:Purchased 1982

T04863 Still Life (circa 1942)
Nature morte
Oc:885x1458:signed:Purchased with assistance from
Cognac Courvoisier 1986

T04923 The Painter and his Family (circa 1939)
Le Peintre et sa famille
Oc:1765x1238:signed:Purchased 1987

DE RIVERA, José born 1904
Modern Collection

T00948 Construction No. 67 (1959)
Sz:737x1391x381:signed:Presented by the artist through
the American Federation of Arts 1967

D'ERLANGER, Rudolphe - see ERLANGER, Rudolphe d'

DE SAINT PHALLE, Niki - see SAINT PHALLE, Niki de

DE SEGONZAC, André Dunoyer - see DUNOYER de SEGONZAC, André

DES GRANGES, David 1611 or 13 - ?1675
British Collection

T02020 The Saltonstall Family (circa 1636-7)
Oc:2140x2762:Purchased with assistance from the
Friends of the Tate Gallery, the National Art Collections
Fund and the Pilgrim Trust 1976

DESNOYER, François 1894-1972
Modern Collection

T03406 Large Port of Sète (1950)
Grand Port de Sète
Oc:1140x1619:signed:Presented by Mme Souza Desnoyer
1982

DESPIAU, Charles 1874-1946
Modern Collection

N04932 Miss Schulte (1934)
Sz:505x451x349:signed:Presented by the National Art
Collections Fund 1938

DE STAEL, Nicolas - see STAEL, Nicolas de

DE TIRTOFF, Romain - see ERTÉ

DE TOULOUSE-LAUTREC, Henri - see TOULOUSE-LAUTREC, Henri de

DEVAS, Anthony 1911-1958
Modern Collection
Tate Gallery Archive holds material concerning this artist

N05110 Mrs Wilson (1939)
Oc:610x508:signed:Presented by the Trustees of the
Chantrey Bequest 1940

T00279 Mrs Dylan Thomas (1942-3)
Oc:762x635:signed:Presented by the Trustees of the
Chantrey Bequest 1959

DEVERELL, Walter Howell 1827-1854
British Collection
Tate Gallery Archive holds material concerning this artist

N02854 A Pet (exhibited 1853)
Oc:838x571:signed:Purchased 1911

N02865 Spencer Deverell
Dπ:92x73:Presented by Wykeham Deverell 1912

N02866 Ruding Deverell (?)
Dπ:67x117:Presented by Wykeham Deverell 1912

N02867 Maria or Jemima Deverell
Dπ:76x51:Presented by Wykeham Deverell 1912

N02868 Louisa
DWπ:140x102:Presented by Wykeham Deverell 1912

N03273 Eustatia (1853)
Oc:559x356:Presented by A.E. Anderson 1918

N03429 Study for 'Twelfth Night' (circa 1850)
Dπ:216x292:Purchased 1919

DEVIS, Arthur 1711-1787
British Collection
Tate Gallery Archive holds material concerning this artist

N03317 Portrait of a Lady (circa 1750-1)
Oc:610x406:Purchased 1918

N03888 Portrait of a Man (circa 1750)
Oc:470x298:Presented by Mr and Mrs John Lane 1924

N05281 The James Family (1751)
Oc:984x1245:signed:Purchased 1941

T01884 A Lady in Blue (1757)
Oc:559x438:signed:Bequeathed by Alan Evans 1974

T03103 Breaking-Up Day at Dr Clayton's School at Salford
(circa 1738)
Oc:1207x1746:Purchased 1980

DEVIS, Anthony Thomas 1729-1817
British Collection

T05474 Hilly Landscape with Sheep
DWπ:136x202:Presented by Miss Marjorie Ball 1988

DE VLAMINCK, Maurice - see VLAMINCK, Maurice de

DE WINT, Peter 1784-1849
British Collection
Tate Gallery Archive holds material concerning this artist

N03477 Knaresborough Castle
Wπ:283x448:Bequeathed by John Henderson 1879

N03478 View near Oxford
Wπ:292x460:Bequeathed by John Henderson 1879

N03479 Lincoln Cathedral, from the Castle Moat
Wπ:400x505:Bequeathed by John Henderson 1879

N03480 Roman Canal, Lincolnshire (circa 1840)
Wπ:238x549:Bequeathed by John Henderson 1879

N03481 Kenilworth Castle
Wπ:274x416:Bequeathed by John Henderson 1879

N03482 Bray on Thames, sketch for No. 3487
Wπ:264x464:Bequeathed by John Henderson 1879

N03483 Cornfield, Ivinghoe, Buckinghamshire
Wπ:298x451:Bequeathed by John Henderson 1879

N03484 A Road in Yorkshire
Wπ:146x368:Bequeathed by John Henderson 1879

N03485 Harvest Time, Lancashire
Wπ:321x619:Bequeathed by John Henderson 1879

N03486 Cottage and Harvesters
Wπ:216x371:Bequeathed by John Henderson 1879

N03487 Bray on Thames from the Towing Path (?circa 1849)
Wπ:371x648:Bequeathed by John Henderson 1879

N03488 Burning Weeds
Wπ:200x543:Bequeathed by John Henderson 1879

N03489 A Warwickshire Lane
WDπ:343x521:Bequeathed by John Henderson 1879

N03490 The Trent near Burton
Wπ:206x432:Bequeathed by John Henderson 1879

N03491 View of Tours
Wπ:149x308:Bequeathed by John Henderson 1879

N03492 Bridge over a Branch of the Wytham, Lincolnshire
Wπ:416x514:Bequeathed by John Henderson 1879

N03493 On the Eden, Cumberland
Wπ:137x505:Bequeathed by John Henderson 1879

N03494 Distant View of Nottingham
Wπ:140x587:Bequeathed by John Henderson 1879

N03495 A Hayfield in Yorkshire
Wπ:241x327:Bequeathed by John Henderson 1879

N03496 Westmorland Hills, Bordering the Ken
Wπ:146x635:Bequeathed by John Henderson 1879

N03497 Ruins of the Bishop's Palace, Lincoln
Wπ:419x521:Bequeathed by John Henderson 1879

N03498 A Cornfield
Wπ:152x476:Bequeathed by John Henderson 1879

N03499 View of London from Greenwich Park
Wπ:127x381:Bequeathed by John Henderson 1879

N03809 View on the Thames
Wπ:152x419:Purchased 1923

N03823 Landscape with Horses Grazing
Oπ:381x584:Purchased 1923

N04879 Harvesting
Oc:692x1168:Purchased 1937

T00987 The Falls of Ogwen
Wπ:330x476:Purchased with assistance from the
National Art Collections Fund (Herbert Powell Bequest)
1967

T03669 Study of Burdock and other Plants
Obw:262x335:Purchased 1983

after
DE WINT, Peter 1784-1849
British Collection
Tate Gallery Archive holds material concerning this artist

Picturesque Views on the Southern Coast of England
(T05218-T05463; complete group; mixed group)

T05267 Hythe, Kent (1816)
Lπ:98x146:Purchased 1988

T05268 Hythe, Kent (1816)
Lπ:98x145:Purchased 1988

T05300 Bognor (1820)
Lπ:98x115:Purchased 1988

T05301 Bognor (1820)
Lπ::Purchased 1988

T05307 Scene on the Beach at Ventnor (1816)
Lπ:126x152:Purchased 1988

T05308 Scene on the Beach at Ventnor (1816)
Lπ:127x152:Purchased 1988

T05310 Undercliff, Isle of Wight, Hampshire (1814)
Lπ:145x220:Purchased 1988

T05311 Undercliff, Isle of Wight, Hampshire (1814)
Lπ:146x222:Purchased 1988

T05312 Black Gang Chine, Isle of Wight, Hampshire (1816)
Lπ:149x213:Purchased 1988

T05313 Black Gang Chine, Isle of Wight, Hampshire (1816)
Lπ:150x215:Purchased 1988

T05318 Cowes Castle, Isle of Wight (1818)
Lπ:136x144:Purchased 1988

T05319　Cowes Castle, Isle of Wight (1818)
　　　　　Lπ:150x163:Purchased 1988

T05424　The Logan Rock, Cornwall (1818)
　　　　　Lπ:116x171:Purchased 1988

T05425　The Logan Rock, Cornwall (1818)
　　　　　Lπ:116x171:Purchased 1988

D. HENRY - see DENTITH, Henry

DIBBETS, Jan born 1941
Modern Collection
Tate Gallery Archive holds material concerning this artist

T01736　Perspective Correction (1968)
　　　　　Fc:1099x1099:signed:Purchased 1973

T01745　Panorama Dutch Mountain 12 x 15 Sea II A (1971)
　　　　　FDb:495x1000:signed:Purchased 1973

P07232　Collage (1973)
　　　　　CFVπ:752x1016:signed:Purchased 1974

DICK, Sir William Reid 1878-1961
British Collection
Tate Gallery Archive holds material concerning this artist

N03449　Androdus (1919)
　　　　　Sz:203x203x152:Presented by the Trustees of the
　　　　　Chantrey Bequest 1919

N05378　Dawn (1921)
　　　　　Ss:248x140x178:signed:Presented by Sir Charles and
　　　　　Lady Tennyson in memory of their son Lieutenant
　　　　　Penrose Tennyson, RNVR 1942

T03329　St George and the Dragon (for E.V. Lucas) (1914)
　　　　　Szs:162x89x108:signed:Presented by the artist's widow
　　　　　1981

T03330　Winged Figure
　　　　　Sz:260x203x60:Presented by the artist's widow 1981

T03331　Sketch for Leverhulme Memorial (Port Sunlight) (circa
　　　　　1930)
　　　　　Sz:184x133x86:signed:Presented by the artist's widow
　　　　　1981

T03332　Sketch for Virgin and Child
　　　　　Szs:219x76x76:Presented by the artist's widow 1981

T03333　Sketch for Memorial Group
　　　　　Sz:194x190x127:Presented by the artist's widow 1981

DICKSEE, Sir Frank 1853-1928
British Collection

N01587　Harmony (1877)
　　　　　Oc:1575x940:signed:Presented by the Trustees of the
　　　　　Chantrey Bequest 1877

N01839　The Two Crowns (1900)
　　　　　Oc:2311x1842:signed:Presented by the Trustees of the
　　　　　Chantrey Bequest 1900

DIEBENKORN, Richard born 1922
Modern Collection

Five Aquatints with Drypoint (P07644; incomplete
group)
P07644　#4 (1978)
　　　　　MIπ:277x200:signed:Purchased 1982

DIGHTON, William Edward 1822-1853
British Collection

N02855　Jerusalem (1852)
　　　　　Wπ:429x756:Presented by subscribers 1911

DILLON, Michael born 1941
Modern Collection

T03717　Op Structure (1967)
　　　　　Sv:910x360x136:Transferred from the Victoria & Albert
　　　　　Museum 1983

T03718　Op Structure (1967)
　　　　　Sv:680x730x460:Transferred from the Victoria & Albert
　　　　　Museum 1983

DILWORTH, Norman born 1933
Modern Collection

P07424　Rational Concepts (1977)
　　　　　MNπ:600x600:signed:Purchased 1981

DIMITRIENKO, Pierre 1925-1974
Modern Collection

T00325　The Petrified Forest (1956)
　　　　　La Forêt pétrifiée
　　　　　Oc:1302x1619:signed:Presented by the Contemporary
　　　　　Art Society 1960

DIMITRIJEVIC, Braco born 1948
Modern Collection

T03684　The Casual Passer-By I Met at 11.28 am, London,
　　　　　October 1972 (1972)
　　　　　3 Fπ:409x1016:signed:Purchased 1983

T03685　Louvre ('J.M.W. Turner' 'Edward Rampton') (1975-9)
　　　　　2 Szs:1870x330x350, 1860x330x350:Purchased 1983

T03686　Louvre ('Leonardo da Vinci' 'Albert Evans') (1975-82)
　　　　　2 Szs:1841x330x350, 1830x330x350:Purchased 1983

T03687　Triptychos Post Historicus or Entrance to the Palace of
　　　　　Light (1982)
　　　　　Fm:1137x1441:Purchased 1983

T03688　Triptychos Post Historicus or Artists' Hats are High
　　　　　above the Rainbow - Portrait of Barry (1982)
　　　　　Fm:1140x1435:Purchased 1983

T04122　Triptychos Post Historicus: Repeated Secret (1978-85)
　　　　　Sv:2020x915x700:Presented by the artist 1985

DINE, Jim born 1935
Modern Collection
Tate Gallery Archive holds material concerning this artist

T00761　Walking Dream with Four Foot Clamp (1965)
　　　　　ODVc:1524x2743x29:signed:Purchased 1965

T03849　The House (Heart) (1983)
　　　　　Sz:1778x1778x356:Presented anonymously 1984

P01790　Throat (1965)
　　　　　CNπ:762x613:signed:Presented by the Museum of
　　　　　Modern Art, New York 1976

P02528　Blue Haircut (1972)
　　　　　CILJπ:537x502:signed:Presented by the artist 1980

P02529　Big Red Wrench in a Landscape (1973)
　　　　　CLπ:765x574:signed:Presented by the artist 1980

P02530　Nutcracker (1973)
　　　　　CLπ:765x572:signed:Presented by the artist 1980

Ten Winter Tools (P02531-P02540; complete group)

P02531　[no title] (1973)
MLπ:707x553:signed:Presented by the artist 1980

P02532　[no title] (1973)
MLπ:708x552:signed:Presented by the artist 1980

P02533　[no title] (1973)
MLπ:708x553:signed:Presented by the artist 1980

P02534　[no title] (1973)
MLπ:710x554:signed:Presented by the artist 1980

P02535　[no title] (1973)
MLπ:710x553:signed:Presented by the artist 1980

P02536　[no title] (1973)
MLπ:700x554:signed:Presented by the artist 1980

P02537　[no title] (1973)
MLπ:707x558:signed:Presented by the artist 1980

P02538　[no title] (1973)
MLπ:707x553:signed:Presented by the artist 1980

P02539　[no title] (1973)
MLπ:707x553:signed:Presented by the artist 1980

P02540　[no title] (1973)
MLπ:708x554:signed:Presented by the artist 1980

P02541　Tinsnip (1973)
CILπ:455x600:signed:Presented by the artist 1980

P02542　Picabia I (Cheer) (1971)
CLπ:1375x918:signed:Presented by the artist 1980

P02543　Picabia II (Forgot) (1971)
CLπ:1375x932:signed:Presented by the artist 1980

P02544　Picabia III (Groans) (1971)
CLπ:1368x928:signed:Presented by the artist 1980

Tool Box (P04216-P04225; complete group)

P04216　Tool Box 1 (1966)
CNπ:605x475:signed:Presented by Rose and Chris Prater through the Institute of Contemporary Prints 1975

P04217　Tool Box 2 (1966)
CNπ:604x475:signed:Presented by Rose and Chris Prater through the Institute of Contemporary Prints 1975

P04218　Tool Box 3 (1966)
CNπ:600x480:signed:Presented by Rose and Chris Prater through the Institute of Contemporary Prints 1975

P04219　Tool Box 4 (1966)
CNπ:605x478:signed:Presented by Rose and Chris Prater through the Institute of Contemporary Prints 1975

P04220　Tool Box 5 (1966)
CNπ:605x478:signed:Presented by Rose and Chris Prater through the Institute of Contemporary Prints 1975

P04221　Tool Box 6 (1966)
CNπ:601x480:signed:Presented by Rose and Chris Prater through the Institute of Contemporary Prints 1975

P04222　Tool Box 7 (1966)
CNπ:603x480:signed:Presented by Rose and Chris Prater through the Institute of Contemporary Prints 1975

P04223　Tool Box 8 (1966)
CNπ:602x476:signed:Presented by Rose and Chris Prater through the Institute of Contemporary Prints 1975

P04224　Tool Box 9 (1966)
CNπ:601x475:signed:Presented by Rose and Chris Prater through the Institute of Contemporary Prints 1975

P04225　Tool Box 10 (1966)
CNπ:603x478:signed:Presented by Rose and Chris Prater through the Institute of Contemporary Prints 1975

P04226　Four Hearts (1969)
CNπ:324x318:signed:Presented by Rose and Chris Prater through the Institute of Contemporary Prints 1975

P04227　Palette II (1969)
CNπ:711x511:signed:Presented by Rose and Chris Prater through the Institute of Contemporary Prints 1975

P07757　Two Hearts in a Forest (1981)
WCJπ:915x1527:signed:Purchased 1982

P08151　Welcome Home Rare Birds (1969)
MNa:152x137:Transferred from the Library 1979

DINKEL, Ernest M.　1894-1983
Modern Collection
Tate Gallery Archive holds material concerning this artist

N04477　The Deluge (exhibited 1929)
Tw:470x464:Presented by the Trustees of the Chantrey Bequest 1929

DISLER, Martin　born 1949
Modern Collection

T03862　Untitled (1984)
Ohne Titel
Dπ:1354x2730:signed:Purchased 1984

Endless Modern Licking of Crashing Globe by Black Doggie - Time Bomb (P07790-P07846; complete group)

P07839　[no title] (1981)
MIπ:530x730:signed:Purchased 1983

P07840　[no title] (1981)
MIπ:530x730:signed:Purchased 1983

P07841　[no title] (1981)
MIπ:530x737:signed:Purchased 1983

P07842　[no title] (1981)
MIπ:527x730:signed:Purchased 1983

P07843　[no title] (1981)
MIπ:530x730:signed:Purchased 1983

P07844　[no title] (1981)
MIπ:527x730:signed:Purchased 1983

P07845　[no title] (1981)
MIπ:527x730:signed:Purchased 1983

P07846　[no title] (1981)
MIπ:530x730:signed:Purchased 1983

P07990　[no title] (1981)
MIπ:556x750:signed:Purchased 1983

P77159　Untitled (1986)
Ohne Titel
3 Iπ:1685x993:signed:Purchased 1986

P77269　Untitled (1986)
Ohne Titel
Iπ:800x1200:Purchased 1989

DISMORR, Jessica　1885-1939
Modern Collection
Tate Gallery Archive holds material concerning this artist

T01084　Abstract Composition (circa 1915)
Ob:413x508:Purchased 1968

T02322　Related Forms (1937)
Tb:556x657:signed:Presented by Quentin Stevenson in memory of Catherine Giles and R.H.M. Ody 1978

DIXON, Harry 1861-1942
British Collection

N01705   Lions (1891)
Wπ:648x1181:signed:Presented by the Trustees of the Chantrey Bequest 1891

DIXON, William ?1784 or 5 - circa 1834
British Collection

T03855   Cottages near a Track
Oπc:163x202:Purchased 1984

T03856   Hops
Oπb:116x141:signed:Purchased 1984

DOBSON, Frank 1888-1963
Modern Collection
Tate Gallery Archive holds material concerning this artist

N04437   Head of a Girl (1925)
Szs:305x241x254:Presented by the Contemporary Art Society 1929

N04510   Truth (1930)
Sz:1270x762x635:signed:Presented by the Contemporary Art Society 1930

N04550   The Earl of Oxford and Asquith (1921)
Sz:330x203x229:Presented by Viscount D'Abernon 1930

N04796   Miss Jeanne de Casalis (1934)
Sz:495x356x241:Presented by Douglas Stephenson 1935

N04922   Noon (1936)
Sp:254x305x343:signed:Presented by the Contemporary Art Society 1938

N05028   Margaret Rawlings (1937)
Sz:571x559x546:signed:Presented anonymously 1937

N05040   Susanna (circa 1925)
Sz:584x406x330:signed:Presented by the Contemporary Art Society 1939

N05874   Torso (1933)
Ss:673x203x203:Purchased 1948

N05938   Sir Osbert Sitwell, Bt (1923)
Sm:318x178x229:Presented by the executors of T.E. Lawrence 1950

T00663   Female Nude (circa 1927-8)
Sz:400x102x76:Presented by the Trustees of the Chantrey Bequest 1964

T01322   The Man Child (1921)
Ss:768x559x324:Presented by the Trustees of the Chantrey Bequest 1971

T02317   Nude (1946)
Dπ:305x457:signed:Presented by S.G. Hand in memory of Mrs I.M. Whitaker 1978

T03719   Charnaux Venus (1933-4)
Sv:1700x500x400:Transferred from the Victoria & Albert Museum 1983

T03720   Kneeling Figure (1935)
Sp:210x130x143:signed:Transferred from the Victoria & Albert Museum 1983

T03721   Crouching Woman (1923)
Sz:110x145x190:Transferred from the Victoria & Albert Museum 1983

DOBSON, William 1611-1646
British Collection

N01249   Endymion Porter (circa 1642-5)
Oc:1499x1270:Purchased 1888

N04619   Portrait of an Officer (circa 1645)
Oc:1022x762:Bequeathed by Mrs E.K. Hornsby-Drake 1932

DOBSON, William Charles Thomas 1817-1898
British Collection

T03448   The Child Jesus Going Down with His Parents to Nazareth (1856)
Oc:1090x900:signed:Purchased 1982

DODD, Francis 1874-1949
British Collection
Tate Gallery Archive holds material concerning this artist

N03957   A Smiling Woman (1904)
Oc:610x508:signed:Presented by the Trustees of the Chantrey Bequest 1924

N04227   Edward Garnett (exhibited 1926)
Dπ:368x267:signed:Purchased 1926

N04507   Cumberland Market
Wπ:203x229:signed:Purchased 1930

N04962   In the Parlour (1937)
Oc:762x622:signed:Presented by the Trustees of the Chantrey Bequest 1938

N05324   Ely (1926)
Oc:508x762:signed:Bequeathed by Frank Pick 1942

DODGSON, John 1890-1969
Modern Collection
Tate Gallery Archive holds material concerning this artist

T00349   Giant Snail (1951-9)
Oc:635x762:signed:Purchased 1960

DOESBURG, Theo van 1883-1931
Modern Collection

T03374   Counter-Composition VI (1925)
Contre-compositie
Oc:500x500:signed:Purchased 1982

DOMJAN, Joseph born 1907
Modern Collection

P01387   Alpine Moon (1973)
CJπ:476x359:signed:Presented by the artist through the Institute of Contemporary Prints 1975

P01388   Bird Song (1973)
CJπ:473x359:signed:Presented by the artist through the Institute of Contemporary Prints 1975

P01389   Blue Poppy (1973)
CJπ:473x362:signed:Presented by the artist through the Institute of Contemporary Prints 1975

P01390   Golden Queen Anne's Lace (1973)
CJπ:473x362:signed:Presented by the artist through the Institute of Contemporary Prints 1975

P01391   Happy Dragon (1973)
CJπ:476x359:signed:Presented by the artist through the Institute of Contemporary Prints 1975

P01392   Heraldic Eagle (1973)
CJπ:473x362:signed:Presented by the artist through the Institute of Contemporary Prints 1975

P01393   Moon Dragon (1973)
CJπ:473x362:signed:Presented by the artist through the Institute of Contemporary Prints 1975

P01394 Morning Star (1973)
CJπ:476x359:signed:Presented by the artist through the Institute of Contemporary Prints 1975

P01395 Ornate Vision (1973)
CJπ:473x362:signed:Presented by the artist through the Institute of Contemporary Prints 1975

P01396 Pink Sunset Cloud (1975)
CJπ:473x362:signed:Presented by the artist through the Institute of Contemporary Prints 1975

DONAGH, Rita born 1939
Modern Collection
Tate Gallery Archive holds material concerning this artist

T01687 Reflection on Three Weeks in May 1970 (1971)
ODc:1524x1524:signed:Purchased 1972

DONALDSON, Andrew Brown 1840-1919
British Collection

N01723 Puente San Martin, Toledo (1889)
Wπ:641x311:signed:Presented by Miss Louisa Twining 1899

DONALDSON, Antony born 1939
Modern Collection
Tate Gallery Archive holds material concerning this artist

T00590 Take Five (1962)
Oc:1524x1524:signed:Purchased 1963

P01397 Christine (1973)
CLπ:502x508:signed:Presented by Christie's Contemporary Art through the Institute of Contemporary Prints 1975

DORAZIO, Piero born 1927
Modern Collection
Tate Gallery Archive holds material concerning this artist

T00804 Very Sharp (1965)
Molto a punta
Oc:1556x2349:signed:Purchased 1966

DÖRFLINGER, Johannes born 1941
Modern Collection

T04899 Mountain Figure (1984)
Dπ:685x1014:signed:Purchased 1987

T04900 Cassida (1986)
PDπ:685x1014:signed:Purchased 1987

T04901 Wing (1986)
PDπ:692x1015:signed:Purchased 1987

T04902 Wave (1985)
PDπ:685x1014:signed:Purchased 1987

P06724 Tarot (1972)
CLπ:337x460:Presented by Curwen Studio 1976

D'ORSAY, Count Alfred 1801-1852
British Collection

T05029 Portrait of J.M.W. Turner ('The Fallacy of Hope'), engraved by J. Hogarth (published 1851)
Lπ:328x225:Presented by Richard Godfrey in memory of Wilfred Yee Huie 1988

DOTREMONT, Christian born 1922
Modern Collection

For Jorn (P03241-P03255; complete group; mixed group)
Pour Jorn

P03247 [no title] (1975-6)
CLπ:492x733:signed:Presented by the Asger Jorn Foundation 1978

DOTTORI, Gerardo 1884-1977
Modern Collection

T01336 Explosion of Red on Green (1910)
Esplosione dirosso sul verde
Oc:492x695:signed:Presented by the artist 1971

DOUBLEDAY, John born 1947
Modern Collection

T03722 Maquette for 'Building Blocks' (1964)
Sz:270x130x70:signed:Transferred from the Victoria & Albert Museum 1983

attributed to
DOUGHTY, William 1757-1782
British Collection

N05598 Caricature Group (circa 1780)
Oc:775x1041:signed:Purchased 1939

DOUGLAS, Edwin 1848-1914
British Collection

N01558 Alderneys (Mother and Daughter) (1875)
Oc:1422x1118:signed:Presented by Sir Henry Tate 1894

DOUGLAS, Sir William Fettes 1822-1891
British Collection

N00617 Bibliomania (?1852)
Oc:889x1295:signed:Bequeathed by Jacob Bell 1859

DOVA, Gianni born 1925
Modern Collection

T00085 Explosion (1953)
Esplosione
Ec:797x702:signed:Presented by Charles Damiano 1956

T00086 Sudden Aggression (1955)
Aggressione improvvisa
Oc:597x800:signed:Presented by Charles Damiano 1956

DOWNARD, Ebenezer Newman active 1849-1889
British Collection

T01139 A Mountain Path at Capel Curig, Wales (1860)
Oc:352x502:signed:Purchased 1969

DOWNMAN, John circa 1750-1824
British Collection

N02233 Lady Clarges (1790)
WDπ:203x165:Bequeathed by Miss Julia Emily Gordon 1896

N03316 Sir Ralph Abercromby (?) and Companion (?circa 1795-1800)
Oc:762x635:Presented by Louis Duveen through the National Art Collections Fund 1918

N03544 Lady Delaval (?) (1792)
Oc:781x781:signed:Presented by Alfred A. de Pass 1920

T01885 Miss Jackson (1778)
Om:229x190:signed:Bequeathed by Alan Evans 1974

DOWNSBROUGH, Peter born 1940
Modern Collection

Jam Press Phase One (P08006-P08014; complete group;
mixed group)

P08008 1. 4 (1973-4)
MLπ:441x559:Transferred from the Library 1977
after

DOYLE, John 1797-1868
British Collection

T04907 Samuel Rogers at his Breakfast Table, engraved by
Charles Mottram (circa 1823)
MIπ:580x866:Presented by Dr David Blayney Brown 1987

DOYLE, John born 1928
Modern Collection
Tate Gallery Archive holds material concerning this artist

P06110 Canterbury Cathedral (1974)
CLπ:419x654:signed:Presented by Curwen Studio
through the Institute of Contemporary Prints 1975

DRAPER, Herbert 1863-1920
British Collection
Tate Gallery Archive holds material concerning this artist

N01679 The Lament for Icarus (exhibited 1898)
Oc:1829x1556:signed:Presented by the Trustees of the
Chantrey Bequest 1898

DRESSLER, Conrad 1856-1940
British Collection

N02242 John Ruskin (1885)
Sp:406x305x279:signed:Presented by T. Thornton 1902

DREVER, Timothy born 1935
Modern Collection

P04228 Untitled (1969)
CNπ:610x610:signed:Presented by Rose and Chris Prater
through the Institute of Contemporary Prints 1975

DROUNGAS, Achilles born 1940
Modern Collection

P01398 Measure of Understanding (1972)
CLπ:597x279:signed:Presented by Christie's
Contemporary Art through the Institute of
Contemporary Prints 1975

P01399 City under Siege (1973)
CLπ:530x692:signed:Presented by Editions Alecto
through the Institute of Contemporary Prints 1975

P01400 A Fig, a Plumb, a Quince, an Apple, a Pear (1973)
CLπ:524x698:signed:Presented by Editions Alecto
through the Institute of Contemporary Prints 1975

DRUMMOND, Malcolm 1880-1945
Modern Collection

T00611 Boyne Hill Vicarage, Maidenhead (circa 1910)
Oc:508x406:Purchased 1963

T00893 Girl with Palmettes (circa 1920)
Oc:498x403:Purchased 1966

DRURY, Alfred 1856-1944
British Collection

N01757 Griselda (1896)
Sz:533x483x254:signed:Presented by the Trustees of the
Chantrey Bequest 1896

DRYSDALE, Russell born 1912
Modern Collection

N05986 War Memorial (1950)
Oc:660x1016:signed:Purchased 1951

DUBSKY, Mario 1939-1985
Modern Collection

T04908 Cabaret Valhalla (1983)
Oc:2130x2132:signed:Presented by Barbara Dubsky, the
artist's sister 1987

DUBUFFET, Jean 1901-1985
Modern Collection
Tate Gallery Archive holds material concerning this artist

T00243 Man with a Hod (1955-6)
L'Homme à la hotte
Vπ:1022x505:signed:Bequeathed by E.C. Gregory 1959

T00801 Spinning Round (1961)
Vire-volte
Oc:975x1304:signed:Presented by Mrs Cynthia Fraser in
memory of her husband, W. Lionel Fraser 1965

T00867 The Busy Life (1953)
La Vie affairée
Oc:1302x1956:signed:Presented by the artist 1966

T00868 The Exemplary Life of the Soil (Texturology LXIII)
(1958)
Vie exemplaire du sol (Texturologie LXIII)
Oc:1295x1619:signed:Purchased 1966

T00869 Nimble Free Hand to the Rescue (1964)
Main leste et rescousse
Ac:1499x2007:signed:Presented by Galerie Beyeler, Basle
and Galerie Jeanne Bucher, Paris 1966

T00870 Site Inhabited by Objects (1965)
Site habité d'objets
Ac:1295x1619:signed:Purchased 1966

T01575 Hopes and Options (1971)
Voeux et options
Sv:2521x4128:Presented by Alistair McAlpine (later Lord
McAlpine of West Green) 1972

T03080 Monsieur Plume with Creases in his Trousers (Portrait of
Henri Michaux) (1947)
Monsieur Plume plis au pantalon (Portrait d'Henri
Michaux)
OVc:1302x965:signed:Purchased 1980

T03679 Vicissitudes (1977)
Les Vicissitudes
Aπc:2100x3390:signed:Purchased 1983

P07781 Man in a Cap (1953)
L'Homme à la casquette
MLπ:503x150:signed:Purchased 1983

P77031 Fern in the Hat (1953)
Fougère au chapeau
CLπ:527x400:signed:Purchased 1984

P77118 Gold and Shadow [from 'Land Registry'] (1958, published 1960)
Or et ombre [from 'Cadastre']
CLπ:443x386:signed:Purchased 1985

P77137 Typist [from 'Matter and Memory'] (1944, published 1945)
Dactylographe [from 'Matière et mémoire']
MLπ:255x153:signed:Purchased 1986

P77160 Peopling of the Lands (1953)
Peuplement des terres
CLπ:645x500:signed:Purchased 1986

P77184 Leaves with Bird (1953)
Feuillages à l'oiseau
MLπ:472x487:signed:Purchased 1987

P77185 Inhabited Landscape (1946)
Paysage habité
CLπ:217x335:signed:Purchased 1987

DUCHAMP, Marcel 1887-1968
Modern Collection
Tate Gallery Archive holds material concerning this artist

T03253 Coffee Mill (1911)
Moulin à café
Ob:330x127:signed:Purchased 1981

DUCHAMP, Marcel and HAMILTON, Richard 1887-1968, born 1922
Modern Collection
Tate Gallery Archive holds material concerning these artists

T02011 The Bride Stripped Bare by her Bachelors, Even (The Large Glass) (1915-23, replica 1965-6)
La Mariée mise à nu par ses célibataires, même
SOVg:2775x1759:signed:Presented by William N. Copley through the American Federation of Arts 1975

DUCHAMP-VILLON, Raymond 1876-1918
Modern Collection

T00371 The Lovers (1913, posthumous cast)
Les Amants
Rm:673x997x121:Presented by the Friends of the Tate Gallery 1960

T02307 Large Horse (1914, cast 1961)
Le Grand cheval
Sz:1000x987x660:signed:Purchased 1978

DUFRESNE, Charles 1876-1938
Modern Collection

N04213 Spahi Attacked by a Lion (1919)
Spahi attaqué par un lion
WGπ:394x505:signed:Presented by C.L. Rutherston 1926

DUFY, Raoul 1877-1953
Modern Collection
Tate Gallery Archive holds material concerning this artist

N04850 Olive Trees by the Golfe Juan (circa 1927)
Oliviers au Golfe Juan
Wπ:508x660:signed:Presented by the Contemporary Art Society 1936

N05943 Deauville, Drying the Sails (1933)
Deauville, le séchage des voiles
Oc:464x1102:signed:Purchased 1950

T02133 The Baou de Saint-Jeannet (1923)
Le Baou de Saint-Jeannet
Oc:645x806:signed:Bequeathed by John Levy 1977

T03564 The Harvest (1929)
La Moisson
Oc:1300x1620:signed:Bequeathed by Mrs A.F. Kessler 1983

T03565 Open Window at Saint-Jeannet (circa 1926-7)
Fenêtre ouverte à Saint-Jeannet
Gπ:656x507:signed:Bequeathed by Mrs A.F. Kessler 1983

T03566 The Kessler Family on Horseback (1931)
La Famille Kessler à cheval
Gπ:500x669:Bequeathed by Mrs A.F. Kessler 1983

T03567 Landscape Study for 'The Kessler Family on Horseback' (1931)
Etude du paysage de 'La Famille Kessler à cheval'
Gπ:503x660:Bequeathed by Mrs A.F. Kessler 1983

T05500 The Kessler Family on Horseback (1932)
Oc:2195x2673:signed:Bequeathed by Mrs A.F. Kessler 1983

School Prints (P01698-P01727; complete group; mixed group)

P01703 The Band (1946-9)
CLπ:495x759:signed:Presented by Patrick Seale Prints 1975

DUGDALE, Thomas 1880-1952
Modern Collection
Tate Gallery Archive holds material concerning this artist

N04788 The Red Jacket (exhibited 1924)
Oc:762x641:signed:Presented by Francis Howard 1935

DUGGER, John born 1948
Modern Collection
Tate Gallery Archive holds material concerning this artist

T03166 Sports Banner (1980)
ADcw:1187x1997:signed:Presented by E.J. Power through the Friends of the Tate Gallery 1980

DUNBAR, Evelyn 1906-1960
Modern Collection

N05212 Winter Garden (circa 1929-37)
Oc:305x914:signed:Purchased 1940

N05213 Study for Decoration: Flight (1930)
OWπ:381x394:signed:Purchased 1940

N05688 A Land Girl and the Bail Bull (1945)
Oc:914x1829:signed:Presented by the War Artists' Advisory Committee 1946

DUNLOP, Ronald Ossory 1894-1973
Modern Collection
Tate Gallery Archive holds material concerning this artist

N04897 Lifeboat, Walberswick (1936)
Oc:1016x1270:signed:Presented by the Trustees of the Chantrey Bequest 1937

N05336 Rosalind Iden, as Ophelia (1940)
Oc:1010x762:signed:Presented by the Trustees of the Chantrey Bequest 1940

T00171 Myself with Cadger's Pipe (1950)
Oc:610x502:signed:Presented by Edward Le Bas 1958

DUNOYER de SEGONZAC, André
1884-1974
Modern Collection

N05043 The Road from Grimaud (1937)
La Route de Grimaud
DWπ:495x718:signed:Purchased 1939

N05069 The Farm on the Estate (1923)
La Ferme dans la terre
Oc:600x810:signed:Bequeathed by Frank Hindley Smith 1940

N05070 Nude with a Newspaper (1921)
Nu au journal
Oc:924x600:signed:Bequeathed by Frank Hindley Smith 1940

N05415 Still Life with a Cabbage (1919-20)
Nature morte au chou
Oc:730x921:Presented by Sir Michael Sadler 1941

DUNSTAN, Bernard born 1920
Modern Collection
Tate Gallery Archive holds material concerning this artist

P06111 Interior, Viterbo (1974)
CLπ:311x298:signed:Presented by Curwen Studio through the Institute of Contemporary Prints 1975

P06775 Albergo Stella (1978)
CLπ:318x298:signed:Presented by Curwen Studio 1978

attributed to
DUPONT, Gainsborough 1754-1797
British Collection

N00311 Cottage Children
Oc:457x356:Presented by Robert Vernon 1847

N01271 Marie-Auguste Vestris (circa 1780-5)
Oc:318x267:Presented by James Rannie Swinton 1888

N01488 Rustics with Donkey
Oc:452x546:Presented by the Misses Lane 1896

DURRANT, Jennifer born 1942
Modern Collection

T03305 Other Cloud Painting (1978)
Ac:2616x3137:signed:Purchased 1981

T03306 Sweet Pea Painting (1978-9)
Ac:2616x3073:Purchased 1981

DURST, Alan L. 1883-1970
Modern Collection
Tate Gallery Archive holds material concerning this artist

N04615 Feline (1930)
Ss:190x267x210:signed:Presented by the executor of Mrs Herbert Gibson 1932

T00722 Girl Binding her Hair (1929)
Ss:406x292x241:Presented by the Trustees of the Chantrey Bequest 1965

DYCE, William 1806-1864
British Collection
Tate Gallery Archive holds material concerning this artist

N01407 Pegwell Bay, Kent - a Recollection of October 5th 1858 (?1858-60)
Oc:635x889:Purchased 1894

N01426 St John Leading Home his Adopted Mother (1844-60)
Oπ:762x1099:Presented anonymously 1894

N03461 Boy Reclining by a Pool
Lπ:83x127:Presented by Miss Dyce 1919

N03462 Cottage Interior
Lπ:83x127:Presented by Miss Dyce 1919

N03463 Old Woman
Lπ:232x184:Presented by Miss Dyce 1919

N03464 Girl at a Crescent
Lπ:121x79:Presented by Miss Dyce 1919

N03465 An Old Mill
Lπ:102x149:Presented by Miss Dyce 1919

T00618 Madonna and Child (circa 1827-30)
Oc:1029x806:Bequeathed by Colonel Ernest Carrick Freeman 1963

DYCK, Sir Anthony van - see VAN DYCK, Sir Anthony

DZAMONJA, Dusan born 1928
Modern Collection

T00430 Metal Sculpture 14 (1960)
Sm:730x457x356:Purchased 1961

EARDLEY, Joan 1921-1963
Modern Collection
Tate Gallery Archive holds material concerning this artist

T04133 Salmon Net Posts (circa 1961-62)
Ob:1185x2175:Presented by the Friends of the Tate
Gallery 1986

EAST, Sir Alfred 1849-1913
British Collection

N04917 Golden Autumn (?1904)
Oc:1219x1530:signed:Presented by Mrs Mildred Donald
1938

EASTLAKE, Sir Charles Lock 1793-1865
British Collection
Tate Gallery Archive holds material concerning this artist

N00397 Christ Lamenting over Jerusalem (?1842)
Oc:1048x1562:Presented by Robert Vernon 1847

N00398 Haidee, a Greek Girl (1827)
Oc:635x508:Presented by Robert Vernon 1847

N00399 Escape of the Carrara Family from the Pursuit of the
Duke of Milan 1389 (1849)
Oc:1270x1016:Presented by Robert Vernon 1847

N00898 Lord Byron's Dream (1827)
Oc:1181x1708:Bequeathed by Thomas Howard 1872

N01395 Mrs Charles H. Bellenden Ker (1835)
Oc:762x635:Bequeathed by C.H. Bellenden Ker 1893

T00664 The Colosseum from the Esquiline (1822)
Oc:527x654:Presented by the Friends of the Tate Gallery
1964

T00665 The Colosseum from the Campo Vaccino (1822)
Oc:527x648:Presented by the Friends of the Tate Gallery
1964

EDRIDGE, Henry 1769-1821
British Collection

N04299 Landscape with Mill
Dπ:257x400:Bequeathed by J.R. Holliday 1927

N04300 Seashore with Cliff (1818)
Dπ:241x375:signed:Bequeathed by J.R. Holliday 1927

after
EDRIDGE, Henry 1769-1821
British Collection

Picturesque Views on the Southern Coast of England
(T05218-T05463; complete group; mixed group)

T05284 The Beach at Brighton, Sussex (1814)
Lπ:138x238:Purchased 1988

T05285 The Beach at Brighton, Sussex (1814)
Lπ:139x239:Purchased 1988

EDWARDS, Edwin 1823-1879
British Collection

N01690 The Thames from a Wharf at Waterloo Bridge (?1866)
Oc:654x1448:Presented by Mrs E. Edwards 1900

EDWARDS, Jeffrey born 1945
Modern Collection

P03111 Points to Remember when Buying a House (1970)
CNπ:511x664:signed:Presented by Andrew Dickerson
1975

P03112 Severe Sweat Stains (1970)
CNπ:495x495:signed:Presented by Andrew Dickerson
1975

P03113 Work (1972)
CNπ:391x302:signed:Presented by Andrew Dickerson
1975

P03114 A Narrow Escape (1973)
CNπ:660x813:signed:Presented by Andrew Dickerson
1975

P03115 Moonlight (1974)
CNπ:533x562:signed:Presented by Andrew Dickerson
1975

EGG, Augustus Leopold 1816-1863
British Collection
Tate Gallery Archive holds material concerning this artist

N00444 Scene from 'Le Diable Boiteux' (exhibited 1844)
Oc:864x1118:Presented by Robert Vernon 1847

N01385 Beatrix Knighting Esmond (1857)
Oc:851x1156:Purchased 1893

N03278 Past and Present, No. 1 (1858)
Oc:635x762:signed:Presented by Sir Alec and Lady
Martin in memory of their daughter Nora 1918

N03279 Past and Present, No. 2 (1858)
Oc:635x762:signed:Presented by Sir Alec and Lady
Martin in memory of their daughter Nora 1918

N03280 Past and Present, No. 3 (1858)
Oc:635x762:signed:Presented by Sir Alec and Lady
Martin in memory of their daughter Nora 1918

EGLEY, William Maw 1826-1916
British Collection
Tate Gallery Archive holds material concerning this artist

N05779 Omnibus Life in London (1859)
Oc:448x419:signed:Bequeathed by Miss J.L.R. Blaker
1947

EHRLICH, Georg 1897-1966
Modern Collection
Tate Gallery Archive holds material concerning this artist

N05394 Italian Boy (1935)
Sz:292x187x203:signed:Presented by Erich Goeritz 1942

T00369 Head of a Horse (1955-6)
Sz:438x140x251:Presented by the Trustees of the
Chantrey Bequest 1960

ELK, Ger van born 1941
Modern Collection
Tate Gallery Archive holds material concerning this artist

T03108 Lunch II (1976)
FDOim:800x1000:signed:Purchased 1980

P07434 Roquebrune (1979/80)
CNFπ:816x1702:signed:Purchased 1981

ELLIOTT, Geoffrey born 1935
Modern Collection
Tate Gallery Archive holds material concerning this artist

P06112 Brighton Fish Market (1968)
CLπ:448x591:Presented by Curwen Studio through the
Institute of Contemporary Prints 1975

ELMORE, Alfred 1815-1881
British Collection

N04736 Study for 'Invention of the Combing Machine' (circa 1862)
Ob:311x400:Presented by Capt. R.R. Trout 1934

ELWELL, Frederick W. 1870-1958
British Collection

N03450 The 'Beverley Arms' Kitchen (1919)
Oc:1283x1022:signed:Presented by the Trustees of the Chantrey Bequest 1919

ELWYN, John born 1916
Modern Collection
Tate Gallery Archive holds material concerning this artist

P06113 Caernarvon Castle (1969)
CLπ:460x610:signed:Presented by Curwen Studio through the Institute of Contemporary Prints 1975

P06114 Harlech Castle (1969)
CLπ:460x610:signed:Presented by Curwen Studio through the Institute of Contemporary Prints 1975

EMANUEL, Frank L. 1865-1948
British Collection
Tate Gallery Archive holds material concerning this artist

N02894 Kensington Interior (1912)
Oc:1168x908:signed:Presented by the Trustees of the Chantrey Bequest 1912

EMETT, Rowland 1906-1990
Modern Collection

T03940 Dawn Flight: Mist Clearing, Mallard Rising and the Early Up Slow Surprised (1978)
DWπ:540x760:signed:Presented by the artist and his wife 1985

EMILIAN, Céline born 1902
Modern Collection
Tate Gallery Archive holds material concerning this artist

N05051 Angela (1930)
Sz:318x146x210:signed:Presented by the artist 1939

ENGELBACH, Florence 1872-1951
British Collection

N04978 Roses (circa 1934-8)
Oc:356x406:signed:Presented anonymously 1939

ENSOR, James 1860-1949
Modern Collection
Tate Gallery Archive holds material concerning this artist

N04846 Effect of Light (1935)
Le Coup de lumière
Oc:508x616:signed:Presented by Georges Wildenstein 1936

EPSTEIN, Sir Jacob 1880-1959
Modern Collection
Tate Gallery Archive holds material concerning this artist

N03187 Euphemia Lamb (1908)
Sz:375x400x203:signed:Presented by the Contemporary Art Society 1917

N03646 Nan (1909)
Sz:445x381x229:Presented by the Trustees of the Chantrey Bequest 1922

N03849 Jacob Kramer (1921)
Sz:635x533x254:Presented by the Contemporary Art Society 1924

N04238 The Visitation (1926)
Sz:1651x470x457:Presented by the Contemporary Art Society 1927

N04418 Mrs Godfrey Phillips (1928)
Sz:457x432x248:Presented by A.E. Anderson through the National Art Collections Fund 1928

N04424 The Little Negress (1928)
Dπ:476x559:signed:Purchased 1928

N04425 Negress (1928)
Dπ:457x559:signed:Purchased 1928

N04754 Albert Einstein (1933)
Sz:432x279x254:Presented by the Trustees of the Chantrey Bequest 1934

N05579 Esther (1930)
Sz:533x635x254:Presented by Howard Bliss 1945

N05689 The Rt Hon. Ernest Bevin (1943)
Sz:260x216x248:Presented by the War Artists' Advisory Committee 1946

N06089 Kathleen (1921)
Sz:470x470x305:Presented by the Contemporary Art Society 1952

N06132 Somerset Maugham (1951)
Sz:477x225x250:Presented by William Somerset Maugham 1952

N06139 Mrs Mary McEvoy (circa 1910)
Sz:419x394x229:Presented by the Trustees of the Chantrey Bequest 1953

T00340 Torso in Metal from 'The Rock Drill' (1913-14)
Sz:705x584x445:Purchased 1960

T00363 Study for 'The Rock Drill' (circa 1913)
Dπ:641x533:Purchased 1960

T01691 Female Figure in Flenite (1913)
Ss:457x95x121:Purchased 1972

T01820 Doves (1914-15)
Ss:648x787x343:Purchased 1973

T03358 Totem (circa 1913)
DWπ:580x415:signed:Purchased 1982

T04940 Ann Freud (1949-50)
Sz:280x190x203:Bequeathed by Alison, Lady Hayter 1987

T05758 Dahlias
WGπ:572x448:signed:Bequeathed by Helena and Kenneth Levy 1990

T05759 Dahlias and Sunflowers
WGπ:575x452:signed:Bequeathed by Helena and Kenneth Levy 1990

T05760 Epping Forest
WGπ:451x574:Bequeathed by Helena and Kenneth Levy 1990

ERLANGER, Rodolphe d' 1872-1932
Modern Collection

N03669 Street in Cairo (?circa 1920-2)
Ow:178x117:Presented by Lord Duveen 1922

ERMA, Thomas 1939-1964
Modern Collection

T01573 Collage Painting (1962)
Dπ:1626x1302:signed:Presented by David Kluger
through the American Federation of Arts 1972

ERNEST, John born 1922
Modern Collection
Tate Gallery Archive holds material concerning this artist

T00872 Mosaic Relief No. 4 (1966)
Rv:1067x1372x73:Presented by Sir George Labouchere
through the Friends of the Tate Gallery 1966

T03723 Triangulated Relief (1965)
Rw:530x700x60:Transferred from the Victoria & Albert
Museum 1983

ERNST, Max 1891-1976
Modern Collection
Tate Gallery Archive holds material concerning this artist

N05289 The Entire City (1934)
La Ville entière
Oc:502x613:signed:Purchased with assistance from the
Knapping Fund 1941

T00336 Men Shall Know Nothing of This (1923)
Les Hommes n'en sauront rien
Oc:803x638:Purchased 1960

T00548 Forest and Dove (1927)
Forêt et colombe
Oc:1003x813:signed:Presented by the Friends of the Tate
Gallery 1962

T00619 Moon in a Bottle (1955)
La Lune en bouteille
Oc:600x813:signed:Presented by Sir Robert Adeane
through the Friends of the Tate Gallery 1963

T01988 Celebes (1921)
Oc:1254x1079:signed:Purchased 1975

T03252 Pietà or Revolution by Night (1923)
Pietà ou La révolution la nuit
Oc:1162x889:Purchased 1981

T03707 Dadaville (circa 1924)
Dpwc:680x560x63:Purchased 1983

P77271 Untitled from 'La Brebis galante' (1949)
Iπ:237x192:Purchased 1989

P77348 Dangerous Correspondances (1947)
Correspondances dangereuses
Iπ:300x222:Purchased 1990

ERTÉ (Romain de Tirtoff) 1892-1990
Modern Collection

Numerals (P06115-P06123; incomplete group)
P06115 Zero (1968)
CLπ:670x520:Presented by Curwen Studio through the
Institute of Contemporary Prints 1975

P06116 Number One (1968)
CLπ:671x519:Presented by Curwen Studio through the
Institute of Contemporary Prints 1975

P06117 Number Two (1968)
CLπ:651x503:Presented by Curwen Studio through the
Institute of Contemporary Prints 1975

P06118 Number Three (1968)
CLπ:650x502:Presented by Curwen Studio through the
Institute of Contemporary Prints 1975

P06119 Number Five (1968)
CLπ:649x501:Presented by Curwen Studio through the
Institute of Contemporary Prints 1975

P06120 Number Six (1968)
CLπ:649x502:Presented by Curwen Studio through the
Institute of Contemporary Prints 1975

P06121 Number Seven (1968)
CLπ:648x502:Presented by Curwen Studio through the
Institute of Contemporary Prints 1975

P06122 Number Eight (1968)
CLπ:648x502:Presented by Curwen Studio through the
Institute of Contemporary Prints 1975

P06123 Number Nine (1968)
CLπ:649x503:Presented by Curwen Studio through the
Institute of Contemporary Prints 1975

Precious Stones (P06124-P06129; complete group)
P06124 Amethyst (1969)
CLπ:648x499:Presented by Curwen Studio through the
Institute of Contemporary Prints 1975

P06125 Diamond (1969)
CLπ:648x500:Presented by Curwen Studio through the
Institute of Contemporary Prints 1975

P06126 Emerald (1969)
CLπ:645x499:Presented by Curwen Studio through the
Institute of Contemporary Prints 1975

P06127 Ruby (1969)
CLπ:648x490:Presented by Curwen Studio through the
Institute of Contemporary Prints 1975

P06128 Sapphire (1969)
CLπ:648x496:Presented by Curwen Studio through the
Institute of Contemporary Prints 1975

P06129 Topaz (1969)
CLπ:648x500:Presented by Curwen Studio through the
Institute of Contemporary Prints 1975

ESTES, Richard born 1936
Modern Collection

P07261 Untitled (1973-4)
CNπ:851x1191:signed:Purchased 1979

P77083 Holland Hotel (1984)
CNπ:1157x1832:signed:Purchased 1985

ESTEVE, Maurice born 1904
Modern Collection

T00254 Composition 166 (1957)
Wπ:505x638:Purchased 1959

ETCHELLS, Frederick 1886-1973
Modern Collection
Tate Gallery Archive holds material concerning this artist

N04572 The Fair, fragment (1911)
Tc:2508x6147:Purchased 1931

N05403 Still Life (circa 1913)
Gb:749x629:Presented by Duncan Grant 1943

N05404 Portrait (circa 1911)
Oc:610x508:Presented by Duncan Grant 1943

T00192 The Big Girl (circa 1912)
Tb:749x629:Purchased 1958

T03724 Inscription 'Let us now Praise Famous Men' (1925)
Rs:510x910x25:Transferred from the Victoria & Albert
Museum 1983

ETROG, Sorel born 1933
Modern Collection

T01218 Prophet II (1967-8)
Sz:632x559x165:signed:Presented by Mrs Ayala Zacks 1970

ETTY, William 1787-1849
British Collection
Tate Gallery Archive holds material concerning this artist

N00356 Youth on the Prow, and Pleasure at the Helm (exhibited 1832)
Oc:1587x1175:signed:Presented by Robert Vernon 1847

N00357 The Persian (exhibited 1834)
Oc:406x305:signed:Presented by Robert Vernon 1847

N00358 Candaules, King of Lydia, Shews his Wife by Stealth to Gyges (exhibited 1830)
Oc:451x559:Presented by Robert Vernon 1847

N00359 The Lute Player (exhibited 1835)
Ow:629x533:signed:Presented by Robert Vernon 1847

N00360 The Dangerous Playmate (exhibited 1833)
Ow:267x279:Presented by Robert Vernon 1847

N00361 The Saviour or the Disciple
Ob:483x378:Presented by Robert Vernon 1847

N00362 Christ Appearing to Mary Magdalene after the Resurrection (exhibited 1834)
Oc:400x660:Presented by Robert Vernon 1847

N00363 The Duet (1834-8)
Ow:381x492:signed:Presented by Robert Vernon 1847

N00364 Window in Venice, during a Festa (exhibited 1831)
Oc:610x502:Presented by Robert Vernon 1847

N00365 The Magdalen (?exhibited 1842)
Ob:492x391:signed:Presented by Robert Vernon 1847

N00366 Bathers Surprised by a Swan. Verso: Terpsichore (?) with Putti (exhibited 1841)
Ow:987x978:Presented by Robert Vernon 1847

N00614 Musidora: The Bather 'At the Doubtful Breeze Alarmed', replica (?exhibited 1846)
Oc:651x502:Bequeathed by Jacob Bell 1859

N01795 Study for 'Pandora Crowned by the Seasons' (circa 1824)
ODπ:156x187:Bequeathed by Henry Vaughan 1900

N04108 The Fairy of the Fountain (1845)
Ob:708x508:Presented in memory of Lord Leverhulme by his executors through the National Art Collections Fund 1925

N04384 Study of a Peacock for 'The Judgement of Paris' (?circa 1826)
Ob:502x641:Purchased 1928

N05305 Standing Female Nude (circa 1835-40)
Oc:1016x648:Presented by the National Art Collections Fund 1941

N05614 The Parting of Hero and Leander (exhibited 1827)
Oc:825x838:signed:Purchased 1945

N06268 Miss Mary Arabella Jay (exhibited 1819)
Oc:762x632:Bequeathed by Mrs Rose Mary Chamberlen 1956

N06354 The Coral Finder: Venus and her Youthful Satellites, replica (circa 1820-48)
Oc:743x991:Bequeathed by Mrs M. Orr-Ewing 1964

T00199 Britomart Redeems Faire Amoret (exhibited 1833)
Oc:908x660:Purchased 1958

EURICH, Richard born 1903
Modern Collection
Tate Gallery Archive holds material concerning this artist

N05344 Antwerp (1939)
Oc:1016x1270:signed:Presented by the Trustees of the Chantrey Bequest 1940

N05690 Night Raid on Portsmouth Docks (1941)
Oc:787x1270:signed:Presented by the War Artists' Advisory Committee 1946

N05691 The Landing at Dieppe, 19th August 1942 (1942-3)
Ow:1219x1753:signed:Presented by the War Artists' Advisory Committee 1946

N05692 Survivors from a Torpedoed Ship (1942)
Oc:356x610:signed:Presented by the War Artists' Advisory Committee 1946

T03217 Beach with Bathers (1969)
Ob:406x1219:signed:Presented by the Trustees of the Chantrey Bequest 1981

EVANS, Garth born 1934
Modern Collection
Tate Gallery Archive holds material concerning this artist

T00672 White No. 34 (1964)
Rwba:1226x1486x89:signed:Purchased 1964

P02469 Untitled (1971)
Mlπ:515x640:signed:Presented by the artist 1978

P02470 Untitled (1971)
Mlπ:515x642:signed:Presented by the artist 1978

P02471 Untitled (1971)
Mlπ:514x644:signed:Presented by the artist 1978

P02472 Untitled (1971)
Mlπ:512x640:signed:Presented by the artist 1978

P02473 Untitled (1971)
Mlπ:518x641:signed:Presented by the artist 1978

P02474 Untitled (1971)
Mlπ:590x765:signed:Presented by the artist 1978

EVANS, Leslie - see BOYD and EVANS

EVANS, Merlyn O. 1910-1973
Modern Collection
Tate Gallery Archive holds material concerning this artist

N06147 Souvenir of Suez (1952)
Oc:737x1270:signed:Purchased 1953

T00830 The Conquest of Time (1934)
Oc:1016x816:signed:Presented by the Trustees of the Chantrey Bequest 1966

T02099 The Mark of the Beast (1940)
Oc:908x711:Purchased 1976

P01872 Conquest of Time (1934)
Mlπ:254x203:signed:Presented by Margerie Evans 1979

P01873 Tragic Group (1949-50)
Mlπ:556x657:Presented by Margerie Evans 1979

P01874 The Chess Players (1951)
Mlπ:410x416:signed:Presented by Margerie Evans 1979

P01875 Pentaptych No. 3 (1961)
Mlπ:1006x502:signed:Presented by Margerie Evans 1979

P01876 Triptych No. 1 (1964)
Mlπ:698x546:signed:Presented by Margerie Evans 1979

P01877 Triptych No. 2 (1964)
Mlπ:608x546:signed:Presented by Margerie Evans 1979

Penwith Portfolio (P01416, P06005, P06108, P06130, P06241, P06324, P06346, P06359, P06399, P06519, P06700; complete group; mixed group)

P06130 St Ives Beach (1973)
CLπ:508x724:signed:Presented by Curwen Studio through the Institute of Contemporary Prints 1975

EVANS, Sebastian active 1885
British Collection

T05475 Allegorical Subject: The Unfaithful Poet
Dπ:248x172:Presented by Miss Marjorie Ball 1988

EVES, Reginald G. 1876-1941
British Collection
Tate Gallery Archive holds material concerning this artist

N04461 Thomas Hardy (1924)
Oc:762x635:signed:Presented by Francis Howard 1929

N04895 Max Beerbohm (1936)
Oc:724x635:signed:Presented by the Trustees of the Chantrey Bequest 1937

EWORTH, Hans active 1540-1573
British Collection

T00606 Portrait of an Unknown Lady (1557)
Ow:597x483:signed:Purchased 1963

T01569 Elizabeth Roydon, Lady Golding (1563)
Ow:378x302:Bequeathed by Miss Rachel and Miss Jean Alexander 1972

T03896 Portrait of a Lady, Probably of the Wentworth Family (circa 1565-8)
Ow:998x619:Purchased with assistance from the Friends of the Tate Gallery 1984

EYTON, Anthony born 1923
Modern Collection
Tate Gallery Archive holds material concerning this artist

T03339 Open Window, Spitalfields (1976-81)
Oc:2438x1727:signed:Presented by the Trustees of the Chantrey Bequest 1982

FABRO, Luciano born 1936
Modern Collection

T05537 Ovaries (1988)
Ovaie
2 Smv:75x11250x1500:Presented by the Patrons of New
Art through the Friends of the Tate Gallery 1989

P07994 SS Redentore (1972)
4 MNπ:5300x1800, 4100x8100, 5300x1705,
4800x3400:signed:Purchased 1984

FAED, Thomas 1826-1900
British Collection

N01525 The Silken Gown (1860 or 63)
Oc:940x749:signed:Presented by Sir Henry Tate 1894

N01526 Faults on Both Sides (1861)
Oc:673x552:signed:Presented by Sir Henry Tate 1894

N01527 Highland Mother (exhibited 1870)
Oc:267x203:signed:Presented by Sir Henry Tate 1894

FAGAN, Robert circa 1745-1816
British Collection

T03249 Anna Maria Ferri, the Artist's First Wife (circa 1790-2)
Oc:737x616:Purchased 1981

FAIRWEATHER, Ian 1891-1974
Modern Collection

N04801 Bathing Scene, Bali (circa 1933-4)
Tπ:889x1321:Presented by the Contemporary Art Society
1935

FALKENSTEIN, Clare born 1909
Modern Collection

T01228 Point as a Set No. 26 (1970-71)
Sm:762x762x762:Presented by the artist 1970

FANTIN-LATOUR, Henri 1836-1904
Modern Collection
Tate Gallery Archive holds material concerning this artist

N01952 Mr and Mrs Edwin Edwards (1875)
Oc:1308x981:signed:Presented by Mrs E. Edwards 1904

N02133 Roses (1864)
Oc:565x464:signed:Bequeathed by Mrs Edwin Edwards
1907

N02134 A Plate of Apples (1861)
Oc:210x264:signed:Bequeathed by Mrs Edwin Edwards
1907

N04580 Judgment of Paris (circa 1863)
Jugement de Paris
Oc:229x279:signed:Bequeathed by Hans Velten 1931

N04581 Self-Portrait (1860)
Oc:314x254:signed:Bequeathed by Hans Velten 1931

FARINGTON, Joseph 1747-1821
British Collection

N04296 Landscape at Sandringham, with Trees and Wagon (1787)
DWπ:219x270:signed:Bequeathed by J.R. Holliday 1927

N04297 Landscape, with Castle (1787)
DWπ:295x222:signed:Bequeathed by J.R. Holliday 1927

N04298 Cockermouth Castle (1786)
DWπ:159x298:signed:Bequeathed by J.R. Holliday 1927

T00786 The Oak Tree (circa 1785-90)
Oc:635x610:Purchased 1965

FARQUARSON, David 1839-1907
British Collection

N01648 In a Fog (1897)
Oc:1206x1816:signed:Presented by the Trustees of the
Chantrey Bequest 1897

N02072 Birnam Wood (1906)
Oc:1676x2438:signed:Presented by the Trustees of the
Chantrey Bequest 1906

FARQUARSON, Joseph 1847-1935
British Collection
Tate Gallery Archive holds material concerning this artist

N01626 The Joyless Winter Day (exhibited 1883)
Oc:1041x1803:signed:Presented by the Trustees of the
Chantrey Bequest 1906

FARRERAS, Francisco born 1927
Modern Collection

T00484 No. 139 (1961)
Vw:1397x1702:signed:Presented by the Spanish
Government 1962

FAUTRIER, Jean 1897-1964
Modern Collection

P77119 Reclining Woman IV (circa 1942, published circa 1960-4)
Femme étendue IV
MIπ:155x274:signed:Purchased 1985

P77120 Hostages on a Black Ground (1946, published circa
1960-4)
Otages fond noir
MIπ:242x327:signed:Purchased 1985

P77121 Dark Landscape (circa 1945 / circa 1960-4, published
circa 1960-4)
Paysage sombre
CIπ:142x177:signed:Purchased 1985

P77139 Violet Hostage (1949, published circa 1960-4)
Otage violet
CIπ:265x309:signed:Purchased 1986

P77140 Baby Mine (1947, published circa 1960-4)
Les Seins et le sexe de la femme
CIπ:278x336:signed:Purchased 1986

P77161 The Executed (1943, published circa 1960-4)
Les Fusillés
MIπ:335x269:signed:Purchased 1986

FAZZINI, Pericle 1913-1987
Modern Collection

T00373 Seated Woman (1959)
Dπ:689x476:signed:Purchased 1960

FEARON, Hilda 1878-1917
British Collection

N04832 The Tea Party (1916)
Oc:546x660:signed:Presented by Algernon Talmage 1936

FEDDEN, Mary born 1915

Modern Collection
Tate Gallery Archive holds material concerning this artist

P01096 Ginger Beer Bottle (1972)
CLπ:416x578:signed:Presented by Waddington Galleries through the Institute of Contemporary Prints 1975

P06131 Basket of Lemons (1971)
CLπ:749x549:signed:Presented by Curwen Studio through the Institute of Contemporary Prints 1975

P06132 Pot of Shells (1971)
CLπ:549x752:signed:Presented by Curwen Studio through the Institute of Contemporary Prints 1975

P06133 Shells and Pebbles (1971)
CLπ:546x749:signed:Presented by Curwen Studio through the Institute of Contemporary Prints 1975

P06134 Straw Plate (1971)
CLπ:749x549:signed:Presented by Curwen Studio through the Institute of Contemporary Prints 1975

P06135 Etching Table (1972)
CLπ:413x568:signed:Presented by Curwen Studio through the Institute of Contemporary Prints 1975

P06136 Figs (1972)
CLπ:410x568:signed:Presented by Curwen Studio through the Institute of Contemporary Prints 1975

P06137 Fritillaries (1972)
CLπ:778x575:signed:Presented by Curwen Studio through the Institute of Contemporary Prints 1975

P06138 Ivy (1972)
CLπ:568x410:signed:Presented by Curwen Studio through the Institute of Contemporary Prints 1975

P06139 The Lamp (1972)
CLπ:562x413:signed:Presented by Curwen Studio through the Institute of Contemporary Prints 1975

FEHR, Henry C. 1867-1940

British Collection

N01749 The Rescue of Andromeda (1893)
Sz:2743x2591x2184:signed:Presented by the Trustees of the Chantrey Bequest 1894

FEIBUSCH, Hans born 1898

Modern Collection
Tate Gallery Archive holds material concerning this artist

School Prints (P01698-P01727; complete group; mixed group)

P01704 Mandrill and Mangabeys (1946-9)
CLπ:495x762:signed:Presented by Patrick Seale Prints 1975

FEILER, Paul born 1918

Modern Collection
Tate Gallery Archive holds material concerning this artist

T00741 Inclined Oval Brown (1964-5)
Oc:914x1016:signed:Purchased 1965

FELL, Sheila 1931-1979

Modern Collection

T00473 Snowscape IV (1961)
Oc:251x302:Purchased 1962

T01065 Haystack in a Field (1967)
Oc:711x914:signed:Presented by the Trustees of the Chantrey Bequest 1968

T03159 Maryport, Cumbria (1965)
Oc:1019x1270:signed:Presented by the Trustees of the Chantrey Bequest 1980

FERGUSON, William Gow circa 1633-1695

British Collection

T00061 Still Life (1684)
Oc:654x540:Purchased 1955

FERGUSSON, J.D. 1874-1961

British Collection
Tate Gallery Archive holds material concerning this artist

N05880 Café-Concert des Ambassadeurs (1907)
Ob:375x413:signed:Presented by Sir Louis Fergusson 1949

T00667 Blue Beads, Paris, 1910 (1910)
Ob:502x457:signed:Presented by the Friends of the Tate Gallery 1964

T00668 Oak Rhythm (1925)
Sw:425x127x76:Presented by the Friends of the Tate Gallery 1964

FERNANDEZ, Armand - see ARMAN

FERNELEY, John, I 1782-1860

British Collection

N05429 The Bay Horse (1826)
Oc:838x1048:signed:Presented by Major Guy Paget 1943

T03423 John Burgess of Clipstone, Nottinghamshire, on a Favourite Horse, with his Harriers (1838)
Oc:959x1397:signed:Bequeathed by Mrs F. Ambrose Clark through the British Sporting Art Trust 1982

T03424 Sir Robert Leighton after Coursing, with a Groom and a Couple of Greyhounds (1816)
Oc:1051x1397:signed:Bequeathed by Mrs F. Ambrose Clark through the British Sporting Art Trust 1982

T03425 Mr Powell and his Son, with Norton, a Grey Hunter (1816)
Oc:860x1076:signed:Bequeathed by Mrs F. Ambrose Clark through the British Sporting Art Trust 1982

T03426 Defiance, a Brood Mare, with Reveller, a Foal (1833)
Oc:712x940:signed:Bequeathed by Mrs F. Ambrose Clark through the British Sporting Art Trust 1982

T03439 Major Healey, Wearing Raby Hunt Uniform, Riding with the Sedgefield Hunt (circa 1833)
Oc:764x970:signed:Presented by Miss Violet N. Cross through the British Sporting Art Trust 1982

FERNELEY, John, II circa 1815-1862

British Collection

T03427 Hunt Scurry (1832)
Oc:450x904:signed:Bequeathed by Mrs F. Ambrose Clark through the British Sporting Art Trust 1982

FEW, Elsie 1909-1980

Modern Collection
Tate Gallery Archive holds material concerning this artist

T03285 Bradfields (1947)
Ow:305x356:signed:Purchased 1981

T03286 Wrapping Paper (1977)
Vb:991x686:signed:Purchased 1981

FIELDING, Anthony Vandyke Copley
1798-1855
British Collection

N01720 A View in Sussex (1834)
Wπ:229x343:signed:Presented by E. Homan 1899

T00988 Cader Idris from the Barmouth Sands (1810)
Wπ:213x654:signed:Presented by the National Art
Collections Fund (Herbert Powell Bequest) 1967

T05473 Loch Earn with Ben Vorlich
Wπ:96x200:Presented by Miss Marjorie Ball 1988

FIJALKOWSKI, Stanislaw born 1922
Modern Collection

P07921 October 18, 1971 (1971)
MJπ:400x308:signed:Purchased 1983

P07922 Motorway XLV (1976)
MJπ:521x410:signed:Purchased 1983

FILDES, Sir Luke 1844-1927
British Collection
Tate Gallery Archive holds material concerning this artist

N01522 The Doctor (exhibited 1891)
Oc:1664x2419:Presented by Sir Henry Tate 1894

T01227 Applicants for Admission to a Casual Ward (after 1908)
Oc:571x940:Purchased 1970

FINDEN, William 1787-1852
British Collection

T05706 Colonel Manwaring, Hazlewood and the Smugglers
(1836)
Iπ:82x134:Presented by William Drummond 1989

FINE, Lois born 1931
Modern Collection

P06140 Sphinx (1972)
MLπ:483x692:signed:Presented by Curwen Studio
through the Institute of Contemporary Prints 1975

FINLAY, Ian Hamilton born 1925
Modern Collection
Tate Gallery Archive holds material concerning this artist

T02034 Starlit Waters (1967)
Swv:311x2400x133:Purchased 1976

T02408 Sea Poppy I (1968)
Sg:349x305x63:Presented by the Contemporary Art
Society 1979

T02409 Sea Poppy II (1968)
Sg:346x298x63:Presented by the Contemporary Art
Society 1979

P07014 Marine [collaboration with Patrick Caulfield] (1968)
CNπ:459x520:Purchased 1974

P07015 Poem/Print No. 11 [collaboration with John Furnival]
(1969)
CNπ:511x716:Purchased 1974

P07016 Homage to Mozart [collaboration with Ron Costley]
(1970)
CNπ:330x457:signed:Purchased 1974

P07017 Catameringue [collaboration with Peter Grant] (1970)
CNπ:355x439:Purchased 1974

P07018 The Little Seamstress [collaboration with Richard
Demarco] (1970)
CNπ:460x589:Purchased 1974

P07019 Seashells [collaboration with Ian Procktor] (1971)
CNπ:267x230:signed:Purchased 1974

P07020 Interior/Interieur Homage to Vuillard [collaboration with
Michael Harvey] (1971)
CNπ:252x252:Purchased 1974

P07021 A Rock Rose [collaboration with Richard Demarco]
(1971)
CNπ:381x562:Purchased 1974

P07022 The Washington Fountain [collaboration with Karl
Torok] (1972)
CLπ:230x330:Purchased 1974

P07023 Homage to Modern Art [collaboration with Jim
Nicholson] (1972)
CNπ:762x538:signed:Purchased 1974

P07024 Sail Wholemeal [collaboration with Jim Nicholson]
(1972)
CNπ:762x538:signed:Purchased 1974

P07025 Arcadia [collaboration with George Oliver] (1973)
CNπ:355x437:Purchased 1974

P07450 Acrobats (1966)
CNπ:388x279:Purchased 1981

P07451 Sea Poppy I [collaboration with Alistair Cant] (1966)
CNπ:337x305:Purchased 1981

P07452 Star/Steer (1966)
CNπ:571x444:Purchased 1981

P07453 Summer Sails [collaboration with Jim Nicholson] (1966)
CNπ:586x447:Purchased 1981

P07454 La Belle Hollandaise [collaboration with Herbert
Rosenthal] (1967)
CNπ:565x432:Purchased 1981

P07455 Land/Sea [collaboration with Herbert Rosenthal] (1967)
CNπ:431x562:Purchased 1981

P07456 Seams (1969)
CNπ:435x562:Purchased 1981

P07457 Errata [collaboration with David Button] (1970)
CNJπ:252x508:signed:Purchased 1981

P07458 Scottish Zulu [collaboration with David Button] (1970)
CNπ:360x435:Purchased 1981

P07459 Glossary [collaboration with Richard Demarco] (1971)
CNπ:228x825:signed:Purchased 1981

P07460 D1 [collaboration with Michael Harvey] (1972)
CNπ:242x322:signed:Purchased 1981

P07461 Spiral Binding (1972)
CNVπ:454x190:signed:Purchased 1981

P07462 Topiary Aircraft Carrier [collaboration with Ian Gardner]
(1972)
CNπ:305x438:Purchased 1981

P07463 Necktank [collaboration with Michael Harvey] (1973)
CNπ:356x438:Purchased 1981

P07464 Gourd [collaboration with Ron Costley] (1975)
CNπ:280x418:signed:Purchased 1981

P07465 Midway (1975)
CNv:153x153:Purchased 1981

P07466 Sea Poppy (1975)
CNv:153x153:Purchased 1981

P07467 Tree Shells (1975)
CNv:153x153:Purchased 1981

P07468 U.S.S. Enterprise (1975)
CNv:153x153:Purchased 1981

P07469 Flowers (1977)
CNJπ:232x840:signed:Purchased 1981

P07645 Sailing Barge Red Wing (1975)
CNπ:328x305:signed:Purchased 1982

P07646 At the Field's Edge (1978)
MNπ:296x504:signed:Purchased 1982

P07647 Homage to Agam (1978)
CNπ:380x264:signed:Purchased 1982

Two Trees [collaboration with Richard Healy]
(P07923-P07924; complete group)

P07923 [no title] (1982)
CJπ:92x116:Purchased 1983

P07924 [no title] (1982)
CJπ:92x116:Purchased 1983

P07925 Homage to Malevich (1978)
CNπ:251x251:signed:Purchased 1983

P07926 Propaganda for the Wood Elves (collaboration with
Harvey Dwight) (1981)
MFπ:210x148:Purchased 1983

Posters from the Little Spartan War (P07927-P07930;
complete group)

P07927 The Arts Council must be Utterly Destroyed (1982)
MJπ:305x432:Purchased 1983

P07928 Death to the Arts Council (1982)
MJπ:305x432:Purchased 1983

P07929 Let Perish the Money Tyrants (1982)
MJπ:305x432:Purchased 1983

P07930 Peace to the Cottages - War to the Arts Council (1982)
Nπ:302x432:Purchased 1983

P07931 Apollo and Daphne (1975)
CNπ:497x360:Purchased 1983

P07932 Midway I (1977)
CNπ:565x687:Purchased 1983

P07933 Midway II (1977)
CNπ:565x687:Purchased 1983

P07934 Venus of the Hours (1975)
CNπ:749x368:Purchased 1983

P08027 Porphyry [collaboration with Ron Costley] (1977)
MLπ:95x121:Transferred from the Library 1978

FINLAY, Ian Hamilton and ANDREW, John
born 1925, born 1933
Modern Collection
Tate Gallery Archive holds material concerning these
artists

T02252 Lyre (Mk. 2) (1977)
Ss:232x324x121:Purchased 1977

FINNIE, John born 1935
Modern Collection

P06141 Silver Arcade, Leicester (1956)
CLπ:591x489:Presented by Curwen Studio through the
Institute of Contemporary Prints 1975

FISHER, Brian born 1939
Modern Collection

Centennial Suite (P03217-P03225, P03228-P03229;
complete group; mixed group)

P03222 Untitled (1967)
CNπ:470x343:Presented by Simon Fraser University,
British Columbia 1977

FISHER, Joel born 1947
Modern Collection

T03445 Untitled (1981-82)
3 Sp, 3 Dπb:448x1737x155:Purchased 1982

FISHER, Mark 1841-1923
British Collection
Tate Gallery Archive holds material concerning this artist

N03028 A Vision of the Sea (exhibited 1915)
Oc:737x813:Presented by the Trustees of the Chantrey
Bequest 1915

N03553 Feeding the Fowls (exhibited 1920)
Oc:610x787:signed:Presented by the Trustees of the
Chantrey Bequest 1920

N03835 Cows in the Orchard
Oc:457x635:signed:Presented by W.H. Wood 1924

N03871 Road through Clover (exhibited 1896)
Oc:343x343:signed:Presented by W.H. Wood 1924

N05396 Snow Scene (1894)
Oc:457x660:signed:Presented by the Trustees of the
Chantrey Bequest 1942

FISHER, Melton 1859-1939
Modern Collection

N01678 In Realms of Fancy (exhibited 1898)
Oc:1232x1219:signed:Presented by the Trustees of the
Chantrey Bequest 1898

FISHER, Roy born 1930
Modern Collection

Cultures [collaboration with Ian Tyson] (P03127-P03131;
complete group)

P03127 [no title] (1975)
MJπ:248x248:Presented by Tetrad Press 1975

P03128 [no title] (1975)
MJπ:248x248:Presented by Tetrad Press 1975

P03129 [no title] (1975)
MJπ:248x248:Presented by Tetrad Press 1975

P03130 [no title] (1975)
MJπ:248x248:Presented by Tetrad Press 1975

P03131 [no title] (1975)
MJπ:248x248:Presented by Tetrad Press 1975

FITTON, James 1899-1982
Modern Collection
Tate Gallery Archive holds material concerning this artist

N06219 Frying Tonight (1954)
Ob:775x1041:signed:Presented by the Trustees of the
Chantrey Bequest 1954

FITZGERALD, John Anster 1819-1906
British Collection

T01083 The Fairy's Lake (?exhibited 1866)
Ob:152x203:signed:Purchased 1968

FLANAGAN, Barry born 1941
Modern Collection
Tate Gallery Archive holds material concerning this artist

T01120 aaing j gni aa (1965)
Sv:1829x914x914:Purchased 1969

T01699 Sixties' Dish (1970)
Sv:1575x1346x952:Presented by Alistair McAlpine (later Lord McAlpine of West Green) 1972

T01716 Pile 3 (1968/1985)
Sc:318x521x483:signed:Purchased 1973

T01717 June 2 '69 (1969)
Scw:2921x5080x889:signed:Purchased 1973

T01718 No. 5 1971 (1971)
Sfw:635x2642x2515:Purchased 1973

T02061 Four Casb 2 '67 (1967)
4 Scv:1829x381x381:Purchased 1976

T02062 Ringl l'67 (1967)
Sv::Purchased 1976

T02063 Rope (Gr 2sp 60) 6 '67 (1967)
Sv:67x67x3909:Purchased 1976

T03059 A Nose in Repose (1977-9)
Ssw:895x751x305:Purchased 1980

T03267 Hare and Helmet II (1981)
Sz:1260x521x610:Presented by the Sainsbury Charitable Fund through the Friends of the Tate Gallery 1981

T03608 Carving No. 13 (1981)
Ss:355x1410x585:Purchased 1983

T03609 Carving No. 2 (1981)
Ss:622x609x609:Purchased 1983

T03725 Sand Muslin 2 (1966)
2 Sv:181x302x302:Transferred from the Victoria & Albert Museum 1983

Portfolio of Etchings (P01401-P01404; complete group)

P01401 Grate (1971)
MIπ:166x200:signed:Presented by the Institute of Contemporary Prints 1975

P01402 Joke Ink Blot (1971)
MIπ:166x202:signed:Presented by the Institute of Contemporary Prints 1975

P01403 60's Dish (1971)
MIπ:205x173:signed:Presented by the Institute of Contemporary Prints 1975

P01404 When Attitude Offend Form (1971)
MIπ::signed:Presented by the Institute of Contemporary Prints 1975

P01405 What Can the Poor Apache Do (1971)
MIπ:249x247:signed:Presented by the Institute of Contemporary Prints 1975

P02723 Colours Up (Induction) (1972, reprinted circa 1983)
MIπ:151x251:signed:Presented by Sue Flanagan, the artist's former wife 1985

P02724 Foolsproof (1972, reprinted circa 1983)
MIπ:203x162:signed:Presented by Sue Flanagan, the artist's former wife 1985

P02725 Think of Courage (without Fear not) (1972, reprinted circa 1983)
MIπ:152x201:signed:Presented by Sue Flanagan, the artist's former wife 1985

P02726 Left Hand By Right Hand (1970)
MIπ:248x248:signed:Presented by Sue Flanagan, the artist's former wife 1985

P02727 O'Rembrandt (1970)
MIπ:165x204:signed:Presented by Sue Flanagan, the artist's former wife 1985

P02728 To Draw Fire (1970, reprinted circa 1983)
MIπ:247x245:signed:Presented by Sue Flanagan, the artist's former wife 1985

P02729 Withdrawal From Stone Wall Street (1970, reprinted circa 1983)
MIπ:247x245:signed:Presented by Sue Flanagan, the artist's former wife 1985

P02730 Left Hand By Left Hand (1971)
MIπ:247x246:signed:Presented by Sue Flanagan, the artist's former wife 1985

P02731 Left Hand By Right Hand (1971)
MIπ:210x295:signed:Presented by Sue Flanagan, the artist's former wife 1985

P02732 Dedicated to Vincent Price (1971)
MIπ:247x246:signed:Presented by Sue Flanagan, the artist's former wife 1985

P02733 Abstract (1972, reprinted circa 1983)
MIπ:200x250:signed:Presented by Sue Flanagan, the artist's former wife 1985

P02734 Abstract (1972)
MIπ:200x253:signed:Presented by Sue Flanagan, the artist's former wife 1985

P02735 Abstract (1972, reprinted circa 1983)
MIπ:202x250:signed:Presented by Sue Flanagan, the artist's former wife 1985

P02736 Alan Sekers (1972)
MIπ:202x150:signed:Presented by Sue Flanagan, the artist's former wife 1985

P02737 The Anesthesiologist (1972)
MIπ:197x247:signed:Presented by Sue Flanagan, the artist's former wife 1985

P02738 Appointment Book (1972)
MIπ:199x245:signed:Presented by Sue Flanagan, the artist's former wife 1985

P02739 At the Goslings (1972)
MIπ:176x252:signed:Presented by Sue Flanagan, the artist's former wife 1985

P02740 Black Dog (1972)
MIπ:162x197:signed:Presented by Sue Flanagan, the artist's former wife 1985

P02741 Boo (1972, reprinted circa 1983)
MIπ:248x200:signed:Presented by Sue Flanagan, the artist's former wife 1985

P02742 Bubblegum (1972)
MIπ:201x150:signed:Presented by Sue Flanagan, the artist's former wife 1985

P02743 Bungo the Elephant by Tara (1972, reprinted circa 1983)
MIπ:202x253:signed:Presented by Sue Flanagan, the artist's former wife 1985

P02744 The Cat's Whiskers (1972, reprinted circa 1983)
MIπ:222x150:signed:Presented by Sue Flanagan, the artist's former wife 1985

P02745 Dancing Dog (1972)
MIπ:248x209:signed:Presented by Sue Flanagan, the artist's former wife 1985

P02746 David King (1972)
MIπ:252x200:signed:Presented by Sue Flanagan, the artist's former wife 1985

P02747 David Sylvester (1972)
MIπ:202x304:signed:Presented by Sue Flanagan, the artist's former wife 1985

P02748 Studies (1972, reprinted circa 1983)
MIπ:204x302:signed:Presented by Sue Flanagan, the artist's former wife 1985

P02749 Diagram of a Conversation, George Melly (1972)
MIπ:245x192:signed:Presented by Sue Flanagan, the artist's former wife 1985

P02750 Four Kings (1972, reprinted circa 1983)
MIπ:250x201:signed:Presented by Sue Flanagan, the artist's former wife 1985

P02751 George (1972)
MIπ:248x199:signed:Presented by Sue Flanagan, the artist's former wife 1985

P02752 George Melly (1972)
MIπ:249x201:signed:Presented by Sue Flanagan, the artist's former wife 1985

P02753 George Melly (1972)
MIπ:247x175:signed:Presented by Sue Flanagan, the artist's former wife 1985

P02754 Gilbert (1972)
MIπ:252x201:signed:Presented by Sue Flanagan, the artist's former wife 1985

P02755 Gilbert and George (1972)
MIπ:200x252:signed:Presented by Sue Flanagan, the artist's former wife 1985

P02756 Grown Upstalking (1972)
MIπ:163x200:signed:Presented by Sue Flanagan, the artist's former wife 1985

P02757 Himself (1972, reprinted circa 1983)
MIπ:247x190:signed:Presented by Sue Flanagan, the artist's former wife 1985

P02758 Jan Craig-Martin (1972, reprinted circa 1983)
MIπ:247x197:signed:Presented by Sue Flanagan, the artist's former wife 1985

P02759 Judy Greenwood (1972)
MIπ:253x200:signed:Presented by Sue Flanagan, the artist's former wife 1985

P02760 Lion at 30 mph (1972)
MIπ:164x200:signed:Presented by Sue Flanagan, the artist's former wife 1985

P02761 Mark Glazebrook (1972)
MIπ:199x149:signed:Presented by Sue Flanagan, the artist's former wife 1985

P02762 Mark Glazebrook (1972)
MIπ:200x151:signed:Presented by Sue Flanagan, the artist's former wife 1985

P02763 Michael Craig-Martin (1972)
MIπ:248x196:signed:Presented by Sue Flanagan, the artist's former wife 1985

P02764 Miles and Joanna (1972)
MIπ:166x201:signed:Presented by Sue Flanagan, the artist's former wife 1985

P02765 Nigel Greenwood (1972)
MIπ:256x206:Presented by Sue Flanagan, the artist's former wife 1985

P02766 Nigel and Maud Gosling (1972)
MIπ:175x251:signed:Presented by Sue Flanagan, the artist's former wife 1985

P02767 Nigel and Maud Gosling (1972)
MIπ:199x248:signed:Presented by Sue Flanagan, the artist's former wife 1985

P02768 Nina King (1972)
MIπ:248x201:signed:Presented by Sue Flanagan, the artist's former wife 1985

P02769 Numbers (1972, reprinted circa 1983)
MIπ:203x251:signed:Presented by Sue Flanagan, the artist's former wife 1985

P02770 One of the Lads (1972, reprinted circa 1983)
MIπ:252x200:signed:Presented by Sue Flanagan, the artist's former wife 1985

P02771 Paul DuFeu (1972)
MIπ:253x200:signed:Presented by Sue Flanagan, the artist's former wife 1985

P02772 Peter Townsend (1972)
MIπ:200x163:signed:Presented by Sue Flanagan, the artist's former wife 1985

P02773 A Pound Note, by a Governed Imagination (1972)
MIπ:150x202:signed:Presented by Sue Flanagan, the artist's former wife 1985

P02774 Richard Alston (circa 1971-2)
MIπ:252x200:signed:Presented by Sue Flanagan, the artist's former wife 1985

P02775 Richard Hamilton Working (1972)
MIπ:247x197:signed:Presented by Sue Flanagan, the artist's former wife 1985

P02776 Samantha (1972)
MIπ:251x200:signed:Presented by Sue Flanagan, the artist's former wife 1985

P02777 Samantha (1972)
MIπ:202x152:signed:Presented by Sue Flanagan, the artist's former wife 1985

P02778 Self-Portrait (1972)
MIπ:250x201:signed:Presented by Sue Flanagan, the artist's former wife 1985

P02779 Sue (1972)
MIπ:258x197:signed:Presented by Sue Flanagan, the artist's former wife 1985

P02780 Tara (1972)
MIπ:247x200:signed:Presented by Sue Flanagan, the artist's former wife 1985

P02781 Telephone (1972)
MIπ:201x163:signed:Presented by Sue Flanagan, the artist's former wife 1985

P02782 Tim Craig (1972)
MIπ:196x159:signed:Presented by Sue Flanagan, the artist's former wife 1985

P02783 Tim Craig (1972, reprinted circa 1983)
MIπ:246x244:signed:Presented by Sue Flanagan, the artist's former wife 1985

P02784 Tom Raworth (1972)
MIπ:201x252:signed:Presented by Sue Flanagan, the artist's former wife 1985

P02785 To the Last of the Imaginary Solutions (1972, reprinted circa 1983)
MIπ:202x250:signed:Presented by Sue Flanagan, the artist's former wife 1985

P02786 Wendy/Mayla (1972)
MIπ:250x197:signed:Presented by Sue Flanagan, the artist's former wife 1985

P02787 Cup and Quill (1972, published 1983)
MIπ:162x200:signed:Presented by Sue Flanagan, the artist's former wife 1985

P02788 Truffle Hunt (1972, published 1983)
MIπ:127x178:signed:Presented by Sue Flanagan, the artist's former wife 1985

P02789 The Wren's Nest (1972, published 1983)
MIπ:200x250:signed:Presented by Sue Flanagan, the artist's former wife 1985

P02790 Herbert Distel Walking (1973)
MIπ:247x198:signed:Presented by Sue Flanagan, the artist's former wife 1985

P02791 His Master's Voice (1973)
MIπ:209x245:signed:Presented by Sue Flanagan, the artist's former wife 1985

P02792 Larry Weiner (1973, reprinted circa 1983)
MIπ:248x197:signed:Presented by Sue Flanagan, the artist's former wife 1985

P02793 The Clay Pit (1975, published 1976)
CJπ:178x178:signed:Presented by Sue Flanagan, the artist's former wife 1985

P02794 Motif (1975)
CJπ:89x89:signed:Presented by Sue Flanagan, the artist's former wife 1985

P02795 The Abbey (1976)
CJπ:308x496:signed:Presented by Sue Flanagan, the artist's former wife 1985

P02796 At River Oich (1976)
MIπ:155x232:signed:Presented by Sue Flanagan, the artist's former wife 1985

P02797 Beacon (1976)
CJπ:154x137:signed:Presented by Sue Flanagan, the artist's former wife 1985

P02798 Cat (1976, reprinted circa 1983)
MIπ:250x202:signed:Presented by Sue Flanagan, the artist's former wife 1985

P02799 Graphics (1976)
CJπ:311x267:signed:Presented by Sue Flanagan, the artist's former wife 1985

P02800 Herring Drifter at Fort Augustus Swing Bridge at Night (1976)
CJπ:127x180:signed:Presented by Sue Flanagan, the artist's former wife 1985

P02801 Loch Ness (1976)
MIπ:157x231:signed:Presented by Sue Flanagan, the artist's former wife 1985

P02802 Loch Ness (1976)
MIπ:157x231:signed:Presented by Sue Flanagan, the artist's former wife 1985

P02803 Loch Tarff (1976)
CJπ:332x317:signed:Presented by Sue Flanagan, the artist's former wife 1985

P02804 On the Ness (1976)
MIπ:127x261:signed:Presented by Sue Flanagan, the artist's former wife 1985

P02805 Stones (1976)
CJπ:127x261:signed:Presented by Sue Flanagan, the artist's former wife 1985

P02806 Urquheart (1976, reprinted circa 1983)
MIπ:156x232:signed:Presented by Sue Flanagan, the artist's former wife 1985

P02807 Urquheart Castle (1976)
CJπ:285x504:signed:Presented by Sue Flanagan, the artist's former wife 1985

P02808 View (1976)
CJπ:131x178:signed:Presented by Sue Flanagan, the artist's former wife 1985

P02809 Water Folding Over A Stone (1976)
MIπ:156x232:signed:Presented by Sue Flanagan, the artist's former wife 1985

P02810 Atlantic Moon (1977, reprinted circa 1983)
CJπ:200x148:signed:Presented by Sue Flanagan, the artist's former wife 1985

P02811 Eve (1977, reprinted circa 1983)
MIπ:250x201:signed:Presented by Sue Flanagan, the artist's former wife 1985

P02812 Eve (1977)
CJπ:134x139:signed:Presented by Sue Flanagan, the artist's former wife 1985

P02813 Out of Oban (1977)
CJπ:176x287:signed:Presented by Sue Flanagan, the artist's former wife 1985

P02814 Out of Oban (1977, reprinted circa 1983)
CJπ:178x286:signed:Presented by Sue Flanagan, the artist's former wife 1985

P02815 Rembrandt Study (1977, reprinted circa 1983)
MIπ:249x202:signed:Presented by Sue Flanagan, the artist's former wife 1985

P02816 Whisky's Tale (1977)
CJπ:204x143:signed:Presented by Sue Flanagan, the artist's former wife 1985

P02817 McBrayne's Ferry (1977, published 1983)
CJπ:303x358:signed:Presented by Sue Flanagan, the artist's former wife 1985

P02818 Killary Bay (1979-80, published 1983)
CJπ:283x322:signed:Presented by Sue Flanagan, the artist's former wife 1985

P02819 Killary Harbour I (1979-80, published 1983)
CJπ:272x324:signed:Presented by Sue Flanagan, the artist's former wife 1985

P02820 Killary Harbour II (1979-80, published 1983)
CJπ:258x308:signed:Presented by Sue Flanagan, the artist's former wife 1985

P02821 Llandudno (1979, reprinted circa 1983)
CJπ:257x245:signed:Presented by Sue Flanagan, the artist's former wife 1985

P02822 Llandudno (1979, reprinted circa 1983)
CJπ:256x235:signed:Presented by Sue Flanagan, the artist's former wife 1985

P02823 Llandudno (1979, reprinted circa 1983)
CJπ:267x250:signed:Presented by Sue Flanagan, the artist's former wife 1985

P02824 Llandudno (1979, reprinted circa 1983)
CJπ:176x170:signed:Presented by Sue Flanagan, the artist's former wife 1985

P02825 Llandudno (1979, reprinted circa 1983)
CJπ:299x288:signed:Presented by Sue Flanagan, the artist's former wife 1985

P02826 Willie's Rocks (1979)
CJπ:261x347:signed:Presented by Sue Flanagan, the artist's former wife 1985

P02827 Cob Study (1983)
CJπ:216x153:signed:Presented by Sue Flanagan, the artist's former wife 1985

P02828 Ganymede (1983)
CJπ:365x252:Presented by Sue Flanagan, the artist's former wife 1985

P02829 Jolly Dog (1972, reprinted circa 1983)
MIπ:250x198:Presented by Sue Flanagan, the artist's former wife 1985

P02830 Mule (1983)
MIπ:183x219:Presented by Sue Flanagan, the artist's former wife 1985

P02831 Stepney Green (1983)
MIπ:173x218:Presented by Sue Flanagan, the artist's former wife 1985

P02832 Welsh Girl (1983)
CJπ:230x314:Presented by Sue Flanagan, the artist's former wife 1985

P02833 Welsh Lights (1983)
CJπ:363x252:signed:Presented by Sue Flanagan, the artist's former wife 1985

P02834 Yacht II (1983)
CJπ:220x422:signed:Presented by Sue Flanagan, the artist's former wife 1985

For John Constable (P03149-P03157, P03159-P03161, P03180-P03185; complete group; mixed group)
P03153 Untitled (1976)
MIπ:162x235:signed:Presented by Bernard Jacobson Gallery 1976

P07431 Pilgrim (1981)
MJπ:260x146:signed:Purchased 1981

P07432 Valentine (1981)
CJπ:305x203:signed:Purchased 1981

P07935 Field Day (1983)
MIπ:184x216:signed:Purchased 1983

P07936 Welsh Cob (1983)
MJπ:358x254:signed:Purchased 1983

FLAVIN, Dan born 1933
Modern Collection
Tate Gallery Archive holds material concerning this artist

T01323 'Monument' for V. Tatlin (1966-9)
RV:3054x584x89:Purchased 1971

T01824 Untitled (Corner Piece) (1969)
RV:1226x1226x203:Purchased 1973

FLAXMAN, John 1755-1826
British Collection
Tate Gallery Archive holds material concerning this artist

N03623 Woman and Child
DWπ:140x79:Purchased 1922

T05476 Classical Figure Studies (1792)
Dπ:68x242:Presented by Miss Marjorie Ball 1988

FLORENCE, Mary Sargent 1857-1954
British Collection

N04705 'Suffer Little Children to Come unto Me' (1913)
DGπ:1226x2286:signed:Presented by the Trustees of the Chantrey Bequest 1932

N04706 Pentecost (circa 1913)
DGπ:1206x2299:Presented by the Trustees of the Chantrey Bequest 1932

N05960 Children at Chess (circa 1903)
Tw:902x400:signed:Presented by the Trustees of the Chantrey Bequest 1949

FOLEY, John Henry 1818-1874
British Collection

N01770 Sir Joshua Reynolds, P.R.A.
Ss:2032x787x660:Bequeathed by Henry Vaughan 1900

FONTANA, Lucio 1899-1968
Modern Collection

T00234 Spatial Concept (1958)
Concetto spaziale
Pc:1638x1206:signed:Purchased 1959

T00694 Spatial Concept 'Waiting' (1960)
Concetto spaziale 'Attesa'
C:930x730:signed:Purchased 1964

T03588 Nature (1959-60)
Natura
Sz:610x730:Purchased 1983

T03961 Spatial Concept 49-50 B4 (1949-50)
49-50 B4 Concetto Spaziale
c:550x846:signed:Purchased with assistance from the Friends of the Tate Gallery 1985

FORAIN, Jean-Louis 1852-1931
Modern Collection
Tate Gallery Archive holds material concerning this artist

N03288 The Tribunal (circa 1902-3)
Le Tribunal
Oc:603x730:signed:Purchased 1918

N04789 Counsel and Accused (1908)
Avocat et accusé
Oc:651x813:signed:Purchased 1935

N05294 The Tub (circa 1886-7)
Oc:654x546:signed:Bequeathed by Sir Hugh Walpole 1941

FORBES, Elizabeth 1859-1912
British Collection

T04171 Volendam, Holland, from the Zuidende (?1895)
Ow:268x174:Presented by the Friends of the Tate Gallery 1986

FORBES, Stanhope Alexander 1857-1947
British Collection
Tate Gallery Archive holds material concerning this artist

N01544 The Health of the Bride (1889)
Oc:1524x2000:signed:Presented by Sir Henry Tate 1894

FORBES, Vivian 1891-1937
Modern Collection

N04682 The Fallen Statue (1932)
Oc:381x552:signed:Purchased 1933

FORBES-ROBERTSON, Eric 1865-1935
British Collection

T01825 In the Forest, Pont-Aven (circa 1895)
Oc:686x905:Purchased 1973

FORD, Mary born 1946
Modern Collection

P01865 Boats-Antibes (1978)
CNπ:210x483:signed:Presented by Christie's Contemporary Art 1979

FORD, Onslow Edward 1852-1901
British Collection

N01753 The Singer (exhibited 1889)
Szv:902x216x432:signed:Presented by Sir Henry Tate 1894

N01758 Folly (exhibited 1886)
Sz:887x415x330:Presented by the Trustees of the Chantrey Bequest 1886

N02971 Sir W.Q. Orchardson, R.A. (exhibited 1895)
Sz:622x305x229:Presented by the Orchardson Memorial Committee 1914

FÖRG, Günther born 1952
Modern Collection

Space (P77349-P77360; complete group)
Raum
P77349   [no title] (1987)
    Lπ:575x305:signed:Purchased 1990
P77350   [no title] (1987)
    Lπ:440x260:signed:Purchased 1990
P77351   [no title] (1987)
    Lπ:160x400:signed:Purchased 1990
P77352   [no title] (1987)
    Lπ:520x355:signed:Purchased 1990
P77353   [no title] (1987)
    Lπ:510x355:signed:Purchased 1990
P77354   [no title] (1987)
    Lπ:520x375:signed:Purchased 1990
P77355   [no title] (1987)
    Lπ:475x307:signed:Purchased 1990
P77356   [no title] (1987)
    Lπ:475x315:signed:Purchased 1990
P77357   [no title] (1987)
    Lπ:475x308:signed:Purchased 1990
P77358   [no title] (1987)
    Lπ:440x258:signed:Purchased 1990
P77359   [no title] (1987)
    Lπ:438x258:signed:Purchased 1990
P77360   [no title] (1987)
    Lπ:440x260:signed:Purchased 1990

FORGE, Andrew born 1923
Modern Collection
Tate Gallery Archive holds material concerning this artist

T00491   Orange Nude: S. Undressing (1961)
    Oc:1022x762:Purchased 1962

FOSTER, Myles Birket 1825-1899
British Collection

N01977   Lane Scene at Hambledon (?exhibited 1862)
    Wπ:425x635:signed:Bequeathed by C. Fraser 1905
N04016   The Country Inn (published 1863)
    Mπ:178x137:signed:Presented by Gilbert Dalziel 1924
N04050   Landscape
    Jπ:140x114:signed:Presented by Harold Hartley 1925
N04950   Eel Bucks (circa 1890)
    Wπ:102x140:signed:Bequeathed by R.H. Williamson 1938
N04951   The Smithy (circa 1890)
    Wπ:102x140:signed:Bequeathed by R.H. Williamson 1938

FOX PITT, Douglas 1864-1922
British Collection

N03994   Concert on the West Pier, Brighton (?circa 1911-18)
    DWπ:210x279:signed:Presented by Miss Patience Scott 1924

FRAENKEL, Elsa 1892-1975
Modern Collection

N06088   A Young Frenchman (1935)
    Sz:343x181x219:signed:Presented by the artist 1952

FRAMPTON, Edward Reginald 1872-1923
British Collection
Tate Gallery Archive holds material concerning this artist

T03414   Brittany: 1914 (circa 1920)
    Oc:768x926:signed:Purchased 1982

FRAMPTON, Sir George 1860-1928
British Collection

N01954   Charles Keene (1896)
    Sz:902x597x76:signed:Presented by the artist 1905
N05998   Charles Keene, Plaster for N01954 (1896)
    Sp:902x597x76:signed:Presented by Mrs E. Edwards 1905

FRAMPTON, Meredith 1894-1984
Modern Collection
Tate Gallery Archive holds material concerning this artist

N04820   Portrait of a Young Woman (1935)
    Oc:2057x1079:signed:Presented by the Trustees of the Chantrey Bequest 1935
T03415   Marguerite Kelsey (1928)
    Oc:1208x1412:signed:Presented by the Friends of the Tate Gallery 1982
T03981   Nude with Flying Swans (1919)
    Tw:180x241:signed:Presented by the executors of Mrs Hilda Frampton, the artist's widow 1985
P11080   Near Dieppe (1919)
    MIπ:231x292:Presented by the executors of Mrs Hilda Frampton, the artist's widow 1985
P11081   Sir George Frampton (1919)
    MIπ:196x245:Presented by the executors of Mrs Hilda Frampton, the artist's widow 1985

after
FRANCIA, François Louis Thomas 1772-1839
British Collection

Picturesque Views on the Southern Coast of England (T05218-T05463; complete group; mixed group)
T05298   Worthing Point, from Shoreham (1814)
    Iπ:128x136:Purchased 1988
T05299   Worthing Point, from Shoreham (1814)
    Iπ:138x142:Purchased 1988

FRANCIA, Peter de - see DE FRANCIA, Peter

FRANCIS, Sam born 1923
Modern Collection
Tate Gallery Archive holds material concerning this artist

T00148   Painting (1957)
    Wπ:629x486:Purchased 1957
T00634   Around the Blues (1957/62)
    OAc:2743x4877:signed:Purchased 1964
P11070   Damn Braces (1960)
    CLπ:851x632:signed:Presented by J.G. Cluff 1984
P11071   Blue Blood Stone (1960)
    CLπ:844x632:signed:Presented by J.G. Cluff 1984
P77042   Concert Hall I (1976)
    CLπ:561x447:signed:Purchased 1984

FRANKENTHALER, Helen born 1928
Modern Collection

P07394   Door (1976-9)
CLπ:581x781:signed:Purchased 1980

FRASER, Alexander 1786-1865
British Collection

N00453   Interior of a Highland Cottage
Oc:698x889:Presented by Robert Vernon 1847

N01789   Figures Outside an Inn: Scene from 'Peveril of the Peak'
Oc:432x343:Bequeathed by Henry Vaughan 1900

FRASER, Claud Lovat 1890-1921
Modern Collection

T01989   The Slave Market (1912-13)
GWDc:610x914:Purchased 1975

T01990   Seated Female Nude (1919)
WDπ:359x241:signed:Presented by Mrs Grace Lovat Fraser, the artist's widow 1975

T01991   Nude Study: Two Seated Women (circa 1919)
DWπ:321x295:signed:Presented by Mrs Grace Lovat Fraser, the artist's widow 1975

FREEDMAN, Barnett 1901-1958
Modern Collection
Tate Gallery Archive holds material concerning this artist

N05201   Street Scene (1933-9)
Oc:1829x2146:signed:Purchased 1939

N05610   Illustrations for Walter de la Mare's 'Love' (1942)
DWπ:140x89:signed:Purchased 1945

N05693   Personnel of an Aircraft Factory (1942)
DWπ:1086x2203:signed:Presented by the War Artists' Advisory Committee 1946

N05694   Interior of a Submarine (1943)
DWπ:600x940:signed:Presented by the War Artists' Advisory Committee 1946

N06137   Music (1951)
Oc:762x1016:signed:Presented by J. Lyons and Co. 1953

P01804   Illustrations for 'Wuthering Heights' I-XVI (1941)
16 CLπ:952x591:Presented by Robert Simon 1976

P01805   Illustrations for 'Jane Eyre' I-XVI (1942)
16 CLπ:940x584:Presented by Robert Simon 1976

P01806   Illustrations for 'Anna Karenina' I-XIV (1950)
14 CLπ:968x629:Presented by Robert Simon 1976

P06707   The Darts Champion (1956)
CLπ:483x733:Presented by Curwen Studio 1976

FREILES, Antonio born 1943
Modern Collection

P02517   Situation 377 (1976)
Situazione 377
CNπ:622x451:signed:Presented by the artist 1979

P02518   Situation 507 (1978)
Situazione 507
CNπ:800x584:signed:Presented by the artist 1979

P02519   Situation 514 (1979)
Situazione 514
MIπ:337x248:signed:Presented by the artist 1979

FRÉLAUT, Jean 1879-1954
Modern Collection

N04797   Wedding Feast in Brittany (1908)
Repas de noce en Bretagne
Oc:895x1308:Presented by P.M. Turner 1935

FRENKEL, Vera born 1938
Modern Collection

Homage to Albert Dumouchel (P03166-P03178; complete group; mixed group)
Hommage à Albert Dumouchel
P03172   Poem for Albert (1971)
Poème pour Albert
CLπ:533x235:signed:Presented by the University of Quebec 1976

FREUD, Lucian born 1922
Modern Collection
Tate Gallery Archive holds material concerning this artist

N06039   Girl with a White Dog (1950-1)
Oc:762x1016:Purchased 1952

N06040   Francis Bacon (1952)
Om:178x127:Purchased 1952

T00422   Self-Portrait (1946)
Oc:610x502:signed:Purchased 1961

T01972   Naked Portrait (1972-3)
Oc:610x610:Purchased 1975

T03105   Two Plants (1977-80)
Oc:1499x1200:Purchased 1980

T05722   Standing by the Rags (1988-9)
Oc:1689x1384:Purchased with assistance from the National Art Collections Fund, the Friends of the Tate Gallery and anonymous donors 1990

P07782   Head of a Woman (1982)
MIπ:127x127:signed:Purchased 1982

P07783   The Painter's Mother (1982)
MIπ:178x152:signed:Purchased 1982

P77182   Man Posing (1985)
Lπ:695x543:signed:Purchased 1987

P77186   Blond Girl (1985)
Lπ:695x545:signed:Purchased 1987

P77265   Girl with a Fig Leaf (1947)
Lπ:298x238:signed:Purchased 1988

FRIEDENSON, Arthur 1872-1955
British Collection

N02138   Runswick Bay (1907)
Oc:1059x1537:signed:Presented by the Trustees of the Chantrey Bequest 1907

FRIEND, Ian born 1951
Modern Collection

P77111   Three Sculptural Images (1984)
MLπ:488x775:signed:Purchased 1985

FRIESZ, Othon 1879-1949
Modern Collection
Tate Gallery Archive holds material concerning this artist

N05071 Woman at a Window (1919)
Jeune femme à la fenêtre
Oc:730x600:signed:Bequeathed by Frank Hindley Smith
1940

N06179 The Castle of Falaise (Evening) (1904)
Le Château de Falaise (soir)
Oc:730x600:signed:Presented by Dr Hermann Ganz 1953

FRINK, Dame Elisabeth born 1930
Modern Collection
Tate Gallery Archive holds material concerning this artist

N06140 Bird (1952)
Sz:203x241x362:Purchased 1952

T00580 Harbinger Bird IV (1960)
Sz:483x213x356:signed:Purchased 1963

T03416 In Memoriam I (1981)
Sz:1275x1100x680:signed:Purchased 1982

T03417 In Memoriam II (1981)
Sz:1245x1170x680:signed:Purchased 1982

The Canterbury Tales I (P01097-P01101; complete
group)
P01097 [title not known] (1970)
MIπ:270x311:signed:Presented by Waddington Galleries
through the Institute of Contemporary Prints 1975

P01098 [title not known] (1970)
MIπ:250x303:signed:Presented by Waddington Galleries
through the Institute of Contemporary Prints 1975

P01099 The Miller's Tale I (1970)
MIπ:304x205:signed:Presented by Waddington Galleries
through the Institute of Contemporary Prints 1975

P01100 The Miller's Tale (1970)
MIπ:302x250:signed:Presented by Waddington Galleries
through the Institute of Contemporary Prints 1975

P01101 [title not known] (1970)
MIπ:273x300:signed:Presented by Waddington Galleries
through the Institute of Contemporary Prints 1975

P01102 Horse and Rider VI (1970)
CLπ:584x781:signed:Presented by Waddington Galleries
through the Institute of Contemporary Prints 1975

P01103 Horse's Head (1970)
MLπ:387x587:signed:Presented by Waddington Galleries
through the Institute of Contemporary Prints 1975

P01104 Small Horse and Rider (1970)
MLπ:384x591:signed:Presented by Waddington Galleries
through the Institute of Contemporary Prints 1975

P01105 Man and Horse IV (1971)
CLπ:594x803:signed:Presented by Waddington Galleries
through the Institute of Contemporary Prints 1975

P01106 Small Boar (1971)
CLπ:511x638:signed:Presented by Waddington Galleries
through the Institute of Contemporary Prints 1975

Chaucer's 'Canterbury Tales' (P01107-P01125; complete
group)
P01107 [title not known] (1972)
MIπ:498x347:signed:Presented by Waddington Galleries
through the Institute of Contemporary Prints 1975

P01108 The Knight's Tale (1972)
MIπ:497x345:signed:Presented by Waddington Galleries
through the Institute of Contemporary Prints 1975

P01109 The Miller's Tale I (1972)
MIπ:500x345:signed:Presented by Waddington Galleries
through the Institute of Contemporary Prints 1975

P01110 The Miller's Tale II (1972)
MIπ:499x346:signed:Presented by Waddington Galleries
through the Institute of Contemporary Prints 1975

P01111 [title not known] (1972)
MIπ:499x347:signed:Presented by Waddington Galleries
through the Institute of Contemporary Prints 1975

P01112 The Shipman's Tale (1972)
MIπ:496x345:signed:Presented by Waddington Galleries
through the Institute of Contemporary Prints 1975

P01113 The Prioress's Tale (1972)
MIπ:500x345:signed:Presented by Waddington Galleries
through the Institute of Contemporary Prints 1975

P01114 Chaucer's Tale of Sir Topaz (1972)
MIπ:499x346:signed:Presented by Waddington Galleries
through the Institute of Contemporary Prints 1975

P01115 The Nun's Priests' Tale (1972)
MIπ:497x345:signed:Presented by Waddington Galleries
through the Institute of Contemporary Prints 1975

P01116 The Physician's Tale (1972)
MIπ:498x347:signed:Presented by Waddington Galleries
through the Institute of Contemporary Prints 1975

P01117 The Pardoner's Tale (1972)
MIπ:497x345:signed:Presented by Waddington Galleries
through the Institute of Contemporary Prints 1975

P01118 The Wife of Bath's Tale (1972)
MIπ:502x348:signed:Presented by Waddington Galleries
through the Institute of Contemporary Prints 1975

P01119 The Summoner's Tale (1972)
MIπ:500x346:signed:Presented by Waddington Galleries
through the Institute of Contemporary Prints 1975

P01120 The Clerk's Tale (1972)
MIπ:500x347:signed:Presented by Waddington Galleries
through the Institute of Contemporary Prints 1975

P01121 The Merchant's Tale (1972)
MIπ:500x347:signed:Presented by Waddington Galleries
through the Institute of Contemporary Prints 1975

P01122 The Squire's Tale (1972)
MIπ:498x347:signed:Presented by Waddington Galleries
through the Institute of Contemporary Prints 1975

P01123 The Franklin's Tale (1972)
MIπ:500x347:signed:Presented by Waddington Galleries
through the Institute of Contemporary Prints 1975

P01124 The Second Nun's Tale (1972)
MIπ:497x345:signed:Presented by Waddington Galleries
through the Institute of Contemporary Prints 1975

P01125 The Manciple's Tale (1972)
MIπ:497x345:signed:Presented by Waddington Galleries
through the Institute of Contemporary Prints 1975

P01126 Goggled Head (1973)
CLπ:559x441:signed:Presented by Waddington Galleries
through the Institute of Contemporary Prints 1975

Birds of Prey (P01127-P01135; incomplete group)
P01127 Golden Eagle (1974)
CLπ:536x464:signed:Presented by Waddington Galleries
through the Institute of Contemporary Prints 1975

P01128 Goshawk (1974)
CLπ:540x465:signed:Presented by Waddington Galleries
through the Institute of Contemporary Prints 1975

P01129 Honey Buzzard (1974)
CLπ:540x465:signed:Presented by Waddington Galleries
through the Institute of Contemporary Prints 1975

P01130 Kestrel (1974)
CIπ:542x465:signed:Presented by Waddington Galleries through the Institute of Contemporary Prints 1975

P01131 Lammergeier (1974)
CIπ:541x467:signed:Presented by Waddington Galleries through the Institute of Contemporary Prints 1975

P01132 Marsh Harrier (1974)
CIπ:535x468:signed:Presented by Waddington Galleries through the Institute of Contemporary Prints 1975

P01133 Osprey (1974)
CIπ:541x465:signed:Presented by Waddington Galleries through the Institute of Contemporary Prints 1975

P01134 Peregrine Falcon (1974)
CIπ:540x465:signed:Presented by Waddington Galleries through the Institute of Contemporary Prints 1975

P01135 Sparrow Hawk (1974)
CIπ:530x467:signed:Presented by Waddington Galleries through the Institute of Contemporary Prints 1975

P06142 Spinning Man I (1965)
MLπ:575x810:signed:Presented by Curwen Studio through the Institute of Contemporary Prints 1975

P06143 Spinning Man II (1965)
MLπ:572x800:signed:Presented by Curwen Studio through the Institute of Contemporary Prints 1975

P06144 Spinning Man III (1965)
MLπ:812x578:signed:Presented by Curwen Studio through the Institute of Contemporary Prints 1975

P06145 Spinning Man IV (1965)
MLπ:801x572:signed:Presented by Curwen Studio through the Institute of Contemporary Prints 1975

P06146 Spinning Man V (1965)
MLπ:795x571:signed:Presented by Curwen Studio through the Institute of Contemporary Prints 1975

P06147 Spinning Man VI (1965)
MLπ:803x570:signed:Presented by Curwen Studio through the Institute of Contemporary Prints 1975

P06148 Spinning Man VII (1965)
MLπ:576x813:signed:Presented by Curwen Studio through the Institute of Contemporary Prints 1975

P06149 Spinning Man VIII (1965)
MLπ:571x803:signed:Presented by Curwen Studio through the Institute of Contemporary Prints 1975

P06150 Guillemot (1967)
CLπ:530x737:Presented by Curwen Studio through the Institute of Contemporary Prints 1975

Images 67 (P06151-P06159; complete group)
P06151 Bull (1967)
CLπ:778x599:Presented by Curwen Studio through the Institute of Contemporary Prints 1975

P06152 Ducks (1967)
CLπ:592x779:Presented by Curwen Studio through the Institute of Contemporary Prints 1975

P06153 Cormorant (1967)
CLπ:510x738:Presented by Curwen Studio through the Institute of Contemporary Prints 1975

P06154 Hare (1967)
CLπ:591x780:Presented by Curwen Studio through the Institute of Contemporary Prints 1975

P06155 Horse (1967)
CLπ:778x594:Presented by Curwen Studio through the Institute of Contemporary Prints 1975

P06156 Lioness (1967)
CLπ:780x594:Presented by Curwen Studio through the Institute of Contemporary Prints 1975

P06157 Owl (1967)
CLπ:780x594:Presented by Curwen Studio through the Institute of Contemporary Prints 1975

P06158 Wild Boar (1967)
CLπ:780x594:Presented by Curwen Studio through the Institute of Contemporary Prints 1975

P06159 Wild Goat (1967)
CLπ:781x596:Presented by Curwen Studio through the Institute of Contemporary Prints 1975

P06160 Wood Pigeons (1967)
CLπ:584x784:Presented by Curwen Studio through the Institute of Contemporary Prints 1975

P06161 Æsop's Fables (1968)
MLπ:537x759:Presented by Curwen Studio through the Institute of Contemporary Prints 1975

Wild Animals (P06162-P06169; complete group)
P06162 Badger (1970)
CLπ:520x660:signed:Presented by Curwen Studio through the Institute of Contemporary Prints 1975

P06163 Bear (1970)
CLπ:518x658:signed:Presented by Curwen Studio through the Institute of Contemporary Prints 1975

P06164 Boar (1970)
CLπ:524x654:signed:Presented by Curwen Studio through the Institute of Contemporary Prints 1975

P06165 Hare (1970)
CLπ:511x646:signed:Presented by Curwen Studio through the Institute of Contemporary Prints 1975

P06166 Lynx (1970)
CLπ:520x655:signed:Presented by Curwen Studio through the Institute of Contemporary Prints 1975

P06167 [title not known] (1970)
CLπ:521x660:signed:Presented by Curwen Studio through the Institute of Contemporary Prints 1975

P06168 Wild Cat (1970)
CLπ:519x660:signed:Presented by Curwen Studio through the Institute of Contemporary Prints 1975

P06169 Wolf (1970)
CLπ:521x660:signed:Presented by Curwen Studio through the Institute of Contemporary Prints 1975

P06170 Horse and Rider (1970)
CLπ:591x781:signed:Presented by Curwen Studio through the Institute of Contemporary Prints 1975

P06171 Man and Horse I (1971)
CLπ:602x798:signed:Presented by Curwen Studio through the Institute of Contemporary Prints 1975

P06172 Man and Horse II (1971)
CLπ:595x797:signed:Presented by Curwen Studio through the Institute of Contemporary Prints 1975

P06173 Man and Horse III (1971)
CLπ:596x798:signed:Presented by Curwen Studio through the Institute of Contemporary Prints 1975

P06174 Man and Horse V (1971)
CLπ:595x800:signed:Presented by Curwen Studio through the Institute of Contemporary Prints 1975

P06175 [title not known] (1971)
CLπ:591x796:signed:Presented by Curwen Studio through the Institute of Contemporary Prints 1975

P06176 Horse and Rider I (1970-1)
CLπ:585x778:signed:Presented by Curwen Studio through the Institute of Contemporary Prints 1975

P06177 Horse and Rider II (1970-1)
CLπ:586x778:signed:Presented by Curwen Studio
through the Institute of Contemporary Prints 1975

P06178 Horse and Rider III (1970-1)
CLπ:584x778:signed:Presented by Curwen Studio
through the Institute of Contemporary Prints 1975

P06179 Horse and Rider IV (1970-1)
CLπ:584x778:signed:Presented by Curwen Studio
through the Institute of Contemporary Prints 1975

P06180 Horse and Rider V (1970-1)
CLπ:584x778:signed:Presented by Curwen Studio
through the Institute of Contemporary Prints 1975

P06181 Horse and Rider (1970-1)
CLπ:592x785:signed:Presented by Curwen Studio
through the Institute of Contemporary Prints 1975

P06182 The Three Riders (1972-4)
CLπ:575x778:signed:Presented by Curwen Studio
through the Institute of Contemporary Prints 1975

P06183 Corrida One (1973)
CLπ:571x775:signed:Presented by Curwen Studio
through the Institute of Contemporary Prints 1975

P06184 Corrida Two (1973)
CLπ:576x775:signed:Presented by Curwen Studio
through the Institute of Contemporary Prints 1975

P06185 Corrida Three (1973)
CLπ:574x775:signed:Presented by Curwen Studio
through the Institute of Contemporary Prints 1975

P06186 Corrida Four (1973)
CLπ:574x775:signed:Presented by Curwen Studio
through the Institute of Contemporary Prints 1975

P06187 Corrida Five (1973)
CLπ:576x775:signed:Presented by Curwen Studio
through the Institute of Contemporary Prints 1975

P06188 Rejoneadora One (1973)
CLπ:571x775:signed:Presented by Curwen Studio
through the Institute of Contemporary Prints 1975

P06189 Rejoneadora Two (1973)
CLπ:571x775:signed:Presented by Curwen Studio
through the Institute of Contemporary Prints 1975

P06190 Rejoneadora Three (1973)
CLπ:573x775:signed:Presented by Curwen Studio
through the Institute of Contemporary Prints 1975

The Odyssey (P06191-P06202; complete group)

P06191 Telemachus and Nector (1973-4)
CLπ:254x165:signed:Presented by Curwen Studio
through the Institute of Contemporary Prints 1975

P06192 Nausicaa (1973-4)
CLπ:254x165:signed:Presented by Curwen Studio
through the Institute of Contemporary Prints 1975

P06193 Calypso (1973-4)
CLπ:254x164:signed:Presented by Curwen Studio
through the Institute of Contemporary Prints 1975

P06194 Circe (1973-4)
CLπ:254x166:signed:Presented by Curwen Studio
through the Institute of Contemporary Prints 1975

P06195 Odysseus and Penelope (1973-4)
CLπ:256x163:signed:Presented by Curwen Studio
through the Institute of Contemporary Prints 1975

P06196 [title not known] (1973-4)
CLπ:252x161:signed:Presented by Curwen Studio
through the Institute of Contemporary Prints 1975

P06197 Cyclops (1973-4)
CLπ:255x160:signed:Presented by Curwen Studio
through the Institute of Contemporary Prints 1975

P06198 The Book of the Dead (1973-4)
CLπ:251x164:signed:Presented by Curwen Studio
through the Institute of Contemporary Prints 1975

P06199 Menelaus and Helen (1973-4)
CLπ:198x160:signed:Presented by Curwen Studio
through the Institute of Contemporary Prints 1975

P06200 [title not known] (1973-4)
CLπ:254x159:signed:Presented by Curwen Studio
through the Institute of Contemporary Prints 1975

P06201 The Great Bow (1973-4)
CLπ:256x156:signed:Presented by Curwen Studio
through the Institute of Contemporary Prints 1975

P06202 Odysseus Meets his Son (1973-4)
CLπ:250x166:signed:Presented by Curwen Studio
through the Institute of Contemporary Prints 1975

P06203 Cormorant (1974)
CLπ:610x502:signed:Presented by Curwen Studio
through the Institute of Contemporary Prints 1975

P06204 Gull (1974)
CLπ:610x476:signed:Presented by Curwen Studio
through the Institute of Contemporary Prints 1975

P06205 Horse and Jockey (1974)
CLπ:486x546:signed:Presented by Curwen Studio
through the Institute of Contemporary Prints 1975

P06206 Osprey (1974)
CLπ:610x476:signed:Presented by Curwen Studio
through the Institute of Contemporary Prints 1975

P06207 Shearwater (1974)
CLπ:610x476:signed:Presented by Curwen Studio
through the Institute of Contemporary Prints 1975

P06725 Eagle Owl (1972-3)
CLπ:775x571:signed:Presented by Curwen Studio 1977

P06726 Lying Down Horse (1972-3)
CLπ:575x775:signed:Presented by Curwen Studio 1977

FRITH, William Powell 1819-1909
British Collection
Tate Gallery Archive holds material concerning this artist

N00615 The Derby Day (1856-8)
Oc:1016x2235:Bequeathed by Jacob Bell 1859

N01781 Uncle Toby and the Widow Wadman (1865)
Oc:756x521:signed:Bequeathed by H.S. Ashbee 1900

T00041 Dolly Varden (circa 1842-9)
Ow:273x216:Bequeathed by Mrs E.J. Thwaites 1955

FROHNER, Adolf born 1934
Modern Collection

P08016 Looking Up to the Woman (circa 1975)
Auf die Frau hinaufschauend
MIπ:178x140:signed:Transferred from the Library 1978

FROST, Terry born 1915
Modern Collection
Tate Gallery Archive holds material concerning this artist

T00268 Khaki and Lemon (1956)
Oc:762x635:signed:Purchased 1959

T00829 June, Red and Black (1965)
Ac:2445x1835:signed:Purchased 1966

T01501 Green, Black and White Movement (1951)
Oc:1092x851:signed:Presented by the Contemporary Art
Society 1971

T01924 Winter 1956, Yorkshire (1956)
Ob:2467x1248:signed:Purchased 1974

T02022 Through Blacks (1969)
Ac:1981x2591:Purchased 1976

T02236 Brown and Yellow (circa 1951-2)
Ob:610x203:Bequeathed by Miss E.M. Hodgkins 1977

T05718 Untitled Composition (circa 1955)
Oπ:768x395:Purchased 1989

T05719 Untitled Composition (1954-6)
Wπ:570x438:Purchased 1989

P01136 Lace I (1968)
CLVπ:768x584:signed:Presented by Waddington Galleries through the Institute of Contemporary Prints 1975

P01137 Red and Black Solid (1968)
CLπ:622x435:signed:Presented by Waddington Galleries through the Institute of Contemporary Prints 1975

P01138 Black and Purple on Blue (1969)
CLπ:587x457:signed:Presented by Waddington Galleries through the Institute of Contemporary Prints 1975

P01139 Blues (1969)
CLπ:460x460:signed:Presented by Waddington Galleries through the Institute of Contemporary Prints 1975

P01140 Colour on the Side (1969)
CLπ:765x562:signed:Presented by Waddington Galleries through the Institute of Contemporary Prints 1975

P01141 Ochre, Red, Blue (1969)
CLπ:784x584:signed:Presented by Waddington Galleries through the Institute of Contemporary Prints 1975

P01142 Red, Blue, Orange on Yellow (1969)
CLπ:457x460:signed:Presented by Waddington Galleries through the Institute of Contemporary Prints 1975

P01143 Blue Suspended Form (1970)
CLπ:905x635:signed:Presented by Waddington Galleries through the Institute of Contemporary Prints 1975

P01144 Green and Orange (1970)
CLπ:508x657:signed:Presented by Waddington Galleries through the Institute of Contemporary Prints 1975

P01145 Orange Dusk (1970)
CLπ:676x518:signed:Presented by Waddington Galleries through the Institute of Contemporary Prints 1975

P01146 Red with Black on the Side (1970)
CLπ:606x511:signed:Presented by Waddington Galleries through the Institute of Contemporary Prints 1975

P01147 Stacked on the Side (1970)
CLπ:492x702:signed:Presented by Waddington Galleries through the Institute of Contemporary Prints 1975

P01148 Lace II (1971)
CLVπ:537x930:signed:Presented by Waddington Galleries through the Institute of Contemporary Prints 1975

P01149 Alhambra (1972)
CLπ:619x759:signed:Presented by Waddington Galleries through the Institute of Contemporary Prints 1975

P01150 Ice Blue (1972)
CLπ:654x518:signed:Presented by Waddington Galleries through the Institute of Contemporary Prints 1975

P01151 Moonship (1972)
CLπ:1057x752:signed:Presented by Waddington Galleries through the Institute of Contemporary Prints 1975

P01152 Red, Blue, Green (1972)
CLπ:638x905:signed:Presented by Waddington Galleries through the Institute of Contemporary Prints 1975

P01153 Straw, Orange, Blue (1972)
CLπ:635x508:signed:Presented by Waddington Galleries through the Institute of Contemporary Prints 1975

P01154 Suspended Form (1972)
CLπ:762x562:signed:Presented by Waddington Galleries through the Institute of Contemporary Prints 1975

P01155 Zebra (1972)
CLπ:784x581:signed:Presented by Waddington Galleries through the Institute of Contemporary Prints 1975

IAA Portfolio (P03096-P03104, P03107; complete group; mixed group)

P03099 Untitled (1975)
CLπ:486x686:Presented by the International Association of Art 1975

P04229 Black and Red on Blue (1968)
CNπ:575x772:signed:Presented by Rose and Chris Prater through the Institute of Contemporary Prints 1975

P04230 Black on Mauve Grey (1968)
CNπ:772x559:signed:Presented by Rose and Chris Prater through the Institute of Contemporary Prints 1975

P04231 Red and Black on Green (1968)
CNπ:559x765:signed:Presented by Rose and Chris Prater through the Institute of Contemporary Prints 1975

P04232 Red and Black on Grey (1968)
CNπ:556x695:signed:Presented by Rose and Chris Prater through the Institute of Contemporary Prints 1975

P06208 Red and Black Linear (1967-8)
CLπ:606x441:signed:Presented by Curwen Studio through the Institute of Contemporary Prints 1975

P06209 Red and Black Solid (1967-8)
CLπ:622x435:signed:Presented by Curwen Studio through the Institute of Contemporary Prints 1975

P06210 Lace I (trial Proof) (1968)
CLπ:762x603:signed:Presented by Curwen Studio through the Institute of Contemporary Prints 1975

P07981 Blue Moon (1952)
CLπ:355x273:Purchased 1983

P07982 Boat Shapes (1952)
CJπ:132x143:signed:Purchased 1983

P07983 Boat Shapes (circa 1954)
MJπ:131x155:signed:Purchased 1983

P07984 Boat Shapes (1954)
MJπ:193x267:signed:Purchased 1983

P07985 Leeds (1956)
MIπ:125x167:signed:Purchased 1983

P07986 Camping, Anduze (1979)
MIπ:257x209:signed:Purchased 1983

P07987 Umea, Sweden (1979)
MIπ::signed:Purchased 1983

P07988 Self-Portrait (1980)
MIπ:277x200:signed:Purchased 1983

P77162 Composition (1957)
Iπ:354x252:signed:Purchased 1986

FROST, William Edward 1810-1877
British Collection

N04970 Warrior Seated at a Table
WDπ:108x83:Presented by Alex Fraser 1938

T00047 Meditation
Ob:292x229:Purchased 1955

FROY, Martin born 1926
Modern Collection
Tate Gallery Archive holds material concerning this artist

N06077 Young Man Doing Up his Shoe (1951-2)
Ob:1219x762:Purchased 1952

T00458 Two Figures Summer '61 (1961)
Oc:1524x1219:Purchased 1961

FRY, Anthony born 1927
Modern Collection

T00161 Dancing Figures (exhibited 1957)
Oc:508x660:Purchased 1957

T00399 Dance, Blue and Yellow (1960)
Oc:762x1010:Purchased 1961

T03282 Nude X (1980-81)
Oc:1016x1372:Presented anonymously through the
Friends of the Tate Gallery 1981

FRY, Roger 1866-1934
British Collection
Tate Gallery Archive holds material concerning this artist

N04571 The Zoo, Two Fragments (1911)
Tc:1346x1105, 2470x1213:Purchased 1931

T00101 Still Life: Flowers (circa 1912)
Oc:965x610:Purchased 1956

T01778 Landscape with Shepherd, near Villa Madama, Rome
(1891)
Oc:362x464:Presented by Mrs Pamela Diamand, the
artist's daughter 1973

T01779 River with Poplars (circa 1912)
Ow:565x708:Presented by Mrs Pamela Diamand, the
artist's daughter 1973

T01780 Still Life with T'ang Horse (circa 1919-21)
Oc:356x457:Presented by Mrs Pamela Diamand, the
artist's daughter 1973

T01781 Bridge over the Allier (circa 1933)
Ob:314x410:Presented by Mrs Pamela Diamand, the
artist's daughter 1973

T01957 Essay in Abstract Design (1914 or 1915)
OVw:362x270:Presented by Mrs Pamela Diamand, the
artist's daughter 1975

Ten Architectural Lithographs (P08164-P08173;
complete group)

P08164 Arles sur Tech (1930)
MLπ:376x276:signed:Transferred from the Library 1979

P08165 Baroque Altar, Perpignon (1930)
MLπ:360x274:signed:Transferred from the Library 1979

P08166 Cluny Museum, Paris (1930)
MLπ:380x274:signed:Transferred from the Library 1979

P08167 Elne (1930)
MLπ:380x280:signed:Transferred from the Library 1979

P08168 Notre Dame, Clermont Ferrand (1930)
MLπ:375x278:signed:Transferred from the Library 1979

P08169 Rock-cut Church, Aubeterre (1930)
MLπ:378x280:signed:Transferred from the Library 1979

P08170 Rock-cut Church, Saint Emilion (1930)
MLπ:375x274:signed:Transferred from the Library 1979

P08171 A Staircase / Narbonne (1930)
MLπ:370x274:signed:Transferred from the Library 1979

P08172 Trinity College Library, Cambridge (1930)
MLπ:318x235:signed:Transferred from the Library 1979

P08173 [title not known] (1930)
MLπ::signed:Transferred from the Library 1979

FUCHS, Emil 1866-1929
Modern Collection

N05999 Sir Joseph Duveen (1903)
Oc:1676x1060:signed:Presented by Lord Duveen 1910

FULLARD, George 1923-1973
Modern Collection
Tate Gallery Archive holds material concerning this artist

T02014 Death or Glory (1963-4)
Sw:1880x1911x972:Purchased 1975

T03218 Infant with Flower (1958, cast 1960)
Sz:762x419x381:signed:Presented by the Trustees of the
Chantrey Bequest 1981

FULLER, Isaac circa 1606-1672
British Collection

T00056 Portrait of an Unknown Man (circa 1660)
Oc:1245x1022:Purchased 1955

FULLER, Sue born 1914
Modern Collection
Tate Gallery Archive holds material concerning this artist

T00757 String Composition 128 (1964)
V:914x914x38:signed:Presented by Emerson Crocker
through the Friends of the Tate Gallery 1965

FULLEYLOVE, John 1845-1908
British Collection

N03568 South Entrance, Church of the Holy Sepulchre,
Jerusalem (1901)
Dπ:352x251:Bequeathed by Mrs E.J. Thwaites 1955

FULTON, Hamish born 1946
Modern Collection
Tate Gallery Archive holds material concerning this artist

T01762 A Condor (1972)
Fb:565x819:Purchased 1973

T03268 France on the Horizon (1975)
FDπ:1099x1295:Purchased 1981

P07350 Northern France/Southern England (1977)
MFπ:514x600:Purchased 1979

P07382 No Darkness (1979)
MFπ:1372x1099:Purchased 1980

P07383 Slioch Hilltop Cairn/Circling Buzzards (1980)
MFπ:1181x870:Purchased 1980

FURSE, Charles Wellington 1868-1904
British Collection
Tate Gallery Archive holds material concerning this artist

N01963 The Return from the Ride (1902)
Oc:2159x2775:Presented by the Trustees of the Chantrey
Bequest 1905

N02059 Diana of the Uplands (1903-4)
Oc:2369x1791:Purchased 1906

N04611 Field-Marshal Earl Roberts, KG, VC, OM (1893-5)
Oc:3404x4547:Presented by the artist's widow 1932

T00615 Field-Marshal Earl Roberts on his Charger 'Vonolel' (circa 1893-1900)
Oc:914x705:signed:Bequeathed by Mary Elizabeth, Lady Hudson 1963

FUSELI, Henry 1741-1825
British Collection

N01228 Titania and Bottom (circa 1790)
Oc:2172x2756:signed:Presented by Miss Julia Carrick Moore in accordance with the wishes of her sister 1887

N03396 The Debutante (1807)
WDπ:371x241:Presented by Lady Holroyd in accordance with the wishes of the late Sir Charles Holroyd 1919

N05304 Percival Delivering Belisane from the Enchantment of Urma (exhibited 1783)
Oc:991x1257:Presented by the National Art Collections Fund 1941

T00733 Lady Macbeth Seizing the Daggers (?exhibited 1812)
Oc:1016x1270:Purchased 1965

T00876 The Shepherd's Dream, from 'Paradise Lost' (1793)
Oc:1543x2153:Purchased 1966

FUSSELL, Michael 1927-1974
Modern Collection
Tate Gallery Archive holds material concerning this artist

T00477 Skywards (1961)
OVc:305x305:signed:Purchased 1962

FYZEE-RAHAMIN, Samuel 1880-1964
Modern Collection

N04095 Raagni Todi, Goddess Tune (1913)
WDπ:514x362:signed:Presented by Sir Victor Sassoon 1925

N04096 A Rajput Sirdar (circa 1914-5)
WDπ:495x292:signed:Presented by the State of Bhavnagar 1925

GABO, Naum 1890-1977
Modern Collection
Tate Gallery Archive holds material concerning this artist

T00190 Spiral Theme (1941)
Sa:140x244x244:Purchased 1958

T00191 Linear Construction No. 1 (1942-3)
Sa:349x349x89:Purchased 1958

T00826 Bronze Spheric Theme (circa 1960)
Sz:921x667x724:Purchased 1966

T00827 Kinetic Construction (Standing Wave) (1919-20, replica 1985)
KSm:616x241x190:Presented by the artist through the American Federation of Arts 1966

T01105 Linear Construction No. 2 (1970-71)
Sa:1149x835x835:Presented by the artist through the American Federation of Arts 1969

T01171 Torsion (Project for a Fountain) (1960-4)
Sz:762x841x841:Presented by the artist through the American Federation of Arts 1969

T01520 Head No. 2 (Enlarged Version 1964) (1916)
Sm:1753x1340x1226:Purchased 1972

T01754 Revolving Torsion, Fountain (1972-3)
Sm:3099x3353x3353:Presented by Alistair McAlpine (later Lord McAlpine of West Green) 1973

T02142 Circular Relief (circa 1925)
Raw:498x498x229:signed:Presented by the artist 1977

T02143 Construction in Space 'Two Cones' (1927)
Sa:251x311x419:Presented by the artist 1977

T02144 Red Cavern (circa 1926)
Samw:660x514x279:signed:Presented by the artist 1977

T02145 Construction in a Niche (1930)
Samw:610x279x584:signed:Presented by the artist 1977

T02146 Torsion (1928-36)
Sa:352x410x400:Presented by the artist 1977

T02147 Stone with Collar (1930-1)
Ss:178x152x79:Presented by the artist 1977

T02148 Quartz Stone Carving (1936-40)
Ss:159x248x200:Presented by the artist 1977

T02149 Sketch (1917)
Dπ:244x168:signed:Presented by the artist 1977

T02150 Sketch (1917)
Dπ:283x286:signed:Presented by the artist 1977

T02151 Sketch for Relief Construction (1917)
Dπ:181x143:signed:Presented by the artist 1977

T02152 Design for a Construction in a Niche (1918)
Dπ:244x194:signed:Presented by the artist 1977

T02153 Sketch (1917)
Dπ:305x222:signed:Presented by the artist 1977

T02154 Sketch for a Kinetic Construction (1922)
Dπ:432x314:signed:Presented by the artist 1977

T02155 Sketch for a Mobile Construction (circa 1918)
Db:337x260:signed:Presented by the artist 1977

T02156 First Sketch for a Monument for an Institute of Physics and Mathematics (1919)
Dπ:330x229:signed:Presented by the artist 1977

T02157 Sketch (1918-19)
Dπ:241x203:signed:Presented by the artist 1977

T02158 Sketch for a Stone Carving (1933)
Dπ:140x219:signed:Presented by the artist 1977

T02159 Sketch for 'Spiral Theme' (circa 1940-1)
Dπ:124x241:signed:Presented by the artist 1977

T02160 Urn, Sketch for an Imaginary Construction (Logan Rock) (circa 1933)
Dπ:279x219:Presented by the artist 1977

T02161 Sketch for 'Spheric Theme' (1935-7)
Dπ:197x321:signed:Presented by the artist 1977

T02162 Sketch for 'Spheric Theme' (circa 1937)
Dπ:241x203:signed:Presented by the artist 1977

T02163 Sketch for 'Construction Through a Plane' (circa 1935)
Dπ:241x206:signed:Presented by the artist 1977

T02164 Sketch for Kinetic Construction (1949)
DWπ:333x254:signed:Presented by the artist 1977

T02165 Cover Design for a Portfolio of Prints (circa 1975)
Dπ:511x432:signed:Presented by the artist 1977

T02166 Two Cubes (Demonstrating the Stereometric Method) (1930)
Sw:305x305x305:Presented by the artist 1977

T02167 Model for 'Column' (1920-21)
Sa:143x95x95:Presented by the artist 1977

T02168 Model for Monument for an Airport (circa 1932)
Sa:63x121x76:Presented by the artist 1977

T02169 Model for 'Construction in Space 'Two Cones'' (1927)
Sa:86x108x124:Presented by the artist 1977

T02170 Model for 'Double Relief in a Niche' (1929-30)
Sabw:114x222x51:signed:Presented by the artist 1977

T02171 Model for 'Torsion' (circa 1928)
Sa:89x95x95:Presented by the artist 1977

T02172 Model for 'Stone with Collar' (1930-1)
Ss:48x51x44:Presented by the artist 1977

T02173 Model for 'Spheric Theme' (circa 1937)
Sa:83x102x83:Presented by the artist 1977

T02174 Model for 'Spheric Theme with Centre' (circa 1937)
Sm:102x76x83:Presented by the artist 1977

T02175 Model for 'Monument to the Astronauts' (circa 1966-8)
Sav:89x76x57:Presented by the artist 1977

T02176 Spheric Theme (Penetrated Variation) (circa 1937-40)
Sz:330x330x302:Presented by the artist 1977

T02177 Model for 'Construction Through a Plane' (circa 1935-7)
Sa:152x152x32:Presented by the artist 1977

T02178 Model for 'Construction on a Line' (circa 1937)
Sa:108x102x38:Presented by the artist 1977

T02179 Model for 'Construction in Space 'Crystal'' (1937)
Sa:76x76x38:Presented by the artist 1977

T02180 Model for 'Construction in Space with Crystalline Centre' (1938)
Sa:102x156x57:Presented by the artist 1977

T02181 Model for 'Spiral Theme' (1941)
Sa:63x171x114:Presented by the artist 1977

T02182 Model for the Baltimore 'Construction Suspended in Space' (1950)
Sa:216x51x51:Presented by the artist 1977

T02183 Model for 'Shadow Piece' (1951-2)
Szv:108x222x57:Presented by the artist 1977

T02184 Model for the Esso Project, Radio City, New York (1949)
Sam:89x127x51:Presented by the artist 1977

T02185 Model for 'Linear Construction No. 3 with Red' (1952)
Sa:95x63x60:Presented by the artist 1977

T02186 First Model for a 'Monument to the Unknown Politcal Prisoner' (1952)
Sam:127x32x25:Presented by the artist 1977

T02187 Model for a 'Monument to the Unknown Political Prisoner' (1952)
Sam:381x89x95:Presented by the artist 1977

T02188 Model for a Construction at the Bijenkorf Building, Rotterdam (1955)
Sa:251x44x44:Presented by the artist 1977

T02189 Linear Form (part of the model for the First Bijenkorf Project) (circa 1954)
Sam:41x41:Presented by the artist 1977

T02190 Linear Form (probably part of the model for the First Bijenkorf Project) (circa 1954)
Sam:57x41x41:Presented by the artist 1977

T02191 Linear Form (possible part of the model for the First Bijenkorf Project) (circa 1954)
Sa:57x44x41:Presented by the artist 1977

T02192 Linear Form (curved) (circa 1954)
Sam:86x41x41:Presented by the artist 1977

T02193 Model for Hanging Construction (1950s)
Sa:114x197x114:Presented by the artist 1977

T02194 Model for Hanging Piece (circa 1957)
Sa:152x95x38:Presented by the artist 1977

T02195 Model for 'Vertical Construction No. 1' (circa 1964)
Szm:117x32x32:Presented by the artist 1977

T02196 Model for 'Construction in Space, Suspended' (1965)
Sa:108x102x38:Presented by the artist 1977

T02197 Carving (circa 1960-70)
Sp:60x127x98:Presented by the artist 1977

T02198 Carving (circa 1960-70)
Ss:25x117x76:Presented by the artist 1977

T02199 Carving (circa 1960-70)
Ss:38x105x76:Presented by the artist 1977

T02200 Carving (circa 1960-70)
Ss:51x156x133:Presented by the artist 1977

T02201 Carving (circa 1960-70)
Ss:19x83x41:Presented by the artist 1977

T02202 Carving (circa 1960-70)
Ss:38x41x44:Presented by the artist 1977

T02203 Carving (circa 1960-70)
Ss:25x73x41:Presented by the artist 1977

T02204 Plaster Cast of the Alabaster in 'Construction with Alabaster Carving' (1938-9, cast 1963)
Sp:213x152x38:signed:Presented by the artist 1977

T02205 Cast of One Side of the Alabaster in 'Construction with Alabaster Carving' (1938-9, cast 1963)
Sp:222x152x38:signed:Presented by the artist 1977

T02206 Model for 'Construction in Space 'Arch'' (1937)
Sa:102x203x51:Presented by the artist 1977

T03054 Construction on a Line (1935-7)
Sa:451x432x89:Purchased 1980

T04146 Model for the Set of 'La Chatte' (1926-27)
Swmf:603x801x547:Presented by Nina Williams, the artist's daughter and her husband Graham Williams 1986

Opus 2 (P01921-P01925, P02002; incomplete group)
P01921 [no title] (1950)
MJπ:204x155:signed:Presented by Miriam and Nina Gabo, the artist's widow and daughter 1979

P01922 [no title] (1950)
MJπ:205x154:signed:Presented by Miriam and Nina Gabo, the artist's widow and daughter 1979

P01923 [no title] (1950)
MJπ:206x155:signed:Presented by Miriam and Nina Gabo, the artist's widow and daughter 1979

P01924 [no title] (1950)
MJπ:205x152:signed:Presented by Miriam and Nina Gabo, the artist's widow and daughter 1979

P01925 [no title] (1950)
MJπ:204x155:signed:Presented by Miriam and Nina Gabo, the artist's widow and daughter 1979

Opus 3 (P01926, P02003; incomplete group)
P01926 [no title] (1950)
CJπ:203x144:signed:Presented by Miriam and Nina Gabo, the artist's widow and daughter 1979

Opus 4 (P01927, P02004; incomplete group)
P01927 [no title] (1950)
MJπ:160x139:signed:Presented by Miriam and Nina Gabo, the artist's widow and daughter 1979

Opus 5 (P01928, P02005; incomplete group)
P01928 [no title] (1950)
CJπ:241x203:signed:Presented by Miriam and Nina Gabo, the artist's widow and daughter 1979

Opus 11 (P01929; incomplete group)
P01929 [no title] (circa 1955)
MJπ:184x190:signed:Presented by Miriam and Nina Gabo, the artist's widow and daughter 1979

Opus 6 (P01930-P01937, P02006; incomplete group)
P01930 [no title] (circa 1955-6)
CJπ:385x334:signed:Presented by Miriam and Nina Gabo, the artist's widow and daughter 1979

P01931 [no title] (circa 1955-6)
CJπ:384x333:signed:Presented by Miriam and Nina Gabo, the artist's widow and daughter 1979

P01932 [no title] (circa 1955-6)
CJπ:385x334:signed:Presented by Miriam and Nina Gabo, the artist's widow and daughter 1979

P01933 [no title] (circa 1955-6)
CJπ:384x334:signed:Presented by Miriam and Nina Gabo, the artist's widow and daughter 1979

P01934 [no title] (circa 1955-6)
CJπ:384x333:signed:Presented by Miriam and Nina Gabo, the artist's widow and daughter 1979

P01935 [no title] (circa 1955-6)
CJπ:385x334:signed:Presented by Miriam and Nina Gabo, the artist's widow and daughter 1979

P01936 [no title] (circa 1955-6)
CJπ:386x334:signed:Presented by Miriam and Nina Gabo, the artist's widow and daughter 1979

P01937 [no title] (circa 1955-6)
CJπ:385x334:signed:Presented by Miriam and Nina Gabo, the artist's widow and daughter 1979

Opus 7 (P01938-P01940; incomplete group)
P01938 [no title] (1956-73)
MJπ:202x253:signed:Presented by Miriam and Nina Gabo, the artist's widow and daughter 1979

P01939 [no title] (1956-73)
MJπ:262x382:signed:Presented by Miriam and Nina Gabo, the artist's widow and daughter 1979

P01940 [no title] (1956-73)
MJπ:203x256:signed:Presented by Miriam and Nina Gabo, the artist's widow and daughter 1979

Opus 12 (P01941; incomplete group)
P01941 [no title] (circa 1950)
MJπ:151x151:signed:Presented by Miriam and Nina Gabo, the artist's widow and daughter 1979

P01942 Untitled (circa 1965-73)
MJπ:148x148:signed:Presented by Miriam and Nina Gabo, the artist's widow and daughter 1979

P01943 Untitled (1965-73)
MJπ:277x202:Presented by Miriam and Nina Gabo, the artist's widow and daughter 1979

P01944 Untitled (1965-73)
MJπ:179x129:signed:Presented by Miriam and Nina Gabo, the artist's widow and daughter 1979

P01945 Untitled (1965-73)
CJπ:180x130:signed:Presented by Miriam and Nina Gabo, the artist's widow and daughter 1979

Opus 8 (P01946, P02007; incomplete group)
P01946 [no title] (1970)
MJπ:304x238:Presented by Miriam and Nina Gabo, the artist's widow and daughter 1979

Opus 10 (P01947-P01948; incomplete group)
P01947 [no title] (circa 1969)
MJπ:305x355:signed:Presented by Miriam and Nina Gabo, the artist's widow and daughter 1979

P01948 [no title] (circa 1969)
MJπ:305x357:signed:Presented by Miriam and Nina Gabo, the artist's widow and daughter 1979

Opus 9 (P01949; incomplete group)
P01949 [no title] (1973)
MJπ:238x277:signed:Presented by Miriam and Nina Gabo, the artist's widow and daughter 1979

Opus 1 (P02001; incomplete group)
P02001 [no title] (1950)
MJπ:160x145:signed:Presented by the artist 1967

Opus 2 (P01921-P01925, P02002; incomplete group)
P02002 [no title] (1950)
MJπ:204x154:signed:Presented by the artist 1967

Opus 3 (P01926, P02003; incomplete group)
P02003 [no title] (1950)
MJπ:265x199:signed:Presented by the artist 1967

Opus 4 (P01927, P02004; incomplete group)
P02004 [no title] (1950)
MJπ:160x140:signed:Presented by the artist 1967

Opus 5 (P01928, P02005; incomplete group)
P02005 [no title] (1950)
MJπ:243x302:signed:Presented by the artist 1967

Opus 6 (P01930-P01937, P02006; incomplete group)
P02006 [no title] (1955-6)
MJπ:385x333:signed:Presented by the artist 1971

Opus 8 (P01946, P02007; incomplete group)
P02007 [no title] (1968-70)
MJπ:303x239:signed:Presented by the artist 1971

GAINSBOROUGH, Thomas 1727-1788
British Collection
Tate Gallery Archive holds material concerning this artist

N00308 Musidora (circa 1780-8)
Oc:1880x1530:Presented by Robert Vernon 1847

N00309 Boy Driving Cows near a Pool (circa 1786)
Oc:584x762:Presented by Robert Vernon 1847

N00310 Sunset: Carthorses Drinking at a Stream (circa 1760)
Oc:1435x1537:Presented by Robert Vernon 1847

N00678 Abel Moysey (circa 1764)
Oc:578x457:Presented by H.G. and the Rev. F.L. Moysey 1861

N00789 The Baillie Family (circa 1784)
Oc:2508x2273:Bequeathed by Alexander Baillie 1868

N01044 The Rev. Sir Henry Bate-Dudley, Bart (circa 1780)
Oc:724x578:Presented by T. Birch Wolfe 1878

N01283 Wooded Landscape with a Peasant Resting (circa 1747)
Oc:625x781:Purchased 1889

N01482 The Artist's Daughter Margaret (circa 1772)
Oc:756x629:Presented by the family of Richard J. Lane 1896

N01483 Tristram and Fox (circa 1775-85)
Oc:610x508:Presented by the family of Richard J. Lane 1896

N01484 An Old Horse (circa 1755)
Oc:552x648:Presented by the family of Richard J. Lane 1896

N01485 Landscape with a Peasant on a Path (circa 1746-7)
Oc:222x171:Presented by the family of Richard J. Lane 1896

N01486 Landscape with Figures under a Tree (circa 1746-7)
Oc:222x171:Presented by the family of Richard J. Lane 1896

N01825 Woody Landscape with Building (circa 1768-71)
Oc:425x543:Bequeathed by Henry Vaughan 1900

N02210 Wooded Landscape with Figures and Cows at a Watering Place (The Watering Place) (circa 1776-7)
Lπ:244x324:Presented by A.E. Anderson 1907

N02223 Wooded Landscape with Shepherd and Sheep (circa 1785-8)
Dπ:264x368:Presented by T. Birch Wolfe 1878

N02224 Mountain Landscape with Pool (circa 1785-8)
Dπ:264x368:Presented by T. Birch Wolfe 1878

N02225 Wooded Landscape with Horsemen Travelling along a Country Track (circa 1775-80)
Dπ:254x314:Presented by T. Birch Wolfe 1878

N02226 Upland Landscape with River and Horsemen Crossing a Bridge (circa 1785-8)
Dπ:264x368:Presented by T. Birch Wolfe 1878

N02227 Wooded Landscape with Peasant Asleep and Horses outside a Shed (circa 1775-80)
Dπ:254x314:Presented by T. Birch Wolfe 1878

N02228 Wooded Landscape with Figures and Pool (circa 1785-8)
Dπ:260x368:Presented by T. Birch Wolfe 1878

N02229 Wooded Mountain Landscape with Figures, Church and River (circa 1785-8)
Dπ:264x368:Presented by T. Birch Wolfe 1878

N02284 The Bridge (circa 1786)
Oc:400x483:Bequeathed by Martin H. Colnaghi 1908

N02637 Sir William Blackstone (1774)
Oc:762x635:Bequeathed by George Salting 1910

N02638 Miss Elizabeth Singleton (?1769)
Oc:349x298:Bequeathed by George Salting 1910

N02717 Wooded Landscape with Peasant Reading Tombstone, Rustic Lovers and Ruined Church (1779-80)
Lπ:298x394:Presented by A.E. Anderson 1910

N02718 Wooded Landscape with Two Country Carts and Figures (1779-80)
Lπ:298x394:Presented by A.E. Anderson 1910

N02720 Wooded River Landscape with Shepherd and Sheep (circa 1785)
Lπ:248x343:Presented by A.E. Anderson 1910

N02721 Wooded Landscape with Country Cart, Cottage and Figures (1785)
Lπ:248x321:Presented by A.E. Anderson 1910

N02722 Wooded Landscape with Three Cows at a Pool (circa 1785)
Lπ:276x346:Presented by A.E. Anderson 1910

N02921 Wooded Landscape with Buildings on a Hillside (early 1780s)
Dπ:254x324:Presented by Sir Edward Poynter Bt 1913

N02928 The Housemaid (circa 1782-6)
Oc:2349x1486:Presented by Rosalind, Countess of Carlisle 1913

N04690 Admiral Sir Charles Thompson, Bt (1774)
Oc:1270x1016:Bequeathed by Sir Edward Stern 1933

N04777 John Needham, 10th Viscount Kilmorey (circa 1768)
Oc:2337x1562:Purchased 1934

N05400 Figure Study for 'The Housemaid' (circa 1785-8)
Dπ:346x248:Presented by Percy Moore Turner 1943

N05638 The Artist's Daughter Mary (1777)
Oc:775x648:signed:Bequeathed by Sir Otto Beit 1945

N05803 Gypsy Encampment, Sunset (circa 1778-80)
Oc:1206x1505:Presented by Frederick John Nettlefold 1947

N05844 Pomeranian Bitch and Puppy (circa 1777)
Oc:832x1118:Bequeathed by Mrs Arthur James 1948

N05845 Landscape with Gipsies (circa 1753-4)
Oc:483x622:Bequeathed by Mrs Arthur James 1948

N05925 Sir Francis Gregg (circa 1770)
Oc:749x629:Purchased 1950

N06242 Gainsborough Dupont (circa 1770-5)
Oc:445x362:Bequeathed by Lady d'Abernon 1954

T00642 An Officer of the 16th Light Dragoons (circa 1765)
Oc:737x597:Bequeathed by Thomas Bruce Ismay 1963

T00726 Mrs Susanna Gardiner (circa 1780-5)
Oc:756x629:Presented by Miss Marjorie Gainsborough Gardiner 1965

T00727 Edward Richard Gardiner (circa 1760-8)
Oc:622x502:Presented by Miss Marjorie Gainsborough Gardiner 1965

T00989 Village Scene with Figures (circa 1771-2)
WGπ:222x314:Presented by the National Art Collections Fund (Herbert Powell Bequest) 1967

T01422 Wooded Landscape with Cows beside a Pool, Figures and Cottage (circa 1775-80)
Bm:279x349:Purchased 1971

T01423 Wooded Landscape with Country Cart and Figures (circa 1775-80)
Bm:279x349:Purchased 1971

T01424 Wooded Landscape with Figures and Cows at a Watering Place (The Watering Place) (circa 1776-7)
Bm:279x349:Purchased 1971

T01425 Wooded Landscape with Country Cart, Cottage and Figures (circa 1785)
Bm:283x349:Purchased 1971

T01426 Wooded River Landscape with Shepherd and Sheep
Bm:292x381:Purchased 1971

T01427 Wooded Landscape with Riders (circa 1785)
Bm:184x244:Purchased 1971

T01428 Wooded Landscape with Three Cows at a Pool (circa 1785)
Bm:283x349:Purchased 1971

T01429 Wooded Landscape with Riders and Packhorses
Bm:276x356:Purchased 1971

T01430 Wooded Landscape with Country Cart and Figures (circa 1785-8)
Bm:283x349:Purchased 1971

T01431 Wooded Landscape with Herdsman and Four Cows (circa 1785-8)
Bm:279x349:Purchased 1971

T01432 Wooded Landscape with Herdsman and Three Cows (circa 1785-8)
Bm:279x349:Purchased 1971

T01433 Wooded Landscape with Cows beside a Pool, Figures and Cottage (circa 1775-80, reprinted 1971)
Lπ:257x327:Purchased 1971

T01434 Wooded Landscape with Country Cart and Figures (circa 1775-80, reprinted 1971)
Lπ:257x327:Purchased 1971

T01435 Wooded Landscape with Figures and Cows at a Watering Place (The Watering Place) (circa 1776-7, reprinted 1971)
Lπ:248x327:Purchased 1971

T01436 Wooded Landscape with Country Cart, Cottage and Figures (circa 1785, reprinted 1971)
Lπ:257x324:Purchased 1971

T01437 Wooded River Landscape with Shepherd and Sheep (reprinted 1971)
Lπ:251x340:Purchased 1971

T01438 Wooded Landscape with Riders (circa 1785, reprinted 1971)
Lπ:184x244:Purchased 1971

T01439 Wooded Landscape with Three Cows at a Pool (circa 1785, reprinted 1971)
Lπ:270x349:Purchased 1971

T01440 Wooded Landscape with Riders and Packhorses (reprinted 1971)
Lπ:241x318:Purchased 1971

T01441 Wooded Landscape with Country Cart and Figures (circa 1785-8, reprinted 1971)
Lπ:283x349:Purchased 1971

T01442 Wooded Landscape with Herdsman and Four Cows (circa 1785-8, reprinted 1971)
Lπ:257x324:Purchased 1971

T01443 Wooded Landscape with Herdsman and Three Cows (circa 1785-8, reprinted 1971)
Lπ:267x340:Purchased 1971

T02000 Giovanna Baccelli (exhibited 1782)
Oc:2267x1486:Purchased 1975

T02261 Sir Benjamin Truman (circa 1770-4)
Oc:2378x1514:Purchased with assistance from subscribers 1978

T03895 The Rev. John Chafy Playing the Violoncello in a Landscape (circa 1750-2)
Oc:749x609:Purchased with assistance from the Friends of the Tate Gallery, the National Heritage Memorial Fund and the National Art Collections Fund 1984

A00190 Wooded Landscape with Herdsmen and Three Cows (circa 1785-8)
Mπ:279x346:Presented by A.E. Anderson 1910

after
GAINSBOROUGH, Thomas 1727-1788
British Collection

N01174 Copy of 'The Watering Place'
Oc:419x546:Bequeathed by Mrs Elizabeth Vaughan 1885

N02719 Cattle and Tree, engraved by Thomas Rowlandson
Lπ:152x206:Presented by A.E. Anderson 1910

manner of
GAINSBOROUGH, Thomas 1727-1788
British Collection

N04845 Mrs Sarah Walker (circa 1770)
Oc:749x622:Presented by Miss F.R. Wilkinson in the name of herself and her late sister, Mrs Garrett 1936

N06281 Landscape: Sheep in a Woodland Glade
Oc:622x749:Bequeathed by R.W. Lloyd 1958

GALE, William 1823-1909
British Collection

T00045 The Confidante (1857)
Ow:248x171:Purchased 1955

GALLERY, LONDON, The (GRYLLS, Vaughan and WEGNER, Nicholas) born ?, born 1948
Modern Collection
Tate Gallery Archive holds material concerning these artists

Jam Press Phase One (P08006-P08014; complete group; mixed group)

P08011 7 Kölner Kunstmarkt (1973-4)
MLπ:559x441:Transferred from the Library 1977

GARBE, Richard 1876-1957
British Collection
Tate Gallery Archive holds material concerning this artist

N04100 A Drake (1924)
Ss:292x203x216:signed:Presented by the Trustees of the Chantrey Bequest 1925

N04480 Sea Lion (1929)
Ss:756x552x235:signed:Presented by the Trustees of the Chantrey Bequest 1929

N04549 Autumn (1930)
Si:914x210x178:signed:Presented by the Trustees of the Chantrey Bequest 1930

GARDINER, Clive 1891-1960
Modern Collection
Tate Gallery Archive holds material concerning this artist

T00675 Churchyard, Old Town, St Mary's IV (?1956)
Oc:254x356:Presented by the artist's family 1964

GARDNER, Daniel 1750-1805
British Collection

N04740 The Wife and Children of John Moore, Archbishop of Canterbury, 1783-1805
Pπ:622x851:Bequeathed by Admiral Sir Arthur Moore 1934

N04954 Portrait of a Lady
Oc:895x698:Purchased 1938

GARET, Jedd born 1955
Modern Collection

T04127 To Rule the World (1985)
2 Ac:3465x1860:signed:Presented by Mr Frederic Mueller through the American Federation of Arts 1985

GARRARD, George 1760-1826
British Collection

T02358 Bay Hunter by a Lake (circa 1790)
Oc:571x813:Presented by Paul Mellon through the British Sporting Art Trust 1979

T03299 Coombe Hill (1791)
Ob:137x184:Purchased 1981

GARSTIN, Norman 1847-1926
British Collection
Tate Gallery Archive holds material concerning this artist

N04234 A Woman Reading a Newspaper (1891)
Ow:254x216:signed:Presented by Mrs Garstin 1927

T03163 Haycocks and Sun (circa 1886)
Ob:203x270:signed:Presented by the Contemporary Art Society 1980

T03164 Mount's Bay and Tolcarne from Trewidden Farm Footpath with Alethea and her Mother (circa 1898)
Ow:200x260:signed:Presented by the Contemporary Art Society 1980

T03165 The Bull Hotel, Burford (?circa 1916)
Ow:210x267:signed:Presented by the Contemporary Art Society 1980

GASCOYNE, David born 1916
Modern Collection

T05025 Perseus and Andromeda (1936)
Vπ:178x248:signed:Purchased 1987

GASTINEAU, Henry 1791-1876
British Collection

N02420 Ruin with Farm-Buildings (published 1826)
Lπ:175x260:Presented by Edmund Houghton 1898

T05477 Landscape with a Ruined Abbey
DWπ:201x298:signed:Presented by Miss Marjorie Ball 1988

GAUDIER-BRZESKA, Henri 1891-1915
Modern Collection
Tate Gallery Archive holds material concerning this artist

N03339 A Wolf (1913)
Dπ:248x343:signed:Presented by Miss Sophie Brzeska 1918

N03341 A Dog (circa 1913)
Dπ:178x318:Presented by Miss Sophie Brzeska 1918

N04514 Singer (1913)
Ss:851x216x159:Presented by C. Frank Stoop through the Contemporary Art Society 1930

N04515 Red Stone Dancer (circa 1913)
Ss:432x229x229:signed:Presented by C. Frank Stoop through the Contemporary Art Society 1930

N04516 The Imp (circa 1914)
Ss:406x89x83:Presented by C. Frank Stoop through the Contemporary Art Society 1930

N04517 Man on a Horse (1913)
Dπ:419x521:signed:Presented by C. Frank Stoop through the Contemporary Art Society 1930

N04518 Head of a Child (circa 1912-13)
Dπ:387x254:signed:Presented by C. Frank Stoop through the Contemporary Art Society 1930

N04519 Head of a Girl (circa 1912-13)
Dπ:381x254:signed:Presented by C. Frank Stoop through the Contemporary Art Society 1930

N04520 Tiger (1913)
Dπ:387x260:signed:Presented by C. Frank Stoop through the Contemporary Art Society 1930

N04521 Lion (circa 1912-13)
Dπ:235x349:Presented by C. Frank Stoop through the Contemporary Art Society 1930

N04522 Leopard I (circa 1912-13)
Dπ:254x387:Presented by C. Frank Stoop through the Contemporary Art Society 1930

N04523 Leopard II (circa 1912-13)
Dπ:254x387:Presented by C. Frank Stoop through the Contemporary Art Society 1930

N04524 Jaguar (circa 1912-13)
Dπ:254x387:Presented by C. Frank Stoop through the Contemporary Art Society 1930

N04525 Puma I (circa 1912-13)
Dπ:203x368:Presented by C. Frank Stoop through the Contemporary Art Society 1930

N04526 Puma II (circa 1912-13)
Dπ:254x387:Presented by C. Frank Stoop through the Contemporary Art Society 1930

N04527 Eland (circa 1912-13)
Dπ:254x387:Presented by C. Frank Stoop through the Contemporary Art Society 1930

N04528 Verso: Traces of Sketch of Bison (circa 1912-13)
Dπ:216x343:Presented by C. Frank Stoop through the Contemporary Art Society 1930

N04529 Studies of Birds (circa 1912-13)
Dπ:254x356:Presented by C. Frank Stoop through the Contemporary Art Society 1930

N04530 Vulture I (circa 1912-13)
Dπ:387x254:Presented by C. Frank Stoop through the Contemporary Art Society 1930

N04531 Vulture II (circa 1912-13)
Dπ:387x254:Presented by C. Frank Stoop through the Contemporary Art Society 1930

N04532 Vulture III (circa 1912-13)
Dπ:394x254:Presented by C. Frank Stoop through the Contemporary Art Society 1930

N04533 Vulture IV (circa 1912-13)
Dπ:381x254:Presented by C. Frank Stoop through the Contemporary Art Society 1930

N04534 Torso of a Woman (1913, posthumous cast)
Sz:210x89x83:Presented by the Earl of Sandwich 1930

T00129 Horace Brodzky (1913, posthumous cast)
Sz:679x533x368:signed:Presented by the Trustees of the Chantrey Bequest 1957

T00147 Sophie Brzeska (1913)
Pπ:559x384:Purchased 1957

T00365 Garden Ornament (1914)
Sp:635x216x222:Presented by Hanover Gallery 1960

T00403 Garden Ornament, cast of T00365 (1914, posthumous cast)
Sz:635x216x222:Purchased 1961

T00542 Sepulchral Figure (1913)
Ss:406x368x203:Bequeathed by the Earl of Sandwich 1962

T00658 Bird Swallowing a Fish (circa 1913-14, posthumous cast)
Sz:318x603x279:Purchased 1964

T00762 The Dancer (1913, posthumous cast)
Sz:775x178x197:Presented by Sir Edward Beddington-Behrens 1965

T00836 Seated Woman (1914, posthumous cast)
Sz:470x343x216:Presented by Kettle's Yard Collection Cambridge 1966

T00837 Wrestlers (1914, posthumous cast)
Rp:711x927x76:signed:Presented by Kettle's Yard Collection Cambridge 1966

T00838 Maternity (1913, posthumous cast)
Sz:279x260x197:Presented by Kettle's Yard Collection Cambridge 1966

T00839 Garden Ornament (1914, posthumous cast)
Sz:349x279x279:Presented by Kettle's Yard Collection Cambridge 1966

T00840 Head (1914, posthumous cast)
Sp:298x229x178:Presented by Kettle's Yard Collection Cambridge 1966

T00841 Doorknocker (1914, posthumous cast)
Sz:171x79x29:Presented by Kettle's Yard Collection Cambridge 1966

T00842 Duck (1914, posthumous cast)
Sz:63x121x35:Presented by Kettle's Yard Collection Cambridge 1966

T00843 Monkeys (1912, posthumous cast)
Sp:178x159x95:Presented by Kettle's Yard Collection Cambridge 1966

T00844 Relief Head (circa 1913, posthumous cast)
Rz:130x70x25:Presented by Kettle's Yard Collection Cambridge 1966

T00845 Dog (1914, posthumous cast)
Sz:152x352x79:Presented by Kettle's Yard Collection Cambridge 1966

T00846 Mermaid (1913 or 1914, posthumous cast)
Sz:114x273x197:Presented by Kettle's Yard Collection Cambridge 1966

T00847 Standing Female Nude, One Hand on Hip (1913)
Dπ:387x254:Presented by Kettle's Yard Collection Cambridge 1966

T00848 Standing Female Nude, Hands on Hips (1913)
Dπ:381x254:Presented by Kettle's Yard Collection Cambridge 1966

T00849 Standing Female Nude, Arms Outstretched (1913)
Dπ:381x248:Presented by Kettle's Yard Collection Cambridge 1966

T00850 Wrestler (1913)
Dπ:384x251:Presented by Kettle's Yard Collection Cambridge 1966

T00851 Abstract Drawing (circa 1914)
Dπ:318x479:Presented by Kettle's Yard Collection Cambridge 1966

T00852 Head, Left Profile (circa 1914)
Dπ:248x190:Presented by Kettle's Yard Collection Cambridge 1966

T01097 Ornament (1914)
Sz:156x38x32:signed:Presented by Mr Dermot Freyer 1968

T01160 Major R.H. Smythies (1912)
Sp:445x229x235:signed:Presented by the Contemporary Art Society 1969

T01492 Major R.H. Raymond Smythies (1912, posthumous cast)
Sz:445x229x235:Purchased 1971

T03726 The Dancer (1913)
Sp:787x230x216:signed:Transferred from the Victoria & Albert Museum 1983

T03727 Fallen Workman (1912, posthumous cast)
Szs:321x368x381:Transferred from the Victoria & Albert Museum 1983

T03728 Sleeping Fawn (1913, posthumous cast)
Sp:114x254x216:Transferred from the Victoria & Albert
Museum 1983

T03729 Crouching Fawn (1913, posthumous cast)
Sp:254x305x127:Transferred from the Victoria & Albert
Museum 1983

T03730 The Idiot (circa 1912)
Sp:181x140x165:Transferred from the Victoria & Albert
Museum 1983

T03731 Torso (1914)
Ss:252x982x77:Transferred from the Victoria & Albert
Museum 1983

T03732 Figure (circa 1913-14, ?posthumous cast)
Sz:121x51x38:Transferred from the Victoria & Albert
Museum 1983

GAUGUIN, Paul 1848-1903
Modern Collection

N03167 Tahitians (circa 1891)
Tahitiens
ODπ:854x1019:Presented by the Contemporary Art
Society 1917

N03470 Faa Iheihe (1898)
Oc:540x1695:signed:Presented by Lord Duveen 1919

T00895 Harvest: Le Pouldu (1890)
Oc:730x921:signed:Accepted by the Commissioners of
Inland Revenue in lieu of tax and allocated 1966

circle of
GAUGUIN, Paul 1848-1903
Modern Collection

T00544 Study of a Tree. Verso: Portrait Study of a Man (?Paul
Gauguin) (?1887)
Etude d'arbre
DGπ:203x267:Bequeathed by the Earl of Sandwich 1962

GAULD, Peter born 1930
Modern Collection

P06211 Farningham (1972-4)
CLπ:495x559:signed:Presented by Curwen Studio
through the Institute of Contemporary Prints 1975

P06212 Scotney Castle (1973-4)
CLπ:511x546:signed:Presented by Curwen Studio
through the Institute of Contemporary Prints 1975

P06213 Union Mill, Cranbrook (1973-4)
CLπ:575x530:signed:Presented by Curwen Studio
through the Institute of Contemporary Prints 1975

P06214 The Pantiles, Tunbridge Wells (1974)
CLπ:479x537:signed:Presented by Curwen Studio
through the Institute of Contemporary Prints 1975

GEAR, William born 1915
Modern Collection
Tate Gallery Archive holds material concerning this artist

T00405 Interior (1949)
Oc:1003x819:signed:Purchased 1961

T00406 Feature in Landscape (1960)
Oc:1219x813:signed:Purchased 1961

T00469 Landscape Structure (1948)
Gb:508x648:signed:Presented by the artist 1961

T04995 Danse Macabre (1948)
DGπ:369x539:signed:Purchased 1987

P77163 Trellis (1952)
Lπ:282x400:signed:Purchased 1986

P77260 Black Tree (1950)
Lπ:500x377:signed:Purchased 1988

GEDDES, Andrew 1783-1844
British Collection

N00355 Dull Reading (circa 1826)
Ow:254x330:Presented by Robert Vernon 1847

N02472 The Artist's Mother (1822)
Lπ:152x124:Presented by J.P. Heseltine 1909

N03995 Sir William Allan in Circassian Costume (1815)
Lπ:216x146:Presented by Sir Charles Holmes 1924

N03996 Head of an Old Woman
Lπ:95x70:Presented by Sir Charles Holmes 1924

N04007 Old Woman with a Ring (after Jordaens)
Lπ:127x108:Presented by Sir Charles Holmes 1924

N05068 Mrs Greatorex (exhibited 1840)
Oc:1270x1016:Presented by W. Graham Robertson 1940

GEDEN, Dennis born 1944
Modern Collection

Crow Messenger Portfolio (P06634-P06635,
P06727-P06728; complete group)
P06634 1. Star Juggler (1976)
CLπ:663x471:signed:Presented by Curwen Studio 1976

P06635 5. Thumb Tiddler (1976)
CLπ:661x472:signed:Presented by Curwen Studio 1976

P06727 3. Crow Messenger (1976)
CLπ:471x661:signed:Presented by Curwen Studio 1976

P06728 2. Still Life and 3. Quiet Horse (1976)
CLπ:471x312:signed:Presented by Curwen Studio 1976

GENTLEMAN, David born 1930
Modern Collection
Tate Gallery Archive holds material concerning this artist

Fortifications (P04233-P04238; complete group)
P04233 Beaumaris (1971)
CNπ:684x685:signed:Presented by Rose and Chris Prater
through the Institute of Contemporary Prints 1975

P04234 Caerphilly (1971)
CNπ:685x636:signed:Presented by Rose and Chris Prater
through the Institute of Contemporary Prints 1975

P04235 Deal (1971)
CNπ:636x686:signed:Presented by Rose and Chris Prater
through the Institute of Contemporary Prints 1975

P04236 Fortress (1971)
CNπ:686x687:signed:Presented by Rose and Chris Prater
through the Institute of Contemporary Prints 1975

P04237 Francesco di Georgio I (1971)
CNπ:687x685:signed:Presented by Rose and Chris Prater
through the Institute of Contemporary Prints 1975

P04238 Francesco di Georgio II (1971)
CNπ:685x687:signed:Presented by Rose and Chris Prater
through the Institute of Contemporary Prints 1975

Ten Topographical Lithographs (P06215-P06224;
complete group)
P06215 [title not known] (1970)
CLπ::Presented by Curwen Studio through the Institute
of Contemporary Prints 1975

P06216 Abbeygate, Bury St Edmunds (1970)
CLπ:646x518:Presented by Curwen Studio through the Institute of Contemporary Prints 1975

P06217 Hardwick Hall (1970)
CLπ:513x654:Presented by Curwen Studio through the Institute of Contemporary Prints 1975

P06218 Heningham Hall (1970)
CLπ:519x657:Presented by Curwen Studio through the Institute of Contemporary Prints 1975

P06219 Kelmscott House, Chiswick (1970)
CLπ:643x528:Presented by Curwen Studio through the Institute of Contemporary Prints 1975

P06220 Little Moreton Hall (1970)
CLπ:510x650:Presented by Curwen Studio through the Institute of Contemporary Prints 1975

P06221 The Maltings, Snape (1970)
CLπ:643x518:Presented by Curwen Studio through the Institute of Contemporary Prints 1975

P06222 Orford Castle, Suffolk (1970)
CLπ:654x518:Presented by Curwen Studio through the Institute of Contemporary Prints 1975

P06223 [title not known] (1970)
CLπ:518x648:Presented by Curwen Studio through the Institute of Contemporary Prints 1975

P06224 The Gatehouse, Stanway (1970)
CLπ:533x644:Presented by Curwen Studio through the Institute of Contemporary Prints 1975

The Charleston Suite (P06225-P06232; complete group)
P06225 St James, Goose Creek (1971-2)
CLπ:400x534:signed:Presented by Curwen Studio through the Institute of Contemporary Prints 1975

P06226 [title not known] (1971-2)
CLπ:390x532:signed:Presented by Curwen Studio through the Institute of Contemporary Prints 1975

P06227 Charleston Market (1971-2)
CLπ:407x530:signed:Presented by Curwen Studio through the Institute of Contemporary Prints 1975

P06228 Gaillard - Bennett House (1971-2)
CLπ:405x514:signed:Presented by Curwen Studio through the Institute of Contemporary Prints 1975

P06229 Mulberry Plantation House (1971-2)
CLπ:385x514:signed:Presented by Curwen Studio through the Institute of Contemporary Prints 1975

P06230 Nathaniel Russell House (1971-2)
CLπ:392x532:signed:Presented by Curwen Studio through the Institute of Contemporary Prints 1975

P06231 Miles Brewton House (1971-2)
CLπ:390x514:signed:Presented by Curwen Studio through the Institute of Contemporary Prints 1975

P06232 The Wedge Plantation House (1971-2)
CLπ:384x505:signed:Presented by Curwen Studio through the Institute of Contemporary Prints 1975

Covent Garden Suite (P06233-P06239; incomplete group)
P06233 Endell Street (1972)
CLπ:497x775:signed:Presented by Curwen Studio through the Institute of Contemporary Prints 1975

P06234 The Flower Market, Covent Garden (1972)
CLπ:535x420:signed:Presented by Curwen Studio through the Institute of Contemporary Prints 1975

P06235 Foreign Fruit Market (1972)
CLπ:396x523:signed:Presented by Curwen Studio through the Institute of Contemporary Prints 1975

P06236 Seven Dials: Monmouth St, Shelton St and Mercer St (1972)
CLπ:610x499:signed:Presented by Curwen Studio through the Institute of Contemporary Prints 1975

P06237 Southern Section of Piazza (James Butler) (1972)
CLπ:402x530:signed:Presented by Curwen Studio through the Institute of Contemporary Prints 1975

P06238 Warehouse in Mercer St (1972)
CLπ:523x394:signed:Presented by Curwen Studio through the Institute of Contemporary Prints 1975

P06239 Warehouses between Shelton St and Earlham St (1972)
CLπ:400x508:signed:Presented by Curwen Studio through the Institute of Contemporary Prints 1975

P06240 Dunstanburgh Castle (1973)
CLπ:445x645:signed:Presented by Curwen Studio through the Institute of Contemporary Prints 1975

The Bath Suite (P06636-P06642; complete group)
P06636 Dundas Aqueduct (1975)
CLπ:503x389:signed:Presented by Curwen Studio 1976

P06637 Camden Crescent (1975)
CLπ:506x384:signed:Presented by Curwen Studio 1976

P06638 Ralph Allen's Sham Castle (1975)
CLπ:412x532:signed:Presented by Curwen Studio 1976

P06639 Lansdowne Crescent (1975)
CLπ:402x517:signed:Presented by Curwen Studio 1976

P06640 Canal in Sydney Gardens (1975)
CLπ:5805x370:signed:Presented by Curwen Studio 1976

P06641 Great Roman Bath (1975)
CLπ:390x512:signed:Presented by Curwen Studio 1976

P06642 Bath Abbey Precinct (1975)
CLπ:394x525:signed:Presented by Curwen Studio 1976

P06643 St Thomas's Hospital (1975)
CLπ:574x774:signed:Presented by Curwen Studio 1976

P06644 House on the Quayside (1975)
CLπ:572x775:signed:Presented by Curwen Studio 1976

P06729 Ellen Keeley's Shop (1972)
CLπ:393x530:Presented by Curwen Studio 1977

P06730 Piazza Looking South Past St Paul's (1972)
CLπ:398x527:Presented by Curwen Studio 1977

P06776 Seven Sisters (1976)
CLπ:390x515:signed:Presented by Curwen Studio 1978

P06777 Garrick Club (1977)
CLπ:530x415:signed:Presented by Curwen Studio 1978

P06778 Gordale Scar (1978)
CLπ:400x510:signed:Presented by Curwen Studio 1978

GENTLEMAN, Tom 1882-1966
Modern Collection
Tate Gallery Archive holds material concerning this artist

School Prints (P01698-P01727; complete group; mixed group)
P01705 The Grey Horses (1946-9)
CLπ:496x765:Presented by Patrick Seale Prints 1975

GEOFFREY, Iqbal born 1939
Modern Collection
Tate Gallery Archive holds material concerning this artist

T00539 Epitaph 1958 (1958)
OEVb:257x381:signed:Presented by A.S. Alley 1962

GEORGE - see GILBERT and GEORGE

GEORGE, Patrick born 1923
Modern Collection
Tate Gallery Archive holds material concerning this artist

T00421 Natalie Dower (1958)
Oc:1524x1219:signed:Purchased 1961

T00908 Hickbush (1961-5)
Oc:1060x1524:Presented by the Trustees of the Chantrey
Bequest 1967

T03099 Hickbush, the Grove I (1975-6)
Oc:530x1270:Purchased 1980

GEORGE, Thomas born 1918
Modern Collection

T00521 CP-Five (1961)
DPπ:635x470:signed:Presented by Mrs John Barry Ryan
through the Friends of the Tate Gallery 1962

GERE, Charles M. 1869-1957
British Collection
Tate Gallery Archive holds material concerning this artist

N04226 Provence (1926)
WDπ:324x457:signed:Purchased 1927

N04501 Trial by Jury (1919)
DWπ:270x375:signed:Purchased 1930

GERE, Margaret 1878-1965
British Collection

N03168 Noah's Ark (circa 1909)
Tf:264x264:signed:Presented by the Contemporary Art
Society 1917

GERRARD, A.H. born 1899
Modern Collection

P07026 Eternal Life (1924)
MJπ:222x171:Purchased 1926

GERTLER, Mark 1891-1939
Modern Collection
Tate Gallery Archive holds material concerning this artist

N03807 Portrait of a Girl (1912)
Ow:508x406:signed:Presented by A.E. Anderson through
the National Art Collections Fund 1923

N05121 The Artist's Mother (1911)
Dπ:375x254:signed:Presented by Rowland
Burdon-Muller 1940

N05124 Violin Case and Flowers (1930)
Oc:711x914:signed:Presented by the Contemporary Art
Society 1940

N05311 The Servant Girl (1923)
Oc:635x470:Purchased 1941

N05557 The Artist's Mother (1911)
Oc:660x559:signed:Presented by the Trustees of the
Chantrey Bequest 1944

N05835 The Tea Pot (1918)
Oc:406x508:signed:Purchased 1948

N06033 Acrobats (1917)
Sz:597x419x375:Purchased 1951

N06231 Jewish Family (1913)
Oc:660x508:signed:Bequeathed by Sir Edward Marsh
through the Contemporary Art Society 1954

N06232 Sketch for 'The Servant Girl' (1923)
Db:406x311:signed:Bequeathed by Sir Edward Marsh
through the Contemporary Art Society 1954

T00605 Queen of Sheba (1922)
Oc:940x1073:signed:Purchased 1963

T01043 The Basket of Fruit (1925)
Oc:787x1003:signed:Presented by the National Art
Collections Fund (Thomas Balston Bequest) 1968

T01044 Mandolinist (1934)
Ob:762x559:signed:Presented by the National Art
Collections Fund (Thomas Balston Bequest) 1968

T03846 Merry-Go-Round (1916)
Oc:1892x1422:signed:Purchased 1984

GETHIN, Percy Francis 1874-1916
British Collection

N04173 Sémur, General View through Viaduct (1911-2)
DWπ:346x263:signed:Purchased 1926

N04174 Athlone
WDπ:203x305:signed:Purchased 1926

N04175 View from Château Chinon (1911-2)
Wπ:219x279:Purchased 1926

GHEERAERTS, Marcus, II 1561 or 2 - 1636
British Collection

T01872 Mary Rogers, Lady Harington (1592)
Ow:1130x851:Purchased with assistance from the
National Art Collections Fund and subscribers 1974

T03028 Captain Thomas Lee (1594)
Oc:2305x1508:Purchased with assistance from the
Friends of the Tate Gallery, the National Art Collections
Fund and the Pilgrim Trust 1980

T03456 Portrait of a Woman in Red (1620)
Ow:1143x902:Purchased 1982

T03466 Portrait of a Man in Masque Dress, Probably Philip
Herbert, 4th Earl of Pembroke (circa 1610)
Ow:556x446:Purchased 1982

attributed to
GHEERAERTS, Marcus, II 1561 or 2 - 1636
British Collection

T03030 Gertrude Sadler, Lady Aston (circa 1620-3)
Oc:2273x1334:Purchased with assistance from the
Friends of the Tate Gallery, the National Art Collections
Fund and the Pilgrim Trust 1980

GHIKA, Nicolas born 1906
Modern Collection

T00010 Small Composition in Grey (1953)
Petite Composition en gris
Ow:413x330:signed:Presented by a number of the artist's
friends through the Contemporary Art Society 1955

GIACOMETTI, Alberto 1901-1966
Modern Collection
Tate Gallery Archive holds material concerning this artist

N05908 Interior (1949)
Intérieur
Oc:651x537:signed:Purchased 1949

N05909 Seated Man (1949)
Homme assis
Oc:800x540:signed:Purchased 1949

N05939 Man Pointing (1947)
Homme signalant
Sz:1780x950x520:signed:Purchased 1949

T00238 Venice Woman IX (1956)
Femme de Venise IX
Sz:1130x165x346:signed:Purchased 1959

T00258 Two Figures (1947)
Deux figures
Oπ:419x597:Purchased 1959

T00358 Diego (1959)
Oc:610x498:signed:Purchased 1960

T00773 Four Figurines on a Base (1950/1965, cast circa 1965-6)
Quatre figurines sur base
Sz:1562x419x314:signed:Purchased with assistance from the Friends of the Tate Gallery 1965

T00774 Bust of Diego (1955)
Buste de Diego
Sz:565x320x145:signed:Purchased with assistance from the Friends of the Tate Gallery 1965

T00775 Standing Woman (circa 1958-9, cast released by the artist 1964)
Femme debout
Sz:686x140x270:signed:Purchased with assistance from the Friends of the Tate Gallery 1965

T00776 Standing Woman (circa 1958-9, cast released by the artist 1964)
Femme debout
Sz:692x137x241:signed:Purchased with assistance from the Friends of the Tate Gallery 1965

T00777 Standing Woman (circa 1958-9, cast released by the artist 1964)
Femme debout
Sz:651x121x200:signed:Purchased with assistance from the Friends of the Tate Gallery 1965

T00778 Annette IV (1962, cast 1965)
Sz:584x235x229:signed:Purchased with assistance from the Friends of the Tate Gallery 1965

T00779 Chiavenna Bust I (1964)
Buste de Chiavenna I
Sz:410x197x152:signed:Purchased with assistance from the Friends of the Tate Gallery 1965

T00780 Standing Woman (1948-9)
Femme debout
Sz:1680x159x340:signed:Presented by the artist 1965

T00781 Caroline (1965)
Oc:1295x806:signed:Purchased with assistance from the Friends of the Tate Gallery 1965

T00782 Caroline (1965)
Oc:1302x813:signed:Purchased with assistance from the Friends of the Tate Gallery 1965

T01519 Walking Woman (1932-3/1936, cast 1966)
Femme qui marche
Sz:1499x276x378:signed:Presented by the artist and Mrs Erica Brausen 1972

T01981 Hour of the Traces (1930)
L'Heure des traces
Spm:686x362x286:Purchased with assistance from the Friends of the Tate Gallery 1975

T04905 Jean Genet (1955)
Oc:653x543:signed:Accepted by the Commissioners of Inland Revenue in lieu of tax and allocated 1987

P77122 The Studio I (1954)
Atelier I
MLπ:540x439:signed:Purchased 1984

GIARDELLI, Arthur born 1911
Modern Collection
Tate Gallery Archive holds material concerning this artist

T03799 The Sea is All About Us (1982)
RAWπw:813x813:signed:Presented by Mr and Mrs Eric Estorick 1983

GIBB, Phelan 1870-1948
British Collection

N04405 Belgrave Square and Wilton Crescent (1928)
WDπ:343x483:signed:Presented by Lady Ian Hamilton 1928

GIBBONS, John born 1949
Modern Collection

T05215 Desire (1985-6)
Sm:1290x510x330:Purchased 1988

GIBBS, Evelyn born 1905
Modern Collection
Tate Gallery Archive holds material concerning this artist

P06779 Gozo Fields (1977)
CLπ:505x670:Presented by Curwen Studio 1978

P06780 Low Tide, Hammersmith (1977)
CLπ:489x625:Presented by Curwen Studio 1978

P06781 Rock Landscape (1977)
CLπ:489x648:signed:Presented by Curwen Studio 1978

P06782 Santu Pietru (1977)
CLπ:505x670:signed:Presented by Curwen Studio 1978

GIBSON, John 1790-1866
British Collection

N01746 Hylas and the Water-Nymphs (1826)
Ss:1600x1194x718:signed:Presented by Robert Vernon 1847

GILBERT, Sir Alfred 1854-1934
British Collection
Tate Gallery Archive holds material concerning this artist

N01949 George Frederic Watts, O.M., R.A. (1888-9)
Sz:584x584x368:Presented by Mrs Watts by the wish of the late George Frederic Watts 1904

N03039 Mrs Macloghlin (1906-7)
Sz:438x216x190:signed:Presented by Mrs Macloghlin 1915

N04176 Model for 'Eros' on the Shaftesbury Memorial, Piccadilly Circus (1891, cast 1925)
Sz:610x267x679:Presented by the Trustees of the Chantrey Bequest 1925

N04586 Mother Teaching Child (1881)
Ss:1035x673x660:Bequeathed by H.L. Dalton 1931

N04755 Ignacy Jan Paderewski (?circa 1900)
Sz:603x262x267:signed:Presented by the Trustees of the Chantrey Bequest 1934

N04827 Icarus (1882-4)
Sz:495x210x159:signed:Bequeathed by Frederick Harrison 1936

N04828 Perseus Arming (1881-3)
Sz:368x178x121:Bequeathed by Frederick Harrison 1936

N04829 Comedy and Tragedy: 'Sic Vita' (circa 1890-2)
Sz:349x152x140:signed:Bequeathed by Frederick Harrison 1936

N04977 The Broken Shrine (?circa 1900)
Sz:352x200x190:signed:Presented by Maurice Yorke 1938

N05885 John Howard, the Prison Philanthropist (circa 1893-4)
Sz:381x127x127:Bequeathed by Mrs J. Margaret Hadley 1949

T00167 Charity (1877)
Sp:327x95x89:Purchased 1958

T00168 Mourning Angel (1877)
Sp:318x127x76:Purchased 1958

GILBERT and GEORGE born 1943, born 1942
Modern Collection
Tate Gallery Archive holds material concerning these artists

T01701 Balls: The Evening Before the Morning After - Drinking Sculpture (1972)
114 Fπ:2108x4382:Purchased 1972

T01702 In the Bush (1972)
X::Purchased 1972

T01703 Gordon's Makes Us Drunk (1972)
X::Purchased 1972

T01704 A Portrait of the Artists as Young Men (1972)
X::Purchased 1972

T03241 Postcard Sculpture 1974 (1974)
πb:1270x943:signed:Purchased 1981

T03297 England (1980)
30 Fπ:3026x3026:signed:Purchased 1981

T03352 Coronation Cross (1981)
πb:1330x997:signed:Purchased 1982

T03452 The Nature of Our Looking (1970)
5 HDπ::signed:Purchased 1982

GILBERT, Charles Web 1867-1925
British Collection

N03220 The Critic (1916)
Ss:406x254x248:signed:Presented by the Trustees of the Chantrey Bequest 1917

GILBERT, Sir John 1817-1897
British Collection

N01931 Old Gravel Pit in Greenwich Park (1893)
Wπ:394x622:signed:Bequeathed by George Gilbert 1904

N01932 Bringing up the Guns (1889)
Wπ:343x451:signed:Bequeathed by George Gilbert 1904

N01933 Cardinal Wolsey and the Duke of Buckingham (1861)
DWπ:159x254:signed:Bequeathed by George Gilbert 1904

N01934 The Happiest Land (1862)
Wπ:213x190:signed:Bequeathed by George Gilbert 1904

N04017 The Merry Wives of Windsor, engraved by the Dalziel Brothers (published 1858-60)
Jπ:190x127:Presented by Gilbert Dalziel 1924

N04051 The Deserted Cottage, engraved by the Dalziel Brothers
Jπ:108x102:Presented by Harold Hartley 1925

GILBERT, Stephen born 1910
Modern Collection
Tate Gallery Archive holds material concerning this artist

T00464 Structure 14c (1961)
Sm:775x1219x813:Purchased 1961

T03698 Untitled (1948)
Oc:535x715:signed:Purchased 1983

T04933 Untitled (1948)
Dπ:314x234:signed:Purchased 1987

T04934 Untitled (1948)
WDπ:235x312:signed:Purchased 1987

T04935 Untitled (1948)
DWπ:330x261:signed:Purchased 1987

P77187 Untitled (1949)
Lπ:564x436:signed:Purchased 1987

P77188 Untitled (1949)
Jπ:314x235:signed:Purchased 1987

GILIOLI, Emile 1911-1977
Modern Collection

N06167 Prayer and Force (1952)
Prière et force
Ss:486x460x286:signed:Purchased 1953

GILL, Charles 1742 - after 1828
British Collection

T01886 The Lethbridge Children (1785)
Oc:711x902:signed:Bequeathed by Alan Evans 1974

GILL, Colin 1892-1940
Modern Collection

N03659 Study for 'L'Allegro' (1921)
Dπ:546x610:signed:Purchased 1922

GILL, Eric 1882-1940
Modern Collection
Tate Gallery Archive holds material concerning this artist

N03563 Crucifixion (1910)
Rs:946x781x127:Presented by the Contemporary Art Society 1920

N04487 The East Wind (1928)
Ss:254x705x102:Purchased 1929

N04808 Prospero and Ariel (1931)
Ss:1270x457x356:Purchased 1935

N05388 Mankind (1927-8)
Ss:2413x610x457:Purchased with assistance from Eric Kennington, the Knapping Fund and subscribers 1938

T00583 Eve (1928)
Ss:737x152x152:signed:Bequeathed by Hugh W. Rawlinson 1963

T03449 Christ Child (1922)
Sw:141x341x12:Purchased 1982

T03477 Ecstasy (1910-11)
Rs:1372x457x228:signed:Purchased 1982

T03733 Alphabet and Numerals (1909)
Rs:329x618x60:signed:Transferred from the Victoria & Albert Museum 1983

T03734 Two Alphabets and Numerals (1909)
Rs:265x400x28:signed:Transferred from the Victoria & Albert Museum 1983

T03735 Alphabet (1909)
Rs:325x431x28:signed:Transferred from the Victoria & Albert Museum 1983

T03736 Crucifix (circa 1913)
Rs:455x175x38:Transferred from the Victoria & Albert Museum 1983

T03737 The North Wind (1929)
Rs:254x698x101:Transferred from the Victoria & Albert Museum 1983

T03738 Inscription 'Ex Divina Pulchritudine' (1926)
Rs:306x457x38:Transferred from the Victoria & Albert Museum 1983

T03739 Alphabet of Raised Letters (1927)
Rs:533x546x44:signed:Transferred from the Victoria & Albert Museum 1983

T03740 Alphabet (1927)
Rs:512x543x44:signed:Transferred from the Victoria & Albert Museum 1983

T03741 Inscription 'Homines Divites' (1922)
Rs:237x897x35:Transferred from the Victoria & Albert Museum 1983

T03742 Inscription 'In Terra Pax' (1922)
Rs:155x830x30:Transferred from the Victoria & Albert Museum 1983

T03743 Inscription 'Gloria in Altissimis Deo' (1922)
Rs:255x530x25:Transferred from the Victoria & Albert Museum 1983

T03744 Sundial (1923-4)
SRms:460x375x240:Transferred from the Victoria & Albert Museum 1983

T03745 St Sebastian (1920)
Ss:1040x202x254:Transferred from the Victoria & Albert Museum 1983

P08039 Nativity with Midwife (1913)
MJπ:51x51:Transferred from the Library 1979

P08040 Slaughter of the Innocents (1914)
MJπ:60x51:Transferred from the Library 1979

P08041 Calvary, Five Stalks of Leaves, and Ship (1915)
MJπ:175x79:Transferred from the Library 1979

P08042 Crucifix, Chalice & Host (1915)
MJπ:124x79:Transferred from the Library 1979

P08043 Dumb-Driven Cattle (1915)
MJπ:95x79:signed:Transferred from the Library 1979

P08044 Hog and Wheatsheaf (1915)
MJπ:133x133:Transferred from the Library 1979

P08045 The Purchaser (1915)
MJπ:124x79:signed:Transferred from the Library 1979

P08046 Adeste Fideles, Three Kings, The Manger, Cantet Nunc Io, Madonna & Child with Chalice (1916)
MJπ:200x133:Transferred from the Library 1979

P08047 Animals All (1916)
MJπ:51x51:Transferred from the Library 1979

P08048 Christmas Gifts: Daylight, and Christmas Gifts: Dawn
MJπ:175x89:Transferred from the Library 1979

P08049 Initial S with Church, Chalice & Host with Ω & A, Gravestone with Angel, Semi-Circular Device, and Circular Device (1916)
5 MJπ:175x165:Transferred from the Library 1979

P08050 Madonna and Child with Angel (1916)
MJπ:60x60:Transferred from the Library 1979

P08051 Jesus is Condemned to Death (1917)
MJπ:54x54:Transferred from the Library 1979

P08052 Jesus Receives His Cross (1917)
MJπ:54x54:Transferred from the Library 1979

P08053 Jesus Falls the First Time (1917)
MJπ:54x54:Transferred from the Library 1979

P08054 Jesus Meets His Mother (1917)
MJπ:54x54:Transferred from the Library 1979

P08055 Simon of Cyrene Helps Jesus to Carry the Cross (1917)
MJπ:54x54:Transferred from the Library 1979

P08056 Jesus Meets Veronica (1917)
MJπ:54x54:Transferred from the Library 1979

P08057 Jesus Falls the Second Time (1917)
MJπ:54x54:Transferred from the Library 1979

P08058 Jesus Speaks to the Women of Jerusalem (1917)
MJπ:54x54:Transferred from the Library 1979

P08059 Jesus Falls the Third Time (1917)
MJπ:54x54:Transferred from the Library 1979

P08060 Jesus is Stripped (1917)
MJπ:54x54:Transferred from the Library 1979

P08061 Jesus is Nailed to the Cross (1917)
MJπ:54x54:Transferred from the Library 1979

P08062 Jesus Dies Upon the Cross (1917)
MJπ:54x54:Transferred from the Library 1979

P08063 The Body of Jesus is Taken Down from the Cross (1917)
MJπ:54x54:Transferred from the Library 1979

P08064 The Body of Jesus is Laid in the Tomb (1917)
MJπ:54x54:Transferred from the Library 1979

P08065 Crucifix (1917)
CJπ:124x79:Transferred from the Library 1979

P08066 Epiphany, Palm Sunday, and Adam & Eve
MJπ:181x63:Transferred from the Library 1979

P08067 The Last Judgement (1917)
MJπ:44x54:Transferred from the Library 1979

P08068 Resurrection (1917)
MJπ:140x89:signed:Transferred from the Library 1979

P08069 Spray of Leaves, Stalk, Initial O with Speedwell, Paschal Lamb, Axe & Block, and Hangman's Rope (1917)
MJπ:171x140:Transferred from the Library 1979

P08070 Ascension (1918)
MJπ:140x89:Transferred from the Library 1979

P08071 Madonna & Child in Vesica (1918)
MJπ:105x44:Transferred from the Library 1979

P08072 Christ and the Money-Changers (1919)
MJπ:51x70:Transferred from the Library 1979

P08073 Christ and the Money-Changers (1919)
MJπ:140x89:Transferred from the Library 1979

P08074 Crucifix (1919)
CJπ:130x102:Transferred from the Library 1979

P08075 Madonna & Child (1919)
MJπ:165x95:Transferred from the Library 1979

P08076 Spoil Bank Crucifix (1919)
MJπ:51x76:Transferred from the Library 1979

P08077 Bookplate: Girl with Deer (1920)
MJπ:60x60:Transferred from the Library 1979

P08078 Hottentot (1920)
MJπ:197x44:Transferred from the Library 1979

P08079 New England Woods (1920)
MJπ:89x57:Transferred from the Library 1979

P08080 Our Lady of Lourdes (1920)
MJπ:302x241:Transferred from the Library 1979

P08081 Dress: 1860 (1921)
MJπ:70x51:Transferred from the Library 1979

P08082 Dress: 1920 (1921)
MJπ:89x76:Transferred from the Library 1979

P08083 The Lion (1921)
MJπ:54x76:signed:Transferred from the Library 1979

P08084 Bookplate: S. Helena, and Bookplate: S. Angela (1922)
MJπ:171x35:Transferred from the Library 1979

P08085 Christmas Card: Madonna & Child (1922)
MJπ:89x63:Transferred from the Library 1979

P08086 Clare (1922)
MJπ:165x114:Transferred from the Library 1979

P08087 Divine Lovers: I (1922)
MJπ:89x76:Transferred from the Library 1979

P08088 Girl in Bath: I (1922)
MJπ:105x105:signed:Transferred from the Library 1979

P08089 The Plait (1922)
MJπ:165x102:signed:Transferred from the Library 1979

P08090 Actor on Stage (1923)
MJπ:105x181:Transferred from the Library 1979

P08091 Autumn Midnight (1923)
MJπ:114x79:signed:Transferred from the Library 1979

P08092 Girl in Bath: II (1923)
MJπ:105x105:signed:Transferred from the Library 1979

P08093 [title not known] (1923)
15 MJπ:216x159:Transferred from the Library 1979

P08094 Mother and Child (1923)
MJπ:140x83:signed:Transferred from the Library 1979

P08095 Daily Herald Order of Industrial Heroism (1923)
CJπ:124x194:Transferred from the Library 1979

P08096 Sculpture I, Sculpture II, and Woman's Head (1923)
MJπ:165x130:Transferred from the Library 1979

P08097 The Tennis Player (1923)
MJπ:114x105:Transferred from the Library 1979

P08098 Toilet (1923)
MJπ:108x63:Transferred from the Library 1979

P08099 Eliz. G. (1924)
MJπ:171x121:signed:Transferred from the Library 1979

P08100 Gordian G. (1924)
MJπ:171x124:signed:Transferred from the Library 1979

P08101 Madonna & Child (1924)
MJπ:38x146:Transferred from the Library 1979

P08102 Mother and Child (1924)
MJπ:83x86:Transferred from the Library 1979

P08103 Mrs Williams (1924)
MJπ:219x159:signed:Transferred from the Library 1979

P08104 Naked Girl on Grass (1924)
MJπ:38x76:Transferred from the Library 1979

P08105 Portrait of a Lady (1924)
MIπ:175x114:signed:Transferred from the Library 1979

P08106 Ruth Lowinsky (1924)
MJπ:229x152:signed:Transferred from the Library 1979

P08107 Thomas Edmond Lowinsky (1924)
MJπ:270x181:signed:Transferred from the Library 1979

P08108 Xenia Noelle Lowinsky (1924)
MJπ:229x152:signed:Transferred from the Library 1979

P08109 Girl Sleeping (1925)
MJπ:35x89:Transferred from the Library 1979

P08110 The Harem (1925)
MJπ:121x95:Transferred from the Library 1979

P08111 Ibi Dabo Tibi (1925)
MJπ:76x89:Transferred from the Library 1979

P08112 Madonna and Child (1925)
MJπ:89x51:Transferred from the Library 1979

P08113 Madonna and Child, with Children (1925)
MJπ:51x76:Transferred from the Library 1979

P08114 My Love among the Lilies (1925)
MJπ:51x76:Transferred from the Library 1979

P08115 On My Bed by Night (1925)
MJπ:63x95:Transferred from the Library 1979

P08116 Stay Me with Apples (1925)
MJπ:63x60:Transferred from the Library 1979

P08117 Swineherd (1925)
MJπ:57x83:Transferred from the Library 1979

P08118 Beatrice Warde (1926)
MJπ:229x149:signed:Transferred from the Library 1979

P08119 Bookplate (1926)
MIπ:57x32:Transferred from the Library 1979

P08120 Bookplate: S. Anthony (1926)
MJπ:121x86:Transferred from the Library 1979

P08121 The Carrying of the Cross (1926)
MJπ:108x108:Transferred from the Library 1979

P08122 David (1926)
MIπ:111x70:Transferred from the Library 1979

P08123 Device: S. Thomas's Hands (1926)
MJπ:29x35:Transferred from the Library 1979

P08124 Earth Waiting (1926)
MJπ:89x76:Transferred from the Library 1979

P08125 Eve (1926)
MJπ:235x117:Transferred from the Library 1979

P08126 Flying Buttress (1926)
MJπ:111x70:Transferred from the Library 1979

P08127 The Good Shepherd (1926)
MJπ:76x38:Transferred from the Library 1979

P08128 Mary Magdalen (1926)
MJπ:63x63:Transferred from the Library 1979

P08129 Miss R. Rothenstein (1926)
MJπ:222x159:Transferred from the Library 1979

P08130 Prior of Caldey (1926)
MIπ:222x159:signed:Transferred from the Library 1979

P08131 Skaters (1926)
MIπ:102x108:Transferred from the Library 1979

P08132 Woman with Balloons (1926)
MJπ:102x44:Transferred from the Library 1979

P08133 Border: Lovers Facing Left, and Border: Lovers (1926-7)
MJπ:178x130:Transferred from the Library 1979

P08134 Adam & Eve in Heaven (1927)
MIπ:111x70:Transferred from the Library 1979

P08135 Bookplate: Girl with Three Scallops (1927)
MIπ:89x57:signed:Transferred from the Library 1979

P08136 Border: Chaucer & Cupid, and Chaucer Writing (1927)
MJπ:171x133:Transferred from the Library 1979

P08137 Border: Our Lord on Tree (1927)
MJπ:178x41:Transferred from the Library 1979

P08138 Chalice and Host (1927)
MJπ:67x41:Transferred from the Library 1979

P08139 Clothes: For Dignity & Adornment (1927)
MIπ:111x70:Transferred from the Library 1979

P08140 The Good Shepherd (1927)
MJπ:86x51:Transferred from the Library 1979

P08141 Self-Portrait (1927)
MJπ:181x121:Transferred from the Library 1979

P08142 The Soul and the Bridegroom (1927)
MJπ:79x51:Transferred from the Library 1979

P08143 Title Page: Troilus and Criseyde (1927)
MJπ:178x114:Transferred from the Library 1979

P11046 The Martyrdom of St Saturus (1928)
CJπ:83x108:Bequeathed by Mrs E. West 1982

P11047 The Triumph of St Perpetua (1928)
CJπ:90x83:Bequeathed by Mrs E. West 1982

GILL, Macdonald 1884-1947
Modern Collection
Tate Gallery Archive holds material concerning this artist

N04570 Punch and Judy (1911)
Tc:2286x1861:Purchased 1931

GILLIAM, Sam born 1933
Modern Collection

T01326 Simmering (1970)
RAc:2159x1353:signed:Presented by Mrs Nesta Dorrance
through the American Federation of Arts 1974

GILLIES, Sir William 1898-1973
Modern Collection
Tate Gallery Archive holds material concerning this artist

T00007 Summer Stream (1954)
Oc:470x571:signed:Purchased 1955
T00008 Esperston (1950)
Oc:356x660:signed:Purchased 1955
T00009 Summer Morning (1954)
DWπ:670x575:signed:Purchased 1955
T00771 The Marble-Topped Table (1965)
Ob:1003x749:signed:Presented by the Trustees of the
Chantrey Bequest 1965
T01126 Still Life with Blue Gloves (1968)
Wπ:654x914:signed:Presented by the Trustees of the
Chantrey Bequest 1969

GILMAN, Harold 1876-1919
British Collection
Tate Gallery Archive holds material concerning this artist

N03684 Canal Bridge, Flekkefjord (circa 1913)
Oc:457x610:signed:Purchased 1922
N04273 Leeds Market (circa 1913)
Oc:508x610:signed:Presented by the Very Rev. E.
Milner-White 1927
N05317 Mrs Mounter at the Breakfast Table (exhibited 1917)
Oc:610x406:signed:Purchased 1942
N05555 The Artist's Mother (exhibited 1913)
Oc:610x508:signed:Presented by the Trustees of the
Chantrey Bequest 1943
N05783 French Interior (circa 1905-7)
Oc:622x514:signed:Purchased 1947
N05831 Lady on a Sofa (exhibited 1910)
Oc:305x406:signed:Purchased 1948
T00026 Study for 'Canal Bridge, Flekkefjord' (circa 1913)
Dπ:229x292:Purchased 1955
T00096 Edwardian Interior (circa 1900-05)
Oc:533x540:signed:Presented by the Trustees of the
Chantrey Bequest 1956
T00143 Study for 'Leeds Market' (circa 1913)
Dπ:248x298:signed:Purchased 1957

GILPIN, Sawrey and BARRET, George
Senior 1733-1807, 1728 or 32 - 1784
British Collection

T02359 Broodmares and Colts in a Landscape (?exhibited 1783)
Oc:629x749:Presented by Paul Mellon through the
British Sporting Art Trust 1979

GINESI, Edna born 1902
Modern Collection

N04969 Landscape, North Wales (1937)
Oc:635x813:signed:Presented by Mrs Hazel McKinley
1938
T00688 Everglades (1964)
Oc:1016x1270:signed:Presented by Mrs H.G. McKinley
1964

GINGER, Phyllis born 1907
Modern Collection
Tate Gallery Archive holds material concerning this artist

School Prints (P01698-P01727; complete group; mixed
group)
P01706 Town Centre (1946-9)
CLπ:495x762:Presented by Patrick Seale Prints 1975

GINNER, Charles 1878-1952
British Collection
Tate Gallery Archive holds material concerning this artist

N03838 Porthleven (exhibited 1922)
Oc:508x692:signed:Presented by the Contemporary Art
Society 1924
N03873 From a Hampstead Window (exhibited 1924)
DWπ:445x314:signed:Purchased 1924
N05050 The Café Royal (1911)
Oc:635x483:signed:Presented by Edward Le Bas 1939
N05270 Claverton Street: Snow in Pimlico (1939)
Oc:406x356:signed:Purchased 1941
N05276 Flask Walk, Hampstead, on Coronation Day (1937)
Oc:610x508:signed:Purchased 1941
N05306 Hartland Point from Boscastle (1941)
Oc:584x857:signed:Presented by the Trustees of the
Chantrey Bequest 1941
N05695 Emergency Water Storage Tank (1941-2)
Oc:686x508:signed:Presented by the War Artists'
Advisory Committee 1946
T01099 Study for 'Flask Walk, Hampstead, on Coronation Day'
(1937)
Dw:445x311:Presented by the Friends of the Tate Gallery
1968
T03096 Piccadilly Circus (1912)
Oc:813x660:signed:Purchased 1980
T03841 Victoria Embankment Gardens (1912)
Oc:664x461:signed:Purchased 1984

GIOBBI, Edward born 1926
Modern Collection

T00673 November 22nd No. 3 (1964)
ODcb:1683x1683:signed:Purchased 1964

GIRTIN, Thomas 1775-1802
British Collection
Tate Gallery Archive holds material concerning this artist

N04360 The River Tweed near Kelso (1800)
Wπ:267x324:Bequeathed by J.R. Holliday 1927
N04409 Bamburgh Castle, Northumberland (circa 1797-9)
Wπ:549x451:signed:Presented by A.E. Anderson in
memory of his brother Frank through the National Art
Collections Fund 1928

N04728 The White House at Chelsea (1800)
Wπ:298x514:signed:Bequeathed by Mrs Ada Montefiore 1933

T00990 La Rue St Denis (1802)
IWπ:229x489:Presented by the National Art Collections Fund (Herbert Powell Bequest) 1967

T00991 A Winding Estuary (1798)
Wπ:117x533:Presented by the National Art Collections Fund (Herbert Powell Bequest) 1967

T00992 A Temple of Vesta
Wπ:289x305:Presented by the National Art Collections Fund (Herbert Powell Bequest) 1967

T00993 Guisborough Priory, Yorkshire (1801)
Wπ:629x508:signed:Presented by the National Art Collections Fund (Herbert Powell Bequest) 1967

T00994 Landscape (1800)
Wπ:70x241:Presented by the National Art Collections Fund (Herbert Powell Bequest) 1967

T00995 Pont-y-Pair (1798-9)
Wπ:381x581:Presented by the National Art Collections Fund (Herbert Powell Bequest) 1967

T03340 The Ruins of the Emperor Julian's Baths, Hôtel de Cluny, Paris (1801-2)
Wπ:314x232:Purchased 1982

after
GIRTIN, Thomas 1775-1802
British Collection

The Rivers of England (T04868-T04871; complete group)

T04868 Kirkstall Abbey on the River Aire, engraved by W. Say (published 1824)
Iπ:145x213:Purchased 1987

T04869 York Minster on the River Foss, engraved by T. Lupton (published 1824)
Iπ:147x229:Purchased 1987

T04870 The Rivers of England ('River Scenery'): Ripon Minster on the Rivers Ure and Skell, engraved by T. Lupton (1825)
Iπ:147x224:Purchased 1987

T04871 Bolton Abbey on the River Wharfe, engraved by J. Bromley (published 1825)
Iπ:139x229:Purchased 1987

GLEHN, Wilfred Gabriel de - see DE GLEHN, Wilfred Gabriel

GLEICHEN, Feodora 1861-1922
British Collection

N04590 Head of a Girl (1921)
Sp:337x254x254:signed:Presented by the Geichen Family 1931

GLEIZES, Albert 1881-1953
Modern Collection

T00550 Painting (1921)
Tableau
Gw:921x730:signed:Purchased 1962

T02410 Portrait of Jacques Nayral (1911)
Portrait de Jacques Nayral
Oc:1619x1140:signed:Purchased 1979

GLENDENNING, Alfred 1861-1907
British Collection

N01718 Haymaking (1898)
Wπ:597x914:signed:Presented by the Trustees of the Chantrey Bequest 1898

GLENDENNING, Ronald
Modern Collection

P06708 Cycle Racing (circa 1956)
CLπ:483x737:signed:Presented by Curwen Studio 1976

P06783 Landscape (1978)
CLπ:435x533:signed:Presented by Curwen Studio 1978

GLOVER, John 1767-1849
British Collection

N01186 Landscape with Cattle
Oc:521x718:Bequeathed by Mrs Elizabeth Vaughan 1885

T05561 Thirlmere (circa 1820-30)
Oc:760x1012:Purchased 1989

GOENEUTTE, Norbert 1854-1894
Modern Collection

N04538 The Boulevard de Clichy under Snow (1876)
Le Boulevard de Clichy, par un temps de neige
Oc:600x733:signed:Purchased 1930

GOGH, Vincent van 1853-1890
Modern Collection
Tate Gallery Archive holds material concerning this artist

N04713 Farms near Auvers (1890)
Oc:502x1003:Bequeathed by C. Frank Stoop 1933

N04714 The Oise at Auvers (1890)
DGπ:473x629:Bequeathed by C. Frank Stoop 1933

N04715 Thatched Roofs (1884)
DGπ:305x448:Bequeathed by C. Frank Stoop 1933

N04716 A Corner of the Garden of St Paul's Hospital at St Rémy (1889)
Dπ:622x483:Bequeathed by C. Frank Stoop 1933

GOLDEN, Grace born 1904
Modern Collection

N04898 Summer Evening, Embankment Gardens (circa 1934)
DWπ:457x622:signed:Presented by the Trustees of the Chantrey Bequest 1937

N05338 Free Speech (1940)
Oc:406x559:signed:Presented by the Trustees of the Chantrey Bequest 1940

GOLDING, John born 1929
Modern Collection
Tate Gallery Archive holds material concerning this artist

T01857 CV (1973)
Ac:2134x3048:signed:Purchased 1974

T03859 H13 (Pleated Light-Verona) (1983)
Af:1753x2747:signed:Purchased 1984

GOLDSCHMIDT, Hilde 1897-1980
Modern Collection
Tate Gallery Archive holds material concerning this artist

T03350　The Sphinx (1948)
Oc:889x610:signed:Bequeathed by the artist 1982

GOLUB, Leon born 1922
Modern Collection

P77249　Fighter (1965)
Lπ:765x565:signed:Purchased 1988
P77250　Wounded Sphinx (1965)
Lπ:755x1050:signed:Purchased 1988
P77251　White Squad (1987)
Lπ:755x1060:Purchased 1988

GONTCHAROVA, Nathalie 1881-1962
Modern Collection

N06193　Three Young Women (1920)
Trois jeunes filles
Oc:1019x683:signed:Presented by Eugène Mollo and the artist 1953
N06194　Linen (1913)
Oc:956x838:signed:Presented by Eugène Mollo and the artist 1953
T00468　Gardening (1908)
Oc:1029x1232:signed:Presented by the artist 1961
T01119　Rayonist Composition (circa 1912-3)
Composition rayonniste
Pπ:318x216:signed:Presented by Eugène Rubin 1969

GONZALEZ, Joan 1868-1908
Modern Collection
Tate Gallery Archive holds material concerning this artist

T01640　Couple in the Undergrowth (circa 1900-1)
Couple dans les sous-bois
Dπ:324x502:Presented by Mme Roberta Gonzalez-Richard, the artist's niece 1972
T01641　Peasant Woman at a Fountain (circa 1902)
Paysanne à la fontaine
Gπ:489x489:signed:Presented by Mme Roberta Gonzalez-Richard, the artist's niece 1972
T01642　Catalan Landscape (circa 1902)
Paysage catalan
WGπ:511x549:Presented by Mme Roberta Gonzalez-Richard, the artist's niece 1972
T01643　Portrait of a Young Man (circa 1903-4)
Portrait de jeune homme
Dπ:397x311:Presented by Mme Roberta Gonzalez-Richard, the artist's niece 1972
T01644　Three Ladies (circa 1908)
Les Trois Dames
Pπ:425x302:signed:Presented by Mme Roberta Gonzalez-Richard, the artist's niece 1972
T01645　Woman with an Eye-Glass (circa 1902-3)
Femme au lorgnon
DWπ:317x241:Presented by Mme Roberta Gonzalez-Richard, the artist's niece 1972
T01646　Clearing with Ferns. Verso: Trunks of Birch Trees (circa 1901-2)
Clairière aux fougères. Verso: Les Troncs de bouleaux
PWπ:454x333:Presented by Mme Roberta Gonzalez-Richard, the artist's niece 1972

T01647　Twilight (circa 1904-5)
Crépuscule
WGπ:318x483:Presented by Mme Roberta Gonzalez-Richard, the artist's niece 1972
T01648　Nude with a Veil (circa 1905-6)
Nu au voile
Pπ:541x314:Presented by Mme Roberta Gonzalez-Richard, the artist's niece 1972
T01649　Nude Seated by a Tree (circa 1905-6)
Nu assis à l'arbre
Pπ:251x162:Presented by Mme Roberta Gonzalez-Richard, the artist's niece 1972
T01650　A Large Cloud (circa 1905)
Le Grand Nuage
Dπ:311x483:Presented by Mme Roberta Gonzalez-Richard, the artist's niece 1972
T01651　A Tower (circa 1906-7)
La Tour
Wπ:298x473:Presented by Mme Roberta Gonzalez-Richard, the artist's niece 1972
T01652　Landscape Known As 'The Iron Gate' (1904)
Paysage dit 'La Grille'
Gπ:470x610:signed:Presented by Mme Roberta Gonzalez-Richard, the artist's niece 1972
T01653　Arid Landscape (circa 1905)
Paysage aride
Pπ:324x498:Presented by Mme Roberta Gonzalez-Richard, the artist's niece 1972
T01654　Four Trees (circa 1905)
Les Quatre Arbres
WGπ:479x622:Presented by Mme Roberta Gonzalez-Richard, the artist's niece 1972
T01655　Spring Undergrowth (circa 1901-2)
Sous-bois printanier
Gπ:648x502:signed:Presented by Mme Roberta Gonzalez-Richard, the artist's niece 1972
T01656　Black Landscape (circa 1903-4)
Paysage noir
Pπ:476x616:Presented by Mme Roberta Gonzalez-Richard, the artist's niece 1972
T01657　Fantastic Landscape (circa 1906-7)
Paysage fantastique
Pπ:327x502:Presented by Mme Roberta Gonzalez-Richard, the artist's niece 1972
T01658　Girl in a Red Dress (circa 1902-3)
Jeune fille à la robe rouge
Pπ:556x225:Presented by Mme Roberta Gonzalez-Richard, the artist's niece 1972
T01659　Black Tree (1903)
L'Arbre noir
Pπ:502x651:signed:Presented by Mme Roberta Gonzalez-Richard, the artist's niece 1972
T01660　Face of a Woman (circa 1902)
Visage de femme
Dπ:295x190:signed:Presented by Mme Roberta Gonzalez-Richard, the artist's niece 1972
T01661　Three Trees (circa 1903-4)
Les Trois Arbres
Dπ:479x622:Presented by Mme Roberta Gonzalez-Richard, the artist's niece 1972
T01662　White Clouds (circa 1903-4)
Les Nuages blancs
Pπ:229x292:Presented by Mme Roberta Gonzalez-Richard, the artist's niece 1972

T01663 Girl with Black Gloves (circa 1905)
Jeune femme gantée de noir
Pπ:483x168:Presented by Mme Roberta
Gonzalez-Richard, the artist's niece 1972

T01664 Earth and Sky (circa 1902)
Terre et ciel
Gπ:264x498:signed:Presented by Mme Roberta
Gonzalez-Richard, the artist's niece 1972

T01665 A Pretty Parisian (circa 1902-3)
La Jolie Parisienne
Pπ:327x254:signed:Presented by Mme Roberta
Gonzalez-Richard, the artist's niece 1972

T01666 Part of a Landscape (circa 1901-2)
Paysage découpé
Pπ:235x333:Presented by Mme Roberta
Gonzalez-Richard, the artist's niece 1972

T01667 Two Women (circa 1905)
Deux femmes
Pπ:483x305:Presented by Mme Roberta
Gonzalez-Richard, the artist's niece 1972

T01668 Girl in a White Dress (circa 1908)
Jeune femme en robe blanche
Pπ:321x241:Presented by Mme Roberta
Gonzalez-Richard, the artist's niece 1972

T01669 Strange Landscape (circa 1907-8)
Paysage bizarre
Pπ:318x241:Presented by Mme Roberta
Gonzalez-Richard, the artist's niece 1972

T01670 Nude with Drapery (circa 1907-8)
Nu à la draperie
Pπ:318x244:Presented by Mme Roberta
Gonzalez-Richard, the artist's niece 1972

T01671 Girls at a Fountain (circa 1907-8)
Jeune fille à la fontaine
Pπ:241x318:Presented by Mme Roberta
Gonzalez-Richard, the artist's niece 1972

T01672 Strange Park (circa 1903-4)
L'Etrange Parc
Pπ:622x483:Presented by Mme Roberta
Gonzalez-Richard, the artist's niece 1972

T01673 Two Parisians (circa 1902-3)
Deux parisiennes
Pπ:324x254:Presented by Mme Roberta
Gonzalez-Richard, the artist's niece 1972

T01674 Two Parisians (circa 1903-4)
Deux parisiennes
Pπ:406x232:Presented by Mme Roberta
Gonzalez-Richard, the artist's niece 1972

T01675 The Chinchilla Collar (circa 1908)
Le Col de chinchilla
Pπ:318x241:Presented by Mme Roberta
Gonzalez-Richard, the artist's niece 1972

T01676 Tree and Stone Hut (1904)
L'Arbre et la hutte de pierre
Dπ:311x460:signed:Presented by Mme Roberta
Gonzalez-Richard, the artist's niece 1972

T01677 The Enclosure (The Wall of Enclosure) (circa 1905-6)
La Clôture (Le Mur de clôture)
Pπ:324x495:signed:Presented by Mme Roberta
Gonzalez-Richard, the artist's niece 1972

T01678 Black and Pink Trees (circa 1905-6)
Arbres noirs et roses
Pπ:505x324:signed:Presented by Mme Roberta
Gonzalez-Richard, the artist's niece 1972

T01679 Two Olive Trees (1904)
Les Deux Oliviers
Gπ:476x597:Presented by Mme Roberta
Gonzalez-Richard, the artist's niece 1972

GONZALEZ, Julio 1876-1942
Modern Collection

T01242 Maternity (1934)
Maternité
Sm:1305x406x235:Purchased 1970

T01262 Self-Portrait (1941)
Autoportrait
DWπ:264x190:signed:Presented by Mme Roberta
Gonzalez-Richard, the artist's niece 1972

T01263 Figure of Terror II (1941)
Personnage terrible II
DWπ:321x241:signed:Presented by Mme Roberta
Gonzalez-Richard, the artist's niece 1972

T01264 Aerial Figure (1941)
Personnage aerien
DWπ:318x248:signed:Presented by Mme Roberta
Gonzalez-Richard, the artist's niece 1972

T01500 Study for 'Maternity' (1934)
Etude pour 'La Maternité'
Dπ:244x159:signed:Presented by Mme Roberta
Gonzalez-Richard, the artist's niece 1972

T01590 Woman Dressing (circa 1905-8)
Femme s'habillant
Pπ:448x270:Presented by Mme Roberta
Gonzalez-Richard, the artist's niece 1972

T01591 Sleeping Girl (circa 1904-5)
Jeune femme endormie
Pπ:483x308:Presented by Mme Roberta
Gonzalez-Richard, the artist's niece 1972

T01592 Portrait of a Girl. Verso: The Frill (circa 1908-9)
Portrait de jeune fille. Verso: Le Jabot
Pπ:394x279:Presented by Mme Roberta
Gonzalez-Richard, the artist's niece 1972

T01593 Peasant Gardening (circa 1910)
Paysanne jardinant
Pπ:324x251:Presented by Mme Roberta
Gonzalez-Richard, the artist's niece 1972

T01594 Profile of a Girl in a Head-Dress (circa 1904)
Profil de jeune fille à la coiffe
Pπ:362x267:Presented by Mme Roberta
Gonzalez-Richard, the artist's niece 1972

T01595 Nude Girl Washing Herself (circa 1914-18)
Jeune fille nue se lavant
Pπ:356x273:Presented by Mme Roberta
Gonzalez-Richard, the artist's niece 1972

T01596 Nude Girl (circa 1914-18)
Jeune fille nue
Pπ:518x286:Presented by Mme Roberta
Gonzalez-Richard, the artist's niece 1972

T01597 Large Tree (1919)
Le Grand Arbre
Pπ:629x260:Presented by Mme Roberta
Gonzalez-Richard, the artist's niece 1972

T01598 Large Trees (1919)
Les Grands Arbres
Pπ:324x248:signed:Presented by Mme Roberta
Gonzalez-Richard, the artist's niece 1972

T01599 Peasant with a Bundle of Sticks (circa 1919-23)
Paysan au fagot
Pπ:251x327:Presented by Mme Roberta
Gonzalez-Richard, the artist's niece 1972

T01600 Apple Picking (circa 1920)
La Cueillette de pommes
Pπ:378x295:Presented by Mme Roberta
Gonzalez-Richard, the artist's niece 1972

T01601 Peasant Couple with Apple-Trees (circa 1920)
Couple de paysans aux pommiers
Pπ:352x327:Presented by Mme Roberta
Gonzalez-Richard, the artist's niece 1972

T01602 Peasant with a Large Pitchfork (circa 1920)
Paysan à la grande fourche
Pπ:279x479:Presented by Mme Roberta
Gonzalez-Richard, the artist's niece 1972

T01603 Work in the Fields (circa 1920)
Travaux aux champs
Pπ:324x251:Presented by Mme Roberta
Gonzalez-Richard, the artist's niece 1972

T01604 Transplanting and Watering (1921)
Dépiquage et arrosage
Wπ:251x324:signed:Presented by Mme Roberta
Gonzalez-Richard, the artist's niece 1972

T01605 Imaginary Face (1934)
Visage fantastique
Dπ:327x251:signed:Presented by Mme Roberta
Gonzalez-Richard, the artist's niece 1972

T01606 Sulky Face (1936)
Visage boudeur
DWπ:308x232:signed:Presented by Mme Roberta
Gonzalez-Richard, the artist's niece 1972

T01607 Stern Mask with a Beard (1936)
Masque rigoureux à la barbe
Dπ:314x244:signed:Presented by Mme Roberta
Gonzalez-Richard, the artist's niece 1972

T01608 Stern Face (1936)
Visage sévère
DWπ:241x159:signed:Presented by Mme Roberta
Gonzalez-Richard, the artist's niece 1972

T01609 Reclining Figure with a Large Hand (1936)
Dπ:194x283:signed:Presented by Mme Roberta
Gonzalez-Richard, the artist's niece 1972

T01610 Noble Woman (1936)
Dπ:305x203:signed:Presented by Mme Roberta
Gonzalez-Richard, the artist's niece 1972

T01611 Figure at a Window (1936)
DWπ:229x156:signed:Presented by Mme Roberta
Gonzalez-Richard, the artist's niece 1972

T01612 Figure with a White Rectangle (1937)
Personnage au rectangle blanc
Dπ:327x254:signed:Presented by Mme Roberta
Gonzalez-Richard, the artist's niece 1972

T01613 Fantastic Figure (1937)
Personnage fantastique
DWπ:327x254:signed:Presented by Mme Roberta
Gonzalez-Richard, the artist's niece 1972

T01614 Vibrating Figure (1938)
Personnage vibrant
DWπ:327x254:signed:Presented by Mme Roberta
Gonzalez-Richard, the artist's niece 1972

T01615 Figure with Balls, known as 'Severe' (1938)
Personnage aux boules dit 'Sévère'
Dπ:356x279:signed:Presented by Mme Roberta
Gonzalez-Richard, the artist's niece 1972

T01616 Figure with Balls (1938)
Personnage aux boules
DWπ:318x241:signed:Presented by Mme Roberta
Gonzalez-Richard, the artist's niece 1972

T01617 Head with a Long Neck (1939)
Tête au long cou
Dπ:330x241:signed:Presented by Mme Roberta
Gonzalez-Richard, the artist's niece 1972

T01618 Shrieking Head, called 'The Shriek' (1939)
Tête criant dite 'Le Cri'
Dπ:279x337:signed:Presented by Mme Roberta
Gonzalez-Richard, the artist's niece 1972

T01619 V-Shaped Head (1939)
Tête au V
DWπ:406x305:Presented by Mme Roberta
Gonzalez-Richard, the artist's niece 1972

T01620 Face with a Black Sun (1939)
Visage au soleil noir
Dπ:241x346:signed:Presented by Mme Roberta
Gonzalez-Richard, the artist's niece 1972

T01621 Stern Mask (1940)
Masque rigoureux
DWπ:311x241:Presented by Mme Roberta
Gonzalez-Richard, the artist's niece 1972

T01622 Figure in Glory (1940)
Personnage en gloire
DWπ:264x190:signed:Presented by Mme Roberta
Gonzalez-Richard, the artist's niece 1972

T01623 Architectural Figure No. 2 (1940)
Personnage architectural no. 2
DWπ:318x241:signed:Presented by Mme Roberta
Gonzalez-Richard, the artist's niece 1972

T01624 Maltese Face (1940)
Visage maltais
DWπ:318x241:signed:Presented by Mme Roberta
Gonzalez-Richard, the artist's niece 1972

T01625 Native Woman (1940)
Femme sauvage
DWπ:318x241:signed:Presented by Mme Roberta
Gonzalez-Richard, the artist's niece 1972

T01626 Solemn Maternity (1940)
Maternité grave
DWπ:483x321:signed:Presented by Mme Roberta
Gonzalez-Richard, the artist's niece 1972

T01627 Standing Woman Shouting (1940)
Femme debout criant
DWπ:321x238:signed:Presented by Mme Roberta
Gonzalez-Richard, the artist's niece 1972

T01628 Man Enigma (1941)
Homme fusée
DWπ:318x241:signed:Presented by Mme Roberta
Gonzalez-Richard, the artist's niece 1972

T01629 Brown and Blue Night (1941)
Brun et bleu Nuit
DWGπ:248x162:signed:Presented by Mme Roberta
Gonzalez-Richard, the artist's niece 1972

T01630 Maternity (1941)
Maternité
DWπ:260x194:signed:Presented by Mme Roberta
Gonzalez-Richard, the artist's niece 1972

T01631 Screaming Head with a White Veil (1941)
Tête criant au voile blanc
DGπ:318x238:signed:Presented by Mme Roberta
Gonzalez-Richard, the artist's niece 1972

T01632 Self-Portrait (1941)
Autoportrait
Dπ:311x203:Presented by Mme Roberta
Gonzalez-Richard, the artist's niece 1972

T01633 Figure known as 'The Shell-Fish' (1941)
Personnage dit 'Le Coquillage'
DWπ:244x321:signed:Presented by Mme Roberta
Gonzalez-Richard, the artist's niece 1972

T01634 Houses and Sky (1941)
Maisons et ciel
Dπ:159x238:signed:Presented by Mme Roberta
Gonzalez-Richard, the artist's niece 1972

T01635 Marie-Thérèse with a Veil No. 2 (1941)
Marie-Thérèse au voile No. 2
Pπ:314x241:signed:Presented by Mme Roberta
Gonzalez-Richard, the artist's niece 1972

T01636 Marie-Thérèse Sad (1942)
Marie-Thérèse triste
Pπ:375x267:Presented by Mme Roberta
Gonzalez-Richard, the artist's niece 1972

T01637 Figure with Three Balls, No. 2 (1942)
Personnage aux trois boules no. 2
Pπ:267x190:signed:Presented by Mme Roberta
Gonzalez-Richard, the artist's niece 1972

T01638 Solemn Head in Profile (1942)
Tête profil grave
DWπ:187x267:Presented by Mme Roberta
Gonzalez-Richard, the artist's niece 1972

T01639 Girl Dressing her Hair (1942)
Jeune femme se coiffant
DWπ:267x371:signed:Presented by Mme Roberta
Gonzalez-Richard, the artist's niece 1972

T01698 Head called 'The Tunnel' (1933-4)
Tête dite 'Le Tunnel'
Sm:467x216x308:Purchased 1972

GOOD, Thomas Sword 1789-1872
British Collection

N00378 The Newspaper
Ow:241x190:Presented by Robert Vernon 1847

N00917 No News (exhibited 1833)
Ow:533x432:Presented by the artist's widow 1874

N00918 Fisherman with a Gun (?1832)
Ow:375x476:Presented by the artist's widow 1874

N00919 Study of a Boy
Ow:302x243:Presented by the artist's widow 1874

GOODALL, Frederick 1822-1904
British Collection
Tate Gallery Archive holds material concerning this artist

N00450 A Village Holiday of the Olden Time: 'When the Merry
Bells Ring Round' (1847)
Oc:1067x1714:signed:Presented by Robert Vernon 1847

N00451 The Tired Soldier Resting at a Roadside Well (exhibited
1842)
Oc:698x914:Presented by Robert Vernon 1847

N01562 The Ploughman and the Shepherdess: Time of the
Evening Prayer (1897)
Oc:1905x2413:signed:Presented by subscribers 1898

GOODWIN, Albert 1845-1932
British Collection

N01550 Shipwreck: Sinbad the Sailor Storing his Raft (1887)
Oc:1245x2007:signed:Presented by Sir Henry Tate 1894

N01900 Ali Baba and the Forty Thieves (1901)
Oc:1060x1397:signed:Presented by the Trustees of the
Chantrey Bequest 1901

N02296 The Gate of the Pass, Maloja
Gπ:257x365:signed:Presented by Miss Evelyn de
Ponsonby McGhee 1908

N02297 Torre del Greco and Capri (1900 and 1904)
Gπ:248x375:signed:Presented by Miss Evelyn de
Ponsonby McGhee 1908

N02298 Folkestone Harbour (1907)
Wπ:254x384:signed:Presented by Miss Evelyn de
Ponsonby McGhee 1908

N02299 Ely Cathedral (1908)
Wπ:254x375:signed:Presented by Miss Evelyn de
Ponsonby McGhee 1908

N04219 Salisbury
Wπ:95x140:signed:Bequeathed by Miss Amy Mary
Benecke 1926

GORDINE, Dora born 1906
Modern Collection
Tate Gallery Archive holds material concerning this artist

N04419 Mongolian Head (1928)
Sz:330x190x241:signed:Presented anonymously through
the National Art Collections Fund 1928

N04695 Javanese Head (circa 1929-33)
Sz:362x210x279:signed:Presented by the Hon. Richard
Hare 1933

N04860 A Malay Sultana (1933)
Sz:273x222x349:signed:Bequeathed by Mrs Rhoda
Symons 1937

T03746 Guadaloupe Head (circa 1925-7)
Sz:360x230x230:signed:Transferred from the Victoria &
Albert Museum 1983

GORDON, Sir John Watson 1788-1864
British Collection

N03562 Mrs George Baird of Strichen (exhibited 1862)
Ob:356x279:Presented by A. Kay through the National
Art Collections Fund 1920

GORE, Spencer 1878-1914
British Collection
Tate Gallery Archive holds material concerning this artist

N03558 From a Window in Cambrian Road, Richmond (1913)
Oc:559x686:Presented by subscribers 1920

N03839 Houghton Place (1912)
Oc:508x610:Presented by the Contemporary Art Society
1927

N04675 Letchworth (1912)
Oc:508x610:Purchased 1933

N05099 Mornington Crescent (1911)
Oc:635x762:Bequeathed by Lady Henry
Cavendish-Bentinck 1940

N05100 Richmond Park (1913-14)
Oc:508x762:Bequeathed by Lady Henry
Cavendish-Bentinck 1940

N05263 The Blacksmith's Shop (circa 1903)
WDπ:225x302:Presented by Albert Rutherston 1941

N05307 Dancing in the Street (circa 1904)
DWπ:251x356:Presented by Albert Rutherston 1941

N05859 Inez and Taki (1910)
Oc:406x508:signed:Purchased 1948

N06016 Ballet Scene (circa 1906-11)
WDπ:375x279:Presented by Albert Rutherston 1951

T00027 North London Girl (circa 1911-12)
Oc:762x610:Bequeathed by J.W. Freshfield 1955

T00028 The Fig Tree (1912)
Oc:635x762:signed:Bequeathed by J.W. Freshfield 1955

T00446 Sketch for a Mural Decoration for 'The Cave of the
Golden Calf' (1912)
Oπ:305x603:signed:Purchased 1961

T00496 The Gas Cooker (1913)
Oc:730x368:Presented by the Trustees of the Chantrey
Bequest 1962

T01859 The Beanfield, Letchworth (1912)
Oc:305x406:signed:Purchased 1974

T01960 The Cinder Path (1912)
Oc:686x787:Purchased 1975

T02260 A Singer at the Bedford Music Hall (1912)
Oc:533x432:signed:Presented by Mr and Mrs Robert
Lewin through the Friends of the Tate Gallery 1978

T03561 The Artist's Wife (1913)
Oc:765x636:Presented by Frederick Gore, the artist's son
1983

GORKY, Arshile 1904-1948
Modern Collection

T01319 Waterfall (1943)
Oc:1537x1130:signed:Purchased with assistance from the
Friends of the Tate Gallery 1971

GORMLEY, Antony born 1950
Modern Collection
Tate Gallery Archive holds material concerning this artist

T03681 Natural Selection (1981)
Smv:11960x150x150:Presented by the Contemporary Art
Society 1983

T04860 Seed (1985)
DOπ:1367x1014:signed:Presented by Weltkunst
Foundation 1986

T04875 Space (1986)
DOπ:1366x1016:signed:Purchased 1986

T05004 Untitled (for Francis) (1985)
Sv:1900x1170x290:Purchased 1987

GOSSE, Sylvia 1881-1968
Modern Collection

N04364 Walter Richard Sickert (1923-5)
Oc:508x305:signed:Presented anonymously 1927

GOTCH, Thomas Cooper 1854-1931
British Collection

N01590 Alleluia (exhibited 1896)
Oc:1333x1841:signed:Presented by the Trustees of the
Chantrey Bequest 1896

GOTLIB, Henryk 1890-1966
Modern Collection
Tate Gallery Archive holds material concerning this artist

T03185 Rembrandt in Heaven (circa 1948-58)
Oc:1333x1632:signed:Purchased 1980

GOTTLIEB, Adolph 1903-1974
Modern Collection

T03094 The Alchemist (1945)
Oc:711x908:signed:Purchased 1980

T03095 Labyrinth No. 2 (1950)
Oc:914x1219:signed:Purchased 1980

T03276 Wedge (1961)
Oc:1829x1219:signed:Presented anonymously 1981

P04239 Blues on Green (1971)
CNπ::signed:Presented by Rose and Chris Prater through
the Institute of Contemporary Prints 1975

GÖTZ, Karl-Otto born 1914
Modern Collection

P08216 Untitled (1953)
CLπ:260x208:signed:Transferred from the Library 1987

P11204 Untitled (circa 1946)
Jπ:365x530:Presented by William Gear 1988

P11205 Bird Plant (1946)
Vogelpflanze
Jπ:270x435:signed:Presented by William Gear 1988

P11206 Gilgamesh (1947)
Gilgamesch
Jπ:400x560:signed:Presented by William Gear 1988

GOUK, Alan born 1939
Modern Collection

T04925 Cretan Premonition (1985-6)
Oc:1708x4381:signed:Purchased 1987

GOW, Andrew Carrick 1848-1920
British Collection

N01529 A Musical Story by Chopin (1879)
Oc:698x902:signed:Presented by Sir Henry Tate 1894

N01530 A Lost Cause: Flight of King James II after the Battle of
the Boyne (1888)
Oc:1181x1511:signed:Presented by Sir Henry Tate 1894

N01588 Cromwell at Dunbar (1886)
Oc:1206x1511:signed:Presented by the Trustees of the
Chantrey Bequest 1886

GOW, Mary 1851-1929
British Collection

N02263 Marie-Antoinette (1908)
Wπ:775x1333:signed:Presented by the Trustees of the
Chantrey Bequest 1908

GOWER, George circa 1540-1596
British Collection

N06090 Sir Thomas Kytson (1573)
Ow:527x400:Purchased 1952

N06091 Lady Kytson (1573)
Ow:679x521:Purchased 1952

GOWING, Sir Lawrence 1918-1991
Modern Collection
Tate Gallery Archive holds material concerning this artist

N05627 Mrs Roberts (1944)
Oc:406x508:signed:Presented by the Contemporary Art
Society 1945

T00475 Path with Elder and Hazel (1959)
Oc:635x762:signed:Presented by the Contemporary Art Society 1962

T00719 Wood: Parabolic Perspective (1963)
Ow:1149x1327:Purchased 1965

T03208 Portrait of Sir Norman Reid (1980)
Oc:660x451:Presented by the Trustees of the Tate Gallery 1981

GRAESER, Camille born 1918
Modern Collection

P03179 Untitled (1976)
Ohne Titel
CNπ:524x260:Presented by Kunsthaus Zürich 1976

GRAEVENITZ, Gerhard von 1934-1983
Modern Collection

T01822 5 Black Rectangles on White (1973)
Rw:1200x1197x121:Purchased 1973

GRAHAM, Dan born 1942
Modern Collection
Tate Gallery Archive holds material concerning this artist

T01737 Two Correlated Rotations (1970/72)
KFV::Purchased 1973

GRAHAM, Peter 1836-1921
British Collection
Tate Gallery Archive holds material concerning this artist

N01524 A Rainy Day (1871)
Oc:1168x1803:signed:Presented by Sir Henry Tate 1894

GRAND, Roger born 1922
Modern Collection

N06071 Nude (1951)
Dπ:260x137:signed:Purchased 1952

GRANGES, David des - see DES GRANGES, David

GRANT, Alistair born 1925
Modern Collection
Tate Gallery Archive holds material concerning this artist

P01156 Ghost II (1971)
CLπ:534x775:signed:Presented by Waddington Galleries through the Institute of Contemporary Prints 1975

P01157 Ghost V (1971)
CLπ:533x773:signed:Presented by Waddington Galleries through the Institute of Contemporary Prints 1975

P01158 Ghost VI (1971)
CLπ:540x775:signed:Presented by Waddington Galleries through the Institute of Contemporary Prints 1975

P02488 Ghost I (1971)
CLπ:575x770:signed:Presented by the artist 1979

P02489 Ghost III (1971)
CLπ:575x783:signed:Presented by the artist 1979

P02490 Ghost IV (1971)
CLπ:570x778:signed:Presented by the artist 1979

P07254 St Valery (1972-8)
CLNVπ:492x616:signed:Purchased 1979

P07255 Galopin II (1976-9)
CLNVπ:568x787:signed:Purchased 1979

GRANT, Duncan 1885-1978
Modern Collection
Tate Gallery Archive holds material concerning this artist

N03169 The Queen of Sheba (1912)
Ow:1200x1200:Presented by the Contemporary Art Society 1917

N03666 Lemon Gatherers (1910)
Ob:565x813:signed:Purchased 1922

N04443 South of France (1922)
Oc:648x806:signed:Presented by the Contemporary Art Society 1929

N04566 Football (1911)
Tc:2273x1968:Purchased 1931

N04567 Bathing (1911)
Tc:2286x3061:Purchased 1931

N05075 Landscape, Sussex (1920)
Oc:457x762:signed:Bequeathed by Frank Hindley Smith 1940

N05076 Portrait of a Woman (1927)
Oπ:724x584:signed:Bequeathed by Frank Hindley Smith 1940

N05171 Girl at the Piano (1940)
Oc:1175x1473:signed:Presented by the Trustees of the Chantrey Bequest 1940

N05405 Vanessa Bell (1942)
Oc:1016x610:Purchased 1943

N05428 The Hayrick (1940)
Oc:610x660:signed:Purchased 1943

N05764 Lytton Strachey (circa 1909)
Oc:533x660:Purchased 1947

N05765 James Strachey (1910)
Oc:635x762:Purchased 1947

N06143 Still Life with Carrots (circa 1921)
Oc:508x686:Bequeathed by Sir Edward Marsh through the Contemporary Art Society 1953

N06181 Dancers (circa 1910-11)
Ow:533x660:Bequeathed by Sir Edward Marsh through the Contemporary Art Society 1953

T00294 The Kitchen (1902)
Oc:508x406:signed:Presented by the Trustees of the Chantrey Bequest 1959

T00723 The Tub (circa 1913)
WTπ:762x559:signed:Presented by the Trustees of the Chantrey Bequest 1965

T01143 Interior at Gordon Square (circa 1915)
Ow:400x321:Purchased 1969

T01328 The Mantelpiece (1914)
OVb:457x394:signed:Purchased 1971

T01514 Venus and Adonis (circa 1919)
Oc:635x940:Purchased 1972

T01744 Abstract Kinetic Collage Painting with Sound (1914)
GWc:279x4502:Purchased 1973

T03847 Head of Eve (1913)
Ob:756x635:Purchased 1984

T05757 Garden Path in Spring (1944)
Oc:913x832:signed:Bequeathed by Helena and Kenneth Levy 1990

For John Constable (P03149-P03157, P03159-P03161, P03180-P03185; complete group; mixed group)

P03181 Untitled (1976)
MIπ:267x340:signed:Presented by Bernard Jacobson Gallery 1976

Penwith Portfolio (P01416, P06005, P06108, P06130, P06241, P06324, P06346, P06359, P06399, P06519, P06700; complete group; mixed group)

P06241 Interior (1973)
CLπ:368x305:signed:Presented by Curwen Studio through the Institute of Contemporary Prints 1975

P06242 Standing Woman (1973-4)
CLπ:746x432:signed:Presented by Curwen Studio through the Institute of Contemporary Prints 1975

P06243 Washerwoman (1973-4)
CLπ:730x524:signed:Presented by Curwen Studio through the Institute of Contemporary Prints 1975

A01111 Kinetic Realisation of T01744 made for Tate Gallery (1974)
KF::Purchased 1975

GRAU, Enrici
Modern Collection

P06784 Jewel Box (1977)
MLπ:645x540:Presented by Curwen Studio 1978

GRAVENEY, William 1904-1984
Modern Collection

N04209 Cormorants (exhibited 1926)
Sw:235x254x152:signed:Presented by Sir Philip Sassoon 1926

GRAVES, Morris born 1910
Modern Collection

T00520 Spring with Machine Age Noise No. 1 (1957)
TDπ:673x1368:signed:Presented by Sir Robert Adeane through the Friends of the Tate Gallery 1962

GRAY, Douglas S. 1890-1959
Modern Collection

N04193 Rosalind (1924-5)
Oc:1295x927:signed:Presented by the Trustees of the Chantrey Bequest 1926

GRAY, Ronald 1868-1951
British Collection
Tate Gallery Archive holds material concerning this artist

N04098 My Mother (1908)
Oc:737x610:signed:Presented by the Trustees of the Chantrey Bequest 1925

GRAYSON, Roy born 1936
Modern Collection
Tate Gallery Archive holds material concerning this artist

Jam Press Phase One (P08006-P08014; complete group; mixed group)
P08009 1. 5 (1973-4)
MLπ:559x441:Transferred from the Library 1977

GREAVES, Derrick born 1927
Modern Collection
Tate Gallery Archive holds material concerning this artist

T00033 Domes of Venice (1953-4)
Oc:1841x1549:signed:Presented by the Trustees of the Chantrey Bequest 1955

Approval Stamp Offer (P01676-P01687; complete group; mixed group)
P01676 [no title] (1972)
MJπ:50x50:Presented by Tetrad Press through the Institute of Contemporary Prints 1975

P01677 Snow in the Alps (1972)
MJπ:50x50:Presented by Tetrad Press through the Institute of Contemporary Prints 1975

P01678 Four Rooms (1972)
MJπ:51x51:Presented by Tetrad Press through the Institute of Contemporary Prints 1975

Tetrad Pamphlets Vol. I Nos. I-X (P01688-P01697; complete group; mixed group)
P01688 Poem 1968 (1970)
CNπ:305x511:Presented by Tetrad Press through the Institute of Contemporary Prints 1975

P01689 Sweet Pictorial Reason (1971)
CNπ::Presented by Tetrad Press through the Institute of Contemporary Prints 1975

Also (P04240-P04246; complete group)
P04240 [title not known] (1972)
CNπ:471x650:signed:Presented by Rose and Chris Prater through the Institute of Contemporary Prints 1975

P04241 [title not known] (1972)
CNπ:474x650:signed:Presented by Rose and Chris Prater through the Institute of Contemporary Prints 1975

P04242 [title not known] (1972)
CNπ:472x650:signed:Presented by Rose and Chris Prater through the Institute of Contemporary Prints 1975

P04243 [title not known] (1972)
CNπ:477x650:signed:Presented by Rose and Chris Prater through the Institute of Contemporary Prints 1975

P04244 [title not known] (1972)
CNπ:473x649:signed:Presented by Rose and Chris Prater through the Institute of Contemporary Prints 1975

P04245 [title not known] (1972)
CNπ:477x650:signed:Presented by Rose and Chris Prater through the Institute of Contemporary Prints 1975

P04246 [title not known] (1972)
CNπ:477x650:signed:Presented by Rose and Chris Prater through the Institute of Contemporary Prints 1975

P05503 Abstract Painting with Fruit (1979)
CNπ:508x381:signed:Presented by Rose and Chris Prater 1979

P05504 Begonia (1979)
CNπ:508x381:signed:Presented by Rose and Chris Prater 1979

Europaeische Graphik VII (P06244, P06289-P06291, P06319, P06340-P06341, P06549; incomplete group; mixed group)
P06244 Vase and Falling Petal (1971)
CLπ:648x495:signed:Presented by Curwen Studio through the Institute of Contemporary Prints 1975

P06245 White Vase (1972)
CLπ:641x483:signed:Presented by Curwen Studio through the Institute of Contemporary Prints 1975

GREAVES, Walter 1846-1930
British Collection
Tate Gallery Archive holds material concerning this artist

N03643 Hammersmith Bridge on Boat-race Day (circa 1862)
Oc:914x1397:Presented by the Trustees of the Chantrey Bequest 1922

N04564 Walter Greaves and Alice Greaves on the Embankment (circa 1880-90)
Oc:305x508:Presented by Lord Henry Bentinck 1931

N04598 Old Battersea Bridge (1874)
Oc:584x762:signed:Presented by the Trustees of the Chantrey Bequest 1931

N04599 The Green Dress (circa 1875)
Oc:1930x914:Presented by the Trustees of the Chantrey Bequest 1931

N05216 Battersea Reach (circa 1870)
Oc:641x768:signed:Purchased 1940

N06246 Self-Portrait
Oπ:400x321:signed:Purchased 1954

GRECO, Emilio born 1913
Modern Collection
Tate Gallery Archive holds material concerning this artist

T00014 Large Seated Figure (1951)
Grande figura seduta
Sz:1321x406x635:signed:Purchased 1955

T00015 Head and Shoulders of a Girl (1954)
Dπ:502x356:signed:Purchased 1955

T00016 Head of a Girl (1954)
Dπ:498x356:signed:Purchased 1955

T00198 Large Bather I (1956)
La grande bagnante no. 1
Sz:2134x514x724:signed:Presented by Count Manassei 1958

Six Drawings for 'Pinocchio' (A01074-A01079; complete group)
A01074 [title not known] (1953)
Dπ:660x467:signed:Presented by the artist 1960

A01075 [title not known] (1953)
Dπ:660x467:signed:Presented by the artist 1960

A01076 [title not known] (1953)
Dπ:660x467:signed:Presented by the artist 1960

A01077 [title not known] (1953)
Dπ:660x467:signed:Presented by the artist 1960

A01078 [title not known] (1953)
Dπ:660x467:signed:Presented by the artist 1960

A01079 [title not known] (1953)
Dπ:660x467:signed:Presented by the artist 1960

Two Drawings for Large Bather I (A01080-A01081; complete group)
A01080 [title not known] (1959)
Dπ:635x410:signed:Presented by the artist 1960

A01081 [title not known] (1959)
Dπ:660x467:signed:Presented by the artist 1960

GREEN, Alan born 1932
Modern Collection
Tate Gallery Archive holds material concerning this artist

T03443 One to Four (1982)
3 Oc:1706x5118:signed:Purchased 1982

T03835 Check (1973)
Ac:2134x2743:signed:Purchased 1984

Three Variations (P01406-P01408; complete group)
P01406 Variation A (1974)
Clπ:548x696:signed:Presented by Annely Juda and Editions Alecto through the Institute of Contemporary Prints 1975

P01407 Variation B (1974)
Clπ:550x695:signed:Presented by Annely Juda and Editions Alecto through the Institute of Contemporary Prints 1975

P01408 Variation C (1974)
Clπ:547x695:signed:Presented by Annely Juda and Editions Alecto through the Institute of Contemporary Prints 1975

P01774 Four Rectangles (1975)
Clπ:546x692:signed:Presented by the Artist and Annely Juda Fine Art 1976

P01775 Second State (1975)
Clπ:543x692:signed:Presented by the Artist and Annely Juda Fine Art 1976

P01776 Second State (1975)
Clπ:550x692:signed:Presented by the Artist and Annely Juda Fine Art 1976

Four to One (P01777-P01785; complete group)
P01777 Black (1976)
Clπ:546x692:Presented by the Artist and Annely Juda Fine Art 1977

P01778 Black on Black (1976)
Clπ:548x692:Presented by the Artist and Annely Juda Fine Art 1977

P01779 Cream over Crimson (1976)
Clπ:332x547:Presented by the Artist and Annely Juda Fine Art 1977

P01780 White on Brown (1976)
Clπ:345x693:Presented by the Artist and Annely Juda Fine Art 1977

P01781 1/4 Black Diagonal (1976)
Clπ:293x350:Presented by the Artist and Annely Juda Fine Art 1977

P01782 1/4 Black Red (1976)
Clπ:272x348:Presented by the Artist and Annely Juda Fine Art 1977

P01783 1/2 Black (1976)
Clπ:339x544:Presented by the Artist and Annely Juda Fine Art 1977

P01784 1/2 Red Black (1976)
Clπ:349x544:Presented by the Artist and Annely Juda Fine Art 1977

P01785 1/2 to the Right (1976)
Clπ:349x545:Presented by the Artist and Annely Juda Fine Art 1977

Three to Four (P01856-P01859; complete group)
P01856 1. Black Vertical on Black (1977)
CLπ:660x660:signed:Presented by the Artist and Annely Juda Fine Art 1978

P01857 2. 90% on White (1977)
CLπ:660x660:signed:Presented by the Artist and Annely Juda Fine Art 1978

P01858 3. Grey on 180 (1977)
CLπ:660x665:signed:Presented by the Artist and Annely Juda Fine Art 1978

P01859 4. White Horizontal, Black Verticals (1977)
CLπ:660x660:signed:Presented by the Artist and Annely Juda Fine Art 1978

Two Plus Two (P03117-P03120; complete group)

P03117 Black Diagonal to Edge (1975)
CLπ:546x694:Presented by Annely Juda Fine Art 1975

P03118 Black over White (1975)
CLπ:545x692:Presented by Annely Juda Fine Art 1975

P03119 White Diagonal to Edge (1975)
CLπ:546x691:Presented by Annely Juda Fine Art 1975

P03120 White over Black (1975)
CLπ:547x694:Presented by Annely Juda Fine Art 1975

GREEN, Anthony born 1939
Modern Collection
Tate Gallery Archive holds material concerning this artist

T01064 Souvenir de Jeunesse: Madeleine Joscelyne's Lounge (1967)
Oc:1524x1448:signed:Presented by the Trustees of the Chantrey Bequest 1968

T03259 Casimir Dupont (1980)
Ob:2172x2169:signed:Purchased 1981

T03295 L'Heure du Thé, Argenton-sur-Creuse (1980)
Ob:1994x2210:signed:Presented by the Trustees of the Chantrey Bequest 1981

GREENE, Stephen born 1918
Modern Collection

T00526 The Return (1950)
Oc:1318x838:signed:Presented by R. Kirk Askew, Jnr through the Friends of the Tate Gallery 1962

GREENFIELD, Graham born 1951
Modern Collection

P01409 Glass Table (1974)
CLπ:197x305:signed:Presented by Christie's Contemporary Art through the Institute of Contemporary Prints 1975

P01410 Still Life with Flowers (1974)
CLπ:302x203:signed:Presented by Christie's Contemporary Art through the Institute of Contemporary Prints 1975

GREENHAM, Peter born 1909
Modern Collection

T00769 Jane (1964)
Oc:610x508:signed:Presented by the Trustees of the Chantrey Bequest 1965

T02401 Father d'Arcy (1975)
Oc:762x521:Presented by the Trustees of the Chantrey Bequest 1979

T03219 Life Class (1979)
Oc:1219x2146:Presented by the Trustees of the Chantrey Bequest 1981

GREENWOOD, Phillip born 1934
Modern Collection

P01411 Snow Night (1974)
CLπ:448x559:signed:Presented by Christie's Contemporary Art through the Institute of Contemporary Prints 1975

P01866 Woodshade (1977)
CLπ:279x254:signed:Presented by Christie's Contemporary Art 1979

GREGORY, Edward John 1850-1909
British Collection

N01704 Marooning (1887)
Wπ:368x457:signed:Presented by Sir Henry Tate 1894

GREIFFENHAGEN, Maurice 1862-1931
British Collection

N02974 Women by a Lake (1914)
Oc:1537x1524:signed:Presented by the Trustees of the Chantrey Bequest 1914

N04192 Dawn (1926)
Ow:959x2019:signed:Presented by the Trustees of the Chantrey Bequest 1926

P03030 Restoration of Alsace-Lorraine to France (1917)
CLπ:695x445:signed:Presented by the Ministry of Information 1918

GREY, Roger de - see DE GREY, Roger

GRIFFIER, John, the Elder 1646 or 52 - 1718
British Collection

T00408 View of Hampton Court Palace (circa 1710)
Om:381x505:signed:Presented by the Friends of the Tate Gallery 1961

T04129 A Turkey and other Fowl in a Park (1710)
Oc:1146x1390:signed:Purchased 1985

GRIFFITHS, John 1838-1918
British Collection

N03432 A Sannyasi - A Religious Mendicant (exhibited 1882)
Wπ:483x343:Presented by Miss Griffiths 1919

GRIMM, Samuel Hieronymous 1733-1794
British Collection

T03603 The Glacier of Simmenthal (1774)
Wπ:295x371:signed:Purchased 1983

GRIMSHAW, Atkinson 1836-1893
British Collection

T00626 View of Heath Street by Night (1882)
Ob:368x537:signed:Purchased 1963

T00902 Liverpool Quay by Moonlight (1887)
Oc:610x914:signed:Purchased 1967

T03683 Bowder Stone, Borrowdale (circa 1863-8)
Oc:400x536:signed:Purchased with assistance from the Friends of the Tate Gallery 1983

GRIMSHAW, Trevor born 1947
Modern Collection

P01412 Northern Townscape (1974)
CLπ:324x422:signed:Presented by Christie's Contemporary Art through the Institute of Contemporary Prints 1975

P01413 Open Space (1974)
CLπ:327x422:signed:Presented by Christie's Contemporary Art through the Institute of Contemporary Prints 1975

GRIS, Juan 1887-1927
Modern Collection
Tate Gallery Archive holds material concerning this artist

N05747 The Sunblind (1914)
La Jalousie
VDc:921x727:signed:Purchased 1946

N05935 Violin and Fruit-Dish (1924)
Violon et compotier
Oc:387x600:signed:Purchased 1950

GROSS, Anthony 1905-1984
Modern Collection
Tate Gallery Archive holds material concerning this artist

N05696 Desert Patrol (1942)
DWπ:324x498:signed:Presented by the War Artists'
Advisory Committee 1946

N05697 Liberation and Battle of France: The Church of St Jean
among the Ruins of Caen, Normandy (1944)
DWπ:394x571:signed:Presented by the War Artists'
Advisory Committee 1946

N05698 Liberation and Battle of France: The Fall of the Arsenal
at Cherbourg (1944)
DWπ:394x571:signed:Presented by the War Artists'
Advisory Committee 1946

N05699 Liberation and Battle of France: Cherbourg, Battalion
H.Q. of the East Yorks (1944)
DWπ:394x571:signed:Presented by the War Artists'
Advisory Committee 1946

N05700 Gateway into Germany: The Maas in Flood near the Berg
Bridge (1944)
DWπ:413x591:signed:Presented by the War Artists'
Advisory Committee 1946

N05701 Final Stages of the German War: Krupp's Works at Essen
(1945)
DWπ:394x571:signed:Presented by the War Artists'
Advisory Committee 1946

T00146 Grey Landscape, Le Boulvé (1955)
Oc:648x921:signed:Purchased 1957

T00735 Foothills (1964)
DWπ:251x406:signed:Purchased 1965

T02111 Quercy Blanc (1975-7)
DWGπ:394x565:signed:Purchased 1977

T02393 Pech de Murat (1978)
Oc:895x1308:signed:Presented by the Trustees of the
Chantrey Bequest 1979

T03318 Place du Théâtre, Brive-la-Gaillarde (1929)
Oc:813x1000:signed:Purchased 1981

T03328 La Route de Ste. Livrade (1932)
Oc:495x645:signed:Presented by the artist 1981

For John Constable (P03149-P03157, P03159-P03161,
P03180-P03185; complete group; mixed group)

P03154 [no title] (1976)
MIπ:270x346:signed:Presented by Bernard Jacobson
Gallery 1976

P07245 Sortie d'Usine No. 4 (1931)
MIπ:314x238:signed:Purchased 1978

P07246 La Bourdette (1932)
MIπ:216x340:signed:Purchased 1978

P07247 Burgundy Canal (1937)
MIπ:210x318:signed:Purchased 1978

P07248 Children Going Out to the Fields (small plate) (1955)
MIπ:222x283:signed:Purchased 1978

P07249 Les Mamelons (1962)
MIπ:378x492:signed:Purchased 1978

P07250 Wheatfield (1966)
MIπ:305x375:signed:Purchased 1978

P07251 Winter Grasses (1972)
MIπ:356x492:signed:Purchased 1978

P07252 Coulourgues (1977)
MIπ:200x238:signed:Purchased 1978

GROSZ, George 1893-1959
Modern Collection
Tate Gallery Archive holds material concerning this artist

T00019 A Married Couple (1930)
Ehepaar
Wπ:660x473:signed:Presented by the Contemporary Art
Society 1955

T00020 Drawing for 'The Mirror of the Bourgeoisie' (circa 1925)
Drawing for 'Der Spiesser-Spiegel'
Dπ:629x505:signed:Presented by the Contemporary Art
Society 1955

T02053 Suicide (1916)
Selbstmörder
Oc:1000x775:signed:Purchased with assistance from the
National Art Collections Fund 1976

GROTH, Jan born 1938
Modern Collection

T02244 Drawing, Untitled (1971)
Dπ:625x879:signed:Presented by Steingrim Laursen 1977

T02245 Drawing, Untitled (1975)
Dπ:625x879:signed:Presented by Steingrim Laursen 1977

GROUP ONE FOUR - see BERRY, John;
KUNST, Mauro; YALE, Brian

GRUBER, Francis 1912-1948
Modern Collection

T00180 Job (1944)
Oc:1619x1299:signed:Purchased 1958

GRYLLS, Vaughan - see GALLERY,
LONDON, The

GUEVARA, Alvaro 1894-1951
Modern Collection

N03509 Dame Edith Sitwell (exhibited 1919)
Oc:1829x1219:Presented by Lord Duveen, Walter Taylor
and George Eumorfopoulos through the National Art
Collections Fund 1920

N06218 The Artist's Mother (?exhibited 1919)
Oc:267x197:Presented by Colonel F. Beddington in
memory of the artist 1954

T01992 Meraud Guinness Guevara (1930)
Oc:622x464:Presented by the Trustees of the Chantrey
Bequest 1975

GUEVARA, Meraud born 1904
Modern Collection
Tate Gallery Archive holds material concerning this artist

T02331 Seated Woman with Small Dog (circa 1939)
Femme assise au petit chien
ODc:889x651:Presented by Salander Galleries, New York
1979

GUILLAUMIN, Armand 1841-1927
Modern Collection

N04824 Moret-sur-Loing (1902)
Oc:600x730:signed:Purchased 1936

GULICH, John 1864-1898
British Collection

N01725 A Violin Concerto (1898)
Wπ:889x711:signed:Presented by Sir Henry Tate 1899

GURSCHNER, Herbert 1901-1975
Modern Collection
Tate Gallery Archive holds material concerning this artist

N04593 The Annunciation (1929-30)
Oc:1626x1918:signed:Presented by Lord Duveen 1931

GUSTON, Philip 1913-1980
Modern Collection

T00252 The Return (1956-8)
Oc:1781x1991:Purchased 1959

T03364 Black Sea (1977)
Oc:1730x2970:signed:Purchased 1982

T04885 Cornered (1971)
Oπb:769x1017:signed:Presented by Michael Elias in
memory of Frederick Elias through the American
Federation of Arts 1986

P07999 Door (1980)
MLπ:495x749:signed:Purchased 1983

P11072 Room (1980)
MLπ:730x1016:signed:Presented by David and Renée
McKee through the American Federation of Arts 1984

P11073 East Side (1980)
MLπ:762x1010:signed:Presented by David and Renée
McKee through the American Federation of Arts 1984

P11074 Rug (1980)
MLπ:495x736:signed:Presented by David and Renée
McKee through the American Federation of Arts 1984

P11075 Summer (1980)
MLπ:464x730:signed:Presented by David and Renée
McKee through the American Federation of Arts 1984

P11076 Sea (1980)
MLπ:584x990:signed:Presented by David and Renée
McKee through the American Federation of Arts 1984

P11077 Car (1980)
MLπ:463x762:signed:Presented by David and Renée
McKee through the American Federation of Arts 1984

P11078 Elements (1980)
MLπ:679x990:signed:Presented by David and Renée
McKee through the American Federation of Arts 1984

P11079 Coat (1980)
MLπ:604x959:signed:Presented by David and Renée
McKee through the American Federation of Arts 1984

P77009 Painter (1980)
MLπ:813x1079:signed:Purchased 1983

GUTFREUND, Oto 1889-1927
Modern Collection

T01234 Cubist Bust (1912-13, cast circa 1962-3)
Sz:616x591x445:Purchased 1970

GUTHRIE, Sir James 1859-1930
British Collection
Tate Gallery Archive holds material concerning this artist

T03446 The Wash (1882-3)
Oc:940x735:signed:Purchased 1982

GUTHRIE, Robin born 1902
Modern Collection
Tate Gallery Archive holds material concerning this artist

N04233 Head of a Woman (circa 1921)
Oc:508x406:Presented by Professor Frederick Brown
1927

GUTTUSO, Renato 1912-1987
Modern Collection
Tate Gallery Archive holds material concerning this artist

N05947 Sulphur Miners (1949)
Wπ:692x1045:signed:Purchased 1950

N05948 Campieri (1949)
Wπ:521x689:signed:Purchased 1950

T00420 The Discussion (1959-60)
La discussione
TOVc:2200x2480:signed:Purchased 1961

GWYNNE-JONES, Allan 1892-1982
Modern Collection
Tate Gallery Archive holds material concerning this artist

N04971 A Fair by Night (1938)
Oc:1079x1486:Presented by Fairfax Hall 1938

N05262 The Mantelpiece (1939)
Oc:406x508:signed:Presented by the Contemporary Art
Society 1941

N06221 Peaches in a Basket (1948)
Oc:343x432:signed:Presented by the Trustees of the
Chantrey Bequest 1954

T02077 Self-Portrait (circa 1926)
Oc:432x330:Presented by the Trustees of the Chantrey
Bequest 1976

HAACKE, Hans born 1936
Modern Collection

T05206 A Breed Apart (1978)
7 Fπ:910x910:Presented by the Patrons of New Art
through the Friends of the Tate Gallery 1988

HACKER, Arthur 1858-1919
British Collection

N01576 The Annunciation (1892)
Oc:2311x1257:signed:Presented by the Trustees of the
Chantrey Bequest 1892

HADEN, Sir Francis Seymour 1818-1910
British Collection

N02427 Battersea Reach (1863)
IMπ:127x229:Presented by Ernest Marsh 1909

HAESE, Günther born 1924
Modern Collection
Tate Gallery Archive holds material concerning this artist

T00810 After the Rain 1 (1965)
Nach dem Regen 1
Sm:298x248x349:signed:Purchased 1965

HAGHE, Louis 1806-1885
British Collection

N00456 Council of War at Courtray (1839)
Wπ:762x711:Presented by Robert Vernon 1847

HAILE, Sam 1909-1948
Modern Collection
Tate Gallery Archive holds material concerning this artist

T00942 Surgical Ward (1939)
Oc:610x762:Presented by Mrs Marriane Haile 1967

after
HAKEWILL, James 1778-1843
British Collection

Picturesque Views on the Southern Coast of England
(T05218-T05463; complete group; mixed group)
T05274 South Gate, Winchelsea
Iπ:109x135:Purchased 1988
T05283 Lewes Castle
Iπ:109x141:Purchased 1988

HALFORD, Mary - see DAVIS, Lady

HALL, David born 1937
Modern Collection
Tate Gallery Archive holds material concerning this artist

T01210 Nine (1967)
SAb:76x5182x5486:Purchased 1970

HALL, Harry ?1813-1882
British Collection

T01887 John Barham Day with his Sons John and William on
Newmarket Heath (1841)
Oc:632x765:signed:Bequeathed by Alan Evans 1974

HALL, Nigel born 1943
Modern Collection
Tate Gallery Archive holds material concerning this artist

T01405 Plateau Marker 1 (1970)
Sam:3048x4115x914:Purchased 1971
T01845 Untitled Drawing (1973)
Dπ:813x584:signed:Purchased 1974
T05523 Gaze Large (1988)
Sz:2428x1775x1355:Presented by Tom Bendhem 1989

HALL, Oliver 1869-1957
British Collection

N03003 Avignon (1911)
Oc:914x1219:signed:Presented by Francis Howard
through the National Loans Exhibition Committee 1914
N03555 Shap Moors (1919)
Oc:1016x1270:signed:Presented by the Trustees of the
Chantrey Bequest 1920
N04835 Vale of Festiniog (circa 1936)
Oc:559x813:signed:Presented by the Trustees of the
Chantrey Bequest 1936

HALSWELLE, Keeley 1832-1891
British Collection

N01548 Pangbourne (1881)
Oc:908x1359:signed:Presented by Sir Henry Tate 1894

HAMBLING, Maggi born 1945
Modern Collection

T03542 Max Wall and his Image (1981)
Oc:1677x1219:signed:Presented by the Trustees of the
Chantrey Bequest 1983
T05023 Minotaur Surprised while Eating (1986-87)
Oc:1448x1222:signed:Purchased with assistance from the
Friends of the Tate Gallery 1987

HAMILTON, Cuthbert 1885-1959
Modern Collection

T00758 Reconstruction (1919-20)
DGπ:559x419:signed:Purchased 1965

HAMILTON, Gavin 1723-1798
British Collection

T00864 Priam Pleading with Achilles for the Body of Hector
(?engraved 1775)
Oc:635x991:Purchased 1966
T03365 Agrippina Landing at Brindisium with the Ashes of
Germanicus (1765-72)
Oc:1825x2560:Purchased 1982

attributed to
HAMILTON, Gawen circa 1698-1737
British Collection

T00943 An Elegant Company Playing Cards (circa 1725)
Oc:692x577:Purchased 1967

attributed to
HAMILTON, James 1640-1720
British Collection

T02266 Two Hounds Chasing a Hare (circa 1700)
Oc:1105x1572:signed:Bequeathed by Miss Agnes Clarke
1978

HAMILTON, Richard born 1922
Modern Collection
Tate Gallery Archive holds material concerning this artist

T00705 Towards a Definitive Statement on the Coming Trends in
Men's Wear and Accessories: (a) Together let us explore
the Stars (1962)
OVw:610x813:Purchased 1964

T00912 Interior II (1964)
OAVw:1219x1626:Purchased 1967

T01144 Swingeing London 67 (f) (1968-9)
Amc:673x851:Purchased 1969

T01190 $he (1958-61)
OVb:1219x813:Purchased 1970

T01195 The Solomon R. Guggenheim Museum (Neapolitan)
(1965-6)
RAa:1219x1219x178:Purchased 1970

T01201 Trainsition IIII (1954)
Ow:914x1219:Purchased 1970

T03980 The citizen (1981-3)
2 Oc:2000x1009, 2000x1000:Purchased 1985

P01019 People (1968)
FGNVπ:384x591:signed:Presented by Dr and Mrs
C.W.L. Smith 1971

Five Tyres Remoulded (P01730-P01738; complete group)
P01730 [no title] (1972)
:605x845x3:signed:Presented by the Contemporary Art
Society 1975

P01731 Dimensional Data (1972)
:600x850:signed:Presented by the Contemporary Art
Society 1975

P01732 Perspective Scheme (1972)
:600x850:signed:Presented by the Contemporary Art
Society 1975

P01733 Radial Sections (1972)
:600x850:signed:Presented by the Contemporary Art
Society 1975

P01734 Circumferential Sections (1972)
:600x850:signed:Presented by the Contemporary Art
Society 1975

P01735 Treads (Line) (1972)
:600x850:signed:Presented by the Contemporary Art
Society 1975

P01736 Treads (Area) (1972)
:600x850:signed:Presented by the Contemporary Art
Society 1975

P01737 Depth of Cut (1972)
:600x850:signed:Presented by the Contemporary Art
Society 1975

P01738 [no title] (1972)
CJπ:600x851:signed:Presented by the Contemporary Art
Society 1975

P01855 Swingeing London 67 (1967-8)
CLπ:711x498:signed:Presented by Rita Donagh, the
artist's wife 1978

Release Stage Proofs (P02416-P02432; incomplete
group)
P02416 Stage Proof 1 (1972)
CNπ:684x859:signed:Presented by the artist 1977

P02417 Stage Proof 2 (1972)
CNπ:680x859:signed:Presented by the artist 1977

P02418 Stage Proof 3 (1972)
CNπ:681x859:signed:Presented by the artist 1977

P02419 Stage Proof 4 (1972)
CNπ:681x858:signed:Presented by the artist 1977

P02420 Stage Proof 5 (1972)
CNπ:681x858:signed:Presented by the artist 1977

P02421 Stage Proof 6 (1972)
CNπ:681x857:signed:Presented by the artist 1977

P02422 Stage Proof 7 (1972)
CNπ:681x857:signed:Presented by the artist 1977

P02423 Stage Proof 8 (1972)
CNπ:682x857:signed:Presented by the artist 1977

P02424 Stage Proof 9 (1972)
CNπ:682x857:signed:Presented by the artist 1977

P02425 Stage Proof 10 (1972)
CNπ:682x857:signed:Presented by the artist 1977

P02426 Stage Proof 11 (1972)
CNπ:682x857:signed:Presented by the artist 1977

P02427 Stage Proof 12 (1972)
CNπ:682x857:signed:Presented by the artist 1977

P02428 Stage Proof 13 (1972)
CNπ:681x857:signed:Presented by the artist 1977

P02429 Stage Proof 16 (1972)
CNπ:682x857:signed:Presented by the artist 1977

P02430 Stage Proof 17 (1972)
CNπ:682x857:signed:Presented by the artist 1977

P02431 Stage Proof 18 (1972)
CNπ:683x862:signed:Presented by the artist 1977

P02432 Stage Proof 19 (1972)
CNπ:683x857:signed:Presented by the artist 1977

P04247 Adonis in Y Fronts (1962-3)
CNπ:610x816:signed:Presented by Rose and Chris Prater
through the Institute of Contemporary Prints 1975

The Institute of Contemporary Arts Portfolio (P04016,
P04038, P04053, P04076, P04115, P04125, P04166,
P04248, P04256, P04315-P04316, P04334,
P04378-P04380, P04419, P04635, P04752, P04938,
P05138, P05155, P05248; complete group; mixed group)
P04248 5 Tyres Abandoned (1964)
CNπ:448x749:signed:Presented by Rose and Chris Prater
through the Institute of Contemporary Prints 1975

P04249 A Little Bit of Roy Lichtenstein for ... (1964)
CNπ:511x692:signed:Presented by Rose and Chris Prater
through the Institute of Contemporary Prints 1975

P04250 Interior (1964-5)
CNπ:495x638:signed:Presented by Rose and Chris Prater
through the Institute of Contemporary Prints 1975

P04251 My Marilyn (1965)
CNπ:518x632:signed:Presented by Rose and Chris Prater
through the Institute of Contemporary Prints 1975

P04252 The Solomon R. Guggenheim (1965)
CNπ:559x559:signed:Presented by Rose and Chris Prater
through the Institute of Contemporary Prints 1975

P04253 Toaster (1967)
CNLVπ:787x854:signed:Presented by Rose and Chris
Prater through the Institute of Contemporary Prints 1975

P04254 Release (1972)
CNπ:683x857:signed:Presented by Rose and Chris Prater through the Institute of Contemporary Prints 1975

P04255 Swingeing London III (1972)
CNπ:679x857:signed:Presented by Rose and Chris Prater through the Institute of Contemporary Prints 1975

P07446 Interior with Monochromes (1979)
CLNπ:498x698:signed:Purchased 1981

P07447 Soft Pink Landscape (1980)
CLNπ:730x918:signed:Purchased 1981

P07448 Dedicated Follower of Fashion (1980)
MIπ:584x381:signed:Purchased 1981

Reaper (P07648-P07653; incomplete group)
P07648 Reaper (d) (1949)
MIπ:173x270:Purchased 1982

P07649 Reaper (e) (1949)
MIπ:175x222:signed:Purchased 1982

P07650 Reaper (g) (1949)
MIπ:225x325:signed:Purchased 1982

P07651 Reaper (h) (1949)
MIπ:171x247:signed:Purchased 1982

P07652 Reaper (i) (1949)
MIπ:200x277:signed:Purchased 1982

P07653 Reaper (j) (1949)
MIπ:99x225:signed:Purchased 1982

P07654 Microcosmos (Plant Cycle) (1950)
MIπ:177x225:signed:Purchased 1982

P07655 Structure (1950)
MIπ:400x303:signed:Purchased 1982

P07656 Heteromorphism (1951)
MIπ:255x200:signed:Purchased 1982

P07657 Self-Portrait (1951)
MIπ:300x196:signed:Purchased 1982

P07658 Still Life? (1955)
MIπ:245x175:signed:Purchased 1982

P07659 Picasso's Meninas (1973)
MIπ:570x490:signed:Purchased 1982

P07937 Fashion Plate (1969-70)
CLNVπ:749x650:signed:Purchased 1983

P77043 Kent State (1970)
CNπ:672x872:signed:Purchased 1984

HAMILTON, Richard - see DUCHAMP, Marcel and HAMILTON, Richard

attributed to
HAMILTON, William 1751-1801
British Collection

T00939 The Invasion of a Harem
Oc:470x698:Purchased 1967

HAMMERSHOI, Vilhelm 1864-1916
Modern Collection

N04106 Interior (1899)
Oc:645x581:signed:Presented in memory of Leonard Borwick by his friends through the National Art Collections Fund 1926

N04509 Interior, Sunlight on the Floor (1906)
Oc:514x441:signed:Purchased 1930

HANCOCK, Charles 1795-1868
British Collection

N05661 Lord Fitzhardinge and Some of his Hounds
Oc:1626x2146:Presented by Lord Howard de Walden 1946

HAND, Thomas active circa 1790-1804
British Collection

N02474 Cottage and Hilly Landscape (1797)
Oc:711x908:signed:Presented by Lockett Agnew 1909

HARDAKER, Charles born 1934
Modern Collection

T00861 Still Life: Vertical Structures, Three Times Three (1965)
Oc:1219x914:signed:Presented by the Trustees of the Chantrey Bequest 1966

HARDING, James Duffield 1798-1863
British Collection

N02444 South Brent (1858)
Dπ:254x352:signed:Presented by Charles Newton-Robinson 1909

T00996 Twickenham (1839)
DWπ:270x384:Presented by the National Art Collections Fund (Herbert Powell Bequest) 1967

T00997 Vicenza (1834)
DWπ:375x264:Presented by the National Art Collections Fund (Herbert Powell Bequest) 1967

HARRISON, Margaret
Modern Collection
Tate Gallery Archive holds material concerning this artist

P06246 Good Enough to Eat (1971)
CLπ:571x784:signed:Presented by Curwen Studio through the Institute of Contemporary Prints 1975

P06247 Take One Lemon (1971)
CLπ:787x575:signed:Presented by Curwen Studio through the Institute of Contemporary Prints 1975

HART, James Turpin 1835-1899
British Collection

T03396 A Rustic Timepiece (1856)
Oc:533x432:signed:Purchased 1982

HART, Solomon Alexander 1806-1881
British Collection

N00424 Interior of Jewish Synagogue at the Time of the Reading of the Law (1830)
Oc:813x673:Presented by Robert Vernon 1847

HARTRICK, Archibald Standish 1864-1950
British Collection
Tate Gallery Archive holds material concerning this artist

N04752 The Penitents' Bench (1904)
Wπ:267x365:signed:Presented by the Trustees of the Chantrey Bequest 1934

N05973 Toulouse-Lautrec (circa 1933)
DWπ:248x190:Purchased 1951

The Great War: Britain's Efforts and Ideals
(P03001-P03007, P03011-P03023, P03031-P03036,
P03039-P03044; incomplete group; mixed group)
Women's Work (P03031-P03036; complete group)

P03031 On the Land - Ploughing (circa 1917)
MLπ:466x356:signed:Presented by the Ministry of
Information 1918

P03032 On the Railway - Engine and Carriage Cleaners (circa
1917)
MLπ:461x359:signed:Presented by the Ministry of
Information 1918

P03033 In the Towns: A Bus Conductress (circa 1917)
MLπ:465x362:signed:Presented by the Ministry of
Information 1918

P03034 On Munitions - Skilled Work (circa 1917)
MLπ:464x360:signed:Presented by the Ministry of
Information 1918

P03035 On Munitions - Dangerous Work (Packing T.N.T.) (circa
1917)
MLπ:460x353:signed:Presented by the Ministry of
Information 1918

P03036 On Munitions - Heavy Work (Drilling and Casting)
(circa 1917)
MLπ:461x357:signed:Presented by the Ministry of
Information 1918

HARTUNG, Hans 1909-1989
Modern Collection
Tate Gallery Archive holds material concerning this artist

T00816 T1963-R6 (1963)
Ac:1797x1410:signed:Purchased 1966

P01791 No. 77 (1958)
MLπ:514x349:Presented by the Museum of Modern Art,
New York 1976

P77141 L10 (1957)
CLπ:520x320:signed:Purchased 1986

P77142 L36 (1957)
CLπ:501x320:signed:Purchased 1986

P77200 24 (1953)
Iπ:378x517:signed:Purchased 1987

HARTWELL, Charles Leonard 1873-1951
British Collection

N02267 A Foul in the Giants' Race (1908)
Sz:260x216x286:signed:Presented by the Trustees of the
Chantrey Bequest 1908

N02975 Dawn (1913-4)
Ss:1930x1181x940:signed:Presented by the Trustees of
the Chantrey Bequest 1914

HASELTINE, Herbert 1877-1962
Modern Collection

N04560 Suffolk Punch Stallion: Sudbourne Premier (1931-2)
Szv:552x660x210:signed:Purchased 1932

HATHERELL, William 1855-1928
British Collection

N02937 O, Romeo, Romeo, Wherefore Art Thou Romeo? (circa
1912)
Gπ:241x178:signed:Presented by the Trustees of the
Chantrey Bequest 1913

HAUSMANN, Raoul 1886-1971
Modern Collection
Tate Gallery Archive holds material concerning this artist

T01918 The Art Critic (1919-20)
Der Kunstkritiker
FVπ:318x254:Purchased 1974

HAVELL, William 1782-1857
British Collection

T00998 Landscape
Wπ:365x343:Presented by the National Art Collections
Fund (Herbert Powell Bequest) 1967

T01095 Caversham Bridge (1805)
Oπ:276x219:signed:Purchased 1968

T03393 The Thames near Moulsford (1807)
Obw:482x623:signed:Purchased 1982

T03394 Windsor Castle (circa 1807)
Ob:117x219:signed:Purchased 1982

after
HAVELL, William 1782-1857
British Collection

Picturesque Views on the Southern Coast of England
(T05218-T05463; complete group; mixed group)

T05275 Hastings, Sussex (first plate) (1816)
Iπ:149x228:Purchased 1988

T05276 Hastings, Sussex (second plate) (1816)
Iπ:152x224:Purchased 1988

T05277 Hastings, Sussex (second plate) (1816)
Iπ:152x224:Purchased 1988

HAYDEN, Henri 1883-1970
Modern Collection

T00559 The Red Plain (1962)
La Plaine rouge
Oc:540x730:signed:Purchased 1962

T00818 Chess Board in Ochre (1961)
Echecs en ochre
Oc:591x914:signed:Presented by Victor and Mabel
Waddington through the Institute of Contemporary
Prints in memory of Eliza Heygate 1975

P01159 Bottle and Fruit (1968)
Bouteille et fruits
CLπ:375x511:signed:Presented by Waddington Galleries
through the Institute of Contemporary Prints 1975

P01160 The Red Hill (1968)
La Colline rouge
CLπ:365x514:signed:Presented by Waddington Galleries
through the Institute of Contemporary Prints 1975

P01161 Fay-le-Bac (1968)
Fay-le-Bac
CLπ:384x518:signed:Presented by Waddington Galleries
through the Institute of Contemporary Prints 1975

P01162 Brown Still Life (1968)
Nature morte brune
CLπ:356x530:signed:Presented by Waddington Galleries
through the Institute of Contemporary Prints 1975

P01163 Blue Landscape (1968)
Paysage bleu
CLπ:397x559:signed:Presented by Waddington Galleries
through the Institute of Contemporary Prints 1975

P01164 Green Landscape (1968)
Paysage vert
CLπ:346x495:signed:Presented by Waddington Galleries through the Institute of Contemporary Prints 1975

P01165 Black Vase (1968)
Potiche noir
CLπ:349x502:signed:Presented by Waddington Galleries through the Institute of Contemporary Prints 1975

P01166 The Sun (1968)
Le Soleil
CLπ:378x571:signed:Presented by Waddington Galleries through the Institute of Contemporary Prints 1975

P01167 Red and Blue Teapot (1968)
Théière rouge et bleu
CLπ:378x470:signed:Presented by Waddington Galleries through the Institute of Contemporary Prints 1975

P01168 Courtablon (1969)
Courtablon
CLπ:365x495:signed:Presented by Waddington Galleries through the Institute of Contemporary Prints 1975

P01169 Still Life (1969)
Nature morte
CLπ:381x556:signed:Presented by Waddington Galleries through the Institute of Contemporary Prints 1975

P01170 Hayden Landscape (1969)
Paysage Hayden
CLπ:387x521:signed:Presented by Waddington Galleries through the Institute of Contemporary Prints 1975

P01171 Orange Landscape (1969)
Paysage orange
CLπ:394x524:signed:Presented by Waddington Galleries through the Institute of Contemporary Prints 1975

P01172 Untitled (Blue Landscape) (1971)
CLπ:381x584:signed:Presented by Waddington Galleries through the Institute of Contemporary Prints 1975

HAYDON, Benjamin Robert 1786-1846
British Collection
Tate Gallery Archive holds material concerning this artist

N00682 Punch or May Day (1829)
Oc:1505x1851:Bequeathed by George Darling 1862

N00786 The Raising of Lazarus (1821-3)
Oc:4267x6325:Presented by R.E. Lofft 1868

N05352 Study for 'The Mock Election' (1827)
Dπ:187x229:Presented by Iolo Williams 1942

N05644 Chairing the Member (1828)
Oc:1524x1918:signed:Purchased 1946

T01173 Gentleman with a Horse (1844)
Oc:632x762:signed:Presented by Mrs M. Bernard 1970

A00192 Sketches of Sir George Beaumont (1819)
Dπ:121x98:Presented by Charles Newton-Robinson 1909

HAYES, Edwin 1819-1904
British Collection

N01603 Sunset at Sea: From Harlyn Bay, Cornwall (exhibited 1894)
Oc:927x1264:signed:Presented by the Trustees of the Chantrey Bequest 1894

HAYMAN, Francis 1708-1776
British Collection

N06206 The Wrestling Scene from 'As You Like It' (circa 1740-2)
Oc:527x921:Purchased 1953

T00052 Thomas Nuthall and his Friend Hambleton Custance (circa 1748)
Oc:710x915:Bequeathed by Ernest E. Cook through the National Art Collections Fund 1955

T00524 See-Saw (circa 1742)
Oc:1390x2415:Presented by the Friends of the Tate Gallery 1962

HAYMAN, Patrick 1915-1988
Modern Collection
Tate Gallery Archive holds material concerning this artist

T02239 Mother and Child near a Town (1952)
Ocb:256x179:signed:Bequeathed by Miss E.M. Hodgkins 1977

P11094 Birds and Trees (1951)
CJπ:102x151:signed:Presented by Warren MacKenzie 1986

P11095 Dog on the Shore (1951)
CJπ:102x151:signed:Presented by Warren MacKenzie 1986

HAYNES-WILLIAMS, John 1836-1908
British Collection

N01554 Ars Longa, Vita Brevis (1877)
Oc:1289x2115:signed:Presented by Sir Henry Tate 1894

HAYTER, Stanley William 1901-1988
Modern Collection
Tate Gallery Archive holds material concerning this artist

N06069 Fish in the Escoutay (1951)
Oc:546x1480:signed:Purchased 1952

T00637 Deliquescence (1935)
Ow:991x2000:Presented by Sir John Rothenstein through the Friends of the Tate Gallery 1964

T01752 Untitled (1946)
Oc:1016x1270:signed:Presented by Robert Jay Wolff 1973

T03407 Teatro Olimpico (1980)
Ac:1137x1458:signed:Presented by the artist 1982

T03408 Ophelia (1936)
OTc:1000x1445:signed:Purchased 1982

P07027 Myth of Creation (1940)
CLπ:251x200:signed:Purchased 1972

P07028 Le Chas de l'aiguille (1946)
MLπ:302x187:signed:Purchased 1972

P07470 Ripple (1970)
CLπ:470x594:signed:Purchased 1981

P07471 Pillars (1974)
CLπ:591x425:signed:Purchased 1981

P07472 Chute (1975)
CLπ:597x489:signed:Purchased 1981

P07473 Cirque Chinois (1976)
CLπ:492x396:signed:Purchased 1981

P07474 Styx (1976)
CLπ:485x593:signed:Purchased 1981

P07475 Loop (1978)
CLπ:641x492:signed:Purchased 1981

P07476 Hang Glider (1979)
CLπ:495x638:signed:Purchased 1981

P07477 Ceiling (1980)
CLπ:489x591:signed:Purchased 1981

P07478 Hex (1981)
CLπ:495x492:signed:Purchased 1981

P08178 Cover Illustration to 'Tides' by John Montagu (1970)
CLπ:121x114:Transferred from the Library 1980

HAYWARD, Alfred Robert 1875-1971
British Collection

N03661 Composition: Late Evening (1920)
DWπ:235x352:signed:Purchased 1922

N04674 Sunset on the Lagoon, Venice (1925)
Oc:559x762:signed:Purchased 1933

HEAD, Tim born 1946
Modern Collection
Tate Gallery Archive holds material concerning this artist

T02078 Displacements (1975-6)
FV:4877x8915x8915:Purchased 1976

T04932 Deep Freeze (1987)
Ac:2136x1526:signed:Purchased 1987

T05709 Drawing for 'Project for Guggenheim Spiral' (1980)
Dπ:760x1020:Presented by Esso UK plc to mark the first anniversary of the opening of the Tate Gallery Liverpool 1989

T05710 Drawing for 'Project for Guggenheim Spiral' (1980)
Dπ:760x1020:Presented by Esso UK plc to mark the first anniversary of the opening of the Tate Gallery Liverpool 1989

T05711 Drawing for 'Project for Guggenheim Spiral' (1980)
Dπ:760x1020:Presented by Esso UK plc to mark the first anniversary of the opening of the Tate Gallery Liverpool 1989

T05712 Drawing for 'Project for Guggenheim Spiral' (1980)
Dπ:760x1020:Presented by Esso UK plc to mark the first anniversary of the opening of the Tate Gallery Liverpool 1989

T05713 Drawing for 'Project for Guggenheim Spiral' (1980)
Dπ:760x1020:Presented by Esso UK plc to mark the first anniversary of the opening of the Tate Gallery Liverpool 1989

T05714 Drawing for 'Project for Guggenheim Spiral' (1980)
Dπ:760x1020:Presented by Esso UK plc to mark the first anniversary of the opening of the Tate Gallery Liverpool 1989

T05715 Drawing for 'Project for Guggenheim Spiral' (1980)
Dπ:760x1020:Presented by Esso UK plc to mark the first anniversary of the opening of the Tate Gallery Liverpool 1989

P07515 Equilibrium (1975)
MFπ:384x378:signed:Presented by the artist 1981

P07516 False Alarm I (1978)
CFπ:511x613:Purchased 1981

P07517 False Alarm II (1978)
CFπ:511x613:Purchased 1981

P07518 Dislocations (1980)
CFπ:384x518:Purchased 1981

P07519 Elevation I and II (1980)
CFπ:402x533:Purchased 1981

P07615 Black Light (1973)
MFπ:749x479:Purchased 1982

P07616 Ambidextrous (1974)
CFπ:240x240:Purchased 1982

P77262 Erasers II: On the Rocks (1987)
Fπ:1210x2180:Purchased 1988

HEARNE, Thomas 1744-1817
British Collection

N05792 Edinburgh Castle from Arthur's Seat (1778)
Wπ:356x508:signed:Presented by Frederick John Nettlefold 1947

T00999 Derwentwater (circa 1777-8)
Wπ:206x305:signed:Presented by the National Art Collections Fund (Herbert Powell Bequest) 1967

T01000 Appleby (1778)
Wπ:302x403:signed:Presented by the National Art Collections Fund (Herbert Powell Bequest) 1967

T01001 A Vine-clad Cottage
Wπ:273x203:signed:Presented by the National Art Collections Fund (Herbert Powell Bequest) 1967

HEATH, Adrian born 1920
Modern Collection
Tate Gallery Archive holds material concerning this artist

T00396 Painting Brown and Black (1960)
Oc:1270x1016:signed:Purchased 1960

T00686 Drawing 1964 (Divided Blue) (1964)
Oc:768x559:signed:Purchased 1964

T01338 White Collage (1954)
OVc:508x406:signed:Purchased 1971

The Institute of Contemporary Arts Portfolio (P04016, P04038, P04053, P04076, P04115, P04125, P04166, P04248, P04256, P04315-P04316, P04334, P04378-P04380, P04419, P04635, P04752, P04938, P05138, P05155, P05248; complete group; mixed group)

P04256 Study (1964)
CNπ:914x584:signed:Presented by Rose and Chris Prater through the Institute of Contemporary Prints 1975

P77335 Composition - Black and Yellow (1952)
Jπ:350x247:signed:Purchased 1989

HEEMSKERK, Egbert van, III - see VAN HEEMSKERK, Egbert, III

HEGEDUSIC, Krsto 1901-1975
Modern Collection

N04606 A Fair at Koprivnica (1930)
OTc:730x1041:signed:Presented by Miss I.M. Garrido 1931

HEILIGER, Bernhard born 1915
Modern Collection

T03897 Maquette for Monument for the Unknown Political Prisoner (1953)
Modell zum 'Denkmal des Unbekannten Politischen Gefangenen'
Smz:594x901x901:signed:Presented by the artist 1984

HÉLION, Jean 1904-1987
Modern Collection
Tate Gallery Archive holds material concerning this artist

T00766 Ile de France (1935)
Oc:1454x2000:signed:Purchased 1965

T05497 Nude with Loaves (1952)
Dos aux pains
Oc:1301x970:Purchased 1988

HELLEU, Paul 1859-1927
Modern Collection

N03729 Studies of Mme Helleu and Ellen (circa 1895)
Dπ:419x302:Presented by Dr J.H. Badcock 1923

HELMAN, Robert born 1910
Modern Collection

T00303 Candile (1955)
Oc:797x797:signed:Presented by Mr and Mrs Alexander Margulies 1959

HEMY, Charles Napier 1841-1917
British Collection

N01650 Pilchards (1897)
Oc:1130x2121:signed:Presented by the Trustees of the Chantrey Bequest 1897

N01946 London River (1904)
Oc:1206x1829:signed:Presented by the Trustees of the Chantrey Bequest 1904

N04921 Evening Grey (1866-8)
Oc:571x914:signed:Presented by Godwin King 1938

HENDERSON, Charles Cooper 1803-1877
British Collection

T02360 Changing Horses to a Post-Chaise outside the 'George' Posting-house (circa 1830-40)
Oc:533x762:Presented by Paul Mellon through the British Sporting Art Trust 1979

T03428 Sportsmen in Scottish Dress Driving to the Moors (circa 1845)
Oc:330x613:signed:Bequeathed by Mrs F. Ambrose Clark through the British Sporting Art Trust 1982

T03429 Mail Coach in a Snowstorm (circa 1835-40)
Oc:454x765:signed:Bequeathed by Mrs F. Ambrose Clark through the British Sporting Art Trust 1982

HENDERSON, Elsie Marian 1880-1967
Modern Collection
Tate Gallery Archive holds material concerning this artist

N03206 Three Studies of Leopards (1916)
Dπ:248x375:signed:Presented by the Contemporary Art Society 1917

N03207 A Tiger (1916)
Dπ:216x362:signed:Presented by the Contemporary Art Society 1917

HENDERSON, Nigel 1917-1985
Modern Collection
Tate Gallery Archive holds material concerning this artist

T01915 Collage (1949)
OFb:337x381:Purchased 1974

T01916 Plant Tantrums (1961)
OFb:394x511:signed:Purchased 1974

T01939 Head of a Man (1956)
Fb:1597x1216:Presented anonymously 1975

HENDERSON, William born 1941
Modern Collection
Tate Gallery Archive holds material concerning this artist

T02389 Rougey (1979)
Ac:1753x1451:signed:Purchased 1979

P07351 The Boxer (1979)
MNπ:749x508:signed:Purchased 1979

HENDERSON-BEGG, Liselott
Modern Collection

P06248 Untitled (1971)
CLπ:292x368:signed:Presented by Curwen Studio through the Institute of Contemporary Prints 1975

HENNELL, Thomas 1903-1945
Modern Collection
Tate Gallery Archive holds material concerning this artist

N05287 Landscape: Flint Heap, Road-Making (circa 1937-41)
Wπ:318x483:signed:Presented anonymously 1941

N05411 Interior (circa 1930-2)
Wπ:394x292:Purchased 1940

N05412 The Tree (circa 1938-40)
Wπ:318x483:signed:Purchased 1940

N05413 Portrait Study: Five Figures (circa 1935)
DWπ:264x368:signed:Purchased 1940

N05702 Slipway, Reykjavik Harbour. August 12, 1943 (1943)
Wπ:479x635:signed:Presented by the War Artists' Advisory Committee 1946

HENRI, Robert 1865-1929
Modern Collection

T00440 Market at Concarneau. Verso: Sailing Boats in a Bay (1899)
Ow:159x222:Presented by Hirschl and Adler Gallery, New York through the American Friends of the Tate Gallery 1961

HENRY, D. (Dentith Henry) - see DENTITH, Henry

HEPHER, David born 1935
Modern Collection
Tate Gallery Archive holds material concerning this artist

T02404 Albany Flats (1977-9)
OVc:1975x2794:Purchased 1979

HEPWORTH, Dame Barbara 1903-1975
Modern Collection
Tate Gallery Archive holds material concerning this artist

N05932 Bicentric Form (1949)
Ss:1587x483x311:Purchased 1950

T00269 Two Figures with Folded Arms (1947)
ODw:356x254:signed:Purchased 1959

T00352 Figure (Nanjizal) (1958)
Sw:2496x457x13:Purchased 1960

T00353 Curved Form (Trevalgan) (1956)
Sz:902x597x673:Purchased 1960

T00531 Corinthos (1954-5)
SOw:1041x1067x1016:Purchased 1962

T00696 Three Forms (1935)
Ss:200x533x343:Presented by Mr and Mrs J.R. Marcus Brumwell 1964

T00697 Single Form (Eikon) (1937-8, cast 1963)
Sz:1206x279x260:signed:Presented by the artist 1964

T00698 Forms in Echelon (1938)
Sw:991x597x705:Presented by the artist 1964

T00699 Pelagos (1946)
Swv:368x387x330:Presented by the artist 1964

T00700 Forms (West Penwith) (1958)
ODb:483x362:signed:Presented by the artist 1964

T00701 Perigord (1958)
ODb:483x362:signed:Presented by the artist 1964

T00702 Squares with Two Circles (1963)
Sz:3061x1372x318:signed:Purchased 1964

T00703 Two Figures (Menhirs) (1964)
Ss:756x635x330:Purchased 1964

T00704 Pierced Form (1963-4)
Ss:1264x972x229:Presented by the artist 1964

T00952 Figure of a Woman (1929-30)
Ss:533x305x279:Presented by the artist 1967

T00953 Oval Sculpture (No. 2) (1943)
Sp:286x413x254:Presented by the artist 1967

T00954 Landscape Sculpture (1944, cast 1961)
Sz:318x654x279:signed:Presented by the artist 1967

T00955 Orpheus (Maquette 2) (Version II) (1956)
Smv:1149x432:Presented by the artist 1967

T00956 Cantate Domino (1958)
Sz:2089x527x502:signed:Presented by the artist 1967

T00957 Sea Form (Porthmeor) (1958)
Sz:768x1137x254:Presented by the artist 1967

T00958 Image II (1960)
Ss:749x775x483:Presented by the artist 1967

T00959 Maquette, Three Forms in Echelon (1961)
Sz:679x508x95:signed:Presented by the artist 1967

T00960 Hollow Form with White (1965)
Sw:1346x584x464:Presented by the artist 1967

T01112 Figure (Nyanga) (1959-60)
Sw:908x571:Presented by the artist 1969

T02008 Tides I (1946)
Sw:337x632x298:Presented by Ben Nicholson OM 1975

T02016 Touchstone (1969)
Ss:629x305:Bequeathed by the artist 1976

T02017 Rock Face (1973)
Ss:1022x473x229:Bequeathed by the artist 1976

T02098 Fenestration of the Ear (The Hammer) (1948)
ODb:384x270:signed:Purchased 1976

T02226 Group I (Concourse) February 4 1951 (1951)
Ss:248x505x295:Bequeathed by Miss E.M. Hodgkins 1977

T02227 Two Forms (White and Yellow) (1955)
ODb:425x152:signed:Bequeathed by Miss E.M. Hodgkins 1977

T02228 Family Group - Earth Red and Yellow (1953)
ODb:298x222:signed:Bequeathed by Miss E.M. Hodgkins 1977

T03128 Torso (1928)
Ss:362x171x102:Presented by the executors of the artist's estate 1980

T03129 Infant (1929)
Sw:438x273x254:Presented by the executors of the artist's estate 1980

T03130 Seated Figure (1932-3)
Sw:356x267x203:Presented by the executors of the artist's estate 1980

T03131 Three Forms (1934)
Ss:257x470x216:Presented by the executors of the artist's estate 1980

T03132 Discs in Echelon (1935)
Sz:343x508x273:Presented by the executors of the artist's estate 1980

T03133 Sculpture with Colour (Deep Blue and Red) (1940)
Spv:105x149x105:Presented by the executors of the artist's estate 1980

T03134 Poised Form (1951-2, reworked 1957)
Ss:1168x454x298:Presented by the executors of the artist's estate 1980

T03135 Coré (1955-6)
Sz:743x349x298:Presented by the executors of the artist's estate 1980

T03136 Forms in Movement (Pavan) (1956)
Sz:698x1079x584:signed:Presented by the executors of the artist's estate 1980

T03137 Stringed Figure (Curlew), Version II (1956)
Smv:514x768x432:Presented by the executors of the artist's estate 1980

T03138 Torso II (Torcello) (1958)
Sz:883x298x279:Presented by the executors of the artist's estate 1980

T03139 Garden Sculpture (Model for Meridian) (1958)
Sz:1600x800x298:signed:Presented by the executors of the artist's estate 1980

T03140 Figure for Landscape (1960)
Sz:2603x1257x673:signed:Presented by the executors of the artist's estate 1980

T03141 Pierced Form (Epidauros) (1960)
Sw:737x673x349:Presented by the executors of the artist's estate 1980

T03142 Maquette, Three Forms in Echelon (1961)
Smv:679x521x216:signed:Presented by the executors of the artist's estate 1980

T03143 Single Form (September) (1961)
Sm:825x508x57:Presented by the executors of the artist's estate 1980

T03144 Square Forms (1962)
Sz:343x190x89:Presented by the executors of the artist's estate 1980

T03145 Bronze Form (Patmos) (1962-3)
Sz:654x952x241:Presented by the executors of the artist's estate 1980

T03146 Sphere with Inner Form (1963)
Sz:654x952x241:Presented by the executors of the artist's estate 1980

T03147 Six Forms (2 x 3) (1968)
Sz:571x876x337:signed:Presented by the executors of the artist's estate 1980

T03148 Hollow Form with Inner Form (1968)
Sz:1232x660x660:signed:Presented by the executors of the artist's estate 1980

T03149 Two Forms (Divided Circle) (1969)
Sz:2375x2337x540:signed:Presented by the executors of the artist's estate 1980

T03150 Vertical Forms (St Ives) (1968)
Sz:470x254x102:Presented by the executors of the artist's estate 1980

T03151 Makutu (1969)
Sz:673x248x248:signed:Presented by the executors of the artist's estate 1980

T03152 Oval with Two Forms (1971)
Ss:337x394x330:Presented by the executors of the artist's estate 1980

T03153 Fallen Images (1974-5)
Ss:1219x1302x1302:Presented by the executors of the artist's estate 1980

T03154   The Artist's Hand (1943-4)
Sz:60x190x102:Presented by the executors of the artist's estate 1980

T03155   Two Figures (Heroes) (1954)
Ob:1829x1219:Presented by the executors of the artist's estate 1980

T03399   Ball, Plane and Hole (1936)
Sw:205x610x305:Purchased 1982

T03749   Involute II (1956)
Sz:410x420x360:Transferred from the Victoria & Albert Museum 1983

T03851   Conversation with Magic Stones (1973)
6 Sz:2820x482x533, 2743x584x470, 2690x635x457, 9270x1219x609, 800x1308x914:signed:Accepted by the Commissioners of Inland Revenue in lieu of tax and allocated 1984

Opposing Forms (P01414, P04257-P04264, P04266-P04268; complete group)

P01414   Rangatira II (1970)
CNπ:775x583:signed:Presented by the artist through the Institute of Contemporary Prints 1975

P01415   Kestor Rock, Gleaming Stone (1973)
CLπ:318x203:signed:Presented by the artist through the Institute of Contemporary Prints 1975

Penwith Portfolio (P01416, P06005, P06108, P06130, P06241, P06324, P06346, P06359, P06399, P06519, P06700; complete group; mixed group)

P01416   Moon Landscape (1973)
CLπ:514x473:signed:Presented by the artist through the Institute of Contemporary Prints 1975

Opposing Forms (P01414, P04257-P04264, P04266-P04268; complete group)

P04257   Assembly of Square Forms (1970)
CNπ:773x584:signed:Presented by Rose and Chris Prater through the Institute of Contemporary Prints 1975

P04258   December Forms (1970)
CNπ:777x583:signed:Presented by Rose and Chris Prater through the Institute of Contemporary Prints 1975

P04259   Forms in a Flurry (1970)
CNπ:774x585:signed:Presented by Rose and Chris Prater through the Institute of Contemporary Prints 1975

P04260   High Tide (1970)
CNπ:555x762:signed:Presented by Rose and Chris Prater through the Institute of Contemporary Prints 1975

P04261   November Green (1970)
CNπ:775x584:signed:Presented by Rose and Chris Prater through the Institute of Contemporary Prints 1975

P04262   Two Opposing Forms (1970)
CNπ:772x583:signed:Presented by Rose and Chris Prater through the Institute of Contemporary Prints 1975

P04263   Orchid (1970)
CNπ:582x775:signed:Presented by Rose and Chris Prater through the Institute of Contemporary Prints 1975

P04264   Rangatira I (1970)
CNπ:775x582:signed:Presented by Rose and Chris Prater through the Institute of Contemporary Prints 1975

P04266   Three Forms (1970)
CNπ:775x580:signed:Presented by Rose and Chris Prater through the Institute of Contemporary Prints 1975

P04267   Two Ancestral Figures (1970)
CNπ:775x583:signed:Presented by Rose and Chris Prater through the Institute of Contemporary Prints 1975

P04268   Winter Solstice (1970)
CNπ:774x585:signed:Presented by Rose and Chris Prater through the Institute of Contemporary Prints 1975

P04269   Winter Solstice (1971)
CNπ:305x254:signed:Presented by Rose and Chris Prater through the Institute of Contemporary Prints 1975

P04270   Green Man (1972)
CNπ:673x498:signed:Presented by Rose and Chris Prater through the Institute of Contemporary Prints 1975

P04271   Moonplan (1972)
CNπ:762x562:signed:Presented by Rose and Chris Prater through the Institute of Contemporary Prints 1975

P06249   Untitled (1958)
MLπ:435x298:Presented by Curwen Studio through the Institute of Contemporary Prints 1975

P06250   Three Forms Assembling (1968-9)
CLπ:587x457:signed:Presented by Curwen Studio through the Institute of Contemporary Prints 1975

P06251   Argos (1969)
CLπ:816x587:signed:Presented by Curwen Studio through the Institute of Contemporary Prints 1975

P06252   Autumn Shadows (1969)
CLπ:765x562:signed:Presented by Curwen Studio through the Institute of Contemporary Prints 1975

P06253   Genesis (1969)
CLπ:724x537:signed:Presented by Curwen Studio through the Institute of Contemporary Prints 1975

P06254   Mycenae (1969)
CLπ:810x584:signed:Presented by Curwen Studio through the Institute of Contemporary Prints 1975

P06255   Oblique Forms (1969)
CLπ:556x730:signed:Presented by Curwen Studio through the Institute of Contemporary Prints 1975

P06256   Pastorale (1969)
CLπ:711x511:signed:Presented by Curwen Studio through the Institute of Contemporary Prints 1975

P06257   Porthmeor (1969)
CLπ:724x540:signed:Presented by Curwen Studio through the Institute of Contemporary Prints 1975

P06258   Sea Forms (1969)
CLπ:591x822:signed:Presented by Curwen Studio through the Institute of Contemporary Prints 1975

P06259   Squares and Circles (1969)
CLπ:533x708:signed:Presented by Curwen Studio through the Institute of Contemporary Prints 1975

P06260   Sun and Moon (1969)
CLπ:740x556:signed:Presented by Curwen Studio through the Institute of Contemporary Prints 1975

P06261   Three Forms (1969)
CLπ:457x597:signed:Presented by Curwen Studio through the Institute of Contemporary Prints 1975

P06262   Two Marble Forms (Mykonos) (1969)
CLπ:737x483:signed:Presented by Curwen Studio through the Institute of Contemporary Prints 1975

The Aegean Suite (P06263-P06271; complete group)

P06263   Cool Moon (1971)
CLπ:814x582:signed:Presented by Curwen Studio through the Institute of Contemporary Prints 1975

P06264   Delos (1971)
CLπ:767x545:signed:Presented by Curwen Studio through the Institute of Contemporary Prints 1975

P06265   Decent Forms (1971)
CLπ:769x543:signed:Presented by Curwen Studio through the Institute of Contemporary Prints 1975

P06266 Fragment (1971)
CLπ:776x515:signed:Presented by Curwen Studio through the Institute of Contemporary Prints 1975

P06267 [title not known] (1971)
CLπ:544x765:signed:Presented by Curwen Studio through the Institute of Contemporary Prints 1975

P06268 Olympus (1971)
CLπ:764x543:signed:Presented by Curwen Studio through the Institute of Contemporary Prints 1975

P06269 Sun and Water (1971)
CLπ:765x546:signed:Presented by Curwen Studio through the Institute of Contemporary Prints 1975

P06270 Sun Setting (1971)
CLπ:756x545:signed:Presented by Curwen Studio through the Institute of Contemporary Prints 1975

P06271 Sun and Marble (1971)
CLπ:768x543:signed:Presented by Curwen Studio through the Institute of Contemporary Prints 1975

HERBERT, J.G.S. active 1862
British Collection

T01110 Allegorical Still-Life
Oc:629x781:signed:Purchased 1969

HERBERT, John Rogers 1810-1890
British Collection

N00425 Sir Thomas More and his Daughter (1844)
Oc:851x1105:signed:Presented by Robert Vernon 1847

T01455 Laborare est Orare (1862)
Oc:972x1759:signed:Purchased 1971

HERBIN, Auguste 1882-1960
Modern Collection
Tate Gallery Archive holds material concerning this artist

T00517 Nude (1960)
Gb:479x381:signed:Purchased 1962

HERKOMER, Sir Hubert von - see VON HERKOMER, Sir Hubert

HERMAN, Josef born 1911
Modern Collection
Tate Gallery Archive holds material concerning this artist

N06198 Three Miners (1953)
Ow:343x521:Purchased 1953

T00002 In the Miner's Arms (1954)
DWπ:197x248:Purchased 1955

T00354 The Pit Pony (1958-9)
Oc:1118x1854:signed:Purchased 1960

T02095 Study for 'In the Mountains' (1965)
DGπ:559x765:Presented by Curwen Studio 1976

T02096 Study for 'Dusk' (1965)
DGπ:562x765:Presented by Curwen Studio 1976

T02097 Two Women Weeding (1965)
DGπ:559x765:Presented by Curwen Studio 1976

T03193 Pregnant Woman with Friend (1946)
PDWπ:648x895:Purchased 1981

Studies for 'The Pit Pony' [T00354] (T03194-T03202; complete group)

T03194 Two Sketches of Two Seated Miners, Sketch of a Single Miner (circa 1958)
Dπ:175x225:Presented by the artist 1981

T03195 Two Separate Sketches for Whole Composition, Pony at Right (circa 1958)
Dπ:225x717:Presented by the artist 1981

T03196 Reclining Miner (circa 1958)
Dπ:175x225:Presented by the artist 1981

T03197 Two Separate Sketches for Whole Composition, Pony at Centre (circa 1958)
Dπ:225x171:Presented by the artist 1981

T03198 Seven Separate Sketches (circa 1958)
Dπ:225x175:Presented by the artist 1981

T03199 Three Seated Miners, Miner with Pony in Background (circa 1958)
Dπ:171x225:Presented by the artist 1981

T03200 Two Seated Miners, Miner with Pony in Background (circa 1958)
Dπ:171x225:Presented by the artist 1981

T03201 Two Separate Sketches, Each with a Pony at Right (circa 1958)
Dπ:254x200:Presented by the artist 1981

T03202 Two Separate Sketches, Upper One with a Pony at Right (circa 1958)
Dπ:254x200:Presented by the artist 1981

P06272 The Cart (1960)
CLπ:276x445:Presented by Curwen Studio through the Institute of Contemporary Prints 1975

P06273 Two Miners (1960-2)
CLπ:476x676:Presented by Curwen Studio through the Institute of Contemporary Prints 1975

P06274 Two Miners (circa 1960)
CLπ:454x679:Presented by Curwen Studio through the Institute of Contemporary Prints 1975

P06275 Two Seated Peasants (1961)
CLπ:410x587:Presented by Curwen Studio through the Institute of Contemporary Prints 1975

P06276 Mother and Child (1961-2)
CLπ:670x435:Presented by Curwen Studio through the Institute of Contemporary Prints 1975

P06277 Dusk (1965)
CLπ:508x746:Presented by Curwen Studio through the Institute of Contemporary Prints 1975

P06278 Figure against Dark Sky (1965)
CLπ:533x698:Presented by Curwen Studio through the Institute of Contemporary Prints 1975

P06279 In the Mountains (1965)
CLπ:524x711:Presented by Curwen Studio through the Institute of Contemporary Prints 1975

P06280 Cockle Gatherers (1974)
CLπ:492x648:signed:Presented by Curwen Studio through the Institute of Contemporary Prints 1975

P06281 The First Star (1974-5)
CLπ:314x476:signed:Presented by Curwen Studio through the Institute of Contemporary Prints 1975

P06282 Four Fisherwomen (1974-5)
CLπ:419x610:signed:Presented by Curwen Studio through the Institute of Contemporary Prints 1975

P06283 Scene on the Shore (1974-5)
CLπ:511x635:signed:Presented by Curwen Studio through the Institute of Contemporary Prints 1975

P06284 On the Way Home (1974-5)
CLπ:508x635:signed:Presented by Curwen Studio through the Institute of Contemporary Prints 1975

P06285 The Red Sun (1975)
CLπ:365x438:signed:Presented by Curwen Studio through the Institute of Contemporary Prints 1975

P06711 Figure against a Dark Sky (colour variant) (1965)
CLπ:533x692:Presented by Curwen Studio 1976

HERMES, Gertrude 1901-1983
Modern Collection
Tate Gallery Archive holds material concerning this artist

T00233 Kathleen Raine (1954)
Sz:508x495x330:Presented by Miss Kay M. Murphy 1959

T03221 Baby (1932)
Sz:324x229x206:Presented by the Trustees of the
Chantrey Bequest 1981

T05522 Lady Herbert (1951)
Sz:742x635x578:Bequeathed by Lady Herbert 1989

IAA Portfolio (P03096-P03104, P03107; complete
group; mixed group)
P03100 The Yolk (1954-75)
MJπ:359x308:signed:Presented by the International
Association of Art 1975

P77065 Mistletoe (1930)
MJπ:229x134:signed:Purchased 1984

P77066 Waterlilies (1930)
MJπ:229x134:signed:Purchased 1984

P77067 Fathomless Sounding (1932)
MJπ:381x251:signed:Purchased 1984

P77068 Swallows (1933)
MJπ:190x128:signed:Purchased 1984

P77069 Two People (1934)
MJπ:508x305:signed:Purchased 1984

P77070 One Person (1937)
MJπ:346x337:signed:Purchased 1984

P77071 Ring Net Fishers (1955)
CJπ:558x755:signed:Purchased 1984

HERON, Patrick born 1920
Modern Collection
Tate Gallery Archive holds material concerning this artist

T00392 Green and Purple Painting with Blue Disc: May 1960
(1960)
Oc:1219x1524:signed:Purchased 1960

T00711 Purple Shape in Blue (1964)
Oc:1314x1206:signed:Purchased 1964

T00962 Scarlet, Lemon, and Ultramarine: March 1957 (1957)
Oc:591x794:signed:Purchased 1967

T01101 Soft Green, Blue, Violet, Orange, Brown: January 1968
(1968)
Gπ:591x794:Presented by Philip Goldberg 1968

T01541 Horizontal Stripe Painting: November 1957 - January
1958 (1957-8)
Oc:2743x1548:signed:Purchased 1972

T01878 Brown Ground with Soft Red and Green: August 1958 -
July 1959 (1958-9)
Oc:1520x2138:signed:Purchased 1974

T03106 Harbour Window with Two Figures; St Ives: July 1950
(1950)
Oc:1219x1524:signed:Purchased 1980

T03107 Azalea Garden: May 1956 (1956)
Oc:1524x1276:signed:Purchased 1980

T03660 Cadmium with Violet, Scarlet, Emerald, Lemon and
Venetian:1969 (1969)
Oc:1985x3790:signed:Presented by Lord McAlpine of
West Green 1983

P04272 Blue and Deep Violet with Orange, Brown and Green
(1970)
CNπ:600x781:signed:Presented by Rose and Chris Prater
through the Institute of Contemporary Prints 1975

P04273 Blues Dovetailed in Yellow (1970)
CNπ:597x787:signed:Presented by Rose and Chris Prater
through the Institute of Contemporary Prints 1975

P04274 Four Blues Two Discs (1970)
CNπ:600x784:signed:Presented by Rose and Chris Prater
through the Institute of Contemporary Prints 1975

P04275 Interlocking Pink and Vermilion with Blue (1970)
CNπ:594x787:signed:Presented by Rose and Chris Prater
through the Institute of Contemporary Prints 1975

P04276 Interlocking Scarlet and Pink in Deep Green (1970)
CNπ:594x787:signed:Presented by Rose and Chris Prater
through the Institute of Contemporary Prints 1975

P04277 Magenta Disc and Red Edge (1970)
CNπ:594x781:signed:Presented by Rose and Chris Prater
through the Institute of Contemporary Prints 1975

P04278 Six in Light Orange with Red in Yellow (1970)
CNπ:587x781:signed:Presented by Rose and Chris Prater
through the Institute of Contemporary Prints 1975

P04279 Six in Vermilion with Green in Yellow (1970)
CNπ:587x781:signed:Presented by Rose and Chris Prater
through the Institute of Contemporary Prints 1975

P04280 Six in Vermilion with Red in Red (1970)
CNπ:591x781:signed:Presented by Rose and Chris Prater
through the Institute of Contemporary Prints 1975

P04281 Six in Vermilion with Violet in Red (1970)
CNπ:587x781:signed:Presented by Rose and Chris Prater
through the Institute of Contemporary Prints 1975

P04282 Three Reds in Green and Magenta in Blue (1970)
CNπ:597x784:signed:Presented by Rose and Chris Prater
through the Institute of Contemporary Prints 1975

P04283 Three Reds in Magenta and Green in Blue (1970)
CNπ:597x781:Presented by Rose and Chris Prater
through the Institute of Contemporary Prints 1975

P04284 Two Magenta Discs in Dark Reds (1970)
CNπ:600x787:signed:Presented by Rose and Chris Prater
through the Institute of Contemporary Prints 1975

P04285 Two Pink Discs in Dark Reds (1970)
CNπ:600x787:signed:Presented by Rose and Chris Prater
through the Institute of Contemporary Prints 1975

P04286 Umber Disc and Red Edge (1970)
CNπ:594x781:signed:Presented by Rose and Chris Prater
through the Institute of Contemporary Prints 1975

P04287 Untitled (1971)
CNπ:587x794:signed:Presented by Rose and Chris Prater
through the Institute of Contemporary Prints 1975

P04288 Eight Including Ultramarine (1971)
CNπ:587x794:signed:Presented by Rose and Chris Prater
through the Institute of Contemporary Prints 1975

P04289 Untitled (1972)
CNπ:581x813:signed:Presented by Rose and Chris Prater
through the Institute of Contemporary Prints 1975

January 1973 (P04290-P04307; complete group)
P04290 January 1973: 1 (1973)
CNπ:587x808:signed:Presented by Rose and Chris Prater
through the Institute of Contemporary Prints 1975

P04291 January 1973: 2 (1973)
CNπ:584x813:signed:Presented by Rose and Chris Prater
through the Institute of Contemporary Prints 1975

P04292 January 1973: 3 (1973)
CNπ:586x810:signed:Presented by Rose and Chris Prater through the Institute of Contemporary Prints 1975

P04293 January 1973: 4 (1973)
CNπ:586x810:signed:Presented by Rose and Chris Prater through the Institute of Contemporary Prints 1975

P04294 January 1973: 5 (1973)
CNπ:586x814:signed:Presented by Rose and Chris Prater through the Institute of Contemporary Prints 1975

P04295 January 1973: 6 (1973)
CNπ:586x814:signed:Presented by Rose and Chris Prater through the Institute of Contemporary Prints 1975

P04296 January 1973: 7 (1973)
CNπ:586x814:signed:Presented by Rose and Chris Prater through the Institute of Contemporary Prints 1975

P04297 January 1973: 8 (1973)
CNπ:588x811:signed:Presented by Rose and Chris Prater through the Institute of Contemporary Prints 1975

P04298 January 1973: 10 (1973)
CNπ:588x814:signed:Presented by Rose and Chris Prater through the Institute of Contemporary Prints 1975

P04299 January 1973: 11 (1973)
CNπ:583x795:signed:Presented by Rose and Chris Prater through the Institute of Contemporary Prints 1975

P04300 January 1973: 12 (1973)
CNπ:593x796:signed:Presented by Rose and Chris Prater through the Institute of Contemporary Prints 1975

P04301 January 1973: 13 (1973)
CNπ:592x795:signed:Presented by Rose and Chris Prater through the Institute of Contemporary Prints 1975

P04302 January 1973: 14 (1973)
CNπ:584x814:signed:Presented by Rose and Chris Prater through the Institute of Contemporary Prints 1975

P04303 January 1973: 15 (1973)
CNπ:586x813:signed:Presented by Rose and Chris Prater through the Institute of Contemporary Prints 1975

P04304 January 1973: 16 (1973)
CNπ:586x813:signed:Presented by Rose and Chris Prater through the Institute of Contemporary Prints 1975

P04305 January 1973: 17 (1973)
CNπ:587x814:signed:Presented by Rose and Chris Prater through the Institute of Contemporary Prints 1975

P04306 January 1973: 18 (1973)
CNπ:586x813:signed:Presented by Rose and Chris Prater through the Institute of Contemporary Prints 1975

P04307 January 1973: 19 (1973)
CNπ:586x794:signed:Presented by Rose and Chris Prater through the Institute of Contemporary Prints 1975

Small Red: January 1973 (P04308-P04311; complete group)

P04308 Small Red: January 1973: 1 (1973)
CNπ:428x522:signed:Presented by Rose and Chris Prater through the Institute of Contemporary Prints 1975

P04309 Small Red: January 1973: 2 (1973)
CNπ:428x521:signed:Presented by Rose and Chris Prater through the Institute of Contemporary Prints 1975

P04310 Small Red: January 1973: 3 (1973)
CNπ:427x521:signed:Presented by Rose and Chris Prater through the Institute of Contemporary Prints 1975

P04311 Small Red: January 1973: 4 (1973)
CNπ:428x521:signed:Presented by Rose and Chris Prater through the Institute of Contemporary Prints 1975

P04312 Small Yellow: January 1973 (1973)
CNπ:425x522:signed:Presented by Rose and Chris Prater through the Institute of Contemporary Prints 1975

P06286 Red and Yellow Image (1958)
CNπ:537x387:Presented by Curwen Studio through the Institute of Contemporary Prints 1975

P06287 Grey and Black Stripes (1958)
CNπ:524x419:Presented by Curwen Studio through the Institute of Contemporary Prints 1975

P06709 Black and Blue Stripes (1958)
CLπ::Presented by Curwen Studio 1976

P06710 Grey and Brown Stripes (1958)
CLπ:521x416:Presented by Curwen Studio 1976

P07359 The Shapes of Colour 1943-1978 (1978)
CNπ:502x702:signed:Purchased 1980

The Shapes of Colour (P77362-P77381; complete group)

P77362 [no title] (1978)
CNπ:295x644:signed:Purchased 1980

P77363 [no title] (1978)
CNπ:370x300:signed:Purchased 1980

P77364 [no title] (1978)
CNπ:190x277:signed:Purchased 1980

P77365 [no title] (1978)
CNπ:500x351:signed:Purchased 1980

P77366 [no title] (1978)
CNπ:180x238:signed:Purchased 1980

P77367 [no title] (1978)
CNπ:178x235:signed:Purchased 1980

P77368 [no title] (1978)
CNπ:90x170:signed:Purchased 1980

P77369 [no title] (1978)
CNπ:500x700:signed:Purchased 1980

P77370 [no title] (1978)
CNπ:90x170:signed:Purchased 1980

P77371 [no title] (1978)
CNπ:180x236:signed:Purchased 1980

P77372 [no title] (1978)
CNπ:178x240:signed:Purchased 1980

P77373 [no title] (1978)
CNπ:112x180:signed:Purchased 1980

P77374 [no title] (1978)
CNπ:179x235:signed:Purchased 1980

P77375 [no title] (1978)
CNπ:180x236:signed:Purchased 1980

P77376 [no title] (1978)
CNπ:500x351:signed:Purchased 1980

P77377 [no title] (1978)
CNπ:180x240:signed:Purchased 1980

P77378 [no title] (1978)
CNπ:228x305:signed:Purchased 1980

P77379 [no title] (1978)
CNπ:432x302:signed:Purchased 1980

P77380 [no title] (1978)
CNπ:228x305:signed:Purchased 1980

P77381 [no title] (1978)
CNπ:432x302:signed:Purchased 1980

HERRING, Ed born 1945
Modern Collection
Tate Gallery Archive holds material concerning this artist

Jam Press Phase One (P08006-P08014; complete group; mixed group)
P08010 1. 6 (1973-4)
MLπ:559x441:Transferred from the Library 1977

HERRING, John Frederick 1795-1865
British Collection

N00452 The Frugal Meal (exhibited 1847)
Oc:546x749:Presented by Robert Vernon 1847

T00188 Mazeppa Pursued by Wolves (after Horace Vernet) (1833)
Oc:559x762:Presented by the National Art Collections Fund 1958

T00189 Mazeppa Surrounded by Horses (after Horace Vernet) (circa 1833)
Oc:559x762:Presented by the National Art Collections Fund 1958

T02361 Birmingham with Patrick Conolly Up, and his Owner, John Beardsworth (1830)
Oc:559x762:signed:Presented by Paul Mellon through the British Sporting Art Trust 1979

T02362 Manuella, at Richard Watt's Stud Farm, Bishop Burton, Yorkshire (1825)
Oc:1016x1283:signed:Presented by Paul Mellon through the British Sporting Art Trust 1979

T03430 The Hunting Stud (1845)
Oc:454x708:signed:Bequeathed by Mrs F. Ambrose Clark through the British Sporting Art Trust 1982

attributed to
HERRING, John Frederick, Junior 1816-1907
British Collection

T02018 Farmyard Scene (circa 1870)
Oc:571x838:signed:Bequeathed by Gilbert Charles Dandy 1976

HESSE, Eva 1936-1970
Modern Collection

T02383 Tomorrow's Apples (5 in White) (1965)
REGvb:654x556x159:Purchased 1979

T02394 Addendum (1967)
Rvw:124x3029x206:Purchased 1979

T04151 Untitled (1967)
Dπ:278x216:Presented by Mrs Helen Charash, the artist's sister, through the American Federation of Arts 1986

T04153 Untitled (1965)
Dπ:459x610:signed:Purchased 1986

T04154 Untitled (1965)
DGπ:496x647:signed:Purchased 1986

HEYBOER, Anton born 1924
Modern Collection

P07531 Maria (1978)
OClπ:648x994:signed:Purchased 1981

P07532 Girl of Pleasure (1978)
Meisje van genoegen
OClπ:648x994:signed:Purchased 1981

P07533 Four Women (1980)
Vier Vrouwen
HClπ:641x410:signed:Purchased 1981

HICKEY, Thomas 1741-1824
British Collection

T00351 A Girl Leaning against a Piano (circa 1780)
Oc:908x705:Presented by the Friends of the Tate Gallery 1960

T01208 Dr John Heath (1779)
Oc:746x622:signed:Bequeathed by Mrs Helena Beatrice Anderson 1970

HICKS, George Elgar 1824-1914
British Collection

T00397 Woman's Mission: Companion of Manhood (1863)
Oc:762x641:signed:Presented by David Barclay 1960

HICKS, Phillip born 1928
Modern Collection
Tate Gallery Archive holds material concerning this artist

P01417 Victims I (1970)
CNπ:587x454:signed:Presented by the artist through the Institute of Contemporary Prints 1975

P01418 Aftermath (1971)
CNπ:457x591:signed:Presented by the artist through the Institute of Contemporary Prints 1975

P01419 Old Man and Soldier (1971)
CNπ:657x438:signed:Presented by the artist through the Institute of Contemporary Prints 1975

HIDE, Peter born 1928
Modern Collection
Tate Gallery Archive holds material concerning this artist

T01249 Tripod (1970)
Sm:3137x6756x6756:signed:Purchased 1970

T05517 Seated Figure (1988)
Sm:2945x1422x965:Purchased 1988

HIGHMORE family
British Collection

T04233 [title not known]
DWπ:67x60:Presented by Mrs Joan Highmore Blackhall and Dr R.B. McConnell 1986

T04234 [title not known]
DWπ:240x189:Presented by Mrs Joan Highmore Blackhall and Dr R.B. McConnell 1986

T04235 [title not known]
DWπ::Presented by Mrs Joan Highmore Blackhall and Dr R.B. McConnell 1986

T04236 [title not known]
DWπ::Presented by Mrs Joan Highmore Blackhall and Dr R.B. McConnell 1986

T04237 [title not known]
DWπ::Presented by Mrs Joan Highmore Blackhall and Dr R.B. McConnell 1986

T04238 [title not known]
DWπ::Presented by Mrs Joan Highmore Blackhall and Dr R.B. McConnell 1986

T04239 [title not known]
DWπ::Presented by Mrs Joan Highmore Blackhall and Dr R.B. McConnell 1986

T04240 [title not known]
DWπ::Presented by Mrs Joan Highmore Blackhall and
Dr R.B. McConnell 1986

T04241 [title not known]
DWπ::Presented by Mrs Joan Highmore Blackhall and
Dr R.B. McConnell 1986

T04242 [title not known]
DWπ::Presented by Mrs Joan Highmore Blackhall and
Dr R.B. McConnell 1986

T04243 [title not known]
DWπ::Presented by Mrs Joan Highmore Blackhall and
Dr R.B. McConnell 1986

T04244 [title not known]
DWπ::Presented by Mrs Joan Highmore Blackhall and
Dr R.B. McConnell 1986

T04245 [title not known]
DWπ::Presented by Mrs Joan Highmore Blackhall and
Dr R.B. McConnell 1986

T04246 [title not known]
DWπ::Presented by Mrs Joan Highmore Blackhall and
Dr R.B. McConnell 1986

T04247 [title not known]
DWπ::Presented by Mrs Joan Highmore Blackhall and
Dr R.B. McConnell 1986

T04248 [title not known]
DWπ::Presented by Mrs Joan Highmore Blackhall and
Dr R.B. McConnell 1986

T04249 [title not known]
DWπ::Presented by Mrs Joan Highmore Blackhall and
Dr R.B. McConnell 1986

T04250 [title not known]
DWπ::Presented by Mrs Joan Highmore Blackhall and
Dr R.B. McConnell 1986

T04251 [title not known]
DWπ::Presented by Mrs Joan Highmore Blackhall and
Dr R.B. McConnell 1986

T04252 [title not known]
DWπ::Presented by Mrs Joan Highmore Blackhall and
Dr R.B. McConnell 1986

T04253 [title not known]
DWπ::Presented by Mrs Joan Highmore Blackhall and
Dr R.B. McConnell 1986

T04254 [title not known]
DWπ::Presented by Mrs Joan Highmore Blackhall and
Dr R.B. McConnell 1986

T04255 [title not known]
DWπ::Presented by Mrs Joan Highmore Blackhall and
Dr R.B. McConnell 1986

T04256 [title not known]
DWπ::Presented by Mrs Joan Highmore Blackhall and
Dr R.B. McConnell 1986

T04257 [title not known]
DWπ::Presented by Mrs Joan Highmore Blackhall and
Dr R.B. McConnell 1986

T04258 [title not known]
DWπ::Presented by Mrs Joan Highmore Blackhall and
Dr R.B. McConnell 1986

T04259 [title not known]
DWπ::Presented by Mrs Joan Highmore Blackhall and
Dr R.B. McConnell 1986

T04260 [title not known]
DWπ::Presented by Mrs Joan Highmore Blackhall and
Dr R.B. McConnell 1986

T04261 [title not known]
DWπ::Presented by Mrs Joan Highmore Blackhall and
Dr R.B. McConnell 1986

T04262 [title not known]
DWπ::Presented by Mrs Joan Highmore Blackhall and
Dr R.B. McConnell 1986

T04263 [title not known]
DWπ::Presented by Mrs Joan Highmore Blackhall and
Dr R.B. McConnell 1986

T04264 [title not known]
DWπ::Presented by Mrs Joan Highmore Blackhall and
Dr R.B. McConnell 1986

T04265 [title not known]
DWπ::Presented by Mrs Joan Highmore Blackhall and
Dr R.B. McConnell 1986

T04266 [title not known]
DWπ::Presented by Mrs Joan Highmore Blackhall and
Dr R.B. McConnell 1986

T04267 [title not known]
DWπ::Presented by Mrs Joan Highmore Blackhall and
Dr R.B. McConnell 1986

T04268 [title not known]
DWπ::Presented by Mrs Joan Highmore Blackhall and
Dr R.B. McConnell 1986

T04269 [title not known]
DWπ::Presented by Mrs Joan Highmore Blackhall and
Dr R.B. McConnell 1986

T04270 [title not known]
DWπ::Presented by Mrs Joan Highmore Blackhall and
Dr R.B. McConnell 1986

T04271 [title not known]
DWπ::Presented by Mrs Joan Highmore Blackhall and
Dr R.B. McConnell 1986

T04272 [title not known]
DWπ::Presented by Mrs Joan Highmore Blackhall and
Dr R.B. McConnell 1986

T04273 [title not known]
DWπ::Presented by Mrs Joan Highmore Blackhall and
Dr R.B. McConnell 1986

T04274 [title not known]
DWπ::Presented by Mrs Joan Highmore Blackhall and
Dr R.B. McConnell 1986

T04275 [title not known]
DWπ::Presented by Mrs Joan Highmore Blackhall and
Dr R.B. McConnell 1986

T04276 [title not known]
DWπ::Presented by Mrs Joan Highmore Blackhall and
Dr R.B. McConnell 1986

T04277 [title not known]
DWπ::Presented by Mrs Joan Highmore Blackhall and
Dr R.B. McConnell 1986

T04278 [title not known]
DWπ::Presented by Mrs Joan Highmore Blackhall and
Dr R.B. McConnell 1986

T04279 [title not known]
DWπ::Presented by Mrs Joan Highmore Blackhall and
Dr R.B. McConnell 1986

T04280 [title not known]
DWπ::Presented by Mrs Joan Highmore Blackhall and
Dr R.B. McConnell 1986

T04281 [title not known]
DWπ::Presented by Mrs Joan Highmore Blackhall and
Dr R.B. McConnell 1986

T04282 [title not known]
DWπ::Presented by Mrs Joan Highmore Blackhall and Dr R.B. McConnell 1986

T04283 [title not known]
DWπ::Presented by Mrs Joan Highmore Blackhall and Dr R.B. McConnell 1986

T04284 [title not known]
DWπ::Presented by Mrs Joan Highmore Blackhall and Dr R.B. McConnell 1986

T04285 [title not known]
DWπ::Presented by Mrs Joan Highmore Blackhall and Dr R.B. McConnell 1986

T04286 [title not known]
DWπ::Presented by Mrs Joan Highmore Blackhall and Dr R.B. McConnell 1986

T04287 [title not known]
DWπ::Presented by Mrs Joan Highmore Blackhall and Dr R.B. McConnell 1986

T04288 [title not known]
DWπ::Presented by Mrs Joan Highmore Blackhall and Dr R.B. McConnell 1986

T04289 [title not known]
DWπ::Presented by Mrs Joan Highmore Blackhall and Dr R.B. McConnell 1986

T04290 [title not known]
DWπ::Presented by Mrs Joan Highmore Blackhall and Dr R.B. McConnell 1986

T04291 [title not known]
DWπ::Presented by Mrs Joan Highmore Blackhall and Dr R.B. McConnell 1986

T04292 [title not known]
DWπ::Presented by Mrs Joan Highmore Blackhall and Dr R.B. McConnell 1986

T04293 [title not known]
DWπ::Presented by Mrs Joan Highmore Blackhall and Dr R.B. McConnell 1986

T04294 [title not known]
DWπ::Presented by Mrs Joan Highmore Blackhall and Dr R.B. McConnell 1986

T04295 [title not known]
DWπ::Presented by Mrs Joan Highmore Blackhall and Dr R.B. McConnell 1986

T04296 [title not known]
DWπ::Presented by Mrs Joan Highmore Blackhall and Dr R.B. McConnell 1986

T04297 [title not known]
DWπ::Presented by Mrs Joan Highmore Blackhall and Dr R.B. McConnell 1986

T04298 [title not known]
DWπ::Presented by Mrs Joan Highmore Blackhall and Dr R.B. McConnell 1986

T04299 [title not known]
DWπ::Presented by Mrs Joan Highmore Blackhall and Dr R.B. McConnell 1986

T04300 [title not known]
DWπ::Presented by Mrs Joan Highmore Blackhall and Dr R.B. McConnell 1986

T04301 [title not known]
DWπ::Presented by Mrs Joan Highmore Blackhall and Dr R.B. McConnell 1986

T04302 [title not known]
DWπ::Presented by Mrs Joan Highmore Blackhall and Dr R.B. McConnell 1986

T04303 [title not known]
DWπ::Presented by Mrs Joan Highmore Blackhall and Dr R.B. McConnell 1986

T04304 [title not known]
DWπ::Presented by Mrs Joan Highmore Blackhall and Dr R.B. McConnell 1986

T04305 [title not known]
DWπ::Presented by Mrs Joan Highmore Blackhall and Dr R.B. McConnell 1986

T04306 [title not known]
DWπ::Presented by Mrs Joan Highmore Blackhall and Dr R.B. McConnell 1986

T04307 [title not known]
DWπ::Presented by Mrs Joan Highmore Blackhall and Dr R.B. McConnell 1986

T04308 [title not known]
DWπ::Presented by Mrs Joan Highmore Blackhall and Dr R.B. McConnell 1986

T04309 [title not known]
DWπ::Presented by Mrs Joan Highmore Blackhall and Dr R.B. McConnell 1986

T04310 [title not known]
DWπ::Presented by Mrs Joan Highmore Blackhall and Dr R.B. McConnell 1986

T04311 [title not known]
DWπ::Presented by Mrs Joan Highmore Blackhall and Dr R.B. McConnell 1986

T04312 [title not known]
DWπ::Presented by Mrs Joan Highmore Blackhall and Dr R.B. McConnell 1986

T04313 [title not known]
DWπ::Presented by Mrs Joan Highmore Blackhall and Dr R.B. McConnell 1986

T04314 [title not known]
DWπ::Presented by Mrs Joan Highmore Blackhall and Dr R.B. McConnell 1986

T04315 [title not known]
DWπ::Presented by Mrs Joan Highmore Blackhall and Dr R.B. McConnell 1986

T04316 [title not known]
DWπ::Presented by Mrs Joan Highmore Blackhall and Dr R.B. McConnell 1986

T04317 [title not known]
DWπ::Presented by Mrs Joan Highmore Blackhall and Dr R.B. McConnell 1986

T04318 [title not known]
DWπ::Presented by Mrs Joan Highmore Blackhall and Dr R.B. McConnell 1986

T04319 [title not known]
DWπ::Presented by Mrs Joan Highmore Blackhall and Dr R.B. McConnell 1986

T04320 [title not known]
DWπ::Presented by Mrs Joan Highmore Blackhall and Dr R.B. McConnell 1986

T04321 [title not known]
DWπ::Presented by Mrs Joan Highmore Blackhall and Dr R.B. McConnell 1986

T04322 [title not known]
DWπ::Presented by Mrs Joan Highmore Blackhall and Dr R.B. McConnell 1986

T04323 [title not known]
DWπ::Presented by Mrs Joan Highmore Blackhall and Dr R.B. McConnell 1986

T04324 [title not known]
DWπ::Presented by Mrs Joan Highmore Blackhall and
Dr R.B. McConnell 1986

T04325 [title not known]
DWπ::Presented by Mrs Joan Highmore Blackhall and
Dr R.B. McConnell 1986

T04326 [title not known]
DWπ::Presented by Mrs Joan Highmore Blackhall and
Dr R.B. McConnell 1986

T04327 [title not known]
DWπ::Presented by Mrs Joan Highmore Blackhall and
Dr R.B. McConnell 1986

T04328 [title not known]
DWπ::Presented by Mrs Joan Highmore Blackhall and
Dr R.B. McConnell 1986

T04329 [title not known]
DWπ::Presented by Mrs Joan Highmore Blackhall and
Dr R.B. McConnell 1986

T04330 [title not known]
DWπ::Presented by Mrs Joan Highmore Blackhall and
Dr R.B. McConnell 1986

T04331 [title not known]
DWπ::Presented by Mrs Joan Highmore Blackhall and
Dr R.B. McConnell 1986

T04332 [title not known]
DWπ::Presented by Mrs Joan Highmore Blackhall and
Dr R.B. McConnell 1986

T04333 [title not known]
DWπ::Presented by Mrs Joan Highmore Blackhall and
Dr R.B. McConnell 1986

T04334 [title not known]
DWπ::Presented by Mrs Joan Highmore Blackhall and
Dr R.B. McConnell 1986

T04335 [title not known]
DWπ::Presented by Mrs Joan Highmore Blackhall and
Dr R.B. McConnell 1986

T04336 [title not known]
DWπ::Presented by Mrs Joan Highmore Blackhall and
Dr R.B. McConnell 1986

T04337 [title not known]
DWπ::Presented by Mrs Joan Highmore Blackhall and
Dr R.B. McConnell 1986

T04338 [title not known]
DWπ::Presented by Mrs Joan Highmore Blackhall and
Dr R.B. McConnell 1986

T04339 [title not known]
DWπ::Presented by Mrs Joan Highmore Blackhall and
Dr R.B. McConnell 1986

T04340 [title not known]
DWπ::Presented by Mrs Joan Highmore Blackhall and
Dr R.B. McConnell 1986

T04341 [title not known]
DWπ::Presented by Mrs Joan Highmore Blackhall and
Dr R.B. McConnell 1986

T04342 [title not known]
DWπ::Presented by Mrs Joan Highmore Blackhall and
Dr R.B. McConnell 1986

T04343 [title not known]
DWπ::Presented by Mrs Joan Highmore Blackhall and
Dr R.B. McConnell 1986

T04344 [title not known]
DWπ::Presented by Mrs Joan Highmore Blackhall and
Dr R.B. McConnell 1986

T04345 [title not known]
DWπ::Presented by Mrs Joan Highmore Blackhall and
Dr R.B. McConnell 1986

T04346 [title not known]
DWπ::Presented by Mrs Joan Highmore Blackhall and
Dr R.B. McConnell 1986

T04347 [title not known]
DWπ::Presented by Mrs Joan Highmore Blackhall and
Dr R.B. McConnell 1986

T04348 [title not known]
DWπ::Presented by Mrs Joan Highmore Blackhall and
Dr R.B. McConnell 1986

T04349 [title not known]
DWπ::Presented by Mrs Joan Highmore Blackhall and
Dr R.B. McConnell 1986

T04350 [title not known]
DWπ::Presented by Mrs Joan Highmore Blackhall and
Dr R.B. McConnell 1986

T04351 [title not known]
DWπ::Presented by Mrs Joan Highmore Blackhall and
Dr R.B. McConnell 1986

T04352 [title not known]
DWπ::Presented by Mrs Joan Highmore Blackhall and
Dr R.B. McConnell 1986

T04353 [title not known]
DWπ::Presented by Mrs Joan Highmore Blackhall and
Dr R.B. McConnell 1986

T04354 [title not known]
DWπ::Presented by Mrs Joan Highmore Blackhall and
Dr R.B. McConnell 1986

T04355 [title not known]
DWπ::Presented by Mrs Joan Highmore Blackhall and
Dr R.B. McConnell 1986

T04356 [title not known]
DWπ::Presented by Mrs Joan Highmore Blackhall and
Dr R.B. McConnell 1986

T04357 [title not known]
DWπ::Presented by Mrs Joan Highmore Blackhall and
Dr R.B. McConnell 1986

T04358 [title not known]
DWπ::Presented by Mrs Joan Highmore Blackhall and
Dr R.B. McConnell 1986

T04359 [title not known]
DWπ::Presented by Mrs Joan Highmore Blackhall and
Dr R.B. McConnell 1986

T04360 [title not known]
DWπ::Presented by Mrs Joan Highmore Blackhall and
Dr R.B. McConnell 1986

T04361 [title not known]
DWπ::Presented by Mrs Joan Highmore Blackhall and
Dr R.B. McConnell 1986

T04362 [title not known]
DWπ::Presented by Mrs Joan Highmore Blackhall and
Dr R.B. McConnell 1986

T04363 [title not known]
DWπ::Presented by Mrs Joan Highmore Blackhall and
Dr R.B. McConnell 1986

T04364 [title not known]
DWπ::Presented by Mrs Joan Highmore Blackhall and
Dr R.B. McConnell 1986

T04365 [title not known]
DWπ::Presented by Mrs Joan Highmore Blackhall and
Dr R.B. McConnell 1986

T04366 [title not known]
DWπ::Presented by Mrs Joan Highmore Blackhall and
Dr R.B. McConnell 1986

HIGHMORE, Joseph 1692-1780
British Collection
Tate Gallery Archive holds material concerning this artist

Four Scenes from Samuel Richardson's 'Pamela'
(N03573-N03576; complete group)

N03573 I: Mr B. Finds Pamela Writing (1743-4)
Oc:651x759:Purchased 1921

N03574 VII: Pamela in the Bedroom with Mrs Jewkes and Mr B.
(1743-4)
Oc:627x757:Purchased 1921

N03575 IX: Pamela is Married (1743-4)
Oc:628x760:Purchased 1921

N03576 XI: Pamela Asks Sir Jacob Swinford's Blessing (1743-4)
Oc:632x750:Purchased 1921

N04107 A Gentleman in a Brown Velvet Coat (1747)
Oc:1265x1005:signed:Purchased 1925

N05864 Mr Oldham and his Guests (circa 1735-45)
Oc:1055x1295:Purchased 1948

T00076 The Good Samaritan (1744)
Oc:1595x1448:signed:Presented by C.K. Adams 1955

T04173 A Standing Hound, Looking Up
DWπ:129x166:Presented by Mrs Joan Highmore
Blackhall and Dr R.B. McConnell 1986

T04174 A Family Group of Seven Persons Standing on a Terrace
Dπ:152x184:Presented by Mrs Joan Highmore Blackhall
and Dr R.B. McConnell 1986

T04175 Two Full-length Studies of a Man in Peer's Robes
Dπ:91x137:Presented by Mrs Joan Highmore Blackhall
and Dr R.B. McConnell 1986

T04176 Four Male Academy Studies
Dπ:104x192:Presented by Mrs Joan Highmore Blackhall
and Dr R.B. McConnell 1986

T04177 Sketch of a Helmeted Figure Leading a Blindfolded One
towards an Artist Standing at an Easel
Dπ:121x146:Presented by Mrs Joan Highmore Blackhall
and Dr R.B. McConnell 1986

T04178 Sketch of a Group of Five Gentlemen around a Table
Dπ:207x293:Presented by Mrs Joan Highmore Blackhall
and Dr R.B. McConnell 1986

T04179 Sketch of a Man with a Book, Opening a Door
Dπ:185x155:Presented by Mrs Joan Highmore Blackhall
and Dr R.B. McConnell 1986

T04180 Three Full-length Studies of a Man in Peer's Robes
Dπ:141x171:Presented by Mrs Joan Highmore Blackhall
and Dr R.B. McConnell 1986

T04181 A Family Group of Eight Persons and a Dog, Full-length
Dπ:108x169:Presented by Mrs Joan Highmore Blackhall
and Dr R.B. McConnell 1986

T04182 A Family Group of Five Persons, Knee-length
Dπ:112x136:Presented by Mrs Joan Highmore Blackhall
and Dr R.B. McConnell 1986

T04183 A Group of Four Persons and a Dog in a Garden
Dπ:115x154:Presented by Mrs Joan Highmore Blackhall
and Dr R.B. McConnell 1986

T04184 Sketch of a Child's Head and of a Man on Horseback
DWπ:229x333:Presented by Mrs Joan Highmore
Blackhall and Dr R.B. McConnell 1986

T04185 Two Full-length Studies of a Man Leaning on a Cannon
Dπ:129x198:Presented by Mrs Joan Highmore Blackhall
and Dr R.B. McConnell 1986

T04186 Two Full-length Studies of a Man in Robes
Dπ:189x155:Presented by Mrs Joan Highmore Blackhall
and Dr R.B. McConnell 1986

T04187 Four Full-length Studies of a Man Opening a Door
Dπ:105x201:Presented by Mrs Joan Highmore Blackhall
and Dr R.B. McConnell 1986

T04188 Study of a Female Full-length in an Architectural Setting
DWπ:257x199:Presented by Mrs Joan Highmore
Blackhall and Dr R.B. McConnell 1986

T04189 Two Studies of a Man's Head
DWπ:67x131:Presented by Mrs Joan Highmore Blackhall
and Dr R.B. McConnell 1986

T04190 A Couple Seated on a Garden Bench
DWπ:77x118:Presented by Mrs Joan Highmore Blackhall
and Dr R.B. McConnell 1986

T04191 Putto with a Shepherd's Crook
DWπ:103x76:Presented by Mrs Joan Highmore Blackhall
and Dr R.B. McConnell 1986

T04192 Group of Three Ladies in a Garden
Dπ:96x155:Presented by Mrs Joan Highmore Blackhall
and Dr R.B. McConnell 1986

T04193 Two Studies of a Group of Four Male Figures in an
Architectural Setting
Dπ:190x156:Presented by Mrs Joan Highmore Blackhall
and Dr R.B. McConnell 1986

T04194 The Harlowe Family (circa 1745-7)
Dπ:130x192:Presented by Mrs Joan Highmore Blackhall
and Dr R.B. McConnell 1986

T04195 James Harlowe tries to Join the Hands of Clarissa and
Mr Solmes by Force (circa 1745-7)
Dπ:131x192:Presented by Mrs Joan Highmore Blackhall
and Dr R.B. McConnell 1986

T04196 Clarissa and Mr Lovelace at the Garden Door (circa
1745-7)
Dπ:130x191:Presented by Mrs Joan Highmore Blackhall
and Dr R.B. McConnell 1986

T04197 Portrait of a Man in a Cap
DWπ:108x89:Presented by Mrs Joan Highmore Blackhall
and Dr R.B. McConnell 1986

T04198 Seated Putto. Verso: Fragment of a Figure Holding a Staff
DWπ:56x52:Presented by Mrs Joan Highmore Blackhall
and Dr R.B. McConnell 1986

T04199 A Man Leaning on a Fence
DWπ:68x89:Presented by Mrs Joan Highmore Blackhall
and Dr R.B. McConnell 1986

T04200 Profile of an Old Man
DWπ:60x40:Presented by Mrs Joan Highmore Blackhall
and Dr R.B. McConnell 1986

T04201 Study for Mercury
DWπ:184x146:Presented by Mrs Joan Highmore
Blackhall and Dr R.B. McConnell 1986

T04202 Profile of a Man
Dπ:106x64:Presented by Mrs Joan Highmore Blackhall
and Dr R.B. McConnell 1986

T04203 Family Group of Five Persons, Three-quarter-length
Dπ:105x130:Presented by Mrs Joan Highmore Blackhall
and Dr R.B. McConnell 1986

T04204 Head of an Old Woman
DWπ:143x120:Presented by Mrs Joan Highmore
Blackhall and Dr R.B. McConnell 1986

T04205 Study for a Female Full-length beside a Fountain
Dπ:188x158:Presented by Mrs Joan Highmore Blackhall
and Dr R.B. McConnell 1986

T04206 A Paviour Seen from Behind
Dπ:84x85:Presented by Mrs Joan Highmore Blackhall
and Dr R.B. McConnell 1986

T04207 Classical Female Figure with a Palm Frond
DWπ:82x57:Presented by Mrs Joan Highmore Blackhall
and Dr R.B. McConnell 1986

T04208 Front View of a Bull's Head
DWπ:168x144:Presented by Mrs Joan Highmore
Blackhall and Dr R.B. McConnell 1986

T04209 Side View of a Bull's Head
DWπ:168x132:Presented by Mrs Joan Highmore
Blackhall and Dr R.B. McConnell 1986

T04210 Family Group of Five Persons in a Garden
Dπ:155x191:Presented by Mrs Joan Highmore Blackhall
and Dr R.B. McConnell 1986

T04211 Family Group of Six Persons in a Room
Dπ:127x192:Presented by Mrs Joan Highmore Blackhall
and Dr R.B. McConnell 1986

T04212 Head of an Old Man
DWπ:70x58:Presented by Mrs Joan Highmore Blackhall
and Dr R.B. McConnell 1986

T04213 A Sheet of Two Studies for a Male Full-Length and 'The
Good Samaritan'
Dπ:266x166:Presented by Mrs Joan Highmore Blackhall
and Dr R.B. McConnell 1986

T04214 Two Studies for a Female Full-Length
Dπ:143x172:Presented by Mrs Joan Highmore Blackhall
and Dr R.B. McConnell 1986

T04215 Four Studies for a Male Full-Length
Dπ:255x197:Presented by Mrs Joan Highmore Blackhall
and Dr R.B. McConnell 1986

T04216 Two Classical Heads
DWπ:110x170:Presented by Mrs Joan Highmore
Blackhall and Dr R.B. McConnell 1986

T04217 Two Ladies in an Interior
DWπ:203x161:Presented by Mrs Joan Highmore
Blackhall and Dr R.B. McConnell 1986

T04218 Study for 'The Marriage of Miss Whichcote of Harpswell
with the Dean of York'-I (circa 1749)
Dπ:192x246:Presented by Mrs Joan Highmore Blackhall
and Dr R.B. McConnell 1986

T04219 Study for 'The Marriage of Miss Whichcote of Harpswell
with the Dean of York'-II (circa 1749)
Dπ:193x244:Presented by Mrs Joan Highmore Blackhall
and Dr R.B. McConnell 1986

T04220 Study for 'The Marriage of Miss Whichcote of Harpswell
with the Dean of York'-III (circa 1749)
Dπ:195x250:Presented by Mrs Joan Highmore Blackhall
and Dr R.B. McConnell 1986

T04221 Two Studies for a Male Full-Length
Dπ:127x197:Presented by Mrs Joan Highmore Blackhall
and Dr R.B. McConnell 1986

T04222 A Conversation of Four Persons on a Terrace
Dπ:153x190:Presented by Mrs Joan Highmore Blackhall
and Dr R.B. McConnell 1986

T04223 Head of James Harris of Salisbury
DWπ:196x125:Presented by Mrs Joan Highmore
Blackhall and Dr R.B. McConnell 1986

T04224 The Back of Capt. Grose
Dπ:130x97:Presented by Mrs Joan Highmore Blackhall
and Dr R.B. McConnell 1986

T04225 Four Studies of Heads
Dπ:193x204:Presented by Mrs Joan Highmore Blackhall
and Dr R.B. McConnell 1986

T04226 Sketch of a Girl
Dπ:148x64:Presented by Mrs Joan Highmore Blackhall
and Dr R.B. McConnell 1986

T04227 Portrait of Frank Merrit
Dπ:197x164:Presented by Mrs Joan Highmore Blackhall
and Dr R.B. McConnell 1986

T04228 Studies for a Ceremonial Mace and Hat
Dπ:265x212:Presented by Mrs Joan Highmore Blackhall
and Dr R.B. McConnell 1986

T04229 Portrait of a Young Man, Possibly the Artist's Son
Dπ:188x150:Presented by Mrs Joan Highmore Blackhall
and Dr R.B. McConnell 1986

T04230 Academy Study of a Male Nude
DWπ:233x170:Presented by Mrs Joan Highmore
Blackhall and Dr R.B. McConnell 1986

T04231 Academy Study of a Male Nude
DWπ:241x193:Presented by Mrs Joan Highmore
Blackhall and Dr R.B. McConnell 1986

T04232 Sketchbook of Figure Studies after Classical Statues (six
leaves)
Dπ:359x230:Presented by Mrs Joan Highmore Blackhall
and Dr R.B. McConnell 1986

T04944 Equestrian Portrait of King George II (circa 1743-5)
Oc:750x630:Presented by the Patrons of British Art
through the Friends of the Tate Gallery 1987

HILDITCH, Richard H. 1804-1873
British Collection

T01819 Kew Gardens from Richmond Hill
Oc:203x362:signed:Purchased 1973

HILL, Anthony born 1930
Modern Collection
Tate Gallery Archive holds material concerning this artist

T00567 Relief Construction (1960-2)
Ramb:1105x914x48:signed:Purchased 1963

T01186 Relief Construction (1968-9)
Rmv:610x610x83:Purchased 1970

T01187 S2 (1968-9)
Sam:318x1581x102:Purchased 1970

T01906 Orthogonal / Diagonal Composition (1954)
OEc:606x1216:signed:Purchased 1974

T01907 Painting 55-56 (1955-6)
OEc:1270x508:signed:Purchased 1974

T02027 Relief Construction: December 1956 (1956)
RAm:381x381x41:signed:Purchased 1976

T03750 Relief Construction (1963)
Ram:330x184x321:signed:Transferred from the Victoria
& Albert Museum 1983

T05502 Cut in a Continuum (Relief) (1965)
Rab:915x621x6:Transferred from the Victoria & Albert
Museum 1988

P04313 Parity Study in Blue and Red (1971)
CNπ:705x813:signed:Presented by Rose and Chris Prater
through the Institute of Contemporary Prints 1975

P04314 Vector Rhythms (1972)
MNπ:600x514:signed:Presented by Rose and Chris
Prater through the Institute of Contemporary Prints 1975

P07425 Rational Concepts (1977)
CNπ:597x597:signed:Purchased 1981

HILL, Derek born 1916
Modern Collection
Tate Gallery Archive holds material concerning this artist

T00499 Lancashire Slate Quarry (1961)
Oc:635x743:signed:Purchased 1962

T03888 Sir Frederick Ashton (circa 1964)
Oc:508x609:signed:Presented by the artist in memory of
Sir Colin Anderson 1984

HILL, John circa 1780-1841
British Collection
Tate Gallery Archive holds material concerning this artist

T03668 Interior of the Carpenter's Shop at Forty Hill, Enfield
(?exhibited 1813)
Oc:470x688:Presented by the Friends of the Tate Gallery
1983

HILLER, Susan born 1940
Modern Collection
Tate Gallery Archive holds material concerning this artist

T03923 Belshazzar's Feast, the Writing on Your Wall (1983-4)
12 XF:509x409:Purchased 1984

HILLIARD, John born 1945
Modern Collection
Tate Gallery Archive holds material concerning this artist

T01732 Across the Park (1972)
4 Fb:1016x508:Purchased 1973

T03078 Over Deepdale (1979)
Fb:787x1778:Purchased 1980

T03079 Langdale Fell, Motion Frozen/Frozen Motion (1979)
Fb:746x1041:Purchased 1980

T03116 Camera Recording its Own Condition (7 Apertures, 10
Speeds, 2 Mirrors) (1971)
70 Fπ:2162x1832:Presented anonymously 1980

P07233 Sixty Seconds of Light (1970)
MFπ:400x6001:Purchased 1973

P77030 'Facade' and 'Flight of Happiness' (1982)
2 CFπb:407x699, 178x470, 165x470:signed:Purchased
1984

HILLIER, Tristram 1905-1983
Modern Collection
Tate Gallery Archive holds material concerning this artist

N05447 La Route des Alpes (1937)
Tc:597x806:signed:Presented by the Contemporary Art
Society 1944

N05567 Harness (1944)
Tc:603x813:signed:Presented by Sir Edward Marsh
through the Contemporary Art Society 1944

T00529 Alcañiz (1961)
Oc:698x800:signed:Presented by the Trustees of the
Chantrey Bequest 1962

T03865 Variation on the Form of an Anchor (1939)
Oc:1502x1092:signed:Purchased 1984

HILLS, Robert 1769-1844
British Collection

N04319 Study of a Donkey
Wπ:190x248:Bequeathed by J.R. Holliday 1927

N04320 The Priory, Tonbridge: 3 small sketches
Wπ:279x190:Bequeathed by J.R. Holliday 1927

N04321 A Farm and Study of a Man
DWπ:203x305:Bequeathed by J.R. Holliday 1927

N04322 A Farmyard
Wπ:178x264:Bequeathed by J.R. Holliday 1927

N04323 A Barn
Wπ:133x229:Bequeathed by J.R. Holliday 1927

A00193 Study of Cows
Dπ:235x152:Bequeathed by J.R. Holliday 1927

A00194 Sheep on the Road
Wπ:190x251:Bequeathed by J.R. Holliday 1927

A00195 Cows in a Landscape
Wπ:117x165:Bequeathed by J.R. Holliday 1927

A00196 Study of a Horse
Dπ:216x270:Bequeathed by J.R. Holliday 1927

HILTON, Roger 1911-1975
Modern Collection
Tate Gallery Archive holds material concerning this artist

T00173 January 1957 (1957)
Oc:660x660:signed:Purchased 1958

T00348 Grey Day by the Sea, February 1960 (1960)
Oc:1270x1016:signed:Purchased 1960

T00503 September 1961 (1960)
ODπ:889x1067:signed:Purchased 1962

T00764 March 1960 (1960)
ODπ:1016x1524:signed:Purchased 1965

T01183 Figure, February (1962)
ODc:1473x1829:signed:Purchased 1970

T01230 February 1954 (1954)
Oc:1270x1016:signed:Purchased 1970

T01854 Untitled (?1956-7)
Oc:610x508:signed:Purchased 1974

T01855 Oi Yoi Yoi (1963)
Oc:1524x1270:signed:Purchased 1974

T01856 Two Nude Women (circa 1965)
DPπ:559x762:signed:Purchased 1974

T01932 Untitled (1953)
Oc:362x705:signed:Purchased 1974

T02114 Untitled (1971)
ODc:1016x762:signed:Purchased 1977

T04898 Vertical Composition (1952)
DGπ:1554x500:Purchased 1987

P07479 Untitled (1974)
MLπ::Purchased 1981

P07480 Untitled (1974)
MLπ::Purchased 1981

P07481 Untitled (1974)
CLπ::Purchased 1981

P77164 Woman with Dark Hair (circa 1957)
Lπ:560x380:signed:Purchased 1986

HILTON, William, the Younger 1786-1839
British Collection

N00178 Sir Calepine Rescuing Serena (exhibited 1831)
Oc:1378x2292:Presented by subscribers 1841

N00333 Edith and the Monks Searching for the Body of Harold
(exhibited 1834)
Oc:502x648:Presented by Robert Vernon 1847

N00334 Study of Edith's Head for 'Ediths and the Monks' (circa
1834)
Oc:502x648:Presented by Robert Vernon 1847

N00335 Study of a Monk's Head for 'Edith and the Monks' (circa 1834)
Oc:495x356:Presented by Robert Vernon 1847

N00337 Cupid Disarmed (exhibited 1828)
Oc:724x889:Presented by Robert Vernon 1847

N00338 The Meeting of Abraham's Servants with Rebekah at the Well (exhibited 1833)
Oc:864x1105:Presented by Robert Vernon 1847

N01499 Nature Blowing Bubbles for her Children (exhibited 1821)
Oc:1727x2324:Presented by Charles Butler 1896

N01791 Diana at the Bath (circa 1820)
Ow:216x178:Bequeathed by Henry Vaughan 1900

T04844 Study for 'Sir Calepine Rescuing Serena' (circa 1830)
DWπ:166x258:Purchased 1986

HIRST, Derek born 1930
Modern Collection
Tate Gallery Archive holds material concerning this artist

T01809 Kyoto No. 1 (1972-3)
DVπ:759x565:signed:Purchased 1973

T01810 Kyoto No. 2 (1972-3)
Dπ:759x562:signed:Purchased 1973

T01811 Kyoto No. 3 (1972-3)
Dπ:759x562:signed:Purchased 1973

T01812 Kyoto No. 4 (1972-3)
DVπ:759x562:signed:Purchased 1973

T01813 Kyoto No. 5 (1972-3)
DVπ:759x562:signed:Purchased 1973

T01814 Kyoto No. 6 (1972-3)
DVπ:759x562:signed:Purchased 1973

Paradox I-V (P01878-P01882; complete group)
P01878 Paradox I (1975)
CNπ:533x533:signed:Presented by Editions Alecto 1979

P01879 Paradox II (1975)
CNπ:533x533:signed:Presented by Editions Alecto 1979

P01880 Paradox III (1975)
CNπ:533x533:signed:Presented by Editions Alecto 1979

P01881 Paradox IV (1975)
CNπ:533x533:signed:Presented by Editions Alecto 1979

P01882 Paradox V (1975)
CNπ:533x533:signed:Presented by Editions Alecto 1979

HITCHENS, Ivon 1893-1979
Modern Collection
Tate Gallery Archive holds material concerning this artist

N04923 Winter Stage (1936)
Oc:591x1556:signed:Presented by the Contemporary Art Society 1938

N05255 Damp Autumn (1941)
Oc:406x743:signed:Purchased 1941

N05368 View from Terrace: Ashdown Forest (1938-41)
Oc:813x4305:Presented by Mrs John D. Cowen 1942

T00261 Woodland, Vertical and Horizontal (1958)
Oc:514x1168:signed:Purchased 1959

T00728 Coronation (1937)
Oc:902x1219:signed:Presented by the Trustees of the Chantrey Bequest 1965

T00873 Forest Edge No. 2 (1944)
Oc:591x1613:signed:Presented by Mrs Howard Bliss 1966

T01027 Arno No. 5 (1965)
Oc:584x1549:signed:Presented anonymously 1968

T01205 October Painting, Yellow and Blue (1963)
Oc:622x1384:signed:Presented by Mrs Howard Bliss 1970

T02212 Cartoon Drawing for the Mural Painting at Cecil Sharp House, London (1952)
DPc:867x2959:signed:Presented by the artist 1977

T02213 Study for the Mural Painting at Cecil Sharp House, London (circa 1950)
OTPc:1029x2813:signed:Presented by the artist 1977

T02214 Study for the Mural Painting at Cecil Sharp House, London (circa 1950)
OTPc:1092x3321:signed:Presented by the artist 1977

T02215 Autumn Composition, Flowers on a Table (1932)
Oc:781x1111:signed:Presented by Mrs Mary Hitchens, the artist's wife 1977

T02216 Divided Oak Tree, No. 2 (1958)
Oc:514x1168:signed:Purchased 1977

T03122 Balcony at Cambridge (1929)
Oc:508x610:signed:Purchased 1980

T03123 Abstract Composition (1934)
Oc:679x1019:signed:Purchased 1980

T03124 Triangle to Beyond (1936)
ROcb:762x508:Purchased 1980

T03125 Figures in Sunlight (1942)
Oc:432x759:signed:Purchased 1980

T03126 Boy in Red (1941)
Oc:406x743:signed:Purchased 1980

T03127 A View from my Roof (1978)
Oc:441x1095:signed:Purchased 1980

For John Constable (P03149-P03157, P03159-P03161, P03180-P03185; complete group; mixed group)
P03182 Untitled (1976)
CNπ:378x845:signed:Presented by Bernard Jacobson Gallery 1976

HOARE, Prince - see MASTER OF THE GIANTS

HOARE, William circa 1707-1792
British Collection

T01888 A Gentleman in Brown (1750)
Oc:765x639:Bequeathed by Alan Evans 1974

HOBBS, Peter
Modern Collection
Tate Gallery Archive holds material concerning this artist

P01420 Elba Series (1973)
CNπ:664x486:signed:Presented by Premises through the Institute of Contemporary Prints 1975

HOCKNEY, David born 1937
Modern Collection
Tate Gallery Archive holds material concerning this artist

T00596 The First Marriage (1962)
Oc:1829x2140:signed:Presented by the Friends of the Tate Gallery 1963

T01269 Mr and Mrs Clark and Percy (1970-1)
Ac:2134x3048:Presented by the Friends of the Tate Gallery 1971

T01515 Study for 'Mr and Mrs Clark and Percy' (1970)
Dπ:429x356:Presented by the artist 1972

T01516 Study for 'Mr and Mrs Clark and Percy' (1970)
Dπ:432x352:Presented by the artist 1972

T01517 Study for 'Mr and Mrs Clark and Percy' (1970)
Dπ:270x403:Presented by the artist 1972

T03074 Man in Shower in Beverly Hills (1964)
Ac:1673x1670:signed:Purchased 1980

T03254 A Bigger Splash (1967)
Ac:2426x2438:signed:Purchased 1981

T03255 My Parents (1977)
Oc:1829x1829:signed:Purchased 1981

For John Constable (P03149-P03157, P03159-P03161,
P03180-P03185; complete group; mixed group)

P03184 Untitled (1976)
Mlπ:273x346:signed:Presented by Bernard Jacobson
Gallery 1976

The Institute of Contemporary Arts Portfolio (P04016,
P04038, P04053, P04076, P04115, P04125, P04166,
P04248, P04256, P04315-P04316, P04334,
P04378-P04380, P04419, P04635, P04752, P04938,
P05138, P05155, P05248; complete group; mixed group)

P04315 Cleanliness is Next to Godliness (1964)
CNπ:914x581:signed:Presented by Rose and Chris Prater
through the Institute of Contemporary Prints 1975

P06288 Connoisseur (1970)
MLπ:806x575:Presented by Curwen Studio through the
Institute of Contemporary Prints 1975

Europaeische Graphik VII (P06244, P06289-P06291,
P06319, P06340-P06341, P06549; incomplete group;
mixed group)

P06289 The Print Collector (1970-1)
MLπ:670x530:Presented by Curwen Studio through the
Institute of Contemporary Prints 1975

P06290 Lilies (1970-1)
CLπ:752x533:Presented by Curwen Studio through the
Institute of Contemporary Prints 1975

A Rake's Progress (P07029-P07044; complete group)

P07029 1. The Arrival (1961-3)
CLπ:300x400:signed:Purchased 1971

P07030 1a. Receiving the Inheritance (1961-3)
CLπ:300x400:signed:Purchased 1971

P07031 2. Meeting the Good People (Washington) (1961-3)
CLπ:302x403:signed:Purchased 1971

P07032 2a. The Gospel Singing (Good People) (Madison Square
Garden) (1961-3)
CLπ:304x402:signed:Purchased 1971

P07033 3. The Start of the Spending Spree and the Door Opening
for a Blonde (1961-3)
CLπ:302x400:signed:Purchased 1971

P07034 3a. The Seven Stone Weakling (1961-3)
CLπ:300x400:signed:Purchased 1971

P07035 4. The Drinking Scene (1961-3)
CLπ:295x400:signed:Purchased 1971

P07036 4a. Marries an Old Maid (1961-3)
CLπ:300x400:signed:Purchased 1971

P07037 5. The Election Campaign (with Dark Message) (1961-3)
CLπ:300x400:signed:Purchased 1971

P07038 5a. Viewing a Prison Scene (1961-3)
CLπ:300x400:signed:Purchased 1971

P07039 6. Death in Harlem (1961-3)
CLπ:300x400:signed:Purchased 1971

P07040 6a. The Wallet Begins to Empty (1961-3)
CLπ:300x400:signed:Purchased 1971

P07041 7. Disintegration (1961-3)
CLπ:300x400:signed:Purchased 1971

P07042 7a. Cast Aside (1961-3)
CLπ:300x397:signed:Purchased 1971

P07043 8. Meeting the Other People (1961-3)
CLπ:300x400:signed:Purchased 1971

P07044 8a. Bedlam (1961-3)
CLπ:305x406:signed:Purchased 1971

P07238 Mo with Five Leaves (1971)
MLπ:679x540:signed:Purchased 1978

P07239 Billy Wilder (1976)
CLπ:965x711:signed:Purchased 1978

P07352 Myself and my Heroes (1961)
MLπ:257x502:signed:Purchased 1979

P07353 My Bonnie Lies Over the Ocean (1961-2)
CIVπ:451x451:signed:Purchased 1979

HODGES, William 1744-1797
British Collection

T00690 Tomb and Distant View of Rajmahal Hills (1782)
Oc:622x724:Presented by the Friends of the Tate Gallery
1964

HODGKIN, Eliot 1905-1987
Modern Collection

N04836 October (1935)
Ow:1016x762:signed:Presented by the Trustees of the
Chantrey Bequest 1936

N05558 Undergrowth (1941)
Tc:413x368:signed:Presented by the Trustees of the
Chantrey Bequest 1943

T03222 Pink and White Turnips (1971)
Ob:241x292:signed:Presented by the Trustees of the
Chantrey Bequest 1981

HODGKIN, Howard born 1932
Modern Collection
Tate Gallery Archive holds material concerning this artist

T01117 Mrs Nicholas Monro (1966-9)
Ac:1270x1219:Purchased 1969

T01137 Dinner at West Hill (1964-6)
Oc:1067x1270:signed:Presented by Eliot Hodgkin 1969

T01876 In a Hotel Garden (1974)
Ow:1070x1270:Purchased 1974

T02134 Interior of a Museum (1956-9)
Ow:1016x1270:Purchased 1977

T03069 Mr and Mrs Stephen Buckley (1974-6)
Ow:733x1073:signed:Purchased 1980

T03188 Dinner at Smith Square (1975-9)
Ow:946x1251:Purchased 1980

P01728 Artificial Flowers (1975)
CNπ:292x403:signed:Presented anonymously 1975

P02296 Girl at Night (1966)
CLπ:502x654:signed:Presented by the artist 1976

P02297 Interior with Figure (1966)
CLπ:502x654:signed:Presented by the artist 1976

P02298 Indian Room (1967-8)
CLπ:511x648:signed:Presented by the artist 1976

P02299 Bedroom (1968)
CLπ:514x654:signed:Presented by the artist 1976

P02300 Girl on a Sofa (1968)
CLπ:514x648:signed:Presented by the artist 1976

P02301 Interior (Day) (1974)
CL𝜋:448x603:signed:Presented by the artist 1976

P02302 Interior (Night) (1974)
CL𝜋:445x597:signed:Presented by the artist 1976

For John Constable (P03149-P03157, P03159-P03161, P03180-P03185; complete group; mixed group)

P03155 Untitled (1976)
CL𝜋:451x565:signed:Presented by Bernard Jacobson Gallery 1977

The Institute of Contemporary Arts Portfolio (P04016, P04038, P04053, P04076, P04115, P04125, P04166, P04248, P04256, P04315-P04316, P04334, P04378-P04380, P04419, P04635, P04752, P04938, P05138, P05155, P05248; complete group; mixed group)

P04316 Enter Laughing (1964)
CN𝜋:508x768:signed:Presented by Rose and Chris Prater through the Institute of Contemporary Prints 1975

Indian Views (P04317-P04328; complete group)

P04317 Indian View A (1971)
CN𝜋:580x779:signed:Presented by Rose and Chris Prater through the Institute of Contemporary Prints 1975

P04318 Indian View B (1971)
CN𝜋:577x777:signed:Presented by Rose and Chris Prater through the Institute of Contemporary Prints 1975

P04319 Indian View C (1971)
CN𝜋:577x777:signed:Presented by Rose and Chris Prater through the Institute of Contemporary Prints 1975

P04320 Indian View D (1971)
CN𝜋:575x783:signed:Presented by Rose and Chris Prater through the Institute of Contemporary Prints 1975

P04321 Indian View E (1971)
CN𝜋:581x778:signed:Presented by Rose and Chris Prater through the Institute of Contemporary Prints 1975

P04322 Indian View F (1971)
CN𝜋:580x781:signed:Presented by Rose and Chris Prater through the Institute of Contemporary Prints 1975

P04323 Indian View G (1971)
CN𝜋:581x780:signed:Presented by Rose and Chris Prater through the Institute of Contemporary Prints 1975

P04324 Indian View H (1971)
CN𝜋:581x780:signed:Presented by Rose and Chris Prater through the Institute of Contemporary Prints 1975

P04325 Indian View I (1971)
CN𝜋:580x780:signed:Presented by Rose and Chris Prater through the Institute of Contemporary Prints 1975

P04326 Indian View J (1971)
CN𝜋:587x782:signed:Presented by Rose and Chris Prater through the Institute of Contemporary Prints 1975

P04327 Indian View K (1971)
CN𝜋:580x780:signed:Presented by Rose and Chris Prater through the Institute of Contemporary Prints 1975

P04328 Indian View L (1971)
CN𝜋:580x783:signed:Presented by Rose and Chris Prater through the Institute of Contemporary Prints 1975

P05548 Lotus (1980)
CN𝜋:724x908:signed:Presented by Rose and Chris Prater 1980

Europaeische Graphik VII (P06244, P06289-P06291, P06319, P06340-P06341, P06549; incomplete group; mixed group)

P06291 Arch (1970-1)
CL𝜋:516x657:Presented by Curwen Studio through the Institute of Contemporary Prints 1975

P06292 Untitled (1971)
CL𝜋:273x362:Presented by Curwen Studio through the Institute of Contemporary Prints 1975

P07377 For Bernard Jacobson (1979)
CL𝜋:1057x1499:signed:Purchased 1980

In the Museum of Modern Art (P11005-P11006, P07395-P07396; complete group)

P07395 All alone in the Museum of Art (1979)
GMI𝜋:748x985:signed:Purchased 1980

P07396 Late Afternoon in the Museum of Art (1979)
MI𝜋:757x995:signed:Purchased 1980

P07433 Moonlight (1980)
GCL𝜋:1118x1413:signed:Purchased 1981

P07507 Artist and Model (1980)
GCL𝜋:819x1041:signed:Purchased 1981

P07508 Those ... Plants (1980)
GCL𝜋:822x1041:signed:Purchased 1981

P07617 Souvenir (1981)
MN𝜋:1143x1397:signed:Purchased 1982

In the Museum of Modern Art (P11005-P11006, P07395-P07396; complete group)

P11005 Early Evening in the Museum of Art (1979)
GMI𝜋:750x984:signed:Presented by E.J. Power through the Friends of the Tate Gallery 1980

P11006 Thinking Aloud in the Museum of Art (1979)
MI𝜋:755x1003:signed:Presented by E.J. Power through the Friends of the Tate Gallery 1980

P77044 Nick (1977)
WCI𝜋:445x556:signed:Purchased 1984

P77045 A Storm (1977)
GCL𝜋:517x613:signed:Purchased 1984

P77046 Cardo's Bar (Black) (1979)
OCI𝜋:116x153:signed:Purchased 1984

P77047 Cardo's Bar (Red) (1979)
OWCI𝜋:121x153:signed:Purchased 1984

P77048 Here We are in Croydon (1979)
WGCL𝜋:559x765:signed:Purchased 1984

P77049 Red Eye (1981)
GCL𝜋:262x312:signed:Purchased 1984

P77050 Mourning (1982)
WGCL𝜋:920x1524:signed:Purchased 1984

HODGKINS, Frances 1869-1947
British Collection
Tate Gallery Archive holds material concerning this artist

N05130 The Lake (circa 1930-5)
G𝜋:432x546:signed:Presented by the Contemporary Art Society 1940

N05406 Broken Tractor (1942)
G𝜋:381x571:Purchased 1943

N05456 Loveday and Ann: Two Women with a Basket of Flowers (1915)
Oc:673x673:signed:Purchased 1944

N05857 Seated Woman (circa 1925-30)
D𝜋:940x597:signed:Purchased 1948

N05978 Flatford Mill (1930)
Oc:724x762:signed:Presented by the Contemporary Art Society 1951

N06237 Wings over Water (1930)
Oc:711x914:signed:Presented by Geoffrey, Peter and Richard Gorer in memory of Rèe Alice Gorer 1954

T00163 Still Life (circa 1929)
Dπ:378x445:signed:Presented by Miss Lilian Harmston in accordance with the wishes of Arthur Rowland Howell 1957

HOFLAND, Thomas Christopher 1777-1843
British Collection

N01242 Stirling Castle (circa 1815)
Oc:1321x1841:Purchased 1888

HOFLEHNER, Rudolf born 1916
Modern Collection

T00679 Figure in Iron (1963)
Figur aus Eisen
Sm:2007x508x749:Purchased 1964

HOFMANN, Hans 1880-1966
Modern Collection

T03256 Pompeii (1959)
Oc:2146x1476:signed:Purchased 1981

T04847 Nulli Secundus (1964)
Oc:2136x1318:signed:Purchased 1986

HOGARTH, Paul born 1917
Modern Collection
Tate Gallery Archive holds material concerning this artist

P06646 The Gates of Fez (1975)
CLπ:571x775:Presented by Curwen Studio 1976

HOGARTH, William 1697-1764
British Collection
Tate Gallery Archive holds material concerning this artist

N00112 The Painter and his Pug (1745)
Oc:900x699:signed:Purchased 1824

N01046 Sigismunda Mourning over the Heart of Guiscardo (1759)
Oc:1004x1265:signed:Bequeathed by J.H. Anderdon 1879

N01153 The Strode Family (circa 1738)
Oc:870x915:Bequeathed by Rev. William Finch 1880

N01161 Lavinia Fenton, Duchess of Bolton (circa 1740-50)
Oc:737x584:Purchased 1884

N01374 Heads of Six of Hogarth's Servants (circa 1750-5)
Oc:630x755:Purchased 1892

N01464 O the Roast Beef of Old England ('The Gate of Calais') (1748)
Oc:788x945:Presented by the Duke of Westminster 1895

N01663 Mrs Salter (1741)
Oc:762x635:signed:Purchased 1898

N01935 James Quin, Actor (circa 1739)
Oc:760x622:Purchased 1904

N02437 A Scene from 'The Beggar's Opera' VI (1731)
Oc:572x762:Purchased 1909

N02736 Benjamin Hoadly, Bishop of Winchester (1741)
Oc:1273x1015:signed:Purchased 1910

N05359 The Staymaker (? The Happy Marriage V: The Fitting of the Ball Gown) (circa 1745)
Oc:699x908:Purchased with assistance from the National Art Collections Fund 1942

T00790 Satan, Sin and Death (A Scene from Milton's 'Paradise Lost') (circa 1735-40)
Oc:619x745:Purchased 1966

T00809 Ashley Cowper with his Wife and Daughter (1731)
Oc:533x612:signed:Purchased with assistance from the Friends of the Tate Gallery 1966

T01570 Thomas Pellett, M.D. (circa 1735-9)
Oc:764x635:signed:Bequeathed by Miss Rachel and Miss Jean Alexander 1972

T01789 A Rake's Progress (plate 1) (1735)
Lπ:318x387:Transferred from the reference collection 1973

T01790 A Rake's Progress (plate 3) (1735)
Lπ:318x387:Transferred from the reference collection 1973

T01791 A Rake's Progress (plate 4) (1735)
Lπ:318x387:Transferred from the reference collection 1973

T01792 A Rake's Progress (plate 5) (1735)
Lπ:314x391:Transferred from the reference collection 1973

T01793 A Rake's Progress (plate 7) (1735)
Lπ:318x387:Transferred from the reference collection 1973

T01794 A Rake's Progress (plate 8) (1735-63)
Lπ:318x387:Transferred from the reference collection 1973

T01799 Gin Lane (1751)
Lπ:357x305:Transferred from the reference collection 1973

T01800 The Enraged Musician (1741)
Lπ:332x405:Transferred from the reference collection 1973

T01805 Paul before Felix (1752-62)
Lπ:384x508:Transferred from the reference collection 1973

T01971 Thomas Herring, Archbishop of Canterbury (1744-7)
Oc:1270x1015:signed:Purchased 1975

T03613 The Dance (The Happy Marriage ?VI: The Country Dance) (circa 1745)
Oc:677x892:Purchased with assistance from the National Heritage Memorial Fund 1983

HOGARTH, William and AVILINE, François Antoine 1697-1764, 1727-1780
British Collection

T01797 Four Prints of an Election, plate 4: Chairing the Members (1758)
Lπ:403x540:Transferred from the reference collection 1973

HOGARTH, William and MOSLEY, Charles 1697-1764, 1744 - circa 1770
British Collection

T03918 O the Roast Beef of Old England ('The Gate of Calais') (1749)
Lπ:432x569:Presented by Mrs M.L. Hemphill 1984

HOGARTH, William and SULLIVAN, Luke 1697-1764, 1705-1771
British Collection

T01798 Moses Brought to Pharoah's Daughter (1752-62)
Lπ:390x505:Transferred from the reference collection 1973

T01802 The March to Finchley (1750-61)
Ln:418x542:Transferred from the reference collection
1973

prints after
HOGARTH, William 1697-1764
British Collection

T01680 Satan, Sin and Death, engraved by Thomas Rowlandson
and John Ogbourne after T00790 (1792)
Ln:273x348:Purchased 1972

T01795 Bambridge on Trial for Murder by a Committee of the
House of Commons, engraved by Thomas Cook (1803)
Ln:396x526:Transferred from the reference collection
1973

T01796 Four Prints of an Election, plate 2: Canvassing for Votes,
engraved by Charles Grignion (1757, published 1758)
Ln:405x537:Transferred from the reference collection
1973

T01801 Beggar's Opera, Act III, engraved by William Blake
(1790)
Ln:402x539:Transferred from the reference collection
1973

T01803 Henry the Eighth and Ann Boleyn, engraver unknown
Ln:438x357:Transferred from the reference collection
1973

T01804 The Indian Emperor, engraved by Robert Dodd (1792)
Ln:406x540:Transferred from the reference collection
1973

T03827 Dr Benjamin Hoadly, Bishop of Winchester, engraved by
Thomas Cook (circa 1800)
Ln:321x264:Transferred from the reference collection
1984

T03828 The Staymaker, engraved by Joseph Haynes (1782)
Ln:265x352:Transferred from the reference collection
1984

HOKANSON, Lars born 1942
Modern Collection

P01421 Peaceable Kingdom Revisited (1974)
CLn:394x473:signed:Presented by Christie's
Contemporary Art through the Institute of
Contemporary Prints 1975

follower of
HOLBEIN, Hans, the Younger 1497 or 98 - 1543
British Collection

N04252 William, First Lord de la Warr (?) (circa 1550)
Ow:1327x781:Presented in memory of R.S. Holford and
Sir George Holford by nine members of their family 1927

HOLDEN, Cliff born 1919
Modern Collection
Tate Gallery Archive holds material concerning this artist

T00504 Yellow Seated Figure (1947)
Ob:730x578:signed:Purchased 1962

HOLL, Frank 1845-1888
British Collection
Tate Gallery Archive holds material concerning this artist

N01535 Hush! (1877)
Oc:343x445:signed:Presented by Sir Henry Tate 1894

N01536 Hushed (1877)
Oc:343x445:signed:Presented by Sir Henry Tate 1894

N04065 Samuel Cousins, R.A. (1879)
Oc:1270x1010:signed:Presented by Mrs Frank Holl 1925

N04876 Portrait of My Mother (1882)
Oc:610x508:signed:Presented by Mrs Frank Holl 1937

HOLLAND, Harry born 1941
Modern Collection

P07805 Door (1982)
MLn:195x130:signed:Purchased 1983

P07806 Lovers (1982)
MLn:136x115:signed:Purchased 1983

P07807 T.V. (1982)
MLn:153x157:signed:Purchased 1983

HOLLAND, James 1800-1870
British Collection
Tate Gallery Archive holds material concerning this artist

N01809 The Grand Canal, Venice
Ow:406x737:signed:Bequeathed by Henry Vaughan 1900

N03051 Greenwich Hospital as it was in 1837 (1862)
Ob:203x387:signed:Bequeathed by H.L. Florence 1916

N03326 St Ouen: Rouen (1828)
DWn:432x298:signed:Presented by Lancelot Hannen
through the National Art Collections Fund 1918

N03333 Study of Architecture at Rouen
DWn:432x298:Presented by Lancelot Hannen through
the National Art Collections Fund 1918

N03524 A Recollection of Venice
Ob:419x292:Bequeathed by R.H. Prance 1920

N04236 The Thames below Woolwich, 1843
Oc:610x508:Bequeathed by Miss Susan Field 1927

T01002 Rotterdam (1845)
WDn:432x298:signed:Presented by the National Art
Collections Fund (Herbert Powell Bequest) 1967

T05492 The Tour d'Horloge, Rouen (1850)
Dn:250x180:Purchased 1988

HOLLOWAY, Charles Edward 1838-1897
British Collection

N04149 The St Vincent in Portsmouth Harbour (1893)
Oc:356x254:signed:Purchased 1926

HOLLWEG, Alexander born 1936
Modern Collection

For John Constable (P03149-P03157, P03159-P03161,
P03180-P03185; complete group; mixed group)
P03156 Untitled (1976)
CJn:457x571:signed:Presented by Bernard Jacobson
Gallery 1976

HOLMAN, Francis active 1767-1790
British Collection

T01763 A Dockyard at Wapping (circa 1780-84)
Oc:787x1270:Purchased 1973

HOLMES, Sir Charles John 1868-1936
British Collection
Tate Gallery Archive holds material concerning this artist

N03041 The Burning Kiln (1914)
Oc:686x762:signed:Presented by Michael Sadler through the National Art Collections Fund 1915

N03170 The Red Ruin (1907)
Oc:457x813:signed:Presented by the Contemporary Art Society 1917

N04381 Whernside (1917)
Oc:686x762:signed:Presented by Sir Evan Charteris 1928

HOLMES, Sir Richard Rivington 1835-1911
British Collection

N03618 The Monk (1861)
Dπ:102x57:signed:Presented by Sir Charles Holmes Holmes in memory of Mrs Robert Barclay 1922

HOLROYD, Sir Charles 1861-1917
British Collection
Tate Gallery Archive holds material concerning this artist

N03344 Villa Torlonia, Frascati (circa 1896)
Wπ:279x210:Presented by Lady Holroyd 1918

N03397 Sketch of G.F. Watts (1897)
Oc:559x406:signed:Presented by Lady Holroyd 1919

N03398 Sketch of Alphonse Legros
Oc:533x432:Presented by Lady Holroyd 1919

N03638 Medal of George Meredith
Rz:55x55x4:Presented by Lady Holroyd 1922

N04406 Death of Torrigiano (exhibited 1886)
Oc:927x1200:signed:Presented by Gen. Sir Ian Hamilton 1928

T01925 Wooded Landscape (circa 1906)
Wπ:311x508:signed:Transferred from the reference collection 1974

P01020 Alcantara Bridge, Toledo (1906)
MIπ:89x165:signed:Presented by Lady Holroyd 1918

P01021 Langstrath (1905)
MIπ:203x302:signed:Presented by Lady Holroyd 1918

P01022 Mountain View from the Top of Glaramara, towards Langdale (1907)
MIπ:92x356:signed:Presented by Lady Holroyd 1918

P01023 Honister Crag (1910)
MIπ:225x352:signed:Presented by Lady Holroyd 1918

P01024 Great Gable (1912)
MIπ:229x330:signed:Presented by Lady Holroyd 1918

P01025 The Salute, Venice (1902)
MIπ:302x225:signed:Presented by Lady Holroyd 1918

HOLST, Theodore von - see VON HOLST, Theodore

HOLT, Lilian 1898-1983
Modern Collection
Tate Gallery Archive holds material concerning this artist

T03088 Tajo, Ronda (1956)
Oc:711x911:Purchased 1980

HOLWORTHY, James 1781-1841
British Collection

T04369 Landscape Study
WDπ:61x111:Presented by Miss Marjorie Ball 1986

HOLZER, Jenny born 1950
Modern Collection

T03959 Truisms (1984)
SKV:169x1539x162:Presented by the Patrons of New Art through the Friends of the Tate Gallery 1985

P07847 Inflammatory Essays (1979-82)
CLπ:432x432:signed:Purchased 1983

Inflammatory Essays (P77382-P77412; complete group)

P77382 [no title] (1979-82)
CLπ:431x431:Purchased 1983

P77383 [no title] (1979-82)
CLπ:432x431:Purchased 1983

P77384 [no title] (1979-82)
CLπ:431x431:Purchased 1983

P77385 [no title] (1979-82)
CLπ:431x431:Purchased 1983

P77386 [no title] (1979-82)
CLπ:431x431:Purchased 1983

P77387 [no title] (1979-82)
CLπ:431x431:Purchased 1983

P77388 [no title] (1979-82)
CLπ:431x431:Purchased 1983

P77389 [no title] (1979-82)
CLπ:431x431:Purchased 1983

P77390 [no title] (1979-82)
CLπ:431x431:Purchased 1983

P77391 [no title] (1979-82)
CLπ:431x431:Purchased 1983

P77392 [no title] (1979-82)
CLπ:431x431:Purchased 1983

P77393 [no title] (1979-82)
CLπ:431x431:Purchased 1983

P77394 [no title] (1979-82)
CLπ:431x431:Purchased 1983

P77395 [no title] (1979-82)
CLπ:431x431:Purchased 1983

P77396 [no title] (1979-82)
CLπ:431x431:Purchased 1983

P77397 [no title] (1979-82)
CLπ:431x431:Purchased 1983

P77398 [no title] (1979-82)
CLπ:431x431:Purchased 1983

P77399 [no title] (1979-82)
CLπ:431x431:Purchased 1983

P77400 [no title] (1979-82)
CLπ:431x431:Purchased 1983

P77401 [no title] (1979-82)
CLπ:431x431:Purchased 1983

P77402 [no title] (1979-82)
CLπ:431x431:Purchased 1983

P77403 [no title] (1979-82)
CLπ:431x431:Purchased 1983

P77404 [no title] (1979-82)
CLπ:431x431:Purchased 1983

P77405 [no title] (1979-82)
CLπ:431x431:Purchased 1983

P77406 [no title] (1979-82)
CLπ:431x431:Purchased 1983

P77407 [no title] (1979-82)
CLπ:431x431:Purchased 1983

P77408 [no title] (1979-82)
CLπ:431x431:Purchased 1983

P77409 [no title] (1979-82)
CLπ:431x431:Purchased 1983

P77410 [no title] (1979-82)
CLπ:431x431:Purchased 1983

P77411 [no title] (1979-82)
CLπ:431x431:Purchased 1983

P77412 [no title] (1979-82)
CLπ:431x431:Purchased 1983

HONE, Evie 1894-1955
Modern Collection

T00204 The Crucifixion and Last Supper (circa 1949-50)
Gπ:305x210:Purchased 1958

T00205 Head of Christ (circa 1949-50)
Gπ:552x705:Purchased 1958

T03238 The Crucifixion (1948)
g:394x508:Presented by Derek Hill 1981

HONE, Nathaniel 1718-1784
British Collection

N00675 Mary Hone, the Artist's Wife (?1760)
Oc:289x219:Bequeathed by Richard Frankum 1861

N00760 Edward Orpin, Parish Clerk of Bradford-upon-Avon
(circa 1760-74)
Oc:1219x978:Purchased 1876

T00938 Sketch for 'The Conjuror' (1775)
Ow:575x819:signed:Purchased 1967

HONE, Nathaniel 1831-1917
British Collection

N04104 A Seapiece
Wπ:121x203:Bequeathed by Mrs Magdalene Hone 1925

HOOK, James Clarke 1819-1907
British Collection

N01512 Home with the Tide (1880)
Oc:889x1397:signed:Presented by Sir Henry Tate 1894

N01513 Young Dreams (1887)
Oc:1060x1422:signed:Presented by Sir Henry Tate 1894

N01514 The Seaweed Raker (1889)
Oc:730x1238:signed:Presented by Sir Henry Tate 1894

N01598 The Stream (1885)
Oc:921x1511:signed:Presented by the Trustees of the
Chantrey Bequest 1885

N02252 Wreckage from the Fruiter (1889)
Oc:921x1556:Presented by A.J. and B. Hook 1908

HOPPNER, John ?1758-1810
British Collection
Tate Gallery Archive holds material concerning this artist

N00133 William Smith the Actor (circa 1788)
Oc:792x514:Presented by Serjeant Taddy 1837

N00900 Jane Elizabeth, Countess of Oxford (1797)
Ow:743x635:Bequeathed by Lady Langdale 1873

N01505 Portrait of a Lady
Oc:1264x1003:Presented by Sir Henry Tate 1894

N02765 A Gale of Wind (circa 1794)
Oc:1321x1829:Presented by L. Lesser 1911

N03013 Master Frederick van Diest
Oc:1270x1003:Bequeathed by Miss Julia Crokat 1915

N03014 Miss Louisa van Diest
Oc:1270x1003:Bequeathed by Miss Julia Crokat 1915

N03512 Miss Harriet Cholmondeley (exhibited 1804)
Oc:1283x1022:Bequeathed by Amy, Lady Tate 1920

N04692 Mrs Jordan as Hypolita in 'She Would and She Would
Not' (exhibited 1791)
Oc:775x638:Bequeathed by Sir Edward Stern 1933

N04776 Lord Farnborough (exhibited 1807)
Oc:1270x1010:Presented by Mrs M.V. MacGeorge 1934

N05582 Mrs Williams (circa 1790)
Oc:756x629:Bequeathed by O.S. Ashcroft 1945

studio of
HOPPNER, John ?1758-1810
British Collection

N00233 William Pitt (circa 1806-7)
Oc:1416x1092:Presented by George Moffatt 1853

HOPWOOD, Henry Silkstone 1860-1914
British Collection

N01706 Industry (1894)
Wπ:749x619:signed:Presented by the Trustees of the
Chantrey Bequest 1894

HORNEL, Edward Atkinson 1864-1933
British Collection
Tate Gallery Archive holds material concerning this artist

N04401 Autumn (1904)
Oc:1168x1022:signed:Presented by Sir Hugh Reid 1928

HORSLEY, John Callcott 1817-1903
British Collection
Tate Gallery Archive holds material concerning this artist

N00446 The Pride of the Village (exhibited 1839)
Ow:762x622:Presented by Robert Vernon 1847

N02286 Martin H. Colnaghi (1889)
Oc:1118x870:Presented by Mrs Martin H. Colnaghi 1908

HORTON, Percy 1897-1970
Modern Collection
Tate Gallery Archive holds material concerning this artist

N05133 The Invalid (1934)
Oc:508x406:Purchased 1940

HOSKIN, John 1921-1990
Modern Collection
Tate Gallery Archive holds material concerning this artist

T00412 Standing Figure (1960)
Sm:533x724x178:Purchased 1961

T03752 Black Beetle (1957)
Sm:172x172x314:Transferred from the Victoria & Albert
Museum 1983

HOUGHTON, Arthur Boyd 1836-1875
British Collection

N03620 Punch and Judy
Oc:356x254:Purchased 1922

N03907 Ramsgate Sands (circa 1861)
Oc:241x298:signed:Presented by Miss Helen Devitt in memory of Sir Thomas Devitt Bt 1924

N04019 Child Among the Rocks, engraved by the Dalziel Brothers (published 1865)
Jπ:146x108:Presented by Gilbert Dalziel 1924

N04020 Princess Parizade, engraved by the Dalziel Brothers (published 1864)
Jπ:178x133:Presented by Gilbert Dalziel 1924

N04044 Jew and Gentile, for engraving (published 1864)
DGw:152x127:Presented by Mrs E.C. Davis 1925

N04045 Scotch Scene, for engraving
DGw:114x165:Presented by Mrs E.C. Davis 1925

N04053 The Envious Man Pulling Hairs out of the Cat's Tail, engraved by the Dalziel Brothers (published 1864)
Jπ:178x133:Presented by Harold Hartley 1925

N04122 The Chronicles being Read to the King, engraved by the Dalziel Brothers
Jπ:197x175:Presented by Gilbert Dalziel 1925

N04123 Birth of Camaralzaman (published 1864)
Jπ:171x130:Presented by Gilbert Dalziel 1925

N04151 Mother and Children Reading (circa 1860)
Oc:305x248:Presented by Mrs E.C. Davis 1926

N04152 Lady with a Book (circa 1860)
Oc:241x190:Presented by Mrs E.C. Davis 1926

N04153 The African Magician Offers New Lamps for Old, for engraving (published 1864)
DWπ:171x127:Presented by Mrs E.C. Davis 1926

N04154 The Indian Prostrates Himself Before the King of Persia, for engraving (published 1864)
Dw:171x127:Presented by Mrs E.C. Davis 1926

N04155 Scene from 'The Arabian Nights', for engraving (published 1864)
Dw:127x79:Presented by Mrs E.C. Davis 1926

N04156 Scene from 'The Arabian Nights', for engraving
Dw:95x127:Presented by Mrs E.C. Davis 1926

N04157 Old Woman Seated in a Chair, for engraving
DGw:159x108:Presented by Mrs E.C. Davis 1926

N04158 London Scene, for engraving
DGw:105x89:Presented by Mrs E.C. Davis 1926

N04159 Facing the Camera, for engraving (circa 1865)
DGw:133x102:Presented by Mrs E.C. Davis 1926

N04160 Scene from 'Don Quixote', for engraving (published 1866)
Dw:89x95:Presented by Mrs E.C. Davis 1926

N04161 My Treasure: Mrs A.B. Houghton and Two Children, engraved by the Dalziel Brothers
Jπ:165x121:Presented by Mrs E.C. Davis 1926

N04207 Volunteers
Oc:305x394:Purchased 1926

N04366 The Don on the Island
Oc:292x406:Presented by Mrs and Mrs Gerald Brown 1927

N04397 Head of a Child
Wπ:73x73:signed:Presented by Miss Frances Burlison through the National Art Collections Fund 1928

N04402 Study of a Woman
Wπ:89x63:signed:Presented by Miss Frances Burlison through the National Art Collections Fund 1928

N04403 Head of a Woman and Child
Wπ:79x95:signed:Presented by Miss Frances Burlison through the National Art Collections Fund 1928

T01948 Uncle John with the Young Folk: 'All Prizes and No Blanks!' engraved by the Dalziel Brothers (published 1865)
Jπ:238x346:Transferred from the reference collection 1975

Studies of Children (A00197-A00210; complete group)
A00197 [title not known]
Dπ::Presented by H. Reitlinger 1922

A00198 [title not known]
Dπ::Presented by H. Reitlinger 1922

A00199 [title not known]
Dπ::Presented by H. Reitlinger 1922

A00200 [title not known]
Dπ::Presented by H. Reitlinger 1922

A00201 [title not known]
Dπ::Presented by Mrs E.C. Davis 1926

A00202 [title not known]
Dπ::Presented by Mrs E.C. Davis 1926

A00203 [title not known]
Dπ::Presented by Mrs E.C. Davis 1926

A00204 [title not known]
Dπ::Presented by Mrs E.C. Davis 1926

A00205 [title not known]
Dπ::Presented by Mrs E.C. Davis 1926

A00206 [title not known]
Dπ::Presented by Mrs E.C. Davis 1926

A00207 [title not known]
Dπ::Presented by Mrs E.C. Davis 1926

A00208 [title not known]
Dπ::Presented by Mrs E.C. Davis 1926

A00209 [title not known]
Dπ::Presented by Mrs E.C. Davis 1926

A00210 [title not known]
Dπ::Presented by Mrs E.C. Davis 1926

HOUSE, Gordon born 1932
Modern Collection
Tate Gallery Archive holds material concerning this artist

P01173 Black Quartered Arc (1970)
MLπ:254x254:signed:Presented by Waddington Galleries through the Institute of Contemporary Prints 1975

P01174 Cornered Circuit (1970)
MLπ:251x254:signed:Presented by Waddington Galleries through the Institute of Contemporary Prints 1975

P01175 Diagonal Feint Ruled (1970)
MLπ:257x254:signed:Presented by Waddington Galleries through the Institute of Contemporary Prints 1975

P01176 Embossed Quartered Arc (1970)
MLπ:251x251:signed:Presented by Waddington Galleries through the Institute of Contemporary Prints 1975

P01177 Quartered Arc (1970)
MLπ:168x168:signed:Presented by Waddington Galleries through the Institute of Contemporary Prints 1975

P01178 A. Ladder Box (1970)
MLπ:389x378:signed:Presented by Waddington Galleries through the Institute of Contemporary Prints 1975

P01179 B. Multi-Case (1970)
MLπ:380x380:signed:Presented by Waddington Galleries through the Institute of Contemporary Prints 1975

P01180 C. Vertical Screen (1970)
MIπ:380x384:signed:Presented by Waddington Galleries
through the Institute of Contemporary Prints 1975

P01181 D. Drop Initials (1970)
MIπ:382x380:signed:Presented by Waddington Galleries
through the Institute of Contemporary Prints 1975

P01182 E. Quoined Chase (1970)
MIπ:377x378:signed:Presented by Waddington Galleries
through the Institute of Contemporary Prints 1975

P01183 F. Mitred Matrix (1970)
MIπ:380x380:signed:Presented by Waddington Galleries
through the Institute of Contemporary Prints 1975

P01184 A. Ladder Box (1970)
CLπ:502x502:signed:Presented by Waddington Galleries
through the Institute of Contemporary Prints 1975

P01185 B. Multi-Case (1970)
CLπ:502x502:signed:Presented by Waddington Galleries
through the Institute of Contemporary Prints 1975

P01186 C. Vertical Screen (1970)
CLπ:502x502:signed:Presented by Waddington Galleries
through the Institute of Contemporary Prints 1975

P01187 D. Drop Initials (1970)
CLπ:502x502:signed:Presented by Waddington Galleries
through the Institute of Contemporary Prints 1975

P01188 E. Quoined Chase (1970)
CLπ:502x502:signed:Presented by Waddington Galleries
through the Institute of Contemporary Prints 1975

P01189 F. Mitred Matrix (1970)
CLπ:502x502:signed:Presented by Waddington Galleries
through the Institute of Contemporary Prints 1975

P01190 Vertical Feint Ruled (1970)
MIπ:257x257:signed:Presented by Waddington Galleries
through the Institute of Contemporary Prints 1975

P01191 Arcs with a Square (1971)
MIπ:257x253:signed:Presented by Waddington Galleries
through the Institute of Contemporary Prints 1975

P01192 Arcs with a Square (1971)
MIπ:256x255:signed:Presented by Waddington Galleries
through the Institute of Contemporary Prints 1975

P01193 Arcs with a Square (1971)
MIπ:257x254:signed:Presented by Waddington Galleries
through the Institute of Contemporary Prints 1975

P01194 Arcs with a Square (1971)
MIπ:256x254:signed:Presented by Waddington Galleries
through the Institute of Contemporary Prints 1975

P01195 Arcs with a Square (1971)
MIπ:256x253:signed:Presented by Waddington Galleries
through the Institute of Contemporary Prints 1975

P01196 Arcs with a Square (1971)
MIπ:256x255:signed:Presented by Waddington Galleries
through the Institute of Contemporary Prints 1975

P01197 Arcs with a Square (1971)
MIπ:254x254:signed:Presented by Waddington Galleries
through the Institute of Contemporary Prints 1975

P01198 Triangles within a Square (1971)
MIπ:256x254:signed:Presented by Waddington Galleries
through the Institute of Contemporary Prints 1975

P01199 Triangles within a Square (1971)
MIπ:255x253:signed:Presented by Waddington Galleries
through the Institute of Contemporary Prints 1975

P01200 Triangles within a Square (1971)
MIπ:255x254:signed:Presented by Waddington Galleries
through the Institute of Contemporary Prints 1975

P01201 Triangles within a Square (1971)
MIπ:256x253:signed:Presented by Waddington Galleries
through the Institute of Contemporary Prints 1975

P01202 Triangles within a Square (1971)
MIπ:256x254:signed:Presented by Waddington Galleries
through the Institute of Contemporary Prints 1975

P01203 Triangles within a Square (1971)
MIπ:255x253:signed:Presented by Waddington Galleries
through the Institute of Contemporary Prints 1975

P01204 Triangles within a Square (1971)
MIπ:255x252:signed:Presented by Waddington Galleries
through the Institute of Contemporary Prints 1975

P01205 Triangles within a Square (1971)
MIπ:257x254:signed:Presented by Waddington Galleries
through the Institute of Contemporary Prints 1975

IAA Portfolio (P03096-P03104, P03107; complete
group; mixed group)

P03101 Highbury Quadrant (1975)
CLπ:451x305:signed:Presented by the International
Association of Art 1975

P04329 Blue (1961)
CNπ:406x394:signed:Presented by Rose and Chris Prater
through the Institute of Contemporary Prints 1975

P04330 Brown (1961)
CNπ:406x394:signed:Presented by Rose and Chris Prater
through the Institute of Contemporary Prints 1975

P04331 Grey (1961)
CNπ:406x394:signed:Presented by Rose and Chris Prater
through the Institute of Contemporary Prints 1975

P04332 Orange (1961)
CNπ:406x394:signed:Presented by Rose and Chris Prater
through the Institute of Contemporary Prints 1975

P04333 Yellow (1961)
CNπ:406x394:signed:Presented by Rose and Chris Prater
through the Institute of Contemporary Prints 1975

The Institute of Contemporary Arts Portfolio (P04016,
P04038, P04053, P04076, P04115, P04125, P04166,
P04248, P04256, P04315-P04316, P04334,
P04378-P04380, P04419, P04635, P04752, P04938,
P05138, P05155, P05248; complete group; mixed group)

P04334 Eight Red Arcs (1964)
CNπ::signed:Presented by Rose and Chris Prater through
the Institute of Contemporary Prints 1975

P04335 Series 40cm A (1965)
CNπ:406x406:signed:Presented by Rose and Chris Prater
through the Institute of Contemporary Prints 1975

P04336 Series 40cm B (1965)
CNπ:406x406:signed:Presented by Rose and Chris Prater
through the Institute of Contemporary Prints 1975

P04337 Series 40cm C (1965)
CNπ:406x406:signed:Presented by Rose and Chris Prater
through the Institute of Contemporary Prints 1975

P04338 Series 40cm D (1965)
CNπ:406x406:signed:Presented by Rose and Chris Prater
through the Institute of Contemporary Prints 1975

P04339 Series 40cm E (1965)
CNπ:406x406:signed:Presented by Rose and Chris Prater
through the Institute of Contemporary Prints 1975

P04340 Series 40cm F (1965)
CNπ:406x406:signed:Presented by Rose and Chris Prater
through the Institute of Contemporary Prints 1975

P04341 Dial Set One (1966)
CNπ:521x521:signed:Presented by Rose and Chris Prater
through the Institute of Contemporary Prints 1975

P04342 Dial Set Two (1966)
CNπ:521x521:signed:Presented by Rose and Chris Prater through the Institute of Contemporary Prints 1975

P04343 Dial Set Three (1966)
CNπ:521x521:signed:Presented by Rose and Chris Prater through the Institute of Contemporary Prints 1975

P04344 Dial Set Four (1966)
CNπ:521x521:signed:Presented by Rose and Chris Prater through the Institute of Contemporary Prints 1975

P04345 Dial Set Five (1966)
CNπ:521x521:signed:Presented by Rose and Chris Prater through the Institute of Contemporary Prints 1975

P04346 Dial Set Six (1966)
CNπ:521x521:signed:Presented by Rose and Chris Prater through the Institute of Contemporary Prints 1975

P04347 Black Matrices (1967)
CNπ:511x508:signed:Presented by Rose and Chris Prater through the Institute of Contemporary Prints 1975

P04348 Orange Matrices (1967)
CNπ:511x508:signed:Presented by Rose and Chris Prater through the Institute of Contemporary Prints 1975

P04349 Red Matrices (1967)
CNπ:508x511:signed:Presented by Rose and Chris Prater through the Institute of Contemporary Prints 1975

P04350 4 Blue Arcs (1967)
CNπ:457x457:signed:Presented by Rose and Chris Prater through the Institute of Contemporary Prints 1975

P04351 4 Red Arcs (1967)
CNπ:457x457:signed:Presented by Rose and Chris Prater through the Institute of Contemporary Prints 1975

P04352 Series 40cm Continued G (1969)
CNπ:400x400:signed:Presented by Rose and Chris Prater through the Institute of Contemporary Prints 1975

P04353 Series 40cm Continued H (1969)
CNπ:400x400:signed:Presented by Rose and Chris Prater through the Institute of Contemporary Prints 1975

P04354 Series 40cm Continued I (1969)
CNπ:400x400:signed:Presented by Rose and Chris Prater through the Institute of Contemporary Prints 1975

P04355 Series 40cm Continued J (1969)
CNπ:400x400:signed:Presented by Rose and Chris Prater through the Institute of Contemporary Prints 1975

P04356 Multi/Screen (1969)
CNπ:508x511:signed:Presented by Rose and Chris Prater through the Institute of Contemporary Prints 1975

P04357 Arc A (1971)
CNπ:864x432:signed:Presented by Rose and Chris Prater through the Institute of Contemporary Prints 1975

P04358 Arc B (1971)
CNπ:864x432:signed:Presented by Rose and Chris Prater through the Institute of Contemporary Prints 1975

P04359 Arc C (1971)
CNπ:864x432:signed:Presented by Rose and Chris Prater through the Institute of Contemporary Prints 1975

P04360 Arc D (1971)
CNπ:864x432:signed:Presented by Rose and Chris Prater through the Institute of Contemporary Prints 1975

P04361 Circle E (1971)
CNπ:864x435:signed:Presented by Rose and Chris Prater through the Institute of Contemporary Prints 1975

P04362 Red Quarter Arc (1971)
CNπ:514x518:signed:Presented by Rose and Chris Prater through the Institute of Contemporary Prints 1975

P04363 Triangle A (1971)
CNπ:864x435:signed:Presented by Rose and Chris Prater through the Institute of Contemporary Prints 1975

P04364 Triangle B (1971)
CNπ:864x435:signed:Presented by Rose and Chris Prater through the Institute of Contemporary Prints 1975

P04365 Triangle C (1971)
CNπ:864x435:signed:Presented by Rose and Chris Prater through the Institute of Contemporary Prints 1975

P04366 Triangle D (1971)
CNπ:864x435:signed:Presented by Rose and Chris Prater through the Institute of Contemporary Prints 1975

P04367 Triangle E (1971)
CNπ:864x435:signed:Presented by Rose and Chris Prater through the Institute of Contemporary Prints 1975

P04368 Triangle F (1971)
CNπ:864x435:signed:Presented by Rose and Chris Prater through the Institute of Contemporary Prints 1975

P04369 Triangle G (1971)
CNπ:864x435:signed:Presented by Rose and Chris Prater through the Institute of Contemporary Prints 1975

P04370 Amsterdam B (1971)
CNπ:413x397:signed:Presented by Rose and Chris Prater through the Institute of Contemporary Prints 1975

P04371 Amsterdam A (1971)
CNπ:413x397:signed:Presented by Rose and Chris Prater through the Institute of Contemporary Prints 1975

P04372 Green A (1972)
CNπ:914x305:signed:Presented by Rose and Chris Prater through the Institute of Contemporary Prints 1975

P05505 Crystal Earth (1978-9)
CLπ:419x305:signed:Presented by Rose and Chris Prater 1979

P05506 Directional Pink (1978-9)
CLπ:413x305:signed:Presented by Rose and Chris Prater 1979

P05507 Gothic Green (1978-9)
CLπ:413x305:signed:Presented by Rose and Chris Prater 1979

P05508 Manuscript Red (1978-9)
CLπ:413x305:signed:Presented by Rose and Chris Prater 1979

P05509 Manx Yellow (1978-9)
CLπ:413x305:signed:Presented by Rose and Chris Prater 1979

P05561 Still Life at Millbank (1980)
CNπ:483x635:Presented by Rose and Chris Prater 1980

P07360 An Assemblage of Several Things (1979)
CNπ:502x698:signed:Purchased 1980

HOUSMAN, Laurence 1861-1959
British Collection

N03876 The White Doe (circa 1904)
Dπ:140x83:signed:Purchased 1924

N03877 The Rat-Catcher's Daughter (circa 1904)
Dπ:152x92:signed:Purchased 1924

HOUSHIARY, Shirazeh born 1955
Modern Collection

T05012 Study for 'The Angel of Thought' (1987)
DVπ:498x699:Presented by Weltkunst Foundation 1987

T05013 Study for 'The Earth is an Angel' (1987)
DVπ:509x634:Presented by Weltkunst Foundation 1987

T05014 Study for 'Beating of her Wings' (1987)
DVπ:560x760:Presented by Weltkunst Foundation 1987

T05015 Study for 'Beating of her Wings' (1987)
DVπ:575x760:Presented by Weltkunst Foundation 1987

T05016 Study for 'Beating of her Wings' (1987)
DVπ:379x576:Presented by Weltkunst Foundation 1987

T05017 Study for 'Beating of her Wings' (1987)
DVπ:379x576:Presented by Weltkunst Foundation 1987

T05022 The Earth is an Angel (1987)
Smw:1900x2000x2000:Purchased 1987

HOUTHUESEN, Albert 1903-1979
Modern Collection

N04972 Painted in a Welsh Village (1933)
Oc:940x686:signed:Presented by Dr Edwin Charles
Montgomery-Smith 1938

N05122 Crown of Thorns (1939)
Oc:914x1219:signed:Presented by Lady Matthews 1940

N05328 Maes Gwyn Stack Yard (1935)
Oc:914x1219:signed:Presented by the Trustees of the
Chantrey Bequest 1939

T00425 Ruskin Park II (1959)
Dπ:559x698:signed:Purchased 1961

P06293 Untitled (1969)
CLπ:565x445:Presented by Curwen Studio through the
Institute of Contemporary Prints 1975

P06294 Untitled Sweet Note - Bitter Apple (1969)
MLπ:540x454:signed:Presented by Curwen Studio
through the Institute of Contemporary Prints 1975

P06295 Harry Langdon (Clown with a Small Trilby Hat) (1970)
CLπ:591x460:signed:Presented by Curwen Studio through
the Institute of Contemporary Prints 1975

A Portfolio of Clowns (P06296-P06300; complete group)

P06296 1. White Faced Clown (1970)
CLπ:597x465:signed:Presented by Curwen Studio
through the Institute of Contemporary Prints 1975

P06297 2. Augusti (1970)
CLπ:595x455:signed:Presented by Curwen Studio
through the Institute of Contemporary Prints 1975

P06298 3. Juggler Clowns (1970)
CLπ:5902x469:signed:Presented by Curwen Studio
through the Institute of Contemporary Prints 1975

P06299 4. Night (1970)
CLπ:610x475:signed:Presented by Curwen Studio
through the Institute of Contemporary Prints 1975

P06300 5. Muse and Clown (1970)
CLπ:491x632:signed:Presented by Curwen Studio
through the Institute of Contemporary Prints 1975

P06301 Harry Langdon (1970-4)
MLπ:587x460:signed:Presented by Curwen Studio
through the Institute of Contemporary Prints 1975

P06302 White Face in a Straw Hat (1970-4)
MLπ:559x441:Presented by Curwen Studio through the
Institute of Contemporary Prints 1975

P06303 Philemon (1971)
MLπ:362x311:Presented by Curwen Studio through the
Institute of Contemporary Prints 1975

P06304 Of the Company of St Philemon (1974)
MLπ:759x495:Presented by Curwen Studio through the
Institute of Contemporary Prints 1975

P06305 Clown with Striped Hat (1974)
CLπ:759x495:Presented by Curwen Studio through the
Institute of Contemporary Prints 1975

P06306 Dancer (1974)
MLπ:581x454:signed:Presented by Curwen Studio
through the Institute of Contemporary Prints 1975

P06307 Dancers (1974)
MLπ:546x394:Presented by Curwen Studio through the
Institute of Contemporary Prints 1975

P06308 Laurel (1974)
MLπ:543x425:Presented by Curwen Studio through the
Institute of Contemporary Prints 1975

P06309 Mariner (1974)
MLπ:502x381:Presented by Curwen Studio through the
Institute of Contemporary Prints 1975

P06310 Buster (Keaton) (1974)
MLπ:756x492:Presented by Curwen Studio through the
Institute of Contemporary Prints 1975

P06311 Reflections (1974)
MLπ:664x508:Presented by Curwen Studio through the
Institute of Contemporary Prints 1975

P06312 Stage Actors, Adam and Eve (1974)
MLπ:581x457:Presented by Curwen Studio through the
Institute of Contemporary Prints 1975

P06313 White Face with Plumed Hat (1974)
MLπ:578x448:signed:Presented by Curwen Studio
through the Institute of Contemporary Prints 1975

P06647 Stone Cutter (1974)
MLπ:511x375:signed:Presented by Curwen Studio 1976

P06648 Celebration (1974-5)
CLπ:660x508:signed:Presented by Curwen Studio 1976

P06649 Hubbub (1975)
MLπ:584x457:signed:Presented by Curwen Studio 1976

P06650 Cleft Tree (1975)
MLπ:387x508:signed:Presented by Curwen Studio 1976

P06651 The Beauty Patch (1975)
MLπ:584x457:signed:Presented by Curwen Studio 1976

P06652 Sun over Lake (1975)
MLπ:505x387:signed:Presented by Curwen Studio 1976

P06653 Trilogy (1975)
CLπ:562x410:signed:Presented by Curwen Studio 1976

P06654 Magician (1975)
MLπ:505x311:signed:Presented by Curwen Studio 1976

P06655 Sea Shell (1975)
MLπ:384x505:Presented by Curwen Studio 1976

P06712 Ancestor (1969)
CLπ:352x219:Presented by Curwen Studio 1976

HOW, Beatrice 1867-1932
British Collection

N04837 L'Infirmière (circa 1914-18)
Oc:54x70:signed:Presented by the Trustees of the
Chantrey Bequest 1935

HOWARD, George - see CARLISLE, George Howard, Ninth Earl of

HOWARD, Henry 1769-1847
British Collection
Tate Gallery Archive holds material concerning this artist

N00349 The Flower Girl
Oc:965x610:Presented by Robert Vernon 1847

HOWELL, Peter born 1932
Modern Collection

P06314   The Last Furlong (1973)
CLπ:483x705:signed:Presented by Curwen Studio
through the Institute of Contemporary Prints 1975

HOWITT, Samuel 1756-1822
British Collection

T01003   A Stag Hunt (1793)
Wπ:181x260:signed:Presented by the National Art
Collections Fund (Herbert Powell Bequest) 1967

HOWSON, Peter born 1958
Modern Collection

P77243   Arm Wrestlers: Paisley (1986)
Jπ:750x1040:signed:Purchased 1988

P77244   The Noble Dosser (1987)
Jπ:1774x1167:signed:Purchased 1988

P77245   Rupert (1987)
Iπ:325x248:signed:Purchased 1988

P77246   Amanda (1987)
Iπ:330x245:signed:Purchased 1988

P77247   Bob (1987)
Iπ:326x247:signed:Purchased 1988

P77248   Ned (1987)
Iπ:320x245:signed:Purchased 1988

HOYLAND, John born 1934
Modern Collection
Tate Gallery Archive holds material concerning this artist

T00710   No. 22, 20. 2. 62 (1962)
Oc:1727x1727:signed:Presented by the Contemporary
Art Society 1964

T00886   28. 5. 66 (1966)
Ac:1981x3658:Purchased 1966

T01129   25. 4. 69 (1969)
Ac:2438x914:signed:Presented by the Friends of the Tate
Gallery 1969

T01130   17. 3. 69 (1969)
Ac:1984x3658:signed:Purchased 1969

T02402   Saracen (1977)
Ac:2438x2286:signed:Purchased 1979

T02403   North Sound (1979)
Ac:2438x2286:signed:Purchased 1979

T03701   April 1961 (1961)
Oc:1525x1527:signed:Presented by E.J. Power through
the Friends of the Tate Gallery 1983

T04924   Gadal 10.11.86 (1986)
Ac:2540x2540:signed:Purchased 1987

P01206   Brown-Beige-Pink (1971)
CLπ:530x724:signed:Presented by Waddington Galleries
through the Institute of Contemporary Prints 1975

The New York Suite (P01207-P01215; complete group)
P01207   Green, Orange, Pink (1971)
CNπ:914x660:signed:Presented by Waddington Galleries
through the Institute of Contemporary Prints 1975

P01208   Yellow and Pink (1971)
CNπ:914x660:signed:Presented by Waddington Galleries
through the Institute of Contemporary Prints 1975

P01209   Grey / Blue (1971)
CNπ:914x660:signed:Presented by Waddington Galleries
through the Institute of Contemporary Prints 1975

P01210   Pale Yellow, Pink and Brown (1971)
CNπ:914x660:signed:Presented by Waddington Galleries
through the Institute of Contemporary Prints 1975

P01211   Red Black on Grey (1971)
CNπ:917x660:signed:Presented by Waddington Galleries
through the Institute of Contemporary Prints 1975

P01212   Red Black on Pink (1971)
CNπ:917x660:signed:Presented by Waddington Galleries
through the Institute of Contemporary Prints 1975

P01213   Brown Black on Pink (1971)
CNπ:917x660:signed:Presented by Waddington Galleries
through the Institute of Contemporary Prints 1975

P01214   Grey / Blue on Pink (1971)
CNπ:914x660:signed:Presented by Waddington Galleries
through the Institute of Contemporary Prints 1975

P01215   Grey / Blue on Green (1971)
CNπ:914x660:signed:Presented by Waddington Galleries
through the Institute of Contemporary Prints 1975

P01216   Orange, Pink (1971)
CNπ:445x632:signed:Presented by Waddington Galleries
through the Institute of Contemporary Prints 1975

P01217   Orange-Pink-Green (1971)
CNLπ:486x740:signed:Presented by Waddington
Galleries through the Institute of Contemporary Prints
1975

P01218   Untitled I (1974)
CLπ:771x599:signed:Presented by Waddington Galleries
through the Institute of Contemporary Prints 1975

P01219   Untitled II (1974)
CLπ:773x600:signed:Presented by Waddington Galleries
through the Institute of Contemporary Prints 1975

P01220   Untitled III (1974)
CLπ:778x602:signed:Presented by Waddington Galleries
through the Institute of Contemporary Prints 1975

For John Constable (P03149-P03157, P03159-P03161,
P03180-P03185; complete group; mixed group)
P03185   Untitled (1976)
ACLπ:549x857:signed:Presented by Bernard Jacobson
Gallery 1977

P04373   Blues, Greens (1969)
CNπ:600x908:signed:Presented by Rose and Chris Prater
through the Institute of Contemporary Prints 1975

P04374   Blues, Reds (1969)
CNπ:600x914:signed:Presented by Rose and Chris Prater
through the Institute of Contemporary Prints 1975

P04375   Red, Blue (1969)
CNπ:556x927:signed:Presented by Rose and Chris Prater
through the Institute of Contemporary Prints 1975

P04376   Reds, Greens (1969)
CNπ:597x908:signed:Presented by Rose and Chris Prater
through the Institute of Contemporary Prints 1975

P04377   Yellows (1969)
CNπ:524x908:signed:Presented by Rose and Chris Prater
through the Institute of Contemporary Prints 1975

P05510   Splay (1979)
CIπ:689x543:signed:Presented by Rose and Chris Prater
1979

P05511   Trace (1979)
CIπ:689x546:signed:Presented by Rose and Chris Prater
1979

P05512   Trickster (1979)
CIπ:692x546:signed:Presented by Rose and Chris Prater
1979

P05513   View (1979)
CIπ:689x546:signed:Presented by Rose and Chris Prater 1979

P05549   Memphis (1980)
CIπ:692x543:signed:Presented by Rose and Chris Prater 1980

P05550   Rankin (1979)
CIπ:689x546:signed:Presented by Rose and Chris Prater 1980

P05551   Tembi (1980)
CIπ:546x692:signed:Presented by Rose and Chris Prater 1980

P05567   Vigil (1980)
CIπ:546x689:signed:Presented by Rose and Chris Prater 1981

P07513   Anking (1979)
CIπ:673x533:signed:Purchased 1981

P07514   Dido (1979)
CIπ:676x533:signed:Purchased 1981

HUBBARD, John born 1931
Modern Collection
Tate Gallery Archive holds material concerning this artist

T00589   Autumn on the Chesil Bank (1962)
Oπ:787x648:Purchased 1963

T03371   Light Structure (1966)
Oc:1727x2030:signed:Purchased 1982

T03372   Haytor Quarry (1980-1)
Oc:2032x1930:signed:Purchased 1982

HUDSON, Thomas 1701-1779
British Collection

N01224   Samuel Scott, the Marine Painter (circa 1731-3)
Oc:1220x978:Purchased 1886

N04804   Mrs Collier (1744)
Oc:737x610:Bequeathed by the Misses Mary M. and L.M. Badcock 1935

T00401   Mrs Sarah Ingrams (circa 1750-5)
Oc:1270x1016:Bequeathed by Mrs E.M.E. Commeline 1961

HUEBLER, Douglas born 1924
Modern Collection

T01823   Site Sculpture Project, Windham College Pentagon, Putney, Vermont (1968)
FDCb:622x1276:signed:Presented by Mr and Mrs Joshua A. Gollin through the American Federation of Arts 1973

P07234   Variable Piece No. 44 (1971)
MFVπ:457x613:signed:Purchased 1974

HUGGINS, William 1820-1884
British Collection

T00904   Donkeys and Sheep in a Landscape (1867)
Ow:610x467:signed:Purchased 1967

HUGHES, Arthur 1832-1915
British Collection
Tate Gallery Archive holds material concerning this artist

N02476   April Love (1855-6)
Oc:889x495:signed:Purchased 1909

N04604   The Eve of St Agnes (1856)
Oc:710x1245:signed:Bequeathed by Mrs Emily Toms in memory of her father, Joseph Kershaw 1931

N05244   That was a Piedmontese ... (1862)
Ow:406x298:Bequeathed by Beresford Rimington Heaton 1940

N05245   Aurora Leigh's Dismissal of Romney ('The Tryst') (1860)
Ow:387x305:signed:Bequeathed by Beresford Rimington Heaton 1940

T00176   The Woodman's Child (1860)
Oc:610x641:signed:Presented by Mrs Phyllis L.Holland 1958

T00276   Studies for 'April Love' (circa 1856)
DWπ:254x178:Presented by Charles Alexander Munro 1959

A00211   Illustration for 'At the Back of the North Wind'
Dπ:79x60:Presented by H. Reitlinger 1926

A00212   Illustration for 'At the Back of the North Wind'
Dπ:79x60:signed:Presented by H. Reitlinger 1926

A00213   Illustration for 'At the Back of the North Wind'
Dπ:79x60:signed:Presented by H. Reitlinger 1926

HUGHES, Malcolm born 1920
Modern Collection
Tate Gallery Archive holds material concerning this artist

T00823   White and Aluminium II (1965)
Rv:1829x1829:signed:Purchased 1966

T03753   Maquette for 'Square Relief' (1968)
Rbw:330x310:Transferred from the Victoria & Albert Museum 1983

T03754   Square Relief. White (1968)
HRw:610x610x60:signed:Transferred from the Victoria & Albert Museum 1983

P07426   Rational Concepts (1977)
MNπ:597x597:signed:Purchased 1981

HUGHES, Patrick born 1939
Modern Collection
Tate Gallery Archive holds material concerning this artist

T01512   Collected Works (part two) (1971)
Avb:1219x2032:signed:Purchased 1972

P01808   Infinity (1976)
CNπ:591x1016:signed:Presented by the artist and Bradley Faine 1976

P01867   Over the Moon (1978)
CNπ:721x479:signed:Presented by Christie's Contemporary Art 1979

The Institute of Contemporary Arts Portfolio (P04016, P04038, P04053, P04076, P04115, P04125, P04166, P04248, P04256, P04315-P04316, P04334, P04378-P04380, P04419, P04635, P04752, P04938, P05138, P05155, P05248; complete group; mixed group)

P04378   Brick Door (1964)
CNπ:860x470:signed:Presented by Rose and Chris Prater through the Institute of Contemporary Prints 1975

HUGHES-STANTON, Blair 1902-1981
Modern Collection
Tate Gallery Archive holds material concerning this artist

IAA Portfolio (P03096-P03104, P03107; complete group; mixed group)

P03102 Night (1975)
CJπ:238x330:signed:Presented by the International Association of Art 1975

HUGHES-STANTON, Sir Herbert 1870-1937
British Collection

N02261 A Pasturage among the Dunes, Pas de Calais, France (1908)
Oc:1448x2159:signed:Presented by the Trustees of the Chantrey Bequest 1908

HUMPHREY, Ozias 1742-1810
British Collection

T00756 Elizabeth, Countess of Craven, Later Margravine of Anspach (circa 1780-3)
Oc:603x505:Bequeathed by Cornelia, Countess of Craven 1965

HUNT, Alfred William 1830-1896
British Collection

N01703 Windsor Castle (1889)
Wπ:489x762:signed:Presented by Sir Henry Tate 1894

N05357 Cwm Trefaen (circa 1855-60)
Oc:603x908:Bequeathed by Miss Violet Hunt 1942

N05358 Iron Works, Middlesborough (circa 1865-70)
Oc:438x641:Bequeathed by Miss Violet Hunt 1942

HUNT, William Henry 1790-1864
British Collection

N01970 Portrait Study of a Bearded Man (circa 1835-40)
Wπ:235x203:signed:Presented by Charles Fraser 1905

N01971 A Peasant Girl (1838)
Wπ:394x279:signed:Presented by Charles Fraser 1905

N01972 Fruit
Wπ:216x273:signed:Presented by Charles Fraser 1905

N01973 A Water Carrier
Wπ:375x260:signed:Presented by Charles Fraser 1905

N01974 Apples
Wπ:133x190:signed:Presented by Charles Fraser 1905

N03564 Primroses and Bird's Nest
Wπ:184x273:signed:Bequeathed by Miss Moss 1920

T01154 Study from Nature at Twickenham (circa 1806)
Ob:330x168:Purchased 1969

A00217 Landscape Sketch
Dπ:79x127:signed:Bequeathed by J.R. Holliday 1927

A00218 Landscape Sketch
Dπ:79x127:signed:Bequeathed by J.R. Holliday 1927

HUNT, William Holman 1827-1910
British Collection

N02120 The Ship (1875)
Oc:762x978:signed:Presented by subscribers 1907

N02422 Two Subjects for 'The Germ' (published 1850)
Lπ:200x121:Presented by Edmund Houghton 1898

N03160 John Hunt
Oc:356x305:Presented by Mrs Wyman 1917

N03161 John Key
Oc:356x305:Presented by Mrs Wyman 1917

N03334 The Triumph of the Innocents (1883-4)
Oc:1562x2540:signed:Presented by Sir John Middlemore Bt 1918

N03447 Claudio and Isabella (1850)
Ow:775x457:signed:Presented by the Trustees of the Chantrey Bequest 1919

N04018 Eliezer and Rebekah at the Well, engraved by the Dalziel Brothers (1863)
Jπ:178x137:Presented by Gilbert Dalziel 1924

N04052 The Lady of Shalott, engraved by J. Thompson (published 1857)
Jπ:95x79:Presented by Harold Hartley 1925

N04124 The Lent Jewels, engraved by the Dalziel Brothers (published 1862)
Jπ:127x102:Presented by Gilbert Dalziel 1924

N04624 F.G. Stephens (1847)
Ow:203x175:signed:Bequeathed by H.F. Stephens 1932

N04636 Frontispiece to 'The Germ'
Lπ:203x121:Bequeathed by H.F. Stephens 1932

N05275 Study for 'The Finding of the Saviour in the Temple' (1856)
Dπ:711x508:signed:Presented by A.W.F. Fuller 1941

N05665 Our English Coasts, 1852 ('Strayed Sheep') (1852)
Oc:432x584:signed:Presented by the National Art Collections Fund 1946

T00932 The Haunted Manor (1849)
Ob:2332x337:signed:Purchased 1967

T02075 The Awakening Conscience (1853)
Oc:762x559:signed:Presented by Sir Colin and Lady Anderson through the Friends of the Tate Gallery 1976

T03321 Study for the Christ Child in the Virgin's Arms for 'The Triumph of the Innocents' (first version) (1876)
Dπ:508x356:Purchased 1981

T05468 Cornfield at Ewell (circa 1846)
Ob:202x318:Presented anonymously 1988

HUNT, Walter 1861-1941
British Collection

N01581 The Dog in the Manger (1885)
Oc:1016x1689:signed:Presented by the Trustees of the Chantrey Bequest 1885

HUNTER, Colin 1841-1904
British Collection

N01579 Their Only Harvest (1879)
Oc:1054x1822:signed:Presented by the Trustees of the Chantrey Bequest 1879

HUNTER, Leslie 1877-1931
British Collection

N04795 Kitchen Utensils (circa 1914-18)
Ow:457x381:signed:Presented by William McInnes 1935

HURLSTONE, Frederick Yeates 1800-1869
British Collection

N01967 A Scene from 'Gil Blas' (exhibited 1868)
Oc:1118x1410:Purchased 1905

N04938 Sancho Panza Attended by his State Physician (exhibited 1868)
Oc:1092x1340:Presented by F. Howard 1938

HURRY, Leslie 1909-1978
Modern Collection
Tate Gallery Archive holds material concerning this artist

T04150   Medea's House, Corinth (1948)
TWπ:404x480:signed:Presented by John Hurry
Armstrong, the artist's nephew, in appreciation of Ronald
Alley's services to the Tate Gallery 1986

T04155   A Land Unvisited (1940)
Wπ:450x583:signed:Purchased 1986

T04156   The Courtesan (1941)
Wπ:447x293:signed:Purchased 1986

T05573   Grace Sholto Douglas (1940)
Ob:962x840:Purchased 1989

HUSKISSON, Robert ?1820-1861
British Collection

T01901   The Midsummer Night's Fairies (exhibited 1847)
Ow:289x343:Purchased 1974

HUTCHINSON, Louise 1882-1968
Modern Collection

T03751   Three-fold Head (circa 1953)
Sp:330x320x180:Transferred from the Victoria & Albert
Museum 1983

HUTTON, Clarke born 1898
Modern Collection
Tate Gallery Archive holds material concerning this artist

School Prints (P01698-P01727; complete group; mixed
group)
P01707   Harlequinade (1946-9)
CLπ:495x759:Presented by Patrick Seale Prints 1975

HUXLEY, Paul born 1938
Modern Collection
Tate Gallery Archive holds material concerning this artist

T01056   Untitled No. 92 (1968)
Ac:2032x2032:Purchased 1968

T03589   Fable (1982)
Ac:1956x1956:signed:Purchased 1983

P01422   Untitled No. 8 (1973)
CNπ:600x600:signed:Presented by Christie's
Contemporary Art through the Institute of
Contemporary Prints 1975

HUYSMANS, Jacob circa 1633 - circa 1696
British Collection

T00901   Portrait of a Lady, Perhaps Margaret Blagge, in Masque
Costume as Diana (?circa 1674)
Oc:1197x1013:Presented by the Friends of the Tate
Gallery 1967

IBBETSON, Julius Caesar 1759-1817
British Collection

N01460   Smugglers on the Irish Coast (1808)
Oc:546x851:signed:Purchased 1895

N02948   Sand Quarry at Alum Bay (?exhibited 1792)
Ow:190x254:Bequeathed by Sir Henry Layard 1913

N04910   Two Children (circa 1790)
Oc:743x610:Presented by H.B. Wood 1938

N04920   Two Children
Em:133x108:signed:Presented by H.B. Wood 1938

N05793   A Married Sailor's Return (circa 1800)
Oc:457x610:signed:Presented by Frederick John
Nettlefold 1947

N05794   An Unmarried Sailor's Return (circa 1800)
Oc:464x603:Presented by Frederick John Nettlefold 1947

T01889   Briton Ferry, Glamorgan (circa 1795)
Ow:352x457:Bequeathed by Alan Evans 1974

I CARDONA, Jaume Rocamora - see CARDONA, Jaume Rocamora i

ILLES, Arpad born 1908
Modern Collection

P08017   Jonah and the Whale (1967)
Jónás és a Cethal
MJπ:95x149:signed:Transferred from the Library 1978

IMMENDORFF, Jörg born 1945
Modern Collection

Café Deutschland (P77012; incomplete group)

P77012   We're Coming (1983)
Wir kommen
CJπ:1803x2294:signed:Purchased 1984

INCE, Evelyn circa 1886-1941
Modern Collection

N04751   Flower Piece (circa 1934)
Tw:610x508:signed:Presented by the Trustees of the
Chantrey Bequest 1934

INCHBOLD, John William 1830-1888
British Collection

N01477   The Moorland (Dewar-stone, Dartmoor) (1854)
Oc:356x533:signed:Bequeathed by Sir J. Russell
Reynolds Bt 1896

T05467   Gordale Scar, Yorkshire (exhibited 1876)
Oc:1254x913:signed:Presented by the Patrons of British
Art through the Friends of the Tate Gallery 1988

INLANDER, Henry 1925-1983
Modern Collection
Tate Gallery Archive holds material concerning this artist

T00113   Sienese Hills (1956)
Oc:800x1003:signed:Purchased 1956

T00427   Moving Surface (1961)
Oc:1003x1003:signed:Purchased 1961

INNES, James Dickson 1887-1914
Modern Collection
Tate Gallery Archive holds material concerning this artist

N03468   South of France, Bozouls, near Rodez (1908)
Oc:502x648:signed:Purchased 1919

N03469   Waterfall (1911)
Wπ:356x254:signed:Purchased 1919

N03578   Arenig (1911)
DWπ:254x356:signed:Presented by Mrs Innes 1921

N03579   Vernet (1912)
Wπ:254x356:signed:Presented by Mrs Innes 1921

N03660   Bozouls, near Rodez (1908)
DWπ:349x457:signed:Purchased 1922

N03676   Twilight in Aveyron (1908)
Wπ:241x394:Presented by John Fothergill 1922

N03804   The Waterfall (1910)
Wπ:286x394:signed:Presented by the Trustees of the
Chantrey Bequest 1922

N04385   Arenig, North Wales (1913)
Ow:857x1137:signed:Presented by Rowland
Burdon-Muller 1928

N05308   The Alhambra (circa 1912)
DWπ:324x203:Presented by the Contemporary Art
Society 1941

N05367   Arenig, Sunny Evening (circa 1911-12)
Ow:229x324:Purchased 1942

INSHAW, David born 1943
Modern Collection
Tate Gallery Archive holds material concerning this artist

T03189   The Badminton Game (1972-3)
Oc:1524x1835:signed:Presented by the Friends of the
Tate Gallery 1980

P01221   Girl Sitting in a Garden (1975)
CNπ:467x448:signed:Presented by Waddington Galleries
through the Institute of Contemporary Prints 1975

INTERNATIONAL LOCAL (CHARLESWORTH, Sarah; KOSUTH, Joseph; McCALL, Anthony) born 1945, born 1945, born 1946
Modern Collection

P02338   Where Are You Standing? (1976)
CLπ:1400x991:Presented by the artists 1976

IPOUSTEGUY, Jean born 1920
Modern Collection

T00681   Earth (1962)
La Terre
Sz:1854x686x508:signed:Presented by the Friends of the
Tate Gallery 1964

IRELAND, Geoffrey
Modern Collection
Tate Gallery Archive holds material concerning this artist

P06731   Frail Hunter (1965)
Lπ:505x635:Presented by Curwen Studio 1976

P06759   Sagres (1965)
CLπ:473x610:signed:Presented by Curwen Studio 1976

IRONSIDE, Robin 1912-1965
Modern Collection
Tate Gallery Archive holds material concerning this artist

N05459 The Somnambulist (circa 1943)
Gπ:419x698:Presented by the Contemporary Art Society
1944

IRVIN, Albert born 1922
Modern Collection
Tate Gallery Archive holds material concerning this artist

T03590 Empress (1982)
Ac:2135x3047:signed:Purchased 1983

P08215 [no title] (1987)
CNπ:222x175:signed:Transferred from the Library 1987

IRWIN, Gwyther born 1931
Modern Collection
Tate Gallery Archive holds material concerning this artist

T00478 Parade (1961)
Vπ:1226x762:signed:Purchased 1962

T00613 Forests of the Night (1963)
Vb:762x1073x25:Purchased 1963

The Institute of Contemporary Arts Portfolio (P04016,
P04038, P04053, P04076, P04115, P04125, P04166,
P04248, P04256, P04315-P04316, P04334,
P04378-P04380, P04419, P04635, P04752, P04938,
P05138, P05155, P05248; complete group; mixed group)

P04379 Red Flush (1964)
CNπ:565x825:signed:Presented by Rose and Chris Prater
through the Institute of Contemporary Prints 1975

JACK, Richard 1866-1952
British Collection
Tate Gallery Archive holds material concerning this artist

N02895 Rehearsal with Nikisch (1912)
Oc:1524x2140:signed:Presented by the Trustees of the
Chantrey Bequest 1912

JACKLIN, Bill born 1943
Modern Collection
Tate Gallery Archive holds material concerning this artist

T01494 Catena (1970)
Dπ:737x737:signed:Purchased 1971

Anemones (P02559-P02565; complete group)
P02559 Anemones I (1977)
MIπ:302x206:signed:Presented by the artist 1982
P02560 Anemones II (1977)
MIπ:302x206:signed:Presented by the artist 1982
P02561 Anemones III (1977)
MIπ:302x206:signed:Presented by the artist 1982
P02562 Anemones IV (1977)
MIπ:302x206:signed:Presented by the artist 1982
P02563 Anemones V (1977)
MIπ:302x206:signed:Presented by the artist 1982
P02564 Anemones VI (1977)
MIπ:302x206:signed:Presented by the artist 1982
P02565 Anemones VII (1977)
MIπ:302x206:signed:Presented by the artist 1982

P06656 First Light (1974-5)
CLπ:457x464:signed:Presented by Curwen Studio 1976
P06657 Northern Light (1975)
CLπ:464x464:signed:Presented by Curwen Studio 1976
P06658 Ancient Light (1975)
CLπ:457x476:signed:Presented by Curwen Studio 1976
P06659 Daylight (1975)
CLπ:457x464:signed:Presented by Curwen Studio 1976
P06660 Sky Light (1975)
CLπ:464x464:signed:Presented by Curwen Studio 1976
P06661 Night Light (1975)
CLπ:460x460:signed:Presented by Curwen Studio 1976

JACKSON, Alexander Young 1882-1974
Modern Collection

N03967 The Entrance to Halifax Harbour (1919)
Oc:648x806:signed:Purchased 1924

JACKSON, Arthur born 1911
Modern Collection
Tate Gallery Archive holds material concerning this artist

T00732 Painting (1937)
ODb:254x356:signed:Purchased 1965

JACKSON, F. Ernest 1872-1945
British Collection

N05109 Mrs Beasley (circa 1937)
Oc:533x432:signed:Presented by the Trustees of the Chantrey
Bequest 1940
P03037 United Defence Against Aggression (circa 1917)
CLπ:632x438:signed:Presented by the Ministry of Information
1918

JACKSON, Gilbert active 1622-1640
British Collection

T03237 A Lady of the Grenville Family and her Son (1640)
Oc:742x608:Purchased 1981

JACKSON, John 1778-1831
British Collection
Tate Gallery Archive holds material concerning this artist

N01404 James Northcote (1813 or 1821)
Oc:1321x965:Presented by the Earl of Carlisle 1894
N02279 Sir David Wilkie, R.A. (circa 1815-20)
Dπ:273x213:signed:Presented by Sir J.C. Robinson
through the National Art Collections Fund 1908
N03672 Sir Francis Chantrey (circa 1830)
Ow:1441x1099:Presented by the Trustees of the Chantrey
Bequest 1922
N04082 Sir Henry Webb (1825)
Oc:914x711:signed:Bequeathed by John Lane 1925

JACOBS, Janice born 1947
Modern Collection

P06732 Abstract (1973)
CLπ:708x527:signed:Presented by Curwen Studio 1977

JACOVLEFF, Alexandre 1887-1938
Modern Collection

N04988 A Turkoman (1931)
Un Turcoman
Pπ:759x562:signed:Presented anonymously 1939
N04989 A Coolie (1931)
Pπ:752x556:signed:Presented anonymously 1939
N04990 Verso: Nude Figures in a Room (circa 1937-8)
Tπ:556x381:Presented anonymously 1939
N04991 Nude (circa 1937-8)
Tπ:502x279:Presented anonymously 1939
N04992 Neptune and Andromeda (circa 1937-8)
Tc:521x756:Presented anonymously 1939

Seven Drawings of the Female Model (A01082-A01088;
complete group)
A01082 Female Torso (circa 1933-8)
Dπ:327x340:Presented anonymously 1939
A01083 An Arm and a Hand (circa 1933-8)
Dπ:352x457:Presented anonymously 1939
A01084 Recumbent Model (circa 1933-8)
Dπ:311x505:Presented anonymously 1939
A01085 Reclining Model (circa 1933-8)
Dπ:327x492:Presented anonymously 1939
A01086 Seated Model (circa 1933-8)
Dπ:505x321:Presented anonymously 1939
A01087 Crouching Model from the Side (circa 1933-8)
Dπ:327x479:Presented anonymously 1939
A01088 Crouching Model from the Front (circa 1933-8)
Dπ:505x333:Presented anonymously 1939

JAGGER, Charles Sargeant 1885-1934
Modern Collection
Tate Gallery Archive holds material concerning this artist

N01354 No Man's Land (1919-20)
Rz:1270x3302:signed:Presented by the Council of British
School at Rome 1923

JAMES, A. Gosset 1875-1950
British Collection

N04965 Winter on the Windrush (1938)
Oc:635x1022:Presented by the Trustees of the Chantrey
Bequest 1938

JAMIESON, Alexander 1873-1937
British Collection

N04882 The Tuileries Gardens and the Rue de Rivoli (1901-2)
Oc:610x813:signed:Presented by Mrs E.L. Shute 1937

JANECEK, Ota born 1919
Modern Collection

T00749 The Cell (1964)
Oc:1302x965:signed:Presented by the artist 1965

JANOWICH, Ron born 1948
Modern Collection

P11212 [title not known] (1986)
Jπ:561x336:Presented by Garner H. Tullis and Pamela
Auchincloss 1989

JANSEN, Angela born 1929
Modern Collection

P02444 Untitled (1973)
MIπ:210x178:signed:Presented by the artist 1978
P02445 Station (1974)
MIπ:41x57:signed:Presented by the artist 1978
P02446 Up and Down (1974)
MIπ:38x57:signed:Presented by the artist 1978
P02448 Grass (1977)
MIπ:298x232:signed:Presented by the artist 1978

JAPP, Darsie 1883-1973
Modern Collection
Tate Gallery Archive holds material concerning this artist

N05431 Saddleback from Wallthwaite (1912)
Oc:686x914:Presented by Sir Edward Marsh 1943

JARAY, Tess born 1937
Modern Collection

T01760 Fifteen (1969)
Oc:2235x4318:Presented by E.J. Power through the
Friends of the Tate Gallery 1973

JAVACHEFF, Christo - see CHRISTO

JEANNERET, Charles-Edouard - see LE CORBUSIER

JEMEC, Andrej born 1934
Modern Collection

P02550 Red Dark Red (1979)
CNπ:625x899:signed:Presented by the artist 1981
P07587 Escalation towards Light (1974)
CNπ:597x600:signed:Purchased 1981

JENKINS, Paul born 1923
Modern Collection

T01572 Phenomena, Yonder Near (1964)
Ac:2946x1613:signed:Presented by David Kluger through
the American Federation of Arts 1972

JENNINGS, Humphrey 1907-1950
Modern Collection

T01324 The House in the Woods (1939-44)
Oc:432x533:signed:Presented by Mrs Cicely Jennings
1971
T03212 Train (Locomotive 101) (circa 1939-40)
Oc:635x1013:Presented by the Trustees of the Elephant
Trust 1981
T03213 Swiss Roll (1939)
Ocb:352x445:signed:Presented by the Trustees of the
Elephant Trust 1981

JENNINGS, William George 1763-1854
British Collection

T03349 Heath Scene with a Pond (circa 1831)
Oπ:140x168:Purchased 1982

JESIH, Boris born 1943
Modern Collection

P07588 The Apple Tree and the Grafts (1979)
Jublana Api
CLπ:875x665:signed:Purchased 1981

JOHN, Augustus, OM 1878-1961
British Collection
Tate Gallery Archive holds material concerning this artist

N03171 Woman Smiling (1908-9)
Oc:1960x982:Presented by the Contemporary Art Society
1917
N03172 Walpurgis Night. Verso: Study of a Man (1900)
DWπ:349x483:Presented by the Contemporary Art
Society 1917
N03198 Nirvana (circa 1908)
DWπ:411x305:signed:Presented by Sir William
Rothenstein in memory of Gerard Chowne 1917
N03210 Galway (1916 and 1920)
Oc:2750x11900:Presented by Sir Edmund Davis 1917
N03523 Robin (circa 1912)
Ow:451x305:Presented by Sir Robert Witt through the
National Art Collections Fund 1918
N03565 Rachel (circa 1917)
Oc:762x635:signed:Presented by A.E. Anderson 1920
N03566 Colonel T.E. Lawrence (1919)
Oc:800x597:Presented by the Duke of Westminster 1920
N03581 The Orange Jacket (circa 1916)
Oc:1022x768:Presented by A.E. Anderson 1921
N03730 Washing Day (circa 1912-5)
Ow:406x302:Purchased with assistance from Sir James
Murray 1923
N03731 Portrait of a Woman (1911)
Ow:406x324:Presented by A.E. Anderson with assistance
from the National Art Collections Fund 1923
N03886 Gossiping Women. Verso: A Satyr (1907)
DWπ:498x356:signed:Purchased 1924

N04093 Madame Suggia (1920-3)
Oc:1867x1651:Presented by Lord Duveen through the National Art Collections Fund 1925

N04448 Study for Madame Suggia (circa 1920)
Dπ:470x318:signed:Purchased 1929

N04653 Llyn Treweryn (1911-2)
Ow:316x407:Purchased 1932

N04819 Lord David Cecil (1935)
Oc:921x718:Presented by the Trustees of the Chantrey Bequest 1935

N05097 The Little Railway, Martigues (1928)
Oc:470x546:signed:Bequeathed by Lady Henry Cavendish-Bentinck 1940

N05098 Seated Nude (circa 1920-30)
Dπ:356x216:signed:Bequeathed by Lady Henry Cavendish-Bentinck 1940

N05157 Dorelia (1908)
DWπ:457x273:signed:Bequeathed by Lady Henry Cavendish-Bentinck 1940

N05158 Dorelia (1908)
DWπ:501x354:signed:Bequeathed by Lady Henry Cavendish-Bentinck 1940

N05159 Dorelia (1909)
DWπ:368x445:signed:Bequeathed by Lady Henry Cavendish-Bentinck 1940

N05218 W.B. Yeats (1907)
Oc:508x457:Presented by the Trustees of the Chantrey Bequest 1940

N05259 An Old Lady (1898-9)
Oc:686x558:Purchased 1941

N05268 A Canadian Soldier (1918)
Oc:730x540:Purchased 1941

N05292 Head of Romilly, the Artist's Son (circa 1924)
Oc:457x381:signed:Bequeathed by Sir Hugh Walpole 1941

N05297 The Artist's Children (circa 1915)
Dπ:356x254:Bequeathed by Sir Hugh Walpole 1941

N05298 W.B. Yeats (1907)
Dπ:353x253:signed:Bequeathed by Sir Hugh Walpole 1941

N05299 Two Nudes (circa 1920-6)
Dπ:508x356:signed:Bequeathed by Sir Hugh Walpole 1941

N05346 Blue Cineraria (circa 1928)
Oc:762x686:signed:Presented by the Trustees of the Chantrey Bequest 1940

N05434 Dorelia (circa 1911-2)
OWπ:330x235:signed:Bequeathed by R.J. Dyson 1943

N05645 Joseph Hone (1932)
Oc:508x405:signed:Purchased 1946

N05929 Matthew Smith (1944)
Oc:610x508:signed:Presented by the Trustees of the Chantrey Bequest 1950

N05936 Viscount d'Abernon (1927-32)
Oc:2290x1550:signed:Presented by Viscountess D'Abernon 1950

N06240 Gloxinia (1953)
Oc:762x635:Presented by the Trustees of the Chantrey Bequest 1954

T00071 Rustic Idyll (1902-4)
Pπ:327x298:signed:Purchased 1955

T00072 Composition Sketch (1900)
Dπ:251x324:signed:Purchased 1955

T00138 Edward Grove (1940)
Oc:610x406:signed:Presented by the Trustees of the Chantrey Bequest 1957

T00194 Theodore Powys (circa 1932)
Oc:616x514:Presented by the Trustees of the Chantrey Bequest 1958

T01540 Lyric Fantasy (circa 1913-4)
ODc:2380x4720:Bequeathed by Mrs Reine Pitman 1972

T05805 Arthur Symons (1909)
Dπ:350x251:signed:Bequeathed by Mrs Rhoda Symons 1937

T05806 Arthur Symons (1909)
Dπ:350x251:signed:Bequeathed by Mrs Rhoda Symons 1937

P03038 The Dawn (1917)
MLπ:460x689:signed:Presented by the Ministry of Information 1918

JOHN, Gwen 1876-1939
British Collection
Tate Gallery Archive holds material concerning this artist

N03173 Nude Girl (1909-10)
Oc:445x279:Presented by the Contemporary Art Society 1917

N03174 A Lady Reading (1909-11)
Oc:403x254:Presented by the Contemporary Art Society 1917

N04088 Chloë Boughton-Leigh (circa 1904-8)
Oc:584x381:Purchased 1925

N04861 The Convalescent (1918-9)
Oc:337x254:Bequeathed by Mrs Rhoda Symons 1937

N05152 Study of a Child (circa 1915-20)
Wπ:324x251:Purchased 1940

N05153 Study of a Girl Holding a Doll (circa 1916-20)
Wπ:470x203:Purchased 1940

N05154 Cat (circa 1904-8)
Wπ:111x137:Purchased 1940

N05155 Cat (circa 1904-8)
DWπ:165x117:Purchased 1940

N05162 The Nun (circa 1915-21)
Oc:686x432:Purchased 1940

N05366 Self-Portrait (1902)
Oc:448x349:signed:Purchased 1942

N05744 Young Woman Holding a Black Cat (circa 1920-5)
Oc:457x295:Purchased 1946

N05910 Dorelia in a Black Dress (circa 1903-4)
Oc:730x489:Presented by the Trustees of the Duveen Paintings Fund 1949

T00155 Annabella (circa 1915-20)
DWπ:238x210:Presented by Miss Mary Constance Lloyd 1957

T00156 Cat (circa 1904-8)
Wπ:121x159:Presented by Miss Mary Constance Lloyd 1957

JOHN, Sir William Goscombe 1860-1952
British Collection

N01755 A Boy at Play (circa 1895)
Sz:1302x794x1060:signed:Presented by the Trustees of the Chantrey Bequest 1896

T03747 Pan (1901)
Sz:680x210x120:signed:Transferred from the Victoria & Albert Museum 1983

JOHNS, Jasper born 1930
Modern Collection
Tate Gallery Archive holds material concerning this artist

T00454 Zero Through Nine (1961)
Oc:1372x1048:signed:Presented by the Friends of the Tate Gallery 1961

T03242 Dancers on a Plane; Merce Cunningham (1980)
OAcz:2000x1619:signed:Purchased 1980

P01860 Fool's House (1972)
CLπ:1029x508:signed:Presented by Madame Stassart 1978

P07240 Sketch from Untitled II (1974)
CLπ:708x476:signed:Purchased 1978

P07378 Scent (1975-6)
CLJπ:641x1092:signed:Purchased 1980

P07380 Decoy (1971)
CLπ:1054x752:signed:Purchased 1980

P07397 White Target (1968)
CLπ:342x342:signed:Purchased 1980

P07398 Two Flags (black) (1970-2)
MLπ:627x495:signed:Purchased 1980

P07399 Usuyuki (1979)
CLπ:695x1124:signed:Purchased 1980

P07736 Savarin (1982)
MLπ:1010x759:signed:Purchased 1982

P77165 Ventriloquist (1986)
Lπ:925x616:signed:Purchased 1986

JOHNSON, Ben born 1946
Modern Collection

P01883 Escalator (1975)
CNπ:559x838:signed:Presented by Editions Alecto 1979

JOHNSON, Charles Edward 1832-1913
British Collection

N01606 The Swineherd: Gurth, Son of Beowulph (1879)
Oc:1410x2121:signed:Presented by the Trustees of the Chantrey Bequest 1879

JOHNSON, Cornelius 1593-1661
British Collection

N01320 Apolonius Veth (1644)
Oc:781x635:signed:Presented by Mrs Zouch Troughton 1891

N01321 Cornelia Veth (1644)
Oc:787x635:signed:Presented by Mrs Zouch Troughton 1891

N02530 Portrait of an Unknown Lady (1646)
Oc:794x641:signed:Bequeathed by George Salting 1910

N05927 Cornelia Veth (?) (1659)
Oc:1245x1010:signed:Purchased 1950

T00744 Portrait of an Unknown Gentleman (1629)
Ow:435x318:signed:Purchased 1965

T00745 Portrait of an Unknown Lady (1629)
Ow:410x330:signed:Purchased 1965

T03250 Susanna Temple, Later Lady Lister (1620)
Ow:679x518:signed:Purchased 1981

attributed to
JOHNSON, James 1803-1834
British Collection
Tate Gallery Archive holds material concerning this artist

T01522 The Tranquil Lake: Sunset Seen through a Ruined Abbey (circa 1825-30)
Oc:902x1441:Purchased 1972

JOHNSTONE, William 1897-1981
Modern Collection
Tate Gallery Archive holds material concerning this artist

T03292 Golgotha (1927-8 and circa 1948)
Oc:1381x2416:signed:Purchased 1981

T03293 Littoral (1980)
Oc:1676x1981:signed:Purchased 1981

T03659 Large Brush Drawing (circa 1975-6)
Dπ:916x1318:signed:Presented anonymously in memory of Sir Terence Rattigan 1983

Twenty Poems by Edwin Muir with twenty one Lithographs by William Johnstone (P07534-P07554; complete group)

P07534 [title not known] (1981)
MLπ:324x511:signed:Purchased 1981

P07535 [title not known] (1981)
MLπ:324x511:signed:Purchased 1981

P07536 [title not known] (1981)
MLπ:324x511:signed:Purchased 1981

P07537 [title not known] (1981)
MLπ:324x511:signed:Purchased 1981

P07538 [title not known] (1981)
MLπ:324x511:signed:Purchased 1981

P07539 [title not known] (1981)
MLπ:324x511:signed:Purchased 1981

P07540 [title not known] (1981)
MLπ:324x511:signed:Purchased 1981

P07541 [title not known] (1981)
MLπ:324x511:signed:Purchased 1981

P07542 [title not known] (1981)
MLπ:324x511:signed:Purchased 1981

P07543 [title not known] (1981)
MLπ:324x511:signed:Purchased 1981

P07544 [title not known] (1981)
MLπ:324x511:signed:Purchased 1981

P07545 [title not known] (1981)
MLπ:324x511:signed:Purchased 1981

P07546 [title not known] (1981)
MLπ:324x511:signed:Purchased 1981

P07547 [title not known] (1981)
MLπ:324x511:signed:Purchased 1981

P07548 [title not known] (1981)
MLπ:324x511:signed:Purchased 1981

P07549 [title not known] (1981)
MLπ:324x511:signed:Purchased 1981

P07550 [title not known] (1981)
MLπ:324x511:signed:Purchased 1981

P07551 [title not known] (1981)
MLπ:324x511:signed:Purchased 1981

P07552 [title not known] (1981)
MLπ:324x511:signed:Purchased 1981

P07553 [title not known] (1981)
MLπ:324x511:signed:Purchased 1981

P07554 [title not known] (1981)
MLπ:324x511:signed:Purchased 1981

JONES, Allen born 1937
Modern Collection
Tate Gallery Archive holds material concerning this artist

T01059 Man Woman (1963)
Oc:2146x1886:signed:Presented by the Contemporary
Art Society 1968

T03090 The Battle of Hastings (1961-2)
Oc:1829x1829:signed:Presented by E.J. Power through
the Friends of the Tate Gallery 1980

T03243 Santa Monica Shore (1977)
Oc:1835x1835:Purchased 1981

T03244 Chair (1969)
SAVav:775x571x991:Purchased 1981

T03379 Wet Seal (1966)
Ocw:934x915x100:signed:Purchased 1982

P03092 Legs (1967-8)
CNπ:2032x4572:Presented by the Welsh Arts Council
1975

The Magician Suite (P03192-P03197; complete group)
P03192 I (1976)
CLπ:826x410:signed:Presented by Waddington Galleries
1977

P03193 II (1976)
CLπ:840x412:signed:Presented by Waddington Galleries
1977

P03194 III (1976)
CLπ:832x411:signed:Presented by Waddington Galleries
1977

P03195 IV (1976)
CLπ:824x410:signed:Presented by Waddington Galleries
1977

P03196 V (1976)
CLπ:839x409:signed:Presented by Waddington Galleries
1977

P03197 VI (1976)
CLπ:830x597:signed:Presented by Waddington Galleries
1977

P03198 Black Feat (1976)
CLπ:819x410:signed:Presented by Waddington Galleries
1977

P03199 Red Feat (1976)
CLπ:819x413:signed:Presented by Waddington Galleries
1977

The Institute of Contemporary Arts Portfolio (P04016,
P04038, P04053, P04076, P04115, P04125, P04166,
P04248, P04256, P04315-P04316, P04334,
P04378-P04380, P04419, P04635, P04752, P04938,
P05138, P05155, P05248; complete group; mixed group)
P04380 Dream T-Shirt (1964)
CNπ:737x552:signed:Presented by Rose and Chris Prater
through the Institute of Contemporary Prints 1975

P04381 Three-in-One (1971)
CNπ:816x702:signed:Presented by Rose and Chris Prater
through the Institute of Contemporary Prints 1975

P04382 Cafe Noir (1973)
CNπ:600x797:signed:Presented by Rose and Chris Prater
through the Institute of Contemporary Prints 1975

P04383 One Way Traffic (1974)
CNπ:340x632:signed:Presented by Rose and Chris Prater
through the Institute of Contemporary Prints 1975

P04384 Untitled (1974)
CNπ:190x149:signed:Presented by Rose and Chris Prater
through the Institute of Contemporary Prints 1975

P05421 Crazy Horse (1976)
CNπ:629x775:signed:Presented by Rose and Chris Prater
1978

P05422 Cut-a-Way (1976)
CNπ:686x549:signed:Presented by Rose and Chris Prater
1978

P06337 Untitled (1964)
CLπ:800x571:Presented by Curwen Studio through the
Institute of Contemporary Prints 1975

P06338 Left Hand Lady (1970)
CLπ:575x762:Presented by Curwen Studio through the
Institute of Contemporary Prints 1975

P06339 Right Hand Lady (1970)
CLπ:571x765:Presented by Curwen Studio through the
Institute of Contemporary Prints 1975

Europaeische Graphik VII (P06244, P06289-P06291,
P06319, P06340-P06341, P06549; incomplete group;
mixed group)
P06340 Leg-Splash (1970-1)
CLπ:660x505:Presented by Curwen Studio through the
Institute of Contemporary Prints 1975

P06341 Woman-Splash (1970-1)
CLπ:762x530:Presented by Curwen Studio through the
Institute of Contemporary Prints 1975

P07361 Ways and Means (1976-7)
CNπ:502x702:signed:Purchased 1980

P07449 Box (1980)
CLπ:1060x1520:signed:Purchased 1982

P07759 Take It from the Top (1982)
CLπ:727x940:signed:Purchased 1982

P77051 Exciting Women (1964)
CLπ:409x438:signed:Purchased 1984

JONES, Barbara
Modern Collection

School Prints (P01698-P01727; complete group; mixed
group)
P01708 Fairground (1946-9)
CLπ:495x762:signed:Presented by Patrick Seale Prints
1975

Follies (P06025, P06028-P06029, P06315-P06316,
P06518, P06588-P06589; complete group; mixed group)
P06315 The Aviary, Dropmore (1971)
CLπ:616x483:signed:Presented by Curwen Studio
through the Institute of Contemporary Prints 1975

P06316 Pineapple House, Stirling (1971)
CLπ:629x476:signed:Presented by Curwen Studio
through the Institute of Contemporary Prints 1975

JONES, David 1895-1974
Modern Collection
Tate Gallery Archive holds material concerning this artist

N05054 The Chapel in the Park (1932)
Wπ:622x502:signed:Purchased 1940

N05128 The Terrace (1929)
Wπ:648x502:signed:Presented by the Contemporary Art
Society 1940

N05315 Illustration to the Arthurian Legend: Guenever
(1938-40)
DWπ:622x495:signed:Purchased 1941

N05316 Illustration to the Arthurian Legend: The Four Queens
Find Launcelot Sleeping (1941)
DWπ:629x495:signed:Purchased 1941

T00582 Standing Figure (1921)
Dπ:410x330:signed:Purchased 1963

T02013 The Garden Enclosed (1924)
Ow:356x298:signed:Presented by the Trustees of the
Chantrey Bequest 1975

T02036 Aphrodite in Aulis (1940-1)
WDπ:629x498:Purchased 1976

T02037 Study for Aphrodite in Aulis (circa 1938-40)
Dπ:327x210:Presented by the trustees of the artist's
estate 1976

T02038 Chalice with Flowers and Pepperpot (circa 1954-5)
DWTπ:784x578:Purchased 1976

T03192 Exiit Edictum (1949)
DGπ:406x330:signed:Purchased 1980

T03677 Sanctus Christus de Capel-y-ffin (1925)
GDπ:193x133:signed:Presented by the Friends of the
Tate Gallery 1983

T05503 The Queen's Dish (1932)
Wπ:550x760:Presented by Mrs Doreen Lucas in memory
of her husband N.B.C. Lucas 1988

JONES, Fred Cecil 1891-1956
Modern Collection

N04899 Chimney Stacks and Winding Ways, Whitby (1936)
DWπ:495x419:signed:Presented by the Trustees of the
Chantrey Bequest 1937

JONES, George 1786-1869
British Collection

N00389 The Burning Fiery Furnace (exhibited 1832)
Ow:902x608:Presented by Robert Vernon 1847

N00390 Godiva Preparing to Ride through Coventry (exhibited
1833)
Ow:749x610:Presented by Robert Vernon 1847

N00391 The Battle of Borodino (exhibited 1829)
Oc:1219x2134:Presented by Robert Vernon 1847

N00392 The Town Hall, Utrecht (1829)
Ow:914x711:Presented by Robert Vernon 1847

N00800 Lucknow: Evening. The Sufferers Besieged at Lucknow,
Rescued by General Lord Clyde; November (exhibited
1869)
Oc:1092x2083:Presented by the artist 1869

N00801 Cawnpore, the Passage of the Ganges at Cawnpore on
the 29th and 30th November 1857 (exhibited 1869)
Oc:1092x2083:Presented by the artist 1869

N05994 Cader Idris
Wπ:279x190:Presented by the artist's widow 1888

N05995 Near Dolgelly
Wπ:279x190:Presented by the artist's widow 1888

T01958 The Burning Fiery Furnace, study for N00389 (circa
1832)
Wπ:546x403:signed:Purchased 1975

Sketches of Figures, Costumes, etc. (A00219-A00701)

A00219 [title not known]
Dπ::Presented by the artist's widow 1888

A00220 [title not known]
Dπ::Presented by the artist's widow 1888

A00221 [title not known]
Dπ::Presented by the artist's widow 1888

A00222 [title not known]
Dπ::Presented by the artist's widow 1888

A00223 [title not known]
Dπ::Presented by the artist's widow 1888

A00224 [title not known]
Dπ::Presented by the artist's widow 1888

A00225 [title not known]
Dπ::Presented by the artist's widow 1888

A00226 [title not known]
Dπ::Presented by the artist's widow 1888

A00227 [title not known]
Dπ::Presented by the artist's widow 1888

A00228 [title not known]
Dπ::Presented by the artist's widow 1888

A00229 [title not known]
Dπ::Presented by the artist's widow 1888

A00230 [title not known]
Dπ::Presented by the artist's widow 1888

A00231 [title not known]
Dπ::Presented by the artist's widow 1888

A00232 [title not known]
Dπ::Presented by the artist's widow 1888

A00233 [title not known]
Dπ::Presented by the artist's widow 1888

A00234 [title not known]
Dπ::Presented by the artist's widow 1888

A00235 [title not known]
Dπ::Presented by the artist's widow 1888

A00236 [title not known]
Dπ::Presented by the artist's widow 1888

A00237 [title not known]
Dπ::Presented by the artist's widow 1888

A00238 [title not known]
Dπ::Presented by the artist's widow 1888

A00239 [title not known]
Dπ::Presented by the artist's widow 1888

A00240 [title not known]
Dπ::Presented by the artist's widow 1888

A00241 [title not known]
Dπ::Presented by the artist's widow 1888

A00242 [title not known]
Dπ::Presented by the artist's widow 1888

A00243 [title not known]
Dπ::Presented by the artist's widow 1888

A00244 [title not known]
Dπ::Presented by the artist's widow 1888

A00245 [title not known]
Dπ::Presented by the artist's widow 1888

A00246 [title not known]
Dπ::Presented by the artist's widow 1888

A00247 [title not known]
Dπ::Presented by the artist's widow 1888

A00248 [title not known]
Dπ::Presented by the artist's widow 1888

A00249 [title not known]
Dπ::Presented by the artist's widow 1888

A00250 [title not known]
Dπ::Presented by the artist's widow 1888

A00251 [title not known]
Dπ::Presented by the artist's widow 1888

A00252 [title not known]
Dπ::Presented by the artist's widow 1888

A00253 [title not known]
Dπ::Presented by the artist's widow 1888

A00254 [title not known]
Dπ::Presented by the artist's widow 1888

A00255 [title not known]
Dπ::Presented by the artist's widow 1888

A00256 [title not known]
Dπ::Presented by the artist's widow 1888

A00257 [title not known]
Dπ::Presented by the artist's widow 1888

A00258 [title not known]
Dπ::Presented by the artist's widow 1888

A00259 [title not known]
Dπ::Presented by the artist's widow 1888

A00260 [title not known]
Dπ::Presented by the artist's widow 1888

A00261 [title not known]
Dπ::Presented by the artist's widow 1888

A00262 [title not known]
Dπ::Presented by the artist's widow 1888

A00263 [title not known]
Dπ::Presented by the artist's widow 1888

A00264 [title not known]
Dπ::Presented by the artist's widow 1888

A00265 [title not known]
Dπ::Presented by the artist's widow 1888

A00266 [title not known]
Dπ::Presented by the artist's widow 1888

A00267 [title not known]
Dπ::Presented by the artist's widow 1888

A00268 [title not known]
Dπ::Presented by the artist's widow 1888

A00269 [title not known]
Dπ::Presented by the artist's widow 1888

A00270 [title not known]
Dπ::Presented by the artist's widow 1888

A00271 [title not known]
Dπ::Presented by the artist's widow 1888

A00272 [title not known]
Dπ::Presented by the artist's widow 1888

A00273 [title not known]
Dπ::Presented by the artist's widow 1888

A00274 [title not known]
Dπ::Presented by the artist's widow 1888

A00275 [title not known]
Dπ::Presented by the artist's widow 1888

A00276 [title not known]
Dπ::Presented by the artist's widow 1888

A00277 [title not known]
Dπ::Presented by the artist's widow 1888

A00278 [title not known]
Dπ::Presented by the artist's widow 1888

A00279 [title not known]
Dπ::Presented by the artist's widow 1888

A00280 [title not known]
Dπ::Presented by the artist's widow 1888

A00281 [title not known]
Dπ::Presented by the artist's widow 1888

A00282 [title not known]
Dπ::Presented by the artist's widow 1888

A00283 [title not known]
Dπ::Presented by the artist's widow 1888

A00284 [title not known]
Dπ::Presented by the artist's widow 1888

A00285 [title not known]
Dπ::Presented by the artist's widow 1888

A00286 [title not known]
Dπ::Presented by the artist's widow 1888

A00287 [title not known]
Dπ::Presented by the artist's widow 1888

A00288 [title not known]
Dπ::Presented by the artist's widow 1888

A00289 [title not known]
Dπ::Presented by the artist's widow 1888

A00290 [title not known]
Dπ::Presented by the artist's widow 1888

A00291 [title not known]
Dπ::Presented by the artist's widow 1888

A00292 [title not known]
Dπ::Presented by the artist's widow 1888

A00293 [title not known]
Dπ::Presented by the artist's widow 1888

A00294 [title not known]
Dπ::Presented by the artist's widow 1888

A00295 [title not known]
Dπ::Presented by the artist's widow 1888

A00296 [title not known]
Dπ::Presented by the artist's widow 1888

A00297 [title not known]
Dπ::Presented by the artist's widow 1888

A00298 [title not known]
Dπ::Presented by the artist's widow 1888

A00299 [title not known]
Dπ::Presented by the artist's widow 1888

A00300 [title not known]
Dπ::Presented by the artist's widow 1888

A00301 [title not known]
Dπ::Presented by the artist's widow 1888

A00302 [title not known]
Dπ::Presented by the artist's widow 1888

A00303 [title not known]
Dπ::Presented by the artist's widow 1888

A00304 [title not known]
Dπ::Presented by the artist's widow 1888

A00305 [title not known]
Dπ::Presented by the artist's widow 1888

A00306 [title not known]
Dπ::Presented by the artist's widow 1888

A00307 [title not known]
Dπ::Presented by the artist's widow 1888

A00308 [title not known]
Dπ::Presented by the artist's widow 1888

A00309 [title not known]
Dπ::Presented by the artist's widow 1888

A00310 [title not known]
Dπ::Presented by the artist's widow 1888

A00311 [title not known]
Dπ::Presented by the artist's widow 1888

A00312 [title not known]
Dπ::Presented by the artist's widow 1888

A00313 [title not known]
Dπ::Presented by the artist's widow 1888

A00314 [title not known]
        Dπ::Presented by the artist's widow 1888
A00315 [title not known]
        Dπ::Presented by the artist's widow 1888
A00316 [title not known]
        Dπ::Presented by the artist's widow 1888
A00317 [title not known]
        Dπ::Presented by the artist's widow 1888
A00318 [title not known]
        Dπ::Presented by the artist's widow 1888
A00319 [title not known]
        Dπ::Presented by the artist's widow 1888
A00320 [title not known]
        Dπ::Presented by the artist's widow 1888
A00321 [title not known]
        Dπ::Presented by the artist's widow 1888
A00322 [title not known]
        Dπ::Presented by the artist's widow 1888
A00323 [title not known]
        Dπ::Presented by the artist's widow 1888
A00324 [title not known]
        Dπ::Presented by the artist's widow 1888
A00325 [title not known]
        Dπ::Presented by the artist's widow 1888
A00326 [title not known]
        Dπ::Presented by the artist's widow 1888
A00327 [title not known]
        Dπ::Presented by the artist's widow 1888
A00328 [title not known]
        Dπ::Presented by the artist's widow 1888
A00329 [title not known]
        Dπ::Presented by the artist's widow 1888
A00330 [title not known]
        Dπ::Presented by the artist's widow 1888
A00331 [title not known]
        Dπ::Presented by the artist's widow 1888
A00332 [title not known]
        Dπ::Presented by the artist's widow 1888
A00333 [title not known]
        Dπ::Presented by the artist's widow 1888
A00334 [title not known]
        Dπ::Presented by the artist's widow 1888
A00335 [title not known]
        Dπ::Presented by the artist's widow 1888
A00336 [title not known]
        Dπ::Presented by the artist's widow 1888
A00337 [title not known]
        Dπ::Presented by the artist's widow 1888
A00338 [title not known]
        Dπ::Presented by the artist's widow 1888
A00339 [title not known]
        Dπ::Presented by the artist's widow 1888
A00340 [title not known]
        Dπ::Presented by the artist's widow 1888
A00341 [title not known]
        Dπ::Presented by the artist's widow 1888
A00342 [title not known]
        Dπ::Presented by the artist's widow 1888
A00343 [title not known]
        Dπ::Presented by the artist's widow 1888
A00344 [title not known]
        Dπ::Presented by the artist's widow 1888

A00345 [title not known]
        Dπ::Presented by the artist's widow 1888
A00346 [title not known]
        Dπ::Presented by the artist's widow 1888
A00347 [title not known]
        Dπ::Presented by the artist's widow 1888
A00348 [title not known]
        Dπ::Presented by the artist's widow 1888
A00349 [title not known]
        Dπ::Presented by the artist's widow 1888
A00350 [title not known]
        Dπ::Presented by the artist's widow 1888
A00351 [title not known]
        Dπ::Presented by the artist's widow 1888
A00352 [title not known]
        Dπ::Presented by the artist's widow 1888
A00353 [title not known]
        Dπ::Presented by the artist's widow 1888
A00354 [title not known]
        Dπ::Presented by the artist's widow 1888
A00355 [title not known]
        Dπ::Presented by the artist's widow 1888
A00356 [title not known]
        Dπ::Presented by the artist's widow 1888
A00357 [title not known]
        Dπ::Presented by the artist's widow 1888
A00358 [title not known]
        Dπ::Presented by the artist's widow 1888
A00359 [title not known]
        Dπ::Presented by the artist's widow 1888
A00360 [title not known]
        Dπ::Presented by the artist's widow 1888
A00361 [title not known]
        Dπ::Presented by the artist's widow 1888
A00362 [title not known]
        Dπ::Presented by the artist's widow 1888
A00363 [title not known]
        Dπ::Presented by the artist's widow 1888
A00364 [title not known]
        Dπ::Presented by the artist's widow 1888
A00365 [title not known]
        Dπ::Presented by the artist's widow 1888
A00366 [title not known]
        Dπ::Presented by the artist's widow 1888
A00367 [title not known]
        Dπ::Presented by the artist's widow 1888
A00368 [title not known]
        Dπ::Presented by the artist's widow 1888
A00369 [title not known]
        Dπ::Presented by the artist's widow 1888
A00370 [title not known]
        Dπ::Presented by the artist's widow 1888
A00371 [title not known]
        Dπ::Presented by the artist's widow 1888
A00372 [title not known]
        Dπ::Presented by the artist's widow 1888
A00373 [title not known]
        Dπ::Presented by the artist's widow 1888
A00374 [title not known]
        Dπ::Presented by the artist's widow 1888
A00375 [title not known]
        Dπ::Presented by the artist's widow 1888

A00376 [title not known]
        Dπ::Presented by the artist's widow 1888

A00377 [title not known]
        Dπ::Presented by the artist's widow 1888

A00378 [title not known]
        Dπ::Presented by the artist's widow 1888

A00379 [title not known]
        Dπ::Presented by the artist's widow 1888

A00380 [title not known]
        Dπ::Presented by the artist's widow 1888

A00381 [title not known]
        Dπ::Presented by the artist's widow 1888

A00382 [title not known]
        Dπ::Presented by the artist's widow 1888

A00383 [title not known]
        Dπ::Presented by the artist's widow 1888

A00384 [title not known]
        Dπ::Presented by the artist's widow 1888

A00385 [title not known]
        Dπ::Presented by the artist's widow 1888

A00386 [title not known]
        Dπ::Presented by the artist's widow 1888

A00387 [title not known]
        Dπ::Presented by the artist's widow 1888

A00388 [title not known]
        Dπ::Presented by the artist's widow 1888

A00389 [title not known]
        Dπ::Presented by the artist's widow 1888

A00390 [title not known]
        Dπ::Presented by the artist's widow 1888

A00391 [title not known]
        Dπ::Presented by the artist's widow 1888

A00392 [title not known]
        Dπ::Presented by the artist's widow 1888

A00393 [title not known]
        Dπ::Presented by the artist's widow 1888

A00394 [title not known]
        Dπ::Presented by the artist's widow 1888

A00395 [title not known]
        Dπ::Presented by the artist's widow 1888

A00396 [title not known]
        Dπ::Presented by the artist's widow 1888

A00397 [title not known]
        Dπ::Presented by the artist's widow 1888

A00398 [title not known]
        Dπ::Presented by the artist's widow 1888

A00399 [title not known]
        Dπ::Presented by the artist's widow 1888

A00400 [title not known]
        Dπ::Presented by the artist's widow 1888

A00401 [title not known]
        Dπ::Presented by the artist's widow 1888

A00402 [title not known]
        Dπ::Presented by the artist's widow 1888

A00403 [title not known]
        Dπ::Presented by the artist's widow 1888

A00404 [title not known]
        Dπ::Presented by the artist's widow 1888

A00405 [title not known]
        Dπ::Presented by the artist's widow 1888

A00406 [title not known]
        Dπ::Presented by the artist's widow 1888

A00407 [title not known]
        Dπ::Presented by the artist's widow 1888

A00408 [title not known]
        Dπ::Presented by the artist's widow 1888

A00409 [title not known]
        Dπ::Presented by the artist's widow 1888

A00410 [title not known]
        Dπ::Presented by the artist's widow 1888

A00411 [title not known]
        Dπ::Presented by the artist's widow 1888

A00412 [title not known]
        Dπ::Presented by the artist's widow 1888

A00413 [title not known]
        Dπ::Presented by the artist's widow 1888

A00414 [title not known]
        Dπ::Presented by the artist's widow 1888

A00415 [title not known]
        Dπ::Presented by the artist's widow 1888

A00416 [title not known]
        Dπ::Presented by the artist's widow 1888

A00417 [title not known]
        Dπ::Presented by the artist's widow 1888

A00418 [title not known]
        Dπ::Presented by the artist's widow 1888

A00419 [title not known]
        Dπ::Presented by the artist's widow 1888

A00420 [title not known]
        Dπ::Presented by the artist's widow 1888

A00421 [title not known]
        Dπ::Presented by the artist's widow 1888

A00422 [title not known]
        Dπ::Presented by the artist's widow 1888

A00423 [title not known]
        Dπ::Presented by the artist's widow 1888

A00424 [title not known]
        Dπ::Presented by the artist's widow 1888

A00425 [title not known]
        Dπ::Presented by the artist's widow 1888

A00426 [title not known]
        Dπ::Presented by the artist's widow 1888

A00427 [title not known]
        Dπ::Presented by the artist's widow 1888

A00428 [title not known]
        Dπ::Presented by the artist's widow 1888

A00429 [title not known]
        Dπ::Presented by the artist's widow 1888

A00430 [title not known]
        Dπ::Presented by the artist's widow 1888

A00431 [title not known]
        Dπ::Presented by the artist's widow 1888

A00432 [title not known]
        Dπ::Presented by the artist's widow 1888

A00433 [title not known]
        Dπ::Presented by the artist's widow 1888

A00434 [title not known]
        Dπ::Presented by the artist's widow 1888

A00435 [title not known]
        Dπ::Presented by the artist's widow 1888

A00436 [title not known]
        Dπ::Presented by the artist's widow 1888

A00437 [title not known]
        Dπ::Presented by the artist's widow 1888

A00438 [title not known]
Dπ::Presented by the artist's widow 1888

A00439 [title not known]
Dπ::Presented by the artist's widow 1888

A00440 [title not known]
Dπ::Presented by the artist's widow 1888

A00441 [title not known]
Dπ::Presented by the artist's widow 1888

A00442 [title not known]
Dπ::Presented by the artist's widow 1888

A00443 [title not known]
Dπ::Presented by the artist's widow 1888

A00444 [title not known]
Dπ::Presented by the artist's widow 1888

A00445 [title not known]
Dπ::Presented by the artist's widow 1888

A00446 [title not known]
Dπ::Presented by the artist's widow 1888

A00447 [title not known]
Dπ::Presented by the artist's widow 1888

A00448 [title not known]
Dπ::Presented by the artist's widow 1888

A00449 [title not known]
Dπ::Presented by the artist's widow 1888

A00450 [title not known]
Dπ::Presented by the artist's widow 1888

A00451 [title not known]
Dπ::Presented by the artist's widow 1888

A00452 [title not known]
Dπ::Presented by the artist's widow 1888

A00453 [title not known]
Dπ::Presented by the artist's widow 1888

A00454 [title not known]
Dπ::Presented by the artist's widow 1888

A00455 [title not known]
Dπ::Presented by the artist's widow 1888

A00456 [title not known]
Dπ::Presented by the artist's widow 1888

A00457 [title not known]
Dπ::Presented by the artist's widow 1888

A00458 [title not known]
Dπ::Presented by the artist's widow 1888

A00459 [title not known]
Dπ::Presented by the artist's widow 1888

A00460 [title not known]
Dπ::Presented by the artist's widow 1888

A00461 [title not known]
Dπ::Presented by the artist's widow 1888

A00462 [title not known]
Dπ::Presented by the artist's widow 1888

A00463 [title not known]
Dπ::Presented by the artist's widow 1888

A00464 [title not known]
Dπ::Presented by the artist's widow 1888

A00465 [title not known]
Dπ::Presented by the artist's widow 1888

A00466 [title not known]
Dπ::Presented by the artist's widow 1888

A00467 [title not known]
Dπ::Presented by the artist's widow 1888

A00468 [title not known]
Dπ::Presented by the artist's widow 1888

A00469 [title not known]
Dπ::Presented by the artist's widow 1888

A00470 [title not known]
Dπ::Presented by the artist's widow 1888

A00471 [title not known]
Dπ::Presented by the artist's widow 1888

A00472 [title not known]
Dπ::Presented by the artist's widow 1888

A00473 [title not known]
Dπ::Presented by the artist's widow 1888

A00474 [title not known]
Dπ::Presented by the artist's widow 1888

A00475 [title not known]
Dπ::Presented by the artist's widow 1888

A00476 [title not known]
Dπ::Presented by the artist's widow 1888

A00477 [title not known]
Dπ::Presented by the artist's widow 1888

A00478 [title not known]
Dπ::Presented by the artist's widow 1888

A00479 [title not known]
Dπ::Presented by the artist's widow 1888

A00480 [title not known]
Dπ::Presented by the artist's widow 1888

A00481 [title not known]
Dπ::Presented by the artist's widow 1888

A00482 [title not known]
Dπ::Presented by the artist's widow 1888

A00483 [title not known]
Dπ::Presented by the artist's widow 1888

A00484 [title not known]
Dπ::Presented by the artist's widow 1888

A00485 [title not known]
Dπ::Presented by the artist's widow 1888

A00486 [title not known]
Dπ::Presented by the artist's widow 1888

A00487 [title not known]
Dπ::Presented by the artist's widow 1888

A00488 [title not known]
Dπ::Presented by the artist's widow 1888

A00489 [title not known]
Dπ::Presented by the artist's widow 1888

A00490 [title not known]
Dπ::Presented by the artist's widow 1888

A00491 [title not known]
Dπ::Presented by the artist's widow 1888

A00492 [title not known]
Dπ::Presented by the artist's widow 1888

A00493 [title not known]
Dπ::Presented by the artist's widow 1888

A00494 [title not known]
Dπ::Presented by the artist's widow 1888

A00495 [title not known]
Dπ::Presented by the artist's widow 1888

A00496 [title not known]
Dπ::Presented by the artist's widow 1888

A00497 [title not known]
Dπ::Presented by the artist's widow 1888

A00498 [title not known]
Dπ::Presented by the artist's widow 1888

A00499 [title not known]
Dπ::Presented by the artist's widow 1888

A00500 [title not known]
Dπ::Presented by the artist's widow 1888

A00501 [title not known]
Dπ::Presented by the artist's widow 1888

A00502 [title not known]
Dπ::Presented by the artist's widow 1888

A00503 [title not known]
Dπ::Presented by the artist's widow 1888

A00504 [title not known]
Dπ::Presented by the artist's widow 1888

A00505 [title not known]
Dπ::Presented by the artist's widow 1888

A00506 [title not known]
Dπ::Presented by the artist's widow 1888

A00507 [title not known]
Dπ::Presented by the artist's widow 1888

A00508 [title not known]
Dπ::Presented by the artist's widow 1888

A00509 [title not known]
Dπ::Presented by the artist's widow 1888

A00510 [title not known]
Dπ::Presented by the artist's widow 1888

A00511 [title not known]
Dπ::Presented by the artist's widow 1888

A00512 [title not known]
Dπ::Presented by the artist's widow 1888

A00513 [title not known]
Dπ::Presented by the artist's widow 1888

A00514 [title not known]
Dπ::Presented by the artist's widow 1888

A00515 [title not known]
Dπ::Presented by the artist's widow 1888

A00516 [title not known]
Dπ::Presented by the artist's widow 1888

A00517 [title not known]
Dπ::Presented by the artist's widow 1888

A00518 [title not known]
Dπ::Presented by the artist's widow 1888

A00519 [title not known]
Dπ::Presented by the artist's widow 1888

A00520 [title not known]
Dπ::Presented by the artist's widow 1888

A00521 [title not known]
Dπ::Presented by the artist's widow 1888

A00522 [title not known]
Dπ::Presented by the artist's widow 1888

A00523 [title not known]
Dπ::Presented by the artist's widow 1888

A00524 [title not known]
Dπ::Presented by the artist's widow 1888

A00525 [title not known]
Dπ::Presented by the artist's widow 1888

A00526 [title not known]
Dπ::Presented by the artist's widow 1888

A00527 [title not known]
Dπ::Presented by the artist's widow 1888

A00528 [title not known]
Dπ::Presented by the artist's widow 1888

A00529 [title not known]
Dπ::Presented by the artist's widow 1888

A00530 [title not known]
Dπ::Presented by the artist's widow 1888

A00531 [title not known]
Dπ::Presented by the artist's widow 1888

A00532 [title not known]
Dπ::Presented by the artist's widow 1888

A00533 [title not known]
Dπ::Presented by the artist's widow 1888

A00534 [title not known]
Dπ::Presented by the artist's widow 1888

A00535 [title not known]
Dπ::Presented by the artist's widow 1888

A00536 [title not known]
Dπ::Presented by the artist's widow 1888

A00537 [title not known]
Dπ::Presented by the artist's widow 1888

A00538 [title not known]
Dπ::Presented by the artist's widow 1888

A00539 [title not known]
Dπ::Presented by the artist's widow 1888

A00540 [title not known]
Dπ::Presented by the artist's widow 1888

A00541 [title not known]
Dπ::Presented by the artist's widow 1888

A00542 [title not known]
Dπ::Presented by the artist's widow 1888

A00543 [title not known]
Dπ::Presented by the artist's widow 1888

A00544 [title not known]
Dπ::Presented by the artist's widow 1888

A00545 [title not known]
Dπ::Presented by the artist's widow 1888

A00546 [title not known]
Dπ::Presented by the artist's widow 1888

A00547 [title not known]
Dπ::Presented by the artist's widow 1888

A00548 [title not known]
Dπ::Presented by the artist's widow 1888

A00549 [title not known]
Dπ::Presented by the artist's widow 1888

A00550 [title not known]
Dπ::Presented by the artist's widow 1888

A00551 [title not known]
Dπ::Presented by the artist's widow 1888

A00552 [title not known]
Dπ::Presented by the artist's widow 1888

A00553 [title not known]
Dπ::Presented by the artist's widow 1888

A00554 [title not known]
Dπ::Presented by the artist's widow 1888

A00555 [title not known]
Dπ::Presented by the artist's widow 1888

A00556 [title not known]
Dπ::Presented by the artist's widow 1888

A00557 [title not known]
Dπ::Presented by the artist's widow 1888

A00558 [title not known]
Dπ::Presented by the artist's widow 1888

A00559 [title not known]
Dπ::Presented by the artist's widow 1888

A00560 [title not known]
Dπ::Presented by the artist's widow 1888

A00561 [title not known]
Dπ::Presented by the artist's widow 1888

A00562 [title not known]
Dπ::Presented by the artist's widow 1888

A00563 [title not known]
Dπ::Presented by the artist's widow 1888

A00564 [title not known]
Dπ::Presented by the artist's widow 1888

A00565 [title not known]
Dπ::Presented by the artist's widow 1888

A00566 [title not known]
Dπ::Presented by the artist's widow 1888

A00567 [title not known]
Dπ::Presented by the artist's widow 1888

A00568 [title not known]
Dπ::Presented by the artist's widow 1888

A00569 [title not known]
Dπ::Presented by the artist's widow 1888

A00570 [title not known]
Dπ::Presented by the artist's widow 1888

A00571 [title not known]
Dπ::Presented by the artist's widow 1888

A00572 [title not known]
Dπ::Presented by the artist's widow 1888

A00573 [title not known]
Dπ::Presented by the artist's widow 1888

A00574 [title not known]
Dπ::Presented by the artist's widow 1888

A00575 [title not known]
Dπ::Presented by the artist's widow 1888

A00576 [title not known]
Dπ::Presented by the artist's widow 1888

A00577 [title not known]
Dπ::Presented by the artist's widow 1888

A00578 [title not known]
Dπ::Presented by the artist's widow 1888

A00579 [title not known]
Dπ::Presented by the artist's widow 1888

A00580 [title not known]
Dπ::Presented by the artist's widow 1888

A00581 [title not known]
Dπ::Presented by the artist's widow 1888

A00582 [title not known]
Dπ::Presented by the artist's widow 1888

A00583 [title not known]
Dπ::Presented by the artist's widow 1888

A00584 [title not known]
Dπ::Presented by the artist's widow 1888

A00585 [title not known]
Dπ::Presented by the artist's widow 1888

A00586 [title not known]
Dπ::Presented by the artist's widow 1888

A00587 [title not known]
Dπ::Presented by the artist's widow 1888

A00588 [title not known]
Dπ::Presented by the artist's widow 1888

A00589 [title not known]
Dπ::Presented by the artist's widow 1888

A00590 [title not known]
Dπ::Presented by the artist's widow 1888

A00591 [title not known]
Dπ::Presented by the artist's widow 1888

A00592 [title not known]
Dπ::Presented by the artist's widow 1888

A00593 [title not known]
Dπ::Presented by the artist's widow 1888

A00594 [title not known]
Dπ::Presented by the artist's widow 1888

A00595 [title not known]
Dπ::Presented by the artist's widow 1888

A00596 [title not known]
Dπ::Presented by the artist's widow 1888

A00597 [title not known]
Dπ::Presented by the artist's widow 1888

A00598 [title not known]
Dπ::Presented by the artist's widow 1888

A00599 [title not known]
Dπ::Presented by the artist's widow 1888

A00600 [title not known]
Dπ::Presented by the artist's widow 1888

A00601 [title not known]
Dπ::Presented by the artist's widow 1888

A00602 [title not known]
Dπ::Presented by the artist's widow 1888

A00603 [title not known]
Dπ::Presented by the artist's widow 1888

A00604 [title not known]
Dπ::Presented by the artist's widow 1888

A00605 [title not known]
Dπ::Presented by the artist's widow 1888

A00606 [title not known]
Dπ::Presented by the artist's widow 1888

A00607 [title not known]
Dπ::Presented by the artist's widow 1888

A00608 [title not known]
Dπ::Presented by the artist's widow 1888

A00609 [title not known]
Dπ::Presented by the artist's widow 1888

A00610 [title not known]
Dπ::Presented by the artist's widow 1888

A00611 [title not known]
Dπ::Presented by the artist's widow 1888

A00612 [title not known]
Dπ::Presented by the artist's widow 1888

A00613 [title not known]
Dπ::Presented by the artist's widow 1888

A00614 [title not known]
Dπ::Presented by the artist's widow 1888

A00615 [title not known]
Dπ::Presented by the artist's widow 1888

A00616 [title not known]
Dπ::Presented by the artist's widow 1888

A00617 [title not known]
Dπ::Presented by the artist's widow 1888

A00618 [title not known]
Dπ::Presented by the artist's widow 1888

A00619 [title not known]
Dπ::Presented by the artist's widow 1888

A00620 [title not known]
Dπ::Presented by the artist's widow 1888

A00621 [title not known]
Dπ::Presented by the artist's widow 1888

A00622 [title not known]
Dπ::Presented by the artist's widow 1888

A00623 [title not known]
Dπ::Presented by the artist's widow 1888

A00624 [title not known]
Dπ::Presented by the artist's widow 1888

A00625 [title not known]
Dπ::Presented by the artist's widow 1888

A00626 [title not known]
Dπ::Presented by the artist's widow 1888

A00627 [title not known]
Dπ::Presented by the artist's widow 1888

A00628 [title not known]
Dπ::Presented by the artist's widow 1888

A00629 [title not known]
Dπ::Presented by the artist's widow 1888

A00630 [title not known]
Dπ::Presented by the artist's widow 1888

A00631 [title not known]
Dπ::Presented by the artist's widow 1888

A00632 [title not known]
Dπ::Presented by the artist's widow 1888

A00633 [title not known]
Dπ::Presented by the artist's widow 1888

A00634 [title not known]
Dπ::Presented by the artist's widow 1888

A00635 [title not known]
Dπ::Presented by the artist's widow 1888

A00636 [title not known]
Dπ::Presented by the artist's widow 1888

A00637 [title not known]
Dπ::Presented by the artist's widow 1888

A00638 [title not known]
Dπ::Presented by the artist's widow 1888

A00639 [title not known]
Dπ::Presented by the artist's widow 1888

A00640 [title not known]
Dπ::Presented by the artist's widow 1888

A00641 [title not known]
Dπ::Presented by the artist's widow 1888

A00642 [title not known]
Dπ::Presented by the artist's widow 1888

A00643 [title not known]
Dπ::Presented by the artist's widow 1888

A00644 [title not known]
Dπ::Presented by the artist's widow 1888

A00645 [title not known]
Dπ::Presented by the artist's widow 1888

A00646 [title not known]
Dπ::Presented by the artist's widow 1888

A00647 [title not known]
Dπ::Presented by the artist's widow 1888

A00648 [title not known]
Dπ::Presented by the artist's widow 1888

A00649 [title not known]
Dπ::Presented by the artist's widow 1888

A00650 [title not known]
Dπ::Presented by the artist's widow 1888

A00651 [title not known]
Dπ::Presented by the artist's widow 1888

A00652 [title not known]
Dπ::Presented by the artist's widow 1888

A00653 [title not known]
Dπ::Presented by the artist's widow 1888

A00654 [title not known]
Dπ::Presented by the artist's widow 1888

A00655 [title not known]
Dπ::Presented by the artist's widow 1888

A00656 [title not known]
Dπ::Presented by the artist's widow 1888

A00657 [title not known]
Dπ::Presented by the artist's widow 1888

A00658 [title not known]
Dπ::Presented by the artist's widow 1888

A00659 [title not known]
Dπ::Presented by the artist's widow 1888

A00660 [title not known]
Dπ::Presented by the artist's widow 1888

A00661 [title not known]
Dπ::Presented by the artist's widow 1888

A00662 [title not known]
Dπ::Presented by the artist's widow 1888

A00663 [title not known]
Dπ::Presented by the artist's widow 1888

A00664 [title not known]
Dπ::Presented by the artist's widow 1888

A00665 [title not known]
Dπ::Presented by the artist's widow 1888

A00666 [title not known]
Dπ::Presented by the artist's widow 1888

A00667 [title not known]
Dπ::Presented by the artist's widow 1888

A00668 [title not known]
Dπ::Presented by the artist's widow 1888

A00669 [title not known]
Dπ::Presented by the artist's widow 1888

A00670 [title not known]
Dπ::Presented by the artist's widow 1888

A00671 [title not known]
Dπ::Presented by the artist's widow 1888

A00672 [title not known]
Dπ::Presented by the artist's widow 1888

A00673 [title not known]
Dπ::Presented by the artist's widow 1888

A00674 [title not known]
Dπ::Presented by the artist's widow 1888

A00675 [title not known]
Dπ::Presented by the artist's widow 1888

A00676 [title not known]
Dπ::Presented by the artist's widow 1888

A00677 [title not known]
Dπ::Presented by the artist's widow 1888

A00678 [title not known]
Dπ::Presented by the artist's widow 1888

A00679 [title not known]
Dπ::Presented by the artist's widow 1888

A00680 [title not known]
Dπ::Presented by the artist's widow 1888

A00681 [title not known]
Dπ::Presented by the artist's widow 1888

A00682 [title not known]
Dπ::Presented by the artist's widow 1888

A00683 [title not known]
Dπ::Presented by the artist's widow 1888

A00684 [title not known]
Dπ::Presented by the artist's widow 1888

A00685 [title not known]
Dπ::Presented by the artist's widow 1888

A00686 [title not known]
Dπ::Presented by the artist's widow 1888

A00687 [title not known]
Dπ::Presented by the artist's widow 1888

A00688 [title not known]
Dπ::Presented by the artist's widow 1888

A00689 [title not known]
Dπ::Presented by the artist's widow 1888

A00690 [title not known]
Dπ::Presented by the artist's widow 1888

A00691 [title not known]
Dπ::Presented by the artist's widow 1888

A00692 [title not known]
Dπ::Presented by the artist's widow 1888

A00693 [title not known]
Dπ::Presented by the artist's widow 1888

A00694 [title not known]
Dπ::Presented by the artist's widow 1888

A00695 [title not known]
Dπ::Presented by the artist's widow 1888

A00696 [title not known]
Dπ::Presented by the artist's widow 1888

A00697 [title not known]
Dπ::Presented by the artist's widow 1888

A00698 [title not known]
Dπ::Presented by the artist's widow 1888

A00699 [title not known]
Dπ::Presented by the artist's widow 1888

A00700 [title not known]
Dπ::Presented by the artist's widow 1888

A00701 [title not known]
Dπ::Presented by the artist's widow 1888

JONES, Harold born 1904
Modern Collection

N05211 The Black Door (circa 1935)
Gπ:489x337:signed:Purchased 1940

JONES, Rosura born 1932
Modern Collection

P06568 Helix (1971)
CLπ:749x552:Presented by Curwen Studio through the Institute of Contemporary Prints 1975

P06733 Euston (1965)
CLπ:454x610:Presented by Curwen Studio 1977

P06734 Phoebus (1965)
CLπ:540x692:Presented by Curwen Studio 1977

JONES, Stanley born 1933
Modern Collection
Tate Gallery Archive holds material concerning this artist

P06317 Porthmeor (1959)
CLπ:406x597:signed:Presented by Curwen Studio through the Institute of Contemporary Prints 1975

P06318 Essex Landscape (1962)
CLπ:476x746:signed:Presented by Curwen Studio through the Institute of Contemporary Prints 1975

Europaeische Graphik VII (P06244, P06289-P06291, P06319, P06340-P06341, P06549; incomplete group; mixed group)

P06319 Madron (1970)
CLπ:600x419:signed:Presented by Curwen Studio through the Institute of Contemporary Prints 1975

P06787 Sheelin (1978)
CLπ:600x419:signed:Presented by Curwen Studio 1978

JONES, Thomas 1742-1803
British Collection

T01844 Mount Vesuvius from Torre dell'Annunziata near Naples (1783)
Oπ:381x552:Presented by Mrs Jane Evan-Thomas 1974

T01929 The Outskirts of London: A View Looking towards Queen Square (1785-6)
Oπ:241x330:Purchased 1974

T03367 In the Road to Santa Maria de'Monti, near Naples: Morning (1781)
DWπ:211x278:Purchased 1982

T03544 Excavation of an Antique Building Discovered in a Cava in the Villa Negroni at Rome (?1777, later dated 1779)
Oπ:406x552:signed:Presented by Canon J.H. Adams 1983

T03545 The Capella Nuova outside the Porta di Chiaja, Naples (1782)
Oπ:200x232:signed:Presented by Canon J.H. Adams 1983

T03546 A Scene in the Colosseum, Rome (?1777)
Oπ:432x289:signed:Presented by Canon J.H. Adams 1983

T04872 Naples: Buildings on a Cliff Top (1782)
Oπ:287x387:signed:Purchased 1986

JONES, William active 1738 - 1747 or 8
British Collection

T03111 Damon and Phillida Reconciled: A Scene from Colley Cibber's 'Damon and Phillida' (1740)
Oc:635x762:signed:Purchased 1980

T03112 Phillida Rejecting Mopsus and Cimon: A Scene from Colley Cibber's 'Damon and Phillida' (1740)
Oc:635x762:Purchased 1980

JONZEN, Karin born 1914
Modern Collection
Tate Gallery Archive holds material concerning this artist

T03755 Head of a Youth (circa 1947-8)
Sp:160x100x140:signed:Transferred from the Victoria & Albert Museum 1983

JORN, Asger 1914-1973
Modern Collection
Tate Gallery Archive holds material concerning this artist

T00853 The Timid Proud One (1957)
Le Timide Orgueilleux
Ob:997x806:signed:Purchased 1966

T01253 The Black Flight (1955)
L'Enrol noir
Gπ:479x632:signed:Presented by Sir Dennis Proctor in memory of Dennis Cohen 1970

T03864 Letter to my Son (1956-7)
Lettre à mon fils
Oc:1300x1955:signed:Purchased 1984

JOSEPH, Lily D. 1863-1940
British Collection

N04894 Roofs, High Holborn (circa 1937)
Oc:1346x1473:signed:Presented by the Trustees of the
Chantrey Bequest 1937

JOSEPH, Peter born 1929
Modern Collection

T03467 No. 55 Green with Dark Blue Surround (1981)
Ac:1648x1876:signed:Purchased 1982

JOSEPH, Samuel circa 1790-1850
British Collection

N01764 Sir David Wilkie R.A. (1843)
Ss:2134x686x616:signed:Presented by subscribers 1844

JUDD, Donald born 1928
Modern Collection
Tate Gallery Archive holds material concerning this artist

T01727 Untitled (1973)
Rm:371x1943x749:signed:Purchased 1973

T03087 Untitled (1980)
Sma:229x1016x787:Purchased 1980

T04936 Untitled (1967-8)
HDπ:436x560:signed:Purchased 1987

Untitled (P07555-P07560; complete group)
P07555 [no title] (1980)
MIπ:508x635:signed:Purchased 1981

P07556 [no title] (1980)
MIπ:508x635:signed:Purchased 1981

P07557 [no title] (1980)
MIπ:508x635:signed:Purchased 1981

P07558 [no title] (1980)
MIπ:502x628:signed:Purchased 1981

P07559 [no title] (1980)
MIπ:502x628:signed:Purchased 1981

P07560 [no title] (1980)
MIπ:508x635:signed:Purchased 1981

P77325 [no title] (1974)
Iπ:550x698:Purchased 1989

P77326 [no title] (1974)
Iπ:550x698:Purchased 1989

P77327 [no title] (1974)
Iπ:698x550:Purchased 1989

P77328 [no title] (1974)
Iπ:550x698:Purchased 1989

P77329 [no title] (1974)
Iπ:550x698:Purchased 1989

P77330 [no title] (1974)
Iπ:550x698:signed:Purchased 1989

JUNGMAN, Nico 1872-1935
British Collection

N04363 At Monnikendam (circa 1922-7)
Oc:635x762:signed:Presented by Viscount Lee of
Fareham 1927

KADISHMAN, Menashe born 1932
Modern Collection
Tate Gallery Archive holds material concerning this artist

The Forest (P04385-P04393; complete group)

P04385 [title not known] (1969)
CNπ::signed:Presented by Rose and Chris Prater through the Institute of Contemporary Prints 1975

P04386 [title not known] (1969)
CNπ::signed:Presented by Rose and Chris Prater through the Institute of Contemporary Prints 1975

P04387 [title not known] (1969)
CNπ::signed:Presented by Rose and Chris Prater through the Institute of Contemporary Prints 1975

P04388 [title not known] (1969)
CNπ::signed:Presented by Rose and Chris Prater through the Institute of Contemporary Prints 1975

P04389 [title not known] (1969)
CNπ::signed:Presented by Rose and Chris Prater through the Institute of Contemporary Prints 1975

P04390 [title not known] (1969)
CNπ::signed:Presented by Rose and Chris Prater through the Institute of Contemporary Prints 1975

P04391 [title not known] (1969)
CNπ::signed:Presented by Rose and Chris Prater through the Institute of Contemporary Prints 1975

P04392 [title not known] (1969)
CNπ::signed:Presented by Rose and Chris Prater through the Institute of Contemporary Prints 1975

P04393 [title not known] (1969)
CNπ::signed:Presented by Rose and Chris Prater through the Institute of Contemporary Prints 1975

P04394 Through (1970)
CNπ:571x727:signed:Presented by Rose and Chris Prater through the Institute of Contemporary Prints 1975

P04395 Bridge (1971-4)
CNπ:625x832:signed:Presented by Rose and Chris Prater through the Institute of Contemporary Prints 1975

Cloths 1-3 (P04396, P04400-P04401; complete group)

P04396 Cloths 1 (1973-4)
CNπ:660x813:signed:Presented by Rose and Chris Prater through the Institute of Contemporary Prints 1975

P04397 Cracked Earth (1973-4)
CNπ:791x610:signed:Presented by Rose and Chris Prater through the Institute of Contemporary Prints 1975

P04398 Sculpture (1973-4)
CNπ:756x600:signed:Presented by Rose and Chris Prater through the Institute of Contemporary Prints 1975

P04399 Yellow Rocks (1973-4)
CNπ:546x908:signed:Presented by Rose and Chris Prater through the Institute of Contemporary Prints 1975

Cloths 1-3 (P04396, P04400-P04401; complete group)

P04400 Cloths 2 (1973-4)
CNπ:656x786:signed:Presented by Rose and Chris Prater through the Institute of Contemporary Prints 1975

P04401 Cloths 3 (1973-4)
CNπ:652x788:signed:Presented by Rose and Chris Prater through the Institute of Contemporary Prints 1975

P04402 Mountain A (1974)
CNπ:730x603:signed:Presented by Rose and Chris Prater through the Institute of Contemporary Prints 1975

P04403 Mountain B (1974)
CNπ:730x603:signed:Presented by Rose and Chris Prater through the Institute of Contemporary Prints 1975

Painted Tree I (P04404-P04406; complete group)

P04404 [title not known] (1974)
CNπ:613x914:signed:Presented by Rose and Chris Prater through the Institute of Contemporary Prints 1975

P04405 [title not known] (1974)
CNπ:613x914:signed:Presented by Rose and Chris Prater through the Institute of Contemporary Prints 1975

P04406 [title not known] (1974)
CNπ:613x914:signed:Presented by Rose and Chris Prater through the Institute of Contemporary Prints 1975

Painted Tree II (P04407-P04409; complete group)

P04407 [title not known] (1974)
CNπ:613x914:signed:Presented by Rose and Chris Prater through the Institute of Contemporary Prints 1975

P04408 [title not known] (1974)
CNπ:613x914:signed:Presented by Rose and Chris Prater through the Institute of Contemporary Prints 1975

P04409 [title not known] (1974)
CNπ:613x914:signed:Presented by Rose and Chris Prater through the Institute of Contemporary Prints 1975

P04410 Red Rocks (1974)
CNπ:654x914:signed:Presented by Rose and Chris Prater through the Institute of Contemporary Prints 1975

P05514 Broken Glass (1979)
CNπ:933x467:signed:Presented by Rose and Chris Prater 1979

P05515 Cloths A (1979)
CNπ:580x822:signed:Presented by Rose and Chris Prater 1979

P05516 Cloths B (1979)
CNπ:580x822:signed:Presented by Rose and Chris Prater 1979

P05517 Upright Rags A (1979)
CNπ:864x521:signed:Presented by Rose and Chris Prater 1979

P05518 Upright Rags B (1979)
CNπ:870x521:signed:Presented by Rose and Chris Prater 1979

P05519 Cracked Earth A (1979)
CNπ:791x610:signed:Presented by Rose and Chris Prater 1979

P05520 Cracked Earth B (1979)
CNπ:788x610:signed:Presented by Rose and Chris Prater 1979

P05521 Mountain A (1979)
CNπ:730x603:signed:Presented by Rose and Chris Prater 1979

P05522 Mountain B (1979)
CNπ:730x603:signed:Presented by Rose and Chris Prater 1979

P05523 New York A (1979)
CNπ:807x613:signed:Presented by Rose and Chris Prater 1979

P05524 New York B (1979)
CNπ:812x685:signed:Presented by Rose and Chris Prater 1979

P05525 Sheep A (1979)
CNπ:650x762:signed:Presented by Rose and Chris Prater 1979

P05526 Sheep B (1979)
CNπ:647x775:signed:Presented by Rose and Chris Prater 1979

P05527 Sheep Head A (1979)
CNπ:572x870:signed:Presented by Rose and Chris Prater 1979

P05528 Sheep Head B (1979)
CNπ:572x825:signed:Presented by Rose and Chris Prater 1979

KAHN, Erich 1904-1979
Modern Collection

T03091 The Seven Sisters (1954)
Oc:508x610:signed:Presented by Professor J.P. Hodin 1980

KANDINSKY, Wassily 1866-1944
Modern Collection
Tate Gallery Archive holds material concerning this artist

N04948 Cossacks (1910-1)
Cosaques
Oc:946x1302:signed:Presented by Mrs Hazel McKinley 1938

T02344 Swinging (1925)
Schaukeln
Ob:705x502:signed:Purchased 1979

KANOVITZ, Howard born 1929
Modern Collection

P04411 American Fridge (1969)
CNπ:632x895:signed:Presented by Rose and Chris Prater through the Institute of Contemporary Prints 1975

P04412 Basketball Pinboard (1969)
CNπ:632x889:signed:Presented by Rose and Chris Prater through the Institute of Contemporary Prints 1975

P04413 English Fridge (1969)
CNπ:613x889:signed:Presented by Rose and Chris Prater through the Institute of Contemporary Prints 1975

KAPOOR, Anish born 1954
Modern Collection

T03675 As if to Celebrate, I Discovered a Mountain Blooming with Red Flowers (1981)
3 DSwv:970x762x1600, 330x711x813, 210x153x470:Purchased 1983

T05487 Untitled (1987)
Gπ:390x300:Presented by Weltkunst Foundation 1988

T05488 Untitled (1987-8)
GVπ:540x760:Presented by Weltkunst Foundation 1988

T05489 Untitled (1987-8)
Gπ:420x350:Presented by Weltkunst Foundation 1988

T05490 Untitled (1988)
Gπ:560x560:Presented by Weltkunst Foundation 1988

T05491 Untitled (1986)
Hπ:310x440:Presented by Weltkunst Foundation 1988

T05721 Three (1982)
4 Sv:785x3500x790:Purchased 1989

P11270 Untitled (1989)
Lπ:513x515:signed:Presented by the King Edward's Hospital Fund 1989

P11271 Untitled (1989)
Lπ:513x515:Presented by the King Edward's Hospital Fund 1989

P77318 Untitled 2 (1988)
Lπ:450x350:Purchased 1989

P77319 Untitled 5 (1988)
Lπ:448x350:Purchased 1989

P77320 Untitled 3 (1988)
Lπ:453x353:Purchased 1989

P77321 Untitled I (1988)
Lπ:1133x898:Purchased 1989

P77322 Untitled II (1988)
Lπ:1133x898:Purchased 1989

P77323 Untitled III (1988)
Lπ:898x1133:Purchased 1989

KARLOWSKA, Stanislawa de - see DE KARLOWSKA, Stanislawa

KATZ - see MANE-KATZ

KATZ, Alex born 1927
Modern Collection

T03805 Hiroshi and Marsha (1981)
Oc:1828x2437:Presented by Paul Schupf 1983

KAUFFMAN, Craig born 1932
Modern Collection

T01071 Untitled (1967)
Sa:467x1426x238:Presented anonymously through the American Federation of Arts 1968

KAUFFMANN, Angelica 1741-1807
British Collection

T00928 Portrait of a Lady (circa 1795)
Oc:792x635:Presented by Mrs M. Bernard 1967

manner of
KAUFMANN, Angelica 1741-1807
British Collection

T00025 Hector Taking Leave of Andromache
Oc:1162x1162:Purchased 1955

KAUFMANN, Isidor 1854-1921
Modern Collection

N04464 Young Rabbi from N. (circa 1910)
Ow:381x276:signed:Presented by Viscount Bearsted through the National Art Collections Fund 1929

KAVANAGH, John F. born 1903
Modern Collection

N05441 Russian Peasant (circa 1935-9)
Sz:229x197x241:Presented by the Trustees of the Chantrey Bequest 1943

KEENE, Charles Samuel 1823-1891
British Collection
Tate Gallery Archive holds material concerning this artist

N02446 Drawing for 'Punch'
Dπ::Presented by J.P. Heseltine 1909

N02447 Drawing for 'Punch'
Dπ::Presented by J.P. Heseltine 1909

N02449 Drawing for 'Punch'
Dπ::Presented by J.P. Heseltine 1909

N02450 Drawing for 'Punch'
Dπ::Presented by J.P. Heseltine 1909

N02451 Drawing for 'Punch'
Dπ::Presented by J.P. Heseltine 1909

N02452 Drawing for 'Punch'
Dπ::Presented by J.P. Heseltine 1909

N02453 Drawing for 'Punch'
Dπ::Presented by J.P. Heseltine 1909

N02454 Drawing for 'Punch'
Dπ::Presented by J.P. Heseltine 1909

N02456 Mr Punch
Dπ:102x171:Presented by J.P. Heseltine 1909

N02458 Drawing for 'Punch'
Dπ::Presented by J.P. Heseltine 1909

N02459 Drawing for 'Punch'
Dπ::Presented by J.P. Heseltine 1909

N02460 Drawing for 'Punch'
Dπ::Presented by J.P. Heseltine 1909

N02461 Drawing for 'Punch'
Dπ::Presented by J.P. Heseltine 1909

N02462 Drawing for 'Punch'
Dπ::Presented by J.P. Heseltine 1909

N02463 Drawing for 'Punch'
Dπ::Presented by J.P. Heseltine 1909

N02464 Drawing for 'Punch'
Dπ::Presented by J.P. Heseltine 1909

N02465 Figure Study
Dπ::Presented by J.P. Heseltine 1909

N02466 Figure Study
Dπ::Presented by J.P. Heseltine 1909

N02467 Figure Study
Dπ::Presented by J.P. Heseltine 1909

N02468 Figure Study
Dπ::Presented by J.P. Heseltine 1909

N02469 Figure Study
Dπ::Presented by J.P. Heseltine 1909

N02470 Figure Study
Dπ::Presented by J.P. Heseltine 1909

N03020 Study of a Woman
Wπ:140x89:Presented by J. Bowyer Nichols through the
National Art Collections Fund 1915

N03021 Study of a Boy (circa 1860)
Dπ:102x133:Presented by J. Bowyer Nichols through the
National Art Collections Fund 1915

N03022 Study of the Artist
Dπ:114x171:Presented by J. Bowyer Nichols through the
National Art Collections Fund 1915

N03611 The Artist with a Gun
Dπ:133x70:Presented by H. Reitlinger through the
National Art Collections Fund 1922

N03612 Old Man Seated
Dπ:121x83:Presented by H. Reitlinger through the
National Art Collections Fund 1922

N03613 In the Row
Dπ:111x178:Presented by H. Reitlinger through the
National Art Collections Fund 1922

N03614 Cabman and Policeman
Dπ:111x178:Presented by H. Reitlinger through the
National Art Collections Fund 1922

N03644 Self-Portrait
Ob:289x194:Presented by the Trustees of the Chantrey
Bequest 1922

N04069 The Duel
Wπ:114x108:Presented by the Misses Arber 1925

N04070 Man Polishing Armour
Wπ:210x165:Presented by the Misses Arber 1925

N04071 Cavalier with a Wounded Arm
Dπ:143x92:Presented by the Misses Arber 1925

N04072 Woman and Butler
Dπ:190x130:signed:Presented by the Misses Arber 1925

N04073 Butcher's Shop
Dπ:111x171:signed:Presented by the Misses Arber 1925

N04074 Artist Sketching
Dπ:108x175:Presented by the Misses Arber 1925

N04086 A True Patriot
Dπ:121x181:signed:Bequeathed by John Lane 1926

N04369 Seated Girl (1885)
Dπ:121x83:Presented by John Hipkins 1927

N04370 The Artist Standing (1884)
Dπ:130x83:Presented by John Hipkins 1927

N04371 The Artist in Officer's Uniform (1883)
Dπ:127x83:Presented by John Hipkins 1927

N04372 Sketches of Horace Harral and Edwin Edwards
Dπ:178x133:Presented by John Hipkins 1927

N04373 Scene of the Plague of London (published 1862)
Lπ:152x102:Presented by John Hipkins 1927

N04374 Old Walberswick Pier (1867)
Lπ:105x162:signed:Presented by John Hipkins 1927

T02082 A Lady with Binoculars (1867)
Dπ:197x159:Presented by Mrs Phyllis Keene 1976

T02083 Dorothea Corbould, Reading (?circa 1860)
Dπ:162x102:Presented by Mrs Phyllis Keene 1976

T02084 Study for 'Sam Bentley's Christmas' (?circa 1860)
Dπ:140x127:Presented by Mrs Phyllis Keene 1976

T02085 A Village Street
Dπ:114x181:Presented by Mrs Phyllis Keene 1976

T02086 Study of a Mantelpiece
Dπ:111x178:Presented by Mrs Phyllis Keene 1976

T02087 'Incorrigible!' (1883)
Dπ:175x146:Presented by Mrs Phyllis Keene 1976

T02088 Self-Portrait, Seated (?1885)
Dπ:140x89:Presented by Mrs Phyllis Keene 1976

T02089 Study of a Standing Man
Dπ:203x127:Presented by Mrs Phyllis Keene 1976

T02090 Study of a Man with a Little Girl
Dπ:203x117:Presented by Mrs Phyllis Keene 1976

T03840 Two Artists Working by Lamplight in a Studio (circa
1860)
Dπ:187x127:signed:Purchased 1984

KEEPING, Charles born 1924
Modern Collection
Tate Gallery Archive holds material concerning this artist

P06735 City Tiered Stables (1965)
CLπ:416x670:Presented by Curwen Studio 1977

KEIRINCX, Alexander 1600-1652
British Collection

T04168 Distant View of a Town (called 'Pontefract') (circa
1635-40)
Ow:529x687:signed:Purchased 1986

KELLY, Ellsworth born 1923
Modern Collection
Tate Gallery Archive holds material concerning this artist

T00511 Broadway (1958)
Oc:1981x1768:signed:Presented by E.J. Power through the Friends of the Tate Gallery 1962

T03072 White Curve (1974)
Am:1619x5131:Purchased 1980

P01792 Variant II, yellow (1965)
CLπ:594x394:signed:Presented by the Museum of Modern Art, New York 1976

P11222 Yellow over Dark Blue (1964-5)
Lπ:892x598:signed:Presented by Mary Martin in memory of her husband Bill Morton 1989

The Concorde Series (P77143-P77145; incomplete group)

P77143 Diagonal with Black (State) (1981)
MIπ:402x402:signed:Purchased 1986

P77144 Concorde II (State) (1981)
MIπ:425x284:signed:Purchased 1986

P77145 Concorde IV (State) (1981)
MIπ:405x320:signed:Purchased 1986

KELLY, Felix born 1916
Modern Collection
Tate Gallery Archive holds material concerning this artist

School Prints (P01698-P01727; complete group; mixed group)

P01709 Drifter and Paddle Steamer (1946)
CLπ:594x762:signed:Presented by Patrick Seale Prints 1975

KELLY, Francis born 1927
Modern Collection
Tate Gallery Archive holds material concerning this artist

P01423 Crossroads (1974)
MIπ:346x505:signed:Presented by Christie's Contemporary Art through the Institute of Contemporary Prints 1975

KELLY, Sir Gerald 1879-1972
British Collection
Tate Gallery Archive holds material concerning this artist

N03001 Ma Si Gyaw, Pose IV (1909-14)
Oc:1270x1016:signed:Presented by Francis Howard through the National Loans Exhibition Committee 1914

N04703 The Jester (W. Somerset Maugham) (1911)
Oc:1016x762:Presented by the Trustees of the Chantrey Bequest 1933

T00232 The Vicar in his Study (1912)
Oc:1168x952:signed:Presented by the Trustees of the Chantrey Bequest 1959

T03650 Boulevard Montparnasse (1904)
Ow:180x120:signed:Presented anonymously in memory of Sir Terence Rattigan 1983

T03651 Alex and Demary Dancing in a Music Hall at Algiers (1906)
Ow:148x180:signed:Presented anonymously in memory of Sir Terence Rattigan 1983

T03652 Terrace at Monte Carlo (1908)
Ow:149x180:signed:Presented anonymously in memory of Sir Terence Rattigan 1983

T03653 Beach at Etretât (1908)
Ow:216x270:signed:Presented anonymously in memory of Sir Terence Rattigan 1983

KELLY, Mary born 1941
Modern Collection
Tate Gallery Archive holds material concerning this artist

T03925 Post-Partum Document. Analysed Markings And Diary Perspective Schema (Experimentum Mentis III: Weaning from the Dyad) (1975)
13 DVπ:360x5830:Purchased 1984

KEMENY, Zoltan 1907-1965
Modern Collection

T00815 Suburb of Angels (1957)
Banlieue des anges
Rm:673x959x76:signed:Purchased 1966

T01853 Gravitations Sentimentales (1958)
Rm:860x708:signed:Presented by the Kate Maremont Foundation 1974

T03595 Moonlight (1948)
Clair de lune
ROb:1212x747:signed:Presented by Mrs Madeleine Kemeny, the artist's widow 1983

T03596 Cat Mask (1947)
Masque de chat
RVb:410x585x79:signed:Presented by Mrs Madeleine Kemeny, the artist's widow 1983

KEMP-WELCH, Lucy 1869-1958
British Collection
Tate Gallery Archive holds material concerning this artist

N01649 Colt Hunting in the New Forest (1897)
Oc:1537x3048:signed:Presented by the Trustees of the Chantrey Bequest 1897

N03217 Forward the Guns! (1917)
Oc:1524x3061:signed:Presented by the Trustees of the Chantrey Bequest 1917

KENNET, Lady (Kathleen, Lady Scott; Kathleen Hilton Young) 1878-1947
British Collection

N04467 The Rt. Hon. H.H. Asquith (circa 1912-3)
Sz:311x254x249:Presented by Lord Duveen 1929

KENNINGTON, Eric 1888-1960
Modern Collection
Tate Gallery Archive holds material concerning this artist

N03205 Bayonet Practice (1917)
Dπ:749x651:signed:Presented by Sir William Rothenstein in memory of Gerard Chowne 1917

N03552 A Bantam Hercules (1917)
Dπ:762x483:signed:Presented by Otto Gutekunst 1920

N03593 Sleeping Soldier (exhibited 1918)
Dπ:324x337:Presented by Sir William Nicholson 1921

N03637 Muttar il Hamoud min Beni Hassan (1920)
Pπ:768x559:Presented by T.E. Lawrence 1922

N04075 Raider with a Cosh (1917)
Pπ:629x470:Presented by the Contemporary Art Society 1925

N05029 Earth Child (circa 1936-7)
Ss:1321x597:Presented by the artist 1939

N05438 Head of T.E. Lawrence (1926)
Sz:413x425x254:Presented by The Studio and the
Contemporary Art Society 1943

N05704 Sergeant H.D. Parker, R.A.F. (1941)
Pπ:784x533:signed:Presented by the War Artists'
Advisory Committee 1946

N06230 Reclining Figure of T.E. Lawrence, replica (1939/54)
Sp:597x2095x930:Purchased 1954

The Great War: Britain's Efforts and Ideals
(P03001-P03007, P03011-P03023, P03031-P03036,
P03039-P03044; incomplete group; mixed group)
Making Soldiers (P03039-P03044; complete group)

P03039 Bayonet Practice (circa 1917)
MLπ:465x359:signed:Presented by the Ministry of
Information 1918

P03040 The Gas Mask (circa 1917)
MLπ:470x361:signed:Presented by the Ministry of
Information 1918

P03041 Ready for Service (circa 1917)
MLπ:465x360:signed:Presented by the Ministry of
Information 1918

P03042 In the Trenches (circa 1917)
MLπ:467x360:signed:Presented by the Ministry of
Information 1918

P03043 Over the Top (circa 1917)
MLπ:465x365:signed:Presented by the Ministry of
Information 1918

P03044 Bringing In Prisoners (circa 1917)
MLπ:457x362:signed:Presented by the Ministry of
Information 1918

KENNINGTON, Thomas Benjamin
1856-1916
British Collection

N01560 Orphans (1885)
Oc:1016x762:Presented by Sir Henry Tate 1894

KENNY, Michael born 1941
Modern Collection

T01106 Place (1967)
Sm:591x1041x483:Purchased 1969

KERR, Charles Henry Malcolm 1858-1907
British Collection

N02215 Self-Portrait (exhibited 1899)
Oc:1372x914:signed:Presented by the artist's widow 1908

N04848 The Visitor (exhibited 1905)
Oc:762x321:signed:Presented by the artist's widow 1936

KERR-LAWSON, James 1865-1939
British Collection

N04187 J. Havard Thomas Asleep (1910)
Dπ:127x89:signed:Presented by the artist 1926

KESSELL, Mary 1914-1978
Modern Collection
Tate Gallery Archive holds material concerning this artist

T00391 Still Life under the Sea (1960)
OPc:711x1219:signed:Purchased 1960

KESTLEMAN, Morris born 1905
Modern Collection
Tate Gallery Archive holds material concerning this artist

IAA Portfolio (P03096-P03104, P03107; complete
group; mixed group)

P03103 Bonjour! (1975)
CLπ:511x400:signed:Presented by the International
Association of Art 1975

KETTLE, Tilly 1734 or 5 - 1786
British Collection

N03962 Young Man in a Fawn Coat (circa 1772-3)
Oc:762x629:Bequeathed by Sir Claude Phillips 1925

T03373 Mrs Yates as Mandane in 'The Orphan of China'
(exhibited 1765)
Oc:1924x1295:Purchased with assistance from the
Friends of the Tate Gallery 1982

KEY, Joan born 1948
Modern Collection

P77112 Large Goat's Head (1983)
CLπ:776x575:signed:Purchased 1985

KIDNER, Michael born 1917
Modern Collection
Tate Gallery Archive holds material concerning this artist

T00513 Orange and Violet (1961)
Oc:1270x1041:Purchased 1962

P77023 Square and Circle One (1976, published 1982)
FMLπ:485x579:signed:Purchased 1984

KIEFER, Anselm born 1945
Modern Collection

T03403 Parsifal I (1973)
Oπc:3247x2198:Purchased 1982

T03404 Parsifal II (1973)
HOπc:3247x2188:Purchased 1982

T03405 Parsifal III (1973)
HOπc:3007x4345:Purchased 1982

T04128 The Rhine (1981)
Der Rhein
SJπb:1180x420x95:Presented by the Patrons of New Art
with assistance from Deutsche Bank through the Friends
of the Tate Gallery 1985

KIFF, Ken born 1935
Modern Collection

T03612 Person Cutting an Image (1965-71)
Tb:610x610:signed:Purchased 1983

T04888 Triptych: Shadows (1983-6)
TAOb:1250x3203:signed:Purchased 1987

P11228 [no title] (1988)
Jπ:1065x2100:signed:Presented by Garner H. Tullis and
Pamela Auchincloss 1989

P11229 [no title] (1988)
Jπ:2158x1065:signed:Presented by Garner H. Tullis and
Pamela Auchincloss 1989

KINDERSLEY, David born 1915
Modern Collection

P06320 Letters are Things (1971)
CLπ:584x457:signed:Presented by Curwen Studio through the Institute of Contemporary Prints 1975

P06321 Quality before Quantity (1971)
CLπ:584x457:signed:Presented by Curwen Studio through the Institute of Contemporary Prints 1975

KING, Cecil born 1921
Modern Collection

P01424 Intrusion - Green (1974)
CNπ:514x746:signed:Presented by Editions Alecto through the Institute of Contemporary Prints 1975

P01425 Intrusion - Red (1974)
CNπ:514x746:signed:Presented by Editions Alecto through the Institute of Contemporary Prints 1975

P01426 Threshold - Black (1974)
CNπ:514x743:signed:Presented by Editions Alecto through the Institute of Contemporary Prints 1975

P01427 Threshold - Orange (1974)
CNπ:514x743:signed:Presented by Editions Alecto through the Institute of Contemporary Prints 1975

The Dubai Suite (P01428-P01430; complete group)
P01428 Blue (1975)
CNπ:425x749:signed:Presented by Editions Alecto through the Institute of Contemporary Prints 1975

P01429 Orange (1975)
CNπ:425x749:signed:Presented by Editions Alecto through the Institute of Contemporary Prints 1975

P01430 Red (1975)
CNπ:425x749:signed:Presented by Editions Alecto through the Institute of Contemporary Prints 1975

KING, John Henry Yeend 1855-1924
British Collection

N01673 Milking Time (exhibited 1898)
Oc:1219x1829:signed:Presented by the Trustees of the Chantrey Bequest 1898

KING, Jeremy born 1933
Modern Collection

P06736 A Cheshire Stream (1972-3)
CLπ:381x479:signed:Presented by Curwen Studio 1976

P06788 Maple Durham Hill (1977)
CLπ:394x521:signed:Presented by Curwen Studio 1978

P06789 Temple Henley (1977)
CLπ:394x521:signed:Presented by Curwen Studio 1978

P06790 Silverdale (1978)
CLπ:410x594:signed:Presented by Curwen Studio 1978

P06791 Leighton Moss (1978)
CLπ:410x600:signed:Presented by Curwen Studio 1978

KING, Phillip born 1934
Modern Collection
Tate Gallery Archive holds material concerning this artist

T00737 And the Birds Began to Sing (1964)
SAm:1803x1803x1803:Purchased 1965

T01030 Nile (1967)
Sa:1829x5639x3048:Presented by Mr and Mrs Jack Steinberg through the Friends of the Tate Gallery 1968

T01206 Tra-La-La (1963)
Sa:2743x762x762:Presented by Alistair McAlpine (later Lord McAlpine of West Green) 1970

T01224 Green Streamer (1970)
ASm:1118x3632x2362:Purchased 1970

T01236 Genghis Khan (1963)
SAa:2134x2743x3658:Presented by the Friends of the Tate Gallery 1970

T01360 Call (1967)
SAm:4420x4350x5359:Presented by Alistair McAlpine (later Lord McAlpine of West Green) 1970

T01361 Dunstable Reel (1970)
SAm:1968x5067:Presented by Alistair McAlpine (later Lord McAlpine of West Green) 1970

T02345 Within (1978-9)
Smsw:2210x3200x2590:Purchased 1979

KING, Ronald born 1932
Modern Collection
Tate Gallery Archive holds material concerning this artist

P08177 III the Squire [from the book 'The Prologue'] (1978)
MLπ:279x181:signed:Transferred from the Library 1980

KINLEY, Peter 1926-1988
Modern Collection
Tate Gallery Archive holds material concerning this artist

T00130 Walking Figure (1957)
Oc:1448x889:signed:Purchased 1957

T03476 Fire (1982)
Oc:1676x2134:signed:Purchased 1982

KIRCHNER, Ernst Ludwig 1880-1938
Modern Collection

T03067 Bathers at Moritzburg (1909/26)
Badende Moritzburg
Oc:1511x1997:signed:Purchased 1980

KIRK, Eve 1900-1969
Modern Collection
Tate Gallery Archive holds material concerning this artist

N05041 Avignon (1939)
Oc:502x730:signed:Purchased 1939

KIRKEBY, Per born 1938
Modern Collection

P11220 [title not known] (1988)
Jπ:2132x1072:Presented by Garner H. Tullis and Pamela Auchincloss 1989

P77301 [no title: No. 6] (1987)
Jπ:440x450:signed:Purchased 1989

P77302 [no title: No. 4] (1987)
Jπ:425x460:signed:Purchased 1989

P77303 [no title: No. 9] (1987)
Lπ:785x1187:signed:Purchased 1989

P77304 [no title: No. 13] (1987)
Lπ:788x1198:signed:Purchased 1989

KITAJ, R.B. born 1932
Modern Collection
Tate Gallery Archive holds material concerning this artist

T00561 Isaac Babel Riding with Budyonny (1962)
Oc:1829x1524:Purchased 1963

T01772 The Man of the Woods and the Cat of the Mountains (1973)
Oc:1524x1524:Presented by the Friends of the Tate Gallery 1974

T02141 The Orientalist (1976-7)
Oc:2438x768:Purchased 1977

T03055 The Rise of Fascism (1975-9)
OPπ:851x1584:signed:Purchased 1980

T03082 The Murder of Rosa Luxemburg (1960)
Ovc:1530x1524:signed:Purchased 1980

T04115 Cecil Court, London W.C.2. (The Refugees) (1983-4)
Oc:1830x1830:signed:Purchased 1985

P01431 Robert Duncan (1971)
MIπ:159x159:signed:Presented by Marlborough Graphics through the Institute of Contemporary Prints 1975

In Our Time (P03139-P03141, P04456-P04503; complete group)

P03139 (1) The Tower (1969-70)
CNπ:460x341:signed:Presented by Marlborough Graphics 1976

P03140 (26) Deliverance from Russia (1969-70)
CNπ:580x404:signed:Presented by Marlborough Graphics 1976

P03141 (37) Menschen der Zeit (1969-70)
CNπ:503x367:signed:Presented by Marlborough Graphics 1976

P04414 Acheson Go Home (1963-4)
CNπ:733x527:signed:Presented by Rose and Chris Prater through the Institute of Contemporary Prints 1975

P04415 Errata (1963-4)
CNπ:746x508:Presented by Rose and Chris Prater through the Institute of Contemporary Prints 1975

P04416 Photographs and Philosophy (1963-4)
CNπ:492x772:signed:Presented by Rose and Chris Prater through the Institute of Contemporary Prints 1975

P04417 Boys and Girls! (1964)
CNπ:527x413:signed:Presented by Rose and Chris Prater through the Institute of Contemporary Prints 1975

P04418 Disciple of Bernstein and Kautsky (1964)
CNπ:778x524:signed:Presented by Rose and Chris Prater through the Institute of Contemporary Prints 1975

The Institute of Contemporary Arts Portfolio (P04016, P04038, P04053, P04076, P04115, P04125, P04166, P04248, P04256, P04315-P04316, P04334, P04378-P04380, P04419, P04635, P04752, P04938, P05138, P05155, P05248; complete group; mixed group)

P04419 Good God Where is the King! (1964)
CNπ:765x508:signed:Presented by Rose and Chris Prater through the Institute of Contemporary Prints 1975

P04420 Old and New Tables (1964)
CNπ:552x375:Presented by Rose and Chris Prater through the Institute of Contemporary Prints 1975

P04421 Yaller Bird (1964)
CNπ:619x511:signed:Presented by Rose and Chris Prater through the Institute of Contemporary Prints 1975

P04422 The Desire for Lunch is a Bourgeois Obsessional Neurosis or Grey Schizoids (1965)
CNπ:705x464:signed:Presented by Rose and Chris Prater through the Institute of Contemporary Prints 1975

P04423 The Reduction of Anxiety in Terminal Patients (1965)
CNπ:845x467:signed:Presented by Rose and Chris Prater through the Institute of Contemporary Prints 1975

P04424 World Ruin through Black Magic (1965)
CNπ:1381x981:signed:Presented by Rose and Chris Prater through the Institute of Contemporary Prints 1975

P04425 Mort (1966)
CNπ:1006x689:signed:Presented by Rose and Chris Prater through the Institute of Contemporary Prints 1975

P04426 Pogany (1966)
CNπ:610x914:signed:Presented by Rose and Chris Prater through the Institute of Contemporary Prints 1975

P04427 Truman in the White House (1966)
CNπ:556x797:signed:Presented by Rose and Chris Prater through the Institute of Contemporary Prints 1975

First Series - Some Poets (P04428-P04437; complete group)

P04428 For Love (Robert Creeley) (1966-70)
CNπ::signed:Presented by Rose and Chris Prater through the Institute of Contemporary Prints 1975

P04429 Ed Dorn (1966-70)
CNπ::signed:Presented by Rose and Chris Prater through the Institute of Contemporary Prints 1975

P04430 Revolt on the Clyde (Hugh McDiarmid) (1966-70)
CNπ::signed:Presented by Rose and Chris Prater through the Institute of Contemporary Prints 1975

P04431 Star Betelgeuse (Robert Duncan) (1966-70)
CNπ::signed:Presented by Rose and Chris Prater through the Institute of Contemporary Prints 1975

P04432 Fifties Grand Swank (Morton Feldman) (1966-70)
CNπ::signed:Presented by Rose and Chris Prater through the Institute of Contemporary Prints 1975

P04433 Charles Olson (1966-70)
CNπ::signed:Presented by Rose and Chris Prater through the Institute of Contemporary Prints 1975

P04434 Deerskin (John Wieners) (1966-70)
CNπ::signed:Presented by Rose and Chris Prater through the Institute of Contemporary Prints 1975

P04435 Hail Thee Who Play (Michael McClure) (1966-70)
CNπ::signed:Presented by Rose and Chris Prater through the Institute of Contemporary Prints 1975

P04436 Kenneth Rexroth (1966-70)
CNπ::signed:Presented by Rose and Chris Prater through the Institute of Contemporary Prints 1975

P04437 W.H. Auden (1966-70)
CNπ::signed:Presented by Rose and Chris Prater through the Institute of Contemporary Prints 1975

P04438 Barrio (1967)
CNπ:867x597:signed:Presented by Rose and Chris Prater through the Institute of Contemporary Prints 1975

P04439 Civic Virtue (1967)
CNπ:533x660:signed:Presented by Rose and Chris Prater through the Institute of Contemporary Prints 1975

P04440 Home Truths (1967)
CNπ:568x911:signed:Presented by Rose and Chris Prater through the Institute of Contemporary Prints 1975

P04441 The Romance of the Civil Service (1967)
CNπ:1019x692:signed:Presented by Rose and Chris Prater through the Institute of Contemporary Prints 1975

P04442 Vernissage-Cocktail (1967)
CNπ:1035x695:signed:Presented by Rose and Chris
Prater through the Institute of Contemporary Prints 1975

P04443 The Defects of its Qualities (1967-8)
CNπ:902x610:signed:Presented by Rose and Chris Prater
through the Institute of Contemporary Prints 1975

Struggle in the West - The Bombing of London
(P04444-P04450; complete group)

P04444 Die Guts Alte Zeit (1969-70)
:984x635:signed:Presented by Rose and Chris Prater
through the Institute of Contemporary Prints 1975

P04445 Horizon / Blitz (Prologue) (1969-70)
:761x514:signed:Presented by Rose and Chris Prater
through the Institute of Contemporary Prints 1975

P04446 On the Safeguarding of Life in Theatres (Epilogue)
(1969-70)
:341x457:signed:Presented by Rose and Chris Prater
through the Institute of Contemporary Prints 1975

P04447 Safeguarding of Life (1969-70)
:685x999:signed:Presented by Rose and Chris Prater
through the Institute of Contemporary Prints 1975

P04448 Setpiece I (1969-70)
:443x762:signed:Presented by Rose and Chris Prater
through the Institute of Contemporary Prints 1975

P04449 Setpiece 2 (1969-70)
:431x747:signed:Presented by Rose and Chris Prater
through the Institute of Contemporary Prints 1975

P04450 Setpiece 3 (1969-70)
:441x762:signed:Presented by Rose and Chris Prater
through the Institute of Contemporary Prints 1975

P04451 Bacon I (1968-9)
CNπ:476x1041:signed:Presented by Rose and Chris
Prater through the Institute of Contemporary Prints 1975

P04452 Bacon II (1968-9)
CNπ:1016x375:signed:Presented by Rose and Chris
Prater through the Institute of Contemporary Prints 1975

P04453 Ctric News Topi (1968)
CNπ:991x625:signed:Presented by Rose and Chris Prater
through the Institute of Contemporary Prints 1975

P04454 Plays for Total Stakes (1968)
CNπ:632x632:signed:Presented by Rose and Chris Prater
through the Institute of Contemporary Prints 1975

P04455 Untitled (1969)
CNπ:425x394:signed:Presented by Rose and Chris Prater
through the Institute of Contemporary Prints 1975

In Our Time (P03139-P03141, P04456-P04503; complete
group)

P04456 (2) How to Read (1969-70)
CNπ:458x294:signed:Presented by Rose and Chris Prater
through the Institute of Contemporary Prints 1975

P04457 (3) Four in America (1969-70)
CNπ:458x355:signed:Presented by Rose and Chris Prater
through the Institute of Contemporary Prints 1975

P04458 (4) The Caliph's Design (1969-70)
CNπ:495x316:signed:Presented by Rose and Chris Prater
through the Institute of Contemporary Prints 1975

P04459 (5) Transition (1969-70)
CNπ:382x295:signed:Presented by Rose and Chris Prater
through the Institute of Contemporary Prints 1975

P04460 (6) Partisan Review (1969-70)
CNπ:455x307:signed:Presented by Rose and Chris Prater
through the Institute of Contemporary Prints 1975

P04461 (7) Der Russiche Revolutionsfilm (1969-70)
CNπ:381x255:signed:Presented by Rose and Chris Prater
through the Institute of Contemporary Prints 1975

P04462 (8) Die Donan (1969-70)
CNπ:567x431:signed:Presented by Rose and Chris Prater
through the Institute of Contemporary Prints 1975

P04463 (9) The Bronxville Portfolio (1969-70)
CNπ:427x571:signed:Presented by Rose and Chris Prater
through the Institute of Contemporary Prints 1975

P04464 (10) Songs of a Sourdough (1969-70)
CNπ:462x422:signed:Presented by Rose and Chris Prater
through the Institute of Contemporary Prints 1975

P04465 (11) Zeppelin Nights (1969-70)
CNπ:454x327:signed:Presented by Rose and Chris Prater
through the Institute of Contemporary Prints 1975

P04466 (12) Max and the White Phagocytes (1969-70)
CNπ:508x335:signed:Presented by Rose and Chris Prater
through the Institute of Contemporary Prints 1975

P04467 (13) Edward Weston (1969-70)
CNπ:347x264:signed:Presented by Rose and Chris Prater
through the Institute of Contemporary Prints 1975

P04468 (14) The Conga and other Poems (1969-70)
CNπ:459x315:signed:Presented by Rose and Chris Prater
through the Institute of Contemporary Prints 1975

P04469 (15) O'Neill (1969-70)
CNπ:341x458:signed:Presented by Rose and Chris Prater
through the Institute of Contemporary Prints 1975

P04470 (16) China of Today (1969-70)
CNπ:457x580:signed:Presented by Rose and Chris Prater
through the Institute of Contemporary Prints 1975

P04471 (17) Coming of Age in Samoa (1969-70)
CNπ:508x315:signed:Presented by Rose and Chris Prater
through the Institute of Contemporary Prints 1975

P04472 (18) Towards a Better Life (1969-70)
CNπ:456x379:signed:Presented by Rose and Chris Prater
through the Institute of Contemporary Prints 1975

P04473 (19) Edward Hopper (1969-70)
CNπ:407x508:signed:Presented by Rose and Chris Prater
through the Institute of Contemporary Prints 1975

P04474 (20) Marlborough (Mark Rothko) (1969-70)
CNπ:470x427:signed:Presented by Rose and Chris Prater
through the Institute of Contemporary Prints 1975

P04475 (21) Photo-Eye (El Lissitzsky) (1969-70)
CNπ:540x381:signed:Presented by Rose and Chris Prater
through the Institute of Contemporary Prints 1975

P04476 (22) Reklame durch das Schaufenster (1969-70)
CNπ:577x431:signed:Presented by Rose and Chris Prater
through the Institute of Contemporary Prints 1975

P04477 (23) Benia Krik (1969-70)
CNπ:382x244:signed:Presented by Rose and Chris Prater
through the Institute of Contemporary Prints 1975

P04478 (24) Articles and Pamphlets (1969-70)
CNπ:455x387:signed:Presented by Rose and Chris Prater
through the Institute of Contemporary Prints 1975

P04479 (25) The Defence of Terrorism (1969-70)
CNπ:453x338:signed:Presented by Rose and Chris Prater
through the Institute of Contemporary Prints 1975

P04480 (27) Kampflieder - Battle Songs - Canzoni di Guerra
(1969-70)
CNπ:397x557:signed:Presented by Rose and Chris Prater
through the Institute of Contemporary Prints 1975

P04481 (28) Wir haben es nicht vergessen - Nous n'avons pas
oublié - We Have Not Forgotten (1969-70)
CNπ:311x459:signed:Presented by Rose and Chris Prater
through the Institute of Contemporary Prints 1975

P04482 (29) The Jewish Question (1969-70)
CNπ:507x345:signed:Presented by Rose and Chris Prater
through the Institute of Contemporary Prints 1975

P04483 (30) Alkyn (1969-70)
CNπ:212x443:signed:Presented by Rose and Chris Prater
through the Institute of Contemporary Prints 1975

P04484 (31) Plague (1969-70)
CNπ:325x456:signed:Presented by Rose and Chris Prater
through the Institute of Contemporary Prints 1975

P04485 (32) The Prevention of Destitution (1969-70)
CNπ:411x551:signed:Presented by Rose and Chris Prater
through the Institute of Contemporary Prints 1975

P04486 (33) Hollywood, wie es wirklich ist (1969-70)
CNπ:347x457:signed:Presented by Rose and Chris Prater
through the Institute of Contemporary Prints 1975

P04487 (34) Vampyr (1969-70)
CNπ:462x327:signed:Presented by Rose and Chris Prater
through the Institute of Contemporary Prints 1975

P04488 (35) La Lucha del Pueblo Espanol por La Libertad
(1969-70)
CNπ:554x443:signed:Presented by Rose and Chris Prater
through the Institute of Contemporary Prints 1975

P04489 (36) With Scott to the Pole (1969-70)
CNπ:489x377:signed:Presented by Rose and Chris Prater
through the Institute of Contemporary Prints 1975

P04490 (38) Permit me Voyage (1969-70)
CNπ:457x465:signed:Presented by Rose and Chris Prater
through the Institute of Contemporary Prints 1975

P04491 (39) Intelligence Bulletin (1969-70)
CNπ:445x306:signed:Presented by Rose and Chris Prater
through the Institute of Contemporary Prints 1975

P04492 (40) Final - City of Burbank, California, Annual Budget
1968-69 (1969-70)
CNπ:497x383:signed:Presented by Rose and Chris Prater
through the Institute of Contemporary Prints 1975

P04493 (41) Low gehrig (1969-70)
CNπ:493x458:signed:Presented by Rose and Chris Prater
through the Institute of Contemporary Prints 1975

P04494 (42) Industrial Camoflage Manual (1969-70)
CNπ:453x347:signed:Presented by Rose and Chris Prater
through the Institute of Contemporary Prints 1975

P04495 (44) Fighting the Traffic in Young Girls (1969-70)
CNπ:460x350:signed:Presented by Rose and Chris Prater
through the Institute of Contemporary Prints 1975

P04496 (45) Bub and Sis (1969-70)
CNπ:476x353:signed:Presented by Rose and Chris Prater
through the Institute of Contemporary Prints 1975

P04497 (46) Workers in the Dawn (1969-70)
CNπ:455x378:signed:Presented by Rose and Chris Prater
through the Institute of Contemporary Prints 1975

P04498 (47) Hanging in Chains (1969-70)
CNπ:478x286:signed:Presented by Rose and Chris Prater
through the Institute of Contemporary Prints 1975

P04499 (48) The Wording of Police Charges (1969-70)
CNπ:527x349:signed:Presented by Rose and Chris Prater
through the Institute of Contemporary Prints 1975

P04500 (49) Short Takes (1969-70)
CNπ:594x392:signed:Presented by Rose and Chris Prater
through the Institute of Contemporary Prints 1975

P04501 (50) London by Night - Life and Art in Photograph: No.
Four (1969-70)
CNπ:488x385:signed:Presented by Rose and Chris Prater
through the Institute of Contemporary Prints 1975

P04502 (51) The People of the Abyss (1969-70)
CNπ:511x355:signed:Presented by Rose and Chris Prater
through the Institute of Contemporary Prints 1975

P04503 (43) The Pursuit of the House Prat (1969-70)
CNπ:512x339:signed:Presented by Rose and Chris Prater
through the Institute of Contemporary Prints 1975

P04504 Nancy and Jim Dine (1969-70)
CNπ:848x584:signed:Presented by Rose and Chris Prater
through the Institute of Contemporary Prints 1975

P04505 Ezra Pound I (1971)
CNπ:603x956:signed:Presented by Rose and Chris Prater
through the Institute of Contemporary Prints 1975

P04506 Kenneth Koch (1971)
CNπ:933x619:signed:Presented by Rose and Chris Prater
through the Institute of Contemporary Prints 1975

P04507 Notebook (1971)
CNπ:956x587:signed:Presented by Rose and Chris Prater
through the Institute of Contemporary Prints 1975

P04508 Bedroom (1971)
CNπ:689x943:Presented by Rose and Chris Prater
through the Institute of Contemporary Prints 1975

P04509 Outlying London Districts 1 (1971)
CNπ:656x1071:signed:Presented by Rose and Chris
Prater through the Institute of Contemporary Prints 1975

P04510 Outlying London Districts 2 (1971)
CNπ:535x1019:signed:Presented by Rose and Chris
Prater through the Institute of Contemporary Prints 1975

P04511 The Adding Machine (1972)
CNπ:752x549:signed:Presented by Rose and Chris Prater
through the Institute of Contemporary Prints 1975

P04512 Baghdad (1972)
CNπ:502x365:signed:Presented by Rose and Chris Prater
through the Institute of Contemporary Prints 1975

P04513 Belgian Letters (1972)
CNπ:632x425:signed:Presented by Rose and Chris Prater
through the Institute of Contemporary Prints 1975

A Day Book by Robert Creeley (P04514-P04527;
complete group)

P04514 [no title] (1972)
CNπ:624x425:signed:Presented by Rose and Chris Prater
through the Institute of Contemporary Prints 1975

P04515 [no title] (1972)
CNπ:603x446:signed:Presented by Rose and Chris Prater
through the Institute of Contemporary Prints 1975

P04516 [no title] (1972)
CNπ:578x425:signed:Presented by Rose and Chris Prater
through the Institute of Contemporary Prints 1975

P04517 [no title] (1972)
CNπ:618x423:signed:Presented by Rose and Chris Prater
through the Institute of Contemporary Prints 1975

P04518 [no title] (1972)
CLπ:615x422:signed:Presented by Rose and Chris Prater
through the Institute of Contemporary Prints 1975

P04519 [no title] (1972)
CNπ:620x423:signed:Presented by Rose and Chris Prater
through the Institute of Contemporary Prints 1975

P04520 [no title] (1972)
CNπ:615x424:signed:Presented by Rose and Chris Prater
through the Institute of Contemporary Prints 1975

P04521 [no title] (1972)
CNπ:614x424:signed:Presented by Rose and Chris Prater through the Institute of Contemporary Prints 1975

P04522 [no title] (1972)
CNπ:620x430:signed:Presented by Rose and Chris Prater through the Institute of Contemporary Prints 1975

P04523 [no title] (1972)
CNπ:587x447:signed:Presented by Rose and Chris Prater through the Institute of Contemporary Prints 1975

P04524 [no title] (1972)
CNπ:637x422:signed:Presented by Rose and Chris Prater through the Institute of Contemporary Prints 1975

P04525 [no title] (1972)
CNπ:620x422:signed:Presented by Rose and Chris Prater through the Institute of Contemporary Prints 1975

P04526 [no title] (1972)
CNπ:616x425:signed:Presented by Rose and Chris Prater through the Institute of Contemporary Prints 1975

P04527 [no title] (1972)
CNπ:581x425:signed:Presented by Rose and Chris Prater through the Institute of Contemporary Prints 1975

P04528 The Most Important Film Ever Made (1972)
CNVπ:698x1051:signed:Presented by Rose and Chris Prater through the Institute of Contemporary Prints 1975

P04529 Untitled (1972)
CNπ:527x537:signed:Presented by Rose and Chris Prater through the Institute of Contemporary Prints 1975

P04530 Greetings Pablo Ruiz (1972)
CNπ:762x533:signed:Presented by Rose and Chris Prater through the Institute of Contemporary Prints 1975

P04531 Immortal Portraits (1972)
CNπ:721x1143:Presented by Rose and Chris Prater through the Institute of Contemporary Prints 1975

P04532 Jot 'em Down Store (1972)
CNπ:752x552:signed:Presented by Rose and Chris Prater through the Institute of Contemporary Prints 1975

P04533 Madame Jane Junk (1972)
CNπ:521x794:signed:Presented by Rose and Chris Prater through the Institute of Contemporary Prints 1975

P04534 Men and Books (1972)
CNπ:752x549:signed:Presented by Rose and Chris Prater through the Institute of Contemporary Prints 1975

P04535 Men of Europe 1915 (1972)
CNπ:752x549:Presented by Rose and Chris Prater through the Institute of Contemporary Prints 1975

P04536 Modern Painters (1972)
CNπ:508x314:signed:Presented by Rose and Chris Prater through the Institute of Contemporary Prints 1975

P04537 Poison Book (1972)
CNπ:635x489:signed:Presented by Rose and Chris Prater through the Institute of Contemporary Prints 1975

P04538 Boss Tweed (1972)
CNπ:749x549:signed:Presented by Rose and Chris Prater through the Institute of Contemporary Prints 1975

P04539 Cutie (1974)
CNπ:619x467:signed:Presented by Rose and Chris Prater through the Institute of Contemporary Prints 1975

P04540 Ezra Pound II (1974)
CNπ:981x756:signed:Presented by Rose and Chris Prater through the Institute of Contemporary Prints 1975

P04541 French Subjects (1974)
CNπ:997x673:signed:Presented by Rose and Chris Prater through the Institute of Contemporary Prints 1975

P04542 Michael Hamburger (1974)
CNπ:549x514:signed:Presented by Rose and Chris Prater through the Institute of Contemporary Prints 1975

P04543 Waiting for Lefty (1974)
CNπ:940x632:signed:Presented by Rose and Chris Prater through the Institute of Contemporary Prints 1975

P05366 Addled Art Minor Works Volume VI (1975)
CNπ:1048x711:signed:Presented by Rose and Chris Prater 1976

P05367 Frank Auerbach (1975)
CNπ:489x645:signed:Presented by Rose and Chris Prater 1976

P05368 From the Lives of the Saints (1975)
CNπ:1029x714:signed:Presented by Rose and Chris Prater 1976

P05369 Graduate Notebook (1975)
CNπ:727x546:signed:Presented by Rose and Chris Prater 1976

P05370 On Which Side are You, 'Masters of Culture'? (1975)
CNπ:702x483:signed:Presented by Rose and Chris Prater 1976

P05371 The Red Dancer of Moscow (1975)
CNπ:1013x749:Presented by Rose and Chris Prater through the Institute of Contemporary Prints 1976

P05423 Addled Art Minor Works Volume VI [state 1] (1975)
CNπ::Presented by Rose and Chris Prater through the Institute of Contemporary Prints 1978

P05424 Addled Art Minor Works Volume VI [state 2] (1975)
CNπ::Presented by Rose and Chris Prater through the Institute of Contemporary Prints 1978

P05425 The Red Dancer of Moscow [state 1] (1975)
CNπ:1029x762:Presented by Rose and Chris Prater through the Institute of Contemporary Prints 1978

P05426 The Red Dancer of Moscow [state 2] (1975)
CNπ:1029x762:Presented by Rose and Chris Prater through the Institute of Contemporary Prints 1978

P05427 Importing Women for Immoral Purposes (1978)
CNπ:660x518:signed:Presented by Rose and Chris Prater through the Institute of Contemporary Prints 1978

P05428 Man with Matisse Tattoo (1978)
CNπ:784x587:signed:Presented by Rose and Chris Prater through the Institute of Contemporary Prints 1978

P05429 Spirit of the Ghetto (1978)
CNπ:597x454:signed:Presented by Rose and Chris Prater through the Institute of Contemporary Prints 1978

P05562 Chris (1980)
CNπ:585x450:signed:Presented by Rose and Chris Prater through the Institute of Contemporary Prints 1980

Mahler Becomes Politics, Beisbol (P07045-P07059; complete group)

P07045 What is Comparison? (1964)
CNπ:788x562:Purchased 1970

P07046 Republic of the Southern Cross (1965)
CNπ:778x564:Purchased 1970

P07047 The Gay Science (1965)
CNπ:772x587:Purchased 1970

P07048 Hellebore for Georg Traki (1965)
CNπ:769x573:Purchased 1970

P07049 His Every Poor, Defeated, Loser's, Hopeless Move, Loser, Buried (1966)
CNπ:765x506:Purchased 1970

P07050 Go and Get Killed Comrade, We Need a Byron in the Movement (1966)
CNπ:818x557:Purchased 1970

P07051 The Cultural Value of Fear, Distrust and Hypochondria
(1966)
CNπ:523x773:Purchased 1970

P07052 Let Us ... it Arden / And Live in It! (1966)
CNπ::Purchased 1970

P07053 Heart (1966)
CNπ:601x813:Purchased 1970

P07054 I've Balled Every Waitress in this Club (1967)
CNπ:584x828:Purchased 1970

P07055 In his Forthcoming Book on Relative Deprivation (1967)
CNπ:843x509:Purchased 1970

P07056 Glue-Words (1967)
CNπ:838x583:Purchased 1970

P07057 For Fear (1967)
CNπ:510x837:Purchased 1970

P07058 Nerves, Massage, Defeat, Heart (1967)
CNπ:844x575:Purchased 1970

P07059 The Flood of Laymen (1967)
CNπ:826x566:Purchased 1970

KLEE, Paul 1879-1940
Modern Collection
Tate Gallery Archive holds material concerning this artist

N05278 The Castle Mountain of S. (1930)
Der Schlossberg von S.
Gπ:368x467:Presented by the Contemporary Art Society
1941

N05657 Comedy (1921)
Komödie
WOπ:305x454:signed:Purchased 1946

N05658 They're Biting (1920)
Sie beissen an
DOπ:311x235:signed:Purchased 1946

N05659 A Young Lady's Adventure (1922)
Abenteuer eines Fräuleins
Wπ:438x321:signed:Purchased 1946

T00669 Walpurgis Night (1935)
Walpurgisnacht
Gf:508x470:signed:Purchased 1964

KLEIN, Astrid born 1951
Modern Collection

T05034 Petrified Vision (1985)
Versteinerte Vision
Fπ:2469x3596:Purchased 1988

KLEIN, Yves 1928-1962
Modern Collection
Tate Gallery Archive holds material concerning this artist

T01513 IKB 79 (1959)
Afw:1397x1197x32:signed:Purchased 1972

KLINE, Franz 1910-1962
Modern Collection
Tate Gallery Archive holds material concerning this artist

T00926 Meryon (1960-1)
Oc:2359x1956:signed:Purchased 1967

KLINGHOFFER, Clara 1900-1970
Modern Collection

N04704 The Old Troubadour (1926)
Oc:533x648:signed:Presented by the Trustees of the
Chantrey Bequest 1933

KNEALE, Bryan born 1930
Modern Collection
Tate Gallery Archive holds material concerning this artist

T00695 Knuckle (1964)
Sm:851x641x305:Purchased 1964

T00941 Marina (1967)
Sm:984x1029x711:Purchased 1967

T04892 Horse (1983)
Dπ:1831x913:Presented by Sir Richard Attenborough
1987

KNELLER, Sir Godfrey 1646-1723
British Collection
Tate Gallery Archive holds material concerning this artist

N00273 John Smith the Engraver (1696)
Oc:749x622:signed:Presented by William Smith 1856

N03272 The First Marquess of Tweeddale (1695)
Oc:749x635:Presented by Sir George Leon 1917

N03616 A Lady (circa 1715)
Dπ:327x241:Presented by H. Reitlinger through the
National Art Collections Fund 1922

N06222 Elijah and the Angel (1672)
Oc:1765x1486:signed:Purchased 1954

T03982 John Smith, Speaker of the House of Commons (circa
1707-8)
Oc:2205x1565:signed:Purchased 1985

T05019 Portrait of John Banckes (1676)
Oc:1372x1016:signed:Purchased with assistance from the
Friends of the Tate Gallery 1987

KNIGHT, Charles Parsons 1829-1897
British Collection

N01655 The Kyles of Bute (1893)
Oc:622x1105:signed:Presented by Miss A.F.C. Knight
1898

KNIGHT, Harold 1874-1961
British Collection
Tate Gallery Archive holds material concerning this artist

N04957 A Student (exhibited 1938)
Oc:610x508:signed:Presented by the Trustees of the
Chantrey Bequest 1938

KNIGHT, John Baverstock 1785-1859
British Collection

N02733 Axbridge Vale
DWπ:200x295:Presented by the Rev. Alfred Pontifex
1910

N02734 Tievebulliagh from Knocknacarry
DWπ:143x219:Presented by the Rev. Alfred Pontifex
1910

KNIGHT, John Prescott 1803-1881
British Collection

N01498 Sacking a Church at the Time of John Knox (1843)
Oc:1460x1956:signed:Presented by Col. Knight Prescott
1895

KNIGHT, John William Buxton 1842-1908
British Collection

N02262 Old December's Bareness Everywhere (exhibited 1908)
Oc:902x1206:signed:Presented by the Trustees of the
Chantrey Bequest 1908

N04607 Plymouth Harbour (The Wooden Walls of England)
(1891)
Oc:952x1403:signed:Presented by James Ferguson 1931

N05080 Shore Scene
Oc:629x749:Bequeathed by Frank Hindley Smith 1940

KNIGHT, Joseph 1837-1909
British Collection

N01622 A Tidal River (1877)
Oc:851x1245:signed:Presented by the Trustees of the
Chantrey Bequest 1877

KNIGHT, Dame Laura 1877-1970
British Collection
Tate Gallery Archive holds material concerning this artist

N04838 Spring (1916-20)
Oc:1524x1829:signed:Presented by the Trustees of the
Chantrey Bequest 1935

N05330 The Gypsy (exhibited 1939)
Oc:610x406:Presented by the Trustees of the Chantrey
Bequest 1939

KNIGHTS, Winifred 1899-1947
Modern Collection

N03681 Italian Landscape (1921)
Ow:305x324:signed:Purchased 1922

T05532 The Deluge (1920)
Oc:1529x1835:Purchased with assistance from the
Friends of the Tate Gallery 1989

KNOWLES, Justin born 1935
Modern Collection
Tate Gallery Archive holds material concerning this artist

T01982 Two Resin Panels with Black (and Space) (1968-75)
Ra:2743x2134:Purchased 1975

A Series of Four Prints (P04544-P04547; complete
group)
P04544 A. Black (1968)
CNπ:686x1015:signed:Presented by Rose and Chris
Prater through the Institute of Contemporary Prints 1975
P04545 B. Black (1968)
CNπ:686x1015:signed:Presented by Rose and Chris
Prater through the Institute of Contemporary Prints 1975
P04546 C. Red (1968)
CNπ:1015x686:signed:Presented by Rose and Chris
Prater through the Institute of Contemporary Prints 1975
P04547 D. Yellow (1968)
CNπ:686x1015:signed:Presented by Rose and Chris
Prater through the Institute of Contemporary Prints 1975

KOCH, Eleanor born 1926
Modern Collection

P06792 Four Images (1977)
MLπ:635x851:Presented by Curwen Studio 1978

KOENIG, Ghisha born 1921
Modern Collection
Tate Gallery Archive holds material concerning this artist

T04864 The Machine Minders (1956)
Ssmw:1300x1060x600:Purchased 1986

KOHN, Misch born 1916
Modern Collection

P01793 Tiger (1949)
MRπ:416x606:signed:Presented by the Museum of
Modern Art, New York 1976

KOKOSCHKA, Oskar 1886-1980
Modern Collection
Tate Gallery Archive holds material concerning this artist

N05251 Polperro II (1939)
Oc:606x864:signed:Presented by Dr Edvard Benes,
President of Czechoslovakia 1941

N05432 Ambassador Ivan Maisky (1942-3)
Oc:1019x768:signed:Presented by Dr Henry Dreyfuss
1943

T01252 View of the Thames (1959)
Oc:914x1232:signed:Presented by David Hellings 1970

T02208 Dr Fannina W. Halle (circa 1910-12)
Dπ:451x305:signed:Bequeathed by Dr Leopold
Rubinstein 1977

T03829 Study for 'Ambassador Ivan Maisky' (1942)
Dπ:355x253:Presented by Mrs Olda Kokoschka, the
artist's widow 1984

T03830 Study for 'Ambassador Ivan Maisky' (1942)
Dπ:355x253:Presented by Mrs Olda Kokoschka, the
artist's widow 1984

T03834 The Crab (1939-40)
Oc:634x762:signed:Purchased 1984

T03966 Sketchbook (1954)
11 Pπ:253x368:Presented by Mrs Olda Kokoschka, the
artist's widow 1984

T04876 Time, Gentlemen Please (1971-2)
Oc:1300x1000:signed:Purchased 1986

T05485 Marianne-Maquis (1942)
Oc:635x762:Presented by Mrs Olda Kokoschka, the
artist's widow, in honour of the directorship of Sir Alan
Bowness 1988

T05486 Loreley (1941-2)
Oc:635x762:Presented by Mrs Olda Kokoschka, the
artist's widow, in honour of the directorship of Sir Alan
Bowness 1988

KOLAR, Jiri born 1914
Modern Collection

The Flowers of Evil (T05031, T05038-T05040; complete
group)
T05031 The Fine Ship (1972)
Le Beau Navire
FLπ:265x444:signed:Presented by Mr and Mrs Rodney
Capstick-Dale 1988

T05038 Invitation to the Voyage (1972)
L'Invitation au voyage
FLπ:266x408:signed:Presented by Mr and Mrs Rodney
Capstick-Dale 1988

T05039 Metamorphoses of the Vampire (1972)
Les Métamorphoses du vampire
FLπ:253x430:Presented by Mr and Mrs Rodney
Capstick-Dale 1988

T05040 The Little Old Women (1972)
Les Petites Vieilles
FLπ:265x390:signed:Presented by Mr and Mrs Rodney
Capstick-Dale 1988

KOLIBAL, Stanislav born 1925
Modern Collection

T03806 Identity (1982)
RVw:1460x1595x250:signed:Presented by Illa Kodicek
1983

KONZAL, Joseph born 1905
Modern Collection

T00874 Cretan Queen (1963-4)
Sm:1880x470x368:Presented by Joseph L. Shulman
through the American Federation of Arts 1966

KOONING, Willem de - see DE KOONING, Willem

KOPPEL, Heinz 1919-1980
Modern Collection
Tate Gallery Archive holds material concerning this artist

T03798 Snow, Sunshine, Rain (1957)
Oc:1220x2190:Presented anonymously 1983

T05505 Portrait of Helen Lessore (1958)
Oπ:787x484:signed:Presented by John Lessore 1988

KORNER, John born 1913
Modern Collection

Centennial Suite (P03217-P03225, P03228-P03229;
complete group; mixed group)
P03223 Star Flower (1967)
CNπ:305x410:signed:Presented by Simon Fraser
University, British Columbia 1977

KOSSOFF, Leon born 1926
Modern Collection

T00564 Man in a Wheelchair (1959-62)
Ow:2134x1232:Purchased 1963

T01984 Demolition of the Old House, Dalston Junction, Summer
1974 (1974)
Ow:1600x2184:Purchased 1975

T03245 Woman Ill in Bed, Surrounded by Family (1965)
Ob:1854x1245:Purchased 1981

T03246 Children's Swimming Pool, Autumn Afternoon (1971)
Ob:1680x2140:Purchased 1981

T03277 Drawing for 'Woman Ill in Bed Surrounded by Family'
(1965)
Dπ:254x197:Presented by the artist 1981

T03278 Drawing for 'Woman Ill in Bed Surrounded by Family
(Dürer)' (1965)
Dπ:298x222:Presented by the artist 1981

T03279 Drawing for 'Woman Ill in Bed Surrounded by Family
(Rosalind)' (1965)
Dπ:356x254:Presented by the artist 1981

T03280 Drawing for 'Children's Swimming Pool' (1971)
Dπ:419x591:Presented by the artist 1981

T03281 Drawing for 'Children's Swimming Pool' (1971)
Dπ:419x591:Presented by the artist 1981

T03680 Two Seated Figures No. 2 (1980)
Ob:2438x1828:Purchased 1983

T04855 Self-Portrait. Verso: Untitled (Two Figures) (1967)
Dπ:763x556:signed:Presented by Jenny Stein 1986

T05531 Booking Hall, Kilburn Underground (1987)
Ob:1982x1827:Purchased with assistance from the
Friends of the Tate Gallery and the Mail on Sunday
through the Friends of the Tate Gallery 1989

P02933 Outside Kilburn Underground [stage proof] (1979)
MIπ:405x511:Presented by the artist 1986

P02934 Outside Kilburn Underground [stage proof] (1980)
MIπ:405x511:Presented by the artist 1986

P02935 Outside Kilburn Underground [stage proof] (1981)
MIπ:405x511:Presented by the artist 1986

P02936 Outside Kilburn Underground [stage proof] (1983)
MIπ:403x510:Presented by the artist 1986

P02937 Outside Kilburn Underground [stage proof] (1984)
MIπ:405x512:Presented by the artist 1986

P02938 Going Home [stage proof] (1979-84)
MIπ:403x512:Presented by the artist 1986

P02939 Going Home [stage proof] (1979-84)
MIπ:405x511:Presented by the artist 1986

P02940 Going Home [stage proof] (1979-84)
MIπ:403x512:Presented by the artist 1986

P02941 Going Home [stage proof] (1979-84)
MIπ:404x514:Presented by the artist 1986

P77052 Going Home (1984)
MIπ:404x514:signed:Purchased 1984

P77103 Outside Kilburn Underground (1984)
MIπ:405x511:signed:Purchased 1984

KOSUTH, Joseph - see also
INTERNATIONAL LOCAL born 1945
Modern Collection
Tate Gallery Archive holds material concerning this artist

T01909 Clock (One and Five), English/Latin Version (1965)
VFπ:610x2902:Purchased 1974

KOUNELLIS, Jannis born 1936
Modern Collection

T03796 Untitled (1979)
Senza titolo
RVD:3600x5000:Purchased 1983

T04937 Untitled (1983)
Senza titolo
WHOπ:356x430:signed:Purchased 1987

KRAMER, Harry born 1925
Modern Collection

T00714 Torso (1962)
Torse
SKm:1143x679x686:Purchased 1964

T01300 Sledge (1963)
Schlitten
SKm:762x1041x546:Presented by Kate Maremont
Foundation on behalf of Mr and Mrs Arnold H.
Maremont 1971

KRAMER, Jacob 1892-1962
Modern Collection
Tate Gallery Archive holds material concerning this artist

T01973 Jews at Prayer (circa 1919)
Oc:876x498:signed:Purchased 1975

T03964 George Parker (1928)
Oc:764x637:Presented by Mr John Parker 1985

T03965 Dorothy Parker (1928)
Oc:262x638:signed:Presented by Mr John Parker 1985

P07060 The Philosopher (circa 1922)
MLπ:451x302:signed:Purchased 1973

KRASNER, Lee 1908-1984
Modern Collection

T03291 Gothic Landscape (1961)
Oc:1768x2378:signed:Purchased 1981

KRSINIC, Frano born 1897
Modern Collection

N04537 Girl (1930)
Ss:1530x371x311:signed:Purchased 1930

KRUGER, Barbara born 1945
Modern Collection

P77166 Untitled (1985)
9 CLπ:520x520:signed:Purchased 1986

KRZYWOBLOCKI, Wojciech born 1938
Modern Collection

P11084 Earth Sail (1970)
Ziemia Zagiel
MNπ:792x508:signed:Presented by Professor Akumal
Ramachander 1985

KUDRYASHOV, Oleg born 1932
Modern Collection

P77104 Diptych No. 21 (1982)
Diptikha doskai 21
2 CIGπ:719x1217:signed:Purchased 1984

P77105 No. 1077 (1984)
Doskai 1077
WCIπ:919x619:signed:Purchased 1984

KULMER, Ferdinand born 1925
Modern Collection

T00429 Brown Picture (1960)
OTc:1457x972:signed:Purchased 1961

KUNKEL, Don born 1933
Modern Collection

P08018 Untitled (1971)
CNπ:79x79:signed:Transferred from the Library 1978

KUNST, Mauro born 1930
Modern Collection
Tate Gallery Archive holds material concerning this artist

P01764 Black and White (1969)
Negro y blanco
MNπ:457x457:signed:Presented by John Berry 1976

P01765 Pink on Copper (1970)
CNπ:597x502:signed:Presented by John Berry 1976

P01766 Red, Green and Silver (1970)
Verde, rojo y plateado
CNπ:597x505:signed:Presented by John Berry 1976

P01767 Untitled (1970)
CNπ:349x498:signed:Presented by John Berry 1976

P01768 Untitled (1970)
CNπ:597x502:signed:Presented by John Berry 1976

KUPKA, Frantisek 1871-1957
Modern Collection

T00257 The Waterfall (1906)
La Cascade
Oc:648x648:signed:Presented by Mme Eugénie Kupka,
the artist's widow 1959

KUSHNER, Robert born 1949
Modern Collection

P77167 Cupid and Psyche XV (1985)
CIπ:876x1195:signed:Purchased 1986

LAABS, Hans born 1915
Modern Collection

P08019 Untitled (1971)
CNπ:79x79:signed:Transferred from the Library 1978

LACEY, Bruce born 1927
Modern Collection
Tate Gallery Archive holds material concerning this artist

T02023 Boy, Oh Boy, am I Living! (1964)
KSv:1988x1499x381:Purchased 1976

LADBROOKE, Robert 1770-1842
British Collection
Tate Gallery Archive holds material concerning this artist

T01890 Wood Scene (exhibited 1806)
Oc:600x743:Bequeathed by Alan Evans 1974

LA DELL, Edwin born 1919
Modern Collection
Tate Gallery Archive holds material concerning this artist

School Prints (P01698-P01727; complete group; mixed group)

P01710 The Tower of London (1946)
CLπ:496x763:signed:Presented by Patrick Seale Prints 1975

LAIDLAY, William James 1846-1912
British Collection

T01891 On the Nile (1900)
Oc:406x610:signed:Bequeathed by Alan Evans 1974

LAING, Gerald born 1936
Modern Collection

T03842 Skydiver VI (1964)
2 Oc:2032x1467:signed:Purchased 1984

LAM, Wifredo 1902-1982
Modern Collection

N06073 Ibaye (1950)
Oc:1045x876:Purchased 1952

For Jorn (P03241-P03255; complete group; mixed group)
Pour Jorn

P03248 [no title] (1975-6)
CLπ:749x546:signed:Presented by the Asger Jorn Foundation 1978

LAMB, Henry 1883-1960
Modern Collection
Tate Gallery Archive holds material concerning this artist

N03191 A Girl's Head (1909)
Dπ:356x292:signed:Presented by Lord Henry Cavendish-Bentinck through the Contemporary Art Society 1917

N03192 Head of an Irish Girl (1912)
Oc:508x406:Presented by Mr and Mrs J.L. Behrend 1917

N03840 Phantasy (1912)
Oc:864x610:signed:Presented by the Contemporary Art Society 1924

N04749 The Artist's Wife (1933)
Oc:635x762:signed:Presented by the Trustees of the Chantrey Bequest 1934

N05027 Irish Girls (1912)
Oc:749x692:Presented by Julian Lousada 1939

N05630 Death of a Peasant (1911)
Oc:368x318:Presented by the Trustees of the Chantrey Bequest 1944

N05703 H.R.H. the Prince of Luxembourg (1944)
Oc:559x457:signed:Presented by the War Artists' Advisory Committee 1946

T00102 Lamentation (1911)
Oc:914x533:Purchased 1956

T00118 Lytton Strachey (1914)
Oc:2445x1784:Presented by the Trustees of the Chantrey Bequest 1957

T00419 The Artist's Family (1940-3)
Oc:1143x914:signed:Presented by the Trustees of the Chantrey Bequest 1961

LAMB, Lynton born 1907
Modern Collection
Tate Gallery Archive holds material concerning this artist

P06322 Winter Landscape (1962)
CLπ:330x479:signed:Presented by Curwen Studio through the Institute of Contemporary Prints 1975

LAMBERT, George 1700-1765
British Collection

N05981 A View of Box Hill, Surrey (1733)
Oc:908x1804:signed:Purchased 1951

T00211 Classical Landscape (1745)
Oc:1035x1168:signed:Purchased 1958

T04110 Moorland Landscape with Rainstorm (1751)
Oc:303x423:signed:Purchased with assistance from the Friends of the Tate Gallery 1985

LAMBERT, James 1725 - 1779 or 88
British Collection

N01658 Landscape (1769)
Oc:867x1121:signed:Bequeathed by Miss Haines 1898

LAMBERT, Maurice 1901-1964
Modern Collection

N04640 Swan (exhibited 1932)
Ss:387x622x349:signed:Presented by D.H. Conner 1932

N04875 Homo Sapiens (1937)
Sz:1353x521x762:signed:Presented anonymously 1937

N04967 Head of a Woman (exhibited 1938)
Sz:349x194x251:signed:Presented by the Trustees of the Chantrey Bequest 1938

T03756 Man with a Bird (1929)
Ss:890x203x190:signed:Transferred from the Victoria & Albert Museum 1983

LAMBOURN, George 1900-1977
Modern Collection

N04974 Portrait of a Communist (1936)
Oc:546x457:signed:Purchased 1938

LANCASTER, Mark born 1938
Modern Collection
Tate Gallery Archive holds material concerning this artist

T01109   Cambridge Green (1968)
Ac:1727x1727:Purchased 1969

T01238   James Gibbs (1970)
ACc:1727x1727:signed:Purchased 1970

P04548   Eighths (1967)
CNπ:457x686:signed:Presented by Rose and Chris Prater through the Institute of Contemporary Prints 1975

P04549   Sixths (1967)
CNπ:457x686:signed:Presented by Rose and Chris Prater through the Institute of Contemporary Prints 1975

P04550   Fourths (1969)
CNπ:606x914:signed:Presented by Rose and Chris Prater through the Institute of Contemporary Prints 1975

P07618   Zapruder Green (1968)
CLπ:559x768:signed:Purchased 1982

LANCASTER, Osbert 1908-1986
Modern Collection
Tate Gallery Archive holds material concerning this artist

N05379   Greenery Yallery (1939)
Dπ:356x254:Presented by the artist 1942

P06323   Pineapple Poll (1937)
CLπ:419x314:signed:Presented by Curwen Studio through the Institute of Contemporary Prints 1975

LANCASTER, Rev. Richard Hume 1773-1853
British Collection

N01428   A View at Southampton (1817)
Oc:886x1365:signed:Purchased 1894

N01467   Landscape, with a View of Oxford (exhibited 1814)
Oc:508x711:signed:Purchased 1895

LANCE, George 1802-1864
British Collection

N00441   A Basket of Fruit (1834)
Ow:460x521:signed:Presented by Robert Vernon 1847

N00442   The Red Cap (1847)
Ow:448x508:signed:Presented by Robert Vernon 1847

N00443   Fruit Piece (1848)
Oc:711x914:signed:Presented by Robert Vernon 1847

N01184   Fruit Piece
Oc:357x459:Bequeathed by Mrs Elizabeth Vaughan 1885

LANCELEY, Colin born 1938
Modern Collection
Tate Gallery Archive holds material concerning this artist

P01432   Morning and Melancholia (1973)
CLπ:714x918:signed:Presented by Editions Alecto through the Institute of Contemporary Prints 1975

P03265   The Empire Builder (1978)
CLπ:721x952:signed:Presented by Druckma Press 1979

P03266   Two in the Bush (1978)
CLπ:946x679:signed:Presented by Druckma Press 1979

The Miraculous Mandarin Suite (P04551-P04556; complete group)
P04551   1. Arrival of the Mandarin (1966)
CNπ:775x564:signed:Presented by Rose and Chris Prater through the Institute of Contemporary Prints 1975

P04552   2. Chase (1966)
CNπ:775x563:Presented by Rose and Chris Prater through the Institute of Contemporary Prints 1975

P04553   3. Entrance of the Things (1966)
CNπ:769x567:signed:Presented by Rose and Chris Prater through the Institute of Contemporary Prints 1975

P04554   4. Embrace (1966)
CNπ:770x564:signed:Presented by Rose and Chris Prater through the Institute of Contemporary Prints 1975

P04555   5. Strong Motion (1966)
CNπ:766x564:signed:Presented by Rose and Chris Prater through the Institute of Contemporary Prints 1975

P04556   6. Liebestod (1966)
CNπ:776x567:signed:Presented by Rose and Chris Prater through the Institute of Contemporary Prints 1975

P04557   Bluebeard's Castle (1968)
CNπ:1029x1988:signed:Presented by Rose and Chris Prater through the Institute of Contemporary Prints 1975

P04558   Some are More Equal than Others (1969)
CNπ:765x562:signed:Presented by Rose and Chris Prater through the Institute of Contemporary Prints 1975

P04559   Pan Twardowski (1972)
CNπ:775x578:signed:Presented by Rose and Chris Prater through the Institute of Contemporary Prints 1975

P04560   Popiel (1972)
CNπ:775x578:signed:Presented by Rose and Chris Prater through the Institute of Contemporary Prints 1975

Some Adventures of Don Quixote (P04561-P04567; complete group)
P04561   An Adventure with some Windmills (1972)
CNπ:787x583:signed:Presented by Rose and Chris Prater through the Institute of Contemporary Prints 1975

P04562   A Battle with some Wine Skins (1972)
CNπ:795x584:signed:Presented by Rose and Chris Prater through the Institute of Contemporary Prints 1975

P04563   Don Quixote Confined and Confused (1972)
CNπ:781x583:signed:Presented by Rose and Chris Prater through the Institute of Contemporary Prints 1975

P04564   The Don, The Virgin and the Penitents (1972)
CNπ:788x583:signed:Presented by Rose and Chris Prater through the Institute of Contemporary Prints 1975

P04565   The Knight's Penance in the Sierra Morena (1972)
CNπ:793x588:signed:Presented by Rose and Chris Prater through the Institute of Contemporary Prints 1975

P04566   The Liberation of the Galley Stores (1972)
CNπ:788x585:signed:Presented by Rose and Chris Prater through the Institute of Contemporary Prints 1975

P04567   Some Adventures of Don Quixote de la Mancha (1972)
CNπ:780x577:signed:Presented by Rose and Chris Prater through the Institute of Contemporary Prints 1975

The Waste Land (P05372-P05376; complete group)
P05372   The Burial of the Dead (1975)
CNπ:1012x684:signed:Presented by Rose and Chris Prater through the Institute of Contemporary Prints 1976

P05373   A Game of Chess (1975)
CNπ:1015x685:signed:Presented by Rose and Chris Prater through the Institute of Contemporary Prints 1976

P05374   The Final Sermon (1975)
CNπ:1015x682:signed:Presented by Rose and Chris Prater through the Institute of Contemporary Prints 1976

P05375   Death by Water (1975)
CNπ:1012x684:signed:Presented by Rose and Chris Prater through the Institute of Contemporary Prints 1976

P05376 What the Thunder Said (1975)
CNπ:1012x684:signed:Presented by Rose and Chris
Prater through the Institute of Contemporary Prints 1976

LANDER, Reg born 1913
Modern Collection

P06662 Polperro (1975)
CLπ:419x568:signed:Presented by Curwen Studio 1976
P06663 Windsor Castle (1976)
CLπ:257x356:signed:Presented by Curwen Studio 1976

LANDSAAT, Hans born 1935
Modern Collection
Tate Gallery Archive holds material concerning this artist

P05430 Bohemian Reflection (1977)
Boheemse Weerspiegeling
CNπ:502x502:signed:Presented by Rose and Chris Prater
1978

P05431 Flemish Reflection (1977)
Vlaamse Weerspiegeling
CNπ:502x502:signed:Presented by Rose and Chris Prater
1978

P05432 Zeeland Reflection (1977)
Zeeuwse Weerspiegeling
CNπ:502x502:signed:Presented by Rose and Chris Prater
1978

Island Series (P05433-P05436; complete group)
P05433 Island I (1977)
Eiland I
CNπ:236x302:signed:Presented by Rose and Chris Prater
through the Institute of Contemporary Prints 1978

P05434 Island II (1977)
Eiland II
CNπ:216x302:signed:Presented by Rose and Chris Prater
through the Institute of Contemporary Prints 1978

P05435 Island III (1977)
Eiland III
CNπ:267x302:signed:Presented by Rose and Chris Prater
through the Institute of Contemporary Prints 1978

P05436 Gateway (1977)
Poort
CNπ:302x302:signed:Presented by Rose and Chris Prater
through the Institute of Contemporary Prints 1978

Metal Landscape I-IV (P05437-P05440; complete group)
Metalen Landschap I-IV
P05437 I (1978)
CNπ:402x402:signed:Presented by Rose and Chris Prater
through the Institute of Contemporary Prints 1978

P05438 II (1978)
CNπ:236x402:signed:Presented by Rose and Chris Prater
through the Institute of Contemporary Prints 1978

P05439 III (1978)
CNπ:403x403:signed:Presented by Rose and Chris Prater
through the Institute of Contemporary Prints 1978

P05440 IV (1978)
CNπ:402x403:signed:Presented by Rose and Chris Prater
through the Institute of Contemporary Prints 1978

P05477 Bridge (1978)
CNπ:743x825:signed:Presented by Rose and Chris Prater
1979

P05478 Bridge with Matching Cloud (1978)
CNπ:743x825:signed:Presented by Rose and Chris Prater
1979

P05479 Cloud over Land (1979)
CNπ:749x829:signed:Presented by Rose and Chris Prater
1979

P05480 Cloud over Sea (1979)
CNπ:749x829:signed:Presented by Rose and Chris Prater
1979

Franz K. 2 (P05529-P05532; complete group)
P05529 Berlin (1979)
CNπ:350x400:signed:Presented by Rose and Chris Prater
through the Institute of Contemporary Prints 1979

P05530 K. (1979)
CNπ:400x397:signed:Presented by Rose and Chris Prater
through the Institute of Contemporary Prints 1979

P05531 Prague (1979)
CNπ:402x400:signed:Presented by Rose and Chris Prater
through the Institute of Contemporary Prints 1979

P05532 Women (1979)
Vrouwen
CNπ:402x402:signed:Presented by Rose and Chris Prater
through the Institute of Contemporary Prints 1979

P05552 Blue Still Life (1980)
blauw stilleven
CNπ:729x808:signed:Presented by Rose and Chris Prater
through the Institute of Contemporary Prints 1980

P05553 Red Still Life (1980)
rood stilleven
CNπ:730x807:signed:Presented by Rose and Chris Prater
through the Institute of Contemporary Prints 1980

LANDSEER, Charles 1799-1879
British Collection

N00408 Clarissa Harlowe in the Sponging House (exhibited 1833)
Oc:610x508:Presented by Robert Vernon 1847

N00610 Bloodhound and Pups (exhibited 1839)
Oc:711x914:Bequeathed by Jacob Bell 1859

N00611 The Pillaging of a Jew's House in the Reign of Richard I
(exhibited 1839)
Oc:1537x1965:Bequeathed by Jacob Bell 1859

N00612 The Plundering of Basing House (exhibited 1836)
Oc:1003x1257:Bequeathed by Jacob Bell 1859

LANDSEER, Sir Edwin Henry 1803-1874
British Collection
Tate Gallery Archive holds material concerning this artist

N00409 King Charles Spaniels (exhibited 1845)
Oc:698x902:Presented by Robert Vernon 1847

N00411 Highland Music (exhibited 1830)
Ow:470x591:Presented by Robert Vernon 1847

N00412 The Hunted Stag (exhibited 1833)
Ow:405x908:Presented by Robert Vernon 1847

N00415 Dialogue at Waterloo (exhibited 1850)
Oc:1937x3880:Presented by Robert Vernon 1847

N00603 Sleeping Bloodhound (exhibited 1835)
Oc:1016x1270:Bequeathed by Jacob Bell 1859

N00604 Dignity and Impudence (1839)
Oc:889x692:Bequeathed by Jacob Bell 1859

N00605 The Defeat of Comus (1843)
Oc:889x1689:Bequeathed by Jacob Bell 1859

N00606 Shoeing (exhibited 1844)
Oc:1422x1118:Bequeathed by Jacob Bell 1859

N00607 Highland Dogs (circa 1839)
Om:432x543:Bequeathed by Jacob Bell 1859

N00608 Alexander and Diogenes (exhibited 1848)
Oc:1124x1429:Bequeathed by Jacob Bell 1859

N01226 A Distinguished Member of the Humane Society
(exhibited 1838)
Oc:1118x1435:Bequeathed by Newman Smith 1887

N01350 Study of a Lion (circa 1862)
Oc:914x1378:Bequeathed by Thomas Hyde Hills 1892

N01532 A Scene at Abbotsford (exhibited 1827)
Ow:451x610:Presented by Sir Henry Tate 1894

N01533 Uncle Tom
Oc:707x915:Presented by Sir Henry Tate 1894

N01787 Boy, Donkey and Foal - Mischief in Full Play (1822)
Ob:254x321:signed:Bequeathed by Henry Vaughan 1900

N03008 The Duchess of Abercorn and Child (1834-6)
Om:540x432:Presented by Edwin L.MacKenzie 1914

N05777 Loch Avon and the Cairngorm Mountains (circa 1833)
Ow:352x445:Purchased 1947

N06180 The Dog 'Racket' (1813)
Dπ:159x229:signed:Presented by Miss Gladys
Singers-Bigger 1953

T03395 The Harper (1821-2)
Oc:912x710:signed:Purchased 1982

A00702 Low Life (1829)
Ow:457x352:Presented by Robert Vernon 1847

A00703 High Life (1829)
Ow:457x349:Presented by Robert Vernon 1847

LANE, Samuel 1780-1859
British Collection

N04870 Arthur Hughes at the Age of Four (circa 1836)
Ob:305x254:Presented by Miss Emily Hughes 1937

LANE, Theodore 1800-1828
British Collection

N00440 The Enthusiast (The Gouty Angler) (1828)
Ow:406x559:Presented by Robert Vernon 1847

LANG, Daniel born 1935
Modern Collection

P01433 Street Light (1973)
CNπ:559x705:signed:Presented by Christie's
Contemporary Art through the Institute of
Contemporary Prints 1975

P01434 Rosewood (1974)
CNπ:495x686:signed:Presented by Christie's
Contemporary Art through the Institute of
Contemporary Prints 1975

LANGLOIS, Denis
Modern Collection

Homage to Albert Dumouchel (P03166-P03178;
complete group; mixed group)
Hommage à Albert Dumouchel

P03173 Untitled (1971)
MNπ:673x521:signed:Presented by the University of
Quebec 1976

LANTERI, Edouard 1848-1917
British Collection

N01905 Paysan (circa 1901)
Sz:533x495x342:Presented by the artist's pupils 1908

N02853 Bust of Alfred Stevens (1911)
Sz:559x495x286:signed:Presented by the Alfred Stevens
Memorial Committee 1911

N03219 The Sacristan (1917)
Sz:394x222x267:signed:Presented by the Trustees of the
Chantrey Bequest 1917

LANYON, Peter 1918-1964
Modern Collection
Tate Gallery Archive holds material concerning this artist

N06151 Porthleven (1951)
Ob:2445x1219:signed:Presented by the Contemporary
Art Society 1953

T00375 Thermal (1960)
Oc:1829x1524:signed:Purchased 1960

T00950 Porthleven Boats (1950-1)
Smw:629x359x419:signed:Presented by the artist's widow
1967

T01082 Tall Country and Seashore (1951)
Sv:1788x289x203:Presented by the artist's widow 1968

T01496 Construction (1947)
SOwm:260x327x248:Purchased 1971

T01947 Corsham Model (1953)
DGπ:559x762:signed:Purchased 1975

T03209 Zennor Storm (1958)
Ob:1219x1829:signed:Presented by Catherine Viviano
1981

T03324 White Track (1939-40)
RWV:445x495x60:signed:Purchased 1981

T03693 Wreck (1963)
Oc:1220x1830:signed:Presented by the Friends of the
Tate Gallery 1983

Penwith Portfolio (P01416, P06005, P06108, P06130,
P06241, P06324, P06346, P06359, P06399, P06519,
P06700; complete group; mixed group)

P06324 The Returned Seaman (1973)
CLπ:629x698:signed:Presented by Curwen Studio
through the Institute of Contemporary Prints 1975

P07741 The Returned Seaman (1949)
HCJπ:532x736:signed:Purchased 1982

P11082 Underground (1951)
CNπ:265x247:signed:Presented by Warren MacKenzie
1985

P11093 In the Trees (1951)
CNπ:255x242:signed:Presented by Warren MacKenzie
1986

LAPORTE, George Henry 1799-1873
British Collection

T02363 Arab Mare and Foal with Attendant by a Ruined Temple
(circa 1835)
Oc:486x673:Presented by Paul Mellon through the
British Sporting Art Trust 1979

LAPORTE, John 1761-1839
British Collection

N04915 Rob Roy's Cave
Oc:251x349:Presented by Mr and Mrs E. Percival Allam
in memory of their son Stanley 1938

LARIONOV, Michel 1881-1964
Modern Collection
Tate Gallery Archive holds material concerning this artist

N06192 Nocturne (circa 1913-14)
Noktyurn
Oc:502x610:signed:Presented by Eugène Mollo and the artist 1953

T00157 Serge Diaghilev (1915)
Dπ:273x200:signed:Presented by the artist 1957

T00175 White Drawing (?1907)
Dessin blanc
Gπ:229x340:Purchased 1958

T00767 Soldier on a Horse (circa 1911)
Oc:870x991:signed:Presented by Mme Alexandra Larionov, the artist's widow 1965

T01325 Rayonist Drawing (circa 1911-2)
Dπ:241x159:Presented by Eugène Rubin 1971

LAROON, Marcellus, the Younger 1679-1772
British Collection

N03624 Two Gentlemen Going Shooting with a Dog and a Groom with Two Shooting Ponies (1771)
Dπ:475x329:signed:Presented by H. Reitlinger through the National Art Collections Fund 1922

N04420 Interior with Figures (circa 1750)
Oc:457x385:Presented by Julian Lousada through the National Art Collections Fund 1928

T00911 Riders Encountering a Figure of Fate (circa 1730)
Oc:905x699:Purchased 1967

LASZLO de LOMBOS, Phillip Alexius 1869-1937
British Collection

N02957 Lady Wantage (1911)
Oc:737x946:signed:Presented by the artist 1913

LATHAM, James 1696-1747
British Collection

N05801 The Rt Hon. Sir Capel Molyneux (1740)
Oc:1346x1080:Purchased 1947

LATHAM, John born 1921
Modern Collection
Tate Gallery Archive holds material concerning this artist

T00854 Film Star (1960)
Rv:1600x1981x228:Purchased 1966

T01468 P(n)2:3/12 (1963)
Ac:1530x2140:Purchased 1971

T02069 Burial of Count Orgaz (1958)
Rv:1219x914x216:Purchased 1976

T02070 One-Second Drawing (17" 2002) (Time Signature 5:1) (1972)
RAw:267x268x25:signed:Presented by the artist 1976

T02071 Derelict Land Art: Five Sisters (1976)
Sv:1219x1829x241:Purchased 1976

T02072 Five Sisters Bing (1976)
Sv:190x622x457:Purchased 1976

T03706 Observer IV (1960)
RVb:2440x1830x380:Purchased 1983

LA THANGUE, Henry Herbert 1859-1929
British Collection

N01605 The Man with the Scythe (exhibited 1896)
Oc:1676x1664:signed:Presented by the Trustees of the Chantrey Bequest 1896

T03413 The Return of the Reapers (1886)
Oc:1190x695:signed:Purchased 1982

LATTANZI, Luciano born 1925
Modern Collection

P08002 [title not known: from 'Punctualizzazioni a uso Privato'] (1975)
MIπ:114x73:signed:Transferred from the Library 1977

LAURENCIN, Marie 1885-1956
Modern Collection

N04726 Portraits (1915)
Oc:330x460:signed:Bequeathed by C. Frank Stoop 1933

LAURENS, Henri 1885-1954
Modern Collection
Tate Gallery Archive holds material concerning this artist

T00361 Bather (Fragment) (1931, ?later cast)
Baigneuse (Fragment)
Sz:571x670x362:signed:Purchased 1960

T01111 Autumn (1948, ?later cast)
L'Automne
Sz:762x1702x629:Purchased 1969

LAURIE, Robin
Modern Collection

P06325 The Burning Cone (1970)
CLπ:197x117:Presented by Curwen Studio through the Institute of Contemporary Prints 1975

LAUSEN, Jens born 1937
Modern Collection

Map (P04568-P04571; complete group)
Landkarte

P04568 Map No. I Aircastle (1969)
Landkarte Nr. I Luftschloss
CNπ:679x562:signed:Presented by Rose and Chris Prater through the Institute of Contemporary Prints 1975

P04569 Map No. II Paradise (1969)
Landkarte Nr. II Paradies
CNπ:679x562:signed:Presented by Rose and Chris Prater through the Institute of Contemporary Prints 1975

P04570 Map No. III Ariadne's Thread (1969)
Landkarte Nr. III Ariadnes Faden
CNπ:679x562:signed:Presented by Rose and Chris Prater through the Institute of Contemporary Prints 1975

P04571 Map No. IV The Time Before and After Mid Day Homage to C.D. Friedrich (1969)
Landkarte Nr. IV De Zeiträume Vor und Nach Mittag Hommage à C.D. Friedrich
CNπ:679x562:signed:Presented by Rose and Chris Prater through the Institute of Contemporary Prints 1975

LAVERY, Sir John 1856-1941
British Collection
Tate Gallery Archive holds material concerning this artist

N03000 Le Mort du Cygne: Anna Pavlova (1911)
Oc:1981x1467:signed:Presented by F. Howard through the National Loan Exhibition Committee 1914

N03688 The Golf Course, North Berwick (1922)
Oc:635x762:signed:Presented by Lord Duveen 1922

N03958 The Jockeys' Dressing Room at Ascot (1923)
Oc:635x813:Presented by the Trustees of the Chantrey Bequest 1924

N04544 The Chess Players (1929)
Oc:1232x1918:Presented by the Trustees of the Chantrey Bequest 1930

N04553 The Opening of the Modern Foreign and Sargent Galleries at the Tate Gallery, 26 June 1926 (exhibited 1929)
Oc:857x1168:signed:Presented by Lord Duveen 1930

N05271 The Glasgow Exhibition, 1888 (1888)
Ow:235x349:signed:Purchased 1941

N05578 Mrs Guthrie (1898)
Ow:318x171:signed:Purchased 1945

N06063 Auguste Rodin (1912-3)
Oc:1530x1022:signed:Presented by the artist 1914

T04906 King George V, Accompanied by Queen Mary, at the Opening of the Modern Foreign and Sargent Galleries at the Tate Gallery, 26 June 1926 (1926)
Oc:608x507:signed:Presented by the executors of the estate of the Hon Mrs Dorothy Rose Burns 1987

LAW, Bob born 1934
Modern Collection

T01774 Drawing 24.4.60 (1960)
Dπ:679x1006:signed:Purchased 1973

T01775 Drawing 25.4.60 (1960)
Dπ:679x1006:signed:Purchased 1973

T01806 Drawing 4.6.71 (1971)
Dπ:1530x2042:signed:Purchased 1973

T02092 No. 62 (Black/Blue/Violet/Blue) (1967)
Ac:1676x1753:signed:Purchased 1976

T05041 Untitled 29.8.87 (1987)
Wπ:562x763:signed:Presented by Edward Lee through the Karsten Schubert Gallery 1988

LAWES-WITTEWRONGE, Sir Charles, Bt 1843-1911
British Collection

N02871 The Death of Dirce (1906)
Sz:2527x1727x1956:signed:Presented by the artist's widow 1911

LAWRENCE, Eileen born 1946
Modern Collection

T02407 Prayer Stick (1977)
WVπ:2438x152:signed:Presented by the Contemporary Art Society 1979

LAWRENCE, Sir Thomas 1769-1830
British Collection
Tate Gallery Archive holds material concerning this artist

N00136 Miss Laura Dorothea Ross (Mrs Francis Robertson) (circa 1798-1804)
Oc:2397x1473:Presented by Francis Robertson 1837

N00142 John Philip Kemble as Hamlet (1801)
Oc:3061x1981:Presented by King William IV 1836

N00144 Benjamin West, P.R.A. (replica) (circa 1821)
Oc:2683x1768:Presented by King William IV 1836

N00188 Mrs Siddons (1804)
Oc:2540x1480:Presented by Mrs C. FitzHugh 1843

N00324 The Countess of Darnley (circa 1825-30)
Oc:635x505:Presented by Robert Vernon 1847

N00785 Mrs Siddons, ? as Mrs Haller in 'The Stranger' (circa 1796-8)
Oc:762x635:Bequeathed by Mrs Cecilia Combe 1868

N00893 Princess Lieven (?1812-20)
Oc:460x384:Purchased 1871

N00922 Lady Georgiana Fane (?1806)
Oc:1426x1022:signed:Bequeathed by Lady Georgiana Fane 1875

N01238 Sir Samuel Romilly (circa 1810)
Oc:749x622:Bequeathed by Charles Romilly 1887

N01307 Miss Caroline Fry (1827)
Oc:756x629:Presented by Mrs William Wilson 1890

N01413 Philip Sansom (circa 1805-10)
Oc:1264x1016:Bequeathed by Miss Ellen Sansom 1894

N02222 Mrs Siddons (1786)
Pπ:324x273:signed:Bequeathed by Miss Julia Emily Gordon 1896

T00768 Isabel Smith, Called Munia, Nurse to the Angerstein Family (circa 1800)
Dπ:356x302:Bequeathed by Miss May Rowley 1965

T01974 Homer Reciting his Poems (1790)
Oc:940x1111:signed:Purchased 1975

T05466 Philadelphia Hannah, 1st Viscountess Cremone (exhibited 1789)
Oc:2403x1480:Presented by the Patrons of British Art through the Friends of the Tate Gallery 1988

LAWSON, Cecil 1851-1882
British Collection

N01142 The August Moon (1880)
Oc:1689x3061:signed:Presented by the artist's widow 1883

LEACH, Bernard 1887-1979
Modern Collection
Tate Gallery Archive holds material concerning this artist

P06326 Bird Dish (1973-4)
CLπ:483x413:signed:Presented by Curwen Studio through the Institute of Contemporary Prints 1975

P06327 Black Jar (1973-4)
CLπ:483x410:signed:Presented by Curwen Studio through the Institute of Contemporary Prints 1975

P06328 Cornish Coast (1973-4)
CLπ:378x467:signed:Presented by Curwen Studio through the Institute of Contemporary Prints 1975

P06329 Deer Plate (1973-4)
CLπ:483x413:signed:Presented by Curwen Studio through the Institute of Contemporary Prints 1975

P06330 Fish Vase (1973-4)
CLπ:508x298:signed:Presented by Curwen Studio through the Institute of Contemporary Prints 1975

P06331 Lion Tile (1973-4)
CLπ:435x521:signed:Presented by Curwen Studio through the Institute of Contemporary Prints 1975

P06332 Tree Jar (1973-4)
CLπ:448x365:signed:Presented by Curwen Studio through the Institute of Contemporary Prints 1975

Penwith Portfolio (P01416, P06005, P06108, P06130, P06241, P06324, P06346, P06359, P06399, P06519, P06700; complete group; mixed group)

P06359 Drawing for a Pot (1973)
CLπ:302x295:signed:Presented by Curwen Studio through the Institute of Contemporary Prints 1975

LEADER, Benjamin Williams 1831-1923
British Collection

N01540 The Valley of the Llugwy (1883)
Oc:1194x2007:signed:Presented by Sir Henry Tate 1894

LEAR, Edward 1812-1888
British Collection

N02740 S. Francesco di Paola
DWπ:156x108:Presented by the Earl of Northbrook 1910

N02741 Stairs Leading to S. Pietro in Vincoli (1838)
DWπ:356x254:Presented by the Earl of Northbrook 1910

N02742 Back of the Hemicycle Looking on to the Stadium, Palatine (1838)
DWπ:298x175:Presented by the Earl of Northbrook 1910

N02743 Substructure of the Palace of Septimus Severus, Palatine
Wπ:184x330:Presented by the Earl of Northbrook 1910

N02744 St Peter's from Arco Oscuro (1840)
Dπ:330x229:Presented by the Earl of Northbrook 1910

N02745 Fountain of the Sea-Horses in the Garden of the Villa Borghese, Rome
Dπ:235x337:Presented by the Earl of Northbrook 1910

N02746 Piazza di Spagna, Rome
Dπ:232x337:Presented by the Earl of Northbrook 1910

N02747 Church of the SS. Quattro Coronati, Rome
DWπ:235x324:Presented by the Earl of Northbrook 1910

N02748 The Capitol, from the Forum
WDπ:216x305:Presented by the Earl of Northbrook 1910

N02749 Galera (1842)
DWπ:267x489:Presented by the Earl of Northbrook 1910

N02750 The Sirens Isles (1844)
Dπ:225x391:Presented by the Earl of Northbrook 1910

N02751 Pompey's Pillar (1858)
DWπ:337x514:Presented by the Earl of Northbrook 1910

N02752 View near Cairo (1858)
DWπ:165x514:Presented by the Earl of Northbrook 1910

N02753 View of Jerusalem (1858)
DWπ:152x502:Presented by the Earl of Northbrook 1910

N02754 S. Maria Marinasco (1860)
DWπ:311x238:Presented by the Earl of Northbrook 1910

N02755 San Miniato al Monte
DWπ:219x352:Presented by the Earl of Northbrook 1910

N02756 Near Calvi (1868)
Dπ:152x229:Presented by the Earl of Northbrook 1910

N02794 The Baths of Trajan
DWπ:235x302:Presented by the Earl of Northbrook 1910

N02795 Porta Maggiore, Rome
DWπ:235x384:Presented by the Earl of Northbrook 1910

N02796 The Pyramids with the Sphinx and Palms (1858)
DWπ:165x514:Presented by the Earl of Northbrook 1910

N02797 View of Jerusalem (1858)
DWπ:178x502:Presented by the Earl of Northbrook 1910

N02798 Porto Venere (1860)
DWπ:232x324:Presented by the Earl of Northbrook 1910

N02799 Villa S. Firenze (1861)
DWπ:229x352:Presented by the Earl of Northbrook 1910

N02800 Calvi
Dπ:152x235:Presented by the Earl of Northbrook 1910

N02801 Opposite Calvi (1868)
Dπ:187x537:Presented by the Earl of Northbrook 1910

T00630 View of Reggio and the Straits of Messina (1852)
Oc:514x822:signed:Presented by John Witt through the National Art Collections Fund 1963

T01004 Philates (1856)
DWπ:235x321:Presented by the National Art Collections Fund (Herbert Powell Bequest) 1967

T03168 The Monastery of Simopetra on Mount Athos (1856)
DWπ:314x486:Bequeathed by Miss Eveline Annie Dear 1980

T03939 The Fortress of San George, near Argostoli, Cephalonia (1848)
Dπ:356x508:Presented by Denzil Young in accordance with the wishes of his late sister Miss Monica Young 1985

LE BAS, Edward 1904-1966
Modern Collection
Tate Gallery Archive holds material concerning this artist

N05134 Café Scene (1939)
Ob:546x800:signed:Purchased 1940

N05334 Saloon Bar (1940)
Oc:883x1099:signed:Presented by the Trustees of the Chantrey Bequest 1940

N05860 The Tea Table (1947-8)
Ob:667x559:signed:Presented by the Trustees of the Chantrey Bequest 1948

N06010 Interior (1951)
Ob:933x1670:signed:Presented by the Trustees of the Chantrey Bequest 1951

LE BROCQUY, Louis born 1916
Modern Collection
Tate Gallery Archive holds material concerning this artist

T00224 Tinkers Resting (1946)
Ob:508x356:signed:Purchased 1958

T00316 Woman (1959)
OVc:921x730:signed:Purchased 1959

T02335 Study Towards an Image of James Joyce (1977)
Oc:700x700:signed:Purchased 1978

T05708 Image of James Joyce (1977)
Oc:703x704:signed:Presented by the artist 1989

P01744 Cuchulainn (1974)
CLπ:397x397:signed:Presented by Gimpel Fils 1975

P01745 Head and Handprint (1974)
CLπ:397x400:signed:Presented by Gimpel Fils 1975

P01746 Image in Darkness (1974)
CLπ:397x400:signed:Presented by Gimpel Fils 1975

P01747 Lemon (1974)
CLπ:397x397:signed:Presented by Gimpel Fils 1975

P01748 Mycenean Gold Mask (1974)
Clπ:397x400:signed:Presented by Gimpel Fils 1975

P01749 No Lemon (1974)
Clπ:149x171:signed:Presented by Gimpel Fils 1975

P01750 Head on a Red Ground (1974)
Clπ:397x400:signed:Presented by Gimpel Fils 1975

LE BRUN, Christopher born 1951
Modern Collection

T03454 Dream, Think, Speak (1981-2)
Oc:2440x2285:signed:Purchased 1982

T05533 Forest (1987-8)
2 Oc:2355x5660:Purchased 1989

P11199 [no title] (1987)
Jπ:780x570:signed:Presented by Garner H. Tullis and Pamela Auchincloss 1988

P11210 [no title] (1988)
Jπ:780x580:Presented by Garner H. Tullis and Pamela Auchincloss 1989

P11211 [no title] (1988)
Jπ:658x514:Presented by Garner H. Tullis and Pamela Auchincloss 1989

P11224 [no title] (1986)
Jπ:770x575:signed:Presented by Garner H. Tullis and Pamela Auchincloss 1989

P77181 Untitled (1986)
6 Jπ:2280x2240:signed:Purchased 1987

Seven Lithographs (P77294-P77300; complete group)

P77294 [no title] (1989)
Lπ:910x760:signed:Purchased 1989

P77295 [no title] (1989)
Lπ:910x760:signed:Purchased 1989

P77296 [no title] (1989)
Lπ:760x910:signed:Purchased 1989

P77297 [no title] (1989)
Lπ:910x760:signed:Purchased 1989

P77298 [no title] (1989)
Lπ:760x910:signed:Purchased 1989

P77299 [no title] (1989)
Lπ:910x760:signed:Purchased 1989

P77300 [no title] (1989)
Lπ:910x760:signed:Purchased 1989

LE CAPELAIN, Jean 1814-1848
British Collection

N04980 Fishing Boats, Low Tide
Wπ:165x267:Presented by D.C. Fincham 1939

N04981 Fishing Boats, High Tide
Wπ:171x267:Presented by D.C. Fincham 1939

N04982 Harbour with Shipping
Wπ:44x178:Presented by D.C. Fincham 1939

N04983 Fishing Boats Leaving Harbour
Wπ:25x152:Presented by D.C. Fincham 1939

LECK, Bart van der 1876-1958
Modern Collection

T00896 Composition (1918)
Oc:543x425:signed:Purchased 1966

T01098 Study for Compositions No. 3 and No. 4 (Leaving the Factory) (1917)
Fabrieksuitgang
Dπ:965x1499:signed:Presented by Mr and Mrs Robert Lewin through the Friends of the Tate Gallery 1968

LE CORBUSIER (Charles-Edouard Jeanneret) 1887-1965
Modern Collection

N06224 Bull III (1953)
Taureau III
Oc:1619x1137:signed:Purchased 1954

LEDGER, Janet born 1931
Modern Collection

P06793 Factory Gate (1976)
CLπ:292x410:Presented by Curwen Studio 1978

P06794 Play Street (1976)
CLπ:286x406:Presented by Curwen Studio 1978

LEDWARD, Gilbert 1888-1960
Modern Collection
Tate Gallery Archive holds material concerning this artist

N04840 Monolith (exhibited 1936)
Ss:1537x311x324:Presented by the Trustees of the Chantrey Bequest 1936

LEE, Catherine born 1950
Modern Collection

P11225 Unica 39 (1987)
Jπ:570x750:signed:Presented by Garner H. Tullis and Pamela Auchincloss 1989

LEE, Frederick Richard 1799-1879
British Collection

N00419 Showery Weather: Sunrise on the Sea Coast (1834)
Oc:857x1092:signed:Presented by Robert Vernon 1847

N02949 Lake in a Park
Ob:352x457:Bequeathed by Sir Henry Layard 1913

LEE, Frederick Richard and COOPER, Thomas Sidney 1799-1879, 1803-1902
British Collection

N00619 Evening in the Meadows (cattle by Thomas Sidney Cooper) (exhibited 1854)
Oc:952x1308:Bequeathed by Jacob Bell 1859

N00620 A River Scene (cattle by Thomas Sidney Cooper) (1855)
Oc:1270x1829:Bequeathed by Jacob Bell 1859

LEE, Frederick Richard and LANDSEER, Sir Edwin Henry 1799-1879, 1803-1873
British Collection

N00418 Cover Side (figures and animals by Sir E. Landseer) (1839)
Oc:489x406:signed:Presented by Robert Vernon 1847

N01788 Scottish Landscape: Bringing in a Stag (figure and animals by Sir E. Landseer) (1830)
Oc:387x518:signed:Bequeathed by Henry Vaughan 1900

LEE, Sydney 1866-1949
British Collection

N03955 Amongst the Dolomites (1924)
Oc:1187x1454:signed:Presented by the Trustees of the
Chantrey Bequest 1924

N05442 The Top of the St Gotthard (exhibited 1943)
Oc:508x762:signed:Presented by the Trustees of the
Chantrey Bequest 1943

LEE, Thomas Stirling 1857-1916
British Collection

N04430 Margaret Clausen (exhibited 1908)
Ss:540x267x222:Presented by Sir George Clausen 1929

LEES, Derwent 1885-1931
Modern Collection

N04241 Landscape at Collioure (1910)
Wπ:225x340:signed:Presented by F.F. Madan through the
National Art Collections Fund 1927

N05021 Pear Tree in Blossom (1913)
Ow:324x406:signed:Purchased 1939

N05355 Métairie des Abeilles (1912)
Ow:330x406:signed:Bequeathed by Dr John MacGregor
1942

N05356 Métairie des Abeilles (circa 1912)
Wπ:229x305:Bequeathed by Dr John MacGregor 1942

LÉGER, Fernand 1881-1955
Modern Collection
Tate Gallery Archive holds material concerning this artist

N05907 Leaves and Shell (1927)
Feuilles et coquillage
Oc:1295x972:signed:Purchased 1949

N05990 Keys (Composition) (1928)
Les Clés (Composition)
Oc:651x537:signed:Presented by Mrs Fanny Wadsworth
1951

N05991 Playing Card and Pipe (1928)
Carte et pipe
Oc:600x918:signed:Presented by Mrs Fanny Wadsworth
1951

T00246 Two Women Holding Flowers (1954)
Deux femmes tenant des fleurs
Oc:972x1299:signed:Purchased 1959

T02035 Still Life with a Beer Mug (1921-2)
Nature morte à la chope
Oc:921x600:signed:Purchased with assistance from the
Friends of the Tate Gallery 1976

T03118 Acrobat and his Partner (1948)
L'Acrobate et sa partenaire
Oc:1302x1626:signed:Purchased 1980

School Prints (P01698-P01727; complete group; mixed
group)
P01711 The King of Hearts (1946-9)
CLπ:349x514:Presented by Patrick Seale Prints 1975

LEGNAGHI, Igino born 1936
Modern Collection

P01435 Sculptural Image (1973)
CNπ:825x616:signed:Presented by Editions Alecto
through the Institute of Contemporary Prints 1975

LEGROS, Alphonse 1837-1911
British Collection
Tate Gallery Archive holds material concerning this artist

N01501 Femmes en Prière (1888)
Oc:295x727:signed:Presented by subscribers 1897

N02117 John Gray (1883)
Oc:641x457:signed:Presented by Judge Evans 1907

N02433 Memorial Portrait of Alfred Stevens (1907)
Dπ:286x210:signed:Presented by the artist 1909

N02898 Le Repas des Pauvres (1877)
Oc:1130x1429:signed:Presented by Rosalind, Countess of
Carlisle 1912

N02918 The Retreat (exhibited 1872)
Oc:1187x1181:signed:Presented by Mrs Watts by the wish
of the late George Frederic Watts 1913

N03135 Rehearsing the Service (circa 1870)
Oc:914x1168:signed:Bequeathed by Rev. A. Stopford
Brooke 1916

N03274 Cupid and Psyche (exhibited 1867)
Oc:1168x1397:signed:Bequeathed by Sir Charles Holroyd
1918

N03608 Mask of an Old Man
Rz:254x235:Presented by Mrs Knowles 1922

N03609 Mask of an Old Man
Rz:279x241:Presented by Mrs Knowles 1922

N05026 Pour le Monument d'Alfred Stevens
Lπ:140x181:signed:Presented by L. Gantin 1939

Twenty-six Medals (A00704-A00729)
A00704 [title not known]
Rz::Presented by C.A. Ionides 1912

A00705 [title not known]
Rz::Presented by C.A. Ionides 1912

A00706 [title not known]
Rz::Presented by C.A. Ionides 1912

A00707 [title not known]
Rz::Presented by C.A. Ionides 1912

A00708 [title not known]
Rz::Presented by C.A. Ionides 1912

A00709 [title not known]
Rz::Presented by C.A. Ionides 1912

A00710 [title not known]
Rz::Presented by C.A. Ionides 1912

A00711 [title not known]
Rz::Presented by C.A. Ionides 1912

A00712 [title not known]
Rz::Presented by C.A. Ionides 1912

A00713 [title not known]
Rz::Presented by C.A. Ionides 1912

A00714 [title not known]
Rz::Presented by C.A. Ionides 1912

A00715 [title not known]
Rz::Presented by C.A. Ionides 1912

A00716 [title not known]
Rz::Presented by C.A. Ionides 1912

A00717 [title not known]
Rz::Presented by C.A. Ionides 1912

A00718 [title not known]
Rz::Presented by C.A. Ionides 1912

A00719 [title not known]
Rz::Presented by C.A. Ionides 1912

A00720 [title not known]
Rz::Presented by C.A. Ionides 1912

A00721 [title not known]
Rz::Presented by C.A. Ionides 1912

A00722 [title not known]
Rz::Presented by C.A. Ionides 1912

A00723 [title not known]
Rz::Presented by C.A. Ionides 1912

A00724 [title not known]
Rz::Presented by C.A. Ionides 1912

A00725 [title not known]
Rz::Presented by C.A. Ionides 1912

A00726 [title not known]
Rz::Presented by C.A. Ionides 1912

A00727 [title not known]
Rz::Presented by C.A. Ionides 1912

A00728 [title not known]
Rz::Presented by C.A. Ionides 1912

A00729 [title not known]
Rz::Presented by C.A. Ionides 1912

LEHMBRUCK, Wilhelm 1881-1919
Modern Collection

T00543 Inclined Head of a Woman (1910)
Gesenkter Frauenkopf
Sp:425x419x248:signed:Bequeathed by the Earl of
Sandwich 1962

LEIGH, Maude Boughton circa 1881-1945
Modern Collection

N05802 Chloë Boughton-Leigh
Oc:711x508:Purchased 1947

LEIGHTON, Frederic, Lord 1830-1896
British Collection
Tate Gallery Archive holds material concerning this artist

N01511 And the Sea Gave Up the Dead Which Were in It
(exhibited 1892)
Oc:2286x2286:Presented by Sir Henry Tate 1894

N01574 The Bath of Psyche (exhibited 1890)
Oc:1892x622:Presented by the Trustees of the Chantrey
Bequest 1890

N01752 The Sluggard (1885)
Sz:1911x902x597:signed:Presented by Sir Henry Tate 1894

N01754 An Athlete Wrestling with a Python (1877)
Sz:1746x984x1099:signed:Presented by the Trustees of
the Chantrey Bequest 1877

N01761 Sketch for 'An Athlete Wrestling with a Python' (circa
1877)
Sp:251x156x130:signed:Presented by Prof. Alphonse
Legros 1897

N01806 Study for 'The Discovery of Juliet Apparently Lifeless'
(circa 1858)
Ow:210x311:Bequeathed by Henry Vaughan 1900

N02945 Study for 'Needless Alarms' (1886)
Sp:533x225x159:Presented by Charles Fairfax Murray
1913

N03015 Helios and Rhodes
Oc:1658x1099:Purchased 1915

N04006 View in Spain (circa 1886-9)
Oc:213x419:Purchased 1924

N04054 A Recognition from 'Romola', engraved by Swain
(published 1862)
Jπ:159x105:Presented by Harold Hartley 1925

N04731 Mrs John Hanson Walker (1867)
Oc:464x413:Bequeathed by J.H. Hartley 1925

N05120 Needless Alarms (1886)
Sz:508x225x159:Presented by Lady Aberconway 1940

T03053 Lieder ohne Worte (exhibited 1861)
Oc:1016x629:Purchased 1980

Illustrations for 'Dalziel's Bible Gallery', engraved by the
Dalziel Brothers (A00730-A00738; complete group)

A00730 The Spies Escape (published 1881)
Jπ:168x181:Presented by Gilbert Dalziel 1924

A00731 Cain and Abel (published 1881)
Jπ:178x159:Presented by Gilbert Dalziel 1924

A00732 Samson and the Lions (published 1881)
Jπ:184x184:Presented by Gilbert Dalziel 1924

A00733 Abram and the Angel (published 1881)
Jπ:216x152:Presented by Gilbert Dalziel 1924

A00734 Samson at the Mill (published 1881)
Jπ:190x175:Presented by Gilbert Dalziel 1924

A00735 Eliezer and Rebekah (published 1881)
Jπ:175x149:Presented by Gilbert Dalziel 1924

A00736 Moses Views the Promised Land (published 1881)
Jπ:229x137:Presented by Gilbert Dalziel 1924

A00737 Death of the First Born (published 1881)
Jπ:194x175:Presented by Gilbert Dalziel 1924

A00738 Samson Carrying the Gate (published 1881)
Jπ:168x187:Presented by Gilbert Dalziel 1924

LEIRNER, Felicia born 1904
Modern Collection

T00535 Composition (1962)
Composiçao
Sz:1064x686x584:signed:Presented by P.M. Bardi 1962

LELY, Sir Peter 1618-1680
British Collection

N01016 Girl with a Parrot (circa 1670)
Oc:1245x1016:Bequeathed by Wynn Ellis 1876

N03583 Frans Mercurius van Helmont (1670-1)
Oc:1232x1010:Purchased 1921

T00058 Two Ladies of the Lake Family (circa 1660)
Oc:1270x1810:Purchased with assistance from the
National Art Collections Fund 1955

T00070 Elizabeth, Countess of Kildare (circa 1679)
Oc:1257x1022:Purchased 1955

T00452 Susanna and the Elders (circa 1650-5)
Oc:1270x1492:Presented by the Friends of the Tate
Gallery 1961

T00755 Margaret Hughes (circa 1670-5)
Oc:1251x1003:Bequeathed by Cornelia, Countess of
Craven 1965

T00884 Boy Playing a Jew's Harp (circa 1650)
Oc:1410x1029:Presented by the National Art Collections
Fund (Eugene Cremetti Fund) 1966

T00885 Man Playing a Pipe (circa 1650)
Oc:1410x1048:Presented by the National Art Collections
Fund (Eugene Cremetti Fund) 1966

LEMON, Arthur 1850-1912
British Collection

N02935 An Encampment
Oc:711x914:Presented by the Trustees of the Chantrey
Bequest 1913

LENK, Kaspar-Thomas born 1933
Modern Collection
Tate Gallery Archive holds material concerning this artist

T01034 Stratification 10a (Nosferatu) (1967)
Schichtung 10a (Nosferatu)
ASm:1194x1168x356:Purchased 1968

LE PARC, Julio born 1928
Modern Collection

T00678 Continual Mobile, Continual Light (1963)
Continuel-mobile, continuel-lumière
Rv:600x600x10:signed:Purchased 1964

T03774 Virtual Forms in Various Situations (1965)
Formes virtuelles à situations variées
Swm:375x600x370:Transferred from the Victoria &
Albert Museum 1983

P08217 Untitled (1969)
Lπ:229x147:signed:Transferred from the Library 1987

LE PIPER, Francis ?1640-1695
British Collection

T00247 The Combat of Hudibras and Cerdon
Ow:235x432:Purchased 1959

T00248 Hudibras and Ralph Taken Prisoner
Ow:232x432:Purchased 1959

T00620 Hudibras's First Encounter with the Bear-Baiters
Ow:216x435:Presented by Sir John Rothenstein through
the Friends of the Tate Gallery 1963

T00621 Hudibras's Discomfiture at the Hands of the
Skimmington
Ow:232x438:Presented by Sir John Rothenstein through
the Friends of the Tate Gallery 1963

LE SIDANER, Henri 1862-1939
Modern Collection

N03657 Moonlight at Gerberoy (1904)
Clair de Lune à Gerberoy
Oc:654x813:Presented by friends of the Hon. Mr Justice
Peterson 1922

LESLIE, Alexander J. 1873-1930
British Collection

N02789 Dolce Far Niente (circa 1911)
Sz:349x171x209:signed:Presented by the Trustees of the
Chantrey Bequest 1911

LESLIE, Charles Robert 1794-1859
British Collection
Tate Gallery Archive holds material concerning this artist

N00402 Sancho Panza in the Apartment of the Duchess
(exhibited 1844)
Oc:1219x1524:Presented by Robert Vernon 1847

N00403 Uncle Toby and the Widow Wadman in the Sentry Box
(exhibited 1831)
Oc:813x559:Presented by Robert Vernon 1847

N00613 Uncle Toby and the Widow Wadman (1842)
Oc:838x584:Bequeathed by Jacob Bell 1859

N01182 A Scene from Milton's 'Comus' (exhibited 1844)
Oc:311x400:Bequeathed by Mrs Elizabeth Vaughan 1885

N01790 Lady Jane Grey Prevailed on to Accept the Crown
(exhibited 1827)
Oc:445x486:Bequeathed by Henry Vaughan 1900

N01792 Sketch for 'The Duke and Duchess Reading "Don
Quixote"' (circa 1829)
Ob:244x190:signed:Bequeathed by Henry Vaughan 1900

N01793 Sketch for 'Christ Rebuking His Disciples by Calling the
Little Child' (circa 1858)
Oc:203x267:Bequeathed by Henry Vaughan 1900

N01796 Sketch for 'Sancho Panza in the Apartment of the
Duchess' (circa 1844)
Ob:140x168:Bequeathed by Henry Vaughan 1900

N01798 'Slender Courting Anne Page' (circa 1850)
OLπ:381x483:Bequeathed by Henry Vaughan 1900

N01799 Sketch for 'Charles II and Lady Bellenden' (circa 1837)
Ow:264x352:Bequeathed by Henry Vaughan 1900

N01801 Viola and Olivia (1859)
Oπ:229x305:Bequeathed by Henry Vaughan 1900

N01804 Sketch for 'The Rape of the Lock' (circa 1854)
Ow:248x330:Bequeathed by Henry Vaughan 1900

N01805 Sketch for 'Twelfth Night', Act I, Scene 3 (1841)
Ow:222x267:Bequeathed by Henry Vaughan 1900

T03789 The Carved Room, Petworth House, Sussex (c1856).
Verso: Sketch of a Seated Male Figure in Van Dyck
Costume (1844) (circa 1856)
Ow:352x300:Purchased 1983

T04152 Lionel Constable (1854)
Dπ:153x146:signed:Purchased 1986

A00739 Falstaff Personating the King (circa 1851)
Ow:140x216:Bequeathed by Henry Vaughan 1900

A00740 Head of Falstaff (circa 1851)
Ow:140x114:Bequeathed by Henry Vaughan 1900

A00741 Head of Prince Hal (circa 1851)
Oc:140x102:Bequeathed by Henry Vaughan 1900

LESLIE, George Dunlop 1835-1921
British Collection

N01940 Kept in School (1876)
Oc:952x635:signed:Presented by Sir William Agnew Bt
1904

N02070 The Deserted Mill (exhibited 1906)
Oc:1194x940:Presented by the Trustees of the Chantrey
Bequest 1906

LESSORE, Helen born 1907
Modern Collection
Tate Gallery Archive holds material concerning this artist

T03288 Symposium I (1974-77)
Oc:1680x2137:signed:Purchased 1981

LESSORE, John born 1939
Modern Collection

T03223 Annonciade (1961-77)
Oc:1022x1276:signed:Presented by the Trustees of the
Chantrey Bequest 1981

LETHABY, William Richard 1857-1931
British Collection

N04641 Guildford
Wπ:346x248:Presented by Miss Grace A. Crosby 1932

N04642 Sultry Landscape
Wπ:248x346:Presented by Miss Grace A. Crosby 1932

N04643 Blois (1882)
WDπ:248x346:Presented by Miss Grace A. Crosby 1932

N04644 Evening Landscape
Wπ:248x346:Presented by Miss Grace A. Crosby 1932

N04645 The Stream
Wπ:248x346:Presented by Miss Grace A. Crosby 1932

N04646 Trees
Wπ:248x346:Presented by Miss Grace A. Crosby 1932

LEVERETT, David born 1938
Modern Collection

Colour Structure (trial proofs) (P01436-P01437;
incomplete group)

P01436 Colour Structure 1 (trial proof) (1971)
CNπ:665x919:signed:Presented by Clarendon Graphics
through the Institute of Contemporary Prints 1975

P01437 Colour Structure 2 (trial proof) (1971)
CNπ:663x917:signed:Presented by Clarendon Graphics
through the Institute of Contemporary Prints 1975

Equinox (trial proofs) (P01438-P01439, P01444;
incomplete group)

P01438 Equinox (trial proof) (1972)
CLπ:707x713:signed:Presented by Clarendon Graphics
through the Institute of Contemporary Prints 1975

P01439 Equinox (trial proof) (1972)
CLπ:711x712:signed:Presented by Clarendon Graphics
through the Institute of Contemporary Prints 1975

Four Seasons (trial proofs) (P01440-P01443; complete
group)

P01440 Summer (trial proof) (1972)
CLπ:694x689:signed:Presented by Clarendon Graphics
through the Institute of Contemporary Prints 1975

P01441 Autumn (trial proof) (1972)
CLπ:617x617:signed:Presented by Clarendon Graphics
through the Institute of Contemporary Prints 1975

P01442 Winter (trial proof) (1972)
CLπ:620x651:signed:Presented by Clarendon Graphics
through the Institute of Contemporary Prints 1975

P01443 Winter (trial proof) (1972)
CLπ:620x620:signed:Presented by Clarendon Graphics
through the Institute of Contemporary Prints 1975

Equinox (trial proofs) (P01438-P01439, P01444;
incomplete group)

P01444 Equinox (trial proof) (1972)
CLπ:712x718:signed:Presented by Clarendon Graphics
through the Institute of Contemporary Prints 1975

P01445 State of Change (1973)
CLπ:718x921:signed:Presented by Editions Alecto
through the Institute of Contemporary Prints 1975

3 X 3 Shift (P01884-P01886; complete group)

P01884 [no title] (1973)
CNπ:600x900:signed:Presented by Editions Alecto 1979

P01885 [no title] (1973)
CNπ:600x900:signed:Presented by Editions Alecto 1979

P01886 [no title] (1973)
CNπ:600x900:signed:Presented by Editions Alecto 1979

Thought Forms (P02460-P02464; complete group)

P02460 Shift Open (1975-7)
CNπ:570x920:signed:Presented by the artist 1978

P02461 Shift Closed (1975-7)
CNπ:515x850:signed:Presented by the artist 1978

P02462 Colour Satin (1975-7)
CNπ:715x1060:signed:Presented by the artist 1978

P02463 Trace Elements (1975-7)
CNπ:710x1060:signed:Presented by the artist 1978

P02464 Laminations (1975-7)
CNπ:675x980:signed:Presented by the artist 1978

The Janus Suite (P02465-P02467; complete group)

P02465 Historical Utopias (revisited) (1977-8)
CNπ:710x1050:signed:Presented by the artist 1978

P02466 Lost Horizons (1977-8)
CNπ:710x1050:signed:Presented by the artist 1978

P02467 Past Times (1977-8)
CNπ:710x1060:signed:Presented by the artist 1978

The Four Seasons (P02484-P02487; complete group)

P02484 Spring (1971-2)
CNπ:615x610:signed:Presented by the artist 1978

P02485 Summer (1971-2)
CNπ:615x613:signed:Presented by the artist 1978

P02486 Autumn (1971-2)
CNπ:615x615:signed:Presented by the artist 1978

P02487 Winter (1971-2)
CNπ:615x615:signed:Presented by the artist 1978

The Janus Suite (P02465-P02467; complete group)

P02553 Lost Messages (1977-8)
CNπ:595x820:signed:Presented by the artist 1982

P02554 Salient Features (1977-8)
CNπ:595x914:signed:Presented by the artist 1982

P02555 Song for Africa (1977-8)
CNπ:705x1047:signed:Presented by the artist 1982

P02556 Two Faces of a Place (1977-8)
CNπ:712x1050:signed:Presented by the artist 1982

LEVY, Simon 1886-1973
Modern Collection

N05032 The Musician (1925)
La Musicienne
Oc:1213x857:signed:Presented by Lord Ivor Spencer
Churchill 1939

LEWIS, A. Neville 1895-1972
Modern Collection
Tate Gallery Archive holds material concerning this artist

N03641 The Rag and Bone Man (circa 1937)
Dπ:381x279:signed:Purchased 1922

N03841 Charlie, a Little Gipsy Boy (exhibited 1923)
Oc:356x254:signed:Presented by the Contemporary Art
Society 1924

LEWIS, George Robert 1782-1871
British Collection

N02960 Hereford, from the Haywood, Noon (1815)
Oc:416x597:Presented by the Rev. Stopford Brooke 1904

N02961 Hereford, Dynedor and the Malvern Hills, from the
Haywood Lodge, Harvest Scene, Afternoon (1815)
Oc:416x597:Presented by the Rev. Stopford Brooke 1904

T02009 Clearing a Site in Paddington for Development (?circa
1815-23)
DWπ:267x495:signed:Purchased 1975

T03234 Harvest Field with Gleaners, Haywood, Herefordshire
(1815)
Oc:143x195:Purchased 1981

T03235 Harvest Field with Reapers, Haywood, Herefordshire (1815)
Oc:140x195:Purchased 1981

LEWIS, John Frederick 1805-1876
British Collection
Tate Gallery Archive holds material concerning this artist

N01405 Edfu, Upper Egypt (1860)
Ow:298x775:signed:Purchased 1894

N01688 Study for 'The Courtyard of the Coptic Patriarch's House in Cairo' (circa 1864)
Ow:368x356:signed:Purchased 1900

N01729 Spanish Couple Riding a Mule
DGπ:273x356:signed:Presented by Miss Julia Emily Gordon 1888

N02199 Mehemet Ali Pasha
DWπ:381x546:Presented by H. Finch 1907

N02200 Two Turbaned Figures Seated on the Ground in an Eastern Courtyard
DWπ:305x254:Presented by H. Finch 1907

N02201 Corridor Leading to the Sacristy of Santa Croce, Florence (1828)
Dπ:210x286:Presented by H. Finch 1907

N02202 Mirador in Sanchez' Cottage, Alhambra (circa 1832-4)
DWπ:210x279:Presented by H. Finch 1907

N02203 A Pulpit in the Cathedral of Salerno
Dπ:178x260:Presented by H. Finch 1907

N03395 Chapel of the Burning Bush, Mount Sinai (1843)
DWπ:368x495:signed:Presented by Lady Holroyd in accordance with the wishes of the late Sir Charles Holroyd 1919

N03594 The Siesta (1876)
Oc:886x1111:signed:Purchased 1921

N04822 Buck-Shooting in Windsor Great Park (1825)
Oc:991x1372:signed:Presented by the National Art Collections Fund 1936

T00512 Sketch for 'Buck-Shooting in Windsor Great Park' (circa 1825)
Ob:216x324:Purchased 1962

T01005 Study of Rocks in the Val d'Aosta
Wπ:206x289:signed:Presented by the National Art Collections Fund (Herbert Powell Bequest) 1967

T01006 Head of a Lion (1824)
Wπ:343x260:signed:Presented by the National Art Collections Fund (Herbert Powell Bequest) 1967

LEWIS, Morland 1903-1943
Modern Collection

N05561 Quay Street, Ireland (circa 1937)
Ob:222x270:Purchased 1944

N05562 The Bandstand (exhibited 1931)
Oc:451x610:Presented by Sir Kenneth Clark (later Lord Clark of Saltwood) 1944

LEWIS, Wyndham 1882-1957
Modern Collection
Tate Gallery Archive holds material concerning this artist

N04913 Red Scene (1933-6)
Oc:711x914:signed:Purchased 1938

N05039 La Suerte (1938)
Oc:610x457:signed:Presented by the Contemporary Art Society 1939

N05042 Ezra Pound (1939)
Oc:762x1016:Purchased 1939

N05437 Edith Sitwell (1923-35)
Oc:864x1118:signed:Presented by Sir Edward Beddington-Behrens 1943

N05768 The Surrender of Barcelona (1934-7)
Oc:838x597:Purchased 1947

N05886 Composition (1913)
WDπ:343x267:signed:Purchased 1949

N06255 Crouching Woman (circa 1919)
DWπ:279x381:signed:Purchased 1955

N06256 Girl Reclining (circa 1919)
Dπ:381x559:Purchased 1955

N06257 Indian Dance (1912)
DWπ:273x292:signed:Purchased 1955

T00021 Madge Pulsford (1920)
Dπ:279x381:signed:Presented by the Contemporary Art Society 1955

T00022 Portrait Sketch: Seated Woman Wearing Pendant (1923)
Dπ:457x330:signed:Presented by the Contemporary Art Society 1955

T00023 Portrait Sketch: Seated Woman with Beads (circa 1923)
Dπ:381x330:Presented by the Contemporary Art Society 1955

T00024 Crouching Nude (circa 1919)
Dπ:292x229:Presented by the Contemporary Art Society 1955

T00099 Bagdad (1927-8)
Ow:1829x787:Purchased 1956

T00100 Mrs Schiff (1923-4)
Oc:1257x1003:Purchased 1956

T00106 Planners: Happy Day (1912-3)
GDπ:311x381:signed:Purchased 1956

T00107 Creation Myth (1927)
GDVπ:327x298:signed:Purchased 1956

T00108 Two Mechanics (circa 1912)
DWπ:559x337:Purchased 1956

T00135 A Canadian War Factory (1943)
Oc:1143x857:Purchased 1957

T00193 Madge Pulsford (1920)
DWπ:281x279:Purchased 1958

T00625 Vorticist Composition (1915)
GDπ:314x178:signed:Presented by Miss Ethel M. Saunders in memory of her sister 1963

T00689 The Crowd (?exhibited 1915)
ODc:2007x1537:Presented by the Friends of the Tate Gallery 1964

T01931 Workshop (circa 1914-5)
Oc:765x610:Purchased 1974

T04118 Nigel Tangye (1946)
Oc:967x917:signed:Presented by Mr and Mrs E.W.F. Tomlin 1985

LE WITT, Jan 1907-1991
Modern Collection
Tate Gallery Archive holds material concerning this artist

P06333 Axial Image (1966)
CLπ:406x330:Presented by Curwen Studio through the Institute of Contemporary Prints 1975

LeWITT, Sol born 1928
Modern Collection
Tate Gallery Archive holds material concerning this artist

T01766   A Wall Divided Vertically into Fifteen Equal Parts, Each with a Different Line Direction and Colour, and All Combinations (1970)
D::Purchased 1973

T01865   Two Open Modular Cubes/Half-Off (1972)
SEm:1600x3054x2330:Purchased 1974

T03097   Untitled (1965)
Rm:1841x1216x305:signed:Purchased 1980

T03100   Six Geometric Figures (+ Two) (Wall Drawings) (1980-81)
D::Purchased 1980

Straight Lines in Four Directions and All their Possible Combinations (Set of 15+1) (P01054-P01069; complete group)

P01054   [no title] (1973)
MIπ:273x270:signed:Presented by Riva Castleman, Nancy Jennings and Robert Feldman 1975

P01055   [no title] (1973)
MIπ:273x270:signed:Presented by Riva Castleman, Nancy Jennings and Robert Feldman 1975

P01056   [no title] (1973)
MIπ:273x270:signed:Presented by Riva Castleman, Nancy Jennings and Robert Feldman 1975

P01057   [no title] (1973)
MIπ:273x270:signed:Presented by Riva Castleman, Nancy Jennings and Robert Feldman 1975

P01058   [no title] (1973)
MIπ:273x270:signed:Presented by Riva Castleman, Nancy Jennings and Robert Feldman 1975

P01059   [no title] (1973)
MIπ:273x270:signed:Presented by Riva Castleman, Nancy Jennings and Robert Feldman 1975

P01060   [no title] (1973)
MIπ:273x270:signed:Presented by Riva Castleman, Nancy Jennings and Robert Feldman 1975

P01061   [no title] (1973)
MIπ:273x270:signed:Presented by Riva Castleman, Nancy Jennings and Robert Feldman 1975

P01062   [no title] (1973)
MIπ:273x270:signed:Presented by Riva Castleman, Nancy Jennings and Robert Feldman 1975

P01063   [no title] (1973)
MIπ:273x270:signed:Presented by Riva Castleman, Nancy Jennings and Robert Feldman 1975

P01064   [no title] (1973)
MIπ:273x270:signed:Presented by Riva Castleman, Nancy Jennings and Robert Feldman 1975

P01065   [no title] (1973)
MIπ:273x270:signed:Presented by Riva Castleman, Nancy Jennings and Robert Feldman 1975

P01066   [no title] (1973)
MIπ:273x270:signed:Presented by Riva Castleman, Nancy Jennings and Robert Feldman 1975

P01067   [no title] (1973)
MIπ:273x270:signed:Presented by Riva Castleman, Nancy Jennings and Robert Feldman 1975

P01068   [no title] (1973)
MIπ:273x270:signed:Presented by Riva Castleman, Nancy Jennings and Robert Feldman 1975

P01069   [no title] (1973)
MIπ:273x270:signed:Presented by Riva Castleman, Nancy Jennings and Robert Feldman 1975

P01794   Untitled (1971)
MIπ:159x375:signed:Presented by the Museum of Modern Art, New York 1976

Composite Series (set of 5) (P07061-P07065; complete group)

P07061   [no title] (1971)
MLπ:355x355:signed:Purchased 1971

P07062   [no title] (1971)
MLπ:355x355:signed:Purchased 1971

P07063   [no title] (1971)
MLπ:355x355:signed:Purchased 1971

P07064   [no title] (1971)
MLπ:355x355:signed:Purchased 1971

P07065   [no title] (1971)
MLπ:355x355:signed:Purchased 1971

Lines of One Inch, Four Directions, Four Colours (set of 16) (P07066-P07081; complete group)

P07066   [no title] (1971)
CLπ:356x356:signed:Purchased 1971

P07067   [no title] (1971)
CLπ:356x356:signed:Purchased 1971

P07068   [no title] (1971)
CLπ:356x356:signed:Purchased 1971

P07069   [no title] (1971)
CLπ:356x356:signed:Purchased 1971

P07070   [no title] (1971)
CLπ:356x356:signed:Purchased 1971

P07071   [no title] (1971)
CLπ:356x356:signed:Purchased 1971

P07072   [no title] (1971)
CLπ:356x356:signed:Purchased 1971

P07073   [no title] (1971)
CLπ:356x356:signed:Purchased 1971

P07074   [no title] (1971)
CLπ:356x356:signed:Purchased 1971

P07075   [no title] (1971)
CLπ:356x356:signed:Purchased 1971

P07076   [no title] (1971)
CLπ:356x356:signed:Purchased 1971

P07077   [no title] (1971)
CLπ:356x356:signed:Purchased 1971

P07078   [no title] (1971)
CLπ:356x356:signed:Purchased 1971

P07079   [no title] (1971)
CLπ:356x356:signed:Purchased 1971

P07080   [no title] (1971)
CLπ:356x356:signed:Purchased 1971

P07081   [no title] (1971)
CLπ:356x356:signed:Purchased 1971

The Location of Six Geometric Figures (P07660-P07665; complete group)

P07660   [no title] (1975)
MLπ:400x406:signed:Purchased 1982

P07661   [no title] (1975)
MLπ:400x406:signed:Purchased 1982

P07662   [no title] (1975)
MLπ:400x406:signed:Purchased 1982

P07663 [no title] (1975)
MIπ:400x406:signed:Purchased 1982

P07664 [no title] (1975)
MIπ:400x406:signed:Purchased 1982

P07665 [no title] (1975)
MIπ:400x406:signed:Purchased 1982

P77013 A Square Divided Horizontally and Vertically into Four
Equal Parts, Each with a Different Direction of
Alternating Parallel Bands of Lines (1982)
WJπ:607x607:signed:Purchased 1984

Five Forms Derived from a Cube (P77014-P77018;
complete group)

P77014 [no title] (1982)
WJπ:609x603:signed:Purchased 1984

P77015 [no title] (1982)
WJπ:508x305:signed:Purchased 1984

P77016 [no title] (1982)
WJπ:505x597:signed:Purchased 1984

P77017 [no title] (1982)
WJπ:558x597:signed:Purchased 1984

P77018 [no title] (1982)
WJπ:610x470:Purchased 1984

LEYDEN, Ernst van - see VAN LEYDEN, Ernst

LHOTE, André 1885-1962
Modern Collection
Tate Gallery Archive holds material concerning this artist

N05073 Study for 'Homage to Watteau' (1918)
Study for 'Hommage à Watteau'
Oc:333x360:signed:Bequeathed by Frank Hindley Smith
1940

LIBERMAN, Alexander born 1912
Modern Collection
Tate Gallery Archive holds material concerning this artist

T00650 Andromeda (1962)
Ac:1650x1650:signed:Presented by the Montargent
Foundation 1964

LICHTENSTEIN, Roy born 1923
Modern Collection
Tate Gallery Archive holds material concerning this artist

T00897 Whaam! (1963)
Ac:1727x4064:signed:Purchased 1966

T00963 Set of Dinnerware Objects: Dinner Plate, Soup Dish,
Salad Plate, Side Plate, Saucer, Cup (1966)
Vp:260x600x500:Presented by Galerie Ileana Sonnabend,
Paris 1967

T01131 Drawing for 'Whaam!' (1963)
Dπ:149x305:Presented by the artist 1969

T03083 Wall Explosion II (1965)
REm:1702x1880x102:Purchased 1980

P01795 Moonscape (1965)
CNa:508x610:signed:Presented by the Museum of
Modern Art, New York 1976

P01796 Explosion (1965-6)
CLπ:562x435:signed:Presented by the Museum of
Modern Art, New York 1976

P01831 Untitled (Paper Plate) (1969)
CNπ:264x264:Presented by Simon Wilson and the Lisson
Gallery 1978

P07354 Brushstroke (1965)
CNπ:565x724:signed:Purchased 1979

Haystacks (P07407-P07413; complete group)

P07407 Haystacks #1 (1969)
CLNπ:340x597:signed:Purchased 1981

P07408 Haystacks #2 (1969)
CLNπ:342x597:signed:Purchased 1981

P07409 Haystacks #3 (1969)
CLNπ:342x600:signed:Purchased 1981

P07410 Haystacks #4 (1969)
CLNπ:342x597:signed:Purchased 1981

P07411 Haystacks #5 (1969)
CLNπ:342x600:signed:Purchased 1981

P07412 Haystacks #6 (1969)
CLNπ:342x600:signed:Purchased 1981

P07413 Haystacks #7 (1969)
CLNπ:345x600:signed:Purchased 1981

P77053 Still Life with Portrait from 'Six Still Lifes' (1974)
CLNπ:970x724:signed:Purchased 1984

P77054 Painting in Gold Frame from 'Paintings' (1983-4)
CJLNVπ:1098x837:signed:Purchased 1984

LIEBER, Tom born 1949
Modern Collection

P11217 [no title] (1986)
Jπ:1070x1525:Presented by Garner H. Tullis and Pamela
Auchincloss 1989

LIEBERMANN, Max 1847-1935
Modern Collection
Tate Gallery Archive holds material concerning this artist

N04591 Memorial Service for Kaiser Frederick at Kösen (1888)
Kaiser Friedrich Gedächtnisfeier in Kösen
Oc:930x641:signed:Purchased 1931

N04779 Self-Portrait (1934)
Selbstbildnis
Oc:921x733:signed:Presented by Lord Marks 1935

T00632 Professor Richard Cassirer (1918)
Herrenporträt Professor Cassirer
Oc:965x781:signed:Presented by H. Cassirer, son of the
sitter 1963

T03077 After the Bathe (1904)
Nach dem Baden
Oc:629x911:signed:Bequeathed by G.L. Tietz 1980

LIGHTFOOT, Maxwell Gordon 1886-1911
Modern Collection

N04229 Study of a Girl
DWπ:305x244:Purchased 1927

LIJN, Liliane born 1939
Modern Collection
Tate Gallery Archive holds material concerning this artist

T01828 Liquid Reflections (1968)
KSawv:838x1397x1143:Purchased 1973

Koan-Cuts (P01222-P01226; complete group)

P01222 Koan-Cuts I (1971)
CNVπ:560x796:signed:Presented by Waddington
Galleries through the Institute of Contemporary Prints
1975

P01223 Koan-Cuts II (1971)
CNVπ:560x796:signed:Presented by Waddington
Galleries through the Institute of Contemporary Prints
1975

P01224 Koan-Cuts III (1971)
CNVπ:560x797:signed:Presented by Waddington
Galleries through the Institute of Contemporary Prints
1975

P01225 Koan-Cuts IV (1971)
CNVπ:560x776:signed:Presented by Waddington
Galleries through the Institute of Contemporary Prints
1975

P01226 Koan-Cuts V (1971)
CNVπ:560x796:signed:Presented by Waddington
Galleries through the Institute of Contemporary Prints
1975

LIM, Kim born 1936

Modern Collection
Tate Gallery Archive holds material concerning this artist

T02001 Intervals I (1973)
Sw:1829x473x22:signed:Purchased 1975

T02002 Intervals II (1973)
Sw::signed:Purchased 1975

Miscellaneous Etchings (P01227-P01232; complete
group)

P01227 [no title] (1969)
MIπ:90x90:signed:Presented by Waddington Galleries
through the Institute of Contemporary Prints 1975

P01228 [no title] (1969)
MIπ:129x145:signed:Presented by Waddington Galleries
through the Institute of Contemporary Prints 1975

P01229 [no title] (1969)
MIπ:124x125:signed:Presented by Waddington Galleries
through the Institute of Contemporary Prints 1975

P01230 [no title] (1969)
MIπ:80x181:signed:Presented by Waddington Galleries
through the Institute of Contemporary Prints 1975

P01231 [no title] (1969)
MIπ:105x110:signed:Presented by Waddington Galleries
through the Institute of Contemporary Prints 1975

P01232 [no title] (1969)
MIπ:950x980:signed:Presented by Waddington Galleries
through the Institute of Contemporary Prints 1975

P01233 Yellow Ring (1971)
CIπ:254x254:signed:Presented by Waddington Galleries
through the Institute of Contemporary Prints 1975

P01234 Blue Engraving (1972)
CIπ:445x445:signed:Presented by Waddington Galleries
through the Institute of Contemporary Prints 1975

Ladder Series (P01235, P07194-P07196, P07243;
complete group)

P01235 Ladder Series I (1972)
CIπ::signed:Presented by Waddington Galleries through
the Institute of Contemporary Prints 1975

P01236 Red Aquatint (1972)
CIπ:445x445:signed:Presented by Waddington Galleries
through the Institute of Contemporary Prints 1975

P02440 Woodcut Blue (1974)
CJπ:254x511:signed:Presented by the artist 1977

P02441 BX I (1975)
MJπ:198x232:signed:Presented by the artist 1977

P02442 BX II (1975)
MJπ:197x232:signed:Presented by the artist 1977

P02443 Woodcut (1975)
MJπ:240x275:signed:Presented by the artist 1977

P07174 Bridge I (1960)
MLπ:512x761:signed:Purchased 1976

P07175 Bridge II (1960)
MLπ:490x740:signed:Purchased 1976

P07176 Shogan (1960)
MLπ:454x356:signed:Purchased 1976

P07177 Screenprint - Blue on Blue (1968)
CNπ:387x356:signed:Purchased 1976

P07178 Screenprint - White on White (1968)
CNπ:391x356:signed:Purchased 1976

P07179 Green Etching (1969)
MIπ:460x454:signed:Purchased 1976

P07180 Small Etching (1969)
MIπ:86x102:signed:Purchased 1976

P07181 Blue Disc (1970)
CIπ:178x178:signed:Purchased 1976

P07182 Ring (1970)
MIπ:225x241:Purchased 1976

P07183 Silver Engraving (1970)
CIπ:114x114:signed:Purchased 1976

Small Etchings 1971 (P07184-P07186; complete group)

P07184 Small Etching 1971 I (1971)
MIπ:640x640:signed:Purchased 1976

P07185 Small Etching 1971 II (1971)
MIπ:640x640:signed:Purchased 1976

P07186 Small Etching III (1971)
MIπ:63x63:signed:Purchased 1976

P07187 Brown Aquatint (1972)
CIπ:445x438:signed:Purchased 1976

Interval Series (P07188-P07191; complete group)

P07188 [no title] (1972)
CNπ:376x384:signed:Purchased 1976

P07189 [no title] (1972)
CNπ:376x384:signed:Purchased 1976

P07190 [no title] (1972)
CNπ:376x385:signed:Purchased 1976

P07191 [no title] (1972)
CNπ:376x383:signed:Purchased 1976

P07192 Jaune Foncé (1972)
CIπ:225x225:signed:Purchased 1976

P07193 Jaune Foncé Aquatint (1972)
CIπ:225x225:signed:Purchased 1976

Ladder Series (P01235, P07194-P07196, P07243;
complete group)

P07194 Ladder Series III (1972)
CIπ::signed:Purchased 1976

P07195 Ladder Series IV (1972)
CIπ::signed:Purchased 1976

P07196 Ladder Series V (1972)
CIπ::signed:Purchased 1976

P07197 Yellow Ochre Aquatint (1972)
CIπ:270x295:signed:Purchased 1976

P07198 Silver Engraving (1973)
MIπ:419x257:signed:Purchased 1976

Ladder Series (P01235, P07194-P07196, P07243; complete group)
P07243 Ladder Series II (1972)
Iπ::Purchased 1976

P07244 Blue Engraving (1972)
CIπ:445x445:Purchased 1976

LIN, Richard born 1933
Modern Collection
Tate Gallery Archive holds material concerning this artist

T00636 Painting Relief 13 Sept 1963 (1973)
MIπ:419x257:Purchased 1964

P04572 Flirtation (1965)
MNπ:441x562:signed:Presented by Rose and Chris Prater through the Institute of Contemporary Prints 1975

P04573 Relationships I (1965)
MNπ:441x565:signed:Presented by Rose and Chris Prater through the Institute of Contemporary Prints 1975

P04574 Relationships II (1965)
MNπ:441x565:signed:Presented by Rose and Chris Prater through the Institute of Contemporary Prints 1975

The Four Seasons (P04575-P04578; complete group)
P04575 Spring (1966)
CNπ:523x595:signed:Presented by Rose and Chris Prater through the Institute of Contemporary Prints 1975

P04576 Summer (1966)
CNπ:522x595:signed:Presented by Rose and Chris Prater through the Institute of Contemporary Prints 1975

P04577 Autumn (1966)
CNπ:524x596:signed:Presented by Rose and Chris Prater through the Institute of Contemporary Prints 1975

P04578 Winter (1966)
CNπ:524x595:signed:Presented by Rose and Chris Prater through the Institute of Contemporary Prints 1975

P04579 May 1 (1971)
CNπ:507x507:signed:Presented by Rose and Chris Prater through the Institute of Contemporary Prints 1975

P04580 May 2 (1971)
CNπ:508x510:signed:Presented by Rose and Chris Prater through the Institute of Contemporary Prints 1975

P04581 May 3 (1971)
CNπ:507x508:signed:Presented by Rose and Chris Prater through the Institute of Contemporary Prints 1975

P04582 May 4 (1971)
CNπ:508x508:signed:Presented by Rose and Chris Prater through the Institute of Contemporary Prints 1975

LINDNER, Richard 1901-1978
Modern Collection
Tate Gallery Archive holds material concerning this artist

T00538 Homage to a Cat (1952)
Oc:921x603:signed:Presented anonymously 1962

T00877 Stranger No. 2 (1958)
Oc:1524x1016:signed:Presented by the artist through the American Federation of Arts 1967

LINDSTRÖM, Bengt born 1925
Modern Collection

P08218 Red Man (1968)
Rod Man
Lπ:290x224:signed:Transferred from the Library 1987

LING, Rita M. born 1922
Modern Collection

T00038 Galway Cow (1954)
Ss:273x286x356:Presented by the Trustees of the Chantrey Bequest 1955

LINNELL, John 1792-1882
British Collection
Tate Gallery Archive holds material concerning this artist

N00438 Wood-Cutting in Windsor Forest (1834-5)
Ow:235x381:Presented by Robert Vernon 1847

N00439 The Windmill (1844)
Oc:381x457:Presented by Robert Vernon 1847

N01112 Mrs Ann Hawkins (1832)
Ow:232x168:signed:Presented by Fred Piercy 1882

N01546 Reapers, Noonday Rest (1865)
Oc:940x1397:signed:Presented by Sir Henry Tate 1894

N01547 Contemplation (1864-5)
Oc:718x997:signed:Presented by Sir Henry Tate 1894

N02060 Harvest Home, Sunset: The Last Load (1853)
Oc:883x1473:signed:Presented by J.W. Carlile 1906

N05117 Samuel Rogers (1833-5)
Ow:394x349:signed:Bequeathed by Frank Hindley Smith 1940

N05776 Kensington Gravel Pits (1811-12)
Oc:711x1067:signed:Purchased 1947

N05795 The Sandpits (1856)
Oc:914x1219:signed:Presented by Frederick John Nettlefold 1947

T00043 Harvest Moon (1858)
Ow:378x460:Bequeathed by Mrs E.J. Thwaites 1955

T00933 Leading a Barge (circa 1806)
Ob:194x267:Purchased 1967

T00934 At Twickenham (1806)
Ob:165x254:signed:Purchased 1967

T00935 Study of Buildings ('Study from Nature') (1806)
Ob:165x254:signed:Purchased 1967

T01214 At Under River near Sevenoaks (circa 1833)
DWπ:210x327:Purchased 1970

T01490 Study of a Tree ('Study from Nature') (circa 1805-6)
Ob:324x168:signed:Purchased 1971

T03117 Portrait Study of J.M.W. Turner's Father, with a Sketch of Turner's Eyes, Made during a Lecture (1812)
Dπ:187x225:signed:Purchased 1980

T03269 Mrs Phillips, Wife of the China Man, Oxford Street (1814)
Dπ:302x241:signed:Purchased 1981

T04139 Tatham's Garden, Alpha Road, at Evening (1812)
Wπ:102x125:signed:Purchased 1985

Illustrations to Felix Summerley's 'Hand-Book for the National Gallery', engraved by John Jr., James and William Linnell (A00742-A00791; complete group)
A00742 [title not known] (published 1843)
Jπ::Presented by Herbert Linnell 1924

A00743 [title not known] (published 1843)
Jπ::Presented by Herbert Linnell 1924

A00744 [title not known] (published 1843)
Jπ::Presented by Herbert Linnell 1924

A00745 [title not known] (published 1843)
Jπ::Presented by Herbert Linnell 1924

A00746 [title not known] (published 1843)
Jπ::Presented by Herbert Linnell 1924

A00747 [title not known] (published 1843)
Jπ::Presented by Herbert Linnell 1924

A00748 [title not known] (published 1843)
Jπ::Presented by Herbert Linnell 1924

A00749 [title not known] (published 1843)
Jπ::Presented by Herbert Linnell 1924

A00750 [title not known] (published 1843)
Jπ::Presented by Herbert Linnell 1924

A00751 [title not known] (published 1843)
Jπ::Presented by Herbert Linnell 1924

A00752 [title not known] (published 1843)
Jπ::Presented by Herbert Linnell 1924

A00753 [title not known] (published 1843)
Jπ::Presented by Herbert Linnell 1924

A00754 [title not known] (published 1843)
Jπ::Presented by Herbert Linnell 1924

A00755 [title not known] (published 1843)
Jπ::Presented by Herbert Linnell 1924

A00756 [title not known] (published 1843)
Jπ::Presented by Herbert Linnell 1924

A00757 [title not known] (published 1843)
Jπ::Presented by Herbert Linnell 1924

A00758 [title not known] (published 1843)
Jπ::Presented by Herbert Linnell 1924

A00759 [title not known] (published 1843)
Jπ::Presented by Herbert Linnell 1924

A00760 [title not known] (published 1843)
Jπ::Presented by Herbert Linnell 1924

A00761 [title not known] (published 1843)
Jπ::Presented by Herbert Linnell 1924

A00762 [title not known] (published 1843)
Jπ::Presented by Herbert Linnell 1924

A00763 [title not known] (published 1843)
Jπ::Presented by Herbert Linnell 1924

A00764 [title not known] (published 1843)
Jπ::Presented by Herbert Linnell 1924

A00765 [title not known] (published 1843)
Jπ::Presented by Herbert Linnell 1924

A00766 [title not known] (published 1843)
Jπ::Presented by Herbert Linnell 1924

A00767 [title not known] (published 1843)
Jπ::Presented by Herbert Linnell 1924

A00768 [title not known] (published 1843)
Jπ::Presented by Herbert Linnell 1924

A00769 [title not known] (published 1843)
Jπ::Presented by Herbert Linnell 1924

A00770 [title not known] (published 1843)
Jπ::Presented by Herbert Linnell 1924

A00771 [title not known] (published 1843)
Jπ::Presented by Herbert Linnell 1924

A00772 [title not known] (published 1843)
Jπ::Presented by Herbert Linnell 1924

A00773 [title not known] (published 1843)
Jπ::Presented by Herbert Linnell 1924

A00774 [title not known] (published 1843)
Jπ::Presented by Herbert Linnell 1924

A00775 [title not known] (published 1843)
Jπ::Presented by Herbert Linnell 1924

A00776 [title not known] (published 1843)
Jπ::Presented by Herbert Linnell 1924

A00777 [title not known] (published 1843)
Jπ::Presented by Herbert Linnell 1924

A00778 [title not known] (published 1843)
Jπ::Presented by Herbert Linnell 1924

A00779 [title not known] (published 1843)
Jπ::Presented by Herbert Linnell 1924

A00780 [title not known] (published 1843)
Jπ::Presented by Herbert Linnell 1924

A00781 [title not known] (published 1843)
Jπ::Presented by Herbert Linnell 1924

A00782 [title not known] (published 1843)
Jπ::Presented by Herbert Linnell 1924

A00783 [title not known] (published 1843)
Jπ::Presented by Herbert Linnell 1924

A00784 [title not known] (published 1843)
Jπ::Presented by Herbert Linnell 1924

A00785 [title not known] (published 1843)
Jπ::Presented by Herbert Linnell 1924

A00786 [title not known] (published 1843)
Jπ::Presented by Herbert Linnell 1924

A00787 [title not known] (published 1843)
Jπ::Presented by Herbert Linnell 1924

A00788 [title not known] (published 1843)
Jπ::Presented by Herbert Linnell 1924

A00789 [title not known] (published 1843)
Jπ::Presented by Herbert Linnell 1924

A00790 [title not known] (published 1843)
Jπ::Presented by Herbert Linnell 1924

A00791 [title not known] (published 1843)
Jπ::Presented by Herbert Linnell 1924

attributed to
LINNELL, John 1792-1882
British Collection
Tate Gallery Archive holds material concerning this artist

N05185 The Man who Built the Pyramids (after William Blake)
Dπ:298x214:Bequeathed by Miss Alice G.E. Carthew 1940

N05186 The Man Who Taught Blake Painting in his Dreams (after William Blake)
Dπ:260x206:Bequeathed by Miss Alice G.E. Carthew 1940

LINTON, William 1791-1876
British Collection
Tate Gallery Archive holds material concerning this artist

N01029 The Temples of Paestum
Tc:1473x2388:signed:Bequeathed by the artist 1876

LION, Flora 1876-1958
British Collection
Tate Gallery Archive holds material concerning this artist

N03033 My Mother (1909)
Oc:1276x1143:signed:Presented by Francis Howard through the National Loan Exhibitions Committee 1915

LIPCHITZ, Jacques 1891-1973
Modern Collection
Tate Gallery Archive holds material concerning this artist

T00310 Head (1915, later cast)
Tête
Sz:610x210x184:signed:Purchased 1959

T00311 Reclining Woman with Guitar (1928, cast 1950s)
Femme couchée et guitare
Sz:413x746x330:signed:Purchased 1959

T00320 Study for Monument to 'The Spirit of Enterprise' (1953)
Sz:803x724x321:signed:Purchased 1959

T01755 Study for 'Prometheus' (1936)
Etude pour 'Prométheé'
DGπ:308x241:signed:Presented by Mr and Mrs Jack Steinberg through the Friends of the Tate Gallery 1973

T03397 Sculpture (1915-16)
Ss:980x280x180:signed:Purchased with assistance from the Friends of the Tate Gallery, Mrs T. Steinberg and the Rayne Foundation 1982

T03479 Portrait of Gertrude Stein (1938)
Portrait de Gertrude Stein
Sp:305x259x203:signed:Presented by the Lipchitz Foundation 1982

T03480 Sketch for 'Bellerophon Taming Pegasus' (1964)
Sp:522x407x127:Presented by the Lipchitz Foundation 1982

T03481 Sketch for 'Government of the People' (1967-8)
Sp:864x260x260:Presented by the Lipchitz Foundation 1982

T03482 Pregnant Woman (1912)
Sp:642x146x122:Presented by the Lipchitz Foundation 1982

T03483 The Rape of Europa (1938)
L'Enlèvement d'Europe
Sp:407x597x337:Presented by the Lipchitz Foundation 1982

T03484 The Joy of Orpheus II (1945-6)
Le Bonheur d'Orphée II
Sp:521x342x254:Presented by the Lipchitz Foundation 1982

T03485 Spanish Servant Girl (1915, cast 1960s)
Sp:889x228x139:signed:Presented by the Lipchitz Foundation 1982

T03486 Bather III (1917-18, cast 1960s)
Baigneuse III
Sp:737x254x267:Presented by the Lipchitz Foundation 1982

T03487 Toreador (1914-15)
Le Toréador
Sp:845x267x254:Presented by the Lipchitz Foundation 1982

T03488 Seated Man with Clarinet I (1920)
Homme assis à la clarinette I
Sp:775x293x280:signed:Presented by the Lipchitz Foundation 1982

T03489 Song of Songs (1945)
Le Cantique des cantiques
Sp:139x216x89:Presented by the Lipchitz Foundation 1982

T03490 Picador, Bas Relief (circa 1932)
Sp:508x647x102:Presented by the Lipchitz Foundation 1982

T03491 Sketch for 'Our Tree of Life' (1962)
Sp:825x254x267:Presented by the Lipchitz Foundation 1982

T03492 Sculpture (1916)
Sp:1169x368x342:Presented by the Lipchitz Foundation 1982

T03493 Sketch for Enterprise (1953)
Sp:218x330x152:Presented by the Lipchitz Foundation 1982

T03494 Géricault (1933)
Sp:241x177x202:Presented by the Lipchitz Foundation 1982

T03495 David and Goliath, on a Column (1933)
David et Goliath
Sp:330x133x133:signed:Presented by the Lipchitz Foundation 1982

T03496 Head and Hand (1932)
Sp:197x158x95:signed:Presented by the Lipchitz Foundation 1982

T03497 Study for 'Prometheus' (1936)
Etude pour 'Prométheé'
Sp:260x227x114:signed:Presented by the Lipchitz Foundation 1982

T03498 Head, Bust and Arms (1932)
Sp:187x165x95:Presented by the Lipchitz Foundation 1982

T03499 Seated Bather (1916-17)
Sp:736x247x254:Presented by the Lipchitz Foundation 1982

T03500 Study for Prometheus (1936, cast 1960s)
Sp:190x228x890:Presented by the Lipchitz Foundation 1982

T03501 Figure (1915, cast 1964)
Personnage debout
Sp:502x136x101:Presented by the Lipchitz Foundation 1982

T03502 First Study for Pastoral (1934)
Sp:120x127x82:Presented by the Lipchitz Foundation 1982

T03503 Reclining Figure (1929)
Sp:152x254x120:Presented by the Lipchitz Foundation 1982

T03504 Bust of a Woman (1932)
Sp:190x108x108:Presented by the Lipchitz Foundation 1982

T03505 Sketch for a Figure (1926)
Sp:216x108x48:signed:Presented by the Lipchitz Foundation 1982

T03506 The Snuffer (1930, cast 1960s)
Sp:177x152x152:Presented by the Lipchitz Foundation 1982

T03507 Head (1932, cast 1960s)
Tête
Sp:228x146x139:Presented by the Lipchitz Foundation 1982

T03508 Head of a Woman (1911-12)
Tête de fillette
Sp:158x63x54:Presented by the Lipchitz Foundation 1982

T03509 Musical Instruments, Bas Relief (1923)
Nature morte aux instruments de musique
Sp:158x203x25:Presented by the Lipchitz Foundation 1982

T03510 Meditation (1931, cast 1960s)
Sp:197x178x146:Presented by the Lipchitz Foundation 1982

T03511 Woman with Hair (1932, cast 1960s)
Sp:127x89x63:Presented by the Lipchitz Foundation 1982

T03512 First Study for 'Toward a New World' (1934, cast 1965)
Etude pour 'Vers un monde nouveau'
Sp:108x89x51:Presented by the Lipchitz Foundation 1982

T03513 Bull and Condor (1932, cast 1960s)
Le Taureau et le condor
Sp:209x317x158:signed:Presented by the Lipchitz Foundation 1982

T03514 Study for a Monument (1934, cast 1960s)
Etude pour monument
Sp:317x89x89:Presented by the Lipchitz Foundation 1982

T03515 David and Goliath (1933, cast 1963)
David et Goliath
Sp:279x279x152:Presented by the Lipchitz Foundation 1982

T03516 Jacob and the Angel (1931, cast 1960s)
La Lutte de Jacob avec l'ange
Sp:247x349x184:signed:Presented by the Lipchitz Foundation 1982

T03517 First Study for Prometheus (1931, cast 1960s)
Etude pour 'Prométheé'
Sp:120x279x140:Presented by the Lipchitz Foundation 1982

T03518 Musical Instruments, Relief on a Stand (1923, cast 1960s)
Nature morte aux instruments de musique
Sp:248x203x57:Presented by the Lipchitz Foundation 1982

T03519 Hagar (1948)
Sp:152x184x108:Presented by the Lipchitz Foundation 1982

T03520 Reclining Woman (1921)
Femme allongée
Sp:76x108x38:Presented by the Lipchitz Foundation 1982

T03521 Woman Leaning on a Column (1929, cast 1960s)
Sp:254x133x89:Presented by the Lipchitz Foundation 1982

T03522 Dancer with Veil (1928)
Sp:174x79x70:signed:Presented by the Lipchitz Foundation 1982

T03523 Study for a Garden Statue (1921)
Sp:140x35x38:Presented by the Lipchitz Foundation 1982

T03524 Portrait of Annie Dalsace (circa 1921)
Portrait de Annie Dalsace
Sp:335x203x209:signed:Presented by the Lipchitz Foundation 1982

T03525 Sketch for Lower Part of 'Our Tree of Life' (1962)
Sp:558x177x228:Presented by the Lipchitz Foundation 1982

T03526 Musical Instruments, Standing Relief (1924)
Nature morte aux instruments de musique
Sp:388x482x95:Presented by the Lipchitz Foundation 1982

T03527 Variation on the Theme of Hagar (1948)
Sp:152x228x102:Presented by the Lipchitz Foundation 1982

T03528 Sketch for Duluth Monument (1963)
Sp:533x127x127:Presented by the Lipchitz Foundation 1982

T03529 Guitar Player in Armchair (1922)
Joueur de guitare assis
Sp:394x292x304:signed:Presented by the Lipchitz Foundation 1982

T03530 Mother and Child I (1949)
Mère et enfant I
Sp:483x285x254:Presented by the Lipchitz Foundation 1982

T03531 Dancer (1929, cast 1960s)
Danseuse
Sp:82x63x51:Presented by the Lipchitz Foundation 1982

T03532 Song of Songs (1946)
Le Cantique des cantiques
Sp:470x965x273:signed:Presented by the Lipchitz Foundation 1982

T03533 Study for a Monument (circa 1936, cast 1960s)
Etude pour monument
Sp:514x254x222:Presented by the Lipchitz Foundation 1982

T03534 Study for Hagar (1948)
Etude pour Hagar
Spm:241x222x203:signed:Presented by the Lipchitz Foundation 1982

T03535 Dancer (1929)
Danseuse
Sp:82x63x57:signed:Presented by the Lipchitz Foundation 1982

LISSITZKY, El 1890-1941
Modern Collection

Victory Over the Sun (P07137-P07147; complete group)
Sieg über die Sonne

P07137 [title page] (1923)
CLπ:510x440:signed:Purchased 1976

P07138 1. Part of the Show Machinery (1923)
Teil der Schaumaschinerie
CLπ:512x430:signed:Purchased 1976

P07139 2. The Announcer (1923)
Ansager
CLπ:510x428:signed:Purchased 1976

P07140 3. Postman (1923)
Briefträger
CLπ:510x430:signed:Purchased 1976

P07141 4. Anxious People (1923)
Ängstliche
CLπ:512x430:signed:Purchased 1976

P07142 5. Globetrotter (in Time) (1923)
Globetrotter (in der Zeit)
CLπ:510x430:signed:Purchased 1976

P07143 6. Sportsmen (1923)
Sportler
CLπ:510x430:signed:Purchased 1976

P07144 7. Troublemaker (1923)
Zankstifter
CLπ:512x428:signed:Purchased 1976

P07145 8. Old Man (Head 2 Steps behind) (1923)
Alter (Kopf 2 Schritte hinten)
CLπ:510x430:signed:Purchased 1976

P07146 9. Gravediggers (1923)
Totengräber
CLπ:510x431:signed:Purchased 1976

P07147 10. New Man (1923)
Neuer
CLπ:510x430:signed:Purchased 1976

LIVENS, Horace Mann 1862-1936
British Collection

T00326 Three Studies of a Child (circa 1900)
Pπ:305x292:Presented by Robert J. Smith 1960

T00327 Baby with Dummy (circa 1898)
Pπ:368x286:signed:Presented by Robert J. Smith 1960

T00328   Two Children Playing (circa 1902)
Pπ:368x286:signed:Presented by Robert J. Smith 1960

LLEWELLYN, Sir William 1858-1941
British Collection
Tate Gallery Archive holds material concerning this artist

N04960   Sailing at Blakeney (exhibited 1938)
Oc:635x762:signed:Presented by the Trustees of the
Chantrey Bequest 1938

LLOYD, James 1905-1974
Modern Collection
Tate Gallery Archive holds material concerning this artist

T01081   Cat and Mouse (1967)
Gb:381x533:signed:Presented by Eric Lister 1968

LOGAN, Peter born 1943
Modern Collection
Tate Gallery Archive holds material concerning this artist

T01244   Square Dance (1970)
AKm:2102x3600x3600:Presented by the Contemporary
Art Society 1970

LOGSDAIL, William 1859-1944
British Collection

N01621   St Martin-in-the-Fields (1888)
Oc:1435x1181:signed:Presented by the Trustees of the
Chantrey Bequest 1888

LOHSE, Richard Paul born 1902
Modern Collection
Tate Gallery Archive holds material concerning this artist

Untitled (P07666-P07671; complete group)
P07666   [no title] (1981)
CNπ:660x660:signed:Purchased 1982
P07667   [no title] (1981)
CNπ:660x660:signed:Purchased 1982
P07668   [no title] (1981)
CNπ:660x660:signed:Purchased 1982
P07669   [no title] (1981)
CNπ:660x660:signed:Purchased 1982
P07670   [no title] (1981)
CNπ:660x660:signed:Purchased 1982
P07671   [no title] (1981)
CNπ:660x660:signed:Purchased 1982

LOKER, John born 1938
Modern Collection

T02267   Four Shifts I (1977-8)
Ac:2134x1829:signed:Purchased 1978
P07258   Three Horizons II (1975)
CLπ:343x546:signed:Purchased 1979
P11007   Shifts (Gate) (1978)
CLπ:464x394:signed:Presented by E.J. Power through the
Friends of the Tate Gallery 1980

LOMBOS, Phillip Alexius Laszlo de - see
LASZLO de LOMBOS, Phillip Alexius

LONDON GALLERY, The - see GALLERY, LONDON, The

LONG, John St John 1798-1834
British Collection

T04169   The Temptation in the Wilderness (1824)
Ob:226x317:signed:Purchased 1986

LONG, Richard born 1945
Modern Collection
Tate Gallery Archive holds material concerning this artist

T01720   A Hundred Mile Walk (1971-2)
FDVb:216x483:Purchased 1973
T01783   Circle of Sticks (1973)
Sw:10x6706x6706:Purchased 1973
T02065   Untitled (1967)
DFVb:611x819:signed:Purchased 1976
T02066   Cerne Abbas Walk (1975)
2 FDV:724x737, 359x537:Purchased 1976
T02067   119 Stones (1976)
Ss:152x7010x5867:Purchased 1976
T02068   River Avon Driftwood (1976)
Sw::Purchased 1976
T03027   Slate Circle (1979)
Ss::Presented by Anthony d'Offay 1980
T03161   Two Straight Twelve Mile Walks on Dartmoor, England
1980 (1980)
Mπ:1022x1521:Purchased 1980
T03298   A Line in Bolivia - Kicked Stones (2 Versions) (1981)
2 Fb:1241x962, 883x1210:Purchased 1981
T03808   A Sculpture in Bristol (1965/83)
7 Fb, Dπ:276x276:signed:Purchased 1983
T05033   Ten Days Walking and Sleeping on Natural Ground
(1986)
3 Nwπ:1041x1533:Purchased 1988
P03132   Roisin Dubh - A Slow Air (1976)
CLπ:483x508:Presented by the Arts Council of Great
Britain 1976
P07082   Dartmoor Walks (1972)
MNLπ:584x489:signed:Purchased 1973
P07148   Turf Circle (1966)
MFπ:270x305:Purchased 1976
P07149   A Line Made by Walking (1967)
MFπ:375x324:Purchased 1976
P07150   Turf Sculpture (1967)
MFπ:229x229:Purchased 1976
P07151   England (1968)
MFπ:314x476:Purchased 1976
P11266   Waterlines (1989)
Nπ:1277x924:Presented by the King Edward's Hospital
Fund 1989
P77189   Africa Footprints (1986)
Lπ:1006x715:signed:Purchased 1987

LONGO, Robert born 1953
Modern Collection
Tate Gallery Archive holds material concerning this artist

T03782   Sword of the Pig (1983)
3 RV:2480x5880x510:Presented by the Patrons of New
Art through the Friends of the Tate Gallery 1983
P07899   Jules, Gretchen, Mark, State II (1982-3)
MLπ:762x1340:signed:Purchased 1983

LORIMER, John Henry 1856-1936
British Collection

N04540 Sir Robert Lorimer, A.R.A., as a Boy (1875)
Oc:546x381:signed:Presented by the Trustees of the
Chantrey Bequest 1930

LOUIS, Morris 1912-1962
Modern Collection

T00803 Partition (1962)
Ac:2597x445:signed:Presented by Leslie Waddington 1966

T01057 VAV (1960)
Ac:2603x3594:Presented by Mr and Mrs H.J. Heinz II
1968

T01058 Alpha-Phi (1961)
Ac:2591x4951:Presented by Mrs Marcella Lois Brenner,
the artist's widow, through the American Federation of
Arts 1968

LOUTHERBOURG, Philip James de - see DE LOUTHERBOURG, Philip James

LOUW, Roelof born 1936
Modern Collection
Tate Gallery Archive holds material concerning this artist

T01250 Untitled (1968)
SOm:991x5334x5334:Purchased 1970

LOW, Sir David 1891-1963
Modern Collection

N04331 London's New Traffic Problem (1925)
Dπ:273x279:signed:Bequeathed by J.R. Holliday 1927

N05463 The Angels of Peace Descend on Belgium (1940)
Dπ:387x495:signed:Presented by the artist and the
Evening Standard 1944

N05464 Dick Sheppard and Aldous Huxley (1938)
Dπ:419x610:signed:Presented by the artist 1944

N05670 Look Out, Brutus! Caesar is Going to Unseal his Lips!
(1936)
Dπ:368x552:signed:Presented by the artist 1946

LOWE, Peter born 1938
Modern Collection
Tate Gallery Archive holds material concerning this artist

P07427 Rational Concepts (1977)
MNπ:597x597:signed:Purchased 1981

LOWINSKY, Thomas 1892-1947
Modern Collection

N05226 The Dawn of Venus (1922)
Tc:775x724:signed:Purchased 1940

N05322 The Breeze at Morn (1930)
Tc:438x914:signed:Presented by the Contemporary Art
Society 1942

N05329 Mrs James Mackie (1935)
Tc:571x445:signed:Presented by the Trustees of the
Chantrey Bequest 1939

LOWNDES, Alan 1921-1978
Modern Collection
Tate Gallery Archive holds material concerning this artist

P06334 Dartsman Organ Grinder (1972)
MLπ:505x657:signed:Presented by Curwen Studio
through the Institute of Contemporary Prints 1975

P06335 The Doss House (1975)
CLπ:511x410:signed:Presented by Curwen Studio
through the Institute of Contemporary Prints 1975

P06336 The Pawnbroker (1975)
CLπ:495x413:signed:Presented by Curwen Studio
through the Institute of Contemporary Prints 1975

P06737 Stockport Viaduct (1973)
CLπ:410x502:signed:Presented by Curwen Studio 1977

LOWRY, L.S. 1887-1976
Modern Collection
Tate Gallery Archive holds material concerning this artist

N05003 Dwelling, Ordsall Lane, Salford (1927)
Ow:432x533:signed:Purchased 1939

N05912 Coming Out of School (1927)
Ow:347x539:signed:Presented by the Trustees of the
Duveen Paintings Fund 1949

N05992 The Old House, Grove Street, Salford (1948)
Oc:457x610:signed:Purchased 1951

N06027 Study for 'Dwellings, Ordsall Lane, Salford' (1927)
Dπ:283x394:signed:Presented by the artist 1951

N06032 The Pond (1950)
Oc:1143x1524:signed:Presented by the Trustees of the
Chantrey Bequest 1951

T00111 Industrial Landscape (1955)
Oc:1143x1524:signed:Presented by the Trustees of the
Chantrey Bequest 1956

T00142 A Young Man (1955)
Oc:508x610:signed:Purchased 1957

T00591 Hillside in Wales (1962)
Oc:762x1016:signed:Presented by the Trustees of the
Chantrey Bequest 1963

School Prints (P01698-P01727; complete group; mixed
group)

P01712 Punch and Judy (1946-9)
CLπ:495x762:Presented by Patrick Seale Prints 1975

P03267 Bloomsbury Square (1967-8)
MLπ:473x606:signed:Presented by Ganymed Press 1979

P03268 A Hillside (1967-8)
MLπ:473x610:signed:Presented by Ganymed Press 1979

P03269 Seaside Promenade (1967-8)
MLπ:473x610:signed:Presented by Ganymed Press 1979

P03270 Shapes & Sizes (1967-8)
MLπ:476x606:signed:Presented by Ganymed Press 1979

P03271 Sunday Afternoon (1969)
MLπ:476x610:signed:Presented by Ganymed Press 1979

P03272 Tree in a Square (1969)
MLπ:476x610:signed:Presented by Ganymed Press 1979

P03273 Castle on the Sands (1969-70)
MLπ:476x610:signed:Presented by Ganymed Press 1979

P03274 A Northern Town (1969-70)
MLπ:476x610:signed:Presented by Ganymed Press 1979

P03275 Old Steps, Stockport (1969-70)
MLπ:619x483:signed:Presented by Ganymed Press 1979

P03276 The Three Cats, Alstow (1969-70)
MLπ:616x486:signed:Presented by Ganymed Press 1979

P03277 Francis Terrace, Salford (1969-72)
        MLπ:483x616:signed:Presented by Ganymed Press 1979
P03278 The Pavilion (1969-72)
        MLπ:483x619:signed:Presented by Ganymed Press 1979
P03279 The Viaduct, Stockport (1969-72)
        MLπ:483x616:signed:Presented by Ganymed Press 1979
P03280 Winter in Broughton (1969-72)
        MLπ:479x619:signed:Presented by Ganymed Press 1979

LOZOFF, Abrasha 1887-1936
Modern Collection

T00255 Venus and Adonis (circa 1925-30)
        Sw:1118x838x495:Purchased 1959

LUCAS, David - see CONSTABLE, John and LUCAS, David

LUCAS, John Seymour 1849-1923
British Collection
Tate Gallery Archive holds material concerning this artist

N01620 After Culloden, Rebel Hunting (1884)
        Oc:1426x1962:signed:Presented by the Trustees of the
        Chantrey Bequest 1884

LUCY and EEGYUDLUK born circa 1918, born circa 1930
Modern Collection

T00467 The Green Bear (1961)
        Rs:470x876x168:Presented by Charles Gimpel 1961
P01892 Large Bear (1961)
        MLπ:368x549:Presented by Mr and Mrs James Houston
        1961

LUNDQUIST, Evert born 1904
Modern Collection

T00208 Woman in Red (1956-7)
        Oc:1000x902:Purchased 1958

MACALLUM, Hamilton 1841-1896
British Collection

N01502 The Crofter's Team (1896)
Oc:902x1689:signed:Presented by E. Homan 1897

N01714 Gathering Seaweed (1878)
Wπ:343x419:signed:Presented by E. Homan 1897

N01715 A Capri Boy (1883)
Wπ:343x445:signed:Presented by E. Homan 1897

MACBETH, Robert Walker 1848-1910
British Collection
Tate Gallery Archive holds material concerning this artist

N01597 The Cast Shoe (1890)
Oc:832x1372:signed:Presented by the Trustees of the
Chantrey Bequest 1890

MacBRYDE, Robert 1913-1966
Modern Collection
Tate Gallery Archive holds material concerning this artist

T00207 Woman with Paper Flowers (1944)
Oc:533x705:signed:Purchased 1958

T00907 Performing Clown (1946)
Oc:533x705:signed:Presented by the Trustees of the
Chantrey Bequest 1967

P06343 Still Life I (1960)
CLπ:505x349:Presented by Curwen Studio through the
Institute of Contemporary Prints 1975

P06344 Still Life II (1960)
CLπ:613x505:Presented by Curwen Studio through the
Institute of Contemporary Prints 1975

McCALL, Anthony - see INTERNATIONAL LOCAL

MACCALLUM, Andrew 1821-1902
British Collection

N01677 Silvery Moments, Burnham Beeches (1885)
Oc:908x1213:signed:Presented by the artist 1899

N01724 The Monarch of the Glen
Wπ:914x660:signed:Presented by the artist 1899

MACCARI, Mino born 1898
Modern Collection

P08034 Giorgio Morandi (1975)
MIπ:143x127:signed:Transferred from the Library 1978

McCARTNEY, Linda born 1941
Modern Collection

Linda's Pictures (P05441-P05454; complete group)
P05441 Mick Jagger (1977)
CNπ:492x333:signed:Presented by Rose and Chris Prater
1978

P05442 Brian Jones (1977)
CNπ:440x334:signed:Presented by Rose and Chris Prater
1978

P05443 Grace Slick (1977)
CNπ:439x332:signed:Presented by Rose and Chris Prater
1978

P05444 B.B. King (1977)
CNπ:494x333:signed:Presented by Rose and Chris Prater
1978

P05445 Pete Townshend (1977)
CNπ:460x332:signed:Presented by Rose and Chris Prater
1978

P05446 Cups at EMI Studios (1977)
CNπ:493x333:signed:Presented by Rose and Chris Prater
1978

P05447 Brysi Barbados (1977)
CNπ:492x335:signed:Presented by Rose and Chris Prater
1978

P05448 Jimi Hendrix Blue (1977)
CNπ:452x333:signed:Presented by Rose and Chris Prater
1978

P05449 Wrecked Car (1977)
CNπ:486x332:signed:Presented by Rose and Chris Prater
1978

P05450 David Bowie (1977)
CNπ:340x333:signed:Presented by Rose and Chris Prater
1978

P05451 Painted Toenails (1977)
CNπ:333x490:signed:Presented by Rose and Chris Prater
1978

P05452 Mary, Scotland (1977)
CNπ:446x333:signed:Presented by Rose and Chris Prater
1978

P05453 Cinnamon (1977)
CNπ:490x333:signed:Presented by Rose and Chris Prater
1978

P05454 McCartney (1977)
CNπ:480x333:signed:Presented by Rose and Chris Prater
1978

MACCOLL, Dugald Sutherland 1859-1948
British Collection
Tate Gallery Archive holds material concerning this artist

N03149 Dieppe (1899)
WDπ:140x190:signed:Bequeathed by A.N. MacNicholl
1915

N03322 A Belfry at Dinan (exhibited 1906)
WDπ:302x229:signed:Presented by Viscount Bearsted
through the National Art Collections Fund 1918

N03413 Brasenose College, Oxford (?exhibited 1909)
WDπ:235x302:signed:Presented by Geoffrey Blackwell
1919

N03522 Wilmington Barn (1917)
WDb:248x346:signed:Presented by Geoffrey Blackwell
1919

N04508 St Catherine's Quay, Honfleur (exhibited 1906)
WDπ:229x305:signed:Purchased 1930

N05103 Crock and Cottage Loaf No. 2 (exhibited 1931)
Oc:356x279:signed:Presented by the Trustees of the
Chantrey Bequest 1940

McCOMB, Leonard born 1930
Modern Collection
Tate Gallery Archive holds material concerning this artist

T02081 Portrait of Mrs Lilian Kennett (1976)
DWπ:810x549:signed:Purchased 1976

T03601 Portrait of Zarrin Kashi Overlooking Whitechapel High
Street (1981)
WDc:1840x1885:signed:Presented by the Trustees of the
Chantrey Bequest 1983

Blossoms and Flowers (P07501-P07506; complete group)

P07501 Snowdrops (1975-9)
CLπ::Purchased 1981

P07502 Tulips (1975-9)
CLπ:324x254:Purchased 1981

P07503 Rhododendrons (1975-9)
CLπ:400x282:Purchased 1981

P07504 Roses (1975-9)
CLπ:545x314:Purchased 1981

P07505 Apple Blossom I (1975-9)
CLπ:445x349:Purchased 1981

P07506 Apple Blossom II (1975-9)
CLπ:445x346:Purchased 1981

P77233 Jenny Scott (1986)
Mπ:605x475:signed:Purchased 1988

P77234 Rachael House (1987)
Mπ:608x481:signed:Purchased 1988

MACDONALD, Frances born 1914
Modern Collection
Tate Gallery Archive holds material concerning this artist

N05705 Building the Mulberry Harbour, London Docks (1944)
Oc:559x1219:signed:Presented by the War Artists'
Advisory Committee 1946

P06345 Iffley Church (1970-1)
CLπ:394x559:Presented by Curwen Studio through the
Institute of Contemporary Prints 1975

MACDONALD, Georgina (Lady Burne-Jones) 1840-1920
British Collection

N04941 Dead Bird (1857)
Wπ:89x171:Presented by Mrs J.W. Mackail 1938

McEVOY, Ambrose 1878-1927
British Collection
Tate Gallery Archive holds material concerning this artist

N02999 W.A. Jowitt, later Earl Jowitt (1912)
Oc:1283x1022:signed:Presented by Francis Howard
through the National Loans Exhibition Committee 1914

N03175 In a Mirror (exhibited 1911)
WDπ:470x387:Presented by the Contemporary Art
Society 1917

N03176 The Ear-Ring (exhibited 1911)
Oc:762x635:signed:Presented by C.L. Rutherston 1917

N04200 Mrs Claude Johnson (exhibited 1926)
Oc:1016x768:signed:Presented by Mrs C. Johnson in
memory of Claude Johnson 1926

N04230 The Searchlight Tattoo, Wembley (1925)
Oc:762x1270:Presented by the Department of Overseas
Trade 1927

N04447 Euphemia (1909)
Oc:730x483:Purchased 1929

N04476 Michael McEvoy (exhibited 1919)
Oc:762x635:Presented by the Trustees of the Chantrey
Bequest 1929

N04496 The Ferry (1909)
Oc:794x578:Purchased 1930

N04554 A Young Girl
WDπ:559x387:Presented by the artist's widow 1930

N04813 The Hon. Mrs Cecil Baring (circa 1917)
Oc:1270x1022:Presented by the artist's widow 1935

N05217 Two Ballet Dancers with Dresser (circa 1913)
Wπ:483x521:Presented by Francis Howard 1940

N05611 Mother and Son (circa 1910)
Oc:305x232:Purchased 1945

N05832 Self-Portrait (1900)
Dπ:184x127:signed:Presented by Mrs Alan Bazell, the
artist's daughter 1948

N06080 Bessborough Street, Pimlico (1900)
Oc:457x356:Presented by Mrs C. Johnson 1952

N06081 The Artist's Wife (?exhibited 1913)
WDπ:359x254:Presented by Mrs C. Johnson 1952

McEVOY, Mary 1870-1941
British Collection
Tate Gallery Archive holds material concerning this artist

N04362 Interior: Girl Reading (1901)
Oc:533x438:signed:Purchased 1927

McEWEN, Rory 1932-1982
Modern Collection

P04583 Untitled (1969)
CNπ:416x416:signed:Presented by Rose and Chris Prater
through the Institute of Contemporary Prints 1975

P04584 Untitled (1969)
CNπ:305x305:signed:Presented by Rose and Chris Prater
through the Institute of Contemporary Prints 1975

McFALL, David B. 1919-1988
Modern Collection

N05443 Bull Calf (1942-3)
Ss:476x648x565:Presented by the Trustees of the
Chantrey Bequest 1943

MACGREGOR, William York 1855-1923
British Collection

N04201 The Carse of Stirling
Oc:479x610:signed:Purchased 1927

MACH, David born 1956
Modern Collection

T04858 Thinking of England (1983)
Sv:200x1680x2330:Presented by the Contemporary Art
Society 1986

MACHIN, Arnold born 1911
Modern Collection

N05444 St John the Baptist (circa 1944)
Sp:521x311x292:Purchased 1944

N05445 The Annunciation (Two Figures) (circa 1944)
2 Sp:508x286x159, 394x235x156:Purchased 1944

N05773 Spring (exhibited 1947)
Sp:1435x1048x540:Presented by the Trustees of the
Chantrey Bequest 1947

MACK, Heinz born 1931
Modern Collection

T00683 Light Dynamo (1963)
KVWπ:578x571x165:signed:Purchased 1964

T03748 Relief (1964)
Rmb:365x415x40:Transferred from the Victoria & Albert
Museum 1983

MACKAY, Alex
Modern Collection
Tate Gallery Archive holds material concerning this artist

P06738 Two Bird Studies (1976)
MLπ:597x765:signed:Presented by Curwen Studio 1977

McKENNA, Stephen born 1939
Modern Collection

T03540 An English Oak Tree (1981)
Oc:2000x1500:signed:Purchased 1982

T03541 Venus and Adonis (1981)
Oc:1500x2000:signed:Purchased 1982

P77282 Monument for a Fisherman (1988)
Lπ:367x502:Purchased 1989

MACKENNAL, Sir Bertram 1863-1931
British Collection

N02140 The Earth and the Elements (exhibited 1907)
Ss:635x318x318:signed:Presented by the Trustees of the
Chantrey Bequest 1907

N02266 Diana Wounded (circa 1907)
Ss:1473x819x622:signed:Presented by the Trustees of the
Chantrey Bequest 1908

MACKENZIE, Alix 1922-1962
Modern Collection
Tate Gallery Archive holds material concerning this artist

P11096 Gull on Porch (1951)
CDNπ:203x164:signed:Presented by Warren MacKenzie
1986

P11097 Child and Bird (1951)
GCNπ:145x124:Presented by Warren MacKenzie 1986

P11098 Cornish Fields (1951)
CNπ:153x193:Presented by Warren MacKenzie 1986

MACKENZIE, Alexander born 1923
Modern Collection
Tate Gallery Archive holds material concerning this artist

T02240 Drawing, June 1963 (1963)
DPπ:537x645:Bequeathed by Miss E.M. Hodgkins 1977

MACKENZIE, Frederick 1787-1854
British Collection

T03034 The South Ambulatory, Westminster Abbey (1811)
Wπ:784x616:signed:Bequeathed by Leonard James
Penna 1980

MACKENZIE, Warren born 1924
Modern Collection
Tate Gallery Archive holds material concerning this artist

P02942 Untitled (1951)
CNπ:152x191:signed:Presented by the artist 1986

P02943 Untitled (1951)
CNπ:307x146:signed:Presented by the artist 1986

P02944 Untitled (1951)
CNπ:378x210:signed:Presented by the artist 1986

McKINNON, Michael born 1940
Modern Collection

Fibonacci Portfolio (P01887-P01890; complete group)
P01887 Arabian Reel (1976)
Cπ:635x825:signed:Presented by Editions Alecto 1979

P01888 Fibonacci's Garden (1976)
Cπ:635x825:signed:Presented by Editions Alecto 1979

P01889 Phyllotaxis (1976)
Cπ:635x825:signed:Presented by Editions Alecto 1979

P01890 Spiral Prism (1976)
Cπ:635x825:signed:Presented by Editions Alecto 1979

MACKINNON, Sine born 1901
Modern Collection

N05135 Farm Buildings in Provence (1934)
Oc:270x410:Purchased 1940

MACKINTOSH, Charles Rennie 1868-1928
British Collection

N04438 Fetges (circa 1927)
Wπ:464x457:signed:Presented by Walter W. Blackie 1929

MCLACHLAN, Thomas Hope 1845-1897
British Collection

N01656 Evening Quiet (1891)
Oc:584x870:signed:Presented by subscribers 1898

MACLAREN, Donald 1886-1917
Modern Collection

N05778 D.S. MacColl (circa 1906)
Oc:536x340:Presented by D.S. MacColl 1947

McLEAN, Bruce born 1944
Modern Collection
Tate Gallery Archive holds material concerning this artist

T01738 150ft Seaskape, Largiebeg (1969)
Fb:505x787:Purchased 1973

T01739 2 Rock and Shoreskapes, Largiebeg (1969)
Fb:505x787:Purchased 1973

T01740 Six Sculptures (1967-8)
Fb:505x787:Purchased 1973

T03273 Pose Work for Plinths I (1971)
Fb:746x686:Purchased 1981

T03274 Pose Work for Plinths 3 (1971)
Fb:749x683:Purchased 1981

T03275 Study towards the Object of the Exercise (1978)
ADπ:1362x1575:Purchased 1981

T03411 Study for 'Possibly a Nude by a Coal Bunker' (1980)
5 OAFπ:4000x1387:Purchased 1982

P01950 Their Grassy Places (1969)
MFπ:819x914:Presented by the Contemporary Art
Society 1979

P11267 Hot Slick (1989)
Nπ:1012x1274:Presented by the King Edward's Hospital
Fund 1989

P77055 Large Warhead (1984)
CNπ:881x1241:signed:Purchased 1984

P77123 Untitled (1985)
CJπ:806x1175:signed:Purchased 1985

McLEAN, Bruce and WARD, David born 1944, born 1951
Modern Collection
Tate Gallery Archive holds material concerning these artists

T05496 Song for the North (1987)
4 Fπ:1880x1220:Purchased 1988

McLEAN, John born 1939
Modern Collection
Tate Gallery Archive holds material concerning this artist

T05003 Opening (1987)
Ac:750x2285:signed:Purchased 1987

MACLISE, Daniel 1806-1870
British Collection
Tate Gallery Archive holds material concerning this artist

N00422 The Play Scene in 'Hamlet' (exhibited 1842)
Oc:1524x2743:Presented by Robert Vernon 1847

N00423 Malvolio and the Countess (exhibited 1840)
Oc:737x1245:Presented by Robert Vernon 1847

N01250 Charles Dickens (1839)
Oc:870x686:signed:Bequeathed by Rev. Sir Edward R.
Jodrell Bt 1888

McMILLAN, William 1887-1977
Modern Collection

N04602 The Birth of Venus (exhibited 1931)
Ss:1289x533x356:Presented by the Trustees of the
Chantrey Bequest 1931

McTAGGART, William 1835-1910
British Collection
Tate Gallery Archive holds material concerning this artist

N04610 The Emigrants (1883-9)
Oc:946x1410:signed:Purchased 1931

N04701 The Harvest Moon (circa 1899)
Oc:1321x1959:signed:Presented by the Trustees of the
Chantrey Bequest 1933

N06044 Summer Sundown - Tir-nan-og (1880)
Oc:610x914:signed:Bequeathed by Sir James and Lady
Caw 1951

MACTAGGART, Sir William 1903-1981
Modern Collection

T00360 Duet (1958)
Ob:610x1010:signed:Presented by the Trustees of the
Chantrey Bequest 1960

MACWHIRTER, John 1839-1911
British Collection
Tate Gallery Archive holds material concerning this artist

N01571 June in the Austrian Tyrol (exhibited 1892)
Oc:1238x1854:signed:Presented by the Trustees of the
Chantrey Bequest 1892

McWILLIAM, F.E. born 1909
Modern Collection
Tate Gallery Archive holds material concerning this artist

N06164 Cain and Abel (1952)
Sm:460x391:Purchased 1953

T00120 William Scott (1956)
Sz:667x464x273:signed:Purchased 1957

T00121 Mary Scott (1956)
Sz:648x470x267:signed:Purchased 1957

T00407 Pentachord (1959)
Sz:1010x457x127:Purchased 1961

T00599 Profile (1940)
Sw:622x178:Purchased 1963

T00871 Eye, Nose and Cheek (1939)
Ss:889x870x286:Purchased 1966

T03758 Mother and Daughter (1951)
Swam:320x380x120:Transferred from the Victoria &
Albert Museum 1983

Penwith Portfolio (P01416, P06005, P06108, P06130,
P06241, P06324, P06346, P06359, P06399, P06519,
P06700; complete group; mixed group)
P06346 Women of Belfast (1973)
CLπ:460x581:signed:Presented by Curwen Studio
through the Institute of Contemporary Prints 1975

MADDOX, Conroy born 1912
Modern Collection
Tate Gallery Archive holds material concerning this artist

T00640 Winter Criminal Term (1963)
GVπ:381x533:signed:Presented by Miss Pauline Drayson
1964

T01472 The Strange Country (1940)
VWπ:406x279:signed:Purchased 1971

T03052 Passage de l'Opéra (1940)
Oc:1372x940:signed:Purchased 1980

MADDOX, Ronald born 1930
Modern Collection

P06347 The Mansion House, City of London (1974)
MLπ:203x435:signed:Presented by Curwen Studio
through the Institute of Contemporary Prints 1975

P06348 Royal Festival Hall, Queen Elizabeth Hall and Purcell
Room (1974)
MLπ:194x454:Presented by Curwen Studio through the
Institute of Contemporary Prints 1975

P06349 Royal Naval College and Queen's House, Greenwich
(1974)
MLπ:213x454:signed:Presented by Curwen Studio
through the Institute of Contemporary Prints 1975

MAGRITTE, René 1898-1967
Modern Collection
Tate Gallery Archive holds material concerning this artist

T00680 Man with a Newspaper (1928)
L'Homme au journal
Oc:1156x813:signed:Presented by the Friends of the Tate
Gallery 1964

T00892 The Spirit of Geometry (1937)
L'Esprit de géométrie
Gπ:375x292:signed:Presented by the Hon. Ivor Montagu
1966

T01122 The Reckless Sleeper (1928)
Le Dormeur téméraire
Oc:1156x813:signed:Purchased 1969

T03258 The Future of Statues (1937)
L'Avenir des statues
ROp:330x165x203:signed:Purchased 1981

T04367 The Annunciation (1930)
L'Annonciation
Oc:1137x1459:signed:Purchased with assistance from the
Friends of the Tate Gallery 1986

MAHONEY, Charles 1903-1968
Modern Collection
Tate Gallery Archive holds material concerning this artist

N05227 Outhouses (circa 1940)
Oc:305x356:Purchased 1940

N05323 Adam and Eve in the Garden of Eden (exhibited 1936)
Oc:914x762:Presented by the Contemporary Art Society
1942

T02091 Study for 'Adam and Eve' (circa 1936)
WDπ:403x270:signed:Presented by the artist's widow
1976

MAILLOL, Aristide 1861-1944
Modern Collection
Tate Gallery Archive holds material concerning this artist

N04415 Torso of the Monument to Blanqui (1905)
Torse du Monument à Blanqui
Sm:1206x692x527:Purchased 1928

N04576 Venus with a Necklace (circa 1918-28, cast 1930)
Vénus au collier
Sz:1753x610x400:signed:Presented by the Contemporary
Art Society 1931

N05022 The Three Nymphs (1930-8, cast 1937-8)
Les Trois nymphes
Sm:1575x1467x806:signed:Presented by the National Art
Collections Fund 1939

T03757 Large Bather with Raised Arms (circa 1898)
Grande Baigneuse aux bras levés
Sz:264x112x112:signed:Transferred from the Victoria &
Albert Museum 1983

MAISTRE, Roy de - see DE MAISTRE, Roy

MAITEC, Ovidiu born 1925
Modern Collection

T03850 Angels (1971)
Sw:940x880x193:Presented by Jim Ede 1984

MAITIN, Sam born 1928
Modern Collection

P06350 After California (1968)
CLπ::signed:Presented by Curwen Studio through the
Institute of Contemporary Prints 1975

P06351 Again and Now (1968)
CLπ::signed:Presented by Curwen Studio through the
Institute of Contemporary Prints 1975

P06352 Couplets (1968)
CLπ::signed:Presented by Curwen Studio through the
Institute of Contemporary Prints 1975

P06353 For Ollie (1968)
CLπ::signed:Presented by Curwen Studio through the
Institute of Contemporary Prints 1975

P06354 Go and be Gay (1968)
CLπ::signed:Presented by Curwen Studio through the
Institute of Contemporary Prints 1975

P06355 I Have Found It (1968)
CLπ::signed:Presented by Curwen Studio through the
Institute of Contemporary Prints 1975

P06356 Thus Have the Starlings (1968)
CLπ::signed:Presented by Curwen Studio through the
Institute of Contemporary Prints 1975

MAITLAND, Paul 1863-1909
British Collection
Tate Gallery Archive holds material concerning this artist

N03622 Cheyne Walk: The Corner of Beaufort Street
Ow:222x216:signed:Purchased 1922

N04398 Kensington Gardens: Vicinity of the Pond (?1907)
Oc:254x454:signed:Presented by Cyril Andrade 1928

N05879 Barges, Chelsea Riverside, the 'Eighties (?circa 1885-90)
Ow:277x321:signed:Purchased 1948

T03622 Hyacinth (circa 1883)
Oc:305x250:signed:Presented anonymously in memory of
Sir Terence Rattigan 1983

T03623 Factories Bordering the River (circa 1886)
Oc:257x370:signed:Presented anonymously in memory of
Sir Terence Rattigan 1983

T03624 The Sun Pier, Chatham (circa 1897)
Ow:246x272:signed:Presented anonymously in memory of
Sir Terence Rattigan 1983

T03625 The Gardens, Chelsea Embankment (circa 1889)
Ow:280x265:Presented anonymously in memory of Sir
Terence Rattigan 1983

T03626 Surrey Side of the River - Grey Day (circa 1886)
Ow:107x208:signed:Presented anonymously in memory of
Sir Terence Rattigan 1983

T03627 Riverside Industries (circa 1889)
Ow:137x235:signed:Presented anonymously in memory of
Sir Terence Rattigan 1983

T03628 Warehouse Across the River (circa 1886)
Ow:108x152:signed:Presented anonymously in memory of
Sir Terence Rattigan 1983

T03629 Battersea Boat Houses (circa 1888)
Ow:165x130:signed:Presented anonymously in memory of
Sir Terence Rattigan 1983

T03630 By Hyde Park Gate, Kensington Gardens (circa 1906)
Ow:99x180:signed:Presented anonymously in memory of
Sir Terence Rattigan 1983

T03631 Fall of the Leaves, Kensington Gardens (circa 1900)
Ow:136x206:signed:Presented anonymously in memory of
Sir Terence Rattigan 1983

T03632 Autumn, Kensington Gardens (circa 1906)
Ow:102x173:signed:Presented anonymously in memory of
Sir Terence Rattigan 1983

T03633 The Flower Walk, Kensington Gardens (circa 1897)
Ow:128x178:signed:Presented anonymously in memory of
Sir Terence Rattigan 1983

T03634 Kensington Gardens with Chairs and Figures (circa 1907)
Ow:108x175:signed:Presented anonymously in memory of
Sir Terence Rattigan 1983

T03635 The Embankment after a Shower (circa 1888)
Ow:136x220:signed:Presented anonymously in memory of
Sir Terence Rattigan 1983

T03636 In Buckinghamshire (circa 1890)
Ow:146x240:signed:Presented anonymously in memory of
Sir Terence Rattigan 1983

T03637 A Yacht off Sheerness (circa 1896)
Ow:235x137:signed:Presented anonymously in memory of
Sir Terence Rattigan 1983

T03647 The Three Public-Houses, Morning Sun Light (circa
1889)
Oc:760x705:Presented anonymously in memory of Sir
Terence Rattigan 1983

MAKOWSKI, Kazimierz born 1951
Modern Collection

P11085 Defence of the Environment (1983)
Ochrona Srodowiska
MLπ:483x755:signed:Presented by Professor Akumal
Ramachander 1985

P11086 Defence of the Environment (1983)
Ochrona Srodowiska
MLπ:482x766:signed:Presented by Professor Akumal
Ramachander 1985

MALEVICH, Kasimir 1878-1935
Modern Collection

T02319 Dynamic Suprematism (1915 or 1916)
Supremus
Oc:803x800:signed:Purchased with assistance from the
Friends of the Tate Gallery 1978

MALTHOUSE, Eric born 1928
Modern Collection
Tate Gallery Archive holds material concerning this artist

P03093 Midsummer (1967-8)
CNπ:3048x6096:Presented by the Welsh Arts Council
1975

MANBY, Thomas circa 1660-1690
British Collection

T05518 The Ruins of the Colosseum (circa 1660-90)
DWπ:382x279:Purchased 1988

MANCINI, Antonio 1852-1930
Modern Collection

N03687 Portrait of the Artist's Father (circa 1903-4)
Oc:997x597:signed:Presented by L.A. Harrison 1922

T00213 Self-Portrait (circa 1906)
Oπ:546x378:Purchased 1958

MANE-KATZ 1894-1962
Modern Collection

T00304 Orchestra (circa 1949)
Oc:540x651:signed:Presented by Mr and Mrs Alexander
Margulies 1959

MANESSIER, Alfred born 1911
Modern Collection

T00260 -12 (1956)
Oc:1143x1460:Purchased 1959

P08223 Untitled
Lπ:325x500:Transferred from the Library 1989

P08224 Early Spring (1966)
Printemps précoce
Lπ:217x220:signed:Transferred from the Library 1989

MANET, Edouard 1832-1883
Modern Collection

N03295 Woman with a Cat (circa 1880)
La Femme au chat
Oc:921x730:Purchased 1918

MANGOLD, Robert born 1937
Modern Collection
Tate Gallery Archive holds material concerning this artist

Seven Aquatints (P07083-P07089; complete group)
P07083 [title not known] (1973)
CLπ:403x400:signed:Purchased 1974
P07084 [title not known] (1973)
CLπ:403x400:signed:Purchased 1974
P07085 [title not known] (1973)
CLπ:403x400:signed:Purchased 1974
P07086 [title not known] (1973)
CLπ:403x400:signed:Purchased 1974
P07087 [title not known] (1973)
CLπ:403x400:signed:Purchased 1974
P07088 [title not known] (1973)
CLπ:403x400:signed:Purchased 1974
P07089 [title not known] (1973)
CLπ:403x400:signed:Purchased 1974

MANN, Harrington 1864-1937
British Collection

N04887 The Fairy Tale (1902)
Oc:1022x1416:signed:Presented by Francis Howard and
the artist's executors 1937

MAN RAY 1890-1976
Modern Collection
Tate Gallery Archive holds material concerning this artist

T00324 Pisces (1938)
La Femme et son Poisson
Oc:600x730:Presented by William N. Copley 1960

P06459 Untitled I (1969)
CLNπ:581x445:signed:Presented by Curwen Studio
through the Institute of Contemporary Prints 1975

P06460 Untitled II (1969)
CLNπ:581x445:signed:Presented by Curwen Studio
through the Institute of Contemporary Prints 1975

P06461 Untitled III (1969)
CLNπ:581x445:signed:Presented by Curwen Studio
through the Institute of Contemporary Prints 1975

MANSON, James Bolivar 1879-1945
British Collection
Tate Gallery Archive holds material concerning this artist

N01355 Michaelmas Daisies (exhibited 1923)
Oc:610x508:signed:Presented by subscribers 1923

N04929 Self-Portrait (circa 1912)
Oc:508x397:signed:Presented by D.C. Finchman 1938

N05320 Pinks in a Vase (circa 1940)
Oc:508x406:Purchased 1942

MANZONI, Piero 1933-1963
Modern Collection
Tate Gallery Archive holds material concerning this artist

T01871 Achrome (1958)
Vc:1003x1003:signed:Purchased 1974

T01874 Line 4.90m, December 1959 (1959)
SDb:267x70x70:signed:Purchased 1974

T01875 Line 18.82m, September 1959 (1959)
SDb:222x63x63:signed:Purchased 1974

MANZU, Giacomo 1908-1991
Modern Collection

N05854 Cardinal (1947-8)
Cardinale
Sz:502x292x273:signed:Purchased 1948

N05967 Cardinal (1937)
Dπ:451x340:signed:Purchased 1950

N05968 Reclining Woman (1937)
Dπ:343x454:signed:Purchased 1950

N05969 Reclining Woman (1944)
DWπ:254x381:signed:Purchased 1950

N06169 Susanna (1942-52, cast 1953)
Sz:479x1727x527:signed:Purchased with assistance from
the Contemporary Art Society 1953

MARA, Tim born 1948
Modern Collection
Tate Gallery Archive holds material concerning this artist

P03134 Power Cuts Imminent (1975)
CNπ:772x768:Presented by Anderson O'Day 1976

MARAZ, Adriana born 1931
Modern Collection

P02551 Tyrants (1979)
Clπ:489x648:signed:Presented by the artist 1981

P07589 Sunyata (1978)
Mlπ:651x467:signed:Purchased 1981

MARCHAND, Jean 1883-1941
Modern Collection
Tate Gallery Archive holds material concerning this artist

N04417 Maternity (1921)
La Maternité
Oc:1470x978:signed:Presented by Sir Michael and Lady
Sadler through the National Art Collections Fund 1928

N05072 View in the Midi (1913)
Pays du Midi
Oc:730x603:signed:Bequeathed by Frank Hindley Smith
1940

N05101 Landscape at Vence (1927)
Oc:498x613:signed:Bequeathed by Lady Henry
Cavendish-Bentinck 1940

N06203 Angelina (1923)
Oc:1003x810:signed:Presented by Paul Maze 1953

MARCHANT, Paul born 1948
Modern Collection

P06772 Vhinpalashi (Afternoon Rag) (1976)
CLπ:635x508:Presented by Curwen Studio 1978

P06795 Bhupali (Midnight Rag) (1976)
CLπ:635x508:Presented by Curwen Studio 1978

P06796 Rag Vasant (Spring Time) (1978)
CLπ:775x571:Presented by Curwen Studio 1978

MARCOUSSIS, Louis 1878-1941
Modern Collection

N05989 Rain (1929)
Pluie
Oc:610x457:signed:Purchased 1951

T00244 Interior with a Double Bass (1929)
Intérieur à la contrebasse
Oc:495x606:Purchased 1959

MARDEN, Brice born 1938
Modern Collection
Tate Gallery Archive holds material concerning this artist

T04938 I (1986)
Dπ:470x1005:signed:Purchased 1987

T05723 Couplet III (1988-9)
Oc:2740x1520:Purchased with assistance from an
anonymous donor 1990

Five Plates (P01739-P01743; complete group)
P01739 Untitled (a) (1973)
Mlπ:705x508:signed:Presented by the Contemporary Art
Society 1975

P01740 Untitled (b) (1973)
Mlπ:705x508:signed:Presented by the Contemporary Art
Society 1975

P01741 Untitled (c) (1973)
Mlπ:705x508:signed:Presented by the Contemporary Art
Society 1975

P01742 Untitled (d) (1973)
Mlπ:705x508:signed:Presented by the Contemporary Art
Society 1975

P01743 Untitled (e) (1973)
Mlπ:705x508:signed:Presented by the Contemporary Art
Society 1975

Tiles (P07849-P07852; complete group)
P07849 [title not known] (1979)
Mlπ:203x203:signed:Purchased 1983

P07850 [title not known] (1979)
Mlπ:203x203:signed:Purchased 1983

P07851 [title not known] (1979)
Mlπ:203x203:signed:Purchased 1983

P07852 [title not known] (1979)
Mlπ:203x203:signed:Purchased 1983

Etchings to Rexroth (P77208-P77232; complete group)
P77208 1 (1986)
Lπ:202x174:signed:Purchased 1987

P77209 2 (1986)
Lπ:203x174:signed:Purchased 1987

P77210 3 (1986)
Lπ:202x175:signed:Purchased 1987

P77211 4 (1986)
Lπ:202x174:signed:Purchased 1987

P77212 5 (1986)
Lπ:203x175:signed:Purchased 1987

P77213 6 (1986)
Lπ:202x174:signed:Purchased 1987

P77214 7 (1986)
Lπ:202x174:signed:Purchased 1987

P77215 8 (1986)
Lπ:202x175:signed:Purchased 1987

P77216 9 (1986)
Lπ:203x175:signed:Purchased 1987

P77217 10 (1986)
Lπ:201x173:signed:Purchased 1987

P77218 11 (1986)
Lπ:202x175:signed:Purchased 1987

P77219 12 (1986)
Lπ:202x174:signed:Purchased 1987

P77220 13 (1986)
        Lπ:202x174:signed:Purchased 1987
P77221 14 (1986)
        Lπ:202x174:signed:Purchased 1987
P77222 15 (1986)
        Lπ:202x174:signed:Purchased 1987
P77223 16 (1986)
        Lπ:201x173:signed:Purchased 1987
P77224 17 (1986)
        Lπ:202x175:signed:Purchased 1987
P77225 18 (1986)
        Lπ:203x175:signed:Purchased 1987
P77226 19 (1986)
        Lπ:202x175:signed:Purchased 1987
P77227 20 (1986)
        Lπ:200x177:signed:Purchased 1987
P77228 21 (1986)
        Lπ:202x175:signed:Purchased 1987
P77229 22 (1986)
        Lπ:202x175:signed:Purchased 1987
P77230 23 (1986)
        Lπ:200x177:signed:Purchased 1987
P77231 24 (1986)
        Lπ:202x175:signed:Purchased 1987
P77232 25 (1986)
        Lπ:202x175:signed:Purchased 1987

For Caroline (published 1989; P77336-P77347; complete group)

P77336 [no title] (1977)
        Lπ:251x353:Purchased 1989
P77337 [no title] (1977)
        Lπ:251x353:Purchased 1989
P77338 [no title] (1977)
        Lπ:251x353:Purchased 1989
P77339 [no title] (1977)
        Lπ:251x175:Purchased 1989
P77340 [no title] (1977)
        Lπ:251x175:Purchased 1989
P77341 [no title] (1977)
        Lπ:251x352:signed:Purchased 1989
P77342 [no title] (1977)
        Lπ:251x175:signed:Purchased 1989
P77343 [no title] (1977)
        Lπ:251x175:signed:Purchased 1989
P77344 [no title] (1977)
        Lπ:251x175:Purchased 1989
P77345 [no title] (1977)
        Lπ:251x175:signed:Purchased 1989
P77346 [no title] (1977)
        Lπ:251x175:signed:Purchased 1989
P77347 [no title] (1977)
        Lπ:251x175:signed:Purchased 1989

MARIANI, Carlo Maria born 1931
Modern Collection
Tate Gallery Archive holds material concerning this artist

P77029 Offspring of Helios (1982)
        MLπ:622x870:signed:Purchased 1984

MARIN, John 1870-1953
Modern Collection

T00080 Downtown, New York (1923)
        Wπ:679x552:signed:Purchased out of a sum of money
        made availsable from the Bruern Foundation 1956

MARINI, Marino 1901-1980
Modern Collection

N05970 Rider (1948)
        Il cavaliere
        DPπ:454x340:signed:Purchased 1950
N06009 Horseman (1947)
        Il cavaliere
        Sz:1638x1549x673:signed:Purchased 1951
T03157 Portrait Bust of Christian Faerber (circa 1952-3)
        Ritratto di Christian Faerber
        Sz:273x152x219:signed:Presented by Mrs Anna Maria
        Martha Faerber in loving memory of Christian Mario
        Balthasar Faerber 1980

MARKSON, Helena born 1934
Modern Collection
Tate Gallery Archive holds material concerning this artist

P06357 Tower of London (1968)
        CLπ:435x565:signed:Presented by Curwen Studio
        through the Institute of Contemporary Prints 1975

MARLOW, William 1740-1813
British Collection

N06213 Capriccio: St Paul's and a Venetian Canal (?circa 1795)
        Oc:1295x1041:signed:Purchased 1954
T00930 View on the Thames
        Oc:492x787:signed:Purchased 1967
T03602 A Post-House near Florence (circa 1770)
        WDπ:252x356:signed:Purchased 1983

MARSHALL, Benjamin 1768-1835
British Collection

N04825 The Rev. Edward Cage (1826)
        Oc:1003x851:signed:Purchased 1936
T02364 Emilius (?1824)
        Oc:1010x1264:signed:Presented by Paul Mellon through
        the British Sporting Art Trust 1979
T02365 Sir Charles Bunbury with Cox, his Trainer, and a
        Stable-Lad: A Study for 'Surprise and Eleanor' (?1801)
        Oc:470x638:Presented by Paul Mellon through the
        British Sporting Art Trust 1979
T03431 James Belcher, Bare-Knuckle Champion of England
        (?1803)
        Oc:905x702:Bequeathed by Mrs F. Ambrose Clark
        through the British Sporting Art Trust 1982
T03432 Interior of a Barn with a Milkmaid and Farm Labourer
        (circa 1820)
        Oc:876x1041:signed:Bequeathed by Mrs F. Ambrose
        Clark through the British Sporting Art Trust 1982
T03433 Portraits of Cattle of the Improved Short-Horned Breed,
        the Property of J. Wilkinson Esq. of Lenton, near
        Nottingham (1816)
        Oc:1015x1271:signed:Bequeathed by Mrs F. Ambrose
        Clark through the British Sporting Art Trust 1982

MARSHALL, William Calder 1813-1894
British Collection

N01748 The Prodigal Son (1881)
Ss:1245x660x711:signed:Presented by the Trustees of the Chantrey Bequest 1881

MARTIN, Agnes born 1912
Modern Collection
Tate Gallery Archive holds material concerning this artist

T01866 Morning (1965)
ADc:1826x1819:signed:Purchased 1974

MARTIN, Frank born 1921
Modern Collection

P01446 Louise Brooks (1974)
Clπ:371x273:signed:Presented by Christie's Contemporary Art through the Institute of Contemporary Prints 1975

P01447 Vilma Banky (1974)
Clπ:375x273:signed:Presented by Christie's Contemporary Art through the Institute of Contemporary Prints 1975

MARTIN, John 1789-1854
British Collection
Tate Gallery Archive holds material concerning this artist

N05435 The Fallen Angels Entering Pandemonium, from 'Paradise Lost', Book 1 (?exhibited 1841)
Oc:622x765:Purchased 1943

N05613 The Great Day of His Wrath (1851-3)
Oc:1965x3032:signed:Purchased 1945

N05753 The Coronation of Queen Victoria (1839)
Oc:2381x1854:signed:Purchased 1946

T01007 The Garden of Eden (1821)
Wπ:194x264:signed:Presented by the National Art Collections Fund (Herbert Powell Bequest) 1967

T01927 The Last Judgement (1853)
Oc:1968x3258:signed:Bequeathed by Charlotte Frank in memory of her husband Robert Frank 1974

T01928 The Plains of Heaven (1851-3)
Oc:1988x3067:signed:Bequeathed by Charlotte Frank in memory of her husband Robert Frank 1974

T04893 The Crucifixion (published 1834)
Lπ:460x721:Purchased 1987

T04894 Plate from 'Illustrations to the Bible': The Destruction of the Pharoah's Host (published 1833)
Lπ:188x282:Purchased 1987

T04895 Plate from 'Illustrations to the Bible': Moses Breaketh the Tables (published 1833)
Lπ:188x290:Purchased 1987

T04896 Plate from 'Illustrations to the Bible': Belshazzar's Feast (published 1835)
Lπ:190x290:Purchased 1987

T04897 Plate from 'Illustrations to the Bible': The Covenant (published 1832)
Lπ:190x290:Purchased 1987

MARTIN, Kenneth 1905-1984
Modern Collection
Tate Gallery Archive holds material concerning this artist

T00552 Small Screw Mobile (1953)
Sm:635x229:Purchased 1962

T00553 Oscillation (1962)
Szm:216x89x41:Purchased 1962

T00554 Spiral Construction (1961)
Szm:171x171x248:Purchased 1962

T00751 Seventeen Lines (1959-63)
Ob:1524x914:signed:Purchased 1965

T00752 Screw Mobile with Black Centre (circa 1958-65)
Szw:279x629x629:Purchased 1965

T01276 Rotary Rings (Fourth Version) (1968)
SKm:933x584x584:Purchased 1971

T01700 Drawing for a 'Screw Mobile' (1972)
Dπ:794x714:signed:Purchased 1972

T01758 Composition (1949)
Oc:508x410:signed:Purchased 1973

T01765 Linkage (1955)
Kwm:610x1613x343:Purchased 1973

T01847 Chance and Order Group VII, Drawing 6 (1971)
Dπ:343x229:Purchased 1974

T01848 Chance and Order Group VIII, Drawing 6 (1971)
Dπ:343x229:Purchased 1974

T01849 Chance and Order, Change 6 (Monastral Blue) (1972)
Oc:914x914:Purchased 1974

T03190 Chance, Order, Change 6 (Black) (1978-9)
Oc:911x911:Purchased 1980

T03191 Chance, Order, Change 12 (Four Colours) (1980)
Oc:914x911:signed:Purchased 1980

P04585 Chance and Order I (1971-2)
CNπ:686x686:signed:Presented by Rose and Chris Prater 1978

P04586 Chance and Order II (1971-2)
CNπ:686x686:signed:Presented by Rose and Chris Prater 1978

P04587 Chance and Order III (1971-2)
CNπ:686x686:signed:Presented by Rose and Chris Prater 1978

P04588 Chance and Order IV (1971-2)
CNπ:686x686:signed:Presented by Rose and Chris Prater 1978

P04589 Chance and Order V (1971-2)
CNπ:686x686:signed:Presented by Rose and Chris Prater 1978

P05377 Chance and Order VI (1976)
MNπ:705x705:signed:Presented by Rose and Chris Prater 1976

P05455 Rotation 'Frankfurt' I (1977)
CNπ:546x552:signed:Presented by Rose and Chris Prater 1978

P05456 Rotation 'Frankfurt' II (1977)
CNπ:546x552:signed:Presented by Rose and Chris Prater 1978

P05457 Rotation 'Frankfurt' III (1977)
CNπ:546x552:signed:Presented by Rose and Chris Prater 1978

P05458 Rotation 'Frankfurt' IV (1977)
CNπ:546x552:signed:Presented by Rose and Chris Prater 1978

P05475 Rotation 'Frankfurt', Key Drawing (1977)
MNπ:740x740:signed:Presented by Rose and Chris Prater 1978

P07428 Rational Concepts (1977)
MNπ:597x597:signed:Purchased 1981

P07742 Venice (1980)
CNπ:638x895:signed:Purchased 1982

P07743 Pier and Ocean (1980)
CNπ:638x895:signed:Purchased 1982

P77281 Abstract (circa 1950)
Nπ:505x758:Purchased 1989

MARTIN, Mary 1907-1969
Modern Collection
Tate Gallery Archive holds material concerning this artist

T00586 Spiral Movement (1951)
ORb:457x457x95:signed:Purchased 1963

T00645 Spiral (1963)
Rma:533x533x102:signed:Purchased 1964

T01198 Inversions (1966)
Rmow:1829x7315x279:Presented by the Friends of the
Tate Gallery 1970

T05026 Black Relief (1957)
Raw:764x1140x148:signed:Presented by the Friends of
the Tate Gallery 1987

MARTINEAU, Robert Braithwaite 1826-1869
British Collection
Tate Gallery Archive holds material concerning this artist

N01500 The Last Day in the Old Home (1862)
Oc:1073x1448:signed:Presented by E.H. Martineau 1896

N03626 Picciola (1853)
Oc:635x813:Presented by Miss Helen Martineau 1922

N05979 Study of a Man's Head for 'Picciola' (circa 1853)
Ob:197x292:Bequeathed by Miss Helen Martineau 1951

N05980 Study of a Woman
Dπ:343x267:Bequeathed by Miss Helen Martineau 1952

T00011 Kit's Writing Lesson (1852)
Oc:521x705:Purchased 1955

MARX, Enid born 1902
Modern Collection
Tate Gallery Archive holds material concerning this artist

P06358 Budgerigars (1972)
CLπ:575x768:Presented by Curwen Studio through the
Institute of Contemporary Prints 1975

MASI, Denis born 1942
Modern Collection
Tate Gallery Archive holds material concerning this artist

P02226 Project Print (1973)
CNπ:762x508:Presented by the artist 1975

MASI, Denis and COLVERSON, Ian - see COLVERSON, Ian and MASI, Denis

MASON, Arnold 1885-1963
Modern Collection

N05083 Girl with a Hand-Mirror (1929)
Oc:921x718:signed:Purchased 1940

MASON, George 1818-1872
British Collection

N01388 The Cast Shoe (exhibited 1865)
Oc:311x508:Purchased 1893

N01568 Wind on the Wold (1863)
Oc:286x540:Presented by Sir Henry Tate 1894

N02970 Italian Landscape (circa 1845-58)
Oc:403x781:Presented by Sir Thomas Devitt Bt 1914

N04737 Study for 'The Harvest Moon' (circa 1872)
GPπ:184x438:Presented by Mrs Auerbach 1934

N04742 The Harvest Moon (exhibited 1872)
Oc:864x2311:Bequeathed by Lord Faringdon 1934

MASON, Raymond born 1922
Modern Collection
Tate Gallery Archive holds material concerning this artist

T03678 Barcelona Tram (1953, cast 1968)
Rz:780x1250x250:signed:Purchased 1983

T03797 St Mark's Place, East Village, New York City (1972)
SAvw:686x1249x495:signed:Presented by Mme Andrée
Stassart 1983

P77190 Man in the Street (1976)
Lπ:615x540:signed:Purchased 1987

P77191 The Month of May in Paris (1968)
Lπ:650x550:signed:Purchased 1987

MASSON, André 1896-1987
Modern Collection
Tate Gallery Archive holds material concerning this artist

N05646 Ibdes in Aragon (1935)
Ibdès de Aragon
Oc:600x924:signed:Presented by the Contemporary Art
Society 1946

T00073 The Red Lands and the Montagne Sainte Victoire (1948)
Les Terres rouges et la Montagne Ste Victoire
Oc:959x765:signed:Presented by the Contemporary Art
Society 1955

P77114 Childbirth (1955)
L'Enfantement
CLπ:528x435:signed:Purchased 1985

P77115 Les Hain-Teny (1955, published 1956)
Les Hain-Teny
CLπ:430x333:signed:Purchased 1985

attributed to
MASTER of the GIANTS (? Prince Hoare) 1755-1834
British Collection

T01843 Unknown Mythological Subject
Dπ:241x190:Purchased 1974

MATHEWS, Denis born 1913
Modern Collection
Tate Gallery Archive holds material concerning this artist

T00060 Sale of Great Wines at the Hospice de Beaune: Two
Candles Still Burn (circa 1953)
CWGπ:502x406:signed:Purchased 1955

MATISSE, Henri 1869-1954
Modern Collection
Tate Gallery Archive holds material concerning this artist

N04717 Trivaux Pond (1916 or 1917)
L'Etang de Trivaux
Oc:927x743:signed:Bequeathed by C. Frank Stoop 1933

N04718 Nude Study in Blue (circa 1899-1900)
Académie bleue
Oc:730x543:signed:Bequeathed by C. Frank Stoop 1933

N04924 Reading Woman with Parasol (1921)
Liseuse à l'ombrelle
Oc:508x616:signed:Presented by the Contemporary Art
Society 1938

N05141 The Inattentive Reader (1919)
La Liseuse distraite
Oc:730x924:signed:Bequeathed by Montague Shearman
through the Contemporary Art Society 1940

N05905 Notre-Dame (circa 1900)
Oc:460x375:signed:Purchased 1949

N06146 Reclining Nude II (1927)
Nu couché, 2me etat
Sz:283x495x149:signed:Purchased 1953

N06241 André Derain (1905)
Oc:394x289:signed:Purchased with assistance from the
Knapping Fund, the National Art Collections Fund and
the Contemporary Art Society and private subscribers
1954

T00081 Back I (circa 1909-10, cast 1955-6)
Nu de dos I
Rz:1899x1168x184:signed:Purchased 1955

T00082 Back IV (1930, cast 1955-6)
Nu de dos IV
Rz:1892x1130x159:signed:Purchased with assistance
from the Knapping Fund 1955

T00114 Back II (circa 1913-14, cast 1955-6)
Nu de dos II
Rz:1892x1206x190:signed:Purchased with assistance
from the Matisse Appeal Fund 1956

T00160 Back III (circa 1916-17, cast 1955-6)
Nu de dos III
Rz:1880x1130x171:signed:Purchased with assistance
from the Matisse Appeal Fund 1957

T00306 Draped Nude (1936)
Femme nue drapée
Oc:457x375:signed:Purchased 1959

T00368 Standing Nude (1907)
Nu debout
Oc:921x648:signed:Purchased 1960

T00540 The Snail (1953)
L'Escargot
Gπ:2864x2870:signed:Purchased with assistance from the
Friends of the Tate Gallery 1962

T03568 Cap d'Antibes (1922)
Oc:506x612:signed:Bequeathed by Mrs A.F. Kessler 1983

T03889 Studio Interior (circa 1903-4)
Intérieur d'atelier
Oc:550x460:signed:Bequeathed by Lord Amulree 1984

T05756 Reclining Nude
Dπ:400x510:Bequeathed by Helena and Kenneth Levy
1990

School Prints (P01698-P01727; complete group; mixed
group)
P01713 The Dancer (1946-9)
CLπ:495x762:Presented by Patrick Seale Prints 1975

P11048 Little Aurore (1923)
Petite Aurore
MLπ:136x206:signed:Bequeathed by Mrs E. West 1982

MATSCHINSKY-DENNIGHOF, Brigitte
born 1923
Modern Collection

P01448 Untitled A (1964)
MLπ:559x768:signed:Presented by Marlborough
Graphics through the Institute of Contemporary Prints
1975

P01449 Untitled B (1964)
MLπ:559x768:signed:Presented by Marlborough
Graphics through the Institute of Contemporary Prints
1975

MATTA (Roberto Matta Echaurren) born 1912
Modern Collection

T01232 Black Virtue (1943)
La Vertu noire
Oc:765x1826:signed:Purchased 1970

For Jorn (P03241-P03255; complete group; mixed group)
Pour Jorn
P03249 [no title] (1975-6)
CLπ:410x632:signed:Presented by the Asger Jorn
Foundation 1978

MAUFRA, Maxime 1861-1918
Modern Collection

N04947 The Embankment of Lagny under Flood Water (1908)
Le Quai de Lagny inondé
Oc:457x549:signed:Presented by Mr and Mrs Julian
Lousada 1938

MAUNDRELL, Charles 1860 - ?circa 1924
British Collection

N01726 Le Château d'O (exhibited 1899)
WDπ:556x381:signed:Presented by the Trustees of the
Chantrey Bequest 1899

MAURER, Dora born 1937
Modern Collection

P77124 Seven Foldings (1975, published 1978)
Mlπ:578x400:signed:Purchased 1985

P77125 Traces of a Circle (1974)
4 Mlπ:295x297, 294x297, 296x298,
295x298:signed:Purchased 1985

MAUVE, Anton 1838-1888
Modern Collection

N02711 Watering Horses (1871)
Chevaux sortant de l'abreuvoir
Oc:387x600:signed:Presented by J.C.J. Drucker to the
National Gallery 1910

N05569 Milking Time (circa 1871)
Oc:298x502:signed:Bequeathed by Mrs Mary James
Mathews in memory of her husband Frank Claughton
Mathews 1944

N05570 Entering the Fold (circa 1885-8)
DWπ:505x603:signed:Bequeathed by Mrs Mary James
Mathews in memory of her husband Frank Claughton
Mathews 1944

MAXWELL, John 1905-1962
Modern Collection
Tate Gallery Archive holds material concerning this artist

T00006 Cliffs (1959)
Wπ:384x571:signed:Purchased 1955

T00283 Night Flowers (1959)
Oc:914x610:signed:Purchased 1959

MAY, Phil 1864-1903
British Collection

N04265 Lord Rosslyn
Dπ:187x117:signed:Purchased 1927

N04266 Barney Sheppard Sings in the Gloaming (?circa 1889-90)
Dπ:168x264:signed:Purchased 1927

N04267 I Define the Criminal Characteristics in Physiognomy of Chas Peace (?circa 1889-90)
Dπ:159x197:Purchased 1927

N04268 Old Lady and Two Men (?1889-90)
Dπ:200x152:signed:Purchased 1927

N04433 The Drawing Master (1886)
WDπ:244x181:Purchased 1929

MAYOR, Fred 1865-1916
British Collection

N03834 Church at Montreuil (circa 1909)
WDπ:318x394:signed:Presented by the artist's widow 1924

MAZE, Paul 1887-1979
Modern Collection
Tate Gallery Archive holds material concerning this artist

N04812 Yachts (1928)
Oc:330x460:Presented by Lord Duveen 1935

T05205 The Rowley Mile, Newmarket (1929)
Pπ:355x700:Presented by Mrs Maze, the artist's widow, through the Patrons of New Art and the Friends of the Tate Gallery 1988

MEAD, Dorothy 1928-1975
Modern Collection
Tate Gallery Archive holds material concerning this artist

T01493 Chessboard (1958)
Oc:762x635:signed:Presented by Andrew Forge 1971

MEADOWS, Bernard born 1915
Modern Collection
Tate Gallery Archive holds material concerning this artist

N06208 Standing Figure (1951)
Sw:1549x457x381:Presented by the Arts Council of Great Britain 1954

T00329 Four Reliefs (1958)
4 Rz:394x349x38, 394x292x41, 394x324x41, 394x292x41:signed:Purchased 1960

T03409 Black Crab (1951-2)
Sz:425x340x242:signed:Purchased 1982

T03759 Crab (1952)
Sz:155x90x110:Transferred from the Victoria & Albert Museum 1983

T03811 Lovers (1980)
Szs:649x1410x450:Presented by the Friends of the Tate Gallery 1983

P03164 Help (1976)
MLπ:76x152:signed:Presented by Taranman Gallery 1976

P03165 Untitled (1976)
MLπ:152x92:signed:Presented by Taranman Gallery 1976

MEDLEY, Robert born 1905
Modern Collection
Tate Gallery Archive holds material concerning this artist

N05987 Rhododendrons (1950)
Oc:711x908:Purchased 1951

T00331 A Tree Study (1959)
Oc:762x629:signed:Purchased 1960

T00332 Sketch for 'A Tree Study' (1959)
Dπ:387x337:Purchased 1960

T00498 The Antique Room at the Slade: Niobe and Hermes (1952)
Oc:1524x1264:signed:Purchased 1962

T00628 Figuration on White (1963)
Oc:870x1527:Purchased 1963

T01286 Three over Four (1970)
Ac:1829x1829:signed:Purchased 1971

IAA Portfolio (P03096-P03104, P03107; complete group; mixed group)
P03104 Divertimento (1975)
CNπ:318x425:signed:Presented by the International Association of Art 1975

MEDNIKOFF, Reuben 1906-1975
Modern Collection
Tate Gallery Archive holds material concerning this artist

T03890 Untitled Drawing (1936)
Dπ:380x255:Purchased 1984

MEHRING, Howard born 1931
Modern Collection

T01448 Crest (1966)
Ac:2140x1908:signed:Presented by Mrs Nesta Dorrance through the American Federation of Arts 1974

MEIDNER, Else born 1901
Modern Collection

T03694 Death and the Maiden (circa 1918-25)
Dπ:550x497:Presented by Professor J.P. Hodin 1983

MELLIS, Margaret born 1914
Modern Collection
Tate Gallery Archive holds material concerning this artist

T01267 Blue Anemone (1957)
Ob:333x352:signed:Purchased 1971

T04124 Sobranie Collage (1942)
Vbπ:263x370:signed:Purchased 1985

T04929 Marsh White (circa 1972-5)
Oc:569x619:signed:Purchased 1987

T04930 Number Thirty-Five (1983)
Rw:540x755x60:Purchased 1987

MELVILLE, Arthur 1855-1904
British Collection

N04043 Audrey and her Goats (1883-9)
Oc:2045x2134:Presented by W. Graham Robertson 1925

N05067   The Blue Night, Venice (1897)
Wπ:864x610:signed:Presented by W. Graham Robertson 1940

MENEELEY, Ed born 1937
Modern Collection

P01450   Louina's Dream (1973)
CNπ:933x660:signed:Presented by Editions Alecto through the Institute of Contemporary Prints 1975

MENINSKY, Bernard 1891-1950
Modern Collection
Tate Gallery Archive holds material concerning this artist

N04118   Portrait of a Boy (1923)
Oc:914x711:signed:Presented anonymously through the National Art Collections Fund 1925

T00170   Head of a Girl (1944)
Dπ:546x451:signed:Presented by the artist's widow 1958

T01993   Standing Female Nude in a Landscape (circa 1940-3)
Oc:406x254:signed:Bequeathed by Dr Marjorie Franklin 1975

T03348   Sleeping Woman in a Landscape (circa 1945-50)
Oc:613x1070:Purchased 1982

MENPES, Mortimer 1855-1939
British Collection

T01229   Flower of the Tea (1887-8)
Ow:267x171:Purchased 1970

MERCIER, Philip ?1689-1760
British Collection

T00759   A Girl Sewing (circa 1750)
Oc:760x635:signed:Purchased 1965

T00922   A Music Party (circa 1737-40)
Oc:1026x1270:signed:Purchased 1967

T03065   The Schutz Family and their Friends on a Terrace (1725)
Oc:1022x1257:signed:Purchased 1980

MERRITT, Anna Lea 1844-1930
British Collection

N01578   Love Locked Out (1889)
Oc:1156x641:signed:Presented by the Trustees of the Chantrey Bequest 1890

MERZ, Mario born 1925
Modern Collection

T03673   Fibonacci Tables (1974-6)
DAVc:2667x3822:Purchased 1983

T03674   Cone (circa 1967)
Cono
SVw:2210x1295x1295:Purchased 1983

MESENS, E.L.T. 1903-1971
Modern Collection
Tate Gallery Archive holds material concerning this artist

T01102   Thème de Ballet (1960)
Vπ:3x79:signed:Purchased 1969

T01260   The Staff (1962)
L'Etat-Major
VWb:216x276:signed:Purchased 1970

T01261   Mouvement Immobile II (1960)
Mouvement immobile II
Avb:327x251:signed:Purchased 1970

T01265   The Night Prowler (1955)
Le Noctambule
DGVb:571x324:signed:Presented by the artist 1971

MESTROVIC, Ivan 1883-1962
Modern Collection
Tate Gallery Archive holds material concerning this artist

N03284   Portrait of the Artist (1915)
Sp:498x229x235:Presented by the artist 1918

N03460   The Descent from the Cross
Rw:1003x1622:Presented by the Ivan Mestrovic Purchase Fund 1919

N03601   Sir Thomas Beecham, Bt. (1915)
Sz:492x165x213:signed:Presented by Lady Cunard 1921

N04551   Girl with a Lute (1927-8)
Ss:940x794x292:signed:Presented by Lord Duveen 1930

METHUEN, Lord 1886-1974
Modern Collection
Tate Gallery Archive holds material concerning this artist

N05168   Whitehall Palace and Banqueting Hall (1940)
DWπ:533x737:signed:Purchased 1940

N05169   The Tate Gallery from the Surrey Side (1940)
DWπ:324x483:signed:Presented by the artist 1940

N05884   Bath in Midwinter (1936-7)
Ow:495x394:signed:Presented by Mrs Moresby-White 1949

METZINGER, Jean 1883-1956
Modern Collection

T00251   Woman with a Coffee Pot (1919)
La Femme à la cafetière
Oc:1153x810:Purchased 1959

MICHAUX, Henri 1899-1984
Modern Collection

T00577   Untitled Chinese Ink Drawing (1961)
Dπ:746x1099:signed:Purchased 1963

For Jorn (P03241-P03255; complete group; mixed group)
Pour Jorn

P03250   [no title] (1975-6)
MLπ:470x648:signed:Presented by the Asger Jorn Foundation 1978

MICHELL, Keith born 1928
Modern Collection

P04590   Henry VIII (1972)
CNπ:775x533:signed:Presented by Rose and Chris Prater through the Institute of Contemporary Prints 1975

Illustrations of Twelve Shakespeare Sonnets (P06664-P06675; complete group)

P06664   I 'What is your substance, whereof are you made' (1975)
CLπ:521x394:signed:Presented by Curwen Studio 1976

P06665   II 'Not marble, nor the gilded monuments' (1975)
CLπ:521x394:signed:Presented by Curwen Studio 1976

P06666   III 'When I consider everything that grows' (1975)
CLπ:521x394:signed:Presented by Curwen Studio 1976

P06667   IV 'Mine eye hath play'd the painter and hath . . .' (1975)
          CLπ:521x394:signed:Presented by Curwen Studio 1976

P06668   V 'When in disgrace with fortune and men's eyes' (1975)
          CLπ:521x394:signed:Presented by Curwen Studio 1976

P06669   VI 'How heavy do I journey on the way' (1975)
          CLπ:521x394:signed:Presented by Curwen Studio 1976

P06670   VII 'Since I have left you, mine eye is in my mind' (1975)
          CLπ:521x394:signed:Presented by Curwen Studio 1976

P06671   VIII 'Shall I compare thee to a summer's day' (1975)
          CLπ:521x394:signed:Presented by Curwen Studio 1976

P06672   IX 'Look in thy glass and tell the face thou knewest' (1975)
          CLπ:521x394:signed:Presented by Curwen Studio 1976

P06673   X 'My mistress's eyes are nothing like the sun' (1975)
          CLπ:521x394:signed:Presented by Curwen Studio 1976

P06674   XI 'Two loves I have, of comfort and despair' (1975)
          CLπ:521x394:signed:Presented by Curwen Studio 1976

P06675   XII 'Poor soul, the centre of my sinful earth' (1975)
          CLπ:521x394:signed:Presented by Curwen Studio 1976

P06739   Metamorphosis (1973)
          CLπ:603x765:Presented by Curwen Studio 1977

MICHELMORE, Richard and BOMBERG, David - see BOMBERG, David and MICHELMORE, Richard

MIDDLEDITCH, Edward 1923-1987
Modern Collection
Tate Gallery Archive holds material concerning this artist

T00641   Dead Chicken in a Stream (1955)
          Ob:1365x1092:Presented by the Calouste Gulbenkian Foundation 1964

T01046   Sheffield Weir II (1954)
          Ob:914x1505:Presented by the Trustees of the Chantrey Bequest 1968

MILLAIS, Sir John Everett, Bt 1829-1896
British Collection
Tate Gallery Archive holds material concerning this artist

N01494   The Yeoman of the Guard (1876)
          Oc:1397x1118:signed:Bequeathed by Mrs Hodgkinson 1897

N01503   Equestrian Portrait (begun by Sir Edwin Landseer) (1882)
          Oc:3181x2311:signed:Presented anonymously 1897

N01506   Ophelia (1851-2)
          Oc:762x1118:signed:Presented by Sir Henry Tate 1894

N01507   The Vale of Rest (1858-9)
          Oc:1029x1727:Presented by Sir Henry Tate 1894

N01508   The Knight Errant (1870)
          Oc:1841x1353:signed:Presented by Sir Henry Tate 1894

N01509   The North-West Passage (1874)
          Oc:1765x2222:signed:Presented by Sir Henry Tate 1894

N01510   Mercy: St Bartholomew's Day, 1572 (1866)
          Oc:1841x1308:signed:Presented by Sir Henry Tate 1894

N01563   Saint Stephen (1895)
          Oc:1524x1143:signed:Presented by Sir Henry Tate 1894

N01564   A Disciple (1895)
          Oc:1245x876:signed:Presented by Sir Henry Tate 1894

N01584   Speak! Speak! (1895)
          Oc:1676x2108:signed:Presented by the Trustees of the Chantrey Bequest 1895

N01657   The Order of Release 1746 (1852-3)
          Oc:1029x737:signed:Presented by Sir Henry Tate 1898

N01691   The Boyhood of Raleigh (1870)
          Oc:1206x1422:signed:Presented by Amy, Lady Tate in memory of Sir Henry Tate 1900

N01807   A Maid Offering a Basket of Fruit to a Cavalier (1849)
          Ow:152x114:signed:Bequeathed by Henry Vaughan 1900

N01808   Charles I and his Son in the Studio of Van Dyck (1849)
          Ow:159x114:signed:Bequeathed by Henry Vaughan 1900

N01941   Sir Henry Thompson, Bt (1881)
          Oc:1257x914:signed:Bequeathed by Sir Henry Thompson Bt 1904

N03159   Serjeant Ralph Thomas (1848)
          Ow:387x286:Presented by Ralph Thomas 1917

N03414   Mrs Currie (1847)
          Dπ:203x152:signed:Bequeathed by Miss Gore-Currie 1919

N03415   Miss Currie (1847)
          Dπ:203x152:signed:Bequeathed by Miss Gore-Currie 1919

N03416   Master Currie (1847)
          Dπ:203x152:signed:Bequeathed by Miss Gore-Currie 1919

N03584   Christ in the House of His Parents ('The Carpenter's Shop') (1849-50)
          Oc:864x1397:signed:Purchased with assistance from the National Art Collections Fund and various subscribers 1921

N04055   The Good Samaritan, engraved by the Dalziel Brothers (published 1863)
          Jπ:140x108:Presented by Harold Hartley 1929

N04277   A Baron Numbering his Vassals (1850)
          WDπ:292x406:signed:Bequeathed by J.R. Holliday 1927

N04278   Kirk (1853)
          Dπ:190x229:signed:Bequeathed by J.R. Holliday 1927

N04279   The New Ride, Kensington Gardens
          Dπ:203x321:signed:Bequeathed by J.R. Holliday 1927

N04368   Study for 'The Blind Girl'. Verso: Study for 'Peace Concluded' (circa 1854, circa 1855)
          Dπ:187x92:Presented by John Hipkins 1927

N04536   Miss Anne Ryan
          Oc:559x451:signed:Bequeathed by Miss Jennie Lee 1930

N04623   Study for 'Christ in the House of His Parents' (circa 1849)
          Dπ:190x337:signed:Bequeathed by H.F. Stephens 1932

N04792   Study for 'Christ in the House of His Parents' (circa 1849)
          DWπ:190x289:Presented by Sir Hickman Bacon 1935

N05260   Miss Eveleen Tennant (1874)
          Oc:1079x800:signed:Presented by Harold Myers 1941

N05572   Mrs Bischoffsheim (1873)
          Oc:1364x918:signed:Presented by Lady Fitzgerald 1944

N05599   The Disentombment of Queen Matilda (1849)
          Dπ:229x429:signed:Purchased 1945

N05632   The Moon is Up (1890)
          Oc:1041x1689:signed:Presented by Mrs H.S. Neilson 1946

N05770   Hearts are Trumps (1872)
          Oc:1657x2197:signed:Presented by the Trustees of the Chantrey Bequest 1945

T00177   A Spanish Gentleman (after John Jackson's 'Shylock') (circa 1843)
          Oc:533x432:Purchased 1958

T00178   Going to Church (circa 1840-1)
          Wπ:235x333:Purchased 1958

T00179 The Wrestlers (circa 1840-1)
Wπ:362x540:Purchased 1958

T03858 Mrs James Wyatt Jr and her Daughter Sarah (circa 1850)
Ow:353x457:signed:Purchased 1984

Illustrations to 'The Parables of Our Lord', engraved by
the Dalziel Brothers (A00792-A00811; complete group)

A00792 The Lost Sheep (published 1864)
Jπ:140x108:Presented by Gilbert Dalziel 1924

A00793 The Pharisee and the Publican (published 1864)
Jπ:140x108:Presented by Gilbert Dalziel 1924

A00794 The Wise Virgins (published 1864)
Jπ:140x108:Presented by Gilbert Dalziel 1924

A00795 The Unjust Judge and the Importunate Widow
(published 1864)
Jπ:140x108:Presented by Gilbert Dalziel 1924

A00796 The Leaven (published 1864)
Jπ:140x108:Presented by Gilbert Dalziel 1924

A00797 The Rich Man and Lazarus (published 1864)
Jπ:140x108:Presented by Gilbert Dalziel 1924

A00798 The Labourers in the Vineyard (published 1864)
Jπ:140x108:Presented by Gilbert Dalziel 1924

A00799 The Marriage Feast (published 1864)
Jπ:140x108:Presented by Gilbert Dalziel 1924

A00800 The Sower (published 1864)
Jπ:140x108:Presented by Gilbert Dalziel 1924

A00801 The Lost Piece of Silver (published 1864)
Jπ:140x108:Presented by Gilbert Dalziel 1924

A00802 The Foolish Virgins (published 1864)
Jπ:140x108:Presented by Gilbert Dalziel 1924

A00803 The Importunate Friend (published 1864)
Jπ:140x108:Presented by Gilbert Dalziel 1924

A00804 The Pearl of Great Price (published 1864)
Jπ:140x108:Presented by Gilbert Dalziel 1924

A00805 The Tares (published 1864)
Jπ:140x108:Presented by Gilbert Dalziel 1924

A00806 The Good Shepherd (published 1864)
Jπ:140x108:Presented by Gilbert Dalziel 1924

A00807 The Good Samaritan (published 1864)
Jπ:140x108:Presented by Gilbert Dalziel 1924

A00809 The Unmerciful Servant (published 1864)
Jπ:140x108:Presented by Gilbert Dalziel 1924

A00810 The Hidden Treasure (published 1864)
Jπ:140x108:Presented by Gilbert Dalziel 1924

A00811 The Prodigal Son (published 1864)
Jπ:140x108:Presented by Gilbert Dalziel 1924

A00812 Study for 'The Black Brunswicker' (circa 1860)
Dπ:200x117:Presented by Gilbert Dalziel 1924

A00813 Study for 'The Black Brunswicker' (circa 1860)
Dπ:200x117:Presented by Gilbert Dalziel 1924

A00814 Study for 'The Black Brunswicker' (circa 1860)
Dπ:200x117:Presented by Gilbert Dalziel 1924

MILLARES, Manolo 1926-1972
Modern Collection

T00579 Painting 150 (1961)
Cuadro 150
Oc:1308x1619:signed:Purchased 1963

T02385 Painting (1964)
Oc:391x464:signed:Presented by Sir George Labouchere
through the Friends of the Tate Gallery 1979

MILLER, Godfrey 1893-1964
Modern Collection

T00434 Triptych with Figures (circa 1944-50)
Of:654x1041:signed:Purchased 1961

MILLER, Jack born 1935
Modern Collection

West Coast Suburbs (P03135-P03137; complete group)

P03135 Hollywood (1975)
CLπ:362x530:signed:Presented by the artist and Andrew
Dickerson 1976

P03136 Los Angeles, South (1975)
CLπ:323x495:signed:Presented by the artist and Andrew
Dickerson 1976

P03137 Santa Barbara (1975)
CLπ:338x504:signed:Presented by the artist and Andrew
Dickerson 1976

MILLES, Carl 1875-1955
Modern Collection

N04247 Europa and the Bull (1923-4)
Sz:781x667x330:Purchased 1927

N04248 Folke Filbyter (circa 1926)
Sz:730x368x279:Purchased 1927

T02105 The Sun Singer (Torso) (circa 1892)
Sz:911x292x241:signed:Bequeathed by Mrs Muriel
Elverston 1977

MILLET, Francis Davis 1846-1912
Modern Collection

N01611 Between Two Fires (circa 1892)
Oc:740x914:signed:Presented by the Trustees of the
Chantrey Bequest 1892

MILLINGTON, Terence born 1942
Modern Collection

For John Constable (P03149-P03157, P03159-P03161,
P03180-P03185; complete group; mixed group)

P03157 [no title] (1976)
Mlπ:530x394:signed:Presented by Bernard Jacobson
Gallery 1976

MILLNER, William Edward 1849-1895
British Collection

T01140 A Wayside Gossip (1872)
Oc:378x502:signed:Purchased 1969

MILNE, John 1931-1978
Modern Collection
Tate Gallery Archive holds material concerning this artist

T01449 Gnathos (1960)
Szs:641x864x375:Presented by Professor Cosmo
Rodewald 1971

MILNE, Malcolm 1887-1954
Modern Collection

N04260 Lilies of the Valley (1927)
Ob:321x264:signed:Presented by the Daily Express
through the Contemporary Art Society 1927

MILOW, Keith born 1945
Modern Collection

T01213 1 2 3 4 5 6 . . . B (1970)
RADa:1067x2143x102:Purchased 1970

T01279 3nterference (1970-1)
RAv:1524x914x559:Purchased 1971

T04159 Eightieth Cross (1978)
Av:1155x870x210:Presented by the Contemporary Art
Society 1986

T05562 89/5/75/D (1989)
Om:460x355:Purchased 1989

T05563 89/10/80/D (1989)
Om:458x357:Purchased 1989

T05564 88/60/D (1988)
Om:459x358:Purchased 1989

T05565 88/18/D (1988)
Om:458x356:Purchased 1989

T05701 88/49/D (1988)
Om:459x355:Presented by the artist 1989

T05702 88/70/D (1988)
Nπ:458x356:Presented by the artist 1989

15 23/55 55/46 66 (P07090-P07095; complete group)

P07090 PR1NT A (1969)
CNπ:508x762:signed:Purchased 1971

P07091 PR2NT A (1969)
CNπ:508x762:signed:Purchased 1971

P07092 PR3NT A (1969)
CNπ:508x762:signed:Purchased 1971

P07093 PR4NY A (1969)
CNπ:508x762:signed:Purchased 1971

P07094 PR5NT A (1969)
CNπ:508x762:signed:Purchased 1971

P07095 PR6NT A (1969)
CNπ:508x762:signed:Purchased 1971

MILROY, Lisa born 1959
Modern Collection

T05217 Light Bulbs (1988)
Oc:2034x2845:signed:Purchased 1988

MILTON, Peter born 1930
Modern Collection

P03260 Daylilies (1975)
MIπ:505x800:signed:Presented by Impressions
Workshop, Boston 1978

MINAMI, Keiko born 1911
Modern Collection

P01451 Girl with Green Birds (1973)
CLπ:343x292:Presented by Christie's Contemporary Art
through the Institute of Contemporary Prints 1975

MINAUX, André born 1923
Modern Collection

N06168 Arm-chair in an Interior (1951)
Fauteuil dans un intérieur
Oc:1619x968:signed:Purchased 1953

MINGUZZI, Luciano born 1911
Modern Collection

N06165 The Unknown Political Prisoner: Figure within Barbed
Wire (1952)
Figura fra i reticolati
Sz:571x660x330:signed:Purchased 1953

MINTCHINE, Abraham 1898-1931
Modern Collection

N06207 Portrait of the Artist as a Harlequin (1931)
Portrait de l'artiste en arlequin
Oc:724x502:signed:Presented by Mrs Florence Gimpel in
memory of her husband René Gimpel 1954

MINTON, John 1917-1957
Modern Collection
Tate Gallery Archive holds material concerning this artist

T00140 Composition: The Death of James Dean (1957)
Oc:1219x1829:Presented by the Trustees of the Chantrey
Bequest 1957

T00159 Portugese Cannon, Magazan, Morocco (1953)
Oc:1524x1143:Purchased 1957

T00162 Street and Railway Bridge (1946)
Oc:457x610:signed:Purchased 1957

T00237 Corte, Corsica (1947)
DWπ:400x273:signed:Purchased 1959

T04887 Children by the Sea (1945)
Oc:947x760:signed:Purchased 1987

T04926 Landscape with Buildings on a Rock (1939)
Ob:461x550:signed:Purchased 1958, accessioned 1987

MIREA, Joan born 1912
Modern Collection

P06360 Moldavian Nude (1966)
CLπ:556x381:signed:Presented by Curwen Studio
through the Institute of Contemporary Prints 1975

P06361 Transylvanian Nude (1966)
CLπ:556x381:signed:Presented by Curwen Studio
through the Institute of Contemporary Prints 1975

MIRO, Joan 1893-1983
Modern Collection
Tate Gallery Archive holds material concerning this artist

N06007 Women and Bird in the Moonlight (1949)
Femmes, oiseau au clair de lune
Oc:813x660:signed:Purchased 1951

T01318 Painting (1927)
Peinture
OGc:972x1302:signed:Purchased 1971

T03401 Woman (1949)
Femme
Sz:186x264x224:signed:Purchased 1982

T03402 The Tightrope Walker (1970)
L'Equilibriste
Szmw:530x280x130:signed:Purchased 1982

T03690 A Star Caresses the Breast of a Negress (Painting Poem)
(1938)
Une Étoile caresse le sein d'une négresse
(peinture-poème)
Oc:1295x1943:signed:Purchased 1983

T03691 Message from a Friend (1964)
Message d'ami
Oc:2620x2755:signed:Purchased with assistance from
funds bequeathed by Miss H.M. Arbuthnot through the
Friends of the Tate Gallery 1983

P05474 Untitled (1964)
CNπ:660x489:signed:Presented by Rose and Chris Prater
1975

P07356 The Matador (1969)
Le Matador
CIVπ:1067x737:signed:Purchased 1980

P07357 The Great Carnivore (1969)
Le Grand Carnassier
CIπ:1143x692:signed:Purchased 1980

P07358 The Conductor (1976)
Le Chef d'orchestre
CIπ:1143x743:signed:Purchased 1980

P07900 Series II (1952)
Serie II
CIπ:377x455:signed:Purchased 1983

P77064 Composition (1947)
CIπ:127x149:signed:Purchased 1984

P77138 Constellations (1959)
CIπ:277x195:signed:Purchased 1986

MISTRY, Dhruva born 1957
Modern Collection

T05037 Maya Medallion: The Dark One - 2 (1987)
RAp:1160x1160x130:signed:Purchased 1988

MITCHELL, Denis born 1912
Modern Collection
Tate Gallery Archive holds material concerning this artist

T00890 Praze (1964)
Sz:1918x279x286:Presented by T.L. Johnson 1966

T01480 Cauca (1971)
Sz:194x1194x79:Presented by Mrs Marjorie Parr 1971

T02235 Turning Form (1959)
Sz:1422x178x279:signed:Bequeathed by Miss E.M.
Hodgkins 1977

MODIGLIANI, Amedeo 1884-1920
Modern Collection

N04723 Portrait of a Girl (circa 1917)
Oc:806x597:signed:Bequeathed by C. Frank Stoop 1933

N05269 The Little Peasant (circa 1918)
Le Petit Paysan
Oc:1000x645:signed:Presented by Miss Jenny Blaker in
memory of Hugh Blaker 1941

T00149 Caryatid (circa 1913-4)
Cariatide
Dπ:549x448:Purchased 1957

T03569 Madame Zborowska (1918)
La Zborowska en buste
Oc:645x460:signed:Bequeathed by Mrs A.F. Kessler 1983

T03570 Caryatid with a Vase (circa 1914)
Cariatide à la potiche
WHπ:633x481:signed:Bequeathed by Mrs A.F. Kessler
1983

T03760 Head (circa 1911-2)
Tête
Ss:635x125x350:signed:Transferred from the Victoria &
Albert Museum 1983

MOHOLY-NAGY, Laszlo 1895-1946
Modern Collection
Tate Gallery Archive holds material concerning this artist

T00432 K VII (1922)
Oc:1153x1359:signed:Purchased 1961

MOIRA, Gerald 1867-1959
British Collection

N04966 Washing Day (exhibited 1938)
WDπ:387x559:signed:Presented by the Trustees of the
Chantrey Bequest 1938

MONAMY, Peter circa 1682-1749
British Collection

T00807 Ships in Distress in a Storm (circa 1720-30)
Oc:765x1064:signed:Purchased 1965

MONDRIAN, Piet 1872-1944
Modern Collection
Tate Gallery Archive holds material concerning this artist

T00648 Composition with Red, Yellow and Blue (circa 1937-42)
Oc:727x692:signed:Purchased 1964

T00915 Composition with Grey, Red, Yellow and Blue (1920 -
circa 1926)
Oc:997x1003:signed:Purchased 1967

T02211 Tree (circa 1913)
Arbre
Oc:1003x673:signed:Purchased 1977

MONET, Claude 1840-1926
Modern Collection

N04183 Poplars on the Epte (1891)
Les Peupliers au bord de l'Epte
Oc:924x737:signed:Presented by the National Art
Collections Fund 1926

N04184 Woman Seated on a Bench (circa 1874)
Femme assise sur un banc
Oc:737x559:signed:Presented by the National Art
Collections Fund 1926

N06182 The Seine at Port-Villez (1894)
La Seine à Port-Villez
Oc:654x1003:signed:Purchased 1953

MONNINGTON, Sir Thomas 1902-1976
Modern Collection
Tate Gallery Archive holds material concerning this artist

N05036 Allegory (circa 1924)
Tc:1257x2768:Presented by the Contemporary Art
Society 1939

T00924 Square Design (1966)
Oc:933x921:Presented by the Trustees of the Chantrey
Bequest 1967

T03832 Trees and Rocks (1952)
Dπ:503x635:Purchased 1984

T03833 Trees (circa 1938)
Oc:350x452:Purchased 1984

MONRO, Nicholas born 1936
Modern Collection

P04591 Animals Running Through Fire (1970)
CNπ:667x873:signed:Presented by Rose and Chris Prater
through the Institute of Contemporary Prints 1975

P04592 The Balloon Race (1970)
CNπ:673x794:signed:Presented by Rose and Chris Prater through the Institute of Contemporary Prints 1975

P04593 Cosmic Consciousness (1970)
MNπ:635x686:signed:Presented by Rose and Chris Prater through the Institute of Contemporary Prints 1975

P04594 Dancers (1970)
CNπ:806x673:signed:Presented by Rose and Chris Prater through the Institute of Contemporary Prints 1975

P04595 Figure with Crosses (1970)
CNπ:606x930:signed:Presented by Rose and Chris Prater through the Institute of Contemporary Prints 1975

P04596 Girl at Window (1970)
CNπ:552x657:signed:Presented by Rose and Chris Prater through the Institute of Contemporary Prints 1975

P04597 Green Figures (1970)
CNπ:635x902:signed:Presented by Rose and Chris Prater through the Institute of Contemporary Prints 1975

P04598 Hedges (1970)
CNπ:667x933:signed:Presented by Rose and Chris Prater through the Institute of Contemporary Prints 1975

P04599 Hooded Figures (1970)
CNπ:616x784:signed:Presented by Rose and Chris Prater through the Institute of Contemporary Prints 1975

P04600 Hospital (1970)
CNπ:660x829:signed:Presented by Rose and Chris Prater through the Institute of Contemporary Prints 1975

P04601 Operating Theatre (1970)
CNπ:632x654:signed:Presented by Rose and Chris Prater through the Institute of Contemporary Prints 1975

P04602 Sheep (1970)
CNπ:635x899:signed:Presented by Rose and Chris Prater through the Institute of Contemporary Prints 1975

P04603 Stone Circle (1970)
CNπ:622x876:signed:Presented by Rose and Chris Prater through the Institute of Contemporary Prints 1975

P04604 Craters (1971)
CNπ:622x876:signed:Presented by Rose and Chris Prater through the Institute of Contemporary Prints 1975

P04605 The Flood (1971)
CNπ:622x876:signed:Presented by Rose and Chris Prater through the Institute of Contemporary Prints 1975

P04606 Igloos (1971)
CNπ:559x762:signed:Presented by Rose and Chris Prater through the Institute of Contemporary Prints 1975

P04607 Kangaroos (1971)
CNπ:568x772:signed:Presented by Rose and Chris Prater through the Institute of Contemporary Prints 1975

P04608 Colony (1972)
CNπ:610x791:signed:Presented by Rose and Chris Prater through the Institute of Contemporary Prints 1975

P04609 Lobby (1972)
CNπ:587x775:signed:Presented by Rose and Chris Prater through the Institute of Contemporary Prints 1975

P04610 Boats (1973)
CNπ:511x962:signed:Presented by Rose and Chris Prater through the Institute of Contemporary Prints 1975

P04611 Gazelles (1973)
CNπ:565x924:signed:Presented by Rose and Chris Prater through the Institute of Contemporary Prints 1975

P07672 Estuary (1982)
CNπ:705x975:signed:Purchased 1982

MONTPETIT, Guy born 1938
Modern Collection

Homage to Albert Dumouchel (P03166-P03178; complete group; mixed group)
Hommage à Albert Dumouchel

P03174 The Flying Man (1971-2)
L'Homme volant
CLπ:756x559:signed:Presented by the University of Quebec 1976

MOON, Jeremy 1934-1973
Modern Collection
Tate Gallery Archive holds material concerning this artist

T01033 Blue Rose (1967)
Ac:2184x2515:signed:Purchased 1968

T01841 Trellis (1962)
Oc:1384x1067:signed:Purchased 1974

T01842 No. 5/73 (1973)
Oc:1530x711:signed:Purchased 1974

T02052 Untitled 2/72 (1972)
Ac:2032x2896:signed:Purchased 1976

MOON, Michael born 1937
Modern Collection
Tate Gallery Archive holds material concerning this artist

T01255 Untitled (1970)
Aa:2438x3048:Purchased 1970

T02073 Drawing (1976)
Ac:1219x1676:Purchased 1976

T02321 Table (1978)
Ac:2121x1600x95:Purchased 1978

MOORE, Albert 1841-1893
British Collection
Tate Gallery Archive holds material concerning this artist

N01549 Blossoms (1881)
Oc:1473x464:signed:Presented by Sir Henry Tate 1894

N04289 Study for 'Elijah's Sacrifice' (circa 1864)
Wπ:286x216:Bequeathed by J.R. Holliday 1927

N04290 Studies for 'Elijah's Sacrifice' (circa 1864)
Dπ:210x254:Bequeathed by J.R. Holliday 1927

N05082 Portrait Study of a Child
Dπ:305x254:Bequeathed by Frank Hindley Smith 1940

N05876 The Toilet (1886)
Oc:419x235:Bequeathed by W. Graham Robertson 1948

T03064 A Garden (1869)
Oc:1746x879:Purchased with assistance from the Friends of the Tate Gallery 1980

T04877 A Sleeping Girl (circa 1875)
Oc:308x225:Presented by Arthur Grogan 1986

MOORE, Henry 1831-1895
British Collection
Tate Gallery Archive holds material concerning this artist

N01604 Catspaws off the Land (1885)
Oc:902x1359:signed:Presented by the Trustees of the Chantrey Bequest 1885

MOORE, Henry, OM, CH 1898-1986
Modern Collection
Tate Gallery Archive holds material concerning this artist

N05208 Two Seated Figures (1940)
WGDπ:181x270:signed:Purchased 1940

N05209 Two Seated Women (1940)
DTπ:181x270:signed:Purchased 1940

N05210 Standing Figures (1940)
GDπ:264x181:signed:Purchased 1940

N05387 Recumbent Figure (1938)
Ss:889x1327x737:Presented by the Contemporary Art
Society 1939

N05600 Maquette for Madonna and Child (1943)
Sz:140x76x76:signed:Purchased 1945

N05601 Maquette for Madonna and Child (1943)
Sz:146x54x67:signed:Purchased 1945

N05602 Maquette for Madonna and Child (1943)
Sz:156x86x70:signed:Purchased 1945

N05603 Maquette for Madonna and Child (1943)
Sz:184x89x76:signed:Purchased 1945

N05604 Maquette for Family Group (1944)
Sz:137x114x67:signed:Purchased 1945

N05605 Maquette for Family Group (1945)
Sz:127x98x63:signed:Purchased 1945

N05606 Maquette for Family Group (1945)
Sz:178x102x60:signed:Purchased 1945

N05706 Grey Tube Shelter (1940)
WGDπ:279x381:signed:Presented by the War Artists'
Advisory Committee 1946

N05707 Woman Seated in the Underground (1941)
GDπ:483x381:signed:Presented by the War Artists'
Advisory Committee 1946

N05708 A Tilbury Shelter Scene (1941)
WGDπ:419x381:signed:Presented by the War Artists'
Advisory Committee 1946

N05709 Tube Shelter Perspective (1941)
WGDπ:483x438:signed:Presented by the War Artists' Advisory
Committee 1946

N05710 Pale Shelter Scene (1941)
WGDπ:483x432:Presented by the War Artists' Advisory
Committee 1946

N05711 Shelter Scene: Bunks and Sleepers (1941)
WGDπ:483x432:Presented by the War Artists' Advisory
Committee 1946

N05712 Shelterers in the Tube (1941)
WGDπ:381x559:signed:Presented by the War Artists'
Advisory Committee 1946

N05713 Pink and Green Sleepers (1941)
WGDπ:381x559:signed:Presented by the War Artists'
Advisory Committee 1946

N05950 Standing Nude (circa 1925)
Dπ:559x241:signed:Purchased 1950

N06004 Family Group (1949)
Sz:1524x1156x781:signed:Purchased 1950

N06078 Girl (1931)
Ss:737x368x273:Purchased 1952

T00059 Standing Figure (1927)
DWπ:540x318:signed:Purchased 1955

T00228 King and Queen (1952-3, cast 1957)
Sz:1638x1384x845:Presented by the Friends of the Tate
Gallery with funds provided by Associated Rediffusion
Ltd 1959

T00240 Figure (1931)
Sw:248x178x121:Purchased 1959

T00241 Half-figure (1932)
Ss:686x381x279:Bequeathed by E.C. Gregory 1959

T00270 Drawing (1935)
DWπ:343x419:signed:Purchased 1959

T00271 Four Forms, drawing for a Sculpture (1938)
DWπ:279x381:signed:Purchased 1959

T00385 Composition (1932)
Ss:445x457x298:Presented by the Friends of the Tate
Gallery 1960

T00386 Stringed Figure (1938/60)
Szv:273x343x197:Presented by the Friends of the Tate
Gallery 1960

T00387 Reclining Figure (1939)
Sz:137x254x86:Presented by the Friends of the Tate
Gallery 1960

T00388 Helmet Head No. 1 (1950)
Sz:330x260x254:Presented by the Friends of the Tate
Gallery 1960

T00389 Mother and Child (1953)
Sz:508x229x235:Presented by the Friends of the Tate
Gallery 1960

T00390 Working Model for Unesco Reclining Figure (1957)
Sz:1372x2286x1143:Presented by the Friends of the Tate
Gallery 1960

T00395 Two-Piece Reclining Figure No. 2 (1960)
Sz:1257x2578x1086:signed:Purchased 1960

T00603 Working Model for Knife-Edge Two-Piece (1962)
Sz:498x711x330:signed:Purchased 1963

T01172 Upright Form: Knife-Edge (1966)
Ss:597x565x241:Presented by the artist 1970

T02054 Four-Piece Composition: Reclining Figure (1934)
Ss:175x457x203:Purchased with assistance from the
National Art Collections Fund 1976

T02269 Three Points (1939-40)
Sz:140x190x95:Presented by the artist 1978

T02270 Reclining Figure (1951)
Sp:1054x2273x892:Presented by the artist 1978

T02271 Animal Head (1951)
Sp:270x216x295:Presented by the artist 1978

T02272 Upright Internal/External Form (1952-3)
Sp:1956x679x692:Presented by the artist 1978

T02273 Helmet Head and Shoulders (1952)
Sz:165x149x95:Presented by the artist 1978

T02274 Upright Motive No. 1: Glenkiln Cross (1955-6)
Sz:3327x978x965:Presented by the artist 1978

T02275 Upright Motive No. 2 (1955-6)
Sz:3353x768x972:signed:Presented by the artist 1978

T02276 Upright Motive No. 7 (1955-6)
Sz:3404x772x972:signed:Presented by the artist 1978

T02277 Animal Head (1956)
Sz:508x586x568:Presented by the artist 1978

T02278 Falling Warrior (1956-7)
Sz:483x1499x800:Presented by the artist 1978

T02279 Seated Woman (1957)
Sp:1488x1394x914:Presented by the artist 1978

T02280 Woman (1957-8)
Sz:1441x791x921:signed:Presented by the artist 1978

T02281 Three Motives against Wall No. 2 (1959)
Sz:460x1083x381:signed:Presented by the artist 1978

T02282 Bird (1959)
Sz:121x375x130:Presented by the artist 1978

T02283 Headless Animal (1960)
Sz:159x225x95:Presented by the artist 1978

T02284 Relief No. 1 (1959)
Sz:2219x1251x498:signed:Presented by the artist 1978

T02285 Three Part Object (1960)
Sz:1264x718x613:signed:Presented by the artist 1978

T02286 Seated Woman: Thin Neck (1961)
Sz:1702x813x1035:Presented by the artist 1978

T02287 Two Piece Reclining Figure No. 3 (1961)
Sz:1473x2407x1140:Presented by the artist 1978

T02288 Three-Quarter Figure (1961)
Sp:391x232x130:Presented by the artist 1978

T02289 Three Piece Reclining Figure No. 1 (1961-2)
Sz:1700x2800x1370:Presented by the artist 1978

T02290 Large Slow Form (1962-8)
Sz:490x844x460:signed:Presented by the artist 1978

T02291 Helmet Head No 4: Interior - Exterior (1963)
Sz:552x346x391:signed:Presented by the artist 1978

T02292 Three Piece Reclining Figure No. 2: Bridge Prop (1963)
Sz:1054x2365x1102:signed:Presented by the artist 1978

T02293 Locking Piece (1963-4)
Sz:2920x2800x2300:signed:Presented by the artist 1978

T02294 Two Piece Reclining Figure No. 5 (1963-4)
Sz:2375x3683x1988:signed:Presented by the artist 1978

T02295 Working Model for Reclining Figure (Lincoln Centre) (1963-5)
Sz:2349x3721x1651:signed:Presented by the artist 1978

T02296 Atom Piece (Working Model for Nuclear Energy) (1964-5)
Sz:1181x914x914:Presented by the artist 1978

T02297 Moon Head (1964)
Sz:578x441x254:Presented by the artist 1978

T02298 Working Model for Three Way Piece No. 1: Points (1964)
Sz:651x711x743:Presented by the artist 1978

T02299 Working Model for Three Way Piece No. 2: Archer (1964)
Sz:775x787x651:signed:Presented by the artist 1978

T02300 Two Piece Sculpture No. 7: Pipe (1966)
Sz:489x940x460:Presented by the artist 1978

T02301 Two Piece Reclining Figure No. 9 (1968)
Sz:1435x2438x1349:signed:Presented by the artist 1978

T02302 Large Totem Head (1968)
Sz:2457x1340x1257:Presented by the artist 1978

T02303 Working Model for Three Piece No. 3: Vertebrae (1968)
Sz:940x2362x1219:Presented by the artist 1978

T03761 Reclining Figure (1939)
Sm:150x280x100:Transferred from the Victoria & Albert Museum 1983

T03762 Mask (1929)
Sp:200x180x130:Transferred from the Victoria & Albert Museum 1983

T03763 Three Motives against a Wall No. I (1958)
Sz:505x1080x440:Transferred from the Victoria & Albert Museum 1983

P01070 Figures in Settings (trial proof) (1949-51)
CLπ:610x486:signed:Presented by Dr Baer 1975

School Prints (P01698-P01727; complete group; mixed group)

P01714 Sculptural Objects (1946-9)
CLπ:495x762:signed:Presented by Patrick Seale Prints 1975

P02072 Composition for a Poem by Herbert Read (circa 1946)
CLπ:352x279:signed:Presented by the artist 1975

P02073 Figures in Settings (1949-51)
CLπ:613x438:signed:Presented by the artist 1975

P02074 Standing Figures (1949-51)
CLπ:381x470:signed:Presented by the artist 1975

P02075 Two Standing Figures with Studies on the Left (circa 1950)
CLπ:260x359:signed:Presented by the artist 1975

P02076 Two Seated Figures (1951-70)
CLπ:76x127:signed:Presented by the artist 1975

P02077 Reclining Figure (1951-66)
CLπ:76x152:signed:Presented by the artist 1975

P02078 Square Forms (1963-68)
MLπ:543x759:signed:Presented by the artist 1975

P02079 Crowd Looking at a Tied Up Object (1966-8)
Mlπ:216x276:signed:Presented by the artist 1975

P02080 Hommage à Rodin (1966-7)
CLπ:295x235:signed:Presented by the artist 1975

P02081 Ideas for Sculpture (1966-7)
Mlπ:273x216:signed:Presented by the artist 1975

P02082 Six Reclining Figures on Green Ground (1966)
CLπ:340x283:signed:Presented by the artist 1975

P02083 Three Reclining Figures on Pedestals (1966-7)
CLπ:308x273:signed:Presented by the artist 1975

P02084 Two Monumental Reclining Figures (1966)
CLπ:346x279:signed:Presented by the artist 1975

P02085 Two Upright Motives (1966)
CLπ:146x146:signed:Presented by the artist 1975

P02086 Two Seated Women (1966-7)
CLπ:187x203:signed:Presented by the artist 1975

P02087 Concerto (1967-8)
CLπ:130x102:signed:Presented by the artist 1975

P02088 Eight Draped Reclining Figures (1967-71)
Mlπ:308x238:signed:Presented by the artist 1975

P02089 Fantasy (1967-8)
Mlπ:200x254:signed:Presented by the artist 1975

P02090 Four Draped Reclining Figures (1967-8)
CLπ:149x219:signed:Presented by the artist 1975

P02091 Picture Book (1967-71)
Mlπ:102x130:signed:Presented by the artist 1975

P02092 Reading Lesson (1967-8)
Mlπ:152x222:signed:Presented by the artist 1975

P02093 Seated Woman (1967-8)
Mlπ:190x121:signed:Presented by the artist 1975

P02094 Studies for Head and Shoulders Sculpture (1967-70)
Mlπ:308x241:signed:Presented by the artist 1975

P02095 Studies for Sculpture: Two and Three Piece Reclining Figures (1967-71)
Mlπ:308x241:signed:Presented by the artist 1975

P02096 Two Rock Reclining Figures (1967-8)
MLπ:289x229:signed:Presented by the artist 1975

P02097 Ideas for Sculpture [from the book 'Henry Moore' by Ionel Jiahou] (1969)
Mlπ:308x241:signed:Presented by the artist 1975

P02098 Ideas for Sculpture in Landscape [from the book 'Henry Moore' by Ionel Jianou] (1969)
Mlπ:308x241:signed:Presented by the artist 1975

P02099 Projects for Hill Sculpture [from the book 'Henry Moore' by Ionel Jianou] (1969)
Mlπ:308x241:signed:Presented by the artist 1975

P02100 Two Reclining Figures Linear (1969)
Mlπ:308x238:signed:Presented by the artist 1975

Elephant Skull Album (P02102-P02129, P02520;
complete group)

P02102 Elephant Skull Plate I (1969)
MIπ:254x200:signed:Presented by the artist 1975

P02103 Elephant Skull Plate II (1969-70)
MIπ:226x200:signed:Presented by the artist 1975

P02104 Elephant Skull Plate III (1969)
MIπ:252x199:signed:Presented by the artist 1975

P02105 Elephant Skull Plate IV (1969)
MIπ:223x240:signed:Presented by the artist 1975

P02106 Elephant Skull Plate V (1969)
MIπ:253x201:signed:Presented by the artist 1975

P02107 Elephant Skull Plate VI (1970)
MIπ:198x300:signed:Presented by the artist 1975

P02108 Elephant Skull Plate VII (1969)
MIπ:253x199:signed:Presented by the artist 1975

P02109 Elephant Skull Plate VIII (1969)
MIπ:236x308:signed:Presented by the artist 1975

P02110 Elephant Skull Plate IX (1969)
MIπ:278x238:signed:Presented by the artist 1975

P02111 Elephant Skull Plate X (1969)
MIπ:296x201:signed:Presented by the artist 1975

P02112 Elephant Skull Plate XI (1969)
MIπ:254x197:signed:Presented by the artist 1975

P02113 Elephant Skull Plate XII (1969)
MIπ:200x303:signed:Presented by the artist 1975

P02114 Elephant Skull Plate XIII (1969)
MIπ:159x111:signed:Presented by the artist 1975

P02115 Elephant Skull Plate XIV (1969)
MIπ:253x200:signed:Presented by the artist 1975

P02116 Elephant Skull Plate XV (1969)
MIπ:119x192:signed:Presented by the artist 1975

P02117 Elephant Skull Plate XVI (1970)
MIπ:344x250:signed:Presented by the artist 1975

P02118 Elephant Skull Plate XVII (1969)
MIπ:253x201:signed:Presented by the artist 1975

P02119 Elephant Skull Plate XVIII (1970)
MIπ:299x201:signed:Presented by the artist 1975

P02120 Elephant Skull Plate XIX (1969)
MIπ:238x310:signed:Presented by the artist 1975

P02121 Elephant Skull Plate XX (1969)
MIπ:278x236:signed:Presented by the artist 1975

P02122 Elephant Skull Plate XXI (1969)
MIπ:308x240:signed:Presented by the artist 1975

P02123 Elephant Skull Plate XXIII (1969)
MIπ:236x308:signed:Presented by the artist 1975

P02124 Elephant Skull Plate XXIII (1969)
MIπ:252x200:signed:Presented by the artist 1975

P02125 Elephant Skull Plate XXIV (1970)
MIπ:198x300:signed:Presented by the artist 1975

P02126 Elephant Skull Plate XXV (1970)
MIπ:235x280:signed:Presented by the artist 1975

P02127 Elephant Skull Plate XXVI (1969)
MIπ:238x309:signed:Presented by the artist 1975

P02128 Elephant Skull Plate XXVII (1970)
MIπ:347x250:signed:Presented by the artist 1975

P02129 Elephant Skull Plate XXVIII (1969)
MIπ:253x200:signed:Presented by the artist 1975

5 Incisioni di Moore (P02130-P02135; complete group)

P02130 Frontispiece of Il Bisonte Cartella (1970)
CILπ:466x292:signed:Presented by the artist 1975

P02131 Six Sculptural Motives (1970)
CILπ:309x242:signed:Presented by the artist 1975

P02132 Two Draped Standing Figures (1970)
CILπ:318x247:signed:Presented by the artist 1975

P02133 Two Women (1970)
CILπ:315x248:signed:Presented by the artist 1975

P02134 After the Accident (1970)
CILπ:334x240:signed:Presented by the artist 1975

P02135 Two Figures Talking (1970)
CILπ:310x243:signed:Presented by the artist 1975

P02136 Six Sculpture Motives (1970)
MIπ:298x200:signed:Presented by the artist 1975

P02137 Storm at Forte Dei Marmi (1970-1)
CILπ:219x286:signed:Presented by the artist 1975

P02138 Storm at Sea (1970-4)
MIπ:137x244:signed:Presented by the artist 1975

P02139 Three Motives (1970-2)
MIπ:308x241:signed:Presented by the artist 1975

P02140 Three Sculpture Motives (1970-3)
MIπ:298x200:signed:Presented by the artist 1975

P02141 Two Standing Figures (1970)
MIπ:346x251:signed:Presented by the artist 1975

P02142 Two Standing Figures No. V (1970-4)
MIπ:305x241:signed:Presented by the artist 1975

P02143 Two Standing Figures No. XI (1970-1)
MIπ:210x171:signed:Presented by the artist 1975

P02144 Wreck (1970-4)
MIπ:140x238:signed:Presented by the artist 1975

P02145 Two Standing Figures No. XII (1970-1)
MIπ:298x200:signed:Presented by the artist 1975

P02146 Two Seated Figures (1970-3)
CIπ:238x311:signed:Presented by the artist 1975

P02147 Two Tall Figures: Man and Woman (1970-4)
MIπ:295x200:signed:Presented by the artist 1975

P02148 Reclining Figure I (1970-2)
MIπ:120x251:signed:Presented by the artist 1975

P02149 Reclining Figure II (1970-2)
MIπ:110x251:signed:Presented by the artist 1975

P02150 Reclining Figure III (1970-2)
MIπ:119x249:signed:Presented by the artist 1975

P02151 Reclining Figure IV (1970-2)
MIπ:110x242:signed:Presented by the artist 1975

P02152 Two Reclining Figures (1970-2)
MIπ:235x200:signed:Presented by the artist 1975

P02153 Four Sculpture Motives (1971)
MIπ:200x168:signed:Presented by the artist 1975

P02154 Hommage à Seghers Plate I (1971)
MIπ:92x171:signed:Presented by the artist 1975

P02155 Hommage à Seghers Plate II (1971)
MIπ:92x171:signed:Presented by the artist 1975

P02156 Architecture (1971-3)
MIπ:152x156:signed:Presented by the artist 1975

P02157 Three Seated Figures (1971)
MIπ:200x254:signed:Presented by the artist 1975

P02158 Turning Figure No. 1 (1971-3)
CIπ:235x140:signed:Presented by the artist 1975

P02159 Turning Figure No. 2 (1971-3)
CIπ:235x140:signed:Presented by the artist 1975

P02160 Four Mothers (1971-4)
MIπ:305x238:signed:Presented by the artist 1975

P02161 Two Reclining Figures (1971-4)
MIπ:203x168:signed:Presented by the artist 1975

P02162 Reclining Figures and Reclining Mother & Child (1971-4)
CLπ:302x241:signed:Presented by the artist 1975

P02163 Glenkiln Cross Plate I (1972-3)
MIπ:219x159:signed:Presented by the artist 1975

P02164 Glenkiln Cross Plate II (1972-3)
MIπ:219x159:signed:Presented by the artist 1975

P02165 Log Pile I (1972-4)
MIπ:203x190:signed:Presented by the artist 1975

P02166 Log Pile II (1972-4)
MIπ:203x190:signed:Presented by the artist 1975

P02167 Log Pile III (1972-4)
MIπ:203x190:signed:Presented by the artist 1975

P02168 Two Reclining Figures (1972-4)
MIπ:241x143:signed:Presented by the artist 1975

Stonehenge (published 1974; P02169-P02187; complete group)

P02169 Stonehenge Title Page (1973)
MILπ:207x301:signed:Presented by the artist 1975

P02170 Stonehenge A (1973)
MILπ:178x255:signed:Presented by the artist 1975

P02171 Stonehenge B (1972)
MILπ:254x191:signed:Presented by the artist 1975

P02172 Stonehenge C (1972)
MILπ:253x191:signed:Presented by the artist 1975

P02173 Stonehenge I (1973)
MILπ:290x453:signed:Presented by the artist 1975

P02174 Stonehenge II (1973)
MILπ:288x454:signed:Presented by the artist 1975

P02175 Stonehenge III (1973)
MILπ:321x457:signed:Presented by the artist 1975

P02176 Stonehenge IV (1973)
MILπ:291x439:signed:Presented by the artist 1975

P02177 Stonehenge V (1973)
MILπ:293x457:signed:Presented by the artist 1975

P02178 Stonehenge VI (1973)
MILπ:294x457:signed:Presented by the artist 1975

P02179 Stonehenge VII (1973)
MILπ:289x452:signed:Presented by the artist 1975

P02180 Stonehenge VIII (1973)
MILπ:392x293:signed:Presented by the artist 1975

P02181 Stonehenge IX (1973)
MILπ:414x294:signed:Presented by the artist 1975

P02182 Stonehenge X (1973)
MILπ:455x294:signed:Presented by the artist 1975

P02183 Stonehenge XI (1973)
MILπ:452x294:signed:Presented by the artist 1975

P02184 Stonehenge XII (1973)
MILπ:294x408:signed:Presented by the artist 1975

P02185 Stonehenge XIII (1973)
MILπ:293x456:signed:Presented by the artist 1975

P02186 Stonehenge XIV (1973)
MILπ:285x457:signed:Presented by the artist 1975

P02187 Stonehenge XV (1973)
MILπ:290x457:signed:Presented by the artist 1975

P02188 Four Grey Ladies (1973)
CLπ:311x419:signed:Presented by the artist 1975

P02189 Four Silhouette Figures (1973)
Lπ:139x228:signed:Presented by the artist 1975

P02190 Hands I (1973)
MLπ:241x216:signed:Presented by the artist 1975

P02191 Hands II (1973)
MLπ:241x216:signed:Presented by the artist 1975

P02192 Seated Figure & Ideas for Sculpture (1973-4)
CLπ:267x244:signed:Presented by the artist 1975

P02193 Seated Woman in Armchair (1973-4)
MLπ:181x159:signed:Presented by the artist 1975

P02194 Six Stone Figures (1973-4)
CLπ:359x254:signed:Presented by the artist 1975

P02195 Stonehenge, Variant of Title Page (1973)
MIπ:219x305:signed:Presented by the artist 1975

P02196 Three Reclining Figures (1973-4)
MLπ:279x206:signed:Presented by the artist 1975

P02197 Three Reclining Figures with Land Background (1973-4)
CLπ:381x483:signed:Presented by the artist 1975

P02198 Three Reclining Figures with Water Background (1973-4)
CLπ:381x492:signed:Presented by the artist 1975

P02199 Three Standing Figures (1973-4)
CLπ:251x359:signed:Presented by the artist 1975

P02200 Woman Seated on Fireside Stool (1973-4)
CLπ:305x171:signed:Presented by the artist 1975

Auden Poems Moore Lithographs Portfolio (published 1974; P02201-P02219; incomplete group)

P02201 [portfolio folder] (1973)
MLπ:454x514:signed:Presented by the artist 1975

P02202 Sketches of Auden (1973)
MLπ:282x204:signed:Presented by the artist 1975

P02203 Windswept Landscape (1973)
MLπ:419x341:signed:Presented by the artist 1975

P02204 Cavern (1973)
MLπ:320x268:signed:Presented by the artist 1975

P02205 Multitude I (1973)
MLπ:286x225:signed:Presented by the artist 1975

P02206 Multitude II (1973)
MLπ:292x270:signed:Presented by the artist 1975

P02207 Thin Lipped Armourer I (1973)
MLπ:227x296:signed:Presented by the artist 1975

P02208 Thin Lipped Armourer II (1973)
MLπ:217x294:signed:Presented by the artist 1975

P02209 Two Heads (1973)
MLπ:130x200:signed:Presented by the artist 1975

P02210 Lullaby Sketches (1973)
MLπ:241x173:signed:Presented by the artist 1975

P02211 Lullaby (1973)
MLπ:293x305:signed:Presented by the artist 1975

P02212 Lullaby Sleeping Head (1973)
MLπ:276x295:signed:Presented by the artist 1975

P02213 Man and Woman (1973-4)
MLπ:364x264:signed:Presented by the artist 1975

P02214 Fjord (1973)
MLπ:224x256:signed:Presented by the artist 1975

P02215 Divided Landscape (1973)
MLπ:415x342:signed:Presented by the artist 1975

P02216 Split Stone (1973)
MLπ:307x150:signed:Presented by the artist 1975

P02217 Garsdale (1973)
MLπ:251x318:signed:Presented by the artist 1975

P02218 The Forest (1973)
MLπ:291x210:signed:Presented by the artist 1975

P02219 The Bridge (1973)
MLπ:249x342:signed:Presented by the artist 1975

P02220 Six Reclining Figures (1974-5)
CLπ:384x505:signed:Presented by the artist 1975

P02221 Four Standing Women (1974-5)
CLπ:232x403:signed:Presented by the artist 1975

P02222 Mexican Mask (1974-6)
CLπ:238x206:signed:Presented by the artist 1975

P02223 Four Reclining Figures (1974-5)
CLπ:495x594:Presented by the artist 1975

P02227 Seventeen Reclining Figures (1963-9)
MLπ:432x543:signed:Presented by the artist 1975

Sheep Album (P02228-P02244; complete group)
P02228 Sheep Album Cover (1974)
MIπ:330x825:signed:Presented by the artist 1975

P02229 Sheep with Lamb III (1972)
MIπ:145x190:signed:Presented by the artist 1975

P02230 Family (1974)
MIπ:210x251:signed:Presented by the artist 1975

P02231 Sheep in Landscape (1974)
MIπ:329x411:signed:Presented by the artist 1975

P02232 Sheep in Snow Scene (1974)
MIπ:323x412:signed:Presented by the artist 1975

P02233 Sheep in Field (1974)
MIπ:190x254:signed:Presented by the artist 1975

P02234 Sheep with Lamb I (1972)
MIπ:149x208:signed:Presented by the artist 1975

P02235 Sheep with Lamb I (1972)
MIπ:148x210:signed:Presented by the artist 1975

P02236 Sheep with Lamb IV (1972)
MIπ:143x190:signed:Presented by the artist 1975

P02237 Fat Lambs (1974)
MIπ:191x254:signed:Presented by the artist 1975

P02238 Sheep (1972)
MIπ:190x255:signed:Presented by the artist 1975

P02239 Head (1974)
MIπ:189x255:signed:Presented by the artist 1975

P02240 The Snow Sheep (1974)
MIπ:188x254:signed:Presented by the artist 1975

P02241 Ready for Shearing (1974)
MIπ:207x250:signed:Presented by the artist 1975

P02242 Sheep Back View (1972)
MIπ:213x193:signed:Presented by the artist 1975

P02243 Shorn Sheep (1974)
MIπ:190x255:signed:Presented by the artist 1975

P02244 Shorn Sheep with Lamb (1974)
MIπ:183x240:signed:Presented by the artist 1975

P02245 Seated Figure (1973-5)
CLπ:337x279:signed:Presented by the artist 1975

P02246 Six Stones (1973)
MLπ:267x194:signed:Presented by the artist 1975

P02247 Two Reclining Figures (1973-5)
CLπ:441x356:signed:Presented by the artist 1975

P02248 Two Women Bathing Child I (1973)
CLπ:368x413:signed:Presented by the artist 1975

P02249 Two Women Bathing Child (1973)
CLπ:368x413:signed:Presented by the artist 1975

P02250 Mother & Child (1974)
MLπ:279x175:signed:Presented by the artist 1975

P02251 Draped Reclining Figure (1974-5)
CLπ:346x473:signed:Presented by the artist 1975

P02252 Four Reclining Figures (1974-5)
CLπ:489x613:signed:Presented by the artist 1975

P02253 Girl Doing Homework I (1974)
MIπ:210x252:signed:Presented by the artist 1975

P02254 Girl Doing Homework II (1974)
MIπ:177x177:signed:Presented by the artist 1975

P02255 Girl Doing Homework III (1974)
MIπ:227x179:signed:Presented by the artist 1975

P02256 Girl Doing Homework IV (1974)
MIπ:178x178:signed:Presented by the artist 1975

P02257 Girl Doing Homework V (1974)
MIπ:127x140:signed:Presented by the artist 1975

P02258 Girl Doing Homework VI (1974)
MIπ:208x252:signed:Presented by the artist 1975

P02259 Nude (1974-5)
CLπ:283x241:signed:Presented by the artist 1975

P02260 Group of Figures (1974-5)
CLπ:229x333:signed:Presented by the artist 1975

P02261 Three Cloaked Figures I (1974)
CLπ:229x333:signed:Presented by the artist 1975

P02262 Three Cloaked Figures II (1974)
CLπ:229x333:signed:Presented by the artist 1975

Helmet Head Lithographs (published 1975;
P02263-P02267; complete group)
P02263 Contemplative Eye (1974-5)
CLπ:311x318:signed:Presented by the artist 1975

P02264 Direct Eye (1974-5)
CLπ:311x318:signed:Presented by the artist 1975

P02265 Hiding Eye (1974-5)
CLπ:311x318:signed:Presented by the artist 1975

P02266 Superior Eye (1974-5)
CLπ:311x318:signed:Presented by the artist 1975

P02267 Wild Eye (1974-5)
CLπ:311x318:signed:Presented by the artist 1975

P02353 Woman Holding Cat (1949-51)
CLπ:457x568:signed:Presented by the artist 1976

P02354 Figures in Settings & Sculptural Ideas (1949)
CLπ:260x368:signed:Presented by the artist 1976

P02355 Draped Reclining Figure (1951-62)
CLπ:156x203:signed:Presented by the artist 1976

P02356 Eight Reclining Figures in Yellow, Red and Blue (1966-72)
CLπ:318x289:signed:Presented by the artist 1976

P02357 White Forms (1966-9)
CLπ:483x403:signed:Presented by the artist 1976

P02358 Black Figure on Pink Background (1967-8)
CLπ:111x130:signed:Presented by the artist 1976

P02359 Eight Reclining Figures (1967)
CLπ:260x232:signed:Presented by the artist 1976

P02360 Multicoloured Reclining Figures (1967)
CLπ:140x197:signed:Presented by the artist 1976

P02361 Reclining Figure (1967)
CLπ:121x168:signed:Presented by the artist 1976

P02362 Two Forms (1967)
MLπ:219x308:signed:Presented by the artist 1976

P02363 Elephant Skull: Arch Form (1970)
MLπ:149x114:signed:Presented by the artist 1976

P02364 Three Reclining Figures (1971-6)
CLπ:464x387:signed:Presented by the artist 1976

P02365 Three Seated Figures with Children (1973-5)
CLπ:327x460:signed:Presented by the artist 1976

P02366 Girl Seated at Desk I (1974)
CLπ:220x161:signed:Presented by the artist 1976

P02367 Girl Seated at Desk II (1974)
CLπ:254x177:signed:Presented by the artist 1976

P02368 Girl Seated at Desk III (1974)
CLπ:227x178:signed:Presented by the artist 1976

P02369 Girl Seated at Desk (1974)
CLπ:233x184:signed:Presented by the artist 1976

P02370 Reclining Figure (1974)
CLπ:206x289:signed:Presented by the artist 1976

P02371 Reclining Figure (1974)
CLπ:168x244:signed:Presented by the artist 1976

P02372 Reclining Figures Man and Woman I (1975)
CLπ:254x190:signed:Presented by the artist 1976

P02373 Reclining Figures Man and Woman II (1975)
CLπ:254x190:signed:Presented by the artist 1976

P02374 Reclining Figures on Beach (1975-6)
MIπ:175x229:signed:Presented by the artist 1976

P02375 Head (1975)
CLπ:445x359:signed:Presented by the artist 1976

P02376 Ideas for Sculpture (1975)
CLπ:257x356:signed:Presented by the artist 1976

P02377 Reclining Figure (1975)
CLπ:213x286:signed:Presented by the artist 1976

P02378 Seated Mother and Child (1975-6)
CLπ:305x222:signed:Presented by the artist 1976

P02379 Three Graces (1975)
CLπ:241x190:signed:Presented by the artist 1976

P02380 Trapeze Artists (1975-6)
CLπ:238x200:signed:Presented by the artist 1976

P02381 Two Figures at a Table (1975)
CLπ:206x181:signed:Presented by the artist 1976

P02382 Three Reclining Figures (1975)
CLπ:308x229:signed:Presented by the artist 1976

P02383 Four Reclining Figures with Architectural Background (1976)
CLπ:222x356:signed:Presented by the artist 1976

Nudes (published 1976; P02384-P02393; complete group)

P02384 Girl I (1974)
MLπ:232x167:signed:Presented by the artist 1976

P02385 Seated Figures (1974)
MLπ:232x208:signed:Presented by the artist 1976

P02386 Reclining Figure (1974)
MLπ:120x178:signed:Presented by the artist 1976

P02387 Reclining Figure Back (1974)
MLπ:144x180:signed:Presented by the artist 1976

P02388 Seated Girl (1974)
MLπ:178x180:signed:Presented by the artist 1976

P02389 Seated Girl on Bed (1974)
MLπ:220x183:signed:Presented by the artist 1976

P02390 Reclining Girl on Bed (1974)
MLπ:84x179:signed:Presented by the artist 1976

P02391 Seated Figure Back (1974)
MLπ:175x180:signed:Presented by the artist 1976

P02392 Resting Girl (1974)
MLπ:159x172:signed:Presented by the artist 1976

P02393 Girl II (1974)
MLπ:233x186:signed:Presented by the artist 1976

Seated Figures (published 1976; P02394-P02399; complete group)

P02394 Seated Figure I Line Drawing (1974)
:220x160:signed:Presented by the artist 1976

P02395 Seated Figure II Pink Background (1974)
:235x160:signed:Presented by the artist 1976

P02396 Seated Figure III Dark Room (1974)
:243x173:signed:Presented by the artist 1976

P02397 Seated Figure IV Reverse Lighting (1974)
:216x144:signed:Presented by the artist 1976

P02398 Seated Figure V Wickerwork Chair (1974)
:222x173:signed:Presented by the artist 1976

P02399 [title not known] (1976)
::signed:Presented by the artist 1976

P02435 Mother and Child (1976)
CLπ:302x270:signed:Presented by the artist 1977

P02447 Two Reclining Figures (1973-5)
CLπ:441x356:Presented by the artist 1978

P02468 Reclining Figure with Interior Setting II (1977)
CLπ:241x305:signed:Presented by the artist 1978

80th Anniversary Portfolio (P02475-P02483; complete group)

P02475 Reclining Figure with Stormy Sky (1975)
CLπ:158x235:signed:Presented by the artist 1978

P02476 Mother and Child with Wave Background I (1976)
CLπ:175x265:signed:Presented by the artist 1978

P02477 Mother and Child with Wave Background II (1976)
CLπ:175x265:signed:Presented by the artist 1978

P02478 Mother and Child with Wave Background III (1976)
CLπ:175x265:signed:Presented by the artist 1978

P02479 Two Seated Figures against Pillar (1976)
CLπ:135x230:signed:Presented by the artist 1978

P02480 Woman with Arms Crossed (1976)
CLπ:153x182:signed:Presented by the artist 1978

P02481 Woman with Book (1976)
CLπ:200x140:signed:Presented by the artist 1978

P02482 Woman with Clasped Hands (1976)
CLπ:140x178:signed:Presented by the artist 1978

P02483 Woman with Dove (1976)
CLπ:285x210:signed:Presented by the artist 1978

Elephant Skull Album (P02102-P02129, P02520; complete group)

P02520 Elephant Skull Cover (1970)
MLπ::signed:Presented by the artist 1975

P02566 Sheep Walking (1974)
MLπ:127x190:signed:Presented by the artist 1982

P02567 Sheep Resting (1974)
MLπ:127x248:signed:Presented by the artist 1982

P02568 Sheep Grazing (1974)
MLπ:127x190:signed:Presented by the artist 1982

P02569 Sheep Standing (1974)
MLπ:140x190:signed:Presented by the artist 1982

P02570 Sheep Climbing (1974)
MLπ:171x197:signed:Presented by the artist 1982

P02571 Earthquake in Harbour (1973)
CLπ:308x150:signed:Presented by the artist 1982

P02572 Ideas for Wood Sculpture (1973)
CLπ:314x229:signed:Presented by the artist 1982

P02573 Sculptures Dark Interior (1973)
CLπ:254x340:signed:Presented by the artist 1982

P02574 Shipwreck I (1973)
CLπ:257x345:signed:Presented by the artist 1982

P02575 Shipwreck II (1973)
CLπ:257x345:signed:Presented by the artist 1982

P02576 Three Heads (1973)
CLπ:108x159:signed:Presented by the artist 1982

P02577 Black Reclining Figure I (1974)
MLπ:251x324:signed:Presented by the artist 1982

P02578 Black Reclining Figure II (1974)
MLπ:222x270:signed:Presented by the artist 1982

P02579 Black Reclining Figure III (1974)
MLπ:242x322:signed:Presented by the artist 1982

P02580 Black Reclining Figure IV (1974)
MLπ:232x298:signed:Presented by the artist 1982

P02581 Girl Seated at Desk V (1974)
CLπ:133x133:signed:Presented by the artist 1982

P02582 Girl Seated at Desk VI (1974)
CLπ:159x165:signed:Presented by the artist 1982

P02583 Girl Seated at Desk VII (1974)
CLπ:245x175:signed:Presented by the artist 1982

P02584 Girl Seated at Desk IX (1974)
CLπ:276x181:signed:Presented by the artist 1982

P02585 Reclining Figure (1974)
CLπ:160x238:signed:Presented by the artist 1982

P02586 Seated Figure Holding Glass (1974)
CLπ:111x152:signed:Presented by the artist 1982

P02587 Four Grazing Sheep (1974)
MLπ:137x244:signed:Presented by the artist 1982

P02588 Sheep and Lamb (1974)
CLπ:178x184:signed:Presented by the artist 1982

P02589 Sheep Before Shearing (1974)
MLπ:200x283:signed:Presented by the artist 1982

P02590 Sheep in Field (1974)
CLπ:190x276:signed:Presented by the artist 1982

P02591 Sheep in Stormy Landscape (1974)
CLπ:194x279:signed:Presented by the artist 1982

P02592 Three Grazing Sheep (1974)
MLπ:133x241:signed:Presented by the artist 1982

P02593 Two Fat Lambs (1974)
CLπ:165x286:signed:Presented by the artist 1982

P02594 Circus Scenes (1975)
Mlπ:248x206:signed:Presented by the artist 1982

P02595 High Wire Walkers (1975)
Mlπ:251x187:signed:Presented by the artist 1982

P02596 Animal Heads (1975)
CLπ:216x264:signed:Presented by the artist 1982

P02597 Draped Reclining Figure (1975)
CLπ:340x505:signed:Presented by the artist 1982

P02598 Friday Night Camden Town (1975)
CLπ:292x296:signed:Presented by the artist 1982

P02599 Group in Industrial Landscape (1975)
CLπ:168x213:signed:Presented by the artist 1982

P02600 Reclining Woman (1975)
CLπ:130x188:Presented by the artist 1982

P02601 Three Seated Figures in Setting (1975)
CLπ:220x353:signed:Presented by the artist 1982

P02602 Figures in a Forest (1976)
CLπ:291x356:signed:Presented by the artist 1982

P02603 Figures in Snow (1976)
CLπ:343x251:signed:Presented by the artist 1982

P02604 Figures with Smoke Background (1976)
MLπ:343x251:signed:Presented by the artist 1982

P02605 Mother and Child Shell (1976)
CLπ:321x251:signed:Presented by the artist 1982

P02606 Mother and Child with Border Design (1976)
CLπ:318x251:signed:Presented by the artist 1982

P02607 Mother and Child with Dark Background (1976)
CLπ:337x343:signed:Presented by the artist 1982

P02608 Mother and Child with Light Background (1976)
CLπ:337x343:signed:Presented by the artist 1982

P02609 Reclining Figure with Cliff Background (1976)
CLπ:244x338:signed:Presented by the artist 1982

P02610 Seated Mother and Child (1976)
CLπ:260x216:signed:Presented by the artist 1982

P02611 Three Reclining Figures on Pedestals (1976)
CLπ:570x777:signed:Presented by the artist 1982

P02612 Two Reclining Figures (1976)
CLπ:240x290:signed:Presented by the artist 1982

P02613 Two Seated Figures with Children (1976)
CLπ:219x267:Presented by the artist 1982

P02614 Mother and Child Studies and Reclining Figure (1977)
CLπ:382x310:signed:Presented by the artist 1982

P02615 Reclining Figure and Mother and Child Studies (1977)
CLπ:382x310:signed:Presented by the artist 1982

P02616 Reclining Figure Architectural Background I (1977)
CLπ:317x407:signed:Presented by the artist 1982

P02617 Reclining Figure Architectural Background II (1977)
CLπ:498x430:signed:Presented by the artist 1982

P02618 Reclining Figure Architectural Background III (1977)
CLπ:248x305:signed:Presented by the artist 1982

P02619 Reclining Figure Architectural Background IV (1977)
CLπ:317x381:signed:Presented by the artist 1982

P02620 Reclining Figure Interior Setting I (1977)
CLπ:244x317:signed:Presented by the artist 1982

P02621 Stone Reclining Figure (1977)
CLπ:490x705:signed:Presented by the artist 1982

Dante Stones (1980; P02622-P02626; complete group)
P02622 Stone I (1977)
Iπ:292x197:signed:Presented by the artist 1982

P02623 Stone II (1977)
Iπ:292x197:signed:Presented by the artist 1982

P02624 Stone III (1977)
Iπ:292x197:signed:Presented by the artist 1982

P02625 Stone IV (1977)
Iπ:292x197:signed:Presented by the artist 1982

P02626 Stone V (1977)
Iπ:292x197:signed:Presented by the artist 1982

P02627 Girl Reading at Window (1977-8)
CLπ:184x337:signed:Presented by the artist 1982

P02628 Male Figure in Landscape (1977-8)
CLπ:237x292:signed:Presented by the artist 1982

The Reclining Figure (1978; P02629-P02637; complete group)
P02629 Reclining Figure (1978)
Iπ:191x257:signed:Presented by the artist 1982

P02630 Reclining Figure 1 (1977-8)
Iπ:229x305:signed:Presented by the artist 1982

P02631 Reclining Figure 2 (1977-8)
Iπ:229x305:signed:Presented by the artist 1982

P02632 Reclining Figure 3 (1977-8)
Iπ:229x305:signed:Presented by the artist 1982

P02633 Reclining Figure 4 (1977-8)
Iπ:229x305:signed:Presented by the artist 1982

P02634 Reclining Figure 5 (1978)
Lπ:229x305:signed:Presented by the artist 1982

P02635 Reclining Figure 6 (1977-8)
Lπ:229x305:signed:Presented by the artist 1982

P02636 Reclining Figure 7 (1977-8)
Lπ:229x305:signed:Presented by the artist 1982

P02637 Reclining Figure 8 (1977-8)
Lπ:152x203:signed:Presented by the artist 1982

P02640 Reclining Nude I (1978)
CLπ:147x200:signed:Presented by the artist 1982

P02641 Reclining Nude II (1978)
CLπ:147x200:signed:Presented by the artist 1982

P02642 Hands of Dorothy Crowfoot Hodgkin I (1978)
MLπ:147x254:signed:Presented by the artist 1982

P02643 Hands of Dorothy Crowfoot Hodgkin II (1978)
MLπ:147x229:signed:Presented by the artist 1982

P02644 Hands of Dorothy Crowfoot Hodgkin III (1978)
MLπ:130x213:signed:Presented by the artist 1982

P02645 Hands of Dorothy Crowfoot Hodgkin IV (1978)
MLπ:137x200:signed:Presented by the artist 1982

P02646 Hands of Dorothy Crowfoot Hodgkin V (1978)
MLπ:152x238:signed:Presented by the artist 1982

P02647 Four Standing Figures (1978)
CLπ:311x384:signed:Presented by the artist 1982

P02648 Man and Woman Three Quarter Figures (1978)
CLπ:270x368:signed:Presented by the artist 1982

P02649 Reclining Figure against Sea and Rocks (1978)
CLπ:238x353:signed:Presented by the artist 1982

P02650 Reclining Figure Dawn (1978)
CLπ:229x308:signed:Presented by the artist 1982

P02651 Reclining Figure Sunset (1978)
CLπ:234x307:signed:Presented by the artist 1982

P02652 Standing Figure Storm Sky (1978)
CLπ:249x327:signed:Presented by the artist 1982

P02653 Seven Reclining Figures (1978)
CLπ:311x384:signed:Presented by the artist 1982

P02654 Stone Reclining Figure II (1978)
CLπ:584x762:signed:Presented by the artist 1982

P02655 Two Reclining Figures (1978)
CLπ:264x219:signed:Presented by the artist 1982

P02656 Child Study (1979)
MIπ:251x188:signed:Presented by the artist 1982

P02657 Sleeping Child (1979)
MIπ:188x251:signed:Presented by the artist 1982

P02658 Curved Reclining Figure in Landscape I (1979)
MIπ:188x254:signed:Presented by the artist 1982

P02659 Curved Reclining Figure in Landscape II (1979)
MIπ:188x254:signed:Presented by the artist 1982

P02660 Elephants (1979)
MIπ:152x200:signed:Presented by the artist 1982

P02661 Half Figure (1979)
MIπ:127x124:signed:Presented by the artist 1982

P02662 Head of Girl I (1979)
MIπ:229x165:signed:Presented by the artist 1982

P02663 Head of Girl II (1979)
MIπ:254x188:signed:Presented by the artist 1982

P02664 Head of a Girl and Reclining Figure (1979)
MIπ:232x277:signed:Presented by the artist 1982

P02665 Interpretation from Dürer's Portrait of Conrad Verkell
with Landscape (1979)
MIπ:222x168:signed:Presented by the artist 1982

P02666 Mother and Child (1979)
MIπ:279x225:signed:Presented by the artist 1982

P02667 Reclining Figure Distorted (1979)
CIπ:225x283:signed:Presented by the artist 1982

P02668 Reclining Figure Piranesi Background I (1979)
MIπ:159x279:signed:Presented by the artist 1982

P02669 Reclining Figure Piranesi Background II (1979)
MIπ:225x283:signed:Presented by the artist 1982

P02670 Reclining Figure Piranesi Background III (1979)
MIπ:225x283:signed:Presented by the artist 1982

P02671 Reclining Mother and Child I (1979)
MIπ:225x283:signed:Presented by the artist 1982

P02672 Reclining Mother and Child II (1979)
MIπ:225x283:signed:Presented by the artist 1982

P02673 Reclining Mother and Child I Profile (1979)
MIπ:225x283:signed:Presented by the artist 1982

P02674 Seated Figure (1979)
MIπ:225x171:signed:Presented by the artist 1982

P02675 Seated Figure with Architectural Background (1979)
MIπ:175x171:signed:Presented by the artist 1982

P02676 Seated Mother and Child (1979)
MIπ:219x168:signed:Presented by the artist 1982

P02677 Seated Nude (1979)
MIπ:254x188:signed:Presented by the artist 1982

P02678 Seated Woman (1979)
MIπ:225x165:signed:Presented by the artist 1982

P02679 Woman Putting on Stocking I (1979)
MIπ:254x190:signed:Presented by the artist 1982

P02680 Woman Putting on Stocking II (1979)
MIπ:254x190:signed:Presented by the artist 1982

P02681 Female Torso and Sculpture Ideas I (1979)
CLπ:283x403:signed:Presented by the artist 1982

P02682 Female Torso and Sculpture Ideas II (1979)
CLπ:283x403:signed:Presented by the artist 1982

P02683 Homage to Sacheverell Sitwell (1979)
CLπ:271x194:signed:Presented by the artist 1982

P02684 Man and Woman (1979)
CLπ:229x330:signed:Presented by the artist 1982

P02685 Opening Form I (1979)
CLπ:270x343:signed:Presented by the artist 1982

P02686 Reclining Figure Arch Leg (1979)
CLπ:273x410:signed:Presented by the artist 1982

P02687 Reclining Figure Cave (1979)
CLπ:302x410:signed:Presented by the artist 1982

P02688 Reclining Figure Pointed (1979)
MLπ:330x419:signed:Presented by the artist 1982

P02689 Sisters with Children (1979)
CLπ:333x498:signed:Presented by the artist 1982

P02690 Six Sculpture Ideas (1979)
CLπ:317x425:signed:Presented by the artist 1982

P02691 Two Reclining Mother and Child Studies (1979)
CLπ:200x200:signed:Presented by the artist 1982

Trees (published 1980; P02692-P02697; complete group)

P02692 Trees I Bole and Creeper (1979)
Lπ:238x188:signed:Presented by the artist 1982

P02693 Trees II Upright Branches (1979)
Lπ:232x159:signed:Presented by the artist 1982

P02694 Trees III Knuckled Trunk (1979)
Lπ:190x254:signed:Presented by the artist 1982

P02695 Trees IV Tortured Roots (1979)
Lπ:242x188:signed:Presented by the artist 1982

P02696 Trees V Spreading Branches (1979)
Lπ:168x206:signed:Presented by the artist 1982

P02697 Trees VI Dead Ash (1979)
Lπ:222x168:signed:Presented by the artist 1982

P02698 Sheep in Landscape (1974)
CLπ:219x257:signed:Presented by the artist 1982

P02699 Feet on Holiday I (1979)
CLπ:210x257:signed:Presented by the artist 1982

P02700 Feet on Holiday II (1979)
CLπ:215x255:signed:Presented by the artist 1982

P02701 Reclining Figure (1979)
CLπ:170x220:signed:Presented by the artist 1982

P02702 Idea for Relief Sculpture (1980)
CLπ:219x168:signed:Presented by the artist 1982

P02703 Reclining Nude (1980)
CLπ:222x298:signed:Presented by the artist 1982

P02704 Seated Mother and Child (1979-80)
CLπ:420x278:signed:Presented by the artist 1982

P02705 Female Figures with Grey Background (1980)
CLπ:230x445:signed:Presented by the artist 1982

P02706 Mother with Child on Lap (1980)
CLπ:118x93:signed:Presented by the artist 1982

P02707 Seated Figure (1980)
CLπ:320x375:signed:Presented by the artist 1982

P02708 Six Reclining Figures with Blue Background (1980)
CLπ:245x262:signed:Presented by the artist 1982

P02709 Eight Sculpture Ideas (1980-81)
CLπ:380x260:signed:Presented by the artist 1982

P02710 Seated Mother and Child (1980-81)
CLπ:343x260:signed:Presented by the artist 1982

P02711 Seven Sculpture Ideas I (1980-81)
CLπ:376x283:signed:Presented by the artist 1982

P02712 Seven Sculpture Ideas II (1980-81)
CLπ:356x292:signed:Presented by the artist 1982

P02713 Elephants Head I (1981)
CLπ:275x235:signed:Presented by the artist 1982

P02714 Elephant's Head II (1981)
CLπ:230x230:signed:Presented by the artist 1982

P02715 Figures with Sky Background I (1981)
CLπ:268x272:signed:Presented by the artist 1982

P02716 Figures with Sky Background II (1981)
CLπ:258x348:signed:Presented by the artist 1982

P02717 Five Ideas for Sculpture (1981)
CLπ:350x250:signed:Presented by the artist 1982

P02718 Six Reclining Figures (1981)
CLπ:220x248:signed:Presented by the artist 1982

P02719 Six Reclining Figures with Red Background (1981)
CLπ:220x248:signed:Presented by the artist 1982

P02720 Three Sculpture Ideas (1981)
CLπ:368x278:Presented by the artist 1982

P02721 Three Seated Figures (1981)
CLπ:327x283:signed:Presented by the artist 1982

P02722 Three Sisters (1981)
CLπ:349x251:signed:Presented by the artist 1982

P02838 Mary and Martha (1981, published 1983)
CLπ:225x251:signed:Presented by the Henry Moore Foundation 1986

P02839 Nativity (1981, published 1983)
CLπ:225x251:signed:Presented by the Henry Moore Foundation 1986

P02840 Rock Head (1981, published 1983)
CLπ:252x226:signed:Presented by the Henry Moore Foundation 1986

P02841 The Attendants (1981, published 1983)
CLπ:225x251:signed:Presented by the Henry Moore Foundation 1986

P02842 The Observers (1981, published 1983)
CLπ:225x251:signed:Presented by the Henry Moore Foundation 1986

P02843 The Three Marys (1981, published 1983)
CLπ:225x251:signed:Presented by the Henry Moore Foundation 1986

P02844 Two Heads (1981, published 1983)
CLπ:225x251:signed:Presented by the Henry Moore Foundation 1986

P02845 Visitation (1981, published 1983)
CLπ:251x225:signed:Presented by the Henry Moore Foundation 1986

P02846 Woman's Head (1981, published 1983)
CLπ:222x251:signed:Presented by the Henry Moore Foundation 1986

P02847 Reclining Figure (1979, published 1982)
Mlπ:168x222:signed:Presented by the Henry Moore Foundation 1986

P02848 Reclining Mother and Child with Blue Background (1982, published 1983)
CLπ:546x751:signed:Presented by the Henry Moore Foundation 1986

P02849 Reclining Mother and Child with Grey Background (1982, published 1983)
CLπ:546x753:signed:Presented by the Henry Moore Foundation 1986

P02850 Reclining Woman with Yellow Background (1982, published 1984)
CLπ:372x470:signed:Presented by the Henry Moore Foundation 1986

P02851 Six Heads Olympians (1982, published 1983)
CLπ:857x593:signed:Presented by the Henry Moore Foundation 1986

P02852 Reclining Woman on Beach (1980-81, published 1982)
CLπ:552x759:signed:Presented by the Henry Moore Foundation 1986

P02853 Reclining Woman on Sea Shore (1980-81, published 1982)
CLπ:444x610:signed:Presented by the Henry Moore Foundation 1986

P02854 Reclining Woman I (1980-81, published 1982)
CLπ:524x590:signed:Presented by the Henry Moore Foundation 1986

P02855 Reclining Woman II (1980-81, published 1982)
CLπ:419x514:signed:Presented by the Henry Moore Foundation 1986

P02856 Reclining Woman III (1980-81, published 1982)
CLπ:477x648:signed:Presented by the Henry Moore Foundation 1986

P02857 Reclining Woman IV (1980-81, published 1982)
CLπ:488x613:signed:Presented by the Henry Moore Foundation 1986

Sculptural Ideas (published 1981; P02858-P02864; complete group)

P02858 Sculptural Ideas I (1980)
CLπ:251x341:signed:Presented by the Henry Moore Foundation 1986

P02859 Sculptural Ideas 2 (1980)
CLπ:251x341:signed:Presented by the Henry Moore
Foundation 1986

P02860 Sculptural Ideas 3 (1980)
CLπ:219x241:signed:Presented by the Henry Moore
Foundation 1986

P02861 Sculptural Ideas 4 (1980)
CLπ:251x341:signed:Presented by the Henry Moore
Foundation 1986

P02862 Sculptural Ideas 5 (1980)
CLπ:251x341:signed:Presented by the Henry Moore
Foundation 1986

P02863 Sculptural Ideas 6 (1980)
CLπ:251x341:signed:Presented by the Henry Moore
Foundation 1986

P02864 Sculptural Ideas 7 (1980)
CLπ:251x341:signed:Presented by the Henry Moore
Foundation 1986

P02865 Ideas for Metal Sculpture I (1981)
CLπ:224x245:signed:Presented by the Henry Moore
Foundation 1986

P02866 Ideas for Metal Sculpture II (1981)
CLπ:224x245:signed:Presented by the Henry Moore
Foundation 1986

P02867 Ideas for Metal Sculpture III (1981)
CLπ:250x225:signed:Presented by the Henry Moore
Foundation 1986

P02868 Ideas for Metal Sculpture IV (1981)
CLπ:224x245:signed:Presented by the Henry Moore
Foundation 1986

P02869 Ideas for Metal Sculpture V (1981)
CLπ:224x245:signed:Presented by the Henry Moore
Foundation 1986

P02870 Ideas for Metal Sculpture VI (1981)
CLπ:224x248:signed:Presented by the Henry Moore
Foundation 1986

P02871 Ideas for Figures in a Setting (1984)
CLπ:277x219:signed:Presented by the Henry Moore
Foundation 1986

P02872 Man and Woman (1984)
CLπ:304x251:signed:Presented by the Henry Moore
Foundation 1986

P02873 Man and Woman in a Landscape (1984)
CLπ:280x403:signed:Presented by the Henry Moore
Foundation 1986

P02874 Standing Nudes (1984)
CLπ:280x413:signed:Presented by the Henry Moore
Foundation 1986

P02875 Two Ideas for Sculpture (1984)
CLπ:160x354:signed:Presented by the Henry Moore
Foundation 1986

P02876 Two Women Seated on Bench (1984)
CLπ:315x464:signed:Presented by the Henry Moore
Foundation 1986

P02877 Family Group (1984)
CLπ:251x332:signed:Presented by the Henry Moore
Foundation 1986

Seven Ages of Man (published 1986; P02878-P02885;
complete group)

P02878 Man and Woman (1982)
CLπ:238x158:signed:Presented by the Henry Moore
Foundation 1986

P02879 The Infant (1982)
MLπ:285x200:signed:Presented by the Henry Moore
Foundation 1986

P02880 The Schoolboy (1982)
MLπ:267x203:signed:Presented by the Henry Moore
Foundation 1986

P02881 The Lover (1982)
MLπ:242x194:signed:Presented by the Henry Moore
Foundation 1986

P02882 The Soldier (1982)
MLπ:317x210:signed:Presented by the Henry Moore
Foundation 1986

P02883 The Justice (1982)
MLπ:314x213:signed:Presented by the Henry Moore
Foundation 1986

P02884 The Pantaloon (1982)
MLπ:267x206:signed:Presented by the Henry Moore
Foundation 1986

P02885 The Last Scene (1982)
MLπ:308x190:signed:Presented by the Henry Moore
Foundation 1986

P02886 Kneeling Woman (1982, published 1984)
CLπ:325x251:signed:Presented by the Henry Moore
Foundation 1986

P02887 Reclining Figure: Bone (1982, published 1984)
CLπ:252x352:signed:Presented by the Henry Moore
Foundation 1986

P02888 Reclining Figure: Idea for Metal Sculpture (1982,
published 1984)
CLπ:234x307:signed:Presented by the Henry Moore
Foundation 1986

P02889 Four Ideas for Sculpture (1982, published 1984)
CLπ:235x306:signed:Presented by the Henry Moore
Foundation 1986

P02890 Head Study I after Andrea Pisano (1981)
MIπ:276x244:signed:Presented by the Henry Moore
Foundation 1986

P02891 Head Study II after Andrea Pisano (1981)
MIπ:286x248:signed:Presented by the Henry Moore
Foundation 1986

P02892 Head of Girl II (1981)
FIπ:196x144:signed:Presented by the Henry Moore
Foundation 1986

P02893 Head of Girl III (1981)
FIπ:197x147:signed:Presented by the Henry Moore
Foundation 1986

P02894 Adam (1980, published 1983)
CLπ:263x335:signed:Presented by the Henry Moore
Foundation 1986

P02895 Eve (1980, published 1983)
CLπ:266x355:signed:Presented by the Henry Moore
Foundation 1986

P02896 Head of Girl (1981, published 1982)
MIπ:291x308:signed:Presented by the Henry Moore
Foundation 1986

P02897 Opening Form II (1979)
CLπ:225x303:signed:Presented by the Henry Moore
Foundation 1986

P02898 Tunnel Arch and Window (1971, published 1978)
MIπ:149x152:signed:Presented by the Henry Moore
Foundation 1986

P02899 Architecture Doorway (1972, published 1978)
MIπ:191x213:signed:Presented by the Henry Moore
Foundation 1986

P02900 Reclining Figure: Point (1976, published 1979)
CLπ:168x243:signed:Presented by the Henry Moore
Foundation 1986

P02901 Two Reclining Figures (1977-8, published 1978)
MIπ:300x226:signed:Presented by the Henry Moore
Foundation 1986

P02902 Two Reclining Figures (1977-8, published 1979)
MIπ:300x227:signed:Presented by the Henry Moore
Foundation 1986

P02903 Two Reclining Figures (1977-8, published 1978)
MIπ:302x222:signed:Presented by the Henry Moore
Foundation 1986

P02904 Five Reclining Figures (1979, published 1980)
MLπ:277x435:signed:Presented by the Henry Moore
Foundation 1986

P02905 Two Standing Figures No. V (1970, published 1974)
MIπ:306x239:signed:Presented by the Henry Moore
Foundation 1986

P02906 Storm at Sea (1970, published 1974)
MIπ:135x235:signed:Presented by the Henry Moore
Foundation 1986

The Artist's Hand (published 1980; P02907-P02911;
complete group)

P02907 The Artist's Hand I (1979)
MLπ:277x184:signed:Presented by the Henry Moore
Foundation 1986

P02908 The Artist's Hand II (1979)
MIπ:190x254:signed:Presented by the Henry Moore
Foundation 1986

P02909 The Artist's Hand III (1979)
MLπ:317x270:signed:Presented by the Henry Moore
Foundation 1986

P02910 The Artist's Hand IV (1979)
MIπ:220x168:signed:Presented by the Henry Moore
Foundation 1986

P02911 The Artist's Hand V (1979)
MLπ:260x194:signed:Presented by the Henry Moore
Foundation 1986

Animals in the Zoo (published 1983; P02912-P02926;
complete group)

P02912 [title page] (1982)
MIπ:98x123:signed:Presented by the Henry Moore
Foundation 1986

P02913 [accompanying text for 'Animals in the Zoo': (1st Page)]
(1982)
MIπ:97x123:signed:Presented by the Henry Moore
Foundation 1986

P02914 [accompanying text for 'Animals in the Zoo': (2nd Page)]
(1982)
MIπ:98x124:signed:Presented by the Henry Moore
Foundation 1986

P02915 Rhinoceros (1981)
MIπ:213x277:signed:Presented by the Henry Moore
Foundation 1986

P02916 Dromedary (1981)
MIπ:212x277:signed:Presented by the Henry Moore
Foundation 1986

P02917 Vultures (1981)
MIπ:211x277:signed:Presented by the Henry Moore
Foundation 1986

P02918 Elephant (1981)
MIπ:212x276:signed:Presented by the Henry Moore
Foundation 1986

P02919 Leopard (1981)
MIπ:250x195:signed:Presented by the Henry Moore
Foundation 1986

P02920 Zebra (1981)
MIπ:212x275:signed:Presented by the Henry Moore
Foundation 1986

P02921 Bison (1981)
MIπ:211x276:signed:Presented by the Henry Moore
Foundation 1986

P02922 Jaguar (1981)
MIπ:211x276:signed:Presented by the Henry Moore
Foundation 1986

P02923 Antelope (1982)
MIπ:212x276:signed:Presented by the Henry Moore
Foundation 1986

P02924 Tiger (1982)
MIπ:192x240:signed:Presented by the Henry Moore
Foundation 1986

P02925 Tiger (1982)
MIπ:273x352:signed:Presented by the Henry Moore
Foundation 1986

P02926 Elephant (1981)
MIπ:272x352:signed:Presented by the Henry Moore
Foundation 1986

P02927 Elephant's Head (1982)
MIπ:97x121:signed:Presented by the Henry Moore
Foundation 1986

P02928 Bison (1982)
MIπ:97x123:signed:Presented by the Henry Moore
Foundation 1986

P02929 Rhinoceros (1982)
MIπ:98x124:signed:Presented by the Henry Moore
Foundation 1986

P02930 Elephant (1982)
MIπ:122x98:signed:Presented by the Henry Moore
Foundation 1986

P02931 Tiger (1982)
MIπ:123x98:signed:Presented by the Henry Moore
Foundation 1986

P02932 Rhinoceros' Head (1982)
MIπ:123x98:signed:Presented by the Henry Moore
Foundation 1986

P06362 Eight Reclining Figures (1958)
CLπ:311x257:signed:Presented by Curwen Studio
through the Institute of Contemporary Prints 1975

P06363 Black on Red Image (1963)
CLπ:524x483:signed:Presented by Curwen Studio
through the Institute of Contemporary Prints 1975

P06364 Eight Reclining Figures on Rock Background (1963)
CLπ:651x505:signed:Presented by Curwen Studio
through the Institute of Contemporary Prints 1975

P06365 Two Standing Figures (1963)
CLπ:502x660:signed:Presented by Curwen Studio
through the Institute of Contemporary Prints 1975

P06366 Eight Reclining Figures with Architectural Background
(1963)
CLπ:432x330:signed:Presented by Curwen Studio
through the Institute of Contemporary Prints 1975

P06367 Seventeen Reclining Figures with Architectural
Background (1963)
CLπ:521x686:signed:Presented by Curwen Studio
through the Institute of Contemporary Prints 1975

P06368 Five Reclining Figures (1963)
CLπ:768x568:signed:Presented by Curwen Studio
through the Institute of Contemporary Prints 1975

P06369 Single Form (1963)
CLπ:657x505:signed:Presented by Curwen Studio
through the Institute of Contemporary Prints 1975

P06370 Six Reclining Figures (1963)
CLπ:502x660:signed:Presented by Curwen Studio
through the Institute of Contemporary Prints 1975

P06371 Six Reclining Figures in Black (1963)
MLπ:505x657:signed:Presented by Curwen Studio
through the Institute of Contemporary Prints 1975

P06372 Six Reclining Figures with Buff Background (1963)
CLπ:460x591:signed:Presented by Curwen Studio
through the Institute of Contemporary Prints 1975

P06373 Two Reclining Figures with River Background (1963)
CLπ:305x632:signed:Presented by Curwen Studio
through the Institute of Contemporary Prints 1975

P06374 Two Seated Figures in Stone (1963)
MLπ:394x289:signed:Presented by Curwen Studio
through the Institute of Contemporary Prints 1975

P06375 Three Reclining Figures (1971)
CLπ:298x232:signed:Presented by Curwen Studio
through the Institute of Contemporary Prints 1975

P06376 Three Reclining Figures (1971)
CLπ:276x235:signed:Presented by Curwen Studio
through the Institute of Contemporary Prints 1975

P06377 Three Reclining Figures (1971-2)
CLπ:298x229:signed:Presented by Curwen Studio
through the Institute of Contemporary Prints 1975

P06378 Three Reclining Figures (1971-3)
CLπ:298x238:signed:Presented by Curwen Studio
through the Institute of Contemporary Prints 1975

P06379 Three Reclining Figures (1971-3)
CLπ:298x232:signed:Presented by Curwen Studio
through the Institute of Contemporary Prints 1975

P06380 Group of Reclining Figures (1973)
CLπ:464x397:signed:Presented by Curwen Studio
through the Institute of Contemporary Prints 1975

P06381 Pallas Heads (1973)
CLπ:346x464:signed:Presented by Curwen Studio
through the Institute of Contemporary Prints 1975

P06382 Reclining & Standing Figure and Family Group (1973)
CLπ:445x324:signed:Presented by Curwen Studio
through the Institute of Contemporary Prints 1975

P06383 Reclining Figure with Red Stripes (1973)
CLπ:225x206:signed:Presented by Curwen Studio
through the Institute of Contemporary Prints 1975

P06384 Reclining Figure with Sea Background (1973)
CLπ:467x375:signed:Presented by Curwen Studio
through the Institute of Contemporary Prints 1975

P06385 Reclining Figure with Sky Background (1973)
CLπ:441x387:signed:Presented by Curwen Studio
through the Institute of Contemporary Prints 1975

P06386 Six Reclining Figures (1973)
CLπ:321x381:signed:Presented by Curwen Studio
through the Institute of Contemporary Prints 1975

P06387 Two Black Forms: Metal Figures (1973)
MLπ:327x260:signed:Presented by Curwen Studio
through the Institute of Contemporary Prints 1975

P06388 Two Reclining Figures (1973)
CLπ:429x337:signed:Presented by Curwen Studio
through the Institute of Contemporary Prints 1975

P06389 Two Reclining Figures on Striped Background (1973)
CLπ:464x337:signed:Presented by Curwen Studio
through the Institute of Contemporary Prints 1975

P06390 Hommage à Picasso (1973-4)
CLπ:422x629:signed:Presented by Curwen Studio
through the Institute of Contemporary Prints 1975

P06391 Ideas for Wood Sculpture (1973-4)
CLπ:349x267:signed:Presented by Curwen Studio
through the Institute of Contemporary Prints 1975

P06392 Mother and Child (1973-4)
CLπ:241x178:signed:Presented by Curwen Studio
through the Institute of Contemporary Prints 1975

P06393 Three Sculptural Objects (1973-4)
CLπ:343x257:signed:Presented by Curwen Studio
through the Institute of Contemporary Prints 1975

P06394 Four Reclining Figures: Caves (1974)
CLπ:451x600:signed:Presented by Curwen Studio
through the Institute of Contemporary Prints 1975

P06698 Reclining Figures (1973)
CLπ:295x219:signed:Presented by Curwen Studio 1976

P06699 Seven Sculptural Ideas (1973)
CLπ:340x256:signed:Presented by Curwen Studio 1976

Penwith Portfolio (P01416, P06005, P06108, P06130,
P06241, P06324, P06346, P06359, P06399, P06519,
P06700; complete group; mixed group)

P06700 Silhouette Figures with Border Design (1973)
CLπ:487x452:signed:Presented by Curwen Studio 1976

MORANDI, Giorgio 1890-1964
Modern Collection
Tate Gallery Archive holds material concerning this artist

N05782 Still Life (1946)
Natura morta
Oc:375x457:signed:Presented by Studio d'Arte Palma,
Rome 1947

P01919 Hilltop at Evening (1928)
Il poggio di sera
MLπ:140x244:signed:Presented by Senor and Senora Jose
Luis Plaza 1979

P01920 Still Life with Very Fine Hatching (1933)
Natura morta a tratti sottilissimi
MIπ:248x238:signed:Presented by Senor and Senora Jose
Luis Plaza 1979

MORDMULLER, R.G. born 1941
Modern Collection

Imaginations (P08028-P08033; incomplete group)
P08028 [no title] (1977)
CLπ:219x159:Transferred from the Library 1978

P08029 [no title] (1977)
CLπ:219x159:Transferred from the Library 1978

P08030 [no title] (1977)
CLπ:219x159:Transferred from the Library 1978

P08031 [no title] (1977)
CLπ:219x159:Transferred from the Library 1978

P08032 [no title] (1977)
CLπ:219x159:Transferred from the Library 1978

P08033 [no title] (1977)
CLπ:219x159:Transferred from the Library 1978

MORE, Jacob circa 1740-1793
British Collection

T00601 Falls of Clyde: Stonebyres (circa 1771-3)
Oc:803x1006:Purchased 1963

MORELLET, François born 1926
Modern Collection

T01840 Two Warps and Wefts of Short Lines 0 90 (1955-6)
2 Trames de tirets 0-90
Oc:1000x1000:signed:Purchased 1974

MORETON, Warwick born 1947
Modern Collection

P03116 The Gang I (1973)
CNπ:460x225:signed:Presented by Andrew Dickerson 1975

MORISOT, Berthe 1841-1895
Modern Collection

T01079 Girl on a Divan (circa 1885)
Jeune femme au divan
Oc:610x502:signed:Bequeathed by the Hon. Mrs A.E. Pleydell-Bouverie through the Friends of the Tate Gallery 1968

MORLAND, George 1763-1804
British Collection
Tate Gallery Archive holds material concerning this artist

N01030 Inside of a Stable (exhibited 1791)
Oc:1486x2038:signed:Presented by T. Birch Wolfe 1877

N01067 The Gravel Diggers
Ow:178x229:Purchased 1877

N01497 Rabbiting (1792)
Oc:864x1168:signed:Bequeathed by John Travers Smith 1897

N02056 The Fortune Teller
Oc:457x533:Bequeathed by Mrs Behrend 1906

N02639 Outside the Ale-House Door (1792)
Oc:349x273:signed:Bequeathed by George Salting 1910

N02640 Cowherd and Milkmaid (1792)
Oc:508x660:signed:Bequeathed by George Salting 1910

N02641 Roadside Inn (1790)
Oc:511x664:signed:Bequeathed by George Salting 1910

N05796 Morning: Higglers Preparing for Market (1791)
Oc:698x902:signed:Presented by Frederick John Nettlefold 1947

N05849 Outside an Inn, Winter
Oc:718x921:signed:Bequeathed by Mrs Mary Venetia James 1948

T00055 The Tea Garden (engraved 1790)
Oc:406x505:Purchased 1955

MORLAND, Henry Robert 1716-1797
British Collection

N01402 A Lady's Maid Soaping Linen (circa 1765-82)
Oc:743x616:Purchased 1894

N01403 A Laundry Maid Ironing (circa 1765-82)
Oc:743x616:Purchased 1894

N05471 A Girl Singing Ballads by a Paper Lanthorn (circa 1765-82)
Oc:756x622:Bequeathed by Mrs Frances Elinor Pearse 1944

MORLEY, Harry 1881-1943
Modern Collection

N03956 Apollo and Marsyas (1924)
Tc:1067x1016:signed:Presented by the Trustees of the Chantrey Bequest 1924

MORLEY, Malcolm born 1931
Modern Collection

P04612 Horses (1969)
CNπ:629x679:signed:Presented by Rose and Chris Prater through the Institute of Contemporary Prints 1975

P07602 Train Wreck (Gold Version) (1975-81)
CIπ:829x1121:Purchased 1981

MORRICE, James Wilson 1865-1924
Modern Collection
Tate Gallery Archive holds material concerning this artist

N03842 House in Santiago (1915)
Oc:540x648:signed:Presented by the Contemporary Art Society 1924

MORRIS, Sir Cedric, Bt 1889-1982
Modern Collection
Tate Gallery Archive holds material concerning this artist

T03230 Iris Seedlings (1943)
Oc:1219x918:signed:Purchased 1981

T03231 Lucian Freud (1941)
Oc:730x603:signed:Purchased 1981

T03232 David and Barbara Carr (circa 1940)
Oc:1003x746:Purchased 1981

T03592 Patisseries and a Croissant (circa 1922)
Oc:359x327:signed:Presented by Miss Nancy Morris, the artist's sister 1983

T03831 Frances Hodgkins (circa 1917)
Gπ:242x162:Presented by the surviving executor of Frances Hodgkins 1984

T04996 Landscape of Shame (circa 1960)
Oc:756x1002:Presented by the Friends of the Tate Gallery 1987

T05498 Peregrine Falcons (1942)
Oc:620x700:Bequeathed by Miss Nancy Morris, the artist's sister 1988

T05499 Belle of Bloomsbury (1948)
Oc:663x552:Bequeathed by Miss Nancy Morris, the artist's sister 1988

MORRIS, Michael born 1942
Modern Collection
Tate Gallery Archive holds material concerning this artist

Centennial Suite (P03217-P03225, P03228-P03229; complete group; mixed group)
P03224 Screen Test (1967)
CNπ:324x479:signed:Presented by Simon Fraser University, British Columbia 1977

MORRIS, Robert born 1931
Modern Collection
Tate Gallery Archive holds material concerning this artist

T01185 Untitled 1967-8 (1967-8)
Sa:457x2438x2438:Purchased 1970

T01532 Untitled (1965/71)
Sgw:914x914x914:Purchased 1972

P07235 Location Piece (1973)
RVm:537x537x38:Purchased 1974

MORRIS, William 1834-1896
British Collection

N04999 La Belle Iseult (1858)
Oc:718x502:Bequeathed by Miss May Morris 1939

N05219 The Archangel Gabriel
Wπ:2210x610:signed:Presented by the Trustees of the Chantrey Bequest 1940

N05221 Figure of Guinevere (circa 1858)
WDπ:1264x552:Presented by the Trustees of the Chantrey Bequest 1940

N05222 Guinevere and Iseult: Cartoon for Stained Glass (1862)
Wπ:600x686:Presented by the Trustees of the Chantrey Bequest 1940

N05223 Angel of the Resurrection: Cartoon for Stained Glass
Wπ:470x689:Presented by the Trustees of the Chantrey Bequest 1940

A00815 An Angel with a Harp
Dπ:387x190:Bequeathed by J.R. Holliday 1927

A00816 An Angel with a Pipe
Dπ:431x177:Bequeathed by J.R. Holliday 1927

A00817 A Girl with a Flute
Wπ:273x140:Bequeathed by J.R. Holliday 1927

A00818 Design for Tapestry
Dπ:133x349:Bequeathed by J.R. Holliday 1927

attributed to
MORRIS, William 1834-1896
British Collection

A00819 The Archangel Raphael
Wπ:772x187:Presented by the Trustees of the Chantrey Bequest 1940

A00820 The Archangel Gabriel
Wπ:772x187:Presented by the Trustees of the Chantrey Bequest 1940

MORTIMER, John Hamilton 1740-1779
British Collection

The Progress of Virtue (N05837-N05840; complete group)

N05837 I. The Hero Decides to Seek his Fortune (exhibited 1775)
Oc:765x622:Purchased 1948

N05838 II. The Hero's Father Blesses his Departure (exhibited 1775)
Oc:762x635:Purchased 1948

N05839 III. The Hero Rescues the Prisoners (exhibited 1775)
Oc:762x635:Purchased 1948

N05840 IV. The Hero's Father Blesses his Marriage (exhibited 1775)
Oc:752x629:Purchased 1948

N06158 George Thompson, his Wife and (?) his Sister-in-Law (circa 1766-8)
Oc:997x1260:Bequeathed by Mrs Elizabeth Carstairs 1952

T02057 Sir Arthegal, the Knight of Justice, with Talus, the Iron Man (from Spenser's 'Faerie Queene') (exhibited 1778)
Oc:2426x1460:Purchased 1976

after
MORTIMER, John Hamilton 1740-1779
British Collection

T01041 Self-Portrait
Ow:314x254:Presented by Mrs M. Bernard 1968

manner of
MORTIMER, John Hamilton 1740-1779
British Collection

T00342 Rocky Landscape with Banditti (circa 1770-80)
Oc:502x603:Purchased 1960

MORTON, Alastair 1910-1963
Modern Collection
Tate Gallery Archive holds material concerning this artist

T01776 Opus 15 (Light Blue and Yellow) (1938)
Oc:686x991:signed:Purchased 1973

MOSLEY, Charles - see HOGARTH, William and MOSLEY, Charles

MOSS, Marlow 1890-1958
Modern Collection
Tate Gallery Archive holds material concerning this artist

T01113 Composition in Yellow, Black and White (1949)
ROcw:508x356x6:signed:Presented by Miss Erica Brausen 1969

T01114 Balanced Forms in Gunmetal on Cornish Granite (1956-7)
Sms:260x311x273:Presented by Miss Erica Brausen 1969

MOTESICZKY, Marie-Louise von - see VON MOTESICZKY, Marie-Louise

MOTHERWELL, Robert born 1915
Modern Collection
Tate Gallery Archive holds material concerning this artist

T01180 Open No. 122 in Scarlet and Blue (1969)
ADc:2134x2540:signed:Presented by the artist through the American Federation of Arts 1970

T01194 Open No. 121 (Bolton Landing Elegy) (1969)
ADc:2438x4420:signed:Presented by the artist through the American Federation of Arts 1970

P01797 Poet (1) (1961)
MLπ:549x410:signed:Presented by the Museum of Modern Art, New York 1976

'London Series I' (P04613-P04614; incomplete group)
P04613 No. 13 (1970-76)
CNπ:918x610:signed:Presented by Rose and Chris Prater through the Institute of Contemporary Prints 1975

P04614 No. 5 (1970-72)
CNπ:918x613:signed:Presented by Rose and Chris Prater through the Institute of Contemporary Prints 1975

Africa Suite (P04615-P04624; incomplete group)
P04615 Africa 1 (1970)
Nπ:810x597:signed:Presented by Rose and Chris Prater through the Institute of Contemporary Prints 1975

P04616 Africa 6 (1970)
Nπ:810x597:signed:Presented by Rose and Chris Prater through the Institute of Contemporary Prints 1975

P04617 Africa 5 (1970)
Nπ:807x605:signed:Presented by Rose and Chris Prater through the Institute of Contemporary Prints 1975

P04618 Africa 7 (1970)
Nπ:807x597:signed:Presented by Rose and Chris Prater through the Institute of Contemporary Prints 1975

P04619 Africa 2 (1970)
Nπ:810x597:signed:Presented by Rose and Chris Prater through the Institute of Contemporary Prints 1975

P04620 Africa 3 (1970)
Nπ:810x598:signed:Presented by Rose and Chris Prater through the Institute of Contemporary Prints 1975

P04621 Africa 8 (1970)
Nπ:809x600:signed:Presented by Rose and Chris Prater through the Institute of Contemporary Prints 1975

P04622 Africa 10 (1970)
Nπ:810x602:signed:Presented by Rose and Chris Prater through the Institute of Contemporary Prints 1975

P04623 Africa 4 (1970)
Nπ:812x600:signed:Presented by Rose and Chris Prater through the Institute of Contemporary Prints 1975

P04624 Africa 9 (1970)
Nπ:810x600:signed:Presented by Rose and Chris Prater through the Institute of Contemporary Prints 1975

The Basque Suite (P04625-P04634; incomplete group)
P04625 No. 7 (1970)
CNπ:717x560:signed:Presented by Rose and Chris Prater through the Institute of Contemporary Prints 1975

P04626 Untitled C (1970)
CNπ:715x558:signed:Presented by Rose and Chris Prater through the Institute of Contemporary Prints 1975

P04627 No. 3 (1970)
CNπ:715x560:signed:Presented by Rose and Chris Prater through the Institute of Contemporary Prints 1975

P04628 No. 4 (1970)
CNπ:715x560:signed:Presented by Rose and Chris Prater through the Institute of Contemporary Prints 1975

P04629 No. 13 (1970)
CNπ:715x560:signed:Presented by Rose and Chris Prater through the Institute of Contemporary Prints 1975

P04630 Untitled A (1970)
CNπ:718x559:signed:Presented by Rose and Chris Prater through the Institute of Contemporary Prints 1975

P04631 No. 12 (1970)
CNπ:716x560:signed:Presented by Rose and Chris Prater through the Institute of Contemporary Prints 1975

P04632 Untitled B (1970)
CNπ:714x560:signed:Presented by Rose and Chris Prater through the Institute of Contemporary Prints 1975

P04633 No. 8 (1970)
CNπ:714x559:signed:Presented by Rose and Chris Prater through the Institute of Contemporary Prints 1975

P04634 Untitled D (1970)
CNπ:713x559:signed:Presented by Rose and Chris Prater through the Institute of Contemporary Prints 1975

MOTTRAM, Charles - see CRUIKSHANK, George and MOTTRAM, Charles; after DOYLE, John 1807-1876

MOYNIHAN, Rodrigo 1910-1990
Modern Collection

N05714 Private Clarke, A.T.S. (1943)
Oc:457x356:signed:Presented by the War Artists' Advisory Committee 1946

N05771 Still Life with Skull (1945)
Oc:686x559:signed:Presented by the Trustees of the Chantrey Bequest 1946

N06079 Portrait Group (1951)
Oc:2134x3346:Presented by the Trustees of the Chantrey Bequest 1952

T00172 Objective Abstraction (circa 1935-6)
Oc:457x356:Purchased 1958

T00187 Yellow and Violet (1957)
Oc:1270x1016:signed:Purchased 1958

T01583 Interior with a Nude and a Still Life (1937)
Oc:914x1219:signed:Presented by William W. Winkworth 1972

T01770 Painting (1935)
Oc:419x343:Purchased 1973

T03158 Figure in Studio (1977-80)
Oc:410x330:Presented by the Trustees of the Chantrey Bequest 1980

T03931 The Shelf: Objects and Shadows - Front View (1982-3)
Oc:711x915:signed:Presented by the Friends of the Tate Gallery 1984

P06397 Lake Shadow (1972)
CLπ:571x775:signed:Presented by Curwen Studio through the Institute of Contemporary Prints 1975

MOZELEY, Charles
Modern Collection
Tate Gallery Archive holds material concerning this artist

School Prints (P01698-P01727; complete group; mixed group)
P01715 The Ballet (1946-9)
CLπ:495x765:Presented by Patrick Seale Prints 1975

P06395 [title not known] (1959)
CLπ:641x438:Presented by Curwen Studio through the Institute of Contemporary Prints 1975

P06396 [title not known] (1959)
CLπ:603x419:Presented by Curwen Studio through the Institute of Contemporary Prints 1975

MUHRMAN, Henry 1854-1916
British Collection

N02996 Kew Bridge (circa 1898)
Oc:610x927:signed:Presented by F. Howard through the National Loan Exhibition Committee 1914

MUIRHEAD, David 1867-1930
British Collection

N03200 The Avenue (1901)
Oc:445x540:signed:Presented by Mr and Mrs F. Gibson 1917

N03323 Battersea Reach (1917)
Wπ:711x921:signed:Presented by Viscount Bearsted through the National Art Collections Fund 1918

N03906 The Palace, Linlithgow (1923)
Wπ:283x397:signed:Purchased 1924

N04421 Portrait of a Girl (circa 1922)
Oc:283x397:signed:Presented by A.E. Anderson through the National Art Collections Fund 1928

N04781 The Cornfield (exhibited 1911)
Oc:610x914:signed:Presented by Julian Lousada through the National Art Collections Fund 1935

MÜLLER, William James 1812-1845
British Collection

N00379 Eastern Landscape (1843)
Ow:356x521:signed:Presented by Robert Vernon 1847

N01040 A Mountain Stream (circa 1843)
Oc:521x749:Purchased 1878

N01463 View of Bologna: Capriccio with Eastern Figures (circa 1835)
Oc:603x902:Presented by Lady Weston as part of the Sir Joseph Weston Gift 1895

N01474 Dredging on the Medway
Oc:902x1803:Presented by Holbrook Gaskell 1896

N01565 Caernarvon Castle (?1837)
Oc:1016x1524:signed:Presented by Sir Henry Tate 1895

N01728 A Lake-Side Scene (1837)
Wπ:229x305:signed:Bequeathed by Leonard S. Pratten 1890

N02315 Trees, Suffolk (1831)
Wπ:400x270:Presented by Lady Weston as part of the Sir Joseph Weston Gift 1908

N02316 Gateway of Caernarvon Castle (1833)
Wπ:368x267:signed:Presented by Lady Weston as part of the Sir Joseph Weston Gift 1908

N02317 Castle Ditch, Bristol (1831-3)
Wπ:349x248:Presented by Lady Weston as part of the Sir Joseph Weston Gift 1908

N02318 Fourteen Stars Inn, Counterslip (1831-3)
Wπ:457x298:Presented by Lady Weston as part of the Sir Joseph Weston Gift 1908

N02319 Castle, (?Harlech)
Wπ:194x343:Presented by Lady Weston as part of the Sir Joseph Weston Gift 1908

N02320 The Avon, 1 (1834)
Wπ:363x495:signed:Presented by Lady Weston as part of the Sir Joseph Weston Gift 1908

N02321 The Avon, 2 (1834)
Wπ:437x302:signed:Presented by Lady Weston as part of the Sir Joseph Weston Gift 1908

N02322 The Avon, 3: from Leigh Woods (1834)
Wπ:280x404:signed:Presented by Lady Weston as part of the Sir Joseph Weston Gift 1908

N02323 The Avon, 4 (1834)
Wπ:292x441:signed:Presented by Lady Weston as part of the Sir Joseph Weston Gift 1908

N02324 The Avon, 5 (1834)
Wπ:426x286:signed:Presented by Lady Weston as part of the Sir Joseph Weston Gift 1908

N02325 The Avon, 6 (1834)
Wπ:282x448:signed:Presented by Lady Weston as part of the Sir Joseph Weston Gift 1908

N02326 The Avon, 7 (1834)
Wπ:255x376:signed:Presented by Lady Weston as part of the Sir Joseph Weston Gift 1908

N02327 The Avon, 8 (1834)
Wπ:234x368:signed:Presented by Lady Weston as part of the Sir Joseph Weston Gift 1908

N02328 Study of Willows
Dπ:248x317:Presented by Lady Weston as part of the Sir Joseph Weston Gift 1908

N02329 An Interior
WGπ:324x305:Presented by Lady Weston as part of the Sir Joseph Weston Gift 1908

N02330 Bristol Harbour in Ice
WGπ:218x344:signed:Presented by Lady Weston as part of the Sir Joseph Weston Gift 1908

N02331 A Roadside, Leigh (1834)
Wπ:200x267:signed:Presented by Lady Weston as part of the Sir Joseph Weston Gift 1908

N02332 Study of Pines, Rheinwald (1834)
Wπ:269x410:signed:Presented by Lady Weston as part of the Sir Joseph Weston Gift 1908

N02333 Near Wallenstadt (1834)
Wπ:127x206:signed:Presented by Lady Weston as part of the Sir Joseph Weston Gift 1908

N02334 Near Wallenstadt, 2 (1834-5)
Wπ:190x298:signed:Presented by Lady Weston as part of the Sir Joseph Weston Gift 1908

N02336 The Splügen (1834)
WGπ:283x397:signed:Presented by Lady Weston as part of the Sir Joseph Weston Gift 1908

N02337 Via Mala (1834)
WGπ:346x279:signed:Presented by Lady Weston as part of the Sir Joseph Weston Gift 1908

N02338 Lake or River Bank, with Houses
WDπ:106x220:Presented by Lady Weston as part of the Sir Joseph Weston Gift 1908

N02339 Venice
Wπ:342x539:signed:Presented by Lady Weston as part of the Sir Joseph Weston Gift 1908

N02340 The Lagoon, Venice
Wπ:116x414:signed:Presented by Lady Weston as part of the Sir Joseph Weston Gift 1908

N02341 Tivoli: Villa of Maecenas from the North
Wπ:176x437:signed:Presented by Lady Weston as part of the Sir Joseph Weston Gift 1908

N02342 Tivoli: Villa of Maecenas from the North-West
Wπ:298x455:signed:Presented by Lady Weston as part of the Sir Joseph Weston Gift 1908

N02343 Tivoli: The Cascade
Wπ:430x287:signed:Presented by Lady Weston as part of the Sir Joseph Weston Gift 1908

N02344 Tivoli, with the Temple of the Sibyl
Wπ:276x405:signed:Presented by Lady Weston as part of the Sir Joseph Weston Gift 1908

N02345 A Woodland Pool
Wπ:184x267:Presented by Lady Weston as part of the Sir Joseph Weston Gift 1908

N02346 Rocks and Trees
Wπ:432x292:Presented by Lady Weston as part of the Sir Joseph Weston Gift 1908

N02347 Glen Martin Mill, Porlock (1835)
Dπ:257x429:Presented by Lady Weston as part of the Sir Joseph Weston Gift 1908

N02348 Athens, with the Acropolis in Middle Distance (1838)
WDπ:273x422:signed:Presented by Lady Weston as part of the Sir Joseph Weston Gift 1908

N02349 The Parthenon, View from the Interior (1838)
Gπ:419x267:signed:Presented by Lady Weston as part of the Sir Joseph Weston Gift 1908

N02350 The Temple, Aegina (1839)
Wπ:324x484:signed:Presented by Lady Weston as part of
the Sir Joseph Weston Gift 1908

N02351 On the Nile (?near Cairo)
Wπ:221x319:Presented by Lady Weston as part of the Sir
Joseph Weston Gift 1908

N02352 Street in a Near Eastern Town
Wπ:247x145:Presented by Lady Weston as part of the Sir
Joseph Weston Gift 1908

N02353 A Near Eastern Court
Wπ:264x185:Presented by Lady Weston as part of the Sir
Joseph Weston Gift 1908

N02354 Study for 'Arab Shepherds' (circa 1842)
Gπ:102x227:Presented by Lady Weston as part of the Sir
Joseph Weston Gift 1908

N02355 Study of an Aloe
WGπ:287x449:Presented by Lady Weston as part of the
Sir Joseph Weston Gift 1908

N02356 Lighthouse, Naples (1839)
Wπ:287x449:signed:Presented by Lady Weston as part of
the Sir Joseph Weston Gift 1908

N02357 Rouen: La Fierté de St Romain (1840)
Wπ:305x412:signed:Presented by Lady Weston as part of
the Sir Joseph Weston Gift 1908

N02358 Rouen: Apse of St Vincent (1840)
Wπ:438x305:signed:Presented by Lady Weston as part of
the Sir Joseph Weston Gift 1908

N02359 Rouen: Hôtel du Bourgtheroulde (1840)
WDπ:433x290:signed:Presented by Lady Weston as part
of the Sir Joseph Weston Gift 1908

N02360 Diane Chasseresse (1840)
WGπ:278x442:signed:Presented by Lady Weston as part
of the Sir Joseph Weston Gift 1908

N02361 Fountainebleau: The Court of Honour (published 1841)
Wπ:297x432:signed:Presented by Lady Weston as part of
the Sir Joseph Weston Gift 1908

N02362 Fountainebleau: The Palace from the Carp Pond (?1840)
Wπ:286x418:Presented by Lady Weston as part of the Sir
Joseph Weston Gift 1908

N02363 Orleans: House of Francis I (1840)
Wπ:415x297:signed:Presented by Lady Weston as part of
the Sir Joseph Weston Gift 1908

N02364 Sketch for the Frontispiece to the 'Age of Francis I'
(published 1841)
Wπ:571x394:signed:Presented by Lady Weston as part of
the Sir Joseph Weston Gift 1908

N02365 Chambord: The Terrace (published 1841)
Wπ:305x436:signed:Presented by Lady Weston as part of
the Sir Joseph Weston Gift 1908

N02366 Chambord: General View of the Château (?1840)
Wπ:296x431:signed:Presented by Lady Weston as part of
the Sir Joseph Weston Gift 1908

N02367 A Church Interior (?St Denis - Hors, Amboise) (1840)
Wπ:406x280:signed:Presented by Lady Weston as part of
the Sir Joseph Weston Gift 1908

N02368 Azay-le-Rideau: Entrance to the Château (1840)
Wπ:414x285:signed:Presented by Lady Weston as part of
the Sir Joseph Weston Gift 1908

N02369 A Tomb with Effigies
Wπ:254x355:Presented by Lady Weston as part of the Sir
Joseph Weston Gift 1908

N02370 Whitchurch, near Bristol (1840)
Wπ:254x326:signed:Presented by Lady Weston as part of
the Sir Joseph Weston Gift 1908

N02371 Sketch for 'Eel Pots at Goring' (circa 1843)
Wπ:387x511:Presented by Lady Weston as part of the Sir
Joseph Weston Gift 1908

N02372 Camels, a Study in Smyrna (1843)
Wπ:330x544:signed:Presented by Lady Weston as part of
the Sir Joseph Weston Gift 1908

N02374 Lycia: A Turkish Cottage (1843)
Wπ:347x472:signed:Presented by Lady Weston as part of
the Sir Joseph Weston Gift 1908

N02375 Lycia: The Rocky Stair at Tlos (1843-4)
Wπ:347x537:signed:Presented by Lady Weston as part of
the Sir Joseph Weston Gift 1908

N02376 Lycia: The Citadel of Tlos (1844)
Wπ:240x537:signed:Presented by Lady Weston as part of
the Sir Joseph Weston Gift 1908

N02377 Lycia: The Valley of Glaucus (1843)
Wπ:177x553:signed:Presented by Lady Weston as part of
the Sir Joseph Weston Gift 1908

N02378 Arch, Palms, and Shed
Wπ:261x231:Presented by Lady Weston as part of the Sir
Joseph Weston Gift 1908

N02379 Donkey and Fowls
Wπ:127x181:signed:Presented by Lady Weston as part of
the Sir Joseph Weston Gift 1908

N02380 Lynmouth: The River Bank (1844)
Wπ:324x352:signed:Presented by Lady Weston as part of
the Sir Joseph Weston Gift 1908

N02381 Lynmouth: A Bend of the River (?1844)
Wπ:371x570:Presented by Lady Weston as part of the Sir
Joseph Weston Gift 1908

N02382 Rocky Woodland
Wπ:388x416:Presented by Lady Weston as part of the Sir
Joseph Weston Gift 1908

N02383 Leigh Woods (1844)
Wπ:529x349:Presented by Lady Weston as part of the Sir
Joseph Weston Gift 1908

N02384 A Coast Scene
Wπ:292x419:Presented by Lady Weston as part of the Sir
Joseph Weston Gift 1908

N02385 Stonehenge
Wπ:346x553:Presented by Lady Weston as part of the Sir
Joseph Weston Gift 1908

N02386 A Punt
Wπ:342x233:Presented by Lady Weston as part of the Sir
Joseph Weston Gift 1908

N02387 Compton Dando, Somerset (1845)
Wπ:356x559:Presented by Lady Weston as part of the Sir
Joseph Weston Gift 1908

T00044 Waterfall with Fisherman
Oc:508x400:Purchased 1955

A00821 Lycia: A Burdock (1843-4)
Wπ:67x89:Presented by Lady Weston as part of the Sir
Joseph Weston Gift 1908

A00822 Lycia: A Xanthian Youth (1843-4)
Dπ:114x86:signed:Presented by Lady Weston as part of
the Sir Joseph Weston Gift 1908

A00823 Lycia: A Xanthian Boy with a Bow (1843-4)
Dπ:114x70:Presented by Lady Weston as part of the Sir
Joseph Weston Gift 1908

A00824 Lycia: Women in Near Eastern Dress (1843-4)
DWπ:114x105:signed:Presented by Lady Weston as part
of the Sir Joseph Weston Gift 1908

MULLICAN, Matt born 1951
Modern Collection

P77267 Cosmology (1988)
Vπ:764x208:signed:Purchased 1988

MULREADY, William 1786-1863
British Collection
Tate Gallery Archive holds material concerning this artist

N00393 The Last In (1835)
Ow:622x762:signed:Presented by Robert Vernon 1847

N00394 Fair Time (exhibited 1809; background circa 1840)
Oc:787x660:Presented by Robert Vernon 1847

N00395 Crossing the Ford (exhibited 1842)
Ow:606x502:Presented by Robert Vernon 1847

N00396 The Younger Brother (exhibited 1857)
Oc:775x629:Presented by the executors of Robert Vernon 1857

N01181 A Sea-Shore
Oc:375x502:Bequeathed by Mrs Elizabeth Vaughan 1885

N01743 Academy Study (1857)
Dπ:495x216:Presented by Society of Arts 1858

N01744 Academy Study (1846 and 1857)
Dπ:495x356:Presented by Society of Arts 1858

N01745 Academy Study (1842)
Dπ:508x356:Presented by Society of Arts 1858

N01797 Study for 'Interior of an English Cottage' (circa 1828)
Ow:98x70:Bequeathed by Henry Vaughan 1900

T01746 Cottage and Figures (exhibited 1807)
Ob:397x333:Purchased 1973

T01899 The Rattle (exhibited 1808)
Oc:375x340:signed:Purchased 1974

attributed to
MULREADY, William 1786-1863
British Collection

N01038 A Snow Scene
Ob:305x441:Purchased 1878

MUNCASTER, Claude 1903-1974
Modern Collection

N04150 Demolition of Hay's Wharf (1925)
WDπ:292x394:signed:Purchased 1926

MUNCH, Edvard 1863-1944
Modern Collection

N05035 The Sick Child (1907)
Oc:1187x1210:signed:Presented by Thomas Olsen 1939

MUNDY, Henry born 1919
Modern Collection
Tate Gallery Archive holds material concerning this artist

T00709 Float III (1961)
ODb:1600x1981:signed:Presented by the Contemporary Art Society 1964

The Institute of Contemporary Arts Portfolio (P04016, P04038, P04053, P04076, P04115, P04125, P04166, P04248, P04256, P04315-P04316, P04334, P04378-P04380, P04419, P04635, P04752, P04938, P05138, P05155, P05248; complete group; mixed group)

P04635 Untitled (1964)
CNπ:606x584:signed:Presented by Rose and Chris Prater through the Institute of Contemporary Prints 1975

MUNN, Paul Sandby 1773-1845
British Collection

T04172 Bedlam Furnace, Madeley Dale, Shropshire (1803)
DWπ:325x548:signed:Purchased 1986

MUNNINGS, Sir Alfred 1875-1959
British Collection
Tate Gallery Archive holds material concerning this artist

N03554 Epsom Downs - City and Suburban Day (1919)
Oc:794x1283:signed:Presented by the Trustees of the Chantrey Bequest 1920

N04543 From My Bedroom Window (1930)
Oc:914x1016:signed:Presented by the Trustees of the Chantrey Bequest 1930

N04956 Their Majesties' Return from Ascot (1925)
Oc:1480x2445:signed:Presented by the Trustees of the Chantrey Bequest 1937

MUNOZ, Lucio born 1929
Modern Collection

T00476 Panel 21 (1959)
Tabla 21
Ow:698x1089:signed:Presented by the Contemporary Art Society 1962

MURPHY, John born 1945
Modern Collection

T03341 The Blue Veil (1970)
Ac:914x1019:signed:Presented by the Contemporary Art Society 1982

T03342 Delta (1978-9)
ODc:610x584:signed:Purchased 1982

T03343 An Art of Exchange Featuring an Unknown Young Man from a Painting by Albrecht Dürer (1976)
CVπ:616x527:signed:Purchased 1982

T03344 An Art of Exchange Featuring Treasurer H. Urmiller from a Painting by an Unknown Artist (1976)
CVπ:616x527:signed:Purchased 1982

T03345 Silence '. . . augural abscence of a voice which fascinates and . . .' (1980)
WDπ:819x695:signed:Purchased 1982

T03346 Sadness '. . . the incurable imperfection in the very essence of the present moment . . .' (1980)
WDπ:819x695:signed:Purchased 1982

Jam Press Phase One (P08006-P08014; complete group; mixed group)

P08012 1. 8 (1973-4)
MLπ:559x441:Transferred from the Library 1977

MURRAY, Charles 1894-1954
Modern Collection

N05149 Bathers (1940)
Ow:419x584:signed:Purchased 1940

N05150 Trawlers (1940)
Gπ:286x457:Purchased 1940

N05370 Russian Soldiers (1941)
Gπ:318x527:signed:Purchased 1942

N05623 The Resurrection (1944)
Wπ:622x356:signed:Presented by Messrs A.R. Mowbray
and Co 1945

MURRAY, Charles Fairfax 1849-1919
British Collection

N05001 Study of William Morris on his Death-Bed (1896)
Dπ:286x225:signed:Bequeathed by Miss May Morris 1939

MURRAY, Sir David 1849-1933
British Collection
Tate Gallery Archive holds material concerning this artist

N01614 My Love has Gone a-Sailing (exhibited 1883)
Oc:1003x1524:signed:Presented by the Trustees of the
Chantrey Bequest 1884

N01926 In the Country of Constable (1903)
Oc:1219x1829:signed:Presented by the Trustees of the
Chantrey Bequest 1903

N04468 Summer Haze in Sussex (1929)
Oc:610x737:signed:Presented by Sir Alexander Grant
1929

MURRAY, Elizabeth born 1940
Modern Collection

P77126 Untitled (Black Cup) (1984)
HCLπ:1504x921:signed:Purchased 1985

MURTIC, Edo born 1921
Modern Collection

T00426 Red and Brown (1960)
Crveno smede
Oc:1143x1460:signed:Presented by the Yugoslav
Committee of Cultural Relations 1961

MUSIC, Antonio Zoran born 1909
Modern Collection

P77168 Dalmatian Lands (1959)
Lπ:415x572:signed:Purchased 1986

MYERS, Bernard born 1925
Modern Collection
Tate Gallery Archive holds material concerning this artist

P06797 Chrysanthemums (1978)
CLπ:470x635:Presented by Curwen Studio 1978

P06798 Japanese Anemones (1978)
CLπ:479x654:Presented by Curwen Studio 1978

MYTENS, Daniel, the Elder circa 1590-1647
British Collection

N03474 The First Duke of Hamilton (?) as a Boy (1624)
Oc:2007x1251:signed:Presented by Colin Agnew and
Charles Romer Williams 1919

NAGHI BEY, Mohammed 1888-1956
Modern Collection

N04823 Religious Procession, Addis Ababa (1932)
Oc:540x348:signed:Presented by Lord Bossom 1936

NASH, David born 1945
Modern Collection
Tate Gallery Archive holds material concerning this artist

T03471 Rostrum with Bonks (1971)
Sw:1740x630x630:Purchased 1982

T03472 Wood Quarry - Beech, Otterlo (1982)
DVπ:1219x2426:signed:Purchased 1982

T03473 Family Tree, 1970-1982 (1982)
Dπ:965x1884:signed:Purchased 1982

T03932 Flying Frame (1980)
Sw:2160x3430x1200:Exchanged with the artist 1984

NASH, John 1893-1977
Modern Collection
Tate Gallery Archive holds material concerning this artist

N03720 The Lane (exhibited 1923)
WDπ:286x387:Purchased 1923

N05037 The Moat, Grange Farm, Kimble (exhibited 1922)
Oc:762x508:Presented by the Contemporary Art Society
1939

N05140 Dorset Landscape (circa 1915)
WDπ:413x387:Purchased 1940

N05206 Rocks and Sand Dunes, South Wales, Llangeneth (circa
1939)
WDπ:394x571:signed:Presented by the Contemporary
Art Society 1940

N05331 A Suffolk Landscape (circa 1936-7)
Oc:610x813:signed:Presented by the Trustees of the
Chantrey Bequest 1939

N06074 The Cornfield (1918)
Oc:686x762:signed:Presented by the Contemporary Art
Society 1952

N06214 The Blenheim (1947)
WDπ:578x470:signed:Purchased 1954

N06215 Avoncliffe from the Aqueduct (circa 1926)
WDπ:387x495:signed:Purchased 1954

N06234 The Cornfield (1918)
Wπ:187x270:signed:Bequeathed by Sir Edward Marsh
through the Contemporary Art Society 1954

T00035 Fallen Tree (1955)
Wπ:438x552:signed:Presented by the Trustees of the
Chantrey Bequest 1955

T00280 Wild Garden, Winter (1959)
Wπ:406x571:signed:Presented by the Trustees of the
Chantrey Bequest 1959

T00592 Mill Building, Boxted (1962)
Oc:711x813:signed:Presented by the Trustees of the
Chantrey Bequest 1963

T02247 A Path through Trees (circa 1915)
Oc:508x610:signed:Presented by the Trustees of the
Chantrey Bequest 1977

School Prints (P01698-P01727; complete group; mixed
group)

P01716 Harvesting (1946-9)
CLπ:495x762:Presented by Patrick Seale Prints 1975

P01717 Window Plants (1945)
CLπ:498x762:Presented by Patrick Seale Prints 1975

P08020 Cyclamen Periscum (circa 1924-78)
MJπ:171x124:Transferred from the Library 1978

P08021 Epiphyllum in Flower (circa 1925-78)
MJπ:159x124:Transferred from the Library 1978

P08022 A Cottage in Gloucestershire (circa 1925-78)
MJπ:124x171:Transferred from the Library 1978

P08023 Threshing (circa 1925-78)
MJπ:124x203:Transferred from the Library 1978

P08024 Frontispiece for the Book of the Tree (circa 1927-78)
MJπ:140x95:Transferred from the Library 1978

P08025 The Fisherman (circa 1931-78)
MJπ:114x137:Transferred from the Library 1978

NASH, Paul 1889-1946
Modern Collection
Tate Gallery Archive holds material concerning this artist

N03843 Tench Pond in a Gale (1921-2)
DWπ:578x394:signed:Presented by the Contemporary
Art Society 1924

N04259 Behind the Inn (1919-22)
Oc:635x762:signed:Presented by the Daily Express 1927

N05047 Landscape at Iden (1929)
Oc:698x908:signed:Purchased 1939

N05048 Blue House on the Shore (circa 1930-1)
Oc:419x737:signed:Purchased 1939

N05129 London: Winter Scene, No. 2 (1940)
WDπ:289x394:Presented by the Contemporary Art
Society 1940

N05254 Grotto in the Snow (1939)
Oc:718x489:signed:Purchased 1940

N05392 Pillar and Moon (1932-42)
Oc:508x762:signed:Presented by the National Art
Collections Fund 1942

N05667 Landscape from a Dream (1936-8)
Oc:679x1016:signed:Presented by the Contemporary Art
Society 1946

N05715 Bomber in the Corn (1940)
WDπ:394x578:signed:Presented by the War Artists'
Advisory Committee 1946

N05716 The Messerschmidt in Windsor Great Park (1940)
WDπ:400x578:Presented by the War Artists' Advisory
Committee 1946

N05717 Totes Meer (Dead Sea) (1940-1)
Oc:1016x1524:signed:Presented by the War Artists'
Advisory Committee 1946

N06024 Voyages of the Moon (1934-7)
Oc:711x540:signed:Purchased 1951

T00734 Kinetic Feature (1931)
Oc:660x508:signed:Presented by the Friends of the Tate
Gallery 1965

T01251 Equivalents for the Megaliths (1935)
Oc:457x660:signed:Purchased 1970

T01771 Swanage (circa 1936)
FDWπ:400x581:signed:Purchased 1973

T01782 Lavengro and Isopel in the Dingle (1912-13)
Dπ:464x368:signed:Presented by the Friends of the Tate
Gallery 1973

T01821 The Pyramids in the Sea (1912)
Dπ:324x292:signed:Purchased 1973

T01945 Sketch for 'Lavengro and Isopel in the Dingle' (circa
1911-12)
Gπ:267x216:signed:Purchased 1975

T01946 The Orchard (?1914)
DWπ:571x457:signed:Purchased 1975

T02243 In the Marshes (1938)
Vw:241x375:Presented by Anthony and Anne d'Offay
1977

T03098 Lares (1930)
Oc:708x406:signed:Bequeathed by W.N. Sherratt 1980

T03204 Mansions of the Dead (1932)
DWπ:578x394:signed:Purchased 1981

T03205 Three Rooms (1937)
DWπ:394x295:Purchased 1981

T03206 Harbour and Room (1932-6)
Oc:914x711:signed:Purchased 1981

T03820 The Colne (1925)
WDπ:390x570:signed:Bequeathed by Mrs Ernestine
Carter 1984

T04157 Wittenham Clumps (circa 1943-4)
ODc:633x757:Presented by the Trustees of the Paul Nash
Trust 1986

T04161 Landscape at Large (1936)
Vv:262x377:signed:Purchased 1986

P01026 Promenade II (1920-73)
MJπ:137x156:signed:Presented by the Trustees of the
Paul Nash Trust 1971

P01751 The Wall, Dymchurch (circa 1923-75)
Mlπ:127x203:signed:Presented by the Trustees of the
Paul Nash Trust 1976

NASMYTH, Patrick 1787-1831
British Collection

N00380 A Cottage, Formerly in Hyde Park (circa 1807)
Ow:298x391:signed:Presented by Robert Vernon 1847

N00381 The Angler's Nook (1825)
Ow:302x406:signed:Presented by Robert Vernon 1847

N01176 Landscape with a Cottage (1828)
Ow:203x257:signed:Bequeathed by Mrs Elizabeth
Vaughan 1885

N01177 Landscape (1831)
Oc:502x692:signed:Bequeathed by Mrs Elizabeth
Vaughan 1885

N01178 View near Sevenoaks, Kent (1820)
Ow:267x349:signed:Bequeathed by Mrs Elizabeth
Vaughan 1885

N01179 Landscape with a Farm House (1820)
Ow:165x254:signed:Bequeathed by Mrs Elizabeth
Vaughan 1885

N01183 Landscape with a River
Ow:244x314:Bequeathed by Mrs Elizabeth Vaughan 1885

N01384 View in the New Forest near Lyndhurst (1815)
Oc:660x870:signed:Bequeathed by Col. Alexander
Beresford Read 1893

N01828 View in Sussex
Ow:343x445:Bequeathed by Henry Vaughan 1900

N01916 The Severn off Portishead (1827)
Oc:654x908:signed:Bequeathed by Charles Gassiot 1902

N02208 A Pond (1820)
Ow:457x610:Bequeathed by Henry Callcott Brunning
1907

N02950 Falls of the Tummell (1816)
Ow:165x203:signed:Bequeathed by Sir Henry Layard
1913

N02951 Landscape with a Ruin
Ow:152x216:signed:Bequeathed by Sir Henry Layard
1913

N05797 View on the Thames: Greenwich in the Distance (1820)
Oc:660x908:signed:Presented by Frederick John
Nettlefold 1947

NAUMAN, Bruce born 1941
Modern Collection
Tate Gallery Archive holds material concerning this artist

T01753 Corridor with Mirror and White Lights (1971)
Swg:3048x178x1219:Purchased 1973

P07938 NO (Black State) (1981)
MLπ:698x1038:signed:Purchased 1983

NEAGU, Paul born 1938
Modern Collection
Tate Gallery Archive holds material concerning this artist

T05032 Rocking Hyphen (Edge Runner) (1983)
Swmπ:515x1820x780:signed:Presented by Curwen
Gallery 1988

P07259 Jump (1977)
WCNVi:565x762:signed:Purchased 1979

NEBOT, Balthazar active 1730-1765
British Collection

N01453 Covent Garden Market (1737)
Oc:648x1228:signed:Purchased 1895

NECKEMKIN, Sarah
Modern Collection

P06398 Landscape (1960)
CLπ:391x283:Presented by Curwen Studio through the
Institute of Contemporary Prints 1975

NEILAND, Brendan born 1941
Modern Collection
Tate Gallery Archive holds material concerning this artist

P02946 Lloyd's (1986)
Nπ:763x509:signed:Presented by the artist 1987

P03121 Porch (1975)
CLπ:346x686:signed:Presented by Anderson O'Day 1975

P11045 Tolmer Square (1981)
CNπ:781x984:signed:Presented by Elemeta Windows
1981

NELLENS, Roger born 1937
Modern Collection

Machine (P04636-P04639; complete group)
P04636 Machine I (1972)
CNπ:394x701:signed:Presented by Rose and Chris Prater
through the Institute of Contemporary Prints 1975

P04637 Machine II (1972)
CNπ:472x715:signed:Presented by Rose and Chris Prater
through the Institute of Contemporary Prints 1975

P04638 Machine III (1972)
CNπ:574x459:signed:Presented by Rose and Chris Prater
through the Institute of Contemporary Prints 1975

P04639 Machine IV (1972)
CNπ:726x413:signed:Presented by Rose and Chris Prater
through the Institute of Contemporary Prints 1975

NEMON, Oscar 1906-1985
Modern Collection

T03207 Sir John Rothenstein (1960, cast 1982)
Sz:327x260x308:Presented by Lord Charteris of
Amisfield in memory of the Hon. Sir Evan Charteris 1981

NEVELSON, Louise 1899-1988
Modern Collection

T00514 Black Wall (1959)
Sw:2642x2165x648:signed:Presented by the Friends of the
Tate Gallery 1962

T00796 An American Tribute to the British People (1960-4)
SAw:3099x4343x1168:Presented by the artist 1965

T03967 Untitled No. 34 (1980)
Vw:1370x914:signed:Presented by the artist 1985

T03968 Untitled No. 15 (1981)
Vw:1018x814:signed:Presented by the artist 1985

T03969 Untitled No. 16 (1983)
Vw:1018x814:signed:Presented by the artist 1985

T03970 Untitled No. 40 (1983)
Vw:1018x814:signed:Presented by the artist 1985

P77270 Dancing Figure (circa 1953-5)
Lπ:521x353:Purchased 1989

NEVINSON, Christopher Richard Wynne 1889-1946
Modern Collection
Tate Gallery Archive holds material concerning this artist

N03177 La Mitrailleuse (1915)
Oc:610x508:signed:Presented by the Contemporary Art
Society 1917

N04231 A Studio in Montparnasse (exhibited 1926)
Oc:1270x762:signed:Presented by H.G. Wells 1927

N04672 Self-Portrait (1911)
Ow:311x232:signed:Bequeathed by Mrs Margaret Wynne
Nevinson 1932

N04979 Fitzroy Square (1923-4)
Ow:381x276:signed:Presented by D.C. Fincham 1939

T00110 The Arrival (1923-4)
Oc:762x635:signed:Presented by the artist's widow 1956

T00249 Study for 'Returning to the Trenches' (1914-15)
Dπ:146x206:Purchased 1959

T00495 A Star Shell (exhibited 1916)
Oc:508x406:signed:Presented by the Trustees of the
Chantrey Bequest 1962

T00862 Venetian Twilight (circa 1918-19)
Oc:406x508:signed:Purchased 1966

T01913 Dance Hall Scene (circa 1913-14)
GDπ:222x197:signed:Purchased 1974

T03676 Bursting Shell (1915)
Oc:760x560:signed:Purchased 1983

Britain's Efforts and Ideals (P03045-P03050; incomplete
group)
P03045 Making the Engine (1917)
MLπ:402x303:signed:Presented by the Ministry of
Information 1918

P03046 Assembling Parts (1917)
MLπ:402x302:signed:Presented by the Ministry of
Information 1918

P03047 Acetylene Welding (1917)
MLπ:403x298:signed:Presented by the Ministry of
Information 1918

P03048 Sweeping Down on a Taube (1917)
MLπ:400x299:signed:Presented by the Ministry of
Information 1918

P03049 Banking at 4000 Feet (1917)
MLπ:403x316:signed:Presented by the Ministry of
Information 1918

P03050 In the Air (1917)
MLπ:405x302:signed:Presented by the Ministry of
Information 1918

P11049 Survivors at Arras (1917-8)
MLπ::signed:Bequeathed by Mrs E. West 1982

NEWMAN, Avis born 1946
Modern Collection

T03946 The Day's Residues III (1982)
Dπ:1015x1362:signed:Purchased 1985

T03947 The Day's Residues I (1982)
Dπ:1015x1362:signed:Purchased 1985

T03948 The Day's Residues II (1982)
Dπ:1015x1362:signed:Purchased 1985

T03949 The Day's Residues VI (1982)
Dπ:1015x1368:signed:Purchased 1985

T03950 The Day's Residues V (1982)
Dπ:1012x1360:signed:Purchased 1985

NEWMAN, Barnett 1905-1970
Modern Collection
Tate Gallery Archive holds material concerning this artist

T01091 Adam (1951-2)
Oc:2429x2029:signed:Purchased 1968

T03081 Eve (1950)
Oc:2388x1721:Purchased 1980

T05501 Moment (1946)
Oc:762x406:Presented by Mrs Annalee Newman, the
artist's widow, in honour of the Directorship of Sir Alan
Bowness 1988

Eighteen Cantos (P01027-P01044; complete group)
P01027 Canto I (1963-4)
CLπ:420x315:signed:Presented by Mrs Annalee
Newman, the artist's widow 1972

P01028 Canto II (1963-4)
CLπ:385x327:signed:Presented by Mrs Annalee
Newman, the artist's widow 1972

P01029 Canto III (1963-4)
CLπ:424x324:signed:Presented by Mrs Annalee
Newman, the artist's widow 1972

P01030 Canto IV (1963-4)
CLπ:378x320:signed:Presented by Mrs Annalee
Newman, the artist's widow 1972

P01031 Canto V (1963-4)
CLπ:375x334:signed:Presented by Mrs Annalee
Newman, the artist's widow 1972

P01032 Canto VI (1963-4)
CLπ:370x330:signed:Presented by Mrs Annalee
Newman, the artist's widow 1972

P01033 Canto VII (1963-4)
CLπ:375x334:signed:Presented by Mrs Annalee
Newman, the artist's widow 1972

P01034 Canto VIII (1963-4)
CLπ:375x338:signed:Presented by Mrs Annalee
Newman, the artist's widow 1972

P01035 Canto IX (1963-4)
CLπ:370x335:signed:Presented by Mrs Annalee
Newman, the artist's widow 1972

P01036 Canto X (1963-4)
CLπ:373x337:signed:Presented by Mrs Annalee
Newman, the artist's widow 1972

P01037 Canto XI (1963-4)
CLπ:377x335:signed:Presented by Mrs Annalee
Newman, the artist's widow 1972

P01038 Canto XII (1963-4)
CLπ:373x337:signed:Presented by Mrs Annalee
Newman, the artist's widow 1972

P01039 Canto XIII (1963-4)
CLπ:372x334:signed:Presented by Mrs Annalee
Newman, the artist's widow 1972

P01040 Canto XIV (1963-4)
CLπ:375x319:signed:Presented by Mrs Annalee
Newman, the artist's widow 1972

P01041 Canto XV (1963-4)
CLπ:375x322:signed:Presented by Mrs Annalee
Newman, the artist's widow 1972

P01042 Canto XVI (1963-4)
CLπ:375x323:signed:Presented by Mrs Annalee
Newman, the artist's widow 1972

P01043 Canto XVII (1963-4)
CLπ:380x324:signed:Presented by Mrs Annalee
Newman, the artist's widow 1972

P01044 Canto XVIII (1963-4)
CLπ:379x318:signed:Presented by Mrs Annalee
Newman, the artist's widow 1972

P01832 [Eighteen Cantos: title page] (1963-4)
Lπ:400x305:Presented by Mrs Annelee Newman, the
artist's widow 1972

NEWTON, Algernon 1880-1968
Modern Collection
Tate Gallery Archive holds material concerning this artist

N05343 The Surrey Canal, Camberwell (1935)
Oc:718x914:signed:Presented by the Trustees of the
Chantrey Bequest 1940

T00858 A Gleam of Sunlight (1966)
Oc:457x610:signed:Presented by the Trustees of the
Chantrey Bequest 1966

NEWTON, Gilbert Stuart 1794-1835
British Collection

N00353 Yorick and the Grisette (exhibited 1830)
Oc:759x571:Presented by Robert Vernon 1847

N00354 The Window (exhibited 1829)
Ow:371x270:Presented by Robert Vernon 1847

NICHOLLS, Bertram 1883-1974
Modern Collection

N03586 Drying the Sails (1920)
Oc:305x406:signed:Presented by the Trustees of the
Chantrey Bequest 1921

N04091 Steyning Church, Sussex (1921)
Oc:508x406:signed:Presented by Mrs Lucy Carrington
Wertheim through the National Art Collections Fund
1925

NICHOLSON, Ben, OM 1894-1982
Modern Collection
Tate Gallery Archive holds material concerning this artist

N05125 guitar (1933)
Ow:832x197:Presented by the Contemporary Art Society
1940

N05625 St Ives, Cornwall (1943-5)
Ob:406x502:Purchased 1945

N05626 still life (1945)
Oc:838x660:Purchased 1945

N05951 foothills, Cumberland (1928)
Oc:559x686:Presented by Miss D. Noyes and Miss E.
Noyes 1950

T00049 white relief (1935)
ORw:1016x1664:signed:Purchased with assistance from
the Contemporary Art Society 1955

T00050 painting 1937 (1937)
Oc:1594x2013:Purchased 1955

T00051 Feb 28-53 (vertical seconds) (1953)
Oc:756x419:Purchased 1955

T00557 Feb 1960 (ice-off-blue) (1960)
ORb:1219x1829:Purchased 1962

T00588 Dec/62 (interlocking) (1962)
DOπ:349x292:Presented by the Friends of the Tate
Gallery 1963

T00742 August 56 (Val d'Orcia) (1956)
Ob:1219x2134:Purchased 1965

T00743 Le Quotidien (1932)
Ob:375x457:Presented by the Trustees of the Chantrey
Bequest 1965

T00821 1965 (Azetaio) (1965)
DOπ:502x375:Presented by the artist 1966

T00929 1967 (Tuscan relief) (1967)
ORb:1518x1676:Purchased 1967

T00944 Auberge de la sole dieppoise (1932)
Ob:937x759:Presented by Mr and Mrs Michael Sacher
through the Friends of the Tate Gallery 1967

T01028 1966 (Parthenon) (1966)
DOb:375x486:signed:Presented by the artist 1968

T01029 May 1962 (Urbino - footsteps in the dust) (1962)
DOb:483x349:Presented by the artist 1968

T01036 Sept 61 (Paros chapel) (1961)
DWπ:400x495:Purchased 1968

T01037 July 62 (cool moon) (1962)
DOb:254x352:signed:Purchased 1968

T01038 Oct 62 (3 circles) (1962)
DWb:356x330:signed:Presented by the artist 1968

T01054 1967 (nest of circles) (1967)
ORb:1473x711x6:Presented by the artist 1968

T01118 March 63 (Artemission) (1963)
RODb:460x556:signed:Presented by the artist 1969

T01189 painting 1932 (1932)
OGDb:746x1200:signed:Presented by Dame Barbara
Hepworth 1970

T01196 Carnac no. 1 (1969)
ROb:2013x1499x13:signed:Presented by the artist 1970

T02015 Lucignano (1974)
ODb:762x613:Presented by the artist 1976

T02220 Feb 55 (1955)
RODbw:292x232x3:signed:Bequeathed by Miss E.M.
Hodgkins 1977

T02221 Feb 2-54 (1954)
ODc:733x803:Bequeathed by Miss E.M. Hodgkins 1977

T02222 Sept 8-54 (Torcello) (1954)
ODc:978x581:Bequeathed by Miss E.M. Hodgkins 1977

T02223 Oct 55 (concourse of trees, Tuscany) (1955)
DPb:476x368:signed:Bequeathed by Miss E.M. Hodgkins 1977

T02224 Dec 10-54 (1954)
RODw:273x146x6:signed:Bequeathed by Miss E.M. Hodgkins 1977

T02225 July 27-53 (ivory) (1953)
ODc:610x457:Bequeathed by Miss E.M. Hodgkins 1977

T02314 relief 1934 (1934)
ROTbw:718x965x32:Purchased 1978

T02337 Jan 14-65 (Capraia) - project for free standing relief wall (1965)
ROb:349x260x6:Presented by the artist 1979

T02338 wall project 62-75 (1962-75)
ROb:273x603x6:Presented by the artist 1979

T02339 Feb 65 (Cascais) - project for wall with trees & water or rolling countryside trees & sea (1965)
ROb:448x276x10:Presented by the artist 1979

T02340 vertical wall 66 (1966)
ROb:432x267x10:Presented by the artist 1979

T02341 (Forms) Nov 78 (1978)
Ob:232x184:Presented by the artist 1979

T02342 Strange Landscape Nov 78 (1978)
Ob:143x165:Presented by the artist 1979

T03119 painted relief (1939-44)
ROb:165x254x6:Purchased 1980

T03951 16 strings (1978)
WODπ:380x324:signed:Bequeathed by the artist 1985

T03952 nude (circa 1932)
Dπ:498x390:signed:Bequeathed by the artist 1985

T03953 smiling nude (1968)
ODπ:557x686:signed:Bequeathed by the artist 1985

T04119 sculpture (circa 1936)
Sw:228x305x241:signed:Purchased 1985

T04861 first abstract painting, Chelsea (1924)
Ocb:554x612:signed:Accepted by the Commissioners of Inland Revenue in lieu of tax and allocated 1986

T04862 April 20-79 (vertical stripe) (1979)
Ob:730x553:signed:Accepted by the Commissioners of Inland Revenue in lieu of tax and allocated 1986

T05530 Cortivallo, Lugano (1921 - circa 1923)
Oc:457x610:Purchased with assistance from the National Art Collections Fund and the Friends of the Tate Gallery 1989

P01237 San Gimignano (1966)
MIπ:175x238:Presented by Waddington Galleries through the Institute of Contemporary Prints 1975

P01238 Pisa as intended (1967)
MIπ:210x295:Presented by Waddington Galleries through the Institute of Contemporary Prints 1975

P01239 St Ives from Trezion (1967)
MIπ:175x279:Presented by Waddington Galleries through the Institute of Contemporary Prints 1975

P01240 small still life (1967)
MIπ:210x210:Presented by Waddington Galleries through the Institute of Contemporary Prints 1975

P01241 Turkish form (1967)
MIπ:273x146:Presented by Waddington Galleries through the Institute of Contemporary Prints 1975

P01242 untitled (1967)
MIπ:340x181:Presented by Waddington Galleries through the Institute of Contemporary Prints 1975

P02008 small silent siena (1965)
MIπ:203x165:Presented by the artist 1968

P02009 Palastra (1965)
MIπ:162x232:Presented by the artist 1968

P02010 Tuscan pillars (1966)
MIπ:241x146:Presented by the artist 1968

P02011 flowing forms (1967)
MIπ:206x305:Presented by the artist 1968

P02012 Aegean 2 (1967)
MIπ:184x273:Presented by the artist 1968

P02013 two sculptural forms (1967)
MIπ:314x283:Presented by the artist 1968

P02014 Turkish sundial and column (1967)
MIπ:209x232:Presented by the artist 1968

P02015 Rafael (1967)
MIπ:302x264:Presented by the artist 1968

P02016 three forms in a landscape (1967)
MIπ:229x267:Presented by the artist 1968

P02017 glass topped bottle (1967)
MIπ:365x257:Presented by the artist 1968

P02018 Ronco (1967)
MIπ:254x270:Presented by the artist 1968

P02019 two bottles and glass (1967)
MIπ:330x330:Presented by the artist 1968

Penwith Portfolio (P01416, P06005, P06108, P06130, P06241, P06324, P06346, P06359, P06399, P06519, P06700; complete group; mixed group)

P06399 abstract 1936 (1973)
CLπ:667x800:Presented by Curwen Studio through the Institute of Contemporary Prints 1975

P07199 Siena (1967)
MIπ:248x187:Purchased 1976

P07200 Foxy and Frankie (2) (1933)
OMJπ:159x149:signed:Purchased 1976

P07201 Foxy and Frankie (1) (1933)
OMJπ:159x149:signed:Purchased 1976

P07202 abstract (1934)
MJπ:159x203:Purchased 1976

P07203 Paros tree (1967)
MIπ:248x410:Purchased 1976

P07204 three goblets (1967)
MIπ:200x152:Purchased 1976

NICHOLSON, E.Q. born 1908
Modern Collection

T05700 Still Life with Mirror (circa 1949)
WDπ:455x603:Presented by Timothy Nicholson 1989

NICHOLSON, Mabel 1871-1918
British Collection

T03464 The Harlequin (circa 1910)
Oc:1018x643:signed:Presented by Timothy Nicholson 1982

NICHOLSON, Sir William 1872-1949
British Collection
Tate Gallery Archive holds material concerning this artist

N03178 The Lowestoft Bowl (1911)
Oc:476x610:signed:Presented by the Contemporary Art Society 1917

N03689 Lady in Furs, Mme. P. (circa 1907)
Oc:908x705:Presented by R. Phillipson through the
National Art Collections Fund 1927

N04087 Portrait of a Man of Letters: W.E. Henley (1901)
Oc:375x298:signed:Bequeathed by Mrs W.E. Henley 1925

N04936 Silver (1938)
Ow:438x571:signed:Purchased 1938

N05084 Nude (circa 1921)
Ow:406x584:signed:Purchased with assistance from the
Knapping Fund 1940

N05267 Mushrooms (1940)
Ob:349x451:signed:Purchased 1941

N05548 Miss Jekyll's Gardening Boots (1920)
Ow:324x400:signed:Presented by Lady Emily Lutyens
1944

N05642 Studio Still Life (1914)
Oc:1314x1626:signed:Bequeathed by Edward Knoblock
1945

T01047 The Hill above Harlech (circa 1917)
Oc:537x594:signed:Purchased with assistance from the
Knapping Fund 1968

T03792 Harbour in Snow, La Rochelle (1938)
Oc:353x454:signed:Presented by the Friends of the Tate
Gallery 1983

T05520 The Bull Ring, Malaga (1935)
Ow:648x777:Presented by Miss H. Stocks 1989

T05521 The Bull Ring, Malaga (1935)
Dπ:202x252:Presented by Miss H. Stocks 1989

Twelve Portraits (First Series) (P08152-P08163;
complete group)

P08152 The Archbishop of Canterbury (1899)
CLπ:255x228:signed:Transferred from the Library 1979

P08153 Cecil Rhodes (1899)
CLπ:245x232:signed:Transferred from the Library 1979

P08154 H.M. The Queen (1899)
CLπ:242x228:signed:Transferred from the Library 1979

P08155 H.R.H. The Prince of Wales (1899)
CLπ:255x230:signed:Transferred from the Library 1979

P08156 James McNeill Whistler (1899)
CLπ:245x225:signed:Transferred from the Library 1979

P08157 Lord Roberts (1899)
CLπ:242x230:signed:Transferred from the Library 1979

P08158 Prince Bismarck (1899)
CLπ:245x232:signed:Transferred from the Library 1979

P08159 Rudyard Kipling (1899)
CLπ:280x220:signed:Transferred from the Library 1979

P08160 Sarah Bernhardt (1899)
CLπ:238x235:signed:Transferred from the Library 1979

P08161 Sir Henry Hawkins (1899)
CLπ:255x228:signed:Transferred from the Library 1979

P08162 Sir Henry Irving (1899)
CLπ:255x232:signed:Transferred from the Library 1979

P08163 W.E. Gladstone (1899)
CLπ:253x232:signed:Transferred from the Library 1979

NICHOLSON, Winifred 1893-1981
Modern Collection
Tate Gallery Archive holds material concerning this artist

N05126 Window-Sill, Lugano (1923)
Ob:286x508:Presented by the Contemporary Art Society
1940

T01995 Quarante Huit Quai d'Auteuil (1935)
Ob:676x1000:Purchased 1975

T01996 Moonlight and Lamplight (1937)
Oc:762x889:Purchased 1975

T03960 Flower Table (1928-9)
Oc:1128x802:Purchased with assistance from the Carroll
Donner Bequest 1985

T05484 Sandpipers, Alnmouth (1933)
Ob:635x762:Presented by the Friends of the Tate Gallery
1988

NICOL, Erskine 1825-1904
British Collection
Tate Gallery Archive holds material concerning this artist

N01537 Wayside Prayer (1852)
Oc:387x645:signed:Presented by Sir Henry Tate 1894

N01538 The Emigrants (1864)
Oc:457x349:signed:Presented by Sir Henry Tate 1894

N04652 Donnybrook Fair (1859)
Oc:1067x2108:signed:Purchased 1932

NIEUWENHUYS, Constant A. - see CONSTANT

NIMPTSCH, Uli 1897-1977
Modern Collection

T00097 Olympia (circa 1953-6)
Sz:584x1105x610:Purchased 1956

T00277 Seated Girl (1958)
Sz:959x451x375:Purchased 1959

NISBET, Robert Buchan 1857-1942
British Collection

N01711 Evening Stillness (1890)
Wbπ:495x762:signed:Presented by the Trustees of the
Chantrey Bequest 1890

NITSCH, Hermann born 1938
Modern Collection

T03334 Poured Painting (1963)
Schüttbild
Oc:1048x806:signed:Purchased 1981

T03412 Blood Picture (1962)
Blutbild
Vc:1062x804:signed:Purchased 1982

P77169 Towards the Architecture of the O.M. Theatre (1976-9,
1983, 1985)
Zur Architektur des O.M. Theaters
PNf:1460x3570:signed:Purchased 1986

NOBLE, Robert 1857-1917
British Collection

N03313 Dirleton Church, East Lothian (?1912)
Oc:305x603:signed:Presented by subscribers through the
National Art Collections Fund 1918

NOGUCHI, Isamu 1904-1988
Modern Collection

T00338 The Self (1956)
Sm:860x229x210:Purchased 1960

NOLAN, Sir Sidney born 1917
Modern Collection
Tate Gallery Archive holds material concerning this artist

N05993 Inland Australia (1950)
Ab:1219x1524:signed:Purchased 1951

T00150 Glenrowan (1956-7)
Ab:914x1219:signed:Purchased 1957

T00151 Women and Billabong (1957)
Ab:1524x1219:signed:Purchased 1957

T03553 Desert Storm (circa 1955)
Ob:914x1219:Presented by Lord McAlpine of West
Green 1983

T03554 Woman in a Hat (circa 1964)
Ob:1219x1219:Presented by Lord McAlpine of West
Green 1983

T03555 Carcase in Swamp (1955)
Ob:914x1219:signed:Presented by Lord McAlpine of
West Green 1983

T03556 Armoured Helmet (1956)
Ob:1219x914:signed:Presented by Lord McAlpine of
West Green 1983

T03557 In the Cave (1957)
Ob:1219x1524:Presented by Lord McAlpine of West
Green 1983

T03558 Antarctica (1964)
Ob:1219x1219:signed:Presented by Lord McAlpine of
West Green 1983

T03559 Camel and Figure (1966)
Ob:1210x1219:signed:Presented by Lord McAlpine of
West Green 1983

T03560 Peter Grimes's Apprentice (1977)
Ob:914x1219:signed:Presented by Lord McAlpine of
West Green 1983

P01452 By the River (1966-7)
CLπ:524x762:signed:Presented by Marlborough
Graphics through the Institute of Contemporary Prints
1975

P01453 Disguise (1966-7)
CLπ:524x762:signed:Presented by Marlborough
Graphics through the Institute of Contemporary Prints
1975

P01454 Glenrowan (1966-7)
CLπ:762x527:signed:Presented by Marlborough
Graphics through the Institute of Contemporary Prints
1975

P01455 Kelly (1966-7)
CLπ:524x762:signed:Presented by Marlborough
Graphics through the Institute of Contemporary Prints
1975

P01456 Rinder Subject I (1969)
MLπ:505x660:signed:Presented by Marlborough
Graphics through the Institute of Contemporary Prints
1975

P01457 Rinder Subject II (1969)
MLπ:504x658:signed:Presented by Marlborough
Graphics through the Institute of Contemporary Prints
1975

P01458 Rinder Subject III (1969)
MLπ:505x657:signed:Presented by Marlborough
Graphics through the Institute of Contemporary Prints
1975

P01459 Rinder Subject IV (1969)
MLπ:485x500:signed:Presented by Marlborough
Graphics through the Institute of Contemporary Prints
1975

P01460 Rinder Subject V (1969)
MLπ:477x495:signed:Presented by Marlborough
Graphics through the Institute of Contemporary Prints
1975

The Leda Suite (P03281-P03288; complete group)
P03281 1 (1961)
MLπ:440x600:signed:Presented by Ganymed Press 1979

P03282 2 (1961)
MLπ:470x620:signed:Presented by Ganymed Press 1979

P03283 3 (1961)
MLπ:460x635:signed:Presented by Ganymed Press 1979

P03284 4 (1961)
MLπ:482x610:signed:Presented by Ganymed Press 1979

P03285 5 (1961)
MLπ:460x620:signed:Presented by Ganymed Press 1979

P03286 6 (1961)
MLπ:445x590:signed:Presented by Ganymed Press 1979

P03287 7 (1961)
MLπ:450x600:signed:Presented by Ganymed Press 1979

P03288 8 (1961)
MLπ:485x620:signed:Presented by Ganymed Press 1979

P04640 Convict and Cave (1963-4)
CNπ:495x603:signed:Presented by Rose and Chris Prater
through the Institute of Contemporary Prints 1975

P04641 Elephant (1963-5)
CNπ:571x495:signed:Presented by Rose and Chris Prater
through the Institute of Contemporary Prints 1975

P04642 Ned Kelly Washing Feet (1963-5)
CNπ:584x889:signed:Presented by Rose and Chris Prater
through the Institute of Contemporary Prints 1975

P04643 Woman (1963-5)
CNπ:584x889:signed:Presented by Rose and Chris Prater
through the Institute of Contemporary Prints 1975

P04644 Kelly (1964)
CNπ:689x511:signed:Presented by Rose and Chris Prater
through the Institute of Contemporary Prints 1975

P04645 Ned Kelly (1964)
CNπ:775x584:signed:Presented by Rose and Chris Prater
through the Institute of Contemporary Prints 1975

P04646 Illustration to 'News from Mount Amiata' by Mentale
(1965)
MNπ:759x575:signed:Presented by Rose and Chris
Prater through the Institute of Contemporary Prints 1975

P04647 Illustration to 'Pigeons for Hannah Arendt' by Rilke
(1965)
CNπ:565x464:signed:Presented by Rose and Chris Prater
through the Institute of Contemporary Prints 1975

P04648 [title not known] (1965)
CNπ:613x495:signed:Presented by Rose and Chris Prater
through the Institute of Contemporary Prints 1975

P04649 Illustration to the 'Voyage by Beaudelaire' (1965)
CNπ:565x464:signed:Presented by Rose and Chris Prater
through the Institute of Contemporary Prints 1975

P04650 Kelly (1965)
CNπ:638x521:signed:Presented by Rose and Chris Prater
through the Institute of Contemporary Prints 1975

P04651 Kelly (1965)
CNπ:610x495:signed:Presented by Rose and Chris Prater
through the Institute of Contemporary Prints 1975

P04652 Kelly VI (1965)
CNπ:611x488:signed:Presented by Rose and Chris Prater
through the Institute of Contemporary Prints 1975

P04653 Kelly V (1965)
CNπ:612x496:signed:Presented by Rose and Chris Prater through the Institute of Contemporary Prints 1975

P04654 Kelly IV (1965)
CNπ:610x495:signed:Presented by Rose and Chris Prater through the Institute of Contemporary Prints 1975

P04655 Kelly (1965)
CNπ:610x495:signed:Presented by Rose and Chris Prater through the Institute of Contemporary Prints 1975

P04656 Kelly (1965)
CNπ:611x495:signed:Presented by Rose and Chris Prater through the Institute of Contemporary Prints 1975

P04657 Kelly (1965)
CNπ:612x495:signed:Presented by Rose and Chris Prater through the Institute of Contemporary Prints 1975

P04658 Kelly (1965)
CNπ:611x495:signed:Presented by Rose and Chris Prater through the Institute of Contemporary Prints 1975

P04659 Descent (1966)
CNπ:562x464:signed:Presented by Rose and Chris Prater through the Institute of Contemporary Prints 1975

P04660 Figures (1966)
CNπ:562x464:signed:Presented by Rose and Chris Prater through the Institute of Contemporary Prints 1975

P04661 Lighthouse (1966)
CNπ:565x464:signed:Presented by Rose and Chris Prater through the Institute of Contemporary Prints 1975

P04662 Still Life (1966)
CNπ:562x464:signed:Presented by Rose and Chris Prater through the Institute of Contemporary Prints 1975

P04663 Camp (1966-7)
CNπ:692x498:signed:Presented by Rose and Chris Prater through the Institute of Contemporary Prints 1975

P04664 Cross (1966-7)
CNπ:622x457:signed:Presented by Rose and Chris Prater through the Institute of Contemporary Prints 1975

P04665 Girls (1966-7)
CNπ:565x464:signed:Presented by Rose and Chris Prater through the Institute of Contemporary Prints 1975

P04666 Swimmer (1966-7)
CNπ:559x457:signed:Presented by Rose and Chris Prater through the Institute of Contemporary Prints 1975

Inferno (P04667-P04675; complete group)
P04667 Inferno I (1967)
CNπ:755x600:signed:Presented by Rose and Chris Prater through the Institute of Contemporary Prints 1975

P04668 Inferno II (1967)
CNπ:755x609:signed:Presented by Rose and Chris Prater through the Institute of Contemporary Prints 1975

P04669 Inferno III (1967)
CNπ:755x607:signed:Presented by Rose and Chris Prater through the Institute of Contemporary Prints 1975

P04670 Inferno IV (1967)
CNπ:755x606:signed:Presented by Rose and Chris Prater through the Institute of Contemporary Prints 1975

P04671 Inferno V (1967)
CNπ:755x609:signed:Presented by Rose and Chris Prater through the Institute of Contemporary Prints 1975

P04672 Inferno VI (1967)
CNπ:755x608:signed:Presented by Rose and Chris Prater through the Institute of Contemporary Prints 1975

P04673 Inferno VII (1967)
CNπ:753x609:signed:Presented by Rose and Chris Prater through the Institute of Contemporary Prints 1975

P04674 Inferno VIII (1967)
CNπ:760x610:signed:Presented by Rose and Chris Prater through the Institute of Contemporary Prints 1975

P04675 Inferno IX (1967)
CNπ:756x609:signed:Presented by Rose and Chris Prater through the Institute of Contemporary Prints 1975

P04676 The Vanity of Human Wishes (1969)
CNπ:816x597:signed:Presented by Rose and Chris Prater through the Institute of Contemporary Prints 1975

Ned Kelly (P04677-P04692; complete group)
P04677 1. Ned Kelly (1970-1)
CNπ:480x638:signed:Presented by Rose and Chris Prater through the Institute of Contemporary Prints 1975

P04678 2. Constable Fitzpatrick and Kate Kelly (1970-1)
CNπ:475x636:signed:Presented by Rose and Chris Prater through the Institute of Contemporary Prints 1975

P04679 3. Steve Hart Dressed as a Girl (1970-1)
CNπ:473x639:signed:Presented by Rose and Chris Prater through the Institute of Contemporary Prints 1975

P04680 4. Quilting the Armour (1970-1)
CNπ:477x637:signed:Presented by Rose and Chris Prater through the Institute of Contemporary Prints 1975

P04681 5. Death of Constable Scanlon (1970-1)
CNπ:475x636:signed:Presented by Rose and Chris Prater through the Institute of Contemporary Prints 1975

P04682 6. Death of Sergeant Kennedy (1970-1)
CNπ:477x641:signed:Presented by Rose and Chris Prater through the Institute of Contemporary Prints 1975

P04683 7. The Alarm (1970-1)
CNπ:475x636:signed:Presented by Rose and Chris Prater through the Institute of Contemporary Prints 1975

P04684 8. The Pursuit (1970-1)
CNπ:470x640:signed:Presented by Rose and Chris Prater through the Institute of Contemporary Prints 1975

P04685 9. The Marriage of Aaron Sherritt (1970-1)
CNπ:475x640:signed:Presented by Rose and Chris Prater through the Institute of Contemporary Prints 1975

P04686 10. The Defence of Aaron Sherritt (1970-1)
CNπ:635x475:signed:Presented by Rose and Chris Prater through the Institute of Contemporary Prints 1975

P04687 11. Mrs Reardon at Glenrowan (1970-1)
CNπ:480x624:signed:Presented by Rose and Chris Prater through the Institute of Contemporary Prints 1975

P04688 12. Siege at Glenrowan (1970-1)
CNπ:639x480:signed:Presented by Rose and Chris Prater through the Institute of Contemporary Prints 1975

P04689 13. Burning at Glenrowan (1970-1)
CNπ:640x480:signed:Presented by Rose and Chris Prater through the Institute of Contemporary Prints 1975

P04690 14. Glenrowan (1970-1)
CNπ:475x638:signed:Presented by Rose and Chris Prater through the Institute of Contemporary Prints 1975

P04691 15. The Trial (1970-1)
CNπ:479x638:signed:Presented by Rose and Chris Prater through the Institute of Contemporary Prints 1975

P04692 16. The Slip (1970-1)
CNπ:477x640:signed:Presented by Rose and Chris Prater through the Institute of Contemporary Prints 1975

P04693 Ned Kelly (1971)
CNπ:479x638:signed:Presented by Rose and Chris Prater through the Institute of Contemporary Prints 1975

P04694 Stringy Bark Creek (1972)
CNπ:606x806:signed:Presented by Rose and Chris Prater through the Institute of Contemporary Prints 1975

P04695 Kelly and Red Horse (1972)
CNπ:610x813:signed:Presented by Rose and Chris Prater through the Institute of Contemporary Prints 1975

P04696 Imitation I (1972)
CNπ:733x608:signed:Presented by Rose and Chris Prater through the Institute of Contemporary Prints 1975

P04697 Imitation II (1972)
CNπ:733x608:signed:Presented by Rose and Chris Prater through the Institute of Contemporary Prints 1975

P04698 Imitation III (1972)
CNπ:734x608:signed:Presented by Rose and Chris Prater through the Institute of Contemporary Prints 1975

P04699 Imitation IV (1972)
CNπ:733x607:signed:Presented by Rose and Chris Prater through the Institute of Contemporary Prints 1975

P04700 Kelly Head I (1972)
CNπ:609x833:signed:Presented by Rose and Chris Prater through the Institute of Contemporary Prints 1975

P04701 Kelly Head II (1972)
CNπ:832x610:signed:Presented by Rose and Chris Prater through the Institute of Contemporary Prints 1975

P04702 Kelly Head III (1972)
CNπ:830x608:signed:Presented by Rose and Chris Prater through the Institute of Contemporary Prints 1975

P04703 Leda Theme I (1972)
CNπ:602x832:signed:Presented by Rose and Chris Prater through the Institute of Contemporary Prints 1975

P04704 Leda Theme II (1972)
CNπ:609x832:signed:Presented by Rose and Chris Prater through the Institute of Contemporary Prints 1975

P04705 Leda Theme III (1972)
CNπ:610x832:signed:Presented by Rose and Chris Prater through the Institute of Contemporary Prints 1975

Floral Images (P04706-P04720; complete group)
P04706 Print 1 (1972)
CNπ:553x460:signed:Presented by Rose and Chris Prater through the Institute of Contemporary Prints 1975

P04707 Print 2 (1972)
CNπ:545x455:signed:Presented by Rose and Chris Prater through the Institute of Contemporary Prints 1975

P04708 Print 3 (1972)
CNπ:545x457:signed:Presented by Rose and Chris Prater through the Institute of Contemporary Prints 1975

P04709 Print 4 (1972)
CNπ:545x452:signed:Presented by Rose and Chris Prater through the Institute of Contemporary Prints 1975

P04710 Print 5 (1972)
CNπ:545x451:signed:Presented by Rose and Chris Prater through the Institute of Contemporary Prints 1975

P04711 Print 6 (1972)
CNπ:540x456:signed:Presented by Rose and Chris Prater through the Institute of Contemporary Prints 1975

P04712 Print 7 (1972)
CNπ:549x457:signed:Presented by Rose and Chris Prater through the Institute of Contemporary Prints 1975

P04713 Print 8 (1972)
CNπ:549x451:signed:Presented by Rose and Chris Prater through the Institute of Contemporary Prints 1975

P04714 Print 9 (1972)
CNπ:552x460:signed:Presented by Rose and Chris Prater through the Institute of Contemporary Prints 1975

P04715 Print 10 (1972)
CNπ:552x456:signed:Presented by Rose and Chris Prater through the Institute of Contemporary Prints 1975

P04716 Print 11 (1972)
CNπ:559x455:signed:Presented by Rose and Chris Prater through the Institute of Contemporary Prints 1975

P04717 Print 12 (1972)
CNπ:540x457:signed:Presented by Rose and Chris Prater through the Institute of Contemporary Prints 1975

P04718 Print 13 (1972)
CNπ:550x457:signed:Presented by Rose and Chris Prater through the Institute of Contemporary Prints 1975

P04719 Print 14 (1972)
CNπ:548x452:signed:Presented by Rose and Chris Prater through the Institute of Contemporary Prints 1975

P04720 Print 15 (1972)
CNπ:546x452:signed:Presented by Rose and Chris Prater through the Institute of Contemporary Prints 1975

P04721 Kelly II (1973)
CNπ:606x762:signed:Presented by Rose and Chris Prater through the Institute of Contemporary Prints 1975

Landscapes (P04722-P04729; complete group)
P04722 Landscape - Bearded Man (1973)
CNπ:760x762:signed:Presented by Rose and Chris Prater through the Institute of Contemporary Prints 1975

P04723 Landscape - Miner with Dog (1973)
CNπ:762x763:signed:Presented by Rose and Chris Prater through the Institute of Contemporary Prints 1975

P04724 Landscape - Miner and Tree (1973)
CNπ:761x759:signed:Presented by Rose and Chris Prater through the Institute of Contemporary Prints 1975

P04725 Landscape - Miner/Red Helmet (1973)
CNπ:754x760:signed:Presented by Rose and Chris Prater through the Institute of Contemporary Prints 1975

P04726 Landscape - Miner Smoking (1973)
CNπ:762x760:signed:Presented by Rose and Chris Prater through the Institute of Contemporary Prints 1975

P04727 Landscape - Miner and Train (1973)
CNπ:762x762:signed:Presented by Rose and Chris Prater through the Institute of Contemporary Prints 1975

P04728 Landscape - Miner/Yellow Helmet (1973)
CNπ:759x762:signed:Presented by Rose and Chris Prater through the Institute of Contemporary Prints 1975

P04729 Landscape - Scarlet Woman (1973)
CNπ:762x762:signed:Presented by Rose and Chris Prater through the Institute of Contemporary Prints 1975

P04730 Ned Kelly (1973)
CNπ:606x762:signed:Presented by Rose and Chris Prater through the Institute of Contemporary Prints 1975

P04731 Girl in Field (1975)
CNπ:559x752:signed:Presented by Rose and Chris Prater through the Institute of Contemporary Prints 1975

P05378 Burke and Wills Expedition I (1975)
CNπ:647x750:signed:Presented by Rose and Chris Prater 1976

P05379 Burke and Wills Expedition II (1975)
CNπ:651x751:signed:Presented by Rose and Chris Prater 1976

P05380 Burke and Wills Expedition III (1975)
CNπ:650x750:signed:Presented by Rose and Chris Prater 1976

P05381 Burke and Wills Expedition IV (1975)
CNπ:650x747:signed:Presented by Rose and Chris Prater
1976

P05382 Burke and Wills Expedition V (1975)
CNπ:645x749:signed:Presented by Rose and Chris Prater
1976

Ned Kelly II (P05481-P05490; complete group)

P05481 Landscape (1978-9)
CNπ:635x475:signed:Presented by Rose and Chris Prater
1979

P05482 The Burning Tree (1978-9)
CNπ:482x640:signed:Presented by Rose and Chris Prater
1979

P05483 Morning Camp (1978-9)
CNπ:475x635:signed:Presented by Rose and Chris Prater
1979

P05484 First Class Marksman (1978-9)
CNπ:480x635:signed:Presented by Rose and Chris Prater
1979

P05485 Mansfield (1978-9)
CNπ:482x635:signed:Presented by Rose and Chris Prater
1979

P05486 The Watch Tower (1978-9)
CNπ:475x635:signed:Presented by Rose and Chris Prater
1979

P05487 The Encounter (1978-9)
CNπ:482x640:signed:Presented by Rose and Chris Prater
1979

P05488 The Evening (1978-9)
CNπ:482x635:signed:Presented by Rose and Chris Prater
1979

P05489 Bush Picnic (1978-9)
CNπ:482x635:signed:Presented by Rose and Chris Prater
1979

P05490 The Questioning (1978-9)
CNπ:482x635:signed:Presented by Rose and Chris Prater
1979

NOLAND, Kenneth born 1924
Modern Collection

T00763 Drought (1962)
Ac:1765x1765:signed:Purchased 1965

T00898 Gift (1961-2)
Ac:1829x1829:signed:Presented by the artist through the
American Federation of Arts 1966

T01686 Another Line (1970)
Ac:1667x2896:signed:Purchased 1972

NOLDE, Emil 1867-1953
Modern Collection

T00865 The Sea B (1930)
Meer B
Oc:737x1010:signed:Purchased 1966

NORTH, John William 1841-1924
British Collection

N01607 The Winter Sun (exhibited 1891)
Oc:667x984:Presented by the Trustees of the Chantrey
Bequest 1891

N03519 A Bit of Southern England (1868)
Gπ:248x175:signed:Bequeathed by Mrs Louise d'Este
Oliver 1920

N04021 At the Grindstone, engraved by the Dalziel Brothers
(published 1867)
Jπ:165x124:Presented by Gilbert Dalziel 1924

N04022 Vision of a City Tree, engraved by the Dalziel Brothers
(published 1867)
Jπ:162x127:Presented by Gilbert Dalziel 1924

NORTHCOTE, James 1746-1831
British Collection

N04376 A Young Lady Playing the Harp (?exhibited 1814)
Oc:1105x864:Presented in memory of Frank Lloyd by his
daughter Mrs Garwood 1927

OAKLEY, Alfred J. 1878-1959
British Collection

N04194 Mamua (circa 1926)
Sw:476x311x171:signed:Presented by the Trustees of the Chantrey Bequest 1926

O'CONNOR, Andrew 1874-1941
Modern Collection

N04574 The Wife (circa 1923)
Sz:1587x1003x495:Presented anonymously 1931

N04730 The Golden Head (1905)
Sz:359x249x292:signed:Purchased 1934

N04853 Viscount d'Abernon (1934)
Sz:540x194x251:signed:Purchased with assistance from subscribers 1936

O'CONNOR, John born 1913
Modern Collection
Tate Gallery Archive holds material concerning this artist

P06400 Canal Lock (1967)
CLπ:591x813:Presented by Curwen Studio through the Institute of Contemporary Prints 1975

P06401 Kersey Church (1970)
CLπ:486x635:signed:Presented by Curwen Studio through the Institute of Contemporary Prints 1975

O'CONOR, Roderic 1860-1940
British Collection
Tate Gallery Archive holds material concerning this artist

T00133 Still Life with Bottles (1892)
Oc:552x464:signed:Purchased 1957

T00309 Iris (?1913)
Oc:610x502:signed:Presented by the Contemporary Art Society 1959

T00820 Red Roofs (circa 1894)
Oc:318x400:signed:Purchased 1966

T02113 Yellow Landscape (1892)
Oc:676x918:signed:Presented by Mr and Mrs Barnett Shine through the Friends of the Tate Gallery 1977

T02328 Landscape (circa 1895-1900)
Oc:679x924:Presented by Barnett Shine 1978

OELMAN, Michael born 1941
Modern Collection

P01868 Love at First Sight (1978)
CLπ:356x295:signed:Presented by Christie's Contemporary Art 1979

OGBOURNE, John - see prints after HOGARTH, William

O'HARA, Frank - see RIVERS, Larry and O'HARA, Frank

OLDENBURG, Claes born 1929
Modern Collection
Tate Gallery Archive holds material concerning this artist

T01239 Counter and Plates with Potato and Ham (1961)
ESfmp:117x1073x578:signed:Presented by E.J. Power through the Friends of the Tate Gallery 1970

T01257 Soft Drainpipe - Blue (Cool) Version (1967)
SAcm:2591x1876x356:Purchased 1970

T01266 Giant 3-Way Plug Scale 2/3 (1970)
Sw:1473x991x749:Purchased 1971

T01694 Lipsticks in Piccadilly Circus, London (1966)
Vb:254x203:signed:Presented by Hannah Wilke 1972

P07096 System of Iconography - Plug, Mouse, Good Humor, Lipstick, Switches (1970-1)
CLπ:511x391:signed:Purchased 1972

P77106 Screwarch Bridge State II (1980)
MIπ:595x1285:signed:Purchased 1985

P77324 Pizza Pie (1964)
Lπ:438x560:signed:Purchased 1989

OLITSKI, Jules born 1922
Modern Collection

Five Prints Part I (P01243-P01247; complete group)

P01243 Magenta-Orange I (1970)
CNπ:895x664:signed:Presented by Waddington Galleries through the Institute of Contemporary Prints 1975

P01244 Mauve-Blue I (1970)
CNπ:891x661:signed:Presented by Waddington Galleries through the Institute of Contemporary Prints 1975

P01245 Orange-Grey I (1970)
CNπ:891x662:signed:Presented by Waddington Galleries through the Institute of Contemporary Prints 1975

P01246 Pink-Blue I (1970)
CNπ:893x662:signed:Presented by Waddington Galleries through the Institute of Contemporary Prints 1975

P01247 Yellow-Green I (1970)
CNπ:893x663:signed:Presented by Waddington Galleries through the Institute of Contemporary Prints 1975

Five Prints Part II (P01248-P01252; complete group)

P01248 Crimson-Orange II (1970)
CNπ:895x662:signed:Presented by Waddington Galleries through the Institute of Contemporary Prints 1975

P01249 Orange-Ochre II (1970)
CNπ:660x895:signed:Presented by Waddington Galleries through the Institute of Contemporary Prints 1975

P01250 Pale Blue II (1970)
CNπ:893x664:signed:Presented by Waddington Galleries through the Institute of Contemporary Prints 1975

P01251 Pink-Grey II (1970)
CNπ:664x893:signed:Presented by Waddington Galleries through the Institute of Contemporary Prints 1975

P01252 Pink-Yellow II (1970)
CNπ:668x895:signed:Presented by Waddington Galleries through the Institute of Contemporary Prints 1975

OLIVER, Madge 1874-1924
British Collection

N04802 Interior, Pierrefroide (circa 1920-4)
Oc:552x464:Presented by Lord Duveen 1935

N04851 Le Coin de l'Atelier (circa 1920-4)
Oc:425x368:Presented by Miss Ida Brown and Charles Oliver, the artist's brother 1936

OLIVIER, Herbert A. 1861-1952
British Collection

N04883 Mrs Edwin Bale (1900)
Oc:508x610:signed:Presented by the executors of Mrs Viva Jeyes, the sitter's daughter 1937

OLSON, Eric born 1909
Modern Collection

T00792 Optochromi H8 - 1 (1965)
Sv:438x152x95:signed:Presented by the artist 1965

OLSSON, Julius 1864-1942
British Collection
Tate Gallery Archive holds material concerning this artist

N02787 Moonlit Shore (exhibited 1911)
Oc:1175x1537:signed:Presented by the Trustees of the
Chantrey Bequest 1911

O'NEILL, George Bernard 1828-1917
British Collection

N00618 The Foundling (1852)
Oc:698x1194:signed:Bequeathed by Jacob Bell 1859

ONLEY, Toni born 1928
Modern Collection

T00562 Polar No. 1 (1961)
OVc:1172x1397:signed:Presented by Samuel and Ayala
Zacks Award 1963

Centennial Suite (P03217-P03225, P03228-P03229;
complete group; mixed group)
P03225 Landscape (1970)
CNπ:289x387:signed:Presented by Simon Fraser
University, British Columbia 1977

ONO, Yoko born 1933
Modern Collection

P06402 I Ching No. 14 (1970)
CLπ:511x762:Presented by Curwen Studio through the
Institute of Contemporary Prints 1975

ONSLOW-FORD, Gordon born 1912
Modern Collection
Tate Gallery Archive holds material concerning this artist

T01539 Determination of Gender (1939)
Oc:921x727:signed:Purchased 1972

T02391 A Present for the Past (1942)
Oc:1013x1213:signed:Bequeathed by Mrs Jacqueline
Marie Onslow-Ford 1979

OPIE, John 1761-1807
British Collection
Tate Gallery Archive holds material concerning this artist

N00784 William Siddons
Oc:762x635:Bequeathed by Mrs Cecilia Combe 1868

N01026 Portrait of a Lady in the Character of Cressida
(exhibited 1800)
Oc:2337x1448:Bequeathed by George Silk 1834

N01167 Mary Wollstonecraft, Mrs William Godwin (?) (circa
1790-1)
Oc:759x638:Purchased 1884

N01408 Master William Opie (circa 1788)
Oc:521x425:Presented by Edward Opie 1894

N01826 Portrait of the Artist (circa 1790)
Oc:406x330:Bequeathed by Henry Vaughan 1900

N02877 Mrs S.W. Reynolds (1795)
Oc:762x635:Purchased 1912

N03518 The Artist's Mother (circa 1791)
Oc:768x635:Bequeathed by Mrs Louise d'Este Oliver
1920

N04066 Edmund Lenthal Swifte (1802)
Oc:762x635:Bequeathed by Mrs M.E.A. Cuppage 1925

N05834 The Peasant's Family (circa 1783-5)
Oc:1537x1835:Bequeathed by Sir Otto Beit 1948

OPIE, Julian born 1958
Modern Collection
Tate Gallery Archive holds material concerning this artist

T03783 Making It (1983)
SOm:2610x1180x1925:signed:Presented by the Patrons of
New Art through the Friends of the Tate Gallery 1983

OPPENHEIM, Dennis born 1938
Modern Collection
Tate Gallery Archive holds material concerning this artist

T01773 Salt Flat (1968)
FCDb:711x559:signed:Purchased 1973

T03468 Life Support System for a Premature By-Product (from a
Long Distance) (1981)
DHπ:971x2546:signed:Purchased 1982

P07939 The Diamond Cutter's Wedding (1980)
CLπ:968x1267:signed:Purchased 1983

OPSOMER, Isidore 1878-1967
Modern Collection

N04854 Vase with Dahlias (1935)
Kwiaty
Oc:600x498:signed:Presented by Sam Salz 1936

ORCHARDSON, Sir William Quiller
1832-1910
British Collection
Tate Gallery Archive holds material concerning this artist

N01519 Her First Dance (1884)
Oc:1016x1384:signed:Presented by Sir Henry Tate 1894

N01520 The First Cloud (1887)
Oc:832x1213:signed:Presented by Sir Henry Tate 1894

N01521 Her Mother's Voice (exhibited 1888)
Oc:1016x1486:Presented by Sir Henry Tate 1894

N01601 Napoleon on Board the Bellerophon (exhibited 1880)
Oc:1651x2489:Presented by the Trustees of the Chantrey
Bequest 1880

N03212 Charles Moxon (1875)
Oc:1168x838:Bequeathed by Lady Orchardson 1917

N03213 Mrs Charles Moxon (circa 1875)
Oc:1168x838:Bequeathed by Lady Orchardson 1917

N06001 Head of Napoleon, Study for 'Napoleon on Board the
Bellerophon' (circa 1880)
Dπ:540x445:Presented by Mrs A.E. Riviere 1947

ORGAN, Bryan born 1935
Modern Collection

Six British Jockeys (P06403-P06407, P06411; complete
group)
P06403 Geoff Lewis (1974)
CLπ:310x183:signed:Presented by Curwen Studio
through the Institute of Contemporary Prints 1975

P06404 Jimmy Lindley (1974)
CLπ:532x432:signed:Presented by Curwen Studio through the Institute of Contemporary Prints 1975

P06405 Joe Mercer (1974)
CLπ:534x432:signed:Presented by Curwen Studio through the Institute of Contemporary Prints 1975

P06406 Lester Piggott (1974)
CLπ:533x432:signed:Presented by Curwen Studio through the Institute of Contemporary Prints 1975

P06407 Willie Carson (1974)
CLπ:335x292:signed:Presented by Curwen Studio through the Institute of Contemporary Prints 1975

P06408 Monarch of the Glen after Landseer (1974)
CLπ:610x610:signed:Presented by Curwen Studio through the Institute of Contemporary Prints 1975

P06409 Ophelia (1974)
CLπ:483x537:signed:Presented by Curwen Studio through the Institute of Contemporary Prints 1975

P06410 Tiger (1974)
CLπ:651x540:signed:Presented by Curwen Studio through the Institute of Contemporary Prints 1975

Six British Jockeys (P06403-P06407, P06411; complete group)

P06411 Tony Murray (1974)
CLπ:315x196:signed:Presented by Curwen Studio through the Institute of Contemporary Prints 1975

Four Heads of Wild Cats (P06412-P06415; complete group)

P06412 1. Tiger (1974)
CLπ:210x196:signed:Presented by Curwen Studio through the Institute of Contemporary Prints 1975

P06413 2. Lion (1974)
CLπ:199x197:signed:Presented by Curwen Studio through the Institute of Contemporary Prints 1975

P06414 3. Lioness (1974)
CLπ:185x194:signed:Presented by Curwen Studio through the Institute of Contemporary Prints 1975

P06415 4. Cheetah (1974)
CLπ:188x190:signed:Presented by Curwen Studio through the Institute of Contemporary Prints 1975

P06676 Sicilian Window (1975)
CLπ:559x502:signed:Presented by Curwen Studio 1976

P06677 Hotel Timeo (1975)
CLπ:559x498:signed:Presented by Curwen Studio 1976

P06799 Four Birds (1977)
CLπ:660x486:Presented by Curwen Studio 1978

ORPEN, Sir William 1878-1931
British Collection
Tate Gallery Archive holds material concerning this artist

N02940 The Mirror (1900)
Oc:508x406:signed:Presented by Mrs Coutts Michie through the National Art Collections Fund in memory of the George McCulloch Collection 1913

N02997 The Angler (circa 1912)
Oc:914x864:signed:Presented by Francis Howard through the National Loans Exhibition Committee 1914

N03530 The Model (1911)
Wπ:540x692:Presented by Sir Robert Witt through the National Art Collections Fund 1920

N03549 Lady Orpen (exhibited 1907)
Oc:972x864:signed:Presented by Alfred A. de Pass 1920

N03628 Sir William McCormick (1920)
Oc:1270x1016:signed:Presented by the Trustees of the Chantrey Bequest 1921

N04400 Dame Madge Kendal (circa 1927-8)
Oc:1016x857:signed:Presented by Dame Madge Kendall 1928

ORR, Chris born 1943
Modern Collection
Tate Gallery Archive holds material concerning this artist

P03133 Farm (1975)
CLπ:645x854:signed:Presented by Anderson O'Day 1976

ORSAY, Count Alfred d' - see D'ORSAY, Count Alfred

OSBORN, William Evelyn 1868-1906
British Collection

T03648 Royal Avenue, Chelsea (circa 1900)
Oc:505x610:Presented anonymously in memory of Sir Terence Rattigan 1983

T03649 Beach at Dusk, St Ives Harbour (circa 1895)
Oc:610x510:signed:Presented anonymously in memory of Sir Terence Rattigan 1983

OSBORNE, Walter Frederick 1859-1903
British Collection

N01712 Life in the Streets: Hard Times (exhibited 1892)
Pπ:552x368:Presented by the Trustees of the Chantrey Bequest 1892

OSPOVAT, Henry 1877-1909
British Collection

N04367 Jog on, Jog on, the Footpath Way (circa 1900)
DGπ:190x143:signed:Presented by Mrs Wells 1927

T02246 Sketch for Iago and Cassio, and Figure Studies (circa 1900)
Dπ:190x238:Presented by Mrs Wells 1927, accessioned 1977

OTREBA, Ryszard born 1932
Modern Collection

P11087 Initiation I (1973)
Inicjacja I
MRπ:755x557:signed:Presented by Professor Akumal Ramachander 1985

P11088 Discovery V (1975)
Znalezisko V
MRπ:807x548:signed:Presented by Professor Akumal Ramachander 1985

OULESS, Walter William 1848-1933
British Collection

N04734 Philip Westlake (1873)
Oc:902x705:signed:Presented by the artist's daughters 1934

OULTON, Thérèse born 1953
Modern Collection

T05738 Deposition (1989)
Oc:1956x1778:Purchased 1990

P11197 Untitled (1987)
Jπ:439x383:signed:Presented by Garner H. Tullis and Pamela Auchincloss 1988

P11198 Untitled (1987)
Jπ:760x570:signed:Presented by Garner H. Tullis and Pamela Auchincloss 1988

P11226 [no title] (1989)
Jπ:385x343:signed:Presented by Garner H. Tullis and Pamela Auchincloss 1989

P11227 [no title] (1989)
Jπ:1191x1080:signed:Presented by Garner H. Tullis and Pamela Auchincloss 1989

P11265 Smokescreen (1989)
Nπ:1270x1140:Presented by the King Edward's Hospital Fund 1989

OVENDEN, Graham born 1943

Modern Collection
Tate Gallery Archive holds material concerning this artist

Five Girls (P01253-P01257; complete group)

P01253 Lorraine (1970)
MIπ:356x235:signed:Presented by Waddington Galleries through the Institute of Contemporary Prints 1975

P01254 Little Lorraine (1970)
MIπ:354x250:signed:Presented by Waddington Galleries through the Institute of Contemporary Prints 1975

P01255 Belinda (1970)
MIπ:355x220:signed:Presented by Waddington Galleries through the Institute of Contemporary Prints 1975

P01256 Wendy (1970)
MIπ:355x265:signed:Presented by Waddington Galleries through the Institute of Contemporary Prints 1975

P01257 Ashley (1970)
MIπ:356x254:signed:Presented by Waddington Galleries through the Institute of Contemporary Prints 1975

P01258 Contemporary Girl (1971)
MIπ:260x165:signed:Presented by Waddington Galleries through the Institute of Contemporary Prints 1975

P01259 Edwardian Girl (1971)
MIπ:257x162:signed:Presented by Waddington Galleries through the Institute of Contemporary Prints 1975

P01260 Hide and Seek (1971)
CIπ:273x352:signed:Presented by Waddington Galleries through the Institute of Contemporary Prints 1975

P01261 Lure Me (1971)
MIπ:254x349:signed:Presented by Waddington Galleries through the Institute of Contemporary Prints 1975

P01262 The Meeting (1972)
MIπ:356x241:signed:Presented by Waddington Galleries through the Institute of Contemporary Prints 1975

P01263 The Final Reproach (1974-5)
CIπ:330x432:signed:Presented by Waddington Galleries through the Institute of Contemporary Prints 1975

P01264 Initial Rites (1974-5)
MIπ:343x422:signed:Presented by Waddington Galleries through the Institute of Contemporary Prints 1975

P01265 Lolita by the Lake (1974-5)
CIπ:321x381:signed:Presented by Waddington Galleries through the Institute of Contemporary Prints 1975

P01266 Lolita Meditating (1974-5)
CIπ:340x441:signed:Presented by Waddington Galleries through the Institute of Contemporary Prints 1975

P01267 Lolita Perturbed (1974-5)
CIπ:337x429:signed:Presented by Waddington Galleries through the Institute of Contemporary Prints 1975

P01268 Lolita Recumbent (1974-5)
CIπ:273x368:signed:Presented by Waddington Galleries through the Institute of Contemporary Prints 1975

P01269 Lolita Seductive (1974-5)
CIπ:359x460:signed:Presented by Waddington Galleries through the Institute of Contemporary Prints 1975

P01270 Lolita Vanitas (1974-5)
CIπ:346x441:signed:Presented by Waddington Galleries through the Institute of Contemporary Prints 1975

P01271 Lo Scrapes her Knee (1974-5)
CIπ:295x378:signed:Presented by Waddington Galleries through the Institute of Contemporary Prints 1975

P01272 Lo Thoughtful by the Lake (1974-5)
CIπ:321x451:signed:Presented by Waddington Galleries through the Institute of Contemporary Prints 1975

Alice (P04732-P04739; complete group)

P04732 'She kept on growing' (1970)
CNπ:242x181:signed:Presented by Rose and Chris Prater through the Institute of Contemporary Prints 1975

P04733 'You ought to be ashamed of yourself' (1970)
CNπ:242x180:signed:Presented by Rose and Chris Prater through the Institute of Contemporary Prints 1975

P04734 'And Alice looked around eager to see the Queen' (1970)
CNπ:242x180:signed:Presented by Rose and Chris Prater through the Institute of Contemporary Prints 1975

P04735 'We beg your acceptance of this elegant thimble' (1970)
CNπ:243x180:signed:Presented by Rose and Chris Prater through the Institute of Contemporary Prints 1975

P04736 'I don't think they play at all fairly' (1970)
CNπ:244x180:signed:Presented by Rose and Chris Prater through the Institute of Contemporary Prints 1975

P04737 'I don't see how he can finish' (1970)
CNπ:240x180:signed:Presented by Rose and Chris Prater through the Institute of Contemporary Prints 1975

P04738 'But there isn't any wine' (1970)
CNπ:243x180:signed:Presented by Rose and Chris Prater through the Institute of Contemporary Prints 1975

P04739 'Wake up Alice dear' (1970)
CNπ:245x180:signed:Presented by Rose and Chris Prater through the Institute of Contemporary Prints 1975

P04740 The Jane Doll (1971)
CNπ:616x467:signed:Presented by Rose and Chris Prater through the Institute of Contemporary Prints 1975

P04741 Birnham Wood (1972)
CNπ:492x460:signed:Presented by Rose and Chris Prater through the Institute of Contemporary Prints 1975

P04742 The Brigitte Doll (1972)
CNπ:616x470:signed:Presented by Rose and Chris Prater through the Institute of Contemporary Prints 1975

P04743 Great Dunsinane (1972)
CNπ:575x460:signed:Presented by Rose and Chris Prater through the Institute of Contemporary Prints 1975

P04744 The Margie Doll (1972)
CNπ:616x470:signed:Presented by Rose and Chris Prater through the Institute of Contemporary Prints 1975

P04745 This Blasted Heath (1972)
CNπ:622x460:signed:Presented by Rose and Chris Prater through the Institute of Contemporary Prints 1975

OWEN, Rev. Edward Pryce 1788-1863
British Collection

N02408 The Old Welsh Bridge, Shrewsbury (after Paul Sandby)
(1821)
Iπ:305x406:Presented by Edmund Houghton 1898

after
OWEN, Samuel 1768 or 1769-1857
British Collection

Picturesque Views on the Southern Coast of England
(T05218-T05463; complete group; mixed group)
T05221 Reculver Church, Kent (1816)
Iπ:94x152:Purchased 1988

T05222 Reculver Church, Kent (1816)
Iπ:101x157:Purchased 1988

T05242 Dover Castle, Kent (1814)
Iπ:138x226:Purchased 1988

T05243 Dover Castle, Kent (1814)
Iπ:138x228:Purchased 1988

T05252 Shakespeare Cliff, Dover (1816)
Iπ:113x161:Purchased 1988

T05253 Shakespeare Cliff, Dover (1816)
Iπ:123x159:Purchased 1988

T05286 Brighton Church (1814)
Iπ:105x178:Purchased 1988

T05287 Brighton Church (1814)
Iπ:117x177:Purchased 1988

T05402 The Eddystone Light House (1814)
Iπ:104x168:Purchased 1988

T05403 The Eddystone Light House (1814)
Iπ:101x168:Purchased 1988

T05434 Land's End Cornwall, with Long-Ship's Light-House
(1814)
Iπ:128x164:Purchased 1988

T05435 Land's End Cornwall, with Long-Ship's Light-House
(1814)
Iπ:131x166:Purchased 1988

OZENFANT, Amédée 1886-1966
Modern Collection

T00551 Glasses and Bottles (circa 1922-6)
Verres et bouteilles
Oc:727x603:signed:Purchased 1962

PAALEN, Wolfgang 1905-1959
Modern Collection

T02392   The Messenger (1941)
Le Messager
Oc:2000x765:signed:Bequeathed by Mrs Jacqueline
Marie Onslow-Ford 1979

PACKHAM, Alex born 1914
Modern Collection

P06416   The Kitty (1970-1)
CLπ:429x581:Presented by Curwen Studio through the
Institute of Contemporary Prints 1975

PALADINO, Mimmo born 1948
Modern Collection

P07630   Pool Water (1980)
Acqua di stagno
CIπ:572x895:signed:Purchased 1982

P07631   Peter's Stone (1980)
Pietra di Pietro
CIπ:380x370:signed:Purchased 1982

P07854   Menacing Caves (1982)
Caverne minacciose
CIJπ:400x242:signed:Purchased 1983

P77084   Wet Dream (1984)
Sogno umido
CJπ:801x1216:signed:Purchased 1984

P77179   Sirens; Evening; Western Poet (1986)
Sirene, vespero, poeta occidentale
3 VIπ:1873x872, 1862x857, 1868x580:signed:Purchased
1987

PALMER, Garrick born 1933
Modern Collection

P06800   Kennet Lock (1977)
CLπ:349x521:signed:Presented by Curwen Studio 1978

PALMER, Roger born 1946
Modern Collection
Tate Gallery Archive holds material concerning this artist

P08144   Grass (1972)
CNπ:168x286:Transferred from the Library 1979

P08145   Grass Corner (1972)
CNπ:273x171:Transferred from the Library 1979

P08146   Leaves (1972)
CNπ:184x289:Transferred from the Library 1979

P08147   Leaves with Pillar (1972)
CNπ:190x286:Transferred from the Library 1979

P08148   Tarmac Heap (1972)
MNπ:210x295:Transferred from the Library 1979

P08149   Tarmac Strip (1972)
CNπ:267x178:Transferred from the Library 1979

PALMER, Samuel 1805-1881
British Collection
Tate Gallery Archive holds material concerning this artist

N03312   The Bright Cloud (circa 1833-4)
DWπ:229x305:Presented by Hugh Blaker through the
National Art Collections Fund 1917

N03697   Coming from Evening Church (1830)
Tπ:302x200:signed:Purchased 1922

N03698   A Church among Trees (circa 1830)
DWπ:152x184:Purchased 1922

N03699   The Harvest Moon: Drawing for 'A Pastoral Scene' (circa
1831-2)
DWGπ:152x184:Purchased 1922

N03700   Moonlight, a Landscape with Sheep (circa 1831-3)
DWπ:152x184:Purchased 1922

N03701   Landscape, Girl Standing (circa 1826)
DWGπ:114x133:Purchased 1922

N03868   The Weary Ploughman (circa 1858)
Iπ:133x203:Presented by Herbert Linnell 1924

N03869   Evening, engraved by Welby Sherman (1834)
Iπ:149x178:Presented by Herbert Linnell 1924

N04842   The Gleaning Field (circa 1833)
Tw:305x454:signed:Bequeathed by Mrs Louisa Mary
Garrett 1936

N05805   A Hilly Scene (circa 1826-8)
Tπw:206x137:Purchased 1948

N05923   A Dream in the Apennine (exhibited 1864)
GWπ:660x1016:signed:Bequeathed by Mrs Hilda
Fothergill Medlicott 1950

T01008   The Colosseum and the Arch of Constantine from the
Palatine, Rome (1837-9)
WDπ:137x279:Presented by the National Art Collections
Fund (Herbert Powell Bequest) 1967

T01069   The Waterfalls, Pistil Mawddach, North Wales (1835-6)
Oc:406x260:Purchased 1968

PAOLINI, Giulio born 1946
Modern Collection
Tate Gallery Archive holds material concerning this artist

T03320   Portrait of the Artist as a Model (1981)
Ritratto dell'artista come modello
RpcD::Purchased 1981

        Collection (T07673-T07678; complete group)
Collezione

P07673   Isfahan (1974)
CNπ:318x318:signed:Purchased 1982

P07674   Monitor (1974)
CNπ:318x318:signed:Purchased 1982

P07675   Epidaurus (1974)
Epiduaro
CNπ:320x320:signed:Purchased 1982

P07676   Anthology (1974)
Antologia
CNπ:317x317:signed:Purchased 1982

P07677   Rebus (1974)
Rebus
CNπ:350x320:signed:Purchased 1982

P07678   Collection (1974)
Collezione
CNπ:317x315:signed:Purchased 1982

PAOLOZZI, Sir Eduardo born 1924
Modern Collection
Tate Gallery Archive holds material concerning this artist

T00225   Cyclops (1957)
Sz:1111x305x203:signed:Purchased 1958

T00227   Forms on a Bow (1949)
Sm:483x635x216:Presented by the Contemporary Art
Society 1958

T00273   Shattered Head (1956)
Sz:286x241x184:Purchased 1959

T00274 Fisherman and Wife (1946)
DWVπ:768x610:signed:Purchased 1959

T00293 Man's Head (1952-3)
DGπ:718x571:signed:Presented by the Contemporary Art Society 1959

T00450 Study for 'Forms on a Bow' (1949)
Dπ:381x508:signed:Presented by the artist 1961

T00456 Two Forms on a Rod (1948-9, cast circa 1961)
Sm:527x641x324:signed:Presented by the artist 1961

T00627 Conjectures to Identity (1963)
Vπ:759x511:signed:Purchased 1963

T00638 The City of the Circle and the Square (1963 and 1966)
ASm:2108x1022x667:Purchased 1964

T00812 Rizla (1965)
Sm:1651x2108x1499:Purchased 1965

T00917 Tapestry (1966)
Fπ:1930x1321:Presented by Mrs Gabrielle Keiller through the Friends of the Tate Gallery 1967

Ten Collages from BUNK (T01458-T01467; complete group)
T01458 Was This Metal Monster Master - or Slave? (1952)
Vπ:362x248:Presented by the artist 1971

T01459 Meet the People (1948)
Vπ:359x241:Presented by the artist 1971

T01460 Real Gold (1950)
Vπ:356x235:Presented by the artist 1971

T01461 Windtunnel Test (1950)
Vπ:248x365:Presented by the artist 1971

T01462 I was a Rich Man's Plaything (1947)
Vπ:359x238:Presented by the artist 1971

T01463 It's a Psychological Fact Pleasure Helps your Disposition (1948)
Vπ:362x244:Presented by the artist 1971

T01464 Lessons of Last Time (1947)
Vπ:229x311:Presented by the artist 1971

T01465 Yours Till the Boys Come Home (1951)
Vπ:362x248:Presented by the artist 1971

T01466 Sack-o-sauce (1948)
Vπ:356x264:Presented by the artist 1971

T01467 The Ultimate Planet (1952)
Vπ:251x381:Presented by the artist 1971

T01469 Mechaniks Bench (1963)
Sm:1765x1838x483:Purchased 1971

T01475 Varga-Billboard-Girl (1971)
GFb:406x540:Presented by the artist 1971

T01476 Wonder Toy: Robert the Robot (1971)
GFb:422x321:Presented by the artist 1971

T01477 Amir Amur (1967)
Sm:1892x724x533:Purchased 1971

T03764 Mr Cruickshank (1950)
Sz:290x290x200:signed:Transferred from the Victoria & Albert Museum 1983

T03765 Plaster for 'Mr Cruickshank' (1950)
SDp:290x290x200:Transferred from the Victoria & Albert Museum 1983

P01811 Maahantai (1975)
CIπ:625x425x425:signed:Presented by White Ink 1976

P01812 Omaggio a Michelangelo (1975)
CIπ:591x495:Presented by White Ink 1977

P01813 [no title: proof] (1975)
MJπ:575x235:signed:Presented by White Ink 1977

P01814 [no title: proof] (1975)
MJπ:575x235:signed:Presented by White Ink 1977

P01815 For the Four [colour variant of P03144] (1975)
CJπ:403x403:signed:Presented by White Ink 1977

P01816 For the Four [colour variant of P03144] (1975)
CJπ:403x403:signed:Presented by White Ink 1977

P01817 [no title: proof] (1975)
MJπ:406x406:signed:Presented by White Ink 1977

The Ravel Suite (P01825-P01830; complete group)
P01825 Aranjeux (1974)
MIπ:258x190:signed:Presented by White Ink 1977

P01826 Ci Boure (1974)
MIπ:260x214:signed:Presented by White Ink 1977

P01827 Die Versunkene Glocke (1974)
MIπ:230x165:signed:Presented by White Ink 1977

P01828 Jeux d'Eau (1974)
MIπ:257x153:signed:Presented by White Ink 1977

P01829 Olympia (1974)
MIπ:257x170:signed:Presented by White Ink 1977

P01830 Zaspiak-Blat (1974)
MIπ:257x200:signed:Presented by White Ink 1977

P01951 Girot and Plaza (1964)
MNπ:587x914:Presented anonymously through the Friends of the Tate Gallery 1980

P01952 Tafel 16 (circa 1964)
CNπ:651x270:Presented anonymously through the Friends of the Tate Gallery 1980

P01953 [no title: trial proof for As is When] (circa 1964)
CNπ:549x524:Presented anonymously through the Friends of the Tate Gallery 1980

P01954 [no title: trial proof for Moonstrips Empire News] (circa 1967)
MNπ:343x244:Presented anonymously through the Friends of the Tate Gallery 1980

Universal Electronic Vacuum (P04869-P04879, duplicates: P01955-P01957; complete group)
P01955 833. Whipped Cream, A Taste of Honey, Peanuts, Lemon Tree, Others (1967)
CNπ:888x610:Presented anonymously through the Friends of the Tate Gallery 1980

P01956 A formula that can shatter into a million glass bullets (1967)
CNπ:870x610:Presented anonymously through the Friends of the Tate Gallery 1980

P01957 7 Pyramide in form einer achtel skugel (1967)
CNπ:888x610:Presented anonymously through the Friends of the Tate Gallery 1980

P01958 Multi-Channel Prototype (1970)
CNπ:760x510:Presented anonymously through the Friends of the Tate Gallery 1980

P01959 Signs of Death and Decay in the Sky (1969-70)
CLNπ:781x524:Presented anonymously through the Friends of the Tate Gallery 1980

P01960 6228 Plus: Cry on my Shoulder, No Sad Songs etc. (from Zero Energy Experimental Pile Series) (1969-70)
CLNπ:756x502:Presented anonymously through the Friends of the Tate Gallery 1980

Conditional Probability Machine (P01961-P01984, cancelled proof: P11003; complete group)
P01961 Secrets of Life - The Human Machine and How it Works: Perception through Impression (1970)
MIπ:194x306:signed:Presented anonymously through the Friends of the Tate Gallery 1980

P01962 Secrets of Life - The Human Machine and How it Works: Bird (1970)
MIπ:202x140:signed:Presented anonymously through the Friends of the Tate Gallery 1980

P01963 Secrets of Life - The Human Machine and How it Works: Hazardous Journey (1970)
MIπ:134x141:signed:Presented anonymously through the Friends of the Tate Gallery 1980

P01964 Secrets of Life - The Human Machine and How it Works: Reproduction (1970)
MIπ:102x140:signed:Presented anonymously through the Friends of the Tate Gallery 1980

P01965 Secrets of Life - The Human Machine and How it Works: The Moment of Conception (1970)
MIπ:202x285:signed:Presented anonymously through the Friends of the Tate Gallery 1980

P01966 Secrets of Life - The Human Machine and How it Works: Inside the Brain (1970)
MIπ:209x141:signed:Presented anonymously through the Friends of the Tate Gallery 1980

P01967 Manikins for Destruction: Untitled (M.I.R.A. pair) (1970)
MIπ:325x201:signed:Presented anonymously through the Friends of the Tate Gallery 1980

P01968 Manikins for Destruction: Untitled (Monkey No. 9) (1970)
MIπ:132x195:signed:Presented anonymously through the Friends of the Tate Gallery 1980

P01969 Manikins for Destruction: Untitled (U 14322) (1970)
MIπ:148x190:signed:Presented anonymously through the Friends of the Tate Gallery 1980

P01970 Manikins for Destruction: Untitled (School Bus) (1970)
MIπ:255x175:signed:Presented anonymously through the Friends of the Tate Gallery 1980

P01971 Manikins for Destruction: Untitled (Broken Open Dummy Skeleton) (1970)
MIπ:197x145:signed:Presented anonymously through the Friends of the Tate Gallery 1980

P01972 Manikins for Destruction: Untitled (V.W. Dummy) (1970)
MIπ:207x155:signed:Presented anonymously through the Friends of the Tate Gallery 1980

P01973 Pages from the Aerospace Medical Library: Untitled (Baboon on Sled) (1970)
MIπ:152x143:signed:Presented anonymously through the Friends of the Tate Gallery 1980

P01974 Pages from the Aerospace Medical Library: Electrodes etc., Arm Support etc. (1970)
MIπ:292x120:signed:Presented anonymously through the Friends of the Tate Gallery 1980

P01975 Pages from the Aerospace Medical Library: Geometry Relations in Electron Irradiation of a Mouse, 11.47pm, 11.53pm, 12.06am (1970)
MIπ:375x156:signed:Presented anonymously through the Friends of the Tate Gallery 1980

P01976 Pages from the Aerospace Medical Library: Untitled (Decompression Pair) (1970)
MIπ:132x207:signed:Presented anonymously through the Friends of the Tate Gallery 1980

P01977 Pages from the Aerospace Medical Library: Untitled (Tape Dummy) (1970)
MIπ:114x120:signed:Presented anonymously through the Friends of the Tate Gallery 1980

P01978 Pages from the Aerospace Medical Library: Carpenter (1970)
MIπ:200x126:signed:Presented anonymously through the Friends of the Tate Gallery 1980

P01979 From Genot to Unimate: Sim One (1970)
MIπ:162x194:signed:Presented anonymously through the Friends of the Tate Gallery 1980

P01980 From Genot to Unimate: Genot (1970)
MIπ:150x170:signed:Presented anonymously through the Friends of the Tate Gallery 1980

P01981 From Genot to Unimate: Untitled (Walking Machine) (1970)
MIπ:227x190:signed:Presented anonymously through the Friends of the Tate Gallery 1980

P01982 From Genot to Unimate: Untitled (Parade Robot) (1970)
MIπ:152x142:signed:Presented anonymously through the Friends of the Tate Gallery 1980

P01983 From Genot to Unimate: Untitled (Unimate and Egg) (1970)
MIπ:235x190:signed:Presented anonymously through the Friends of the Tate Gallery 1980

P01984 From Genot to Unimate: Untitled (Robot Commander and Boy) (1970)
MIπ:79x67:signed:Presented anonymously through the Friends of the Tate Gallery 1980

P01985 [no title: trial proof for Conditional Probability Machine] (1970)
MIπ:305x219:Presented anonymously through the Friends of the Tate Gallery 1980

P01986 [no title: trial proof for Conditional Probability Machine] (1970)
MIπ:102x76:Presented anonymously through the Friends of the Tate Gallery 1980

P01987 [no title: proof for Mr Peanuts] (1970)
CNπ:698x489:Presented anonymously through the Friends of the Tate Gallery 1980

P01988 [no title: proof for Mr Peanuts] (1970)
CNπ:698x489:Presented anonymously through the Friends of the Tate Gallery 1980

P01989 [no title: proof for Mr Peanuts] (1970)
CNπ:698x489:Presented anonymously through the Friends of the Tate Gallery 1980

P01990 [no title: trial proof] (1973)
CNπ:800x521:Presented anonymously through the Friends of the Tate Gallery 1980

P01991 [title not known] (1974)
CNπ:841x610:Presented anonymously through the Friends of the Tate Gallery 1980

Calcium Light Night (P01992-P01999, P07621; complete group)

P01992 Allegro Moderato Firemans' Parade (1974-6)
CNπ:788x502:signed:Presented anonymously through the Friends of the Tate Gallery 1980

P01993 Central Park in the Dark Some 40 Years Ago (1974-6)
CNπ:788x511:signed:Presented anonymously through the Friends of the Tate Gallery 1980

P01994 The Children's Hour (1974-6)
CNπ:700x524:signed:Presented anonymously through the Friends of the Tate Gallery 1980

P01995 Largo to Presto (1974-6)
CNπ:790x510:signed:Presented anonymously through the Friends of the Tate Gallery 1980

P01996 Aeschylus and Socrates (1974-6)
CNπ:760x545:signed:Presented anonymously through the Friends of the Tate Gallery 1980

P01997 Calcium Night Light (1974-6)
CNπ:676x561:signed:Presented anonymously through the Friends of the Tate Gallery 1980

P01998 Four German Songs (1974-6)
CNπ:697x510:signed:Presented anonymously through the Friends of the Tate Gallery 1980

P01999 From Early Italian Poets (1974-6)
CNπ:737x536:signed:Presented anonymously through the Friends of the Tate Gallery 1980

Bunk (P02020-P02065; complete group)

P02020 1. Evadne in Green Dimension (1972)
CNLVπ:301x213:Presented by the artist 1972

P02021 2. Will Man Outgrow the Earth ? (1972)
CNLVπ:321x242:Presented by the artist 1972

P02022 3. Fun Helped Them Fight (1972)
CNLVπ:371x258:Presented by the artist 1972

P02023 4. The Ultimate Planet (1972)
CNLVπ:253x384:Presented by the artist 1972

P02024 5. See Mom? A Baby's Life is not all Sunshine (1972)
CNLVπ:389x283:Presented by the artist 1972

P02025 6. Sack-O-Sauce (1972)
CNLVπ:362x267:Presented by the artist 1972

P02026 7. Take-off (1972)
CNLVπ:337x242:Presented by the artist 1972

P02027 8a. Hazards include Dust, Hailstones and Bullets. 8b. Survival (1972)
CNLVπ:261x408:Presented by the artist 1972

P02028 9. Was this Metal Monster Master or Slave? (1972)
CNLVπ:361x243:Presented by the artist 1972

P02029 10. Meet the People (1972)
CNLVπ:347x261:Presented by the artist 1972

P02030 11. Improved Beans (1972)
CNLVπ:264x373:Presented by the artist 1972

P02031 12. Refreshing and Delicious (1972)
CNLVπ:378x281:Presented by the artist 1972

P02032 13. You'll soon be Congratulating Yourself! (1972)
CNLVπ:353x259:Presented by the artist 1972

P02033 14. Goering with Wings (1972)
CNLVπ:337x263:Presented by the artist 1972

P02034 15. Real Gold (1972)
CNLVπ:319x243:Presented by the artist 1972

P02035 16. Fantastic Weapons Contrived (1972)
CNLVπ:347x259:Presented by the artist 1972

P02036 17. Has Jazz a Future? (1972)
CNLVπ:262x385:Presented by the artist 1972

P02037 18. Vogue Gorilla with Miss Harper (1972)
CNLVπ:315x239:Presented by the artist 1972

P02038 19. Electric Arms and Hands also Showing Love is Better than Ever (1972)
CNLVπ:333x232:Presented by the artist 1972

P02039 20. It's Daring it's Audacious (1972)
CNLVπ:320x245:Presented by the artist 1972

P02040 21a. North Dakota's Lone Sky Scraper (1972)
CNLVπ:406x281:Presented by the artist 1972

P02041 21b. Will Alien Powers Invade the Earth? (1972)
CNLVπ:186x148:Presented by the artist 1972

P02042 22. Wind Tunnel Test (1972)
CNLVπ:261x377:Presented by the artist 1972

P02043 23. New Life for Old Radios (1972)
CNLVπ:321x242:Presented by the artist 1972

P02044 24. 2000 Horses and Turbo-powered (1972)
CNLVπ:409x287:Presented by the artist 1972

P02045 25. I was a Rich Man's Plaything (1972)
CNLVπ:372x241:Presented by the artist 1972

P02046 26. Never Leave Well Enough Alone (1972)
CNLVπ:265x365:Presented by the artist 1972

P02047 27. No One's Sure How Good It Is (1972)
CNLVπ:344x230:Presented by the artist 1972

P02048 28. Man Holds the Key (1972)
CNLVπ:340x225:Presented by the artist 1972

P02049 29. Merry Xmas with T-1 Space Suits (1972)
CNLVπ:363x227:Presented by the artist 1972

P02050 30. A New Brand of Brilliance (1972)
CNLVπ:410x286:Presented by the artist 1972

P02051 31. Hi-Ho (1972)
CNLVπ:391x262:Presented by the artist 1972

P02052 32. You Can't Beat the Real Thing (1972)
CNLVπ:347x249:Presented by the artist 1972

P02053 33. It's a Psychological Fact Pleasure Helps Your Disposition (1972)
CNLVπ:375x260:Presented by the artist 1972

P02054 34. Mother Goose Goes Hollywood (1972)
CNLVπ:361x259:Presented by the artist 1972

P02055 35. Shots from Peep Show (1972)
CNLVπ:291x242:Presented by the artist 1972

P02056 36. Lessons of Last Time (1972)
CNLVπ:272x363:Presented by the artist 1972

P02057 37. A Funny Thing Happened on the Way to the Airport (1972)
CNLVπ:291x389:Presented by the artist 1972

P02058 38. The Dynamics of Biology (1972)
CNLVπ:400x285:Presented by the artist 1972

P02059 39. Poor Eleanor Knows Them by Heart (1972)
CNLVπ:321x244:Presented by the artist 1972

P02060 40. Write Dept P-1 for Beautiful Full-Colour Catalog (1972)
CNLVπ:330x242:Presented by the artist 1972

P02061 41. Folks Always Invite Me for the Holidays (1972)
CNLVπ:334x245:Presented by the artist 1972

P02062 42. What a Treat for a Nickel! (1972)
CNLVπ:357x285:Presented by the artist 1972

P02063 43. Yours Till the Boys Come Home (1972)
CNLVπ:388x262:Presented by the artist 1972

P02064 44. Headlines from Horrors Ville (1972)
CNLVπ:265x407:Presented by the artist 1972

P02065 45. Trigger Assembly Removed (1972)
CNLVπ:249x385:Presented by the artist 1972

Cloud Atomic Laboratory (P03051-P03058; complete group)

P03051 A. Top: Garco Robot Nailing a Wooden Box. Bottom: Little Boy on his Bed in his Room (1971)
MIπ:353x245:signed:Presented by British Olivetti Ltd 1971

P03052 B. Left: Skull of Test Dummy. Right: Proton-Synchron Electrophysical Laboratory: Vacuum Pumps to the Electromagnet (1971)
MIπ:269x527:signed:Presented by British Olivetti Ltd 1971

P03053 C. Left: Le Robot 'Robert' Voulait Aller à New York Mais le Passager est Trop Lourd: TWA Plane - Steps - Cap 14 Persons with Two Stewardesses. Right: Wonder Toy, Robert the Robot (1971)
MIπ:245x355:signed:Presented by British Olivetti Ltd 1971

P03054 D. Top: Culture: Monkeys May be the Next Space Travellers on US Made Satellites. Bottom: X-15's Maiden Flight (1971)
MIπ:386x190:signed:Presented by British Olivetti Ltd 1971

P03055 E. Left: Pubic Torso on Lorry in Manhattan Street for 'Bonds Clothes for Men'. Right: Varga - Billboard - Girl (1971)
MIπ:227x480:signed:Presented by British Olivetti Ltd 1971

P03056 F. Top: Chimpanzee in a Test Box Designed for Space Flight. Bottom: Mobot Mark I (1971)
MIπ:355x243:signed:Presented by British Olivetti Ltd 1971

P03057 G. Space Age Archaeology. Left: Fathers. Right: Sons (1971)
MIπ:244x422:signed:Presented by British Olivetti Ltd 1971

P03058 H. Left: Television Series 'Lost in Space': Robot as in 'Forbidden Planet'. Right: Soviet Dog and Man Exit from Space Chamber (1971)
MIπ:270x381:signed:Presented by British Olivetti Ltd 1971

For Charles Rennie Mackintosh (P03142-P03147; complete group)

P03142 And King Las (1975)
:404x404:signed:Presented by Marlborough Graphics 1976

P03143 Eros and Dresser (1975)
:405x405:signed:Presented by Marlborough Graphics 1976

P03144 For the Four (1975)
:403x398:signed:Presented by Marlborough Graphics 1976

P03145 Lead Cameron (1975)
:400x403:signed:Presented by Marlborough Graphics 1976

P03146 Pryde - Pierrot (1975)
:404x400:signed:Presented by Marlborough Graphics 1976

P03147 Sobotka (1975)
:406x409:signed:Presented by Marlborough Graphics 1976

P04746 Automobile Head (1954-62)
CNπ:616x413:signed:Presented by Rose and Chris Prater through the Institute of Contemporary Prints 1975

P04747 Standing Figure (1958-62)
CNπ:632x384:signed:Presented by Rose and Chris Prater through the Institute of Contemporary Prints 1975

P04748 Four Stills from the History of Nothing (1962)
CNπ:505x349:signed:Presented by Rose and Chris Prater through the Institute of Contemporary Prints 1975

P04749 Inkwells Gold (1962)
CNπ:470x635:signed:Presented by Rose and Chris Prater through the Institute of Contemporary Prints 1975

P04750 Metafisikal Translations (1962)
CNπ:298x210:signed:Presented by Rose and Chris Prater through the Institute of Contemporary Prints 1975

P04751 Hero as Riddle (1963)
CNπ:867x584:signed:Presented by Rose and Chris Prater through the Institute of Contemporary Prints 1975

The Institute of Contemporary Arts Portfolio (P04016, P04038, P04053, P04076, P04115, P04125, P04166, P04248, P04256, P04315-P04316, P04334, P04378-P04380, P04419, P04635, P04752, P04938, P05138, P05155, P05248; complete group; mixed group)

P04752 Conjectures to Identity (1963-4)
CNπ:756x495:signed:Presented by Rose and Chris Prater through the Institute of Contemporary Prints 1975

P04753 Girot (1964)
CNπ:552x381:signed:Presented by Rose and Chris Prater through the Institute of Contemporary Prints 1975

P04754 Plaza (1964)
CNπ:473x276:signed:Presented by Rose and Chris Prater through the Institute of Contemporary Prints 1975

P04755 Tafel 16 (1964)
CNπ:654x273:signed:Presented by Rose and Chris Prater through the Institute of Contemporary Prints 1975

As Is When (P04756-P04768; complete group)

P04756 Poster (1964)
CNπ:830x511:signed:Presented by Rose and Chris Prater through the Institute of Contemporary Prints 1975

P04757 Artificial Sun (1964)
CNπ:722x557:signed:Presented by Rose and Chris Prater through the Institute of Contemporary Prints 1975

P04758 Assembling Reminders for a Particular Purpose (1965)
CNπ:816x510:signed:Presented by Rose and Chris Prater through the Institute of Contemporary Prints 1975

P04759 Experience (1964)
CNπ:705x498:signed:Presented by Rose and Chris Prater through the Institute of Contemporary Prints 1975

P04760 Futurism at Lenabo (1964)
CNπ:687x547:signed:Presented by Rose and Chris Prater through the Institute of Contemporary Prints 1975

P04761 He Must, So To Speak, Throw Away the Ladder (1965)
CNπ:781x540:signed:Presented by Rose and Chris Prater through the Institute of Contemporary Prints 1975

P04762 Parrot (1964)
CNπ:767x548:signed:Presented by Rose and Chris Prater through the Institute of Contemporary Prints 1975

P04763 Reality (1964)
CNπ:736x515:signed:Presented by Rose and Chris Prater through the Institute of Contemporary Prints 1975

P04764 The Spirit of the Snake (1965)
CNπ:787x530:signed:Presented by Rose and Chris Prater through the Institute of Contemporary Prints 1975

P04765 Tortured Life (1964)
CNπ:785x572:signed:Presented by Rose and Chris Prater through the Institute of Contemporary Prints 1975

P04766 Wittgenstein at the Cinema Admires Betty Grable (1965)
CNπ:833x503:signed:Presented by Rose and Chris Prater through the Institute of Contemporary Prints 1975

P04767 Wittgenstein in New York (1964)
CNπ:763x538:signed:Presented by Rose and Chris Prater through the Institute of Contemporary Prints 1975

P04768 Wittgenstein the Soldier (1964)
CNπ:772x552:signed:Presented by Rose and Chris Prater through the Institute of Contemporary Prints 1975

P04769 Illumination and the Eye (1967)
CNπ:937x610:signed:Presented by Rose and Chris Prater through the Institute of Contemporary Prints 1975

Moonstrips Empire News (P04770-P04867; incomplete group)

P04770 Cover for a Journal (1967)
CNπ:380x255:signed:Presented by Rose and Chris Prater through the Institute of Contemporary Prints 1975

P04771 Donald Duck Meets Mondrian (1967)
CNπ:380x255:signed:Presented by Rose and Chris Prater through the Institute of Contemporary Prints 1975

P04772 Ernie and T.T. at St Louis Airport (1967)
CNπ:380x255:signed:Presented by Rose and Chris Prater through the Institute of Contemporary Prints 1975

P04773 Formica-Formikel (1967)
CNπ:380x255:signed:Presented by Rose and Chris Prater through the Institute of Contemporary Prints 1975

P04774 High Life (1967)
CNπ:380x255:signed:Presented by Rose and Chris Prater through the Institute of Contemporary Prints 1975

P04775 Memory Core Units (1967)
CNπ:380x255:signed:Presented by Rose and Chris Prater through the Institute of Contemporary Prints 1975

P04776 Secrets of Internal Combustion Engine (1967)
CNπ:380x255:signed:Presented by Rose and Chris Prater through the Institute of Contemporary Prints 1975

P04777 The Silken World of Michelangelo (1967)
CNπ:380x255:signed:Presented by Rose and Chris Prater through the Institute of Contemporary Prints 1975

P04778 [no title] (1967)
CNπ:380x255:signed:Presented by Rose and Chris Prater through the Institute of Contemporary Prints 1975

P04779 [no title] (1967)
CNπ:380x255:signed:Presented by Rose and Chris Prater through the Institute of Contemporary Prints 1975

P04780 [no title] (1967)
CNπ:380x255:signed:Presented by Rose and Chris Prater through the Institute of Contemporary Prints 1975

P04781 [no title] (1967)
CNπ:380x255:signed:Presented by Rose and Chris Prater through the Institute of Contemporary Prints 1975

P04782 [no title] (1967)
CNπ:380x255:signed:Presented by Rose and Chris Prater through the Institute of Contemporary Prints 1975

P04783 [no title] (1967)
CNπ:380x255:signed:Presented by Rose and Chris Prater through the Institute of Contemporary Prints 1975

P04784 [no title] (1967)
CNπ:380x255:signed:Presented by Rose and Chris Prater through the Institute of Contemporary Prints 1975

P04785 [no title] (1967)
CNπ:380x255:signed:Presented by Rose and Chris Prater through the Institute of Contemporary Prints 1975

P04786 [no title] (1967)
CNπ:380x255:signed:Presented by Rose and Chris Prater through the Institute of Contemporary Prints 1975

P04787 [no title] (1967)
CNπ:380x255:signed:Presented by Rose and Chris Prater through the Institute of Contemporary Prints 1975

P04788 [no title] (1967)
CNπ:380x255:signed:Presented by Rose and Chris Prater through the Institute of Contemporary Prints 1975

P04789 [no title] (1967)
CNπ:380x255:signed:Presented by Rose and Chris Prater through the Institute of Contemporary Prints 1975

P04790 [no title] (1967)
CNπ:380x255:signed:Presented by Rose and Chris Prater through the Institute of Contemporary Prints 1975

P04791 [no title] (1967)
CNπ:380x255:signed:Presented by Rose and Chris Prater through the Institute of Contemporary Prints 1975

P04792 [no title] (1967)
CNπ:380x255:signed:Presented by Rose and Chris Prater through the Institute of Contemporary Prints 1975

P04793 [no title] (1967)
CNπ:380x255:signed:Presented by Rose and Chris Prater through the Institute of Contemporary Prints 1975

P04794 [no title] (1967)
CNπ:380x255:signed:Presented by Rose and Chris Prater through the Institute of Contemporary Prints 1975

P04795 [no title] (1967)
CNπ:380x255:signed:Presented by Rose and Chris Prater through the Institute of Contemporary Prints 1975

P04796 [no title] (1967)
CNπ:380x255:signed:Presented by Rose and Chris Prater through the Institute of Contemporary Prints 1975

P04797 [no title] (1967)
CNπ:380x255:signed:Presented by Rose and Chris Prater through the Institute of Contemporary Prints 1975

P04798 [no title] (1967)
CNπ:380x255:signed:Presented by Rose and Chris Prater through the Institute of Contemporary Prints 1975

P04799 [no title] (1967)
CNπ:380x255:signed:Presented by Rose and Chris Prater through the Institute of Contemporary Prints 1975

P04800 [no title] (1967)
CNπ:380x255:signed:Presented by Rose and Chris Prater through the Institute of Contemporary Prints 1975

P04801 [no title] (1967)
CNπ:380x255:signed:Presented by Rose and Chris Prater through the Institute of Contemporary Prints 1975

P04802 [no title] (1967)
CNπ:380x255:signed:Presented by Rose and Chris Prater through the Institute of Contemporary Prints 1975

P04803 [no title] (1967)
CNπ:380x255:signed:Presented by Rose and Chris Prater through the Institute of Contemporary Prints 1975

P04804 [no title] (1967)
CNπ:380x255:signed:Presented by Rose and Chris Prater through the Institute of Contemporary Prints 1975

P04805 [no title] (1967)
CNπ:380x255:signed:Presented by Rose and Chris Prater through the Institute of Contemporary Prints 1975

P04806 [no title] (1967)
CNπ:380x255:signed:Presented by Rose and Chris Prater through the Institute of Contemporary Prints 1975

P04807 [no title] (1967)
CNπ:380x255:signed:Presented by Rose and Chris Prater through the Institute of Contemporary Prints 1975

P04808 [no title] (1967)
CNπ:380x255:signed:Presented by Rose and Chris Prater through the Institute of Contemporary Prints 1975

P04809 [no title] (1967)
CNπ:380x255:signed:Presented by Rose and Chris Prater through the Institute of Contemporary Prints 1975

P04810 [no title] (1967)
CNπ:380x255:signed:Presented by Rose and Chris Prater through the Institute of Contemporary Prints 1975

P04811 [no title] (1967)
CNπ:380x255:signed:Presented by Rose and Chris Prater
through the Institute of Contemporary Prints 1975

P04812 [no title] (1967)
CNπ:380x255:signed:Presented by Rose and Chris Prater
through the Institute of Contemporary Prints 1975

P04813 [no title] (1967)
CNπ:380x255:signed:Presented by Rose and Chris Prater
through the Institute of Contemporary Prints 1975

P04814 [no title] (1967)
CNπ:380x255:signed:Presented by Rose and Chris Prater
through the Institute of Contemporary Prints 1975

P04815 [no title] (1967)
CNπ:380x255:signed:Presented by Rose and Chris Prater
through the Institute of Contemporary Prints 1975

P04816 [no title] (1967)
CNπ:380x255:signed:Presented by Rose and Chris Prater
through the Institute of Contemporary Prints 1975

P04817 [no title] (1967)
CNπ:380x255:signed:Presented by Rose and Chris Prater
through the Institute of Contemporary Prints 1975

P04818 [no title] (1967)
CNπ:380x255:signed:Presented by Rose and Chris Prater
through the Institute of Contemporary Prints 1975

P04819 [no title] (1967)
CNπ:380x255:signed:Presented by Rose and Chris Prater
through the Institute of Contemporary Prints 1975

P04820 [no title] (1967)
CNπ:380x255:signed:Presented by Rose and Chris Prater
through the Institute of Contemporary Prints 1975

P04821 [no title] (1967)
CNπ:380x255:signed:Presented by Rose and Chris Prater
through the Institute of Contemporary Prints 1975

P04822 [no title] (1967)
CNπ:380x255:signed:Presented by Rose and Chris Prater
through the Institute of Contemporary Prints 1975

P04823 [no title] (1967)
CNπ:380x255:signed:Presented by Rose and Chris Prater
through the Institute of Contemporary Prints 1975

P04824 [no title] (1967)
CNπ:380x255:signed:Presented by Rose and Chris Prater
through the Institute of Contemporary Prints 1975

P04825 [no title] (1967)
CNπ:380x255:signed:Presented by Rose and Chris Prater
through the Institute of Contemporary Prints 1975

P04826 [no title] (1967)
CNπ:380x255:signed:Presented by Rose and Chris Prater
through the Institute of Contemporary Prints 1975

P04827 [no title] (1967)
CNπ:380x255:signed:Presented by Rose and Chris Prater
through the Institute of Contemporary Prints 1975

P04828 [no title] (1967)
CNπ:380x255:signed:Presented by Rose and Chris Prater
through the Institute of Contemporary Prints 1975

P04829 [no title] (1967)
CNπ:380x255:signed:Presented by Rose and Chris Prater
through the Institute of Contemporary Prints 1975

P04830 [no title] (1967)
CNπ:380x255:signed:Presented by Rose and Chris Prater
through the Institute of Contemporary Prints 1975

P04831 [no title] (1967)
CNπ:380x255:signed:Presented by Rose and Chris Prater
through the Institute of Contemporary Prints 1975

P04832 [no title] (1967)
CNπ:380x255:signed:Presented by Rose and Chris Prater
through the Institute of Contemporary Prints 1975

P04833 [no title] (1967)
CNπ:380x255:signed:Presented by Rose and Chris Prater
through the Institute of Contemporary Prints 1975

P04834 [no title] (1967)
CNπ:380x255:signed:Presented by Rose and Chris Prater
through the Institute of Contemporary Prints 1975

P04835 [no title] (1967)
CNπ:380x255:signed:Presented by Rose and Chris Prater
through the Institute of Contemporary Prints 1975

P04836 [no title] (1967)
CNπ:380x255:signed:Presented by Rose and Chris Prater
through the Institute of Contemporary Prints 1975

P04837 [no title] (1967)
CNπ:380x255:signed:Presented by Rose and Chris Prater
through the Institute of Contemporary Prints 1975

P04838 [no title] (1967)
CNπ:380x255:signed:Presented by Rose and Chris Prater
through the Institute of Contemporary Prints 1975

P04839 [no title] (1967)
CNπ:380x255:signed:Presented by Rose and Chris Prater
through the Institute of Contemporary Prints 1975

P04840 [no title] (1967)
CNπ:380x255:signed:Presented by Rose and Chris Prater
through the Institute of Contemporary Prints 1975

P04841 [no title] (1967)
CNπ:380x255:signed:Presented by Rose and Chris Prater
through the Institute of Contemporary Prints 1975

P04842 [no title] (1967)
CNπ:380x255:signed:Presented by Rose and Chris Prater
through the Institute of Contemporary Prints 1975

P04843 [no title] (1967)
CNπ:380x255:signed:Presented by Rose and Chris Prater
through the Institute of Contemporary Prints 1975

P04844 [no title] (1967)
CNπ:380x255:signed:Presented by Rose and Chris Prater
through the Institute of Contemporary Prints 1975

P04845 [no title] (1967)
CNπ:380x255:signed:Presented by Rose and Chris Prater
through the Institute of Contemporary Prints 1975

P04846 [no title] (1967)
CNπ:380x255:signed:Presented by Rose and Chris Prater
through the Institute of Contemporary Prints 1975

P04847 [no title] (1967)
CNπ:380x255:signed:Presented by Rose and Chris Prater
through the Institute of Contemporary Prints 1975

P04848 [no title] (1967)
CNπ:380x255:signed:Presented by Rose and Chris Prater
through the Institute of Contemporary Prints 1975

P04849 [no title] (1967)
CNπ:380x255:signed:Presented by Rose and Chris Prater
through the Institute of Contemporary Prints 1975

P04850 [no title] (1967)
CNπ:380x255:signed:Presented by Rose and Chris Prater
through the Institute of Contemporary Prints 1975

P04851 [no title] (1967)
CNπ:380x255:signed:Presented by Rose and Chris Prater
through the Institute of Contemporary Prints 1975

P04852 [no title] (1967)
CNπ:380x255:signed:Presented by Rose and Chris Prater
through the Institute of Contemporary Prints 1975

P04853   [no title] (1967)
CNπ:380x255:signed:Presented by Rose and Chris Prater through the Institute of Contemporary Prints 1975

P04854   [no title] (1967)
CNπ:380x255:signed:Presented by Rose and Chris Prater through the Institute of Contemporary Prints 1975

P04855   [no title] (1967)
CNπ:380x255:signed:Presented by Rose and Chris Prater through the Institute of Contemporary Prints 1975

P04856   [no title] (1967)
CNπ:380x255:signed:Presented by Rose and Chris Prater through the Institute of Contemporary Prints 1975

P04857   [no title] (1967)
CNπ:380x255:signed:Presented by Rose and Chris Prater through the Institute of Contemporary Prints 1975

P04858   [no title] (1967)
CNπ:380x255:signed:Presented by Rose and Chris Prater through the Institute of Contemporary Prints 1975

P04859   [no title] (1967)
CNπ:380x255:signed:Presented by Rose and Chris Prater through the Institute of Contemporary Prints 1975

P04860   [no title] (1967)
CNπ:380x255:signed:Presented by Rose and Chris Prater through the Institute of Contemporary Prints 1975

P04861   [no title] (1967)
CNπ:380x255:signed:Presented by Rose and Chris Prater through the Institute of Contemporary Prints 1975

P04862   [no title] (1967)
CNπ:380x255:signed:Presented by Rose and Chris Prater through the Institute of Contemporary Prints 1975

P04863   [no title] (1967)
CNπ:380x255:signed:Presented by Rose and Chris Prater through the Institute of Contemporary Prints 1975

P04864   [no title] (1967)
CNπ:380x255:signed:Presented by Rose and Chris Prater through the Institute of Contemporary Prints 1975

P04865   [no title] (1967)
CNπ:380x255:signed:Presented by Rose and Chris Prater through the Institute of Contemporary Prints 1975

P04866   [no title] (1967)
CNπ:380x255:signed:Presented by Rose and Chris Prater through the Institute of Contemporary Prints 1975

P04867   [no title] (1967)
CNπ:380x255:signed:Presented by Rose and Chris Prater through the Institute of Contemporary Prints 1975

P04868   Theory of Relativity (1967)
CNπ:924x594:signed:Presented by Rose and Chris Prater through the Institute of Contemporary Prints 1975

Universal Electronic Vacuum (P04869-P04879, duplicates: P01955-P01957; complete group)

P04869   Poster (1967)
CNπ:859x611:signed:Presented by Rose and Chris Prater through the Institute of Contemporary Prints 1975

P04870   Computer-Epoch (1967)
CNπ:909x615:signed:Presented by Rose and Chris Prater through the Institute of Contemporary Prints 1975

P04871   883. Whipped Cream, a Taste of Honey, Peanuts, Lemon Tea, Others (1967)
CNπ:889x612:signed:Presented by Rose and Chris Prater through the Institute of Contemporary Prints 1975

P04872   A Formula that can shatter into a million glass bullets (1967)
CNπ:908x610:signed:Presented by Rose and Chris Prater through the Institute of Contemporary Prints 1975

P04873   Horizon of Expectations (1967)
CNπ:925x616:signed:Presented by Rose and Chris Prater through the Institute of Contemporary Prints 1975

P04874   Memory Matrix (1967)
CNπ:915x615:signed:Presented by Rose and Chris Prater through the Institute of Contemporary Prints 1975

P04875   Protocol Sentences (1967)
CNπ:902x611:signed:Presented by Rose and Chris Prater through the Institute of Contemporary Prints 1975

P04876   7 pyramide in form einer aschtelskugel (1967)
CNπ:890x610:signed:Presented by Rose and Chris Prater through the Institute of Contemporary Prints 1975

P04877   Spontaneous Discrimination Non-Spontaneous Discrimination (1967)
CNπ:913x610:signed:Presented by Rose and Chris Prater through the Institute of Contemporary Prints 1975

P04878   Sun City (1967)
CNπ:875x604:signed:Presented by Rose and Chris Prater through the Institute of Contemporary Prints 1975

P04879   War Games Revised (1967)
CNπ:875x605:signed:Presented by Rose and Chris Prater through the Institute of Contemporary Prints 1975

P04880   Hors Concours (1974)
CNπ:838x610:signed:Presented by Rose and Chris Prater through the Institute of Contemporary Prints 1975

Kottbusserdam Pictures and Turkish Music (P04881-P04884; complete group)

P04881   'Franko' Amsterd (1974)
CNπ:802x553:signed:Presented by Rose and Chris Prater through the Institute of Contemporary Prints 1975

P04882   Karakus Döner Havada (1974)
CNπ:812x585:signed:Presented by Rose and Chris Prater through the Institute of Contemporary Prints 1975

P04883   Day and Night (1974)
CNπ:789x559:signed:Presented by Rose and Chris Prater through the Institute of Contemporary Prints 1975

P04884   Turkish Music (1974)
CNπ:803x560:signed:Presented by Rose and Chris Prater through the Institute of Contemporary Prints 1975

P04885   Leonardo (1974)
CNπ:603x425:signed:Presented by Rose and Chris Prater through the Institute of Contemporary Prints 1975

P04886   [title not known] (1974)
CNπ:839x611:signed:Presented by Rose and Chris Prater through the Institute of Contemporary Prints 1975

P04887   [title not known] (1974)
CNπ:641x489:signed:Presented by Rose and Chris Prater through the Institute of Contemporary Prints 1975

P07414   Bash (1971)
CNπ:743x495:signed:Purchased 1981

Calcium Light Night (P01992-P01999, P07621; complete group)

P07621   Nettleton (1977)
CNπ:800x547:signed:Purchased 1982

P07679   Head (1977)
MIπ:284x214:signed:Purchased 1982

P07680   Head (1979)
MIπ:311x207:signed:Purchased 1982

P07681   Head (1980)
Mπ:448x300:signed:Purchased 1982

P07682   Head (1980)
MIπ:454x304:signed:Purchased 1982

P07683 After Biagio di Antonio (1980)
MLπ:152x254:signed:Purchased 1982

P07684 Parkplatz (1980)
MIπ:344x489:signed:Purchased 1982

P11000 Appel-Calder (1975)
CNπ:743x546:signed:Presented anonymously through the
Friends of the Tate Gallery 1980

P11001 Ciao Picasso (1975)
CNπ:737x527:signed:Presented anonymously through the
Friends of the Tate Gallery 1980

P11002 W. 16 (1974)
CNπ:648x451:signed:Presented anonymously through the
Friends of the Tate Gallery 1980

Conditional Probability Machine (P01961-P01984,
cancelled proof: P11003; complete group)

P11003 From Genot to Unimate: Genot (1970)
MIπ:152x170:signed:Presented anonymously through the
Friends of the Tate Gallery 1980

PARC, Julio le - see LE PARC, Julio

PARK, Alistair born 1930
Modern Collection

Jam Press Phase One (P08006-P08014; complete group;
mixed group)

P08013 1. 9 (1973-4)
MLπ:559x441:Transferred from the Library 1977

PARK, John A. 1880-1962
Modern Collection
Tate Gallery Archive holds material concerning this artist

N05337 Snow Falls on Exmoor (1939)
Oc:635x762:signed:Presented by the Trustees of the
Chantrey Bequest 1940

PARKER, Harold 1873-1960
British Collection

N02265 Ariadne (exhibited 1908)
Ss:1041x1422x406:Presented by the Trustees of the
Chantrey Bequest 1904

PARKER, Ray 1922-1990
Modern Collection

T00441 Untitled (1959)
Oc:1778x1800:signed:Purchased 1961

PARKINSON, Valerie
Modern Collection

Untitled (P06417-P06418; complete group)

P06417 [title not known] (1968)
CLπ:241x321:signed:Presented by Curwen Studio
through the Institute of Contemporary Prints 1975

P06418 [title not known] (1968)
CLπ:241x321:signed:Presented by Curwen Studio
through the Institute of Contemporary Prints 1975

PARS, William 1742-1782
British Collection

T04852 Rome: The Forum (circa 1775)
DWπ:402x588:Presented by Mrs Marion Adams in
memory of her husband Canon J.H. Adams 1986

T04853 The Interior of the Colosseum (circa 1775)
DWπ:435x591:Presented by Mrs Marion Adams in
memory of her husband Canon J.H. Adams 1986

PARSONS, Alfred 1847-1920
British Collection
Tate Gallery Archive holds material concerning this artist

N01589 'When Nature Painted all Things Gay' (exhibited 1887)
Oc:1054x1511:signed:Presented by the Trustees of the
Chantrey Bequest 1887

PARTON, Ernest 1845-1938
British Collection

N01628 The Waning of the Year (1879)
Oc:1816x1308:signed:Presented by the Trustees of the
Chantrey Bequest 1879

PARTRIDGE, David born 1919
Modern Collection
Tate Gallery Archive holds material concerning this artist

T00647 Vertebrate Configuration (1963)
ORmb:2057x508x86:signed:Purchased 1964

PASMORE, Victor born 1908
Modern Collection
Tate Gallery Archive holds material concerning this artist

N05253 Lamplight (1941)
Oc:635x762:signed:Purchased 1941

N05974 Square Motif, Blue and Gold: The Eclipse (1950)
Oc:457x610:Purchased 1951

N05975 Reclining Nude (1942)
Oc:305x406:Presented by the Contemporary Art Society
1951

N06191 Spiral Motif in Green, Violet, Blue and Gold: The Coast
of the Inland Sea (1950)
Oc:813x1003:signed:Purchased 1953

T00092 Porthmeor Beach, St Ives (1950)
Dπ:241x289:signed:Purchased 1956

T00094 Abstract in White, Grey and Ochre (1949)
DVc:508x406:signed:Presented by John Piper 1956

T00152 Nude (1941)
Oc:610x508:signed:Presented by Sir Kenneth Clark (later
Lord Clark of Saltwood) 1957

T00166 Abstract in White, Black, Indian and Lilac (1957)
ORw:1067x1168x32:Purchased 1958

T00197 The Quiet River: The Thames at Chiswick (1943-4)
Oc:762x1016:signed:Presented by the Trustees of the
Chantrey Bequest 1958

T00410 Linear Motif in Black and White (1930-1)
OVa:1219x1219:signed:Purchased 1961

T00411 Yellow Abstract (1960-1)
Ob:1219x1219:signed:Purchased 1961

T00587 Black Abstract (1963)
ORb:1524x1524x13:signed:Purchased 1963

T00602 The Jewish Model (1943-5)
Oc:508x406:signed:Purchased 1963

T00609 Relief Construction in White, Black and Maroon
(1962-3)
ORwa:686x737x133:signed:Purchased 1963

T00784 Synthetic Construction (White and Black) (1965-6)
Rv:1226x1226x273:signed:Presented by the artist 1966

T03086 The Green Earth (1979-80)
Ocw:1238x1835:signed:Purchased 1980

T03120 Roses in a Jar (1947)
Oc:610x457:signed:Purchased 1980

P01461 Blue Development (1974)
CIπ:381x381:signed:Presented by Marlborough Graphics through the Institute of Contemporary Prints 1975

P01462 Brown Image (1974)
CINπ:794x203:signed:Presented by Marlborough Graphics through the Institute of Contemporary Prints 1975

Word and Image (P01463-P01469; complete group)
P01463 'Am I the Object Which I See?' (1974)
CIπ:378x381:signed:Presented by Marlborough Graphics through the Institute of Contemporary Prints 1975

P01464 'By What Geometry Must We Construct the Physical World?' (1974)
CIπ:400x392:signed:Presented by Marlborough Graphics through the Institute of Contemporary Prints 1975

P01465 'By what means can we know?' (1974)
CIπ:376x385:signed:Presented by Marlborough Graphics through the Institute of Contemporary Prints 1975

P01466 'Deep inside I looked' (1974)
CIπ:370x382:signed:Presented by Marlborough Graphics through the Institute of Contemporary Prints 1975

P01467 'Quiet is the Island' (1974)
CIπ:407x489:signed:Presented by Marlborough Graphics through the Institute of Contemporary Prints 1975

P01468 'The Tear that Falls' (1974)
CIπ:379x382:signed:Presented by Marlborough Graphics through the Institute of Contemporary Prints 1975

P01469 'When the Curtain Falls' (1974)
CIπ:402x403:signed:Presented by Marlborough Graphics through the Institute of Contemporary Prints 1975

P01470 Linear Development in One Movement (1974)
CIπ:397x400:signed:Presented by Marlborough Graphics through the Institute of Contemporary Prints 1975

P01471 Linear Development in One Movement (1974)
CIπ:330x381:signed:Presented by Marlborough Graphics through the Institute of Contemporary Prints 1975

P01472 Linear Motif in Two Movements (1974)
CINπ:381x400:signed:Presented by Marlborough Graphics through the Institute of Contemporary Prints 1975

P01473 Linear Motif in Three Movements (1974)
CINπ:378x397:signed:Presented by Marlborough Graphics through the Institute of Contemporary Prints 1975

P01474 The Plough and the Stars (1974)
CIπ:381x384:signed:Presented by Marlborough Graphics through the Institute of Contemporary Prints 1975

P01475 Turning and Turning in the Widening Gyre (1974)
CIπ:384x457:signed:Presented by Marlborough Graphics through the Institute of Contemporary Prints 1975

P01476 Vertical Development (1974)
CINπ:667x305:signed:Presented by Marlborough Graphics through the Institute of Contemporary Prints 1975

P01477 When the Lute is Broken (1974)
CIπ:391x397:signed:Presented by Marlborough Graphics through the Institute of Contemporary Prints 1975

P02545 Un Bel di Vedremo (Puccini) (1978)
CIπ:2318x492:signed:Presented by the artist 1981

P02546 Villa dei Misteri (1980)
CIπ:692x1988:signed:Presented by the artist 1981

P03105 Untitled (from IAA Portfolio)
CIπ:245x378:Presented by the International Association of Art 1975

The Cave of Calypso (P03213-P03216; complete group)
P03213 The Cave of Calypso I (1977)
CIπ:375x380:signed:Presented by Marlborough Graphics through the Institute of Contemporary Prints 1977

P03214 The Cave of Calypso II (1977)
CIπ:372x378:signed:Presented by Marlborough Graphics through the Institute of Contemporary Prints 1977

P03215 The Cave of Calypso III (1977)
CIπ:375x378:signed:Presented by Marlborough Graphics through the Institute of Contemporary Prints 1977

P03216 The Cave of Calypso IV (1977)
CIπ:373x378:signed:Presented by Marlborough Graphics through the Institute of Contemporary Prints 1977

P03263 Brown Image Two (1978)
CIπ:1207x984:Presented by Marlborough Graphics 1979

P03264 The Cave of Calypso (1978)
CNπ:679x1010:Presented by Marlborough Graphics 1979

P04888 Points of Contact No. 2 (1964)
CNVπ:679x1010:signed:Presented by Rose and Chris Prater through the Institute of Contemporary Prints 1975

P04889 Points of Contact No. 8 (1966)
CNVπ:813x762:signed:Presented by Rose and Chris Prater through the Institute of Contemporary Prints 1975

P04890 Points of Contact No. 10 (1966)
CNπ:584x1673:signed:Presented by Rose and Chris Prater through the Institute of Contemporary Prints 1975

P04891 Variation of Points of Contact No. 9 (1966)
MNπ:794x591:signed:Presented by Rose and Chris Prater through the Institute of Contemporary Prints 1975

P04892 Points of Contact No. 9 (1966)
CNπ:1524x1273:signed:Presented by Rose and Chris Prater through the Institute of Contemporary Prints 1975

P04893 Points of Contact No. 11 (1967)
CNπ:613x1375:signed:Presented by Rose and Chris Prater through the Institute of Contemporary Prints 1975

P04894 Points of Contact No. 12 (1967)
CNπ:1092x441:signed:Presented by Rose and Chris Prater through the Institute of Contemporary Prints 1975

P04895 Points of Contact A (1969)
CNπ:600x806:signed:Presented by Rose and Chris Prater through the Institute of Contemporary Prints 1975

P04896 Points of Contact No. 13 (1939)
CNπ:559x1308:signed:Presented by Rose and Chris Prater through the Institute of Contemporary Prints 1975

P04897 Points of Contact No. 14 (1969)
CNπ:1908x625:signed:Presented by Rose and Chris Prater through the Institute of Contemporary Prints 1975

P04898 Points of Contact No. 15 (1969)
CNπ:1394x546:signed:Presented by Rose and Chris Prater through the Institute of Contemporary Prints 1975

Points of Contact - Linear Developments Portfolio (P04899-P04906; complete group)
P04899 Linear Development A (1970-1)
CNπ:416x421:signed:Presented by Rose and Chris Prater through the Institute of Contemporary Prints 1975

P04900 Linear Development 1 (1970-1)
CNπ:420x420:signed:Presented by Rose and Chris Prater through the Institute of Contemporary Prints 1975

P04901 Linear Development 2 (1970-1)
CNπ:420x421:signed:Presented by Rose and Chris Prater through the Institute of Contemporary Prints 1975

P04902 Linear Development 3 (1970-1)
CNπ:421x416:signed:Presented by Rose and Chris Prater through the Institute of Contemporary Prints 1975

P04903 Linear Development 4 (1970-1)
CNπ:422x416:signed:Presented by Rose and Chris Prater through the Institute of Contemporary Prints 1975

P04904 Linear Development 5 (1970-1)
CNπ:416x421:signed:Presented by Rose and Chris Prater through the Institute of Contemporary Prints 1975

P04905 Linear Development 6 (1970-1)
CNπ:415x415:signed:Presented by Rose and Chris Prater through the Institute of Contemporary Prints 1975

P04906 Linear Development 7 (1970-1)
CNπ:416x415:signed:Presented by Rose and Chris Prater through the Institute of Contemporary Prints 1975

Points of Contact - Transformations Portfolio (P04907-P04914; complete group)

P04907 Transformation A (1970-1)
CNπ:420x415:signed:Presented by Rose and Chris Prater through the Institute of Contemporary Prints 1975

P04908 Transformation 1 (1970-1)
CNπ:421x416:signed:Presented by Rose and Chris Prater through the Institute of Contemporary Prints 1975

P04909 Transformation 2 (1970-1)
CNπ:421x422:signed:Presented by Rose and Chris Prater through the Institute of Contemporary Prints 1975

P04910 Transformation 3 (1970-1)
CNπ:422x416:signed:Presented by Rose and Chris Prater through the Institute of Contemporary Prints 1975

P04911 Transformation 4 (1970-1)
CNπ:421x421:signed:Presented by Rose and Chris Prater through the Institute of Contemporary Prints 1975

P04912 Transformation 5 (1970-1)
CNπ:415x422:signed:Presented by Rose and Chris Prater through the Institute of Contemporary Prints 1975

P04913 Transformation 6 (1970-1)
CNπ:416x422:signed:Presented by Rose and Chris Prater through the Institute of Contemporary Prints 1975

P04914 Transformation 7 (1970-1)
CNπ:420x420:signed:Presented by Rose and Chris Prater through the Institute of Contemporary Prints 1975

P04915 Abstract (1971)
CNπ:533x508:signed:Presented by Rose and Chris Prater through the Institute of Contemporary Prints 1975

P04916 Linear Development A (1971)
CNπ:635x454:signed:Presented by Rose and Chris Prater through the Institute of Contemporary Prints 1975

P04917 Untitled (1971)
CNπ:657x416:signed:Presented by Rose and Chris Prater through the Institute of Contemporary Prints 1975

Points of Contact - Variations Portfolio (P04918-P04924; complete group)

P04918 Variation No. 2 (1971-2)
CNπ:700x478:signed:Presented by Rose and Chris Prater through the Institute of Contemporary Prints 1975

P04919 Variation No. 7 (1971-2)
CNπ:700x478:signed:Presented by Rose and Chris Prater through the Institute of Contemporary Prints 1975

P04920 Variation No. 8 (1971-2)
CNπ:700x477:signed:Presented by Rose and Chris Prater through the Institute of Contemporary Prints 1975

P04921 Variation No. 1 (1971-2)
CNπ:402x478:signed:Presented by Rose and Chris Prater through the Institute of Contemporary Prints 1975

P04922 Variation No. 3 (1971-2)
CNπ:700x478:signed:Presented by Rose and Chris Prater through the Institute of Contemporary Prints 1975

P04923 Variation No. 5 (1971-2)
CNπ:700x478:signed:Presented by Rose and Chris Prater through the Institute of Contemporary Prints 1975

P04924 Variation No. 4 (1971-2)
CNπ:699x478:signed:Presented by Rose and Chris Prater through the Institute of Contemporary Prints 1975

P04925 What is the Object over There? Points of Contact No. 17 (1973)
CNπ:765x2889:signed:Presented by Rose and Chris Prater through the Institute of Contemporary Prints 1975

P04926 Points of Contact No. 18 (1973-4)
CNπ:562x397:signed:Presented by Rose and Chris Prater through the Institute of Contemporary Prints 1975

P04927 Points of Contact No. 19 (1973-4)
CNπ:559x397:signed:Presented by Rose and Chris Prater through the Institute of Contemporary Prints 1975

P04928 Hear the Sound of a Magic Tune (1974)
CNπ:2429x660:signed:Presented by Rose and Chris Prater through the Institute of Contemporary Prints 1975

P04929 Look into the Pool Narcissus Found (1974)
CNπ:508x3111:signed:Presented by Rose and Chris Prater through the Institute of Contemporary Prints 1975

P04930 Points of Contact No. 20 (1974)
CNπ:559x397:signed:Presented by Rose and Chris Prater through the Institute of Contemporary Prints 1975

P04931 Points of Contact No. 21 (1974)
CNπ:559x397:signed:Presented by Rose and Chris Prater through the Institute of Contemporary Prints 1975

P04932 Points of Contact No. 22 (1974)
CNπ:559x397:signed:Presented by Rose and Chris Prater through the Institute of Contemporary Prints 1975

P04933 Points of Contact No. 23 (1974)
CNπ:768x543:signed:Presented by Rose and Chris Prater through the Institute of Contemporary Prints 1975

P04934 Points of Contact No. 24 (1974)
CNπ:673x600:signed:Presented by Rose and Chris Prater through the Institute of Contemporary Prints 1975

P04935 Points of Contact No. 25 (1974)
CNπ:733x549:signed:Presented by Rose and Chris Prater through the Institute of Contemporary Prints 1975

P04936 Points of Contact No. 26 (1974)
CNπ:584x237:signed:Presented by Rose and Chris Prater through the Institute of Contemporary Prints 1975

P04937 Points of Contact No. 27 (1974)
CNπ:737x578:signed:Presented by Rose and Chris Prater through the Institute of Contemporary Prints 1975

P05459 Interior Image (1977)
CNπ:641x876:signed:Presented by Rose and Chris Prater 1978

P05491 Black Tiger (1979)
CNπ:616x902:signed:Presented by Rose and Chris Prater 1979

P05492 Sun and Sky (1979)
CNπ:800x1041:signed:Presented by Rose and Chris Prater 1979

P05533 Earth from Space (1979)
CNπ:533x940:signed:Presented by Rose and Chris Prater 1979

Points of Contact (P05534-P05537; complete group)

P05534 [title not known] (1979)
CNπ:403x403:signed:Presented by Rose and Chris Prater 1979

P05535 [title not known] (1979)
CNπ:403x403:signed:Presented by Rose and Chris Prater 1979

P05536 [title not known] (1979)
CNπ:403x403:signed:Presented by Rose and Chris Prater 1979

P05537 [title not known] (1979)
CNπ:403x403:signed:Presented by Rose and Chris Prater 1979

P05563 Blue Movement and Green (1980)
CNπ:533x454:signed:Presented by Rose and Chris Prater 1980

P06419 Points of Contact No. 3 (1965)
MLπ:635x864:Presented by Curwen Studio through the Institute of Contemporary Prints 1975

P07097 Abstract (1972)
CIπ:1981x914:signed:Purchased 1972

P07362 The Image in Search of Itself (1971)
CNπ:502x698:signed:Purchased 1980

P07415 Il Mostro (1977)
CIπ:1054x2032:signed:Purchased 1981

P07416 Stromboli (1980)
CIπ:718x1410:signed:Purchased 1981

PASMORE, Wendy born 1915
Modern Collection
Tate Gallery Archive holds material concerning this artist

T00490 Oval Motif in Grey and Ochre (1961)
Ow:533x584:Purchased 1962

PASTERNAK, Leonid 1862-1945
Modern Collection
Tate Gallery Archive holds material concerning this artist

T00343 Boris Pasternak Writing (1919)
Dπ:318x260:signed:Purchased 1960

T00344 On the Sofa (circa 1916)
Wπ:337x445:signed:Purchased 1960

T00345 The Artist's Daughter beside a Stove (1918)
Am Ofen
Dπ:273x432:signed:Purchased 1960

PATRICK, J. McIntosh born 1907
Modern Collection

N04818 Winter in Angus (1935)
Oc:756x1016:signed:Presented by the Trustees of the Chantrey Bequest 1935

PAYNE, William circa 1776 - circa 1830
British Collection

T05478 Wooded Landscape with a Cottage beside a Bridge
Wπ:302x302:signed:Presented by Miss Marjorie Ball 1988

T05479 River Scene with Fishermen Hauling their Nets, Moonlight
DWπ:200x302:Presented by Miss Marjorie Ball 1988

PEACOCK, Ralph 1868-1946
British Collection

N01672 Ethel (1897)
Oc:1321x737:signed:Presented by the Trustees of the Chantrey Bequest 1898

N01772 The Sisters (1900)
Oc:1302x902:signed:Presented by the artist 1900

PEAKE, Robert ?1551-1619
British Collection

T00068 Lady Anne Pope (1615)
Ow:571x445:Purchased 1955

attributed to
PEAKE, Robert ?1551-1619
British Collection

T00067 Lady Elizabeth Pope (circa 1615)
Ow:775x610:Purchased 1955

PEARLSTEIN, Philip born 1924
Modern Collection

P77170 Nude on Striped Hammock (1974)
Iπ:597x655:signed:Purchased 1986

PEARS, Charles 1873-1958
British Collection

The Great War: Britain's Efforts and Ideals (P03001-P03007, P03011-P03023, P03031-P03036, P03039-P03044; incomplete group; mixed group)
Transport by Sea (P03059-P03064; complete group)

P03059 Maintaining Food Supplies (1917)
MLπ:360x459:signed:Presented by the Ministry of Information 1918

P03060 Maintaining Export Trade (1917)
MLπ:355x462:signed:Presented by the Ministry of Information 1918

P03061 Supplying the Navy (1917)
MLπ:358x459:signed:Presented by the Ministry of Information 1918

P03062 Transporting Troops (1917)
MLπ:355x460:signed:Presented by the Ministry of Information 1918

P03063 Maintaining Forces Overseas (1917)
MLπ:360x461:signed:Presented by the Ministry of Information 1918

P03064 Place of Safety (1917)
MLπ:357x460:signed:Presented by the Ministry of Information 1918

PEARSH, Kevin born 1951
Modern Collection

P01809 Rails I (1976)
MIπ:260x349:signed:Presented by Mr and Mrs H. Molesworth 1977

PEGRAM, Henry Alfred 1862-1937
British Collection

N01756 Ignis Fatuus (1889)
Rz:521x521x102:signed:Presented by the Trustees of the Chantrey Bequest 1889

N01945 Sibylla Fatidica (1904)
Ss:1549x1245x978:signed:Presented by the Trustees of the Chantrey Bequest 1904

PENAGOS, Rafael born 1941
Modern Collection

P06740 Woman with Fur Wrap (1976)
MLπ:775x575:Presented by Curwen Studio 1977

P06741 Boy with Mirror (1976)
MLπ:775x571:Presented by Curwen Studio 1977

PENCK, A.R. born 1939
Modern Collection
Tate Gallery Archive holds material concerning this artist

T03303 West (1980)
Westen
Ac:2502x4000:Purchased 1981

T03304 East (1980)
Osten
Ac:2502x4000:Purchased 1981

Expedition to the Holy Land (P77019-P77022; incomplete group)
P77019 Communication (1984)
MIπ:648x934:signed:Purchased 1984

P77020 Concept (1984)
MIπ:645x934:signed:Purchased 1984

P77021 Snow in Jerusalem (1984)
MIπ:645x929:signed:Purchased 1984

P77022 Thoughts in a Kibbutz (1984)
MIπ:645x936:signed:Purchased 1984

P77199 Munich after the Rain (1986-7)
München nach dem Regen
Lπ:480x650:signed:Purchased 1987

PENLEY, Aaron Edwin 1807-1870
British Collection

N02390 Hyde Park Corner (1840)
Dπ:495x343:signed:Presented by Dr Edward J. Steegmann 1908

N02391 Ruins at Torre Wood (1842)
Dπ:254x327:signed:Presented by Dr Edward J. Steegmann 1908

N02392 Willows and Barge
Dπ:229x321:signed:Presented by Dr Edward J. Steegmann 1908

N02393 An Oak Wood near Southampton
Dπ:152x254:signed:Presented by Dr Edward J. Steegmann 1908

PENNY, Edward 1714-1791
British Collection

N03570 Mrs Elizabeth Graves
Oc:368x318:signed:Presented by Algernon Graves 1920

T00643 The Gossiping Blacksmith (exhibited 1769)
Oc:1257x1010:Presented by subscribers 1964

PENONE, Giuseppe born 1947
Modern Collection
Tate Gallery Archive holds material concerning this artist

T03420 Breath 5 (1978)
Soffio 5
Sp:1540x830x840:Purchased 1982

T05557 Tree of 12 Metres (1980-2)
Albero di 12 metri
Sw:6000x500x500:Purchased 1989

PENROSE, Sir Roland 1900-1984
Modern Collection
Tate Gallery Archive holds material concerning this artist

T00671 Le Grand Jour (1938)
Oc:762x1010:signed:Purchased 1964

T02021 Magnetic Moths (1938)
VDWb:813x559:signed:Purchased 1976

T03377 The Last Voyage of Captain Cook (1936/67)
SOpmw:692x660x825:signed:Presented by Mrs Gabrielle Keiller through the Friends of the Tate Gallery 1982

T03400 Portrait (1939)
Oc:762x637:signed:Purchased 1982

T03819 House the Light-house (1983)
GDVπ:590x840:signed:Presented anonymously 1984

PEPLOE, Samuel John 1871-1935
British Collection

N04224 Tulips (exhibited 1926)
Oc:610x508:signed:Purchased 1927

PEPPERCORN, Arthur Douglas 1847-1924
British Collection

N03035 The Path by the River
Oc:914x1372:signed:Presented by Francis Howard through the National Loan Exhibition Committee 1915

PERERA, Ed born 1936
Modern Collection

P06801 Liza (1977)
CLπ:508x603:signed:Presented by Curwen Studio 1978

PERI, Peter 1899-1967
Modern Collection

T05035 Lowering the Girder (1937)
Rp:870x510x190:signed:Purchased 1988

T05036 Mr Collins, A.R.P. Driver (1942)
Sp:675x680x400:signed:Purchased 1988

PERLIN, Bernard born 1918
Modern Collection

N05956 Orthodox Boys (1948)
Tb:762x1016:signed:Presented by Lincoln Kirstein through the Institute of Contemporary Arts 1950

PERMEKE, Constant 1886-1952
Modern Collection

T00218 Harvest (circa 1924-5)
De oogst
Oc:1280x1648:signed:Presented by the Friends of the Tate Gallery 1958

PERRYMAN, Margot born 1938
Modern Collection

T01256 Arcade (1969)
Ac:1727x1473:signed:Purchased 1970

PETERS, Rev. Matthew William 1742-1814
British Collection

T04848 Lydia (circa 1777)
Oc:642x770:Purchased 1986

PETHER, Henry active 1828-1865
British Collection

T00493 Greenwich Reach, Moonlight (exhibited 1854)
Oc:597x889:signed:Purchased 1962

PETTIE, John 1839-1893
British Collection

N01582 The Vigil (exhibited 1884)
Oc:1143x1676:signed:Presented by the Trustees of the
Chantrey Bequest 1884

N02434 Portrait of the Artist (1882)
Ob:305x244:signed:Presented by the John M. Swan
Memorial Fund 1909

PEVSNER, Antoine 1884-1962
Modern Collection
Tate Gallery Archive holds material concerning this artist

N06162 Maquette of a Monument Symbolising the Liberation of
the Spirit (1952)
Maquette d'un monument symbolisant la Liberation de
l'Esprit
Sz:457x457x292:signed:Purchased 1953

T01527 For the Facade of a Museum (1943-4)
Rzw:438x730x391:signed:Purchased 1972

T02241 Head (circa 1923-4)
Sa:76x38x51:Presented by Mrs Miriam Gabo, the artist's
sister-in-law 1977

T02242 Model for the Statue of Aphrodite in the Ballet 'La
Chatte' (1927)
Sa:149x44x51:Presented by Mrs Miriam Gabo, the artist's
sister-in-law 1977

PHALLE, Niki de Saint - see SAINT
PHALLE, Niki de

PHILLIP, John 1817-1867
British Collection

N01534 The Promenade (1859)
Oc:762x568:signed:Presented by Sir Henry Tate 1894

N01908 The Prison Window (1857)
Oc:1041x698:signed:Bequeathed by Charles Gassiot 1902

N05025 The Antonia (1863)
Oc:1118x914:signed:Presented by Lady
Forbes-Robertson 1939

PHILLIPS, Maurice born 1948
Modern Collection

P06420 Two Heads (1969)
MLπ:648x508:Presented by Curwen Studio through the
Institute of Contemporary Prints 1975

PHILLIPS, Peter born 1939
Modern Collection
Tate Gallery Archive holds material concerning this artist

T01159 Random Illusion No. 4 (1968)
ATc:1991x3397:signed:Purchased 1969

T02025 The Entertainment Machine (1961)
Ocw:1829x1829:Purchased 1976

P01273 Collection (1974)
CLπ:797x575:signed:Presented by Waddington Galleries
through the Institute of Contemporary Prints 1975

P01274 Six Times Eight, Dreaming (1974)
CLπ:610x797:signed:Presented by Waddington Galleries
through the Institute of Contemporary Prints 1975

P01478 Custom Print No. 1 (1965)
CLπ:635x511:signed:Presented by the Institute of
Contemporary Prints 1975

Eleven Pop Artists (P01479-P01481; incomplete group)
P01479 Custom Print No. I (1965)
CLπ:611x510:signed:Presented by the Institute of
Contemporary Prints 1975

P01480 Custom Print No. II (1965)
CLπ:610x763:signed:Presented by the Institute of
Contemporary Prints 1975

P01481 Custom Print No. III (1965)
CLπ:619x1008:signed:Presented by the Institute of
Contemporary Prints 1975

P01482 Untitled (1965)
CNπ:664x962:signed:Presented by the Institute of
Contemporary Prints 1975

P01483 Impeller (1972)
CNπ:870x689:signed:Presented by the Institute of
Contemporary Prints 1975

P01484 Impeller (1972)
CNπ:870x689:signed:Presented by the Institute of
Contemporary Prints 1975

P01485 Select-o-Mat Corolla (1972)
CNLVπ:660x987:signed:Presented by the Institute of
Contemporary Prints 1975

P01486 Select-o-Mat Tempest I (1972)
CLπ:576x1041:signed:Presented by the Institute of
Contemporary Prints 1975

P01487 Select-o-Mat Tempest II (1972)
CLπ:561x1040:signed:Presented by the Institute of
Contemporary Prints 1975

P01488 Spectrocoupling (1972)
CNπ:869x667:signed:Presented by the Institute of
Contemporary Prints 1975

P01489 Spectrocoupling (1972)
CNπ:868x670:signed:Presented by the Institute of
Contemporary Prints 1975

P02268 Untitled Composition I (1974)
CNVc:698x1000:signed:Presented by the artist 1975

P02269 Untitled Composition II (1974)
CNVc:698x999:signed:Presented by the artist 1975

P03200 Gravy for the Navy (1968-75)
CNπ:587x949:signed:Presented by Waddington Galleries
through the Institute of Contemporary Prints 1977

P03201 Hunter (1975-6)
CNπ:914x648:signed:Presented by Waddington Galleries
1977

The Institute of Contemporary Arts Portfolio (P04016, P04038, P04053, P04076, P04115, P04125, P04166, P04248, P04256, P04315-P04316, P04334, P04378-P04380, P04419, P04635, P04752, P04938, P05138, P05155, P05248; complete group; mixed group)

P04938 Untitled (1964)
CNπ:914x581:signed:Presented by Rose and Chris Prater through the Institute of Contemporary Prints 1975

pneumatics (P04939-P04946; complete group)

P04939 1. TURBOsonic (1968)
CNπ:591x940:signed:Presented by Rose and Chris Prater through the Institute of Contemporary Prints 1975

P04940 2. PNEUmatics (1968)
CNVπ:591x940:signed:Presented by Rose and Chris Prater through the Institute of Contemporary Prints 1975

P04941 3. Doublebubblebrain (1968)
CNπ:591x940:signed:Presented by Rose and Chris Prater through the Institute of Contemporary Prints 1975

P04942 4. Christmas Eve (1968)
CNπ:591x940:signed:Presented by Rose and Chris Prater through the Institute of Contemporary Prints 1975

P04943 5. THE LION (1968)
CNVπ:591x940:signed:Presented by Rose and Chris Prater through the Institute of Contemporary Prints 1975

P04944 6. Futuristic Revamp (1968)
CNVπ:591x940:signed:Presented by Rose and Chris Prater through the Institute of Contemporary Prints 1975

P04945 7. SUNgleam (1968)
CNVπ:591x940:signed:Presented by Rose and Chris Prater through the Institute of Contemporary Prints 1975

P04946 8. TransORBITALmission (1968)
CNπ:591x940:signed:Presented by Rose and Chris Prater through the Institute of Contemporary Prints 1975

P04947 Untitled (1968)
CNVπ:816x594:signed:Presented by Rose and Chris Prater through the Institute of Contemporary Prints 1975

P04948 Apollo II (1969)
CNπ:597x492:signed:Presented by Rose and Chris Prater through the Institute of Contemporary Prints 1975

PHILLIPS, Thomas 1770-1845
British Collection

N00183 Sir David Wilkie, R.A. (1829)
Oc:997x762:signed:Presented by the artist 1842

PHILLIPS, Tom born 1937
Modern Collection
Tate Gallery Archive holds material concerning this artist

T01327 Benches (1970-1)
Ac:1219x2762:Purchased 1971

T01933 Music Drawing (1963)
Dπ:559x762:signed:Purchased 1974

T01938 Here We Exemplify (1967-8)
Ac:1530x2570:signed:Purchased 1974

A Humument Vol. II (P01490-P01509; complete group)

P01490 [no title: p. 33] (1970)
CJπ:190x140:signed:Presented by the Institute of Contemporary Prints 1975

P01491 [no title: p. 37] (1970)
CJπ:190x140:signed:Presented by the Institute of Contemporary Prints 1975

P01492 [no title: p. 43] (1970)
CJπ:190x140:signed:Presented by the Institute of Contemporary Prints 1975

P01493 [no title: p. 51] (1970)
CJπ:190x140:signed:Presented by the Institute of Contemporary Prints 1975

P01494 [no title: p. 63] (1970)
CJπ:190x140:signed:Presented by the Institute of Contemporary Prints 1975

P01495 [no title: p. 83] (1970)
CJπ:190x140:signed:Presented by the Institute of Contemporary Prints 1975

P01496 [no title: p. 97] (1970)
CJπ:190x140:signed:Presented by the Institute of Contemporary Prints 1975

P01497 [no title: p. 102] (1970)
CJπ:190x140:signed:Presented by the Institute of Contemporary Prints 1975

P01498 [no title: p. 161] (1970)
CJπ:190x140:signed:Presented by the Institute of Contemporary Prints 1975

P01499 [no title: p. 229] (1970)
CJπ:190x140:signed:Presented by the Institute of Contemporary Prints 1975

P01500 [no title: p. 236] (1970)
CJπ:190x140:signed:Presented by the Institute of Contemporary Prints 1975

P01501 [no title: p. 238] (1970)
CJπ:190x140:signed:Presented by the Institute of Contemporary Prints 1975

P01502 [no title: p. 283] (1970)
CJπ:190x140:signed:Presented by the Institute of Contemporary Prints 1975

P01503 [no title: p. 337] (1970)
CJπ:190x140:signed:Presented by the Institute of Contemporary Prints 1975

P01504 [no title: p. 343] (1970)
CJπ:190x140:signed:Presented by the Institute of Contemporary Prints 1975

P01505 [no title: p. 345] (1970)
CJπ:190x140:signed:Presented by the Institute of Contemporary Prints 1975

P01506 [no title: p. 346] (1970)
CJπ:190x140:signed:Presented by the Institute of Contemporary Prints 1975

P01507 [no title: p. 352] (1970)
CJπ:190x140:signed:Presented by the Institute of Contemporary Prints 1975

P01508 [no title: p. 356] (1970)
CJπ:190x140:signed:Presented by the Institute of Contemporary Prints 1975

P01509 [no title: p. 366] (1970)
CJπ:190x140:signed:Presented by the Institute of Contemporary Prints 1975

A Humument Vol. IV (P01510-P01529; complete group)

P01510 [no title] (1970)
CLπ:190x140:signed:Presented by the Institute of Contemporary Prints 1975

P01511 [no title: p. 6] (1970)
CLπ:190x140:signed:Presented by the Institute of Contemporary Prints 1975

P01512 [no title: p. 56] (1970)
CLπ:190x140:signed:Presented by the Institute of Contemporary Prints 1975

P01513   [no title: p. 57] (1970)
CLπ:190x140:signed:Presented by the Institute of
Contemporary Prints 1975

P01514   [no title: p. 113] (1970)
CLπ:190x140:signed:Presented by the Institute of
Contemporary Prints 1975

P01515   [no title: p. 117] (1970)
CLπ:190x140:signed:Presented by the Institute of
Contemporary Prints 1975

P01516   [no title: p. 170] (1970)
CLπ:190x140:signed:Presented by the Institute of
Contemporary Prints 1975

P01517   [no title: p. 196] (1970)
CLπ:190x140:signed:Presented by the Institute of
Contemporary Prints 1975

P01518   [no title: p. 205] (1970)
CLπ:190x140:signed:Presented by the Institute of
Contemporary Prints 1975

P01519   [no title: p. 207] (1970)
CLπ:190x140:signed:Presented by the Institute of
Contemporary Prints 1975

P01520   [no title: p. 225] (1970)
CLπ:190x140:signed:Presented by the Institute of
Contemporary Prints 1975

P01521   [no title: p. 230] (1970)
CLπ:190x140:signed:Presented by the Institute of
Contemporary Prints 1975

P01522   [no title: p. 239] (1970)
CLπ:190x140:signed:Presented by the Institute of
Contemporary Prints 1975

P01523   [no title: p. 240] (1970)
CLπ:190x140:signed:Presented by the Institute of
Contemporary Prints 1975

P01524   [no title: p. 247] (1970)
CLπ:190x140:signed:Presented by the Institute of
Contemporary Prints 1975

P01525   [no title: p. 264] (1970)
CLπ:190x140:signed:Presented by the Institute of
Contemporary Prints 1975

P01526   [no title: p. 271] (1970)
CLπ:190x140:signed:Presented by the Institute of
Contemporary Prints 1975

P01527   [no title: p. 300] (1970)
CLπ:190x140:signed:Presented by the Institute of
Contemporary Prints 1975

P01528   [no title: p. 304] (1970)
CLπ:190x140:signed:Presented by the Institute of
Contemporary Prints 1975

P01529   [no title: p. 317] (1970)
CLπ:190x140:signed:Presented by the Institute of
Contemporary Prints 1975

P01530   Metamorphoses (1970)
MIπ:254x200:signed:Presented by Tetrad Press through
the Institute of Contemporary Prints 1975

Seven Miniatures Opus XIV (P01531-P01537; complete
group)

P01531   [no title] (1971)
CNπ:254x355:signed:Presented by the Institute of
Contemporary Prints 1975

P01532   [no title] (1971)
CNπ:254x355:signed:Presented by the Institute of
Contemporary Prints 1975

P01533   [no title] (1971)
CNπ:254x355:signed:Presented by the Institute of
Contemporary Prints 1975

P01534   [no title] (1971)
CNπ:254x355:signed:Presented by the Institute of
Contemporary Prints 1975

P01535   [no title] (1971)
CNπ:254x355:signed:Presented by the Institute of
Contemporary Prints 1975

P01536   [no title] (1971)
CNπ:254x355:signed:Presented by the Institute of
Contemporary Prints 1975

P01537   [no title] (1971)
CNπ:254x355:signed:Presented by the Institute of
Contemporary Prints 1975

Ein Deutsches Requiem: After Brahms
(P01538-P01549; complete group)

P01538   1 (1972)
CLπ:230x153:signed:Presented by the Institute of
Contemporary Prints 1975

P01539   2 (1972)
CLπ:230x153:signed:Presented by the Institute of
Contemporary Prints 1975

P01540   3 (1972)
CLπ:230x153:signed:Presented by the Institute of
Contemporary Prints 1975

P01541   4 (1972)
CLπ:230x153:signed:Presented by the Institute of
Contemporary Prints 1975

P01542   5 (1972)
CLπ:230x153:signed:Presented by the Institute of
Contemporary Prints 1975

P01543   6 (1972)
CLπ:230x153:signed:Presented by the Institute of
Contemporary Prints 1975

P01544   7 (1972)
CLπ:230x153:signed:Presented by the Institute of
Contemporary Prints 1975

P01545   8 (1972)
CLπ:230x153:signed:Presented by the Institute of
Contemporary Prints 1975

P01546   9 (1972)
CLπ:230x153:signed:Presented by the Institute of
Contemporary Prints 1975

P01547   10 (1972)
CLπ:230x153:signed:Presented by the Institute of
Contemporary Prints 1975

P01548   11 (1972)
CLπ:230x153:signed:Presented by the Institute of
Contemporary Prints 1975

P01549   12 (1972)
CLπ:230x153:signed:Presented by the Institute of
Contemporary Prints 1975

P01550   After Raphael (?) (1973)
CNπ:584x483:signed:Presented by Editions Alecto
through the Institute of Contemporary Prints 1975

The Birth of Art (P01551-P01560; complete group)

P01551   [no title] (1973)
CIπ:280x570:signed:Presented by the Institute of
Contemporary Prints 1975

P01552   [no title] (1973)
CIπ:278x582:signed:Presented by the Institute of
Contemporary Prints 1975

P01553 [no title] (1973)
CIπ:270x580:signed:Presented by the Institute of
Contemporary Prints 1975

P01554 [no title] (1973)
CIπ:270x580:signed:Presented by the Institute of
Contemporary Prints 1975

P01555 [no title] (1973)
CIπ:275x578:signed:Presented by the Institute of
Contemporary Prints 1975

P01556 [no title] (1973)
CIπ:280x580:signed:Presented by the Institute of
Contemporary Prints 1975

P01557 [no title] (1973)
CIπ:278x584:signed:Presented by the Institute of
Contemporary Prints 1975

P01558 [no title] (1973)
CIπ:278x578:signed:Presented by the Institute of
Contemporary Prints 1975

P01559 [no title] (1973)
CIπ:270x580:signed:Presented by the Institute of
Contemporary Prints 1975

P01560 [no title] (1973)
CIπ:272x578:signed:Presented by the Institute of
Contemporary Prints 1975

P01561 Mappin Art Gallery - Conjectured Picture (1974)
CIπ:457x381:signed:Presented by Marlborough Graphics
through the Institute of Contemporary Prints 1975

Approval Stamp Offer (P01676-P01687; complete
group; mixed group)
P01679 [title not known] (1972)
MJπ:51x51:signed:Presented by Tetrad Press through the
Institute of Contemporary Prints 1975

P01680 [title not known] (1972)
MJπ:51x51:signed:Presented by Tetrad Press through the
Institute of Contemporary Prints 1975

P01681 [title not known] (1972)
MJπ:51x51:signed:Presented by Tetrad Press through the
Institute of Contemporary Prints 1975

Tetrad Pamphlets Vol. I Nos. I-X (P01688-P01697;
complete group; mixed group)
P01690 Correspondence (1970)
CNπ:302x508:Presented by Tetrad Press through the
Institute of Contemporary Prints 1975

P01691 The Directions (1970)
CNπ:305x508:Presented by Tetrad Press through the
Institute of Contemporary Prints 1975

P01692 Lesbia Waltz (1971)
CNπ:305x508:Presented by Tetrad Press through the
Institute of Contemporary Prints 1975

A Walk to the Studio (P03202-P03207; complete group)
P03202 Sixty Four Stopcock Box Lids (1976-7)
CNπ:807x598:signed:Presented by Waddington Galleries
1977

P03203 Linoleum (1976-7)
CNπ:811x600:signed:Presented by Waddington Galleries
1977

P03204 Matching Colours Struck by Heatwave (1976-7)
CNπ:843x584:signed:Presented by Waddington Galleries
1977

P03205 A Grammar of Ornament (1976-7)
CNπ:843x584:signed:Presented by Waddington Galleries
1977

P03206 Eleven Elements of Violence (1976-7)
CNπ:802x590:signed:Presented by Waddington Galleries
1977

P03207 Art on the Road (1976-7)
CNπ:810x600:signed:Presented by Waddington Galleries
1977

P03231 A Humument Supplement I (1972)
MIπ:387x425:signed:Presented by Tetrad Press 1978

P04949 A Humument Cartoon (1970)
CNπ:356x505:signed:Presented by Rose and Chris Prater
through the Institute of Contemporary Prints 1975

5 Fragments from a Humument (P04950-P04954;
complete group)
P04950 [no title] (1970)
CNπ:123x122:signed:Presented by Rose and Chris Prater
through the Institute of Contemporary Prints 1975

P04951 [no title] (1970)
CNπ:147x148:signed:Presented by Rose and Chris Prater
through the Institute of Contemporary Prints 1975

P04952 [no title] (1970)
CNπ:113x119:signed:Presented by Rose and Chris Prater
through the Institute of Contemporary Prints 1975

P04953 [no title] (1970)
CNπ:110x203:signed:Presented by Rose and Chris Prater
through the Institute of Contemporary Prints 1975

P04954 [no title] (1970)
CNπ:83x131:signed:Presented by Rose and Chris Prater
through the Institute of Contemporary Prints 1975

A Humument Vol. I (P04955-P04964; complete group)
P04955 [no title: p. 5] (1970)
CNπ:195x140:signed:Presented by Rose and Chris Prater
through the Institute of Contemporary Prints 1975

P04956 [no title: p. 12] (1970)
CNπ:195x140:signed:Presented by Rose and Chris Prater
through the Institute of Contemporary Prints 1975

P04957 [no title: p. 88] (1970)
CNπ:195x140:signed:Presented by Rose and Chris Prater
through the Institute of Contemporary Prints 1975

P04958 [no title: p. 135] (1970)
CNπ:195x140:signed:Presented by Rose and Chris Prater
through the Institute of Contemporary Prints 1975

P04959 [no title: p. 138] (1970)
CNπ:195x140:signed:Presented by Rose and Chris Prater
through the Institute of Contemporary Prints 1975

P04960 [no title: p. 228] (1970)
CNπ:195x140:signed:Presented by Rose and Chris Prater
through the Institute of Contemporary Prints 1975

P04961 [no title: p. 268] (1970)
CNπ:195x140:signed:Presented by Rose and Chris Prater
through the Institute of Contemporary Prints 1975

P04962 [no title: p. 272] (1970)
CNπ:195x140:signed:Presented by Rose and Chris Prater
through the Institute of Contemporary Prints 1975

P04963 [no title: p. 294] (1970)
CNπ:195x140:signed:Presented by Rose and Chris Prater
through the Institute of Contemporary Prints 1975

P04964 [no title: p. 299] (1970)
CNπ:195x140:signed:Presented by Rose and Chris Prater
through the Institute of Contemporary Prints 1975

A Humument Vol. III (P04965-P04994; complete group)
P04965 [no title: p 11] (1970)
CNπ:194x140:signed:Presented by Rose and Chris Prater
through the Institute of Contemporary Prints 1975

P04966 [no title: p. 36] (1970)
CNπ:194x140:signed:Presented by Rose and Chris Prater
through the Institute of Contemporary Prints 1975

P04967 [no title: p. 60] (1970)
CNπ:194x140:signed:Presented by Rose and Chris Prater
through the Institute of Contemporary Prints 1975

P04968 [no title: p. 65] (1970)
CNπ:194x140:signed:Presented by Rose and Chris Prater
through the Institute of Contemporary Prints 1975

P04969 [no title: p. 67] (1970)
CNπ:194x140:signed:Presented by Rose and Chris Prater
through the Institute of Contemporary Prints 1975

P04970 [no title: p. 77] (1970)
CNπ:194x140:signed:Presented by Rose and Chris Prater
through the Institute of Contemporary Prints 1975

P04971 [no title: p. 89] (1970)
CNπ:194x140:signed:Presented by Rose and Chris Prater
through the Institute of Contemporary Prints 1975

P04972 [no title: p. 115] (1970)
CNπ:194x140:signed:Presented by Rose and Chris Prater
through the Institute of Contemporary Prints 1975

P04973 [no title: p. 123] (1970)
CNπ:194x140:signed:Presented by Rose and Chris Prater
through the Institute of Contemporary Prints 1975

P04974 [no title: p. 124] (1970)
CNπ:194x140:signed:Presented by Rose and Chris Prater
through the Institute of Contemporary Prints 1975

P04975 [no title: p. 134] (1970)
CNπ:194x140:signed:Presented by Rose and Chris Prater
through the Institute of Contemporary Prints 1975

P04976 [no title: p. 139] (1970)
CNπ:194x140:signed:Presented by Rose and Chris Prater
through the Institute of Contemporary Prints 1975

P04977 [no title: p. 172] (1970)
CNπ:194x140:signed:Presented by Rose and Chris Prater
through the Institute of Contemporary Prints 1975

P04978 [no title: p. 183] (1970)
CNπ:194x140:signed:Presented by Rose and Chris Prater
through the Institute of Contemporary Prints 1975

P04979 [no title: p. 213] (1970)
CNπ:194x140:signed:Presented by Rose and Chris Prater
through the Institute of Contemporary Prints 1975

P04980 [no title: p. 220] (1970)
CNπ:194x140:signed:Presented by Rose and Chris Prater
through the Institute of Contemporary Prints 1975

P04981 [no title: p. 246] (1970)
CNπ:194x140:signed:Presented by Rose and Chris Prater
through the Institute of Contemporary Prints 1975

P04982 [no title: p. 250] (1970)
CNπ:194x140:signed:Presented by Rose and Chris Prater
through the Institute of Contemporary Prints 1975

P04983 [no title: p. 251] (1970)
CNπ:194x140:signed:Presented by Rose and Chris Prater
through the Institute of Contemporary Prints 1975

P04984 [no title: p. 269] (1970)
CNπ:194x140:signed:Presented by Rose and Chris Prater
through the Institute of Contemporary Prints 1975

P04985 [no title: p. 273] (1970)
CNπ:194x140:signed:Presented by Rose and Chris Prater
through the Institute of Contemporary Prints 1975

P04986 [no title: p. 280] (1970)
CNπ:194x140:signed:Presented by Rose and Chris Prater
through the Institute of Contemporary Prints 1975

P04987 [no title: p. 289] (1970)
CNπ:194x140:signed:Presented by Rose and Chris Prater
through the Institute of Contemporary Prints 1975

P04988 [no title: p. 292] (1970)
CNπ:194x140:signed:Presented by Rose and Chris Prater
through the Institute of Contemporary Prints 1975

P04989 [no title: p. 293] (1970)
CNπ:194x140:signed:Presented by Rose and Chris Prater
through the Institute of Contemporary Prints 1975

P04990 [no title: p. 297] (1970)
CNπ:194x140:signed:Presented by Rose and Chris Prater
through the Institute of Contemporary Prints 1975

P04991 [no title: p. 300] (1970)
CNπ:194x140:signed:Presented by Rose and Chris Prater
through the Institute of Contemporary Prints 1975

P04992 [no title: p. 301] (1970)
CNπ:194x140:signed:Presented by Rose and Chris Prater
through the Institute of Contemporary Prints 1975

P04993 [no title: p. 307] (1970)
CNπ:194x140:signed:Presented by Rose and Chris Prater
through the Institute of Contemporary Prints 1975

P04994 [no title: p. 324] (1970)
CNπ:194x140:signed:Presented by Rose and Chris Prater
through the Institute of Contemporary Prints 1975

Dante's Inferno (P07482-P07497, P07561-P07568,
P07622-P07629, P07685-P07708, P07761-P07803,
P07855-P07898; complete group)
Canto VII (published 1983; P07482-P07485; complete
group)

P07482 [no title] (1981)
CINLπ:330x203:signed:Purchased 1981

P07483 [no title] (1981)
CINLπ:314x225:signed:Purchased 1981

P07484 [no title] (1981)
CINLπ:288x200:signed:Purchased 1981

P07485 [no title] (1981)
CINLπ:317x208:signed:Purchased 1981

Dante's Inferno (P07482-P07497, P07561-P07568,
P07622-P07629, P07685-P07708, P07761-P07803,
P07855-P07898; complete group)
Canto XIII (published 1983; P07486-P07489; complete
group)

P07486 [no title] (1981)
CINLπ:292x203:signed:Purchased 1981

P07487 [no title] (1981)
CINLπ:292x203:signed:Purchased 1981

P07488 [no title] (1981)
CINLπ:315x222:signed:Purchased 1981

P07489 [no title] (1981)
CINLπ:317x229:signed:Purchased 1981

Dante's Inferno (P07482-P07497, P07561-P07568,
P07622-P07629, P07685-P07708, P07761-P07803,
P07855-P07898; complete group)
Canto XV (published 1983; P07490-P07493; complete
group)

P07490 [no title] (1981)
CINLπ:263x202:signed:Purchased 1981

P07491 [no title] (1981)
CINLπ:292x203:signed:Purchased 1981

P07492 [no title] (1981)
CINLπ:317x225:signed:Purchased 1981

P07493 [no title] (1981)
CINLπ:292x203:signed:Purchased 1981

Dante's Inferno (P07482-P07497, P07561-P07568,
P07622-P07629, P07685-P07708, P07761-P07803,
P07855-P07898; complete group)
Canto XIX (published 1983; P07494-P07497; complete
group)

P07494 [no title] (1981)
CINLπ:317x225:signed:Purchased 1981

P07495 [no title] (1981)
CINLπ:242x202:signed:Purchased 1981

P07496 [no title] (1981)
CINLπ:317x222:signed:Purchased 1981

P07497 [no title] (1981)
CINLπ:288x202:signed:Purchased 1981

Dante's Inferno (P07482-P07497, P07561-P07568,
P07622-P07629, P07685-P07708, P07761-P07803,
P07855-P07898; complete group)
Canto III (published 1983; P07561-P07564; complete
group)

P07561 [no title] (1981)
CINLπ:315x228:signed:Purchased 1981

P07562 [no title] (1981)
CINLπ:292x205:signed:Purchased 1981

P07563 [no title] (1981)
CINLπ:295x205:signed:Purchased 1981

P07564 [no title] (1981)
CINLπ:290x204:signed:Purchased 1981

Dante's Inferno (P07482-P07497, P07561-P07568,
P07622-P07629, P07685-P07708, P07761-P07803,
P07855-P07898; complete group)
Canto V (published 1983; P07565-P07568; complete
group)

P07565 [no title] (1981)
CINLπ:290x200:signed:Purchased 1981

P07566 [no title] (1981)
CINLπ:312x228:signed:Purchased 1981

P07567 [no title] (1981)
CINLπ:280x190:signed:Purchased 1981

P07568 [no title] (1981)
CINLπ:312x222:signed:Purchased 1981

Dante's Inferno (P07482-P07497, P07561-P07568,
P07622-P07629, P07685-P07708, P07761-P07803,
P07855-P07898; complete group)
Canto II (published 1983; P07622-P07625; complete
group)

P07622 [no title] (1981)
CINLπ:265x203:signed:Purchased 1981

P07623 [no title] (1981)
CINLπ:293x203:signed:Purchased 1981

P07624 [no title] (1981)
CINLπ:290x203:signed:Purchased 1981

P07625 [no title] (1981)
CINLπ:290x203:signed:Purchased 1981

Dante's Inferno (P07482-P07497, P07561-P07568,
P07622-P07629, P07685-P07708, P07761-P07803,
P07855-P07898; complete group)
Canto XII (published 1983; P07626-P07629; complete
group)

P07626 [no title] (1981)
CINLπ:300x200:signed:Purchased 1981

P07627 [no title] (1981)
CINLπ:290x200:signed:Purchased 1981

P07628 [no title] (1981)
CINLπ:288x203:signed:Purchased 1981

P07629 [no title] (1981)
CINLπ:303x213:signed:Purchased 1981

Dante's Inferno (P07482-P07497, P07561-P07568,
P07622-P07629, P07685-P07708, P07761-P07803,
P07855-P07898; complete group)
Canto I (published 1983; P07685-P07688; complete
group)

P07685 [no title] (1981)
CINLπ:290x203:signed:Purchased 1982

P07686 [no title] (1981)
CINLπ:290x200:signed:Purchased 1982

P07687 [no title] (1981)
CINLπ:312x220:signed:Purchased 1982

P07688 [no title] (1981)
CINLπ:275x203:signed:Purchased 1982

Dante's Inferno (P07482-P07497, P07561-P07568,
P07622-P07629, P07685-P07708, P07761-P07803,
P07855-P07898; complete group)
Canto VIII (published 1983; P07689-P07692; complete
group)

P07689 [no title] (1982)
CINLπ:290x202:signed:Purchased 1982

P07690 [no title] (1982)
CINLπ:314x225:signed:Purchased 1982

P07691 [no title] (1982)
CINLπ:290x203:signed:Purchased 1982

P07692 [no title] (1982)
CINLπ:313x210:signed:Purchased 1982

Dante's Inferno (P07482-P07497, P07561-P07568,
P07622-P07629, P07685-P07708, P07761-P07803,
P07855-P07898; complete group)
Canto X (published 1983; P07693-P07696; complete
group)

P07693 [no title] (1982)
CINLπ:290x203:signed:Purchased 1982

P07694 [no title] (1982)
CINLπ:293x204:signed:Purchased 1982

P07695 [no title] (1982)
CINLπ:290x203:signed:Purchased 1982

P07696 [no title] (1982)
CINLπ:290x203:signed:Purchased 1982

Dante's Inferno (P07482-P07497, P07561-P07568,
P07622-P07629, P07685-P07708, P07761-P07803,
P07855-P07898; complete group)
Canto XVIII (published 1983; P07697-P07700; complete
group)

P07697 [no title] (1982)
CINLπ:300x202:signed:Purchased 1982

P07698 [no title] (1982)
CINLπ:290x200:signed:Purchased 1982

P07699 [no title] (1982)
CINLπ:285x196:signed:Purchased 1982

P07700 [no title] (1982)
CINLπ:305x215:signed:Purchased 1982

Dante's Inferno (P07482-P07497, P07561-P07568,
P07622-P07629, P07685-P07708, P07761-P07803,
P07855-P07898; complete group)
Canto XX (published 1983; P07701-P07704; complete
group)

P07701 [no title] (1982)
CINLπ:290x203:signed:Purchased 1982

P07702 [no title] (1982)
CINLπ:295x203:signed:Purchased 1982

P07703 [no title] (1982)
CINL*π*:290x203:signed:Purchased 1982

P07704 [no title] (1982)
CINL*π*:263x203:signed:Purchased 1982

Dante's Inferno (P07482-P07497, P07561-P07568,
P07622-P07629, P07685-P07708, P07761-P07803,
P07855-P07898; complete group)
Canto XXI (published 1983; P07705-P07708; complete
group)

P07705 [no title] (1982)
CINL*π*:293x203:signed:Purchased 1982

P07706 [no title] (1982)
CINL*π*:310x195:signed:Purchased 1982

P07707 [no title] (1982)
CINL*π*:290x203:signed:Purchased 1982

P07708 [no title] (1982)
CINL*π*:290x203:signed:Purchased 1982

Dante's Inferno (P07482-P07497, P07561-P07568,
P07622-P07629, P07685-P07708, P07761-P07803,
P07855-P07898; complete group)
Canto IV (published 1983; P07761-P07764; complete
group)

P07761 [no title] (1982)
CINL*π*:330x203:signed:Purchased 1983

P07762 [no title] (1982)
CINL*π*:290x200:signed:Purchased 1983

P07763 [no title] (1982)
CINL*π*:290x203:signed:Purchased 1983

P07764 [no title] (1982)
CINL*π*:290x203:signed:Purchased 1983

Canto VI (published 1983; P07765-P07768; complete
group)

P07765 [no title] (1982)
CINL*π*:295x204:signed:Purchased 1983

P07766 [no title] (1982)
CINL*π*:290x203:signed:Purchased 1983

P07767 [no title] (1982)
CINL*π*:290x203:signed:Purchased 1983

P07768 [no title] (1982)
CINL*π*:290x203:signed:Purchased 1983

Dante's Inferno (P07482-P07497, P07561-P07568,
P07622-P07629, P07685-P07708, P07761-P07803,
P07855-P07898; complete group)
Canto IX (published 1983; P07769-P07772; complete
group)

P07769 [no title] (1982)
CINL*π*:290x203:signed:Purchased 1983

P07770 [no title] (1982)
CINL*π*:290x203:signed:Purchased 1982

P07771 [no title] (1982)
CINL*π*:290x200:signed:Purchased 1982

P07772 [no title] (1982)
CINL*π*:290x203:signed:Purchased 1982

Dante's Inferno (P07482-P07497, P07561-P07568,
P07622-P07629, P07685-P07708, P07761-P07803,
P07855-P07898; complete group)
Canto XI (published 1983; P07773-P07776; complete
group)

P07773 [no title] (1982)
CINL*π*:290x204:signed:Purchased 1982

P07774 [no title] (1982)
CINL*π*:290x203:signed:Purchased 1982

P07775 [no title] (1982)
CINL*π*:276x195:signed:Purchased 1982

P07776 [no title] (1982)
CINL*π*:293x203:signed:Purchased 1982

P07777 [title page] (1982)
Cl*π*:150x100:signed:Purchased 1982

P07778 [title page] (1982)
CN*π*:263x203:signed:Purchased 1982

Dante's Inferno (P07482-P07497, P07561-P07568,
P07622-P07629, P07685-P07708, P07761-P07803,
P07855-P07898; complete group)
Canto XIV (published 1983; P07784-P07787; complete
group)

P07784 [no title] (1982)
CINL*π*:292x203:signed:Purchased 1982

P07785 [no title] (1982)
CINL*π*:290x203:signed:Purchased 1982

P07786 [no title] (1982)
CINL*π*:290x203:signed:Purchased 1982

P07787 [no title] (1982)
CINL*π*:292x207:signed:Purchased 1982

Dante's Inferno (P07482-P07497, P07561-P07568,
P07622-P07629, P07685-P07708, P07761-P07803,
P07855-P07898; complete group)
Canto XVI (published 1983; P07788-P07791; complete
group)

P07788 [no title] (1982)
CINL*π*:300x210:signed:Purchased 1982

P07789 [no title] (1982)
CINL*π*:315x225:signed:Purchased 1982

P07790 [no title] (1982)
CINL*π*:302x208:signed:Purchased 1982

P07791 [no title] (1982)
CINL*π*:290x200:signed:Purchased 1982

Dante's Inferno (P07482-P07497, P07561-P07568,
P07622-P07629, P07685-P07708, P07761-P07803,
P07855-P07898; complete group)
Canto XVII (published 1983; P07792-P07795; complete
group)

P07792 [no title] (1982)
CINL*π*:288x204:signed:Purchased 1982

P07793 [no title] (1982)
CINL*π*:294x200:signed:Purchased 1982

P07794 [no title] (1982)
CINL*π*:292x203:signed:Purchased 1982

P07795 [no title] (1982)
CINL*π*:296x207:signed:Purchased 1982

Dante's Inferno (P07482-P07497, P07561-P07568,
P07622-P07629, P07685-P07708, P07761-P07803,
P07855-P07898; complete group)
Canto XXII (published 1983; P07796-P07799; complete
group)

P07796 [no title] (1982)
CINL*π*:302x198:signed:Purchased 1982

P07797 [no title] (1982)
CINL*π*:290x203:signed:Purchased 1982

P07798 [no title] (1982)
CINL*π*:275x222:signed:Purchased 1982

P07799 [no title] (1982)
CINL*π*:293x203:signed:Purchased 1982

Dante's Inferno (P07482-P07497, P07561-P07568, P07622-P07629, P07685-P07708, P07761-P07803, P07855-P07898; complete group)
Canto XXIII (published 1983; P07800-P78003; complete group)

P07800 [no title] (1982)
CINL𝜋:296x203:signed:Purchased 1982

P07801 [no title] (1982)
CINL𝜋:297x203:signed:Purchased 1982

P07802 [no title] (1982)
CINL𝜋:296x203:signed:Purchased 1982

P07803 [no title] (1982)
CINL𝜋:312x210:signed:Purchased 1982

Dante's Inferno (P07482-P07497, P07561-P07568, P07622-P07629, P07685-P07708, P07761-P07803, P07855-P07898; complete group)
Canto XXIV (published 1983; P07855-P07858; complete group)

P07855 [no title] (1983)
CINL𝜋:268x203:signed:Purchased 1983

P07856 [no title] (1983)
CINL𝜋:292x203:signed:Purchased 1983

P07857 [no title] (1983)
CINL𝜋:280x187:signed:Purchased 1983

P07858 [no title] (1983)
CINL𝜋:292x203:signed:Purchased 1983

Dante's Inferno (P07482-P07497, P07561-P07568, P07622-P07629, P07685-P07708, P07761-P07803, P07855-P07898; complete group)
Canto XXVI (published 1983; P07859-P07862; complete group)

P07859 [no title] (1983)
CINL𝜋:292x203:signed:Purchased 1983

P07860 [no title] (1983)
CINL𝜋:292x203:signed:Purchased 1983

P07861 [no title] (1983)
CINL𝜋:285x197:signed:Purchased 1983

P07862 [no title] (1983)
CINL𝜋:292x203:signed:Purchased 1983

Dante's Inferno (P07482-P07497, P07561-P07568, P07622-P07629, P07685-P07708, P07761-P07803, P07855-P07898; complete group)
Canto XXVII (published 1983; P07863-P07866; complete group)

P07863 [no title] (1983)
CINL𝜋:285x197:signed:Purchased 1983

P07864 [no title] (1983)
CINL𝜋:292x203:signed:Purchased 1983

P07865 [no title] (1983)
CINL𝜋:302x203:signed:Purchased 1983

P07866 [no title] (1983)
CINL𝜋:298x200:signed:Purchased 1983

Dante's Inferno (P07482-P07497, P07561-P07568, P07622-P07629, P07685-P07708, P07761-P07803, P07855-P07898; complete group)
Canto XXVIII (published 1983; P07867-P07870; complete group)

P07867 [no title] (1983)
CINL𝜋:292x203:signed:Purchased 1983

P07868 [no title] (1983)
CINL𝜋:292x203:signed:Purchased 1983

P07869 [no title] (1983)
CINL𝜋:292x203:signed:Purchased 1983

P07870 [no title] (1983)
CINL𝜋:302x207:signed:Purchased 1983

Dante's Inferno (P07482-P07497, P07561-P07568, P07622-P07629, P07685-P07708, P07761-P07803, P07855-P07898; complete group)
Canto XXIX (published 1983; P07871-P07874; complete group)

P07871 [no title] (1983)
CINL𝜋:292x203:signed:Purchased 1983

P07872 [no title] (1983)
CINL𝜋:318x222:signed:Purchased 1983

P07873 [no title] (1983)
CINL𝜋:292x203:signed:Purchased 1983

P07874 [no title] (1983)
CINL𝜋:292x203:signed:Purchased 1983

Dante's Inferno (P07482-P07497, P07561-P07568, P07622-P07629, P07685-P07708, P07761-P07803, P07855-P07898; complete group)
Canto XXX (published 1983; P07875-P07878; complete group)

P07875 [no title] (1983)
CINL𝜋:312x222:signed:Purchased 1983

P07876 [no title] (1983)
CINL𝜋:292x203:signed:Purchased 1983

P07877 [no title] (1983)
CINL𝜋:318x222:signed:Purchased 1983

P07878 [no title] (1983)
CINL𝜋:292x203:signed:Purchased 1983

Dante's Inferno (P07482-P07497, P07561-P07568, P07622-P07629, P07685-P07708, P07761-P07803, P07855-P07898; complete group)
Canto XXXI (published 1983; P07879-P07882; complete group)

P07879 [no title] (1983)
CINL𝜋:292x203:signed:Purchased 1983

P07880 [no title] (1983)
CINL𝜋:286x203:signed:Purchased 1983

P07881 [no title] (1983)
CINL𝜋:292x203:signed:Purchased 1983

P07882 [no title] (1983)
CINL𝜋:292x203:signed:Purchased 1983

Dante's Inferno (P07482-P07497, P07561-P07568, P07622-P07629, P07685-P07708, P07761-P07803, P07855-P07898; complete group)
Canto XXV (published 1983; P07883-P07886; complete group)

P07883 [no title] (1983)
CINL𝜋:312x222:signed:Purchased 1983

P07884 [no title] (1983)
CINL𝜋:292x203:signed:Purchased 1983

P07885 [no title] (1983)
CINL𝜋:292x203:signed:Purchased 1983

P07886 [no title] (1983)
CINL𝜋:292x203:signed:Purchased 1983

Dante's Inferno (P07482-P07497, P07561-P07568, P07622-P07629, P07685-P07708, P07761-P07803, P07855-P07898; complete group)
Canto XXXII (published 1983; P07887-P07890; complete group; mixed group)

P07887 [no title] (1983)
CINL𝜋:312x222:signed:Purchased 1983

P07888 [no title] (1983)
CINL𝜋:305x210:signed:Purchased 1983

P07889 [no title] (1983)
CINLπ:292x203:signed:Purchased 1983

P07890 [no title] (1983)
CINLπ:292x203:signed:Purchased 1983

Dante's Inferno (P07482-P07497, P07561-P07568,
P07622-P07629, P07685-P07708, P07761-P07803,
P07855-P07898; complete group)
Canto XXXIII (published 1983; P07891-P07894;
complete group)

P07891 [no title] (1983)
CINLπ:292x203:signed:Purchased 1983

P07892 [no title] (1983)
CINLπ:292x203:signed:Purchased 1983

P07893 [no title] (1983)
CINLπ:292x203:signed:Purchased 1983

P07894 [no title] (1983)
CINLπ:210x203:signed:Purchased 1983

Dante's Inferno (P07482-P07497, P07561-P07568,
P07622-P07629, P07685-P07708, P07761-P07803,
P07855-P07898; complete group)
Canto XXXIV (published 1983; P07895-P07898;
complete group)

P07895 [no title] (1983)
CINLπ:292x203:signed:Purchased 1983

P07896 [no title] (1983)
CINLπ:292x203:signed:Purchased 1983

P07897 [no title] (1983)
CINLπ:254x140:signed:Purchased 1983

P07898 [no title] (1983)
CINLπ:292x203:signed:Purchased 1983

P07989 Colophon (1979-83)
CINLπ:292x204:signed:Purchased 1983

PHILPOT, Glyn Warren 1884-1937
Modern Collection
Tate Gallery Archive holds material concerning this artist

N03002 The Man in Black (1913)
Oc:768x692:signed:Presented by Francis Howard through
the National Loan Exhibitions Committee 1914

N03218 A Young Breton (1917)
Oc:1270x1016:signed:Presented by the Trustees of the
Chantrey Bequest 1917

N04666 Oedipus Replying to the Sphinx (1931)
Sz:838x546x318:Presented by the Contemporary Art
Society 1932

N04893 Mrs Gerard Simpson (1937)
Oc:978x244:Presented by the Trustees of the Chantrey
Bequest 1937

N05382 Three Figures (circa 1921)
DWπ:318x244:Purchased 1942

PICABIA, Francis 1879-1953
Modern Collection

T00305 Conversation I (1922)
DWπ:594x724:signed:Purchased 1959

T03845 The Fig-Leaf (1922)
La Feuille de vigne
Ec:2000x1600:signed:Purchased 1984

PICASSO, Pablo 1881-1973
Modern Collection
Tate Gallery Archive holds material concerning this artist

N04683 Flowers (1901)
Fleurs
Oc:651x489:signed:Purchased with assistance from the
Contemporary Art Society 1933

N04719 Seated Woman in a Chemise (1923)
Femme en chemise assise
Oc:921x730:signed:Bequeathed by C. Frank Stoop 1933

N04720 Girl in a Chemise (circa 1905)
Jeune femme en chemise
Oc:727x600:signed:Bequeathed by C. Frank Stoop 1933

N04721 Horse with a Youth in Blue (1905-6)
Cheval avec jeune homme en bleu
Wπ:498x321:signed:Bequeathed by C. Frank Stoop 1933

N05904 Seated Nude (1909-10)
Femme nue assise
Oc:921x730:signed:Purchased 1949

N05915 Bust of a Woman (1909)
Buste de femme
Oc:727x600:signed:Purchased 1949

N06023 Cock (1932)
Coq
Sz:651x543x318:Purchased 1953

N06205 Nude Woman in a Red Armchair (1932)
Femme nue dans un fauteuil rouge
Oc:1299x972:signed:Purchased 1953

T00145 Goat's Skull, Bottle and Candle (1952)
Crâne de chèvre, bouteille et bougie
Oc:892x1162:signed:Purchased 1957

T00341 Dora Maar Seated (1938)
Dora Maar assise
DWGOπ:689x625:signed:Purchased 1960

T00414 Bottle of Vieux Marc, Glass, Guitar and Newspaper
(1913)
Guitare, journal, verre et bouteille
DVπ:467x625:signed:Purchased 1961

T00729 The Three Dancers (1925)
Les Trois Danseuses
Oc:2153x1422:signed:Purchased with a special
Grant-in-Aid and the Florence Fox Bequest with
assistance from the Friends of the Tate Gallery and the
Contemporary Art Society 1965

T01136 Still Life (1914)
Nature morte
Rwv:254x457x92:Purchased 1969

T03571 Circus Artist and Child (1905)
Artiste de cirque et enfant
DWπ:168x105:Bequeathed by Mrs A.F. Kessler 1983

T03572 Dish of Pears (1936)
Compotier de poires
Oc:380x610:signed:Bequeathed by Mrs A.F. Kessler 1983

T03670 Nude Woman with Necklace (1968)
Femme nue au collier
Oc:1135x1617:signed:Purchased 1983

T05010 Weeping Woman (1937)
Femme en pleurs
Oc:608x500:signed:Accepted by the Commissioners of
Inland Revenue in lieu of tax with additional payment
(Grant-in-Aid) and with assistance from the National
Heritage Memorial Fund, the National Art Collections
Fund and the Friends of the Tate Gallery 1987

School Prints (P01698-P01727; complete group; mixed group)
P01718 Composition (1948)
CLπ:495x762:signed:Presented by Patrick Seale Prints 1975

PICHÉ, Roland born 1938
Modern Collection

P04995 Yellow Square (1969)
CNπ:632x584:signed:Presented by Rose and Chris Prater through the Institute of Contemporary Prints 1975

P04996 Yellow Bridge (1969)
CNπ:692x546:signed:Presented by Rose and Chris Prater through the Institute of Contemporary Prints 1975

P04997 River in Red, Yellow and Blue (1970)
CNπ:629x813:signed:Presented by Rose and Chris Prater through the Institute of Contemporary Prints 1975

P04998 Roundabout (1970)
CNπ:743x616:signed:Presented by Rose and Chris Prater through the Institute of Contemporary Prints 1975

P04999 Summer Portrait (1970)
CNπ:686x705:signed:Presented by Rose and Chris Prater through the Institute of Contemporary Prints 1975

P05001 Yellow and Red Spaceframe (1970)
CNπ:991x724:signed:Presented by Rose and Chris Prater through the Institute of Contemporary Prints 1975

P05002 Essex Landscape (1971)
CNπ:816x638:signed:Presented by Rose and Chris Prater through the Institute of Contemporary Prints 1975

P05003 Bar-B.Q. (1972)
CNπ:660x879:signed:Presented by Rose and Chris Prater through the Institute of Contemporary Prints 1975

P05004 Holland Park (1972)
CNπ:679x991:signed:Presented by Rose and Chris Prater through the Institute of Contemporary Prints 1975

P05005 Portrait Head (1972-3)
CNπ:566x752:signed:Presented by Rose and Chris Prater through the Institute of Contemporary Prints 1975

PICHET, Roland
Modern Collection
Tate Gallery Archive holds material concerning this artist

Homage to Albert Dumouchel (P03166-P03178; complete group; mixed group)
Hommage à Albert Dumouchel
P03175 Silence de Jonille (1971)
Silence de Jonille
CNπ:419x524:signed:Presented by the University of Quebec 1976

PICKARD, Louise 1865-1928
British Collection

N04426 The Green Balcony (circa 1927)
Oc:635x762:Presented by Miss Christina M. Rivington 1928

N05347 Still Life by a Window (circa 1916)
Oc:813x1016:signed:Presented by the Trustees of the Chantrey Bequest 1941

PICKERSGILL, Frederick Richard
1820-1900
British Collection

N00445 Amoret, Aemylia and Prince Arthur in the Cottage of Sclaunder (exhibited 1845)
Oc:591x889:signed:Presented by Robert Vernon 1847

PICKERSGILL, Henry William 1782-1875
British Collection

N00416 Robert Vernon (1846)
Oc:1422x1118:signed:Presented by Robert Vernon 1847

N00417 Syrian Maid (exhibited 1837)
Oc:914x714:signed:Presented by Robert Vernon 1847

N00791 The Nun
Oc:889x686:Presented by the artist 1868

PIGNON, Edouard born 1905
Modern Collection

N06037 The Miner (1949)
Le Mineur
Oc:921x730:signed:Presented by the Contemporary Art Society 1951

T00438 Men Installing Electric Lines at Vallauris (1954)
Les Monteurs de Lignes électriques à Vallauris
Dπ:581x778:signed:Presented by the Friends of the Tate Gallery 1961

PINKNEY, Richard born 1938
Modern Collection
Tate Gallery Archive holds material concerning this artist

P01562 Drawing from the Model (1972)
CNπ:165x276:signed:Presented by Tetrad Press through the Institute of Contemporary Prints 1975

Approval Stamp Offer (P01676-P01687; complete group; mixed group)
P01682 Untitled (1972)
MJπ:51x51:Presented by Tetrad Press through the Institute of Contemporary Prints 1975

P01683 Untitled (1972)
MJπ:51x51:Presented by Tetrad Press through the Institute of Contemporary Prints 1975

P01684 Untitled (1972)
MJπ:51x51:Presented by Tetrad Press through the Institute of Contemporary Prints 1975

Tetrad Pamphlets Vol. I Nos. I-X (P01688-P01697; complete group; mixed group)
P01693 The Alphabet Twice (1971)
CNπ:305x508:Presented by Tetrad Press through the Institute of Contemporary Prints 1975

P01694 A Verse from the Death of a Guiser (1971)
CNπ:305x508:Presented by Tetrad Press through the Institute of Contemporary Prints 1975

P03230 Free Stamp Offer (1971)
MJπ:89x89:Presented by Tetrad Press 1978

Spare Parts (P03232-P03240; complete group)
P03232 [title not known] (1971)
CNπ:254x254:signed:Presented by Tetrad Press 1978

P03233 [title not known] (1971)
CNπ:254x254:signed:Presented by Tetrad Press 1978

P03234 [title not known] (1971)
CNπ:254x254:signed:Presented by Tetrad Press 1978

P03235 [title not known] (1971)
CNπ:254x254:signed:Presented by Tetrad Press 1978

P03236 [title not known] (1971)
CNπ:254x254:signed:Presented by Tetrad Press 1978

P03237 [title not known] (1971)
CNπ:254x254:signed:Presented by Tetrad Press 1978

P03238 [title not known] (1971)
CNπ:254x254:signed:Presented by Tetrad Press 1978

P03239 [title not known] (1971)
CNπ:254x254:signed:Presented by Tetrad Press 1978

P03240 [title not known] (1971)
CNπ:254x254:signed:Presented by Tetrad Press 1978

PINWELL, George John 1842-1875
British Collection

N02689 Study for 'The Pied Piper of Hamelin': The Children (circa 1871)
Gπ:175x295:signed:Presented by Alfred A. de Pass 1910

N02690 Study of Strolling Players
Gπ:267x375:signed:Presented by Alfred A. de Pass 1910

N03625 Landscape
Wπ:152x146:signed:Presented by H. Reitlinger through the National Art Collections Fund 1922

N03973 By the Dovecote, engraved by the Dalziel Brothers (1865)
Jπ:159x127:Purchased 1924

N04023 Shadow and Substance, engraved by the Dalziel Brothers (published 1867)
Jπ:159x127:Presented by Gilbert Dalziel 1924

N04024 The Shadow, engraved by the Dalziel Brothers (published 1867)
Jπ:168x121:Presented by Gilbert Dalziel 1924

N04056 Mrs Malcombe Giving Instructions for her Funeral to her Sons, engraved by Swain (1874)
Jπ:121x165:Presented by Harold Hartley 1925

N04057 Interior of a Barn with Figures and a Lamb, engraved by the Dalziel Brothers (1866)
Jπ:165x124:Presented by Harold Hartley 1925

N04084 Visiting the Poor
Wπ:184x140:signed:Bequeathed by John Lane 1925

N04085 The Connoisseurs
DWπ:114x143:signed:Bequeathed by John Lane 1925

PIPER, Edward 1938-1990
Modern Collection
Tate Gallery Archive holds material concerning this artist

Nudes (P05006-P05011; complete group)

P05006 [title not known] (1970)
:710x551:signed:Presented by Rose and Chris Prater through the Institute of Contemporary Prints 1975

P05007 [title not known] (1970)
:700x533:signed:Presented by Rose and Chris Prater through the Institute of Contemporary Prints 1975

P05008 [title not known] (1970)
:699x548:signed:Presented by Rose and Chris Prater through the Institute of Contemporary Prints 1975

P05009 [title not known] (1970)
:692x538:signed:Presented by Rose and Chris Prater through the Institute of Contemporary Prints 1975

P05010 [title not known] (1970)
:702x533:signed:Presented by Rose and Chris Prater through the Institute of Contemporary Prints 1975

P05011 [title not known] (1970)
:699x535:signed:Presented by Rose and Chris Prater through the Institute of Contemporary Prints 1975

P06742 Telford's Pont-Cysylltau (1965)
CLπ:502x454:Presented by Curwen Studio 1977

P06743 High Level Bridge, Newcastle (1965)
CLπ:508x597:Presented by Curwen Studio 1976

PIPER, Francis le - see LE PIPER, Francis

PIPER, John born 1903
Modern Collection
Tate Gallery Archive holds material concerning this artist

N05215 The Dairy, Fawley Court (1940)
WDπ:514x287:signed:Purchased 1940

N05718 St Mary le Port, Bristol (1940)
Oc:762x635:signed:Presented by the War Artists' Advisory Committee 1946

N05719 All Saints Chapel, Bath (1942)
WDπ:425x559:signed:Presented by the War Artists' Advisory Committee 1946

N05720 Somerset Place, Bath (1942)
WDπ:489x762:Presented by the War Artists' Advisory Committee 1946

N05748 Seaton Delaval (1941)
Ow:711x883:signed:Presented by Sir Kenneth Clark (later Lord Clark of Saltwood) through the Contemporary Art Society 1946

N06212 Abstract I (1935)
OVp:914x1067:signed:Purchased 1954

T00487 Coast of Brittany I (1961)
Vπ:559x775:signed:Presented by the National Art Collections Fund with the assistance of the bequest of Dennis Daybell 1962

T00488 Coast of Brittany II (1961)
Vπ:571x781:signed:Presented by the National Art Collections Fund with the assistance of the bequest of Dennis Daybell 1962

T00494 Three Suffolk Towers (1958)
WDπ:702x375:signed:Presented by the Trustees of the Chantrey Bequest 1962

T00516 The Forum (1961)
Oc:1067x1524:signed:Purchased 1962

T00646 Littlestone-on-Sea (1936)
DVπ:359x476:Purchased 1964

T01026 Construction (1934/1967)
ORwv:1006x1159:signed:Purchased 1968

T03818 Covehithe Church (1983)
Oc:863x1118:signed:Presented by the artist 1984

T03922 Yarnton Monument (1947-8)
Oc:629x753:signed:Bequeathed by Mrs Ernestine Carter 1984

T05030 Beach with Starfish (circa 1933)
GVDπ:380x485:signed:Presented by Charlotte, Lady Bonham-Carter 1988

T05810 Figure Drawing (1941)
DWπ:380x275:signed:Presented by the Contemporary Art Society 1942

T05811 Figure Drawing (1941)
DWπ:376x275:signed:Presented by the Contemporary Art Society 1942

T05812 Figure Drawing (1941)
DWπ:380x275:signed:Presented by the Contemporary Art Society 1942

P01807 Illustrations and Book Jackets for English, Scottish and Welsh Landscapes (1944)
CLπ:940x584:Presented by Robert Simon 1976

Nursery Frieze I-II (P02273-P02274; complete group)
P02273 [title not known] (1939)
CLπ:460x1219:signed:Presented by the artist 1976
P02274 [title not known] (1939)
CLπ:460x1219:signed:Presented by the artist 1976

P02275 Drysllwyn Castle (1953)
MLπ:378x537:Presented by the artist 1976

P02276 Chamecy, Burgundy (1972)
MIπ:692x540:signed:Presented by the artist 1976

P02277 Église de Vernon, Normandy (1972)
MIπ:686x546:signed:Presented by the artist 1976

P02278 Notre Dame de l'Épine, near Rheims (1972)
MIπ:692x540:signed:Presented by the artist 1976

P02279 Rheims Cathedral (1972)
MIπ:686x543:signed:Presented by the artist 1976

P03106 Untitled (from IAA Portfolio) (1975)
CLπ:714x435:Presented by the International Association of Art 1975

80th Anniversary Portfolio (P03297-P03304; complete group)
P03297 Foliate Head (1983)
MINπ:446x645:signed:Presented by Orde Levinson 1983
P03298 Eye and Camera (1983)
MIπ:445x667:signed:Presented by Orde Levinson 1983
P03299 Palazzo Pesaro (1983)
MIπ:450x645:signed:Presented by Orde Levinson 1983
P03300 St Germain de l'Ivret (1983)
MNπ:457x645:signed:Presented by Orde Levinson 1983
P03301 Blenheim Gates (1983)
MIπ:454x663:signed:Presented by Orde Levinson 1983
P03302 Eastnor Castle (1983)
MNπ:460x677:signed:Presented by Orde Levinson 1983
P03303 Saltash Bridge (1983)
MNπ:448x683:signed:Presented by Orde Levinson 1983
P03304 Lower Brockhampton (1983)
MNπ:457x668:signed:Presented by Orde Levinson 1983

P05012 Penybont Ford Congregational Church (1966)
CNπ:708x575:signed:Presented by Rose and Chris Prater through the Institute of Contemporary Prints 1975

Eye and Camera (P05013-P05015; complete group)
P05013 [title not known] (1967)
CNπ::signed:Presented by Rose and Chris Prater through the Institute of Contemporary Prints 1975
P05014 [title not known] (1967)
CNπ::signed:Presented by Rose and Chris Prater through the Institute of Contemporary Prints 1975
P05015 [title not known] (1967)
CNπ::signed:Presented by Rose and Chris Prater through the Institute of Contemporary Prints 1975

Travel Notes (P05016-P05017; complete group)
P05016 [title not known] (1967)
CNπ:746x553:signed:Presented by Rose and Chris Prater through the Institute of Contemporary Prints 1975
P05017 [title not known] (1967)
CNπ:746x553:signed:Presented by Rose and Chris Prater through the Institute of Contemporary Prints 1975

P05018 Besse, Dordogne (1968)
CNπ:781x584:signed:Presented by Rose and Chris Prater through the Institute of Contemporary Prints 1975

P05019 Creysse, Dordogne (1968)
CNπ:448x648:signed:Presented by Rose and Chris Prater through the Institute of Contemporary Prints 1975

P05020 Floirac (1968)
CNπ:438x651:signed:Presented by Rose and Chris Prater through the Institute of Contemporary Prints 1975

P05021 Garn Fawr, Pembrokeshire (1968)
CNπ:432x648:signed:Presented by Rose and Chris Prater through the Institute of Contemporary Prints 1975

P05022 Jazenne, Charente (1968)
CNπ:581x775:signed:Presented by Rose and Chris Prater through the Institute of Contemporary Prints 1975

P05023 La Chapelle St Robert, Dordogne (1968)
CNπ:587x800:signed:Presented by Rose and Chris Prater through the Institute of Contemporary Prints 1975

P05024 Montpellier de Didonne, Charente (1968)
CNπ:768x559:signed:Presented by Rose and Chris Prater through the Institute of Contemporary Prints 1975

P05025 Mosnac, Dordogne (1968)
CNπ:441x660:signed:Presented by Rose and Chris Prater through the Institute of Contemporary Prints 1975

P05026 Near Newcastle Emlyn, Cardigan (1968)
CNπ:438x632:signed:Presented by Rose and Chris Prater through the Institute of Contemporary Prints 1975

P05027 St Amand de Coly, Dordogne (1968)
CNπ:581x775:signed:Presented by Rose and Chris Prater through the Institute of Contemporary Prints 1975

P05028 St Raphael, Dordogne (1968)
CNπ:575x787:signed:Presented by Rose and Chris Prater through the Institute of Contemporary Prints 1975

P05029 St Simon de Pelouialle (1968)
CNπ:568x784:signed:Presented by Rose and Chris Prater through the Institute of Contemporary Prints 1975

P05030 Welsh Landscape, Tretio (1969)
CNπ:486x711:signed:Presented by Rose and Chris Prater through the Institute of Contemporary Prints 1975

P05031 Caernarvon Castle (1971)
CNπ:492x746:Presented by Rose and Chris Prater through the Institute of Contemporary Prints 1975

P05032 Caernarvon Castle (1971)
CNπ:492x746:signed:Presented by Rose and Chris Prater through the Institute of Contemporary Prints 1975

P05033 Chambord (1971)
CNπ:498x686:signed:Presented by Rose and Chris Prater through the Institute of Contemporary Prints 1975

P05034 Corton Church, Suffolk (1971)
CNπ:762x445:signed:Presented by Rose and Chris Prater through the Institute of Contemporary Prints 1975

P05035 Framlingham Castle (1971)
CNπ:486x705:signed:Presented by Rose and Chris Prater through the Institute of Contemporary Prints 1975

P05036 Wymondham, Norfolk (1971)
CNπ:762x559:signed:Presented by Rose and Chris Prater through the Institute of Contemporary Prints 1975

P05037 Abbeville (1972)
CNπ:800x600:signed:Presented by Rose and Chris Prater through the Institute of Contemporary Prints 1975

Eye and Camera (P05038-P05041; complete group)
P05038 [title not known] (1972)
CNπ:483x698:signed:Presented by Rose and Chris Prater through the Institute of Contemporary Prints 1975

P05039 [title not known] (1972)
CNπ:483x698:signed:Presented by Rose and Chris Prater through the Institute of Contemporary Prints 1975

P05040 [title not known] (1972)
CNπ:483x698:signed:Presented by Rose and Chris Prater through the Institute of Contemporary Prints 1975

P05041 [title not known] (1972)
CNπ:483x698:signed:Presented by Rose and Chris Prater through the Institute of Contemporary Prints 1975

P05042 Ludlow Castle (1972)
CNπ:546x803:signed:Presented by Rose and Chris Prater through the Institute of Contemporary Prints 1975

Petit Palais (P05043-P05045; complete group)
P05043 [title not known] (1972)
CNπ:782x572:signed:Presented by Rose and Chris Prater through the Institute of Contemporary Prints 1975

P05044 [title not known] (1972)
CNπ:782x573:signed:Presented by Rose and Chris Prater through the Institute of Contemporary Prints 1975

P05045 [title not known] (1972)
CNπ:783x573:signed:Presented by Rose and Chris Prater through the Institute of Contemporary Prints 1975

P05046 Vaux le Vicomte (1972)
CNπ:559x841:signed:Presented by Rose and Chris Prater through the Institute of Contemporary Prints 1975

P05047 Chambord Rooftops (1973)
CNπ:654x1051:signed:Presented by Rose and Chris Prater through the Institute of Contemporary Prints 1975

Death in Venice (P05048-P05055; complete group)
P05048 [title not known] (1972)
CNπ::signed:Presented by Rose and Chris Prater through the Institute of Contemporary Prints 1975

P05049 [title not known] (1972)
CNπ::signed:Presented by Rose and Chris Prater through the Institute of Contemporary Prints 1975

P05050 [title not known] (1972)
CNπ::signed:Presented by Rose and Chris Prater through the Institute of Contemporary Prints 1975

P05051 [title not known] (1972)
CNπ::signed:Presented by Rose and Chris Prater through the Institute of Contemporary Prints 1975

P05052 [title not known] (1972)
CNπ::signed:Presented by Rose and Chris Prater through the Institute of Contemporary Prints 1975

P05053 [title not known] (1972)
CNπ::signed:Presented by Rose and Chris Prater through the Institute of Contemporary Prints 1975

P05054 [title not known] (1972)
CNπ::signed:Presented by Rose and Chris Prater through the Institute of Contemporary Prints 1975

P05055 [title not known] (1972)
CNπ::signed:Presented by Rose and Chris Prater through the Institute of Contemporary Prints 1975

Eye and Camera (P05056-P05057; complete group)
P05056 [title not known] (1972)
CNπ:476x689:signed:Presented by Rose and Chris Prater through the Institute of Contemporary Prints 1975

P05057 [title not known] (1972)
CNπ:476x689:signed:Presented by Rose and Chris Prater through the Institute of Contemporary Prints 1975

P05058 Three Somerset Towns (1973)
CNπ:654x895:signed:Presented by Rose and Chris Prater through the Institute of Contemporary Prints 1975

P05059 Venetian Backdrop (1973)
CNπ:559x1048:signed:Presented by Rose and Chris Prater through the Institute of Contemporary Prints 1975

P05400 Foliate Heads I (1975)
CNπ:584x768:signed:Presented by Rose and Chris Prater 1976

P05401 Foliate Heads II (1975)
CNπ:584x768:signed:Presented by Rose and Chris Prater 1976

P05402 Horham, Suffolk (1975)
CNπ:546x841:signed:Presented by Rose and Chris Prater 1976

P05403 Kilmory, Argyll (1975)
CNπ:632x841:signed:Presented by Rose and Chris Prater 1976

P05404 Kirkmaiden-in-Fernis (1975)
CNπ:606x918:signed:Presented by Rose and Chris Prater 1976

P05405 Ruined Chapel, Isle of Mull (1975)
CNπ:638x838:Presented by Rose and Chris Prater 1976

P05406 Skeebost, Skye (1975)
CNπ:635x838:signed:Presented by Rose and Chris Prater 1976

P05407 Castlemartin (1976)
CNπ:924x613:signed:Presented by Rose and Chris Prater 1976

P05408 Holkham, Norfolk (1976)
CNπ:613x835:signed:Presented by Rose and Chris Prater 1976

P05409 Moreton Corbett (1976)
CNπ:457x997:signed:Presented by Rose and Chris Prater 1976

P05410 South Lopham (1976)
CNπ:914x524:signed:Presented by Rose and Chris Prater 1976

P05460 Gates of London (1975-8)
CNπ:429x1607:signed:Presented by Rose and Chris Prater 1978

P05461 Buckden in a Storm (1977)
CNπ:578x851:signed:Presented by Rose and Chris Prater 1978

P05462 Capesthorne (1977)
CNπ:641x1019:signed:Presented by Rose and Chris Prater 1978

P05463 Exeter College Chapel, Oxford (1977)
CNπ:819x610:signed:Presented by Rose and Chris Prater 1978

P05464 Eye and Camera (circa 1977)
CNπ:765x1118:signed:Presented by Rose and Chris Prater 1978

P05465 Harlaxton (Blue) (1977)
CNπ:5846x1016:signed:Presented by Rose and Chris Prater 1978

Victorian Dream Palaces (P05466-P05473; complete group)
P05466 Ettingham Park (1977)
CNπ:530x702:signed:Presented by Rose and Chris Prater through the Institute of Contemporary Prints 1978

P05467 Flintham (1977)
CNπ:524x700:signed:Presented by Rose and Chris Prater through the Institute of Contemporary Prints 1978

P05468 Harlaxton through the Gate (1977)
CNπ:715x534:signed:Presented by Rose and Chris Prater through the Institute of Contemporary Prints 1978

P05469 Kelham (1977)
CNπ:472x699:signed:Presented by Rose and Chris Prater through the Institute of Contemporary Prints 1978

P05470 Milton Ernest (1977)
CNπ:510x697:signed:Presented by Rose and Chris Prater through the Institute of Contemporary Prints 1978

P05471 Royal Holloway College (1977)
CNπ:530x705:signed:Presented by Rose and Chris Prater through the Institute of Contemporary Prints 1978

P05472 Shadwell Park (1977)
CNπ:515x697:signed:Presented by Rose and Chris Prater through the Institute of Contemporary Prints 1978

P05473 Wightwick Manor (1977)
CNπ:526x706:signed:Presented by Rose and Chris Prater through the Institute of Contemporary Prints 1978

P05476 Waddesdon (1977)
CNπ:648x991:signed:Presented by Rose and Chris Prater 1978

P05564 Eye and Camera, Red, Blue and Yellow (1980)
CNπ:400x606:signed:Presented by Rose and Chris Prater 1980

Westminster School (P06421-P06422; complete group)
P06421 [title not known] (1961)
CLπ:429x584:signed:Presented by Curwen Studio through the Institute of Contemporary Prints 1975

P06422 [title not known] (1961)
CLπ:429x584:signed:Presented by Curwen Studio through the Institute of Contemporary Prints 1975

P06423 Beach in Brittany (1961-2)
CLπ:473x645:Presented by Curwen Studio through the Institute of Contemporary Prints 1975

P06424 San Marco, Venice (1961-2)
CLπ:645x467:Presented by Curwen Studio through the Institute of Contemporary Prints 1975

P06425 Anglesey Beach (1962-3)
CLπ:559x445:Presented by Curwen Studio through the Institute of Contemporary Prints 1975

P06426 Edington, Wiltshire (1964)
CLπ:530x695:Presented by Curwen Studio through the Institute of Contemporary Prints 1975

A Retrospect of Churches (P06427-P06450; complete group)
P06427 1. Kilpeck, Herefordshire: the Norman South Door (1964)
CLπ:725x515:signed:Presented by Curwen Studio through the Institute of Contemporary Prints 1975

P06428 2. Gaddesby, Leicestershire: Medieval Stonework (1964)
CLπ:672x470:signed:Presented by Curwen Studio through the Institute of Contemporary Prints 1975

P06429 3. Redenhall, Norfolk: the Tower (1964)
CLπ:706x360:signed:Presented by Curwen Studio through the Institute of Contemporary Prints 1975

P06430 4. Warkton, Northamptonshire: Monument by Vangelder, 1775 (1964)
CLπ:692x491:signed:Presented by Curwen Studio through the Institute of Contemporary Prints 1975

P06431 5. Exton, Rutland: Monument by Grinling Gibbons, 1686 (1964)
CLπ:744x516:signed:Presented by Curwen Studio through the Institute of Contemporary Prints 1975

P06432 6. St Kew, Cornwall: Church in a Hilly Landscape (1964)
CLπ:504x701:signed:Presented by Curwen Studio through the Institute of Contemporary Prints 1975

P06433 7. Llan-y-Blodwell, Shropshire: Mid 19th Century Furnishing and Painting (1964)
CLπ:660x460:signed:Presented by Curwen Studio through the Institute of Contemporary Prints 1975

P06434 8. Malmesbury, Wiltshire: the South Porch (1964)
CLπ:615x520:signed:Presented by Curwen Studio through the Institute of Contemporary Prints 1975

P06435 9. Tickencote, Rutland: the Norman Chancel Arch (1964)
CLπ:424x674:signed:Presented by Curwen Studio through the Institute of Contemporary Prints 1975

P06436 10. Rudbaxton, Pembrokeshire: 17th Century Monument, 19th Century Furnishing (1964)
CLπ:473x649:signed:Presented by Curwen Studio through the Institute of Contemporary Prints 1975

P06437 11. Inglesham, Wiltshire: A Rustic Medieval Interior (1964)
CLπ:507x711:signed:Presented by Curwen Studio through the Institute of Contemporary Prints 1975

P06438 12. Lewknor, Oxfordshire: Textured Walls, Traceried Windows (1964)
CLπ:531x709:signed:Presented by Curwen Studio through the Institute of Contemporary Prints 1975

P06439 13. Leckhampstead, Berkshire: a Victorian Church by S.S. Teulor (1964)
CLπ:685x472:signed:Presented by Curwen Studio through the Institute of Contemporary Prints 1975

P06440 14. Fotheringhay, Northamptonshire: Medieval Stone (1964)
CLπ:486x687:signed:Presented by Curwen Studio through the Institute of Contemporary Prints 1975

P06441 15. St Nicholas, Liverpool: Smoke-black Dockland Church (1964)
CLπ:619x454:signed:Presented by Curwen Studio through the Institute of Contemporary Prints 1975

P06442 16. Easton, Portland, Dorset: St George Reforne, an 18th Century Church among the Quarries (1964)
CLπ:501x642:signed:Presented by Curwen Studio through the Institute of Contemporary Prints 1975

P06443 17. North Grimstone, Yorkshire (East Riding): the Deposition - Detail from the 12th Century Font (1964)
CLπ:737x537:signed:Presented by Curwen Studio through the Institute of Contemporary Prints 1975

P06444 18. Gedney, Lincolnshire: a Tower in the Fens (1964)
CLπ:1776x515:signed:Presented by Curwen Studio through the Institute of Contemporary Prints 1975

P06445 19. Llangloffan, Pembrokeshire: the Baptist Chapel (1964)
CLπ:519x616:signed:Presented by Curwen Studio through the Institute of Contemporary Prints 1975

P06446 20. St Anne's, Limehouse, London: by Nicholas Hawksmoor (1964)
CLπ:705x477:signed:Presented by Curwen Studio through the Institute of Contemporary Prints 1975

P06447 21. Christ Church, Spitalfields, London: by Nicholas Hawksmoor (1964)
CLπ:732x483:signed:Presented by Curwen Studio through the Institute of Contemporary Prints 1975

P06448 22. St Matthias, Stoke Newington, London: by William Butterfield (1964)
CLπ:686x520:signed:Presented by Curwen Studio through the Institute of Contemporary Prints 1975

P06449 23. St James the Less, Westminster: by G.E. Street (1964)
CLπ:490x653:signed:Presented by Curwen Studio through the Institute of Contemporary Prints 1975

P06450 24. St Mary's, Paddington: by G.E. Street (1964)
CLπ::signed:Presented by Curwen Studio through the Institute of Contemporary Prints 1975

P06451 Crug Glas, Swansea (1966)
CLπ:505x768:signed:Presented by Curwen Studio through the Institute of Contemporary Prints 1975

P06452 Dylwyn Church (1966)
CLπ:775x546:signed:Presented by Curwen Studio through the Institute of Contemporary Prints 1975

P06453 Ironbridge (1966)
CLπ:483x645:signed:Presented by Curwen Studio through the Institute of Contemporary Prints 1975

P06454 Swansea Chapel (1966)
CLπ:689x518:signed:Presented by Curwen Studio through the Institute of Contemporary Prints 1975

P06455 Bethesda Chapel (1966-7)
CLπ:527x689:signed:Presented by Curwen Studio through the Institute of Contemporary Prints 1975

P06456 Foliate Head (1971)
CLπ:391x264:Presented by Curwen Studio through the Institute of Contemporary Prints 1975

P06457 Annunciation to the Shepherds (from the Penwith Portfolio) (1973)
CLπ:435x549:signed:Presented by Curwen Studio through the Institute of Contemporary Prints 1975

P06744 Avoncroft Museum (1976)
CLπ:422x594:signed:Presented by Curwen Studio 1977

P06802 Mother and Child (1977)
CLπ:597x470:Presented by Curwen Studio 1978

P06803 High Cross (1977-8)
CLπ:406x546:Presented by Curwen Studio 1978

P06804 Holdenby (1977-8)
CLπ:409x603:Presented by Curwen Studio 1978

P06805 Seaton (1977-8)
CLπ:425x597:Presented by Curwen Studio 1978

P07363 Stones and Bones (1978)
CNπ:502x698:signed:Purchased 1980

PIRANDELLO, Fausto 1899-1975
Modern Collection

T05707 Awakening (circa 1948)
Il risveglio
Ob:650x880:Presented by Pierluigi Pirandello, the artist's son 1989

PIRIE, Sir George 1863-1946
British Collection

N05106 Mother Duck (exhibited 1932)
Oc:457x610:signed:Presented by the Trustees of the Chantrey Bequest 1940

PISSARRO, Camille 1830-1903
Modern Collection
Tate Gallery Archive holds material concerning this artist

N04592 Self-Portrait (1903)
Portrait de Camille Pissarro par lui-même
Oc:410x333:signed:Presented by Lucien Pissarro, the artist's son 1931

N04709 A Wool-Carder (1880)
Cardeuse de laine
Op:559x464:signed:Presented by Lucien Pissarro, the artist's son 1933

N05574 Portrait of Felix Pissarro (1881)
Portrait de Félix Pissarro
Oc:552x464:signed:Bequeathed by Lucien Pissarro, the artist's son 1944

N05575 The Little Country Maid (1882)
La Petite Bonne de campagne
Oc:635x530:signed:Bequeathed by Lucien Pissarro, the artist's son 1944

N05576 The Pork Butcher (1883)
La Charcutière
Oc:651x543:signed:Bequeathed by Lucien Pissarro, the artist's son 1944

N05833 The Pilots' Jetty, Le Havre, Morning, Cloudy and Misty Weather (1903)
Anse des pilotes, Le Havre, matin, temps gris, brumeux
Oc:651x813:signed:Presented by Lucien Pissarro, the artist's son 1948

N06003 A Corner of the Meadow at Eragny (1902)
Un Coin du pré à Eragny
Oc:600x813:signed:Presented by Mrs Esther Pissarro, the artist's daughter-in-law 1951

PISSARRO, Lucien 1863-1944
British Collection
Tate Gallery Archive holds material concerning this artist

N03179 High View, Fish Pond (1915)
Oc:533x648:signed:Presented by the Contemporary Art Society 1917

N03865 Les Amandiers, Le Lavandou (1923)
Oc:597x730:signed:Purchased 1924

N04747 April, Epping (1884)
Oc:603x730:signed:Presented by the Trustees of the Chantrey Bequest 1934

N04748 All Saints' Church, Hastings: Sun and Mist (1918)
Oc:648x533:signed:Presented by the Trustees of the Chantrey Bequest 1934

N05552 Ivy Cottage, Coldharbour: Sun and Snow (1916)
Oc:533x648:signed:Presented by the Trustees of the Chantrey Bequest 1943

P07098 Intoxicated with Love [from the book 'Poems taken from 'Livre de Jade''] (1911)
Ivresse d'amour
CJπ:73x73:signed:Purchased 1924

P07099 Le Miroir (circa 1911)
CJπ:67x67:signed:Purchased 1924

P07100 Girl Picking Flowers (1902)
CJπ:117x98:Purchased 1924

P07101 Landscape (circa 1911)
MJπ:79x76:signed:Purchased 1924

P07102 Illustration to The Sleeping Beauty
MJπ:111x89:Purchased 1924

P08182 Le Curé (circa 1884)
MJπ:86x79:Transferred from the Library 1982

P08183 Le Patissier (circa 1884)
MJπ:165x58:Transferred from the Library 1982

P08184 Jeune fille (circa 1884)
MJπ:155x64:Transferred from the Library 1982

P08185 April (1890)
MJπ:98x89:Transferred from the Library 1982

P08186 Floréal (1890)
MJπ:178x64:Transferred from the Library 1982

P08188 Portrait de Camille Pissarro (1893)
MJπ:25x29:Transferred from the Library 1982

P08189 Boy and Pine Tree (1894)
MJπ:29x45:Transferred from the Library 1982

P08190 Un Coeur simple (1900)
MJπ:70x67:Transferred from the Library 1982

P08191 Choix de sonnets (1902)
MJπ:76x76:Transferred from the Library 1982

P08192 Geese (circa 1903)
MJπ:38x54:Transferred from the Library 1982

P08193 Boy Breaking a Stick (circa 1905)
MJπ:64x58:Transferred from the Library 1982

P08194 Consultation (circa 1905)
MJπ:64x70:Transferred from the Library 1982

P08195 Consultation (circa 1905)
MJπ:51x51:Transferred from the Library 1982

P08196 Consultation (circa 1905)
MJπ:83x86:Transferred from the Library 1982

P08197 L'Amour manillé (circa 1905)
MJπ:73x64:Transferred from the Library 1982

P08198 Bookplate and New Year Card (1905)
MJπ:64x64:Transferred from the Library 1982

P08199 Liseuse (circa 1905)
MJπ:64x41:Transferred from the Library 1982

P08200 Women in Roundel (circa 1908)
MJπ:38x38:Transferred from the Library 1982

P08201 New Year Card (1909)
MJπ:44x44:Transferred from the Library 1982

P08202 La Bergère (circa 1912)
MJπ:44x29:Transferred from the Library 1982

P08203 Landscape: Blackpool, Devon (1914)
MJπ:79x76:Transferred from the Library 1982

P08204 Rye (1920)
MJπ:54x38:Transferred from the Library 1982

P08205 New Year Card (1923)
MJπ:38x57:Transferred from the Library 1982

P08206 Christmas Card (1925)
MJπ:51x51:Transferred from the Library 1982

P08207 New Year Card (1925)
MJπ:44x57:Transferred from the Library 1982

P08208 La Bergère (1929)
MJπ:76x73:Transferred from the Library 1982

P08209 Ex Libris Isa Taylor (circa 1892)
MJπ:57x38:Transferred from the Library 1982

P08226 Contentment (1890)
MJπ:98x52:Transferred from the Library 1982

P08227 Le Tennis (1890)
MJπ:98x137:Transferred from the Library 1982

PITCHFORTH, Vivian Roland 1895-1982
Modern Collection
Tate Gallery Archive holds material concerning this artist

N04933 Floods (circa 1935)
Oc:635x813:signed:Purchased 1938

N05173 Night Transport (1939-40)
Oc:508x762:signed:Presented by the Trustees of the
Chantrey Bequest 1940

N05721 Gibraltar Harbour with Escort Groups Going To Sea
(1944)
Wπ:571x787:signed:Presented by the War Artists'
Advisory Committee 1946

T00037 Floods, Madoc Valley, North Wales (1954)
Wπ:432x591:signed:Presented by the Trustees of the
Chantrey Bequest 1955

T03160 Loch Awe
Wπ:483x629:signed:Presented by the Trustees of the
Chantrey Bequest 1980

T03661 Seated Model (circa 1950-60)
Dπ:325x254:Bequeathed by the artist 1983

T03662 Model Seen from the Back (circa 1950-60)
Dπ:254x333:Bequeathed by the artist 1983

T03663 View of Harbour - Folkestone (circa 1920)
DWπ:489x740:Bequeathed by the artist 1983

T03664 Wet Windscreen, Ramsgate Harbour (circa 1971)
Wπ:477x625:Bequeathed by the artist 1983

PLATT, John 1886-1967
Modern Collection

N03875 The Port of St Tropez (1922)
DWπ:470x324:signed:Purchased 1924

PLOWMAN, Chris born 1952
Modern Collection
Tate Gallery Archive holds material concerning this artist

P07260 Clues (1978)
CNπ:508x695:signed:Purchased 1979

PLUMB, John born 1927
Modern Collection

T00509 Edgehill (1962)
AVc:1810x1219:signed:Presented by E.J. Power through
the Friends of the Tate Gallery 1962

T01156 Untitled August 1969 (1969)
Ac:2540x2534:Purchased 1969

P05060 Bermuda (1965)
CNπ:610x508:signed:Presented by Rose and Chris Prater
through the Institute of Contemporary Prints 1975

POCOCK, Nicholas 1741-1821
British Collection

T01009 The Battle of Lissa (1812)
Wπ:302x445:signed:Presented by the National Art
Collections Fund (Herbert Powell Bequest) 1967

POIRIER, Anne and POIRIER, Patrick
born 1942, born 1942
Modern Collection

T03325 Villa Adriana, in memory of Antinous (1979)
Villa Adriana, à la mémoire d'Antinous
SPFV:203x1149x1149:Presented anonymously through
the Contemporary Art Society in memory of Mrs Amy
Colls 1981

POLIAKOFF, Serge 1906-1969
Modern Collection

T00404 Abstract Composition (1954)
Composition abstraite
Oc:1159x889:signed:Purchased 1961

POLKE, Sigmar born 1941
Modern Collection

P77258 Hallo Shiva (1974)
Hallo Shiva
Lπ:203x432:signed:Purchased 1988

P77259 Figure with Hand (1973)
Figur mit Hand
Lπ:626x453:Purchased 1988

POLLARD, James 1792-1867
British Collection

T02366 The Royal Mail Coaches for the North Leaving the
Angel, Islington (1827)
Oc:1032x1464:signed:Presented by Paul Mellon through
the British Sporting Art Trust 1979

T03434 Coursers Taking the Field at Hatfield Park, Herts., the
Seat of the Marquess of Salisbury (exhibited 1824)
Oc:1042x1472:signed:Bequeathed by Mrs F. Ambrose
Clark through the British Sporting Art Trust 1982

T03435 The 'Tally-Ho' London - Birmingham Stage Coach
Passing Whittington College, Highgate (1836)
Oc:369x457:signed:Bequeathed by Mrs F. Ambrose Clark
through the British Sporting Art Trust 1982

T03436 Fly Fishing in the River Lee near the Ferry Boat Inn
(1831)
Oc:356x446:signed:Bequeathed by Mrs F. Ambrose Clark
through the British Sporting Art Trust 1982

T03437 Trolling for Pike in the River Lee (1831)
Oc:356x446:signed:Bequeathed by Mrs F. Ambrose Clark
through the British Sporting Art Trust 1982

POLLOCK, Jackson 1912-1956
Modern Collection

T00384 Number 23 (1948)
Eb:575x784:signed:Presented by the Friends of the Tate
Gallery (purchased out of funds provided by Mr and Mrs
H.J. Heinz II and H.J. Heinz Co. Ltd) 1960

T00436 Yellow Islands (1952)
Oc:1435x1854:signed:Presented by the Friends of the
Tate Gallery (purchased out of funds provided by Mr and
Mrs H.J. Heinz II and H.J. Heinz Co. Ltd) 1961

T03327 Naked Man with Knife (circa 1938-41)
Oc:1270x914:Presented by Frank Lloyd 1981

T03977 Summertime: Number 9A (1948)
OEc:848x5550:signed:Purchased 1988

T03978 Number 14 (1951)
Ec:1465x2695:signed:Purchased with assistance from the
American Fellows of the Tate Gallery Foundation 1988

T03979 Birth (circa 1938-41)
Oc:1164x551:Purchased 1985

POMEROY, Frederick William 1856-1924
British Collection

N01759 The Nymph of Loch Awe (1897)
Ss:267x641x229:signed:Presented by the Trustees of the
Chantrey Bequest 1897

N01762 Dionysus (?1890-1)
Sz:825x318x381:signed:Presented by Henry J. Pfungst
1898

POMODORO, Gio born 1930
Modern Collection

T00677 One (1959)
Uno
Sz:2896x2095x635:Purchased 1964

P08003 Untitled (1975-6)
Mlπ:165x257:signed:Transferred from the Library 1977

POOLE, Henry 1873-1928
British Collection

N04439 Mask of Pan (1926)
Rz:465x225x210:Purchased 1929

N04478 The Little Apple (circa 1927)
Ss:840x430x500:signed:Presented by the Trustees of the
Chantrey Bequest 1929

POOLE, Paul Falconer 1807-1879
British Collection

N01091 The Vision of Ezekiel (exhibited 1875)
Oc:1346x1854:Bequeathed by the artist 1880

N02314 Sketch for 'Vision of Ezekiel' (circa 1875)
Oc:540x762:Purchased 1908

N04909 Sketch for 'The Death of Cordelia' (circa 1858)
Oc:457x597:Presented by F. Howard 1938

N05761 Sketch, (?Ophelia)
Ow:267x368:Purchased 1947

POONS, Larry born 1937
Modern Collection
Tate Gallery Archive holds material concerning this artist

T01053 Out (1967)
Ac:1981x5191:Purchased 1968

POPE, Nicholas born 1949
Modern Collection
Tate Gallery Archive holds material concerning this artist

T02029 Stacked Lead (1976)
Smsw:1219x356x286:Purchased 1976

T03536 Big Hoos (1982)
Sw:2330x1740x890:Purchased 1982

PORTER, Frederick J. 1883-1944
Modern Collection
Tate Gallery Archive holds material concerning this artist

N05079 Winter Lanscape (circa 1929)
Oc:571x737:Bequeathed by Frank Hindley Smith 1940

PORTER, Stephen
Modern Collection

P05061 Untitled (1968)
CNπ:737x533:signed:Presented by Rose and Chris Prater
through the Institute of Contemporary Prints 1975

P05062 Untitled (1968)
CNπ:533x737:signed:Presented by Rose and Chris Prater
through the Institute of Contemporary Prints 1975

P05063 Untitled (1968)
CNπ:533x737:signed:Presented by Rose and Chris Prater
through the Institute of Contemporary Prints 1975

P05064 Untitled (1968)
CNπ:737x533:signed:Presented by Rose and Chris Prater
through the Institute of Contemporary Prints 1975

PORTWAY, Douglas born 1922
Modern Collection

T01479 White Screen (1970-1)
Oc:1016x1270:Presented anonymously 1971

POTTER, Frank Huddlestone 1845-1887
British Collection

N02108 A Music Lesson (1887)
Ow:508x724:signed:Purchased 1907

N02214 Little Dormouse
Oc:562x473:Presented by Amy, Lady Tate in memory of
Sir Henry Tate 1908

N03342 Nothing to Do
Oc:413x241:Presented by W.C. Corke through the
National Art Collections Fund 1918

N04617 Girl Resting at a Piano
Oc:514x714:signed:Purchased 1932

N04621 A Girl Reading
Oc:559x397:Purchased 1932

N05081 Head of a Girl
Oc:102x83:Bequeathed by Frank Hindley Smith 1940

N05364 A Quiet Corner: Miss E.A. Whelan (circa 1887)
Oc:406x305:Purchased 1942

N05446 Rest
Dπ:245x330:Presented by Miss E.A. Whelan 1944

POTTER, Helen Beatrix 1866-1943
British Collection

Illustrations for 'The Tailor of Gloucester'
(A01089-A01110; complete group)

A01089 Frontispiece: The Tailor Mouse (circa 1902)
WDπ:111x92:Presented by Capt. K.W.G. Duke RN 1946

A01090 The Tailor of Gloucester at Work (circa 1902)
WDπ:111x92:Presented by Capt. K.W.G. Duke RN 1946

A01091 Lady Mouse in Mob Cap (circa 1902)
WDπ:111x92:Presented by Capt. K.W.G. Duke RN 1946

A01092 The Tailor Leaving his Workshop (circa 1902)
WDπ:111x92:Presented by Capt. K.W.G. Duke RN 1946

A01093 The Tailor Returning Home (circa 1902)
WDπ:111x92:Presented by Capt. K.W.G. Duke RN 1946

A01094 Simpkin Housekeeping (circa 1902)
WDπ:111x92:Presented by Capt. K.W.G. Duke RN 1946

A01095 The Tailor by the Hearth (circa 1902)
WDπ:111x92:Presented by Capt. K.W.G. Duke RN 1946

A01096 The Tailor Hears Noises (circa 1902)
WDπ:111x92:Presented by Capt. K.W.G. Duke RN 1946

A01097 The Mice Escape (circa 1902)
WDπ:111x92:Presented by Capt. K.W.G. Duke RN 1946

A01098 The Mice Listen to the Tailor's Lament (circa 1902)
WDπ:111x92:Presented by Capt. K.W.G. Duke RN 1946

A01099 'Where is My Twist?' (circa 1902)
WDπ:111x92:Presented by Capt. K.W.G. Duke RN 1946

A01100 The Mice at Work: Threading the Needle (circa 1902)
WDπ:111x92:Presented by Capt. K.W.G. Duke RN 1946

A01101 Simpkin Goes Out (circa 1902)
WDπ:111x92:Presented by Capt. K.W.G. Duke RN 1946

A01102 Simpkin in the Snowy Street (circa 1902)
WDπ:111x92:Presented by Capt. K.W.G. Duke RN 1946

A01103 Simpkin Hears the Mice (circa 1902)
WDπ:111x92:Presented by Capt. K.W.G. Duke RN 1946

A01104 The Mice Sewing the Mayor's Coat (circa 1902)
WDπ:92x111:Presented by Capt. K.W.G. Duke RN 1946

A01105 The Mice Hear Simpkin Outside (circa 1902)
WDπ:92x111:Presented by Capt. K.W.G. Duke RN 1946

A01106 Simpkin at the Tailor's Bedside (circa 1902)
WDπ:111x92:Presented by Capt. K.W.G. Duke RN 1946

A01107 The Tailor and Simpkin Set Out for the Shop (circa 1902)
WDπ:111x92:Presented by Capt. K.W.G. Duke RN 1946

A01108 The Finished Coat (circa 1902)
WDπ:111x92:Presented by Capt. K.W.G. Duke RN 1946

A01109 'No More Twist' (circa 1902)
WDπ:111x92:Presented by Capt. K.W.G. Duke RN 1946

A01110 The Mice Stitching Button-Holes (circa 1902)
WDπ:111x92:Presented by Capt. K.W.G. Duke RN 1946

POTTER, Mary 1900-1981
Modern Collection
Tate Gallery Archive holds material concerning this artist

N05132 Golden Kipper (1939)
Oc:508x406:Purchased 1940

T00584 East Coast Window (exhibited 1959)
Oc:737x914:Presented by the Trustees of the Chantrey
Bequest 1963

T01898 Bonfire (1974)
Oc:1016x1518:signed:Purchased 1974

T05464 Still Life (1959)
Oc:1017x1829:Presented by the Trustees of the Chantrey
Bequest 1988

POTWOROWSKI, Peter 1898-1962
Modern Collection
Tate Gallery Archive holds material concerning this artist

T04125 Forest (Cornwall) (1954)
Oc:641x764:signed:Purchased 1985

POUGNY, Jean - see PUNI, Iwan

POYNTER, Ambrose 1796-1886
British Collection

N01716 A Street
DWπ:159x122:Presented by Miss H.M. Poynter 1898

N01717 Northleach Church, Gloucestershire
Dπ:165x114:Presented by Miss H.M. Poynter 1898

POYNTER, Sir Edward 1836-1919
British Collection
Tate Gallery Archive holds material concerning this artist

N01586 A Visit to Aesculapius (1880)
Oc:1511x2286:signed:Presented by the Trustees of the
Chantrey Bequest 1880

N01948 Outward Bound (1886)
Oc:495x495:signed:Bequeathed by Henry Evans 1904

N03320 Paul and Apollos (1872)
Tp:610x610:signed:Purchased 1918

Illustrations for 'Dalziel's Bible Gallery'
(A00825-A00836; complete group)

A00825 Joseph Presents his Father to Pharoah (1864)
Jπ:137x187:Presented by Gilbert Dalziel 1924

A00826 Moses Keeping Jethro's Sheep (1863)
Jπ:181x159:Presented by Gilbert Dalziel 1924

A00827 Moses and Aaron before Pharoah (1863)
Jπ:203x175:Presented by Gilbert Dalziel 1924

A00828 Pharoah Honours Joseph (1864)
Jπ:197x175:Presented by Gilbert Dalziel 1924

A00829 Moses Strikes the Rock (1865)
Jπ:225x162:Presented by Gilbert Dalziel 1924

A00830 By the Waters of Babylon (1865)
Jπ:222x181:Presented by Gilbert Dalziel 1924

A00831 Miriam (1864)
Jπ:229x168:Presented by Gilbert Dalziel 1924

A00832 Daniel's Prayer (1865)
Jπ:190x175:Presented by Gilbert Dalziel 1924

A00833 Joseph before Pharoah (1864)
Jπ:175x190:Presented by Gilbert Dalziel 1924

A00834 Joseph Distributes Corn (1864)
Jπ:162x187:Presented by Gilbert Dalziel 1924

A00835 The Israelites in Egypt: Water Carriers
Jπ:194x140:Presented by Gilbert Dalziel 1924

A00836 Moses Slaying the Egyptians
Jπ:178x159:Presented by Gilbert Dalziel 1924

PRENDERGAST, Peter born 1946
Modern Collection

T03898 Bethesda Quarry (1980-81)
Ob:1671x1928:Presented by the Contemporary Art
Society 1984

PRIEST, Margaret born 1944
Modern Collection

P03158 Untitled (from Constable Portfolio) (1976)
MIπ:184x251:signed:Presented by Bernard Jacobson
Gallery 1976

PRINGLE, John Quinton 1864-1925
British Collection

T02006 Children at the Burn (1889)
Oc:203x305:signed:Presented by James Meldrum 1975

T02258 Portrait of the Artist's Elder Brother - Christopher
Nisbet Pringle (circa 1890)
Oc:457x305:Presented by Mrs Mary Richmond
Blackwood and Miss Jeanie Nisbet Pringle, the daughters
of the sitter 1977

T02329 The Window (1924)
Oc:562x460:Presented by James Meldrum 1979

T03092 Bosham (1903)
Wπ:289x337:signed:Presented by Mrs Jean Vance Baxter
1980

PRINSEP, Valentine Cameron 1838-1904
British Collection

N01570 Ayesha (exhibited 1887)
Oc:902x698:Presented by the Trustees of the Chantrey
Bequest 1887

PROCKTOR, Patrick born 1936
Modern Collection
Tate Gallery Archive holds material concerning this artist

P01563 Favourites Courtyard (1972)
CIπ:454x603:signed:Presented by Christie's
Contemporary Art through the Institute of
Contemporary Prints 1975

P01564 London Bridge (1973)
CIπ:349x546:signed:Presented by Editions Alecto
through the Institute of Contemporary Prints 1975

South African Suite (P01565-P01570; complete group)

P01565 Leaping Cataract, Victoria Falls (1974)
CIπ:122x205:signed:Presented by Editions Alecto
through the Institute of Contemporary Prints 1975

P01566 Lunch Hour, Johannesburg (1974)
CIπ:126x203:signed:Presented by Editions Alecto
through the Institute of Contemporary Prints 1975

P01567 Municipal Gardens, Johannesburg (1974)
CIπ:182x128:signed:Presented by Editions Alecto
through the Institute of Contemporary Prints 1975

P01568 National Gallery, Johannesburg (1974)
CIπ:203x121:signed:Presented by Editions Alecto
through the Institute of Contemporary Prints 1975

P01569 Sleeping Baby, Johannesburg (1974)
CIπ:126x180:signed:Presented by Editions Alecto
through the Institute of Contemporary Prints 1975

P01570 Victoria Falls (1974)
CIπ:204x124:signed:Presented by Editions Alecto
through the Institute of Contemporary Prints 1975

P01571 Sarum (1974)
CIπ:400x578:signed:Presented by Christie's
Contemporary Art through the Institute of
Contemporary Prints 1975

P01869 Nocturne in North Wales (1976)
CIπ:778x476:signed:Presented by Christie's
Contemporary Art 1979

P06458 Northern Lass (from Europaeische Graphik VII) (1971)
CIπ:657x508:signed:Presented by Curwen Studio
through the Institute of Contemporary Prints 1975

PROCTER, Dod 1892-1972
Modern Collection
Tate Gallery Archive holds material concerning this artist

N04270 Morning (1926)
Oc:762x1524:signed:Presented by the Daily Mail 1927

N04817 Kitchen at Myrtle Cottage (circa 1930-5)
Oc:641x762:signed:Presented by the Trustees of the
Chantrey Bequest 1935

N05325 The Orchard (1934)
Oc:1016x1270:signed:Presented by the Trustees of the
Chantrey Bequest 1937

PROCTER, Ernest 1886-1935
Modern Collection
Tate Gallery Archive holds material concerning this artist

N04839 The Zodiac (1925)
Oc:1524x1676:signed:Presented by the Trustees of the
Chantrey Bequest 1936

PROUT, Margaret Fisher 1875-1963
British Collection
Tate Gallery Archive holds material concerning this artist

N06176 Home Grown (1952)
Ob:991x876:signed:Presented by the Trustees of the
Chantrey Bequest 1953

PROUT, Samuel 1783-1852
British Collection

N01978 House in the Haverwerf, Malines
Wπ:413x286:Bequeathed by C. Fraser 1905

N03430 The Chapel of St Joseph of Arimathea, Glastonbury, from the South-East
Ow:305x394:Presented by Herbert Powell through the National Art Collections Fund 1919

T01010 Fishing Boats, Hastings
DWπ:340x244:Presented by the National Art Collections Fund (Herbert Powell Bequest) 1967

after

PROUT, Samuel 1783-1852
British Collection

Picturesque Views on the Southern Coast of England (T05218-T05463; complete group; mixed group)

T05324 Hurst Castle and the Isle of Wight (1825)
Lπ:72x109:Purchased 1988

T05325 Hurst Castle and the Isle of Wight (1825)
Lπ:73x109:Purchased 1988

T05349 Lulworth Cliffs, Dorsetshire
Lπ:81x109:Purchased 1988

T05350 Lulworth Cliffs, Dorsetshire
Lπ:81x110:Purchased 1988

T05363 Weymouth Castle, Dorsetshire
Lπ:76x115:Purchased 1988

T05364 Weymouth Castle, Dorsetshire
Lπ:77x115:Purchased 1988

T05388 Dartmouth Castle (1825)
Lπ:80x119:Purchased 1988

T05389 Dartmouth Castle (1825)
Lπ:81x119:Purchased 1988

PRYDE, James 1866-1941
British Collection
Tate Gallery Archive holds material concerning this artist

N04488 The Grave (exhibited 1924)
Oc:1524x1403:Presented by Lord Duveen 1929

N05172 The Doctor (exhibited 1909)
Oc:857x1403:Presented by the Trustees of the Chantrey Bequest 1940

N05376 Sketch for 'The Doctor' (circa 1908)
Gπ:149x114:Purchased 1942

PRYSE, Gerald 1880-1957
Modern Collection

P03066 The Third Cavalry Division in Ghent, 12 October 1914 (circa 1917)
CLπ:210x321:signed:Presented by the Ministry of Information 1918

P03067 A Stretcher Party, Champagne, 28 September 1914 (circa 1917)
MLπ:276x435:signed:Presented by the Ministry of Information 1918

P03068 Untitled (Cavalry Halted under Trees) (circa 1917)
MLπ:289x483:signed:Presented by the Ministry of Information 1918

P03069 The Fall of Ostend, October 1914 (circa 1917)
CLπ:264x365:signed:Presented by the Ministry of Information 1918

P03070 The Fall of Ostend: The Digue during Embarkation of the Naval Division from Antwerp (circa 1917)
MLπ:270x419:signed:Presented by the Ministry of Information 1918

P03071 Untitled (Refugees Sheltering among Ruins) (circa 1917)
MLπ:267x406:signed:Presented by the Ministry of Information 1918

P03072 The Retreat of the 7th Division and 3rd Cavalry at Ypres (circa 1917)
MLπ:286x486:signed:Presented by the Ministry of Information 1918

P03073 Antwerp, 10 September 1914 (circa 1917)
MLπ:302x292:signed:Presented by the Ministry of Information 1918

P03074 Indians and Motorbuses near Poperinghe (circa 1917)
MLπ:327x492:signed:Presented by the Ministry of Information 1918

PRZYBYLSKI, Janusz born 1937
Modern Collection

P11089 Mrs Bosom (1983)
MLb:582x453:signed:Presented by Professor Akumal Ramachander 1985

P11090 Mr Jester (1983)
MLb:583x452:signed:Presented by Professor Akumal Ramachander 1985

PULHAM, Peter Rose 1910-1956
Modern Collection

T00560 L'Hôtel Sully, Courtyard with Figures (?1944-5)
Oc:1372x1686:Presented by Richard L. Feigen on behalf of the Richard Feigen Gallery, Chicago, through the Friends of the Tate Gallery 1962

PUNI, Iwan (Jean Pougny) 1892-1956
Modern Collection

T01528 Relief (circa 1915-16)
ROwbm:368x241x73:Purchased 1972

PYNE, James Baker 1800-1870
British Collection

N01545 The Mulgrave Alum Works at Sandsend, Yorkshire Coast (1844)
Oc:927x1429:signed:Presented by Sir Henry Tate 1894

QUAYTMAN, Harvey born 1937
Modern Collection
Tate Gallery Archive holds material concerning this artist

P01893 A'dam I (1978)
Clπ:178x114:signed:Presented by John Walker 1979
P01894 A'dam II (1978)
Clπ:478x114:signed:Presented by John Walker 1979

RACKHAM, Arthur 1867-1939
British Collection
Tate Gallery Archive holds material concerning this artist

N02479 The Dance in Cupid's Alley (1904)
DWπ:324x597:signed:Bequeathed by Major-General Sir Mathew Gossett KCB 1909

RAEBURN, Sir Henry 1756-1823
British Collection

N01146 Mrs Downey
Oc:2375x1499:signed:Bequeathed by Robert Dudgeon 1883

N01435 Lieut-Colonel Bryce McMurdo
Oc:2400x1480:Bequeathed by Gen. Sir Montagu McMurdo 1895

N01837 Mrs H.W. Lauzun (?1796)
Oc:743x610:Bequeathed by Miss Henrietta Frances Todd Lauzun 1891

N02648 Lady Dalrymple
Oc:737x610:Bequeathed by George Salting 1910

N03880 The 1st Viscount Melville (circa 1805)
Oc:749x629:Presented by C. Morland Agnew through the National Art Collections Fund 1924

N03882 A Young Lady (circa 1795-1800)
Oc:737x616:Presented by F.N. and O.S. Ashcroft in memory of their parents 1924

N04693 Mrs Charles Steuart (circa 1794)
Oc:1241x991:Bequeathed by Sir Edward Stern 1933

N04873 Pringle Fraser (circa 1804)
Oc:660x552:Bequeathed by Mrs Mary Woodgate Wharrie 1937

N05639 Mrs Cay
Oc:902x698:Bequeathed by Sir Otto Beit 1941

RAETZ, Marcus born 1941
Modern Collection

T04997 Untitled, Carona (1973)
Ohne Titel, Carona
3 Dπf:1560x766x45:signed:Purchased 1987

T04998 Lisi (1976)
DWGπ:295x208:signed:Purchased 1987

T04999 Lisi (1976)
DWGπ:294x211:Purchased 1987

T05000 Lisi (1976)
DWGπ:295x210:Purchased 1987

T05001 Lisi (1979)
Hπ:301x210:Purchased 1987

RAINER, Arnulf born 1929
Modern Collection

T03385 Untitled (Death Mask) (1978)
Ohne Titel (Totenmaske)
OPFπ:594x425:signed:Purchased 1982

T03386 Untitled (Death Mask) (1978)
Ohne Titel (Totenmaske)
DFπ:592x415:signed:Purchased 1982

T03387 Untitled (Death Mask) (1978)
Ohne Titel (Totenmaske)
OPFπ:609x505:signed:Purchased 1982

T03388 Untitled (Body Language) (circa 1973)
Ohne Titel (Body Language)
POFπ:595x501:signed:Purchased 1982

T03389 Two Flames (Body Language) (1973)
2 Flammen (Body Language)
OFπ:505x607:signed:Purchased 1982

T03390 Untitled (Face Farce) (1971)
Ohne Titel (Face Farce)
OPFπ:608x507:signed:Purchased 1982

T03391 A Nose Adjustment (Face Farce) (1971)
Eine Nasenkorrektur (Face Farce)
OPFπ:608x507:signed:Purchased 1982

T03671 Wine Crucifix (1957/78)
Weinkruzifix
Oc:1680x1030:signed:Purchased 1983

T03905 Untitled (Face Farce) (1970-1)
Ohne Titel (Face Farce)
DFπ:590x417:signed:Purchased 1984

T03906 Rain (1951)
Der Regen
Dπ:859x612:signed:Purchased 1984

Five Reds (P07709-P07713; complete group)
Fünf Rote

P07709 Backbone (1972-9)
Rückgrat
CIπ:530x786:signed:Purchased 1982

P07710 Combed (Belly) (1972-9)
Gekämmt (Bauch)
CIπ:530x786:signed:Purchased 1982

P07711 Red Field (1972-9)
Roter Acker
CIπ:530x786:signed:Purchased 1982

P07712 Head Behind (1972-9)
Kopf dahinter
CIπ:530x786:signed:Purchased 1982

P07713 Violet Furrows (1972-9)
Violette Furchen
CIπ:530x786:signed:Purchased 1982

P07714 Cross I (1977-80)
Kreuz I
MIπ:1340x613:signed:Purchased 1982

P08176 Untitled, from 'Reste' (circa 1978)
MIπ:89x79:signed:Transferred from the Library 1980

Deathmasks (P77072; incomplete group)
Totenmaske

P77072 Johann Wolfgang von Goethe (1982)
Johann Wolfgang von Goethe
MIπ:292x245:signed:Purchased 1984

P77273 Head of the Diver (Deny Your Birth) (1950)
Kopf des Tauchers (Verweigert eure Geburt)
Lπ:508x327:Purchased 1989

P77274 The Water is a Naked Box (1950)
Das Wasser eine nackte Schachtel
Lπ:487x327:Purchased 1989

P77275 Waterworld I (The Fallen Rise) (1950-1)
Wasserwelt I (Die Gestürzten stehen auf)
Lπ:484x632:Purchased 1989

RAINER, Arnulf and BRUS, Günter - see BRUS, Günter and RAINER, Arnulf

RAMSAY, Allan 1713-1784
British Collection

N04083 Portrait of a Man (1743)
Oc:756x632:signed:Bequeathed by John Lane 1925

N06066 Lady Hall of Dunglass (1752)
Oc:1270x1010:signed:Bequeathed by Sophy, Lady Hall in memory of Lt-Col. Sir John Hall, 9th Baronet of Dunglass 1952

T01049 Alexander Boswell, Lord Auchinleck (1754)
Oc:762x635:signed:Presented by the Friends of the Tate Gallery 1968

T01893 Miss Ramsay in a Red Dress (circa 1760-65)
Oc:759x632:Bequeathed by Alan Evans 1974

T03852 Janet Carmichael, Later Countess of Hyndford (1750)
Oc:755x630:signed:Purchased 1984

T05494 Thomas, 2nd Baron Mansel of Margam with his Blackwood Half-Brothers and Sister (1742)
Oc:1245x1003:signed:Purchased with assistance from the National Heritage Memorial Fund, the National Art Collections Fund (Woodroffe Bequest), the Friends of the Tate Gallery, the Mail on Sunday through the Friends of Tate Gallery, Arthur Young, Mrs Sue Hammerson and others 1988

RAMSDEN, Mel - see ART & LANGUAGE (BALDWIN, Michael and RAMSDEN, Mel)

RATCLIFFE, William 1870-1955
British Collection

T00062 The Artist's Room, Letchworth (circa 1932)
Ob:457x552:signed:Presented by S.K. Racliffe, the artist's brother 1955

T03167 Attic Room (1918)
Ow:508x508:signed:Bequeathed by Miss Eveline Annie Dear 1980

T03359 Clarence Gardens (1912)
Oc:570x760:signed:Purchased 1982

RAUSCHENBERG, Robert born 1925
Modern Collection
Tate Gallery Archive holds material concerning this artist

T01135 Almanac (1962)
OVc:2438x1524:signed:Presented by the Friends of the Tate Gallery 1969

T03376 Revenue (Spread) (1980)
RVw:2435x2640x670:signed:Purchased 1982

P07381 Glacial Decoy Series (Lithograph I) (1979)
CLπ:806x1213:signed:Purchased 1980

P07444 Water Stop (1968)
CLπ:1375x806:signed:Purchased 1981

P07445 Glacial Decoy Series (Lithograph IV) (1980)
CLπ:1680x1022:signed:Purchased 1981

P07498 Night Grip (1966)
CLπ:633x457:signed:Purchased 1981

P07715 Preview (1974)
LNVf:1750x2045:signed:Purchased 1982

P77010 Yellow Body (1971)
CNπ:1235x1588:Purchased 1984

P77107 Visitation II (1965)
MLπ:765x564:signed:Purchased 1985

P77108 Pledge (1968)
CLπ:803x584:signed:Purchased 1985

P77127 Bazaar (1984)
CILπ:1073x759:signed:Purchased 1985

P77146 The Razorback Bunch (Etching I) (1980)
MIπ:735x575:signed:Purchased 1985

RAVEN, John Samuel 1829-1877
British Collection

T03326 Study for 'Saintfoin in Bloom': View near Cobham in Kent (1857)
Ob:177x355:Presented by the Friends of the Tate Gallery 1981

RAVEN-HILL, Leonard 1867-1942
British Collection

N04329 Scene on the Deck of a Steamer
DGπ:213x238:signed:Bequeathed by J.R. Holliday 1927

RAVILIOUS, Eric 1903-1942
Modern Collection
Tate Gallery Archive holds material concerning this artist

N05164 The Vale of the White Horse (circa 1939)
WDπ:451x324:signed:Purchased 1940

N05402 The Greenhouse: Cyclamen and Tomatoes (1935)
WDπ:470x597:signed:Presented by Sir Geoffrey and the Hon. Lady Fry in memory of the artist 1943

N05722 Submarines in Dry Dock (1940)
WDπ:432x571:Presented by the War Artists' Advisory Committee 1946

N05723 Midnight Sun (1940)
WDπ:470x591:signed:Presented by the War Artists' Advisory Committee 1946

N05724 Shelling by Night (1941)
WDπ:445x546:signed:Presented by the War Artists' Advisory Committee 1946

N05725 Tiger Moth (1942)
WDπ:457x559:signed:Presented by the War Artists' Advisory Committee 1946

RAYSSE, Martial born 1936
Modern Collection

T03383 Necropolis I (1960)
Nécropole I
Sv:597x125x125:signed:Purchased 1982

READ, David Charles 1790-1851
British Collection

T02249 Castle and Lake (1831)
Iπ:102x146:Presented by Stephen Somerville 1977

T02250 Windermere, Evening (1839 or 1840)
Iπ:95x146:Presented by Stephen Somerville 1977

T02251 Ryde, Isle of Wight (?1843 or 1844)
Iπ:86x251:Presented by Stephen Somerville 1977

REBEYROLLE, Paul born 1926
Modern Collection

T00116 Trout (1956)
Truite
Ow:797x1222:signed:Purchased 1957

P01572 Frogs (1966)
Grenouilles
CLπ:540x756:signed:Presented by Marlborough Graphics through the Institute of Contemporary Prints 1975

P01573   Still Life (1966)
Nature morte
CLπ:533x765:signed:Presented by Marlborough
Graphics through the Institute of Contemporary Prints
1975

REDER, Bernard 1897-1963
Modern Collection

T02320   Two Bathers (1934)
Sp:270x260x184:Presented by Eugene Rosenberg 1978

REDGRAVE, Richard 1804-1888
British Collection

N00428   Country Cousins (exhibited 1848)
Oc:825x1073:Presented by Robert Vernon 1847

T02110   The Emigrant's Last Sight of Home (1858)
Oc:679x984:signed:Purchased with assistance from an
anonymous donor 1977

REDON, Odilon 1840-1916
Modern Collection

T05524   Profile of a Woman with a Vase of Flowers (circa
1895-1905)
Profile de femme avec vase de fleurs
Oc:655x505:Presented anonymously 1989

REDPATH, Anne 1895-1965
Modern Collection
Tate Gallery Archive holds material concerning this artist

T00444   Lenten Roses (1960)
Wb:584x787:signed:Presented by the Trustees of the
Chantrey Bequest 1961

T00770   The Poppy Field (circa 1963)
Oc:762x762:signed:Presented by the Trustees of the
Chantrey Bequest 1965

REEVE, Russell 1895-1970
Modern Collection
Tate Gallery Archive holds material concerning this artist

School Prints (P01698-P01727; complete group; mixed
group)
P01719   The Elephant Act (1946-9)
CLπ:495x762:signed:Presented by Patrick Seale Prints
1975

REGO, Paula born 1935
Modern Collection
Tate Gallery Archive holds material concerning this artist

T03839   Nanny, Small Bears and Bogeyman (1982)
Aπ:1200x1520:signed:Presented by the Patrons of New
Art through the Friends of the Tate Gallery 1984

T05534   The Dance (1988)
Aπc:2126x2740:Purchased 1989

T05538   Drawing for 'The Dance' (1988)
Dπ:297x421:Presented by the artist 1989

T05539   Drawing for 'The Dance' (1988)
Dπ:296x421:Presented by the artist 1989

T05540   Drawing for 'The Dance' (1988)
Dπ:296x422:Presented by the artist 1989

T05541   Drawing for 'The Dance' (1988)
Dπ:297x421:Presented by the artist 1989

T05542   Drawing for 'The Dance' (1988)
Dπ:297x422:Presented by the artist 1989

T05543   Drawing for 'The Dance' (1988)
Dπ:297x422:Presented by the artist 1989

T05544   Drawing for 'The Dance' (1988)
Dπ:298x419:Presented by the artist 1989

T05545   Drawing for 'The Dance' (1988)
Dπ:299x419:Presented by the artist 1989

T05546   Drawing for 'The Dance' (1988)
Dπ:296x421:Presented by the artist 1989

T05547   Drawing for 'The Dance' (1988)
Dπ:299x419:Presented by the artist 1989

T05548   Drawing for 'The Dance' (1988)
Dπ:295x421:signed:Presented by the artist 1989

P77333   Lessons (1982)
Lπ:710x1053:Purchased 1989

P77334   Doctor Dog (1982)
Lπ:710x1053:Purchased 1989

REID, John Robertson 1851-1926
British Collection

N01557   A Country Cricket Match (1878)
Oc:1067x1816:signed:Presented by Sir Henry Tate 1894

N01600   Toil and Pleasure (1879)
Oc:991x1822:signed:Presented by the Trustees of the
Chantrey Bequest 1879

REID, Sir Norman born 1915
Modern Collection
Tate Gallery Archive holds material concerning this artist

T03478   Mr Pencil at Annestown (1960-81)
Ocb:452x518:signed:Presented by Lady d'Avigdor
Goldsmid through the Friends of the Tate Gallery 1982

REINAGLE, Ramsay Richard 1775-1862
British Collection

T01073   A Boy Reading (circa 1795)
Oc:759x632:Bequeathed by Hon. Mrs A.E.
Pleydell-Bouverie through the Friends of the Tate Gallery
1968

T01861   Loughrigg Mountain and River Brathy, near Ambleside -
Sun-Set (1808)
WDπ:511x711:signed:Presented by the Friends of the
Tate Gallery 1974

T05559   A Ruined Castle (1806)
Wπ:632x522:Bequeathed by Miss Mary Holford 1989

REINGANUM, Victor born 1907
Modern Collection
Tate Gallery Archive holds material concerning this artist

T03891   Diagram (1939)
GVπ:334x532:signed:Purchased 1984

REINHARDT, Ad 1913-1967
Modern Collection

T01531   Abstract Painting (circa 1951-2)
Oc:2032x1067:Purchased 1972

T01582   Abstract Painting No. 5 (1962)
Oc:1524x1524:Presented by Mrs Rita Reinhardt through
the American Federation of Arts 1972

RENNELL, Lady Mary born 1901
Modern Collection

P06462   The Boy Jesus and the Shepherd (1974)
CLπ:575x721:signed:Presented by Curwen Studio through the Institute of Contemporary Prints 1975

P06463   Carmelites in Choir (1974)
CLπ:260x302:signed:Presented by Curwen Studio through the Institute of Contemporary Prints 1975

P06678   Carmelite Nun (1975)
CLπ:238x165:signed:Presented by Curwen Studio 1976

P06679   Christmas Card (1975)
CLπ:318x168:signed:Presented by Curwen Studio 1976

P06745   Forest (1972)
CLπ:533x714:signed:Presented by Curwen Studio 1977

P06746   Aborigines (1972)
CLπ:660x505:signed:Presented by Curwen Studio 1977

P06747   Welsh Landscape (1973)
CLπ:765x368:signed:Presented by Curwen Studio 1977

RENOIR, Auguste 1841-1919
Modern Collection
Tate Gallery Archive holds material concerning this artist

N04435   Mother and Child (circa 1916, cast 1927)
Mère et enfant
Sz:533x235x318:signed:Presented by Sir Thomas D. Barlow 1929

N05293   Head of a Girl (1898)
Oc:270x200:signed:Bequeathed by Sir Hugh Walpole 1941

N05933   The Washerwoman (circa 1917-8)
La Laveuse
Sz:1210x749x1289:signed:Purchased 1950

N05934   Venus Victorious (1914, cast ?circa 1916)
Vénus victorieuse
Sz:1848x1118x775:signed:Purchased 1950

T03573   Nude on a Couch (1915)
Femme nue sur un canapé
Oc:518x652:signed:Bequeathed by Mrs A.F. Kessler 1983

T03574   Peaches and Almonds (1901)
Pêches et amandes
Oc:311x413:signed:Bequeathed by Mrs A.F. Kessler 1983

REPIN, Ilya 1844-1930
Modern Collection

T00651   Study of an Old Man (1878)
Oc:883x679:signed:Bequeathed by Peter Provatoroff 1964

REUTER, Ingmar
Modern Collection

P05065   Shop Front (1972)
CNπ:508x695:signed:Presented by Rose and Chris Prater through the Institute of Contemporary Prints 1975

REUTERSWÄRD, Carl Frederik born 1934
Modern Collection

T03109   Portrait of Infinity (1976)
Portrait de l'infini
Sz:70x749x67:Presented by Jean Pierre Cottier 1980

REYNOLDS, Alan born 1926
Modern Collection
Tate Gallery Archive holds material concerning this artist

N06149   Keeper of the Dark Copse II (1951-2)
Ob:792x1067:signed:Presented by R.D.S. May 1953

T00105   Summer: Young September's Cornfield (1954)
Ob:1022x1549:signed:Presented by the Trustees of the Chantrey Bequest 1956

REYNOLDS, Sir Joshua 1723-1792
British Collection

N00079   Three Ladies Adorning a Term of Hymen (1773)
Oc:2337x2908:Bequeathed by the Earl of Blessington 1837

N00106   A Man's Head (circa 1771-3)
Oc:584x457:Presented by Sir George Beaumont Bt 1826

N00107   The Banished Lord (engraved 1777)
Oc:756x622:Presented by the Rev. William Long 1826

N00143   Lord Ligonier (1760)
Oc:2794x2388:Presented by King William IV 1836

N00162   The Infant Samuel (circa 1776)
Oc:914x714:Bequeathed by Lord Farnborough 1828

N00182   A Child's Portrait in Different Views: 'Angel's Heads' (1786-7)
Oc:749x629:Presented by Lady William Gordon 1841

N00305   Sir Abraham Hume (circa 1783)
Oc:698x552:Presented by Robert Vernon 1847

N00306   Self-Portrait (circa 1773)
Oc:737x610:Presented by Robert Vernon 1847

N00307   The Age of Innocence (?1788)
Oc:762x365:Presented by Robert Vernon 1847

N00754   Mr Huddesford and Mr Bampfylde (circa 1778)
Oc:1251x997:Presented by Mrs Plenge in accordance with the wishes of her mother, Mrs Martha Beaumont 1866

N00885   A Nymph and Cupid: 'The Snake in the Grass' (exhibited 1784)
Oc:1245x991:Purchased 1871

N00886   Admiral Viscount Keppel (1780)
Oc:1245x991:Purchased 1871

N00887   Doctor Samuel Johnson (?1772)
Oc:756x622:Purchased 1871

N00889   Self-Portrait when Young (1755-60)
Oc:737x616:Purchased 1871

N00890   George IV when Prince of Wales (1785)
Ow:756x616:Purchased 1871

N00892   Robinetta (circa 1786)
Oc:749x622:Purchased 1871

N01834   Self-Portrait as a Figure of Horror (circa 1784)
Dπ:368x251:Bequeathed by Henry Vaughan 1900

N01840   Sketch for 'The 4th Duke of Marlborough and his Family' (circa 1777)
Oc:552x508:Bequeathed by Henry Vaughan 1900

N01924   Mrs Hartley as a Nymph with a Young Bacchus (exhibited 1773)
Oc:889x686:Presented by Sir William Agnew Bt 1903

N03343   Lady Bampfylde (1776-7)
Oc:2381x1480:Bequeathed by Alfred de Rothschild 1918

N03545   Sir James Hodges (1765)
Oc:1270x1016:Presented by Alfred A. de Pass 1920

N04505   Self-Portrait as a Deaf Man (circa 1775)
Oc:749x622:Bequeathed by Miss Emily Drummond 1930

N04694 The Hon. Miss Monckton (1777-8)
Oc:2400x1473:Bequeathed by Sir Edward Stern 1933

N05023 Admiral Sir Robert Kingsmill (1764 or 66)
Oc:749x622:Presented anonymously 1939

N05564 Portrait of a Lady
Oc:756x622:Presented by Miss M.H. Turner 1944

N05635 The Thames from Richmond Hill (1788)
Oc:698x908:Presented by the National Art Collections
Fund 1945

N05640 Lady Charlotte Hill, Countess Talbot (exhibited 1782)
Oc:2343x1460:Bequeathed by Sir Otto Beit 1941

N05750 Sir Watkin Williams-Wynn and his Mother (circa 1768-9)
Oc:2381x1816:Purchased 1947

N05798 Francis Beckford (1755-6)
Oc:1283x1016:Purchased 1947

N05799 Suzanna Beckford (1756)
Oc:1270x1022:signed:Purchased 1947

N06243 Lady Anstruther (1761)
Oc:1264x991:Bequeathed by Viscountess D'Abernon
1954

N06244 Lord and Lady Ashburton (1782-3)
Oc:1295x1886:Bequeathed by Viscountess D'Abernon
1954

T00066 Mrs Richard Cumberland (?1763)
Oc:749x635:Purchased 1955

A00837 The Holy Family with the Infant St John (1788-9)
Oc:1981x1492:Bequeathed by Capt. L.B. Cumberland
1955

after
REYNOLDS, Sir Joshua 1723-1792
British Collection

N04506 Doctor Johnson Arguing (circa 1770)
Oc:756x629:Bequeathed by Miss Emily Drummond 1930

N05384 Puck or Robin Goodfellow
Oc:368x298:Purchased 1942

N06159 Lady Sarah Bunbury or Lady Beauchamp
Oc:759x629:Bequeathed by Mrs Elizabeth Carstairs 1952

manner of
REYNOLDS, Sir Joshua 1723-1792
British Collection

N00891 Mrs Fox (circa 1780)
Oc:749x622:Purchased 1871

N05843 A Young Black (?Francis Barber)
Oc:451x362:Bequeathed by Mrs Mary Venetia James
1948

T01892 A Young Black (?Francis Barber)
Oc:756x879:Bequeathed by Alan Evans 1974

REYNOLDS-STEPHENS, Sir William 1862-1943
British Collection

N02788 A Royal Game (1906-11)
Szmv:2407x2330x978:Presented by the Trustees of the
Chantrey Bequest 1911

RHOADES, Geoffrey 1898-1980
Modern Collection
Tate Gallery Archive holds material concerning this artist

N05214 Winter Afternoon, Chalk Farm (1935)
Oc:832x1137:signed:Purchased 1940

RICH, Alfred 1856-1921
British Collection

N03037 Shardeloes Park, Bucks. (circa 1913)
Wπ:356x451:signed:Presented by F. Howard through the
National Loan Exhibition Committee 1915

N03180 St Mary's, Oxford (exhibited 1909)
WDπ:235x276:signed:Presented by the Contemporary
Art Society 1917

RICHARDS, Albert 1919-1945
Modern Collection
Tate Gallery Archive holds material concerning this artist

N05726 The Landing: H Hour minus 6. In the Distance Glow of
the Lancasters Bombing Battery to be Attacked (1944)
Wπ:540x737:signed:Presented by the War Artists'
Advisory Committee 1946

N05727 Withdrawing from the Battery after the Battery's Guns
Had Been Destroyed. (1944)
Wπ:540x737:signed:Presented by the War Artists'
Advisory Committee 1946

N05728 Paratroops outside Breville (1944)
Wπ:562x787:signed:Presented by the War Artists'
Advisory Committee 1946

RICHARDS, Ceri 1903-1971
Modern Collection
Tate Gallery Archive holds material concerning this artist

N05354 Blossoms (1940)
Oc:508x610:signed:Purchased 1942

N05949 Cold Light, Deep Shadow (1950)
Oc:914x1168:signed:Purchased 1950

T00083 Cycle of Nature (1955)
Oc:1518x1518:signed:Purchased with assistance from the
Contemporary Art Society 1956

T00209 Interior with Figures and Piano (1946)
DWπ:394x578:signed:Presented by Miss Lilian Harmston
1958

T00210 Interior with Violinist and Pianist (1946)
DWπ:394x571:signed:Presented by Miss Lilian Harmston
1958

T00292 Trafalgar Square, London (1950)
Oc:1511x2438:signed:Presented by the Contemporary
Art Society 1959

T00307 Two Females (1937-8)
Rwm:1600x1168x89:signed:Purchased 1959

T00308 The Sculptor in his Studio (1937)
Rwmv:464x432x44:signed:Presented by Sir Colin and
Lady Anderson through the Contemporary Art Society
1959

T00439 'Do not go gentle into that good night' (1956)
Oc:1067x711:signed:Presented by Abris Silberman
through the Friends of the Tate Gallery 1961

T00474 Design for a Dropcloth: Homage to Dylan Thomas
(1953-4)
DWGVπ:527x781:signed:Presented by the
Contemporary Art Society 1962

T00595 Circular Bases (1961)
Oc:1270x1270:Purchased 1963

T00798 The Female Contains All Qualities (1937)
OVc:1070x892:signed:Purchased 1965

T00802 La Cathédrale Engloutie (Arabesque 3) (1961)
Oc:1524x1524:signed:Presented by Mrs Frances
Richards, the artist's wife 1965

T01862 Still Life with Music (1933)
OVDc:432x486:signed:Purchased 1974

T02040 Drawing (1936)
DWπ:438x584:signed:Purchased 1976

T02041 Study for a Relief Construction (1936)
DWπ:457x584:signed:Purchased 1976

T02042 Rape Scene with Orange and Yellow Woman, Orange Ground (circa 1946-7)
DWπ:178x251:Purchased 1976

T02043 Rape Scene with Yellow Woman (circa 1946-7)
DWπ:178x254:Purchased 1976

T02044 Rape Scene (Woman with Green Arms) (circa 1946-7)
DWπ:178x254:Purchased 1976

T02045 Double Rape Scene, Red and Green Ground (1947)
DWπ:178x254:signed:Purchased 1976

T02046 Rape Scene with Yellow Haired Woman, Black Ground (1947)
DWπ:178x254:Purchased 1976

T02047 Rape Scene in Cavernous Setting (1946)
DWπ:178x251:Purchased 1976

T02048 Rape Scene with Green, Yellow and Red Woman, Blue Ground (circa 1946-7)
DWπ:190x279:Purchased 1976

T02049 Crouching Woman (circa 1946-7)
DWπ:178x229:Purchased 1976

T02050 Rape Scene with Running Woman (1947)
DWπ:203x311:signed:Purchased 1976

T02051 Seated Woman (1947)
DWπ:203x279:signed:Purchased 1976

T02055 The Sculptor and his Object (1943)
DWπ:279x384:signed:Presented by the artist's widow 1976

T02056 The Sculptor and his Object (1936)
DWπ:268x384:signed:Presented by the artist's widow 1976

P01752 Study for the Sabine Theme (1947)
MJπ:283x397:signed:Presented by Mrs Frances Richards, the artist's widow 1976

P01753 Study for the Sabine Theme (1947)
CJπ:213x305:signed:Presented by Mrs Frances Richards, the artist's widow 1976

P01754 Pianist (1948)
CLπ:514x667:signed:Presented by Mrs Frances Richards, the artist's widow 1976

P01755 Arrangement for a Piano (1949)
CLπ:391x575:signed:Presented by Mrs Frances Richards, the artist's widow 1976

P01756 The Sabine Theme (1949)
CLπ:419x552:signed:Presented by Mrs Frances Richards, the artist's widow 1976

P01757 Baroque Interlude (1951)
CLπ:546x387:signed:Presented by Mrs Frances Richards, the artist's widow 1976

P01758 Sunlight in Trafalgar Square (1952)
CLπ:314x565:signed:Presented by Mrs Frances Richards, the artist's widow 1976

P05066 Clair de Lune (1967)
CNπ:530x724:signed:Presented by Rose and Chris Prater through the Institute of Contemporary Prints 1975

P05067 Jardin Sous la Pluie (1967)
CNπ:635x632:signed:Presented by Rose and Chris Prater through the Institute of Contemporary Prints 1975

P05068 Landscape (1967)
CNπ:641x632:signed:Presented by Rose and Chris Prater through the Institute of Contemporary Prints 1975

P05069 Origin of a Rose (1967)
CNπ:527x648:signed:Presented by Rose and Chris Prater through the Institute of Contemporary Prints 1975

P05070 Peu à Peu Sortant de la Brume (1969)
CNπ:505x505:signed:Presented by Rose and Chris Prater through the Institute of Contemporary Prints 1975

Beethoven Suite with Variations (P05071-P05080; complete group)

P05071 Portrait of Beethoven (1970)
CNπ:596x497:signed:Presented by Rose and Chris Prater through the Institute of Contemporary Prints 1975

P05072 Music Room (1970)
CNπ:587x507:signed:Presented by Rose and Chris Prater through the Institute of Contemporary Prints 1975

P05073 Bagatelle (1970)
CNπ:407x583:signed:Presented by Rose and Chris Prater through the Institute of Contemporary Prints 1975

P05074 Violon d'Ingres (1970)
CNπ:402x582:signed:Presented by Rose and Chris Prater through the Institute of Contemporary Prints 1975

P05075 Prometheus II (1970)
CNπ:717x546:signed:Presented by Rose and Chris Prater through the Institute of Contemporary Prints 1975

P05076 Pastorale (1970)
CNπ:762x452:signed:Presented by Rose and Chris Prater through the Institute of Contemporary Prints 1975

P05077 Major-Minor Orange-Blue (1970)
CNπ:526x492:signed:Presented by Rose and Chris Prater through the Institute of Contemporary Prints 1975

P05078 Missa Solemnis (1970)
CNπ:510x476:signed:Presented by Rose and Chris Prater through the Institute of Contemporary Prints 1975

P05079 The Inaudible Tenth (1970)
CNπ:562x482:signed:Presented by Rose and Chris Prater through the Institute of Contemporary Prints 1975

P05080 Prometheus (1970)
CNπ:671x514:signed:Presented by Rose and Chris Prater through the Institute of Contemporary Prints 1975

P05081 Origin of Species (1971)
CNπ:651x806:signed:Presented by Rose and Chris Prater through the Institute of Contemporary Prints 1975

P06464 Trafalgar Square (1958)
MLπ:451x571:Presented by Curwen Studio through the Institute of Contemporary Prints 1975

P06465 Hammerklavier (trial proof) (1959)
CLπ:505x768:Presented by Curwen Studio through the Institute of Contemporary Prints 1975

The Hammerklavier Theme (P06466-P06469; incomplete group)

P06466 Le Poisson d'Or (1959)
CLπ:772x513:signed:Presented by Curwen Studio through the Institute of Contemporary Prints 1975

P06467 Cathédrale Engloutie II (1959)
CLπ:772x510:signed:Presented by Curwen Studio through the Institute of Contemporary Prints 1975

P06468 Cathédrale Engloutie III (1959)
CLπ:453x660:signed:Presented by Curwen Studio through the Institute of Contemporary Prints 1975

P06469 . . . Ce qu'a Vu le Vent d'Ouest (1959)
CLπ:597x470:signed:Presented by Curwen Studio through the Institute of Contemporary Prints 1975

P06470 La Pianiste (1959)
CLπ:489x673:signed:Presented by Curwen Studio through the Institute of Contemporary Prints 1975

P06471 Trafalgar Square (1961-2)
CLπ:521x676:Presented by Curwen Studio through the Institute of Contemporary Prints 1975

P06472 Trafalgar Square (1962)
CLπ:527x778:Presented by Curwen Studio through the Institute of Contemporary Prints 1975

P06473 Trafalgar Square (trial proof) (1962)
CLπ:518x657:Presented by Curwen Studio through the Institute of Contemporary Prints 1975

Twelve Lithographs for Six Poems by Dylan Thomas (P06474-P06485; complete group)
P06474 The Author's Prologue (1965)
CLπ:593x815:signed:Presented by Curwen Studio through the Institute of Contemporary Prints 1975

P06475 The force that through the green fuse drives the flower (1965)
CLπ:597x821:signed:Presented by Curwen Studio through the Institute of Contemporary Prints 1975

P06476 The Crooked Rose (1965)
CLπ:535x688:signed:Presented by Curwen Studio through the Institute of Contemporary Prints 1975

P06477 Blossom (1965)
CLπ:600x822:signed:Presented by Curwen Studio through the Institute of Contemporary Prints 1975

P06478 The force that drives the water through the rocks (1965)
CLπ:435x591:signed:Presented by Curwen Studio through the Institute of Contemporary Prints 1975

P06479 And I am dumb to tell the crooked rose my youth is bent by the same wintry fever (1965)
CLπ:457x631:signed:Presented by Curwen Studio through the Institute of Contemporary Prints 1975

P06480 Green Metaphor (1965)
CLπ:820x595:signed:Presented by Curwen Studio through the Institute of Contemporary Prints 1975

P06481 And death shall have no dominion (1965)
CLπ:562x792:signed:Presented by Curwen Studio through the Institute of Contemporary Prints 1975

P06482 The Flowering Skull (1965)
CLπ:595x817:signed:Presented by Curwen Studio through the Institute of Contemporary Prints 1975

P06483 Do not go gentle into that good night (1965)
CLπ:692x595:signed:Presented by Curwen Studio through the Institute of Contemporary Prints 1975

P06484 Over Sir John's Hill (1965)
CLπ:592x811:signed:Presented by Curwen Studio through the Institute of Contemporary Prints 1975

P06485 Poem on his Birthday (1965)
CLπ:591x820:signed:Presented by Curwen Studio through the Institute of Contemporary Prints 1975

Elegaic Sonnet by Vernon Watkins (P06486-P06487; complete group)
P06486 [title not known] (1970)
CLπ:368x279:signed:Presented by Curwen Studio through the Institute of Contemporary Prints 1975

P06487 [title not known] (1970)
CLπ:368x279:signed:Presented by Curwen Studio through the Institute of Contemporary Prints 1975

Journey Towards the North by Roberto Sansesi (P06488-P06494; complete group)
P06488 Vaucluse (1971)
CLπ:322x242:signed:Presented by Curwen Studio through the Institute of Contemporary Prints 1975

P06489 Journey towards the North (1971)
CLπ:356x272:signed:Presented by Curwen Studio through the Institute of Contemporary Prints 1975

P06490 From a Conversation between Hermes and Menipeus on a Field of Snow (1971)
CLπ:360x291:signed:Presented by Curwen Studio through the Institute of Contemporary Prints 1975

P06491 Improvisation No. 9 upon the Dawn (1971)
CLπ:297x245:signed:Presented by Curwen Studio through the Institute of Contemporary Prints 1975

P06492 The Story Lost in the Snow (1971)
CLπ:410x305:signed:Presented by Curwen Studio through the Institute of Contemporary Prints 1975

P06493 Elegy for Vernon Watkins (1971)
CLπ:322x223:signed:Presented by Curwen Studio through the Institute of Contemporary Prints 1975

P06494 Information Report, XVI (1971)
CLπ:386x282:signed:Presented by Curwen Studio through the Institute of Contemporary Prints 1975

Twelve Lithographs for Six Poems by Dylan Thomas [trial proofs] (P06713-P06718)
P06713 The force that through the green fuse drives the flower (trial proof) (1965)
CLπ:602x824:signed:Presented by Curwen Studio through the Institute of Contemporary Prints 1975

P06714 The Crooked Rose (colour variant) (1965)
CLπ:543x690:signed:Presented by Curwen Studio through the Institute of Contemporary Prints 1975

P06715 The Crooked Rose (colour variant) (1965)
CLπ:536x692:signed:Presented by Curwen Studio through the Institute of Contemporary Prints 1975

P06716 Blossom (trial proof) (1965)
CLπ:597x821:signed:Presented by Curwen Studio through the Institute of Contemporary Prints 1975

P06717 Blossom (trial proof) (1965)
CLπ:395x620:signed:Presented by Curwen Studio through the Institute of Contemporary Prints 1975

P06718 And death shall have no domain (trial proof) (1965)
CLπ:598x823:signed:Presented by Curwen Studio through the Institute of Contemporary Prints 1975

RICHARDS, Frances 1903-1985
Modern Collection
Tate Gallery Archive holds material concerning this artist

T00423 Left and Right of the Long Path (1957)
Tb:457x305:signed:Purchased 1961

Les Illuminations - illustrations to prose poems by Arthur Rimbaud (P06495-P06505; complete group)
P06495 Being Beauteous (1973-5)
CLπ:189x160:signed:Presented by Curwen Studio through the Institute of Contemporary Prints 1975

P06496 Bottom (1973-5)
CLπ:250x203:signed:Presented by Curwen Studio through the Institute of Contemporary Prints 1975

P06497 Bottom (1973-5)
CLπ:237x180:signed:Presented by Curwen Studio through the Institute of Contemporary Prints 1975

P06498 Childhood (1973-5)
CLπ:225x166:signed:Presented by Curwen Studio through the Institute of Contemporary Prints 1975

P06499 Childhood II (1973-5)
CLπ:209x175:signed:Presented by Curwen Studio through the Institute of Contemporary Prints 1975

P06500 Dawn (1973-5)
CLπ:200x163:signed:Presented by Curwen Studio through the Institute of Contemporary Prints 1975

P06501 Dawn (1973-5)
CLπ:214x173:signed:Presented by Curwen Studio through the Institute of Contemporary Prints 1975

P06502 Dawn (1973-5)
CLπ:162x208:signed:Presented by Curwen Studio through the Institute of Contemporary Prints 1975

P06503 Devotion (1973-5)
CLπ:213x206:signed:Presented by Curwen Studio through the Institute of Contemporary Prints 1975

P06504 Mystic (1973-5)
CLπ:188x227:signed:Presented by Curwen Studio through the Institute of Contemporary Prints 1975

P06505 [title page] (1973-5)
CLπ:228x192:signed:Presented by Curwen Studio through the Institute of Contemporary Prints 1975

P06506 Heiratic Floral Figure (1974)
CLπ:581x518:signed:Presented by Curwen Studio through the Institute of Contemporary Prints 1975

The Acts of the Apostles (P07417-P07423; complete group)

P07417 Pentecost (1929-80)
MIπ:190x140:signed:Purchased 1981

P07418 Peter in Prison (1929-80)
MIπ:165x127:signed:Purchased 1981

P07419 Peter on the Housetop (1929-80)
MIπ:172x114:signed:Purchased 1981

P07420 Saul on his Way to Damascus (1929-80)
MIπ:170x115:signed:Purchased 1981

P07421 The Shipwreck (1929-80)
MIπ:152x140:signed:Purchased 1981

P07422 The Stoning of Stephen (1929-80)
MIπ:190x145:signed:Purchased 1981

P07423 Praying to the Animals (1929-80)
MIπ:120x102:signed:Purchased 1981

RICHARDS, John Inigo ?1720-1810
British Collection

T00925 Ivy Bridge, Devon (1768)
Oc:406x498:signed:Presented by Mrs M. Bernard 1967

attributed to
RICHARDSON, Jonathan 1665-1745
British Collection

T01894 Unknown Gentleman (circa 1730-40)
Oc:375x298:Bequeathed by Alan Evans 1974

RICHARDSON-JONES, Keith born 1925
Modern Collection
Tate Gallery Archive holds material concerning this artist

P01574 Untitled (1974)
CNπ:311x384:signed:Presented by the artist through the Institute of Contemporary Prints 1975

P01575 Untitled (1974)
CNπ:381x381:signed:Presented by the artist through the Institute of Contemporary Prints 1975

RICHIER, Germaine 1904-1959
Modern Collection
Tate Gallery Archive holds material concerning this artist

T00075 Water (1953-4)
L'Eau
Sz:1441x625x969:Purchased out of funds provided by Lord Sainsbury and Sir Robert Sainsbury 1956

RICHMOND, George 1809-1896
British Collection
Tate Gallery Archive holds material concerning this artist

N01492 Christ and the Woman of Samaria (1828)
Tw:410x498:signed:Presented by the artist's family 1897

N03692 The Robber
Lπ:70x48:Presented by Mrs John Richmond 1922

N04064 The Shepherd
Lπ:178x114:Presented by Mrs John Richmond 1925

N05858 Abel and the Shepherd (1825)
Tw:229x305:signed:Purchased 1948

T02102 Elijah and the Angel (1824 or 1825)
DWπ:140x140:Purchased 1976

T02103 Study for 'Christ and the Woman of Samaria' (1827 or 1828)
Dπ:108x140:Purchased 1976

T04164 The Creation of Light (1826)
Tw:480x417:signed:Purchased 1986

attributed to
RICHMOND, George 1809-1896
British Collection

A00050 Tracing of Title-Page of Blake's 'Book of Job'
Dπ:214x157:Presented by Mrs John Richmond 1922

A00838 Fettered Nude Figure Reclining by a Rock (circa 1825)
DWπ:235x343:Presented by Mrs John Richmond 1922

RICHMOND, Oliffe 1919-1977
Modern Collection

T02405 Tripod IV (1973)
Swm:3131x1668x1168:Purchased 1979

P06507 Big Man (1966)
MLπ:473x273:Presented by Curwen Studio through the Institute of Contemporary Prints 1975

P06508 Dance (1966)
CLπ:422x327:signed:Presented by Curwen Studio through the Institute of Contemporary Prints 1975

P06509 Discus (1966)
MLπ:483x254:Presented by Curwen Studio through the Institute of Contemporary Prints 1975

P06510 Four Figures (1966)
MLπ:584x797:signed:Presented by Curwen Studio through the Institute of Contemporary Prints 1975

P06511 Marathon (1966)
MLπ:483x251:signed:Presented by Curwen Studio through the Institute of Contemporary Prints 1975

P06512 Standing Group (1966)
MLπ:410x381:signed:Presented by Curwen Studio through the Institute of Contemporary Prints 1975

P06513 Pilot (1966)
MLπ:479x254:Presented by Curwen Studio through the Institute of Contemporary Prints 1975

RICHMOND, Sir William Blake 1842-1921
British Collection
Tate Gallery Archive holds material concerning this artist

N05179 The Libyan Desert, Sunset (1888)
Ow:292x400:signed:Bequeathed by Miss Maud Beddington 1940

RICHTER, Gerhard born 1932
Modern Collection
Tate Gallery Archive holds material concerning this artist

T02348 Abstract Painting No. 439 (1978)
Abstraktes Bild Nr. 439
Oc:2000x2000:signed:Purchased 1979

T02380 Oil Sketch No. 432/11 (1977)
Ölskizze No. 432/11
Oc:524x784:signed:Purchased 1979

T05207 St John (1988)
Oc:2005x2605:signed:Presented by the Patrons of New Art through the Friends of the Tate Gallery 1988

P77207 Elizabeth I (1966)
Lπ:700x595:signed:Purchased 1988

RICHTER, Vjenceslav born 1917
Modern Collection

P07590 Sespo 3 (1980)
MNπ:825x610:signed:Purchased 1981

RICKETTS, Charles 1866-1931
British Collection
Tate Gallery Archive holds material concerning this artist

N03005 Orpheus and Eurydice (circa 1905-7)
Sz:337x241x152:signed:Presented by Francis Howard through the National Loans Exhibition Committee 1914

N03188 Mother and Child (circa 1905-10)
Sz:229x89x121:signed:Presented by the Contemporary Art Society 1917

N03221 Don Juan (circa 1922)
Oc:1162x959:signed:Presented by Sir Otto Beit 1917

N03325 Deposition from the Cross (exhibited 1915)
Oc:711x571:signed:Presented by Viscount Bearsted through the National Art Collections Fund 1918

N04684 Costume Design (circa 1920)
WDπ:292x394:Presented by the National Art Collections Fund 1933

N04685 Costume Design for a Warrior in 'Montezuma' (circa 1925-6)
WDπ:432x340:Presented by the National Art Collections Fund 1933

N04686 Costume Design for 'Montezuma' (circa 1925-6)
WDπ:368x292:Presented by the National Art Collections Fund 1933

N04687 Costume Design for Tubal in 'The Merchant of Venice' (1918)
WDπ:387x279:Presented by the National Art Collections Fund 1933

Illustrations to 'Daphnis and Chlöe' (P01045-P01048; complete group)
P01045 [no title] (circa 1893)
MJπ:165x125:Presented by Sir C. Holmes 1924

P01046 [no title] (circa 1893)
MJπ:78x125:Presented by Sir C. Holmes 1924

P01047 [no title] (circa 1893)
MJπ:160x124:Presented by Sir C. Holmes 1924

P01048 [no title] (circa 1893)
MJπ:161x126:Presented by Sir C. Holmes 1924

P01049 Frontispiece to 'The Dial' (1886)
CJπ:200x137:signed:Presented by Sir C. Holmes 1924

P03065 Italia Redenta (1917)
CLπ:686x425:signed:Presented by the Ministry of Information 1918

RICKEY, George born 1907
Modern Collection

T01051 N Lines Horizontal-Hanging (1967)
Sm:305x2134x610:Presented by Mr and Mrs Norman Laski through the American Federation of Arts 1968

T02019 Four Rectangles Oblique, Bronze (1974)
Rzm:978x965:Presented by Mr and Mrs Leonard S. Field through the American Federation of Arts 1976

RIDLEY, Matthew White 1837-1888
British Collection

N03411 The Pool of London (1862)
Oc:648x914:signed:Presented by the executors of Robert Ross in his memory through the National Art Collections Fund 1919

attributed to
RIGAUD, Hyacinthe 1659-1743
British Collection

T00894 Apollo (1720)
Oc:899x1168:Purchased 1966

RILEY, Bridget born 1931
Modern Collection
Tate Gallery Archive holds material concerning this artist

T00616 Fall (1963)
Ab:1410x1403:signed:Purchased 1963

T01032 Late Morning (1967-8)
Ac:2261x3594:signed:Purchased 1968

T01868 Cantus Firmus (1972-3)
Ac:2413x2159:signed:Purchased 1974

T02030 Deny II (1967)
Ac:2172x2172:Purchased 1976

T03375 To a Summer's Day (1980)
Ac:1155x2810:signed:Purchased 1982

T03816 Achaian (1981)
Oc:2390x2023:signed:Purchased 1983

T04132 Hesitate (1964)
Oc:1067x1124:signed:Presented by the Friends of the Tate Gallery 1985

P01576 Düsseldorf (1971)
CNπ:965x279:signed:Presented by the Institute of Contemporary Prints 1975

Coloured Greys (P01577-P01579; complete group)
P01577 [title not known] (1972)
CNπ:571x584:signed:Presented by the Institute of Contemporary Prints 1975

P01578 [title not known] (1972)
CNπ:571x584:signed:Presented by the Institute of Contemporary Prints 1975

P01579 [title not known] (1972)
CNπ:571x584:signed:Presented by the Institute of
Contemporary Prints 1975

P05082 Untitled (1964)
MNπ:765x356:signed:Presented by Rose and Chris
Prater through the Institute of Contemporary Prints 1975

P05083 Blaze (1964)
MNπ:530x521:signed:Presented by Rose and Chris
Prater through the Institute of Contemporary Prints 1975

Fragments (P07104-P07110; complete group)
P07104 [title not known] (1965)
Mna:657x828:signed:Purchased 1970

P07105 [title not known] (1965)
Mna:694x676:signed:Purchased 1970

P07106 [title not known] (1965)
Mna:615x797:signed:Purchased 1970

P07107 [title not known] (1965)
Mna:699x672:signed:Purchased 1970

P07108 [title not known] (1965)
Mna:614x798:signed:Purchased 1970

P07109 [title not known] (1965)
Mna:625x721:signed:Purchased 1970

P07110 [title not known] (1965)
Mna:691x976:signed:Purchased 1970

Nineteen Greys (P07111-P07114; complete group)
P07111 [title not known] (1968)
CNπ:756x749:signed:Purchased 1970

P07112 [title not known] (1968)
CNπ:756x749:signed:Purchased 1970

P07113 [title not known] (1968)
CNπ:756x749:signed:Purchased 1970

P07114 [title not known] (1968)
CNπ:756x749:signed:Purchased 1970

RILEY, John 1646-1691
British Collection

T00057 James Sotheby (circa 1690)
Oc:1270x1029:Purchased 1955

RINKE, Klaus born 1939
Modern Collection

P07236 Mutations (1970)
MFπ:591x635:signed:Purchased 1973

RIOPELLE, Jean-Paul born 1923
Modern Collection

T00084 Trellis (1952)
Treillis
Wπ:318x406:signed:Presented by Eugène Mollo 1956

T00123 Perspectives (1956)
Oc:806x1000:signed:Purchased 1957

RIPLEY, Edward born 1929
Modern Collection

P06680 Landscape, Cotswold Farm (1975)
CLπ:470x635:signed:Presented by Curwen Studio 1976

RIPPINGILLE, Edward Villiers 1798-1859
British Collection

N00455 Capuchin Friar (circa 1833)
Oc:686x584:Presented by Robert Vernon 1847

RIVERA, Diego 1886-1957
Modern Collection

T00200 Mrs Helen Wills Moody (1930)
Pπ:2280x1603:signed:Presented by the Earl of
Huntingdon 1958

T00317 Still Life (1916)
Nature morte
Ow:6500x400:signed:Purchased 1959

RIVERA, José de - see DE RIVERA, José

RIVERA, Manuel born 1927
Modern Collection

T00485 Metamorphosis (Self-Portrait) (1961)
Metamorfosis (Autoretrato)
Vm:997x721:signed:Purchased 1962

T02384 Metamorphosis (Three Mirrors) (1963)
Metamorfosis (Tres espejos)
RVmfb:895x1200x121:signed:Presented by Sir George
Labouchere through the Friends of the Tate Gallery 1979

RIVERS, Leopold 1850-1905
British Collection

N01710 Stormy Weather (exhibited 1892)
Wπ:546x768:signed:Presented by the Trustees of the
Chantrey Bequest 1892

RIVERS, Larry born 1923
Modern Collection
Tate Gallery Archive holds material concerning this artist

T00522 Parts of the Face: French Vocabulary Lesson (1961)
Oc:749x749:signed:Purchased 1962

P05084 Map with Fraser (1966)
CNVπ:638x514:signed:Presented by Rose and Chris
Prater through the Institute of Contemporary Prints 1975

P05085 Underground with Two Frasers (1966)
CNVπ:902x772:signed:Presented by Rose and Chris
Prater through the Institute of Contemporary Prints 1975

P05086 Fraser (1966)
CNVπ:591x521:signed:Presented by Rose and Chris
Prater through the Institute of Contemporary Prints 1975

P05087 Underground with Fraser (1966)
CNVπ:933x400:signed:Presented by Rose and Chris
Prater through the Institute of Contemporary Prints 1975

Boston Massacre (P05088-P05100; complete group)
P05088 [cover] (1970)
CNVπ:497x759:signed:Presented by Rose and Chris
Prater through the Institute of Contemporary Prints 1975

P05089 Boston Harbor and Shooting (1970)
CNπ:492x695:signed:Presented by Rose and Chris Prater
through the Institute of Contemporary Prints 1975

P05090 Some (Visual) Afterthoughts on the Boston Massacre
(1970)
CNπ::signed:Presented by Rose and Chris Prater through
the Institute of Contemporary Prints 1975

P05091 Enlisted Man and Officer (1970)
CNπ:491x718:signed:Presented by Rose and Chris Prater through the Institute of Contemporary Prints 1975

P05092 40th Regiment (1970)
CNπ:490x711:signed:Presented by Rose and Chris Prater through the Institute of Contemporary Prints 1975

P05093 Ready-Aim (1970)
CNπ:489x708:signed:Presented by Rose and Chris Prater through the Institute of Contemporary Prints 1975

P05094 Ready-Aim and Two Hands (1970)
CNπ::signed:Presented by Rose and Chris Prater through the Institute of Contemporary Prints 1975

P05095 Black Revue (1970)
CNπ:487x695:signed:Presented by Rose and Chris Prater through the Institute of Contemporary Prints 1975

P05096 Victims (1970)
CNπ:488x706:signed:Presented by Rose and Chris Prater through the Institute of Contemporary Prints 1975

P05097 Those who Fire, Those Who Run (1970)
CNVπ::signed:Presented by Rose and Chris Prater through the Institute of Contemporary Prints 1975

P05098 Observation (1970)
CNπ:487x710:signed:Presented by Rose and Chris Prater through the Institute of Contemporary Prints 1975

P05099 Redcoats - Mist (1970)
CNπ:486x711:signed:Presented by Rose and Chris Prater through the Institute of Contemporary Prints 1975

P05100 Redcoats (Fold-Out) (1970)
CNVπ:486x1131:signed:Presented by Rose and Chris Prater through the Institute of Contemporary Prints 1975

P05101 Confederate Soldier (1970)
CNVπ:730x502:signed:Presented by Rose and Chris Prater through the Institute of Contemporary Prints 1975

P05102 Girlie (1970)
CNπ:756x457:signed:Presented by Rose and Chris Prater through the Institute of Contemporary Prints 1975

RIVERS, Larry and O'HARA, Frank born 1923, 1925-1966
Modern Collection

Stones (P77305-P77317; complete group)

P77305 [title page] (1959)
Lπ:315x400:signed:Purchased 1989

P77306 1 (1957)
Lπ:350x450:signed:Purchased 1989

P77307 2 (1958)
Lπ:350x445:signed:Purchased 1989

P77308 3 (1957)
Lπ:350x445:signed:Purchased 1989

P77309 4 (1958)
Lπ:410x450:signed:Purchased 1989

P77310 5 (1959)
Lπ:450x360:signed:Purchased 1989

P77311 6 (1958)
Lπ:360x455:signed:Purchased 1989

P77312 7 (1958)
Lπ:350x450:signed:Purchased 1989

P77313 8 (1958)
Lπ:375x485:signed:Purchased 1989

P77314 9 (1959)
Lπ:360x450:signed:Purchased 1989

P77315 10 (1958)
Lπ:355x450:signed:Purchased 1989

P77316 11 (1958)
Lπ:355x405:signed:Purchased 1989

P77317 12 (1958)
Lπ:320x470:signed:Purchased 1989

RIVIERE, Briton 1840-1920
British Collection
Tate Gallery Archive holds material concerning this artist

N01515 The Miracle of the Gaderene Swine (1883)
Oc:1079x1607:signed:Presented by Sir Henry Tate 1894

N01516 Giants at Play (1882)
Oc:838x1353:signed:Presented by Sir Henry Tate 1894

N01517 Companions in Misfortune (1883)
Oc:876x1283:signed:Presented by Sir Henry Tate 1894

N01518 A Blockade Runner (1888)
Oc:597x438:signed:Presented by Sir Henry Tate 1894

N01566 Sympathy (circa 1878)
Oc:451x375:Presented by Sir Henry Tate 1897

N01577 Beyond Man's Footsteps (exhibited 1894)
Oc:1168x1829:Presented by the Trustees of the Chantrey Bequest 1894

ROBB, Brian born 1913
Modern Collection
Tate Gallery Archive holds material concerning this artist

P06719 Southend Pier (1956)
CLπ:483x733:signed:Presented by Curwen Studio 1976

ROBERTS, David 1796-1864
British Collection

N00400 The Cathedral of Burgos (1835)
Ow:521x460:signed:Presented by Sir Henry Tate 1894

N00401 Chancel of the Collegiate Church of St Paul, at Antwerp (1848)
Oc:1419x1118:signed:Presented by Sir Henry Tate 1894

N01975 The Shrine of Edward the Confessor (1830)
WGπ:321x460:signed:Bequeathed by C. Fraser 1905

N02956 The Porch of St Maclou, Rouen (1829)
Ow:546x406:signed:Bequeathed by Sir Henry Layard 1913

T01011 Ronda (1834)
Wπ:235x330:signed:Presented by the National Art Collections Fund (Herbert Powell Bequest) 1967

ROBERTS, Donald born 1923
Modern Collection
Tate Gallery Archive holds material concerning this artist

P06514 Osseous 68 (1968)
CLπ:591x835:Presented by Curwen Studio through the Institute of Contemporary Prints 1975

P06515 Vair Project - Argent 68 (1968)
CLπ:597x838:signed:Presented by Curwen Studio through the Institute of Contemporary Prints 1975

P06516 Vair Project - Basalt 68 (1968)
CLπ:597x838:signed:Presented by Curwen Studio through the Institute of Contemporary Prints 1975

ROBERTS, William 1895-1980

Modern Collection
Tate Gallery Archive holds material concerning this artist

N04148 The Char (1924)
Oc:432x330:signed:Presented by Lord Duveen 1926

N05372 Self-Portrait Wearing a Cap (1929)
Oc:559x359:signed:Purchased 1942

N06018 Cantering to the Post (1949)
Oc:610x508:signed:Purchased 1951

T00174 The Horse Dealers (1955)
WDπ:508x343:signed:Purchased 1958

T00196 The Cockatoos (1958)
Oc:813x508:signed:Presented by the Trustees of the Chantrey Bequest 1958

T00230 The Diners (1919)
Oc:1524x832:Presented by the Friends of the Tate Gallery 1959

T00322 Athletes Exercising in a Gymnasium (1920)
DWπ:451x359:signed:Purchased 1960

T00528 The Vorticists at the Restaurant de la Tour Eiffel: Spring 1915 (1961-2)
Oc:1829x2134:signed:Presented by the Trustees of the Chantrey Bequest 1962

T00581 Leadenhall Market (1913)
Dπ:587x470:signed:Purchased 1963

T00660 The Lake (1964)
Oc:1905x1295:signed:Presented by the Trustees of the Chantrey Bequest 1964

T00813 The Cinema (1920)
Oc:914x762:signed:Purchased 1965

T00878 The Return of Ulysses (1913)
DWπ:305x457:signed:Purchased 1966

T01100 Study for 'Two Step' (1915)
Dπ:298x229:Purchased 1968

T01184 Esther Lahr (1925)
Oc:508x406:signed:Presented by Charles Lahr in memory of Esther Lahr 1970

T01561 Drawing for 'The Return of Ulysses' (1913)
Dπ:305x460:signed:Purchased 1972

T02346 Playground (The Gutter) (1934-5)
Oc:1432x1594:signed:Purchased 1979

T02347 Skipping (The Gutter) (1934-5)
Oc:1445x705:signed:Purchased 1979

T03075 Portrait of a Man Lighting a Pipe (1948-9)
Oc:514x397:signed:Presented by Ernest Cooper 1980

T03076 L'Algérienne (Portrait of Sarah Roberts) (1962)
Oc:511x410:signed:Presented by Ernest Cooper 1980

T03248 Trooping the Colour (1958-9)
Oc:1829x2743:signed:Purchased 1981

T05761 The Port of London
Oc:533x748:Bequeathed by Helena and Kenneth Levy 1990

ROBERTS-JONES, Ivor born 1916

Modern Collection

T00367 Paul Claudel (circa 1955-7)
Sz:279x203x279:Purchased 1960

ROBINSON, F. Cayley 1862-1927

British Collection

N03954 Pastoral (1923-4)
Oc:6x902x1168:signed:Presented by the Trustees of the Chantrey Bequest 1924

ROBINSON, Sir John Charles 1824-1913

British Collection

N02442 Corfe Castle
Lπ:133x286:Presented by Charles Newton-Robinson 1909

N02443 Newton Manor
Lπ:203x197:Presented by Charles Newton-Robinson 1909

ROBOZ, Zsuzsi born 1939

Modern Collection

Backstage at the Windmill Theatre (P06681-P06686; complete group)

P06681 Closing Day (1975)
MLπ:585x392:signed:Presented by Curwen Studio 1976

P06682 Backstage (1975)
MLπ:475x575:signed:Presented by Curwen Studio 1976

P06683 Connoisseurs (1975)
MLπ:508x572:signed:Presented by Curwen Studio 1976

P06684 Interval (1975)
MLπ:498x389:signed:Presented by Curwen Studio 1976

P06685 Dressing Room (1975)
MLπ:441x560:signed:Presented by Curwen Studio 1976

P06686 Dear Mum (1975)
MLπ:611x457:signed:Presented by Curwen Studio 1976

P06748 Dancing Figure (1976)
MLπ:575x775:signed:Presented by Curwen Studio 1976

P06806 Patricia Ruanne and Nicholas Johnson (1977)
MLπ:368x533:signed:Presented by Curwen Studio 1978

P06807 Rehearsal at Donmar Studios (1977)
MLπ:381x479:signed:Presented by Curwen Studio 1978

ROBSON, George Fennel 1788-1833

British Collection

T01012 Skye
Wπ:213x391:Presented by the National Art Collections Fund (Herbert Powell Bequest) 1967

RODIN, Auguste 1840-1917

Modern Collection
Tate Gallery Archive holds material concerning this artist

N04116 Mrs Charles Hunter (1906)
Ss:876x565x457:signed:Presented by Mrs Charles Hunter 1925

N04589 Balzac (1892)
Sz:311x343x229:signed:Presented by Sir Michael Sadler through the National Art Collections Fund 1931

N05034 Lord Howard de Walden (circa 1905-6)
Sz:552x521x273:Presented by Lord Howard de Walden 1939

N05955 The Fallen Caryatid Carrying her Stone (circa 1880-1, cast 1950)
La Cariatide tombée portant sa pierre
Sz:425x279x330:Purchased 1950

N06070 Woman on a Column (circa 1900-3)
Femme sur une colonne
Sz:908x203x152:signed:Bequeathed by Mrs Rhoda Symons 1952

N06228 The Kiss (1901-4)
Le Baiser
Ss:1822x1219x1530:signed:Purchased with assistance from the National Art Collections Fund and public contributions 1953

T00346 Brother and Sister (1891)
Frère et soeur
Sp:384x209x184:signed:Presented by L.M. Angus
Butterworth in memory of his father Walter Butterworth
through the National Art Collections Fund 1960

ROGERS, Claude 1907-1979
Modern Collection
Tate Gallery Archive holds material concerning this artist

N05345 Mrs Richard Chilver (1937-8)
Oc:908x603:signed:Presented by the Trustees of the
Chantrey Bequest 1940

N06216 Eclipse at Blandford (1952)
Oc:356x305:signed:Purchased 1954

N06217 The Patient Opposite (1952)
Ob:229x267:signed:Purchased 1954

N06227 The Blow Lamp (1953-4)
Oc:622x749:signed:Presented by the Trustees of the
Chantrey Bequest 1954

T02326 The Paraplegic (1970-1)
Ob:486x483:signed:Presented by the Trustees of the
Chantrey Bequest 1978

T03848 Cornfields at Somerton (1961)
Oc:1016x1266:signed:Presented by Lady Proctor in
memory of her husband Sir Dennis Proctor 1984

ROLA, Balthasar Klossowski de - see BALTHUS

ROMBAUX, Egide 1865-1942
Modern Collection

N03031 The First Morning (1913)
Le Premier Matin
Ss:1638x1016x1441:signed:Presented by the artist and
subscribers as a tribute to Belgian Art 1915

ROMITI, Sergio born 1928
Modern Collection

T00380 Composition (1960)
Composizione
Oc:695x648:signed:Presented by Professor Gino
Ghiringhelli 1960

ROMNEY, George 1734-1802
British Collection

N00312 Lady Hamilton as a Bacchante (circa 1786)
Oc:495x400:Presented by Robert Vernon 1847

N01068 A Lady in a Brown Dress: 'The Parson's Daughter' (circa
1785)
Oc:648x648:Purchased 1879

N01396 Mr and Mrs William Lindow (1772)
Oc:1391x1143:Purchased 1893

N01651 Mrs Mark Currie (1789)
Oc:1511x1206:Purchased 1897

N01667 Mrs Johnstone and her Son (?) (circa 1775-80)
Oc:895x705:Bequeathed by Maj.-Gen. John Julius
Johnstone 1898

N01668 Lady Hamilton as Cassandra (circa 1785-6)
Oc:460x460:Bequeathed by Maj.-Gen. John Julius
Johnstone 1898

N01669 Elizabeth, Countess of Craven, Later Margravine of
Anspach (1778)
Oc:673x521:Presented by Lt-Gen. the Hon. Sir Frederick
W. Stopford 1898

N01906 Jacob Morland of Capplethwaite (1763)
Oc:746x629:Bequeathed by Col. John Morland 1902

N02280 William Pitt the Younger (?circa 1783)
Oc:870x660:Bequeathed by Admiral John E. Pringle 1908

N02943 Mrs Robert Trotter of Bush (1788-9)
Oc:756x622:Bequeathed by Alexander Trotter 1913

N03400 The Beaumont Family (1777-9)
Oc:2045x2718:Purchased 1919

N03724 Lady Emilia Kerr (1779-80)
Oc:743x616:Bequeathed by John G. Griffiths 1923

N04489 Dr John Matthews (1786)
Oc:1264x1010:Presented by Miss Winifred Bertha de La
Chere in accordance with the wishes of her uncle, Henry,
1st Viscount Llandaff 1929

N04490 Mrs John Matthews (1786)
Oc:1251x1003:Presented by Miss Winifred Bertha de La
Chere in accordance with the wishes of her uncle, Henry,
1st Viscount Llandaff 1929

N05591 Lady Hamilton as Circe (circa 1782)
Oc:533x495:Bequeathed by Lady Wharton 1945

N05788 Lady Altamont (1788)
Oc:762x635:Presented by Lady Mary Browne through the
National Art Collections Fund 1947

N05850 Tom Hayley as Robin Goodfellow (1789-92)
Oc:756x635:Bequeathed by Mrs Arthur James 1948

T00064 Mrs Richard Cumberland and her Son Charles (circa
1770)
Oc:746x619:Purchased 1955

T00065 Midshipman George Cumberland (circa 1775-80)
Oc:708x549:Purchased 1955

T03547 John Howard Visiting a Lazaretto (circa 1791-2)
Dπ:343x489:Purchased 1982

manner of
ROMNEY, George 1734-1802
British Collection

T00063 Richard Cumberland the Dramatist
Oc:756x635:Purchased 1955

ROOKE, Thomas Matthews 1842-1942
British Collection

The Story of Ruth (A00839-A00841; complete group)
A00839 Ruth and Naomi (1876-7)
Oc:660x394:Presented by the Trustees of the Chantrey
Bequest 1877

A00840 Ruth and Boaz (1876-7)
Oc:660x337:Presented by the Trustees of the Chantrey
Bequest 1877

A00841 Naomi, Ruth and Obed (1876-7)
Oc:660x394:Presented by the Trustees of the Chantrey
Bequest 1877

ROOKER, Michael Angelo 1743-1801
British Collection

T01013 The Abbot's Kitchen, Glastonbury (circa 1795)
Wπ:356x451:signed:Presented by the National Art
Collections Fund (Herbert Powell Bequest) 1967

ROPER, Richard circa 1730 - circa 1775
British Collection

T02367 The Match between Aaron and Driver at Maidenhead,
Aug. 1754: Driver Winning the Third Heat (1754)
Oc:883x1216:Presented by Paul Mellon through the
British Sporting Art Trust 1979

ROSCHLAU, Michael born 1942
Modern Collection

P06517 The Pillar (1972)
CLπ:664x495:Presented by Curwen Studio through the
Institute of Contemporary Prints 1975

ROSENBERG, Isaac 1890-1918
Modern Collection

T01550 Self-Portrait (1911)
Oc:495x387:Presented by David Burton 1972

ROSENQUIST, James born 1933
Modern Collection
Tate Gallery Archive holds material concerning this artist

T01829 Silo (1963-4)
OCwa:2870x3531x562:signed:Purchased 1973

P07241 Marilyn (1974)
CNπ:905x695:signed:Purchased 1978

P07253 Pale Tent II (1976)
WCLπ:137x305:signed:Purchased 1979

P07379 Off the Continental Divide (1973-4)
CLπ:1073x2000:signed:Purchased 1980

P77056 Sunglasses - Landing Net - Triangle (1974)
MIπ:450x895:signed:Purchased 1984

ROSOMAN, Leonard born 1913
Modern Collection
Tate Gallery Archive holds material concerning this artist

N05729 Bomb Falling into Water (1942)
Oc:635x762:signed:Presented by the War Artists'
Advisory Committee 1946

Follies (P06025, P06028-P06029, P06315-P06316,
P06518, P06588-P06589; complete group; mixed group)

P06518 The Gothik Temple, Stowe (1971)
CLπ:511x689:signed:Presented by Curwen Studio
through the Institute of Contemporary Prints 1975

ROSSETTI, Dante Gabriel 1828-1882
British Collection
Tate Gallery Archive holds material concerning this artist

N01210 Ecce Ancilla Domini! (The Annunciation) (1849-50)
Oc:724x419:signed:Purchased 1886

N01279 Beata Beatrix (circa 1864-70)
Oc:864x660:signed:Presented by Georgiana, Baroness
Mount-Temple in memory of her husband, Francis, Baron
Mount-Temple 1889

N01702 Rosa Triplex (1867)
Dπ:508x737:signed:Bequeathed by John J. Lowndes 1892

N02440 Sancta Lilias (1874)
Oc:483x457:signed:Presented by Madame Deschamps in
memory of Georgiana, Baroness Mount-Temple 1909

N02685 Monna Pomona (1864)
Wπ:460x378:signed:Presented by Alfred A. de Pass 1910

N02859 Mary Magdalene (1877)
Wπ:356x206:signed:Purchased 1911

N02860 Mary Nazarene (1857)
Wπ:343x197:Purchased 1911

N03038 Miss Robertson (Mrs Fernandez) (circa 1866)
Dπ:337x254:Presented by Mrs Fernandez 1915

N03053 The Beloved ('The Bride') (1865-6)
Oc:825x762:signed:Purchased with assistance through the
National Art Collections Fund from Sir Arthur Du Cros
Bt and Sir Otto Beit 1916

N03054 Monna Vanna (1866)
Oc:889x864:signed:Purchased with assistance through the
National Art Collections Fund from Sir Arthur Du Cros
Bt and Sir Otto Beit 1916

N03055 Aurelia (Fazio's Mistress) (1863-1873)
Ow:432x368:signed:Purchased with assistance through
the National Art Collections Fund from Sir Arthur Du
Cros Bt and Sir Otto Beit 1916

N03056 Paolo and Francesca (1855)
Wπ:254x449:Purchased with assistance through the
National Art Collections Fund from Sir Arthur Du Cros
Bt and Sir Otto Beit 1916

N03057 The Blue Closet (1857)
Wπ:343x248:signed:Purchased with assistance through
the National Art Collections Fund from Sir Arthur Du
Cros Bt and Sir Otto Beit 1916

N03058 The Wedding of St George and Princess Sabra (1857)
Wπ:365x365:signed:Purchased with assistance through
the National Art Collections Fund from Sir Arthur Du
Cros Bt and Sir Otto Beit 1916

N03059 The Tune of the Seven Towers (1857)
Wπ:314x365:signed:Purchased with assistance through
the National Art Collections Fund from Sir Arthur Du
Cros Bt and Sir Otto Beit 1916

N03060 The Chapel before the Lists (1857-64)
Wπ:400x419:signed:Purchased with assistance through
the National Art Collections Fund from Sir Arthur Du
Cros Bt and Sir Otto Beit 1916

N03061 The Damsel of Sanct Grael (1857)
Wπ:349x127:Purchased with assistance through the
National Art Collections Fund from Sir Arthur Du Cros
Bt and Sir Otto Beit 1916

N03062 The Heart of the Night (Mariana in the Moated Grange)
(1862)
Wπ:270x244:signed:Purchased with assistance through
the National Art Collections Fund from Sir Arthur Du
Cros Bt and Sir Otto Beit 1916

N03063 Lucrezia Borgia (1860-1)
Wπ:419x241:signed:Presented by Charles Ricketts in
memory of Henry Michael Field 1916

N03156 The Passover in the Holy Family (1856)
Wπ:406x432:Presented by Charles Ricketts in memory of
Henry Michael Field 1916

N03283 Arthur's Tomb (1860)
Wπ:235x368:signed:Presented by the National Art
Collections Fund 1918

N03532 Dantis Amor (1860)
Ow:749x813:Presented by F. Treharne James 1920

N03827 Dr Johnson at the Mitre (1860)
Wπ:362x356:signed:Purchased 1923

N03971 Maids of Elfin-Mere, engraved by the Dalziel Brothers
(published 1855)
Jπ:127x76:Purchased 1924

N04058 The Palace of Art, engraved by the Dalziel Brothers
(published 1857)
Jπ:86x79:Presented by Harold Hartley 1925

N04089 Roman de la Rose (1864)
Wπ:343x343:signed:Presented by Andrew Bain 1925

N04283 Study for 'Giotto Painting the Portrait of Dante' (1852)
Dπ:190x168:signed:Bequeathed by J.R. Holliday 1927

N04284 Study for 'The Bride' (1865)
Dπ:419x305:signed:Bequeathed by J.R. Holliday 1927

N04285 Study for the Head of Love, for 'Dante's Dream at the
Time of the Death of Beatrice'
Dπ:610x540:signed:Bequeathed by J.R. Holliday 1927

N04603 St Catherine (1857)
Oc:343x241:signed:Bequeathed by Mrs Emily Toms in
memory of her father, Joseph Kershaw 1931

N04626 Hesterna Rosa (1853)
Dπ:190x235:Bequeathed by H.F. Stephens 1932

N04627 Taurello's First Sight of Fortune (1849)
Dπ:279x279:signed:Bequeathed by H.F. Stephens 1932

N04628 Elizabeth Siddall in a Chair
Dπ:260x184:Bequeathed by H.F. Stephens 1932

N04629 Elizabeth Siddall Plaiting her Hair
Dπ:171x127:Bequeathed by H.F. Stephens 1932

N04872 The Girlhood of Mary Virgin (1848-9)
Oc:832x654:signed:Bequeathed by Lady Jekyll 1937

N04911 Study for 'Desdemona's Death Song' (1870)
Dπ:406x476:Presented by Mrs Eason 1938

N05064 Proserpine (1874)
Oc:1251x610:Presented by W. Graham Robertson 1940

N05228 Dante's Vision of Rachel and Leah (1855)
Wπ:352x314:Bequeathed by Beresford Rimington
Heaton 1940

N05229 Dante's Dream at the Time of the Death of Beatrice
(1856)
Wπ:470x654:signed:Bequeathed by Beresford Rimington
Heaton 1940

N05230 Mary in the House of St John (1859)
Wπ:381x318:signed:Bequeathed by Beresford Rimington
Heaton 1940

N05231 St George and Princess Sabra (1862)
Wπ:524x308:signed:Bequeathed by Beresford Rimington
Heaton 1940

N05232 Bethlehem Gate (1863)
Wπ:448x381:signed:Bequeathed by Beresford Rimington
Heaton 1940

N05233 Woman in Yellow (1863)
Wπ:406x305:signed:Bequeathed by Beresford Rimington
Heaton 1940

N05234 How Sir Galahad, Sir Bors and Sir Percival Were Fed
with the Sanct Grael; but Sir Percival's Sister Died by the
Way (1864)
Wπ:292x419:signed:Bequeathed by Beresford Rimington
Heaton 1940

N05235 Joan of Arc (1864)
Wb:533x571:signed:Bequeathed by Beresford Rimington
Heaton 1940

N05745 Faust: Margaret in the Church (1848)
Dπ:178x121:signed:Presented by E. Percival Allam 1946

N05921 Carlisle Wall (The Lovers) (1853)
Wπ:241x168:signed:Bequeathed by Miss E.K. Virtue
Tebbs 1949

T00287 Study for 'Ecce Ancilla Domini! (The Annunciation)'
(circa 1849)
Dπ:194x137:Purchased 1959

T00333 Mrs Vernon Lushington (1865)
Oπ:225x190:signed:Bequeathed by Miss Susan
Lushington 1960

T03817 Sketch of Angels' Heads (?circa 1875)
Dc:515x567:Presented by W. Graham Robertson 1940

The Seed of David (A00842-A00844; complete group)

A00842 David (1858-64)
Wπ:279x133:Purchased 1924

A00843 The Adoration (1858-64)
Wπ:406x292:Purchased 1924

A00844 King David (1858-64)
Wπ:279x127:Purchased 1924

A00845 Fanny Cornforth (1859)
Dπ:140x146:signed:Bequeathed by J.R. Holliday 1927

A00846 Study of a Man Smoking a Long Pipe (circa 1849)
Dπ:190x92:signed:Bequeathed by J.R. Holliday 1927

ROSSO, Medardo 1858-1928
Modern Collection

T04846 Laughing Woman (Large Version) (circa 1891, cast
?circa 1950)
Grande rieuse
STp:545x510x192:Purchased 1986

ROSZAK, Theodore 1907-1981
Modern Collection

N06163 The Unknown Political Prisoner (Defiant and
Triumphant) (1952)
Sm:371x476x229:Purchased 1953

ROTH, Dieter born 1930
Modern Collection
Tate Gallery Archive holds material concerning this artist

T02209 Self-Portrait as a Drowning Man (1974)
Selbstbild als Ertrunkener
AWVb:800x1003:signed:Purchased 1977

T02210 Self-Portrait at a Table (1973-6)
Selbstbild am Tisch
AOVb:730x1086:signed:Purchased 1977

T03610 Harmonica Curse (1981)
76 F, 74 Vv:1080x1420x18:signed:Purchased 1983

P01833 When G Dug into the Toys he Struck Terrible Shit
(1966-9)
Als g durch das Spielzeug stach er in schreckliche Scheisse
CIπ:505x397:signed:Presented by Richard Hamilton 1978

P01834 Calm Life (1970)
MIπ:489x629:signed:Presented by Richard Hamilton
1978

P01835 Cologne (1970)
Köln
CNπ:705x1000:Presented by Richard Hamilton 1978

German Cities (P01836-P01838; incomplete group)

P01836 Berlin 1 (1970)
CNπ:552x768:Presented by Richard Hamilton 1978

P01837 Berlin 2 (1970)
CNπ:552x768:Presented by Richard Hamilton 1978

P01838 Düsseldorf (1970)
CNπ:552x768:Presented by Richard Hamilton 1978

P01839 Heidelberg (1970)
CNπ:489x730:signed:Presented by Richard Hamilton
1978

P01840 Small Theatre (1970)
Kleines Theater
CNπ:502x702:signed:Presented by Richard Hamilton
1978

P01841 3 Knights (1970)
3 Springer
CNVπ:533x746:signed:Presented by Richard Hamilton
1978

P01842 View of the Emme (1971)
An der Emme
CNπ:581x835:signed:Presented by Richard Hamilton
1978

P01843 Hemdenstein (1971)
MLπ:486x735:Presented by Richard Hamilton 1978

P01844 Quartet (1971)
MIπ:562x679:Presented by Richard Hamilton 1978

P01845 Seminar (in Collaboration with Richard Hamilton)
(1971)
CLπ:711x1045:Presented by Richard Hamilton 1978

P01846 3 Cakes on Swivel Chairs (1971)
3 Kuchen auf Drehstühlen
MNπ:508x730:signed:Presented by Richard Hamilton
1978

A Muse (P01847; incomplete group)
Eine Muse
P01847 3 (1971-2)
MLπ:543x387:Presented by Richard Hamilton 1978

P01848 Messing (1971)
MIπ:330x394:Presented by Richard Hamilton 1978

P01849 By the Sea from Behind (1972)
Am Meer von hinten
CNπ:860x610:signed:Presented by Richard Hamilton
1978

P01850 Big Tardt for Richard (1972)
MLπ:537x749:signed:Presented by Richard Hamilton
1978

P01851 Self Portrait as Pile of Dogs (1973)
Selbstbild als Hundehauf
CNπ:654x768:signed:Presented by Richard Hamilton
1978

P01852 Self Portrait as Jealous Tiger (1973)
Selbstbild als eifersüchtiger Tiger
CNπ:578x686:signed:Presented by Richard Hamilton
1978

P01853 Self Portrait as Jealous Tiger (1973)
Selbstbild als eifersüchtiger Tiger
CNπ:578x686:signed:Presented by Richard Hamilton
1978

P01854 My Eye is my Mouth (1966-9)
Mein Auge ist ein Mund
CIπ:502x397:signed:Presented by Richard Hamilton 1978

P02491 By the Sea (1971)
MIπ:381x587:signed:Presented by the artist 1979

P02492 Double Quartet (1971)
Doppelquartett
CLπ:930x768:signed:Presented by the artist 1979

A Feminine Thought (P02493-P02495; complete group)
Ein weiblicher Gedanke
P02493 [cover] (1971)
Lπ:225x382:signed:Presented by the artist 1979

P02494 A Feminine Thought I (1971)
Ein weiblicher Gedanke I
Lπ:290x243:signed:Presented by the artist 1979

P02495 A Feminine Thought II (1971)
Ein weiblicher Gedanke II
Lπ:290x243:signed:Presented by the artist 1979

P02496 Hemdenstein (1971)
MLπ:486x356:signed:Presented by the artist 1979

P02497 Scrabble (1971)
MLπ:784x1041:signed:Presented by the artist 1979

P02498 Scrapple (1971)
MLπ:806x1041:signed:Presented by the artist 1979

Self Portrait (P02499-P02503; complete group)
Selbstporträt
P02499 [cover] (1971)
Lπ:290x445:signed:Presented by the artist 1979

P02500 [no title] (1971)
Lπ:210x290:signed:Presented by the artist 1979

P02501 [no title] (1971)
Lπ:210x290:signed:Presented by the artist 1979

P02502 [no title] (1971)
Lπ:210x290:signed:Presented by the artist 1979

P02503 [no title] (1971)
Lπ:208x292:signed:Presented by the artist 1979

P02504 Self-Portrait as a Flower Pot (1971)
Selbstbildnis als Topfblume
CLπ:762x991:signed:Presented by the artist 1979

P02505 Two Persons (1971)
MIπ:114x76:signed:Presented by the artist 1979

Alpa (P02506-P02510; complete group)
P02506 [cover] (1972)
CLπ:560x382:signed:Presented by the artist 1979

P02507 [no title] (1972)
CLπ:335x520:signed:Presented by the artist 1979

P02508 [no title] (1972)
CLπ:380x535:signed:Presented by the artist 1979

P02509 [no title] (1972)
CLπ:330x560:signed:Presented by the artist 1979

P02510 [no title] (1972)
CLπ:370x532:signed:Presented by the artist 1979

P02511 Double Self Portrait of the Artist (1972)
MLπ:190x273:signed:Presented by the artist 1979

P02512 Double Somersault (1972)
CLπ:762x994:signed:Presented by the artist 1979

P02513 Double Somersault (1972)
CLπ:755x1003:signed:Presented by the artist 1979

P02514 Large Trolley (1972)
ILVπ:1015x1024:signed:Presented by the artist 1979

P02515 Malego by the Sea (1972)
CLπ:635x648:signed:Presented by the artist 1979

P02516 Palego, Goodbye (1972)
CLπ:635x902:signed:Presented by the artist 1979

ROTH, Frank born 1936
Modern Collection

T00600 Transylvania (1962)
AEOf:1727x2540:signed:Presented by William C. de Vry
through the American Federation of Arts 1963

T00748 Jodrell Bank (1964)
Vc:1734x1727:signed:Presented by Romie Shapiro 1965

ROTHENBERG, Susan born 1945
Modern Collection
Tate Gallery Archive holds material concerning this artist

T04913 Vertical Spin (1986-7)
Oc:3308x2860:signed:Presented by the Patrons of New
Art through the Friends of the Tate Gallery 1987

P07740 Head and Bones (1980)
MJπ:330x286:signed:Purchased 1982

P11203 Untitled (May No. 2) (1979)
Iπ:350x300:signed:Presented in memory of Louise
Bernbaum by her American friends through the Friends
of the Tate Gallery 1988

P77057 Four Green Lines (1984)
CLπ:558x761:signed:Purchased 1984

P77171 Stumblebum (1985-6)
Lπ:2200x1080:signed:Purchased 1986

P77256 Plug (1983)
Lπ:767x560:signed:Purchased 1988

P77257 Untitled (May No. 1) (1979)
Iπ:300x200:signed:Purchased 1988

ROTHENSTEIN, Michael born 1908
Modern Collection
Tate Gallery Archive holds material concerning this artist

N05046 The Crucifixion (1937)
Ob:1016x762:signed:Presented by Mr and Mrs Ellis
Roberts 1939

T00532 Cock's Head (1958)
VGπ:762x559:signed:Purchased 1962

T00889 In Between (1963)
Ow:381x515:signed:Presented anonymously 1966

P01580 Fathers (circa 1970)
CNJπ:562x800:signed:Presented by the artist through the
Institute of Contemporary Prints 1975

Violence (P01581-P01589; complete group)
P01581 Belfast [first version] (circa 1973-4)
CNJπ:634x1023:signed:Presented by the artist through
the Institute of Contemporary Prints 1975

P01582 Belfast [second version] (circa 1973-4)
CNJπ:635x1022:signed:Presented by the artist through
the Institute of Contemporary Prints 1975

P01583 Crash (circa 1973-4)
CNJπ:780x593:signed:Presented by the artist through the
Institute of Contemporary Prints 1975

P01584 Jags (circa 1973-4)
CNJπ:842x565:signed:Presented by the artist through the
Institute of Contemporary Prints 1975

P01585 Jags (circa 1973-4)
CNJπ:748x505:signed:Presented by the artist through the
Institute of Contemporary Prints 1975

P01586 Jags (circa 1973-4)
CNJπ:752x498:signed:Presented by the artist through the
Institute of Contemporary Prints 1975

P01587 Violence I (first version) (circa 1973-4)
CNJπ:623x947:signed:Presented by the artist through the
Institute of Contemporary Prints 1975

P01588 Violence I (second version) (circa 1973-4)
CNJπ:623x947:signed:Presented by the artist through the
Institute of Contemporary Prints 1975

P01589 Violence II (circa 1973-4)
CNJπ:662x959:signed:Presented by the artist through the
Institute of Contemporary Prints 1975

P01590 New York City II (1974)
CNJπ:679x537:signed:Presented by the artist 1962

School Prints (P01698-P01727; complete group; mixed
group)
P01720 Timber Felling in Essex (1946-9)
CLπ:495x762:signed:Presented by Patrick Seale Prints
1975

Affirmations and Defacements (P02400-P02415;
complete group)
P02400 [title not known] (1976)
CNπ:563x395:signed:Presented by the artist through the
Institute of Contemporary Prints 1977

P02401 [title not known] (1976)
CNπ:235x187:signed:Presented by the artist through the
Institute of Contemporary Prints 1977

P02402 [title not known] (1976)
CNπ:566x396:signed:Presented by the artist through the
Institute of Contemporary Prints 1977

P02403 [title not known] (1976)
CNπ:559x377:signed:Presented by the artist through the
Institute of Contemporary Prints 1977

P02404 [title not known] (1976)
CNπ:560x385:signed:Presented by the artist through the
Institute of Contemporary Prints 1977

P02405 [title not known] (1976)
CNπ:560x378:signed:Presented by the artist through the
Institute of Contemporary Prints 1977

P02406 [title not known] (1976)
CNπ:562x385:signed:Presented by the artist through the
Institute of Contemporary Prints 1977

P02407 [title not known] (1976)
CNπ:557x380:signed:Presented by the artist through the
Institute of Contemporary Prints 1977

P02408 [title not known] (1976)
CNπ:563x403:signed:Presented by the artist through the
Institute of Contemporary Prints 1977

P02409 [title not known] (1976)
CNπ:562x377:signed:Presented by the artist through the
Institute of Contemporary Prints 1977

P02410 [title not known] (1976)
CNπ:558x378:signed:Presented by the artist through the
Institute of Contemporary Prints 1977

P02411 [title not known] (1976)
CNπ:508x316:signed:Presented by the artist through the
Institute of Contemporary Prints 1977

P02412 [title not known] (1976)
CNπ:561x378:signed:Presented by the artist through the
Institute of Contemporary Prints 1977

P02413 [title not known] (1976)
CNπ:544x367:signed:Presented by the artist through the
Institute of Contemporary Prints 1977

P02414 [title not known] (1976)
CNπ:557x379:signed:Presented by the artist through the
Institute of Contemporary Prints 1977

P02415 [title not known] (1976)
CNπ:558x376:signed:Presented by the artist through the
Institute of Contemporary Prints 1977

P02948 RIP - Variant (1968)
JFLπ:685x590:signed:Presented by the artist 1987

IAA Portfolio (P03096-P03104, P03107; complete group; mixed group)

P03107 Rush (1975)
CNJπ:483x600:signed:Presented by the International Association of Art 1975

Penwith Portfolio (P01416, P06005, P06108, P06130, P06241, P06324, P06346, P06359, P06399, P06519, P06700; complete group; mixed group)

P06519 Sunrise at 36,000 ft (1973)
CLLπ:483x714:signed:Presented by Curwen Studio through the Institute of Contemporary Prints 1975

P07134 Black Bar (1962)
CJπ:806x575:signed:Purchased 1976

P07135 Black Bar (proof) (1962)
CJπ:810x584:signed:Purchased 1976

P07136 Red Gothic (1962)
CJπ:879x521:signed:Purchased 1976

P11083 The Giraffe (1985)
WCJπ:756x1126:signed:Presented by Angela Flowers 1985

P77172 Fireworks 1 (circa 1953)
Lπ:298x425:signed:Purchased 1986

P77204 Tournament (1963)
JRπ:755x615:signed:Purchased 1987

P77205 Black and Orange (1961)
JRπ:475x720:signed:Purchased 1987

P77206 Untitled (1959)
JRπ:565x865:signed:Purchased 1987

ROTHENSTEIN, Sir William 1872-1945
British Collection
Tate Gallery Archive holds material concerning this artist

N02116 Jews Mourning in a Synagogue (1906)
Oc:1275x1155:Presented by Jacob Moser J.P. through the Trustees and Committee of the Whitechapel Art Gallery in commemoration of the 1906 Jewish Exhibition 1907

N02683 Auguste Rodin (1906)
Dπ:368x311:signed:Presented by George Bernard Shaw through the National Art Collections Fund 1910

N03189 The Doll's House (1899)
Oc:889x610:Presented by C.L. Rutherston 1917

N03190 Sir Rabindranath Tagore (1912)
Dπ:419x308:signed:Presented by Lord Henry Cavendish-Bentinck through the Contemporary Art Society 1917

N03844 Two Women (circa 1895)
Oc:965x768:Presented by the Contemporary Art Society 1924

N03850 Jan Toorop (1894)
Oc:622x508:Purchased 1924

N03887 Arthur Clutton-Brock (1919)
Dπ:343x229:signed:Presented by the artist's friends 1924

N03953 The Princess Badroulbadour (1908)
Oc:1397x1194:Presented by the Trustees of the Chantrey Bequest 1924

N04009 James Havard Thomas (1920)
Dπ:279x190:signed:Purchased 1924

N04010 Charles Conder (1893)
Dπ:508x381:Presented by the artist 1924

N04595 Woman Standing in Doorway (circa 1894)
Oc:813x457:Purchased 1931

N05349 James Stephens (1941)
Oc:768x641:Presented by Miss Flora Russell through the National Art Collections Fund 1942

N05407 Miss Edith Lockyer Williams (1893)
Oc:1232x597:signed:Presented by Professor Basil Williams 1943

N05436 The White Cliffs, Vaucottes (1908)
Oc:756x1010:Purchased 1943

N05553 Barnett Freedman (1925)
Oc:756x508:Presented by the Trustees of the Chantrey Bequest 1943

N05664 Barn at Cherington, Gloucestershire (1935)
Oc:610x749:Bequeathed by the artist 1946

N05946 The Butcher's Shop under the Trees (1899)
Oc:787x584:signed:Presented by Mrs Emily Hesslein 1950

N05997 Norman Hamlet (?exhibited 1910)
Oc:495x597:Presented by the Trustees of the Duveen Paintings Fund 1949

T00569 Study for the Portrait of Barnett Freedman (circa 1925)
Dπ:194x321:signed:Presented by Lady Sykes 1963

T01248 Working Drawing for the Boy in 'The Princess Badroulbadour' (1908)
Dπ:381x283:Presented by Sir John Rothenstein through the Friends of the Tate Gallery 1970

T01869 Portrait of Sir John Rothenstein C.B.E. (1938)
Oc:762x495:Presented by Lady Dynevor through the Friends of the Tate Gallery 1974

T03682 Study for the Attendant in 'The Princess Badroulbadour' (circa 1908)
Dπ:387x281:signed:Presented by Sir John Rothenstein through the Friends of the Tate Gallery 1983

T05075 Mother and Child (1903)
Oc:969x765:signed:Purchased 1988

Work on the Land (P03075-P03081; complete group)

P03075 The Triumph of Democracy (circa 1917)
CLπ:454x708:Presented by the Ministry of Information 1918

P03076 Ploughing (1917)
MLπ:343x460:signed:Presented by the Ministry of Information 1918

P03077 Drilling (1917)
MLπ:352x463:signed:Presented by the Ministry of Information 1918

P03078 Burning Couch Grass (1917)
MLπ:360x466:signed:Presented by the Ministry of Information 1918

P03079 Potato Planting (1917)
MLπ:360x464:signed:Presented by the Ministry of Information 1918

P03080 Timber Hauling (1917)
MLπ:354x459:signed:Presented by the Ministry of Information 1918

P03081 Threshing (1917)
MLπ:344x470:signed:Presented by the Ministry of Information 1918

English Portraits (P11033-P11044; incomplete group)

P11033 Mr Frederick Pollock [Part I] (1897)
MLπ:210x179:signed:Presented by Sir John Rothenstein 1981

P11034 Mr Thomas Hardy [Part I] (1897)
MLπ:384x259:signed:Presented by Sir John Rothenstein 1981

P11035 The Right Rev Dr Creighton [Part III] (1897)
MLπ:380x251:signed:Presented by Sir John Rothenstein 1981

P11036 The Marchioness of Granby [Part III] (1897)
MLπ:380x250:signed:Presented by Sir John Rothenstein 1981

P11037 Mr Robert Bridges [Part VII] (1897)
MLπ:376x258:signed:Presented by Sir John Rothenstein 1981

P11038 Professor Alphonse Legros [Part VII] (1897)
MLπ:377x254:signed:Presented by Sir John Rothenstein 1981

P11039 Professor Charles Villiers Stanford [Part VIII] (1897)
MLπ::signed:Presented by Sir John Rothenstein 1981

P11040 Mr George Bernard Shaw [Part VIII] (1897)
MLπ:375x250:signed:Presented by Sir John Rothenstein 1981

P11041 Mrs Meynell [Part IX] (1897)
MLπ:136x152:signed:Presented by Sir John Rothenstein 1981

P11042 Mr Charles Ricketts and Mr Charles Hazelwood Shannon [Part IX] (1897)
MLπ:377x250:signed:Presented by Sir John Rothenstein 1981

P11043 Sir Frances Seymour Hayden [Part II] (1897)
MLπ:266x242:signed:Presented by Sir John Rothenstein 1981

P11044 Mr William Archer [Part II] (1897)
MLπ:260x115:signed:Presented by Sir John Rothenstein 1981

ROTHKO, Mark 1903-1970
Modern Collection
Tate Gallery Archive holds material concerning this artist

T00275 Light Red Over Black (1957)
Oc:2327x1527:Purchased 1959

T01031 Black on Maroon (1958)
Oc:2667x3658:Presented by the artist through the American Federation of Arts 1968

T01163 Black on Maroon (1959)
Oc:2667x4572:signed:Presented by the artist through the American Federation of Arts 1969

T01164 Black on Maroon (1959)
Oc:2286x2667:signed:Presented by the artist through the American Federation of Arts 1969

T01165 Red on Maroon (1959)
Oc:2667x2388:signed:Presented by the artist through the American Federation of Arts 1969

T01166 Black on Maroon (1958)
Oc:2413x2667:signed:Presented by the artist through the American Federation of Arts 1969

T01167 Red on Maroon (1959)
Oc:1829x4572:signed:Presented by the artist through the American Federation of Arts 1969

T01168 Red on Maroon (1959)
Oc:2667x4572:signed:Presented by the artist through the American Federation of Arts 1969

T01169 Red on Maroon (1959)
Oc:1829x4572:Presented by the artist through the American Federation of Arts 1969

T01170 Black on Maroon (1958)
Oc:2286x2070:signed:Presented by the artist through the American Federation of Arts 1969

T04147 Untitled (circa 1946-7)
Oc:1000x700:signed:Presented by the Mark Rothko Foundation 1986

T04148 Untitled (circa 1951-2)
Oc:1890x1008:Presented by the Mark Rothko Foundation 1986

T04149 Untitled (1968)
Aπ:1730x1235:signed:Presented by the Mark Rothko Foundation 1986

ROUAULT, Georges 1871-1958
Modern Collection
Tate Gallery Archive holds material concerning this artist

N04141 The Meal (1900)
Le Repas
Pπ:276x283:signed:Presented by A.E. Anderson through the National Art Collections Fund 1926

N04799 The Bride (Aunt Sallys) (1907)
La Mariée (Têtes à massacre)
Oπ:749x1054:signed:Presented by the Contemporary Art Society 1935

N05146 The Three Judges (circa 1936)
Les Trois Juges
Ob:784x648:signed:Bequeathed by Montague Shearman through the Contemporary Art Society 1940

N05458 Landscape (1906)
Paysage
WPπ:175x216:signed:Presented by the Contemporary Art Society 1944

N05906 The Italian Woman (1938)
L'Italienne
Oc:651x498:signed:Purchased 1949

ROUSSEAU, Henri ('Le Douanier') 1844-1910
Modern Collection
Tate Gallery Archive holds material concerning this artist

N04727 Bouquet of Flowers (circa 1909-10)
Bouquet de fleurs
Oc:610x495:signed:Bequeathed by C. Frank Stoop 1933

ROUSSEL, Théodore 1847-1926
British Collection

N04361 The Reading Girl (1886-7)
Oc:1524x1613:signed:Presented by Mrs Walter Herriot and Miss R. Herriot in memory of the artist 1927

ROWELL, Kenneth born 1922
Modern Collection

P06520 Untitled I (1964)
CLπ:556x762:Presented by Curwen Studio through the Institute of Contemporary Prints 1975

P06521 Untitled II (1964)
CLπ:556x762:Presented by Curwen Studio through the Institute of Contemporary Prints 1975

P06522 Untitled III (1964)
CLπ:556x762:Presented by Curwen Studio through the Institute of Contemporary Prints 1975

P06523 Untitled IV (1964)
CLπ:556x762:Presented by Curwen Studio through the Institute of Contemporary Prints 1975

P06524 Ceremony (1965)
CLπ:746x495:Presented by Curwen Studio through the Institute of Contemporary Prints 1975

P06525 Ritual Objects (1965)
CLπ:746x492:signed:Presented by Curwen Studio through the Institute of Contemporary Prints 1975

P06749 Two Figures in a Landscape (1963-4)
CLπ:498x721:signed:Presented by Curwen Studio 1976

ROWLANDSON, Thomas 1757-1827
British Collection
Tate Gallery Archive holds material concerning this artist

N04356 Landscape, with Lake (1799)
DWπ:146x235:signed:Bequeathed by J.R. Holliday 1927

N04357 Four Generations
DWπ:203x273:Bequeathed by J.R. Holliday 1927

N04358 Departure from the Wheatsheaf
DWπ:146x235:Bequeathed by J.R. Holliday 1927

N04359 Castle and Bridge, Haverfordwest, Pembrokeshire
DWπ:140x222:Bequeathed by J.R. Holliday 1927

N04585 Camelford Fair
DWπ:210x327:Bequeathed by J.R. Holliday 1931

N05952 The Halt by a Hill
DWπ:184x264:Presented by G.D. Hornblower 1950

T01014 Landscape, Isle of Wight
WDπ:200x276:Presented by the National Art Collections Fund (Herbert Powell Bequest) 1967

ROWLANDSON, Thomas and OGBOURNE, John - see prints after HOGARTH, William

ROWNTREE, Kenneth born 1915
Modern Collection
Tate Gallery Archive holds material concerning this artist

N06210 The Guitar Players (1933)
Ow:241x210:Bequeathed by Albert Rutherston 1953

T03934 Cornish Landscape (1942)
Ob:375x447:signed:Presented by the Friends of the Tate Gallery 1984

T03935 Souvenir of Venice (1961)
Ob:635x762:Presented by the Friends of the Tate Gallery 1984

School Prints (P01698-P01727; complete group; mixed group)

P01721 Tractor in a Landscape (1946-9)
CLπ:498x762:signed:Presented by Patrick Seale Prints 1975

P02835 Welsh Print (1970)
CNπ:300x377:signed:Presented by the artist 1985

P02836 West Front, Durham (1976)
CNπ:483x488:signed:Presented by the artist 1985

P02837 Verlaine (1984)
CNπ:541x404:signed:Presented by the artist 1985

ROY, Pierre 1880-1950
Modern Collection
Tate Gallery Archive holds material concerning this artist

T01182 A Naturalist's Study (1928)
Le Cabinet du naturaliste
Oc:921x654:signed:Bequeathed by Boris Anrep 1969

T03537 Boris Anrep in his Studio, 65 Boulevard Arago (1949)
Oc:653x501:signed:Bequeathed by Mrs M.J.A. Russell 1982

ROZEN, Felix born 1938
Modern Collection

Uncertain Opus (P11052-P11061; complete group)
Opus incertain

P11052 [no title] (1981)
CNπ:327x584:signed:Presented by Mrs Leslie Oliver through the Friends of the Tate Gallery 1983

P11053 [no title] (1981)
CNπ:340x595:signed:Presented by Mrs Leslie Oliver through the Friends of the Tate Gallery 1983

P11054 [no title] (1981)
CNπ:340x595:signed:Presented by Mrs Leslie Oliver through the Friends of the Tate Gallery 1983

P11055 [no title] (1981)
CNπ:340x595:signed:Presented by Mrs Leslie Oliver through the Friends of the Tate Gallery 1983

P11056 [no title] (1981)
CNπ:343x591:signed:Presented by Mrs Leslie Oliver through the Friends of the Tate Gallery 1983

P11057 [no title] (1981)
CNπ:343x591:signed:Presented by Mrs Leslie Oliver through the Friends of the Tate Gallery 1983

P11058 [no title] (1981)
CNπ:343x591:signed:Presented by Mrs Leslie Oliver through the Friends of the Tate Gallery 1983

P11059 [no title] (1981)
CNπ:343x591:signed:Presented by Mrs Leslie Oliver through the Friends of the Tate Gallery 1983

P11060 [no title] (1981)
CNπ:343x591:signed:Presented by Mrs Leslie Oliver through the Friends of the Tate Gallery 1983

P11061 [no title] (1981)
CNπ:343x591:signed:Presented by Mrs Leslie Oliver through the Friends of the Tate Gallery 1983

RÜCKRIEM, Ulrich born 1938
Modern Collection

T05725 Untitled (1989)
Ss:2240x5535x315:Presented by the Patrons of New Art through the Friends of the Tate Gallery 1990

T05741 Double Piece (1982)
Doppelstück
2 Ss:1460x550x550, 215x2420x1100:Presented by the artist 1990

RUGG, Matt born 1935
Modern Collection

T00629 Painted Unit Relief (1963)
ORw:495x495x165:signed:Purchased 1963

RUMNEY, Ralph born 1934
Modern Collection

T05556 The Change (1957)
Ob:1524x1985:Purchased 1989

RUNCIMAN, Alexander 1736-1785
British Collection

T03604 Fingal Encounters Carbon Carglass (first printed circa 1773)
Iπ:149x245:signed:Purchased 1983

T03605 Fingal Encounters Carbon Carglass (upright version) (first printed circa 1773)
Iπ:145x106:signed:Purchased 1983

T03606 Agrippina with the Ashes of Germanicus (first printed circa 1773)
Iπ:144x106:signed:Purchased 1983

RUSCHA, Edward born 1937
Modern Collection
Tate Gallery Archive holds material concerning this artist

P07716 Hollywood (1969)
MLπ:105x430:signed:Purchased 1982

P07940 Roughly 92% Angel but about 8% Devil (1982)
CIπ:368x388:signed:Purchased 1983

P11275 Time Is Up (1989)
Lπ:915x687:signed:Presented by Robert Tibbles 1990

RUSHBURY, Sir Henry 1889-1968
Modern Collection
Tate Gallery Archive holds material concerning this artist

N01360 The Palazzo Ugoccione, Florence (1922)
DWπ:324x502:signed:Presented by J.R. Holliday 1923

N03567 The Forest of Brotonne (1920)
WDπ:254x349:signed:Purchased 1920

N04333 Repairing the Sail (circa 1923)
DWπ:333x352:signed:Bequeathed by J.R. Holliday 1927

N04334 A Ship in Dock (circa 1925-6)
DWπ:295x438:signed:Bequeathed by J.R. Holliday 1927

N04335 La Rochelle (circa 1923)
DWπ:295x448:signed:Bequeathed by J.R. Holliday 1927

N04336 A Brewery Yard (1920)
DWπ:225x254:signed:Bequeathed by J.R. Holliday 1927

N04601 St Paul's (1930)
DWπ:330x492:signed:Presented by the Trustees of the Chantrey Bequest 1931

RUSKIN, John 1819-1900
British Collection
Tate Gallery Archive holds material concerning this artist

N02726 An Olive Spray and Two Leaf Outlines (before 1877)
Dπ:375x279:Presented by Sir Claude Phillips in memory of his sister Eugenie Phillips 1910

N02972 The North-West Angle of the Facade of St Mark's, Venice
WDπ:940x610:Presented by the National Art Collections Fund 1914

N03507 View of Bologna
DWπ:343x489:Purchased 1920

RUSSELL, John 1744-1807
British Collection

N05248 Girl and Cat (1791)
Pπ:587x445:signed:Bequeathed by Lionel Wormser Harris through the National Art Collections Fund 1940

N05249 The Fortune-Teller (exhibited 1790)
Pπ:914x705:signed:Bequeathed by Lionel Wormser Harris through the National Art Collections Fund 1940

RUSSELL, Sir Walter 1867-1949
British Collection
Tate Gallery Archive holds material concerning this artist

N02994 Donkeys and Kites (exhibited 1909)
Oc:762x1016:signed:Presented by Francis Howard through the National Loans Exhibition Committee 1914

N03569 Mr Minney (1920)
Oc:1276x1022:signed:Presented by Charles H. Moore through the National Art Collections Fund 1920

N04099 The Blue Dress (1911)
Oc:1016x762:signed:Presented by the Trustees of the Chantrey Bequest 1925

N04188 The Amber Beads (exhibited 1926)
Oc:749x622:signed:Presented by R. Just Boyd through the National Art Collections Fund 1926

N04542 Cordelia (exhibited 1930)
Oc:914x762:signed:Presented by the Trustees of the Chantrey Bequest 1930

N04746 The Farmyard (exhibited 1934)
Oc:502x756:signed:Presented by the Trustees of the Chantrey Bequest 1934

N04961 High Tide, Blakeney (exhibited 1938)
Oc:470x749:signed:Presented by the Trustees of the Chantrey Bequest 1938

N05105 Carting Sand (exhibited 1910)
Oc:864x1118:signed:Presented by the Trustees of the Chantrey Bequest 1940

RUTHERSTON, Albert 1881-1953
Modern Collection
Tate Gallery Archive holds material concerning this artist

N04569 Paddling (1910)
Tc:2273x2013:signed:Purchased 1931

N04996 Laundry Girls (1906)
Oc:914x1168:signed:Presented by Humbert Wolfe 1939

N05258 The Pump, Nash End (1931)
Oc:406x508:signed:Purchased 1941

RUTLAND, Violet, Duchess of 1856-1937
British Collection

N04914 Recumbent Figure of Lord Haddon (1894-1934)
Sp:1092x1822x825:signed:Presented by the Manners Family 1938

RYAN, Adrian born 1920
Modern Collection
Tate Gallery Archive holds material concerning this artist

T00195 Flowers on a Chair (1958)
Oc:610x432:signed:Presented by the Trustees of the Chantrey Bequest 1958

RYLAND, Adolfine born 1903
Modern Collection

N05112 Isaac Blesses Jacob (1933)
Rs:914x533x102:signed:Presented by the Trustees of the Chantrey Bequest 1940

RYLEY, Charles Reuben circa 1752-1798
British Collection

T03854 Oscar Bringing Back Annir's Daughter (1785)
Oc:314x412:signed:Purchased 1984

RYMAN, Robert born 1930
Modern Collection
Tate Gallery Archive holds material concerning this artist

T03550 Ledger (1983)
Eam:763x711x36:signed:Purchased 1983

Seven Aquatints (P07717-P07723; complete group)
P07717 [title not known] (1972)
Clπ:540x550:signed:Purchased 1982

P07718 [title not known] (1972)
Clπ:300x350:signed:Purchased 1982

P07719 [title not known] (1972)
Clπ:610x610:signed:Purchased 1982

P07720 [title not known] (1972)
Clπ:350x343:signed:Purchased 1982

P07721 [title not known] (1972)
Clπ:553x545:signed:Purchased 1982

P07722 [title not known] (1972)
Clπ:530x540:signed:Purchased 1982

P07723 [title not known] (1972)
Clπ:297x300:signed:Purchased 1982

SADLER, Walter Dendy 1854-1923
British Collection

N01555 Thursday (1880)
Oc:864x1410:signed:Presented by Sir Henry Tate 1894

N01556 A Good Story (1881)
Oc:622x819:signed:Presented by Sir Henry Tate 1894

SAID, Anne born 1914
Modern Collection
Tate Gallery Archive holds material concerning this artist

T00533 Jo's Wild Wood (1961)
Dπ:762x540:signed:Purchased 1962

SAINT PHALLE, Niki de born 1930
Modern Collection

T03824 Shooting Picture (1961)
Tirage
RVp:1430x780x81:Purchased 1984

SAINT-GAUDENS, Augustus 1848-1907
Modern Collection

N03431 Robert Louis Stevenson (circa 1887-93)
Rz:911x902x44:signed:Presented by Miss Mary Hoadley
Dodge 1919

SALLE, David born 1952
Modern Collection
Tate Gallery Archive holds material concerning this artist

T03444 Walking the Dog (1982)
2 AODf:2188x2850:Purchased 1982

Grandiose Synonym for Church (P11221; incomplete
group)
P11221 Untitled (1985)
Iπ:1213x958:signed:Presented by Mr Edward Lee 1989

The Raphael (P77192; incomplete group)
P77192 Untitled (1986)
Iπ:455x604:signed:Purchased 1987

SALT, John born 1937
Modern Collection
Tate Gallery Archive holds material concerning this artist

P11008 Pink Trailer (1977)
CLπ:432x641:signed:Presented by E.J. Power through
the Friends of the Tate Gallery 1980

SANDBY, Paul 1730-1809
British Collection
Tate Gallery Archive holds material concerning this artist

N01853 Edinburgh Castle
Gπ:368x533:Presented by William Sandby 1901

N01854 Carmarthen Castle
Wπ:292x483:Presented by William Sandby 1901

N01855 Part of the Banqueting Hall of the Royal Palace at Eltham
Wπ:254x368:Presented by William Sandby 1901

N01856 The Cemetery Gate of St Augustine's Monastery
Canterbury (1782)
DWπ:324x508:signed:Presented by William Sandby 1901

T01015 Windsor Park
Wπ:216x318:Presented by the National Art Collections
Fund (Herbert Powell Bequest) 1967

SANDBY, Thomas 1721-1798
British Collection

N01852 Design for Freemasons' Hall, London
DWπ:375x368:signed:Presented by William Sandby 1901

SANDER, Ludwig 1906-1975
Modern Collection

P01798 Three Blues (1966)
CLπ:410x464:signed:Presented by the Museum of
Modern Art, New York 1976

SANDLE, Michael born 1936
Modern Collection
Tate Gallery Archive holds material concerning this artist

T04941 The Drummer (1985)
Sz:2640x1340x990:signed:Presented by the Trustees of
the Chantrey Bequest 1987

For John Constable (P03149-P03157, P03159-P03161,
P03180-P03185; complete group; mixed group)
P03159 Untitled (1976)
CLπ:584x791:signed:Presented by Bernard Jacobson
Gallery 1976

SANDS, Ethel 1873-1962
British Collection

N03845 The Chintz Couch (circa 1910)
Cb:464x384:signed:Presented by the Contemporary Art
Society 1924

SANDYS, Edwina born 1938
Modern Collection

P06526 Bowl of Flowers (circa 1972)
CLπ:508x460:signed:Presented by Curwen Studio
through the Institute of Contemporary Prints 1975

P06527 Circus (1972)
CLπ:721x546:Presented by Curwen Studio through the
Institute of Contemporary Prints 1975

P06528 Cardplayers (1974)
CLπ:508x641:signed:Presented by Curwen Studio
through the Institute of Contemporary Prints 1975

P06529 Couples (1974)
CLπ:683x521:signed:Presented by Curwen Studio
through the Institute of Contemporary Prints 1975

P06530 Daffodils (1974)
CLπ:698x460:signed:Presented by Curwen Studio
through the Institute of Contemporary Prints 1975

P06531 Green Nude (1974)
CLπ:419x587:signed:Presented by Curwen Studio
through the Institute of Contemporary Prints 1975

P06532 Moonscape (1974)
CLπ:324x594:signed:Presented by Curwen Studio
through the Institute of Contemporary Prints 1975

P06533 Peace (1974)
CLπ:416x587:signed:Presented by Curwen Studio
through the Institute of Contemporary Prints 1975

P06534 Double Vision (1974)
CLπ:562x787:signed:Presented by Curwen Studio
through the Institute of Contemporary Prints 1975

P06535 Sea Shells (1974)
CLπ:416x591:signed:Presented by Curwen Studio
through the Institute of Contemporary Prints 1975

P06808 Frolic on the Green (1976)
CLπ:521x775:signed:Presented by Curwen Studio 1978

P06809 Backgammon (1976)
CLπ:514x724:signed:Presented by Curwen Studio 1978

P06810 Another Bouquet (1977)
CLπ:670x479:signed:Presented by Curwen Studio 1978

Make Up (P06811-P06814; complete group)

P06811 [no title] (1977)
CLπ:295x435:signed:Presented by Curwen Studio 1978

P06812 [no title] (1977)
CLπ:295x440:signed:Presented by Curwen Studio 1978

P06813 [no title] (1977)
CLπ:295x435:signed:Presented by Curwen Studio 1978

P06814 [no title] (1977)
CLπ:295x435:signed:Presented by Curwen Studio 1978

SANDYS, Frederick 1829-1904
British Collection

N04025 Jacob Hears the Voice of the Lord, engraved by the Dalziel Brothers (published 1881)
Jπ:187x146:Presented by Gilbert Dalziel 1924

N04125 Life's Journey, engraved by the Dalziel Brothers (published 1862)
Jπ:127x102:Presented by Gilbert Dalziel 1925

N04126 The Little Mourner, engraved by the Dalziel Brothers (published 1862)
Jπ:140x108:Presented by Gilbert Dalziel 1925

T00685 Study of Trees and Undergrowth (?circa 1855)
Jπ:311x521:Purchased 1964

T03904 Oriana (1861)
Ow:251x190:signed:Purchased with assistance from the Abbott Fund 1984

T05717 Great Yarmouth and Breydon Water (1871)
Dπ:372x851:Purchased 1989

A00847 Melancholia
JDπ:105x140:Presented by J.R. Holliday 1927

A00848 Study for Illustration
Dπ:146x120:Presented by J.R. Holliday 1927

A00849 Study for Illustration
Jπ:127x114:Presented by J.R. Holliday 1927

SANT, James 1820-1916
British Collection

N03671 Miss Martineau's Garden (1873)
Oc:311x470:signed:Presented by the Trustees of the Chantrey Bequest 1922

N04856 The Duet
Oc:768x641:signed:Bequeathed by Mrs J. Harrold 1936

T02059 Rosalind
Oc:791x664:Presented by Mrs S. Swinton 1976

SARGANT, Francis W. 1870-1960
British Collection

N05409 Carlino (circa 1902)
Ss:381x368x206:Presented by W.L. Sargant, the artist's brother, through the National Art Collections Fund 1943

SARGENT, John Singer 1856-1925
British Collection
Tate Gallery Archive holds material concerning this artist

N01615 Carnation, Lily, Lily, Rose (1885-6)
Oc:1740x1537:signed:Presented by the Trustees of the Chantrey Bequest 1922

N02053 Ellen Terry as Lady Macbeth (1885-6)
Oc:2210x1143:signed:Presented by Sir Joseph Duveen 1906

N03012 Professor Ingram Bywater (exhibited 1901)
Oc:1473x972:signed:Bequeathed by Mrs Ingram Bywater 1914

N03044 Lord Ribblesdale (1902)
Oc:2584x1435:signed:Presented by Lord Ribblesdale as a memorial to Lady Ribblesdale and his sons - Capt. the Hon. Thomas Lister, DSO, 10th Hussars, killed at Jidballi, Somaliland, and Lt the Hon. Charles Lister (HM Diplomatic Service), Hood Battalion, who fell in Gallipoli 1916

N03405 Fountain, with Girl Sketching (circa 1913)
Wπ:270x375:Presented by Lord Duveen 1919

N03406 Riva Degli Schiavoni, Venice (circa 1904)
Wπ:254x356:Presented by Lord Duveen 1919

N03407 Venetian Fishing Boats (circa 1904)
Wπ:489x349:Presented by Lord Duveen 1919

N03408 The Piazzetta, Venice (circa 1904)
Wπ:343x537:Presented by Lord Duveen 1919

N03412 Crucifix (circa 1899)
Rz:1118x787x89:Presented by A.G. Ross in accordance with the wishes of the late Robert Ross through the National Art Collections Fund 1919

N03559 San Vigilio, Lago di Garda (circa 1913)
Wπ:362x533:Presented by Lord Duveen 1919

N03560 Oxen, Carrara (1911-13)
Wπ:400x527:Presented by Lord Duveen 1919

N03658 Miss Eliza Wedgwood and Miss Sargent Sketching (1908)
Wπ:502x356:signed:Bequeathed by William Newall 1922

N03705 Asher Wertheimer (1898)
Oc:1473x978:signed:Presented by the widow and family of Asher Wertheimer in accordance with his wishes 1922

N03706 Mrs Wertheimer (1904)
Oc:1632x1079:signed:Presented by the widow and family of Asher Wertheimer in accordance with his wishes 1922

N03707 Hylda, Daughter of Asher and Mrs Wertheimer (1901)
Oc:2146x1435:signed:Presented by the widow and family of Asher Wertheimer in accordance with his wishes 1922

N03708 Ena and Betty, Daughters of Asher and Mrs Wertheimer (1901)
Oc:1854x1308:signed:Presented by the widow and family of Asher Wertheimer in accordance with his wishes 1922

N03709 Alfred, Son of Asher Wertheimer (?1901)
Oc:1630x1150:signed:Presented by the widow and family of Asher Wertheimer in accordance with his wishes 1922

N03710 Edward, Son of Asher Wertheimer (1902)
Oc:1632x1149:signed:Presented by the widow and family of Asher Wertheimer in accordance with his wishes 1922

N03711 Essie, Ruby and Ferdinand, Children of Asher Wertheimer (1902)
Oc:1613x1937:signed:Presented by the widow and family of Asher Wertheimer in accordance with his wishes 1922

N03712 Hylda, Almina and Conway, Children of Asher Wertheimer (1905)
Oc:1880x1333:signed:Presented by the widow and family of Asher Wertheimer in accordance with his wishes 1922

N03713 Almina, Daughter of Asher Wertheimer (1908)
Oc:1340x1010:signed:Presented by the widow and family
of Asher Wertheimer in accordance with his wishes 1922

N04102 Study of Mme Gautreau (circa 1884)
Oc:2064x1079:Presented by Lord Duveen through the
National Art Collections Fund 1925

N04103 Claude Monet Painting at the Edge of a Wood (circa
1887)
Oc:540x648:Presented by Miss Emily Sargent and Mrs
Ormond through the National Art Collections Fund 1925

N04180 The Misses Hunter (1902)
Oc:2292x2299:signed:Presented by Mrs Charles Hunter
through the National Art Collections Fund 'in memory of
a great artist and a great friend' 1926

N04465 Miss Priestley (circa 1889)
Oc:914x635:Presented by Miss Emily Sargent in memory
of her brother through the National Art Collections Fund
1929

N04466 Lady Fishing - Mrs Ormond (1889)
Oc:1848x978:Presented by Miss Emily Sargent in
memory of her brother through the National Art
Collections Fund 1929

N04469 Mrs Charles Hunter (1898)
Oc:1480x895:Presented by Mrs Charles Hunter through
the National Art Collections Fund 'in memory of a great
artist and a great friend' 1929

N04783 The Black Brook (circa 1908)
Oc:552x698:signed:Purchased 1935

N04787 Vernon Lee (1881)
Oc:537x432:signed:Bequeathed by Miss Vernon Lee
through Miss Cooper Willis 1935

N04791 Val d'Aosta (circa 1908-10)
Oc:921x978:signed:Presented by Miss Emily Sargent 1935

N05052 Sir Philip Sassoon (1923)
Oc:952x578:signed:Bequeathed by Miss Vernon Lee
through Miss Cooper Willis 1935

N05066 W. Graham Robertson (1894)
Oc:2305x1187:signed:Presented by W. Graham
Robertson 1940

N05246 Colonel Ian Hamilton, CB, DSO (1898)
Oc:1384x787:signed:Presented by Gen. Sir Ian Hamilton
1940

N05247 Jean, Wife of Colonel Ian Hamilton (1896)
Oc:1302x921:signed:Presented by Gen. Sir Ian Hamilton
1940

N05901 Mrs Frederick Barnard (1885)
Oc:1041x571:signed:Bequeathed by Miss Dorothy
Barnard 1949

T00124 The Mountains of Moab (1905)
Oc:654x1111:Purchased 1957

T00125 The Plains of Esdraelon (1905)
Oc:711x1105:Purchased 1957

T00158 Mrs Philip Leslie Agnew (1902)
Oc:908x743:Purchased 1957

T03927 A Nude Boy on a Beach (1878)
Ow:268x351:Bequeathed by John Tillotson 1984

A00850 Dorothy Barnard
Dπ:248x210:signed:Bequeathed by Miss Dorothy
Barnard 1949

A00851 Polly Barnard
Dπ:279x235:signed:Bequeathed by Miss Dorothy
Barnard 1949

SARTORIUS, Francis 1734-1804
British Collection

T00888 A Black Horse with Two Dogs (1793)
Oc:346x416:signed:Presented by Alistair McAlpine (later
Lord McAlpine of West Green) 1966

SARTORIUS, John Nost 1759-1828
British Collection

T02368 The Earl of Darlington Fox-Hunting with the Raby Pack:
Drawing Cover (1805)
Oc:705x908:signed:Presented by Paul Mellon through the
British Sporting Art Trust 1979

T02369 The Earl of Darlington Fox-Hunting with the Raby Pack:
Going to Cover (1805)
Oc:714x914:signed:Presented by Paul Mellon through the
British Sporting Art Trust 1979

T02370 The Earl of Darlington Fox-Hunting with the Raby Pack:
Full Cry (1804)
Oc:702x899:signed:Presented by Paul Mellon through the
British Sporting Art Trust 1979

T02371 The Earl of Darlington Fox-Hunting with the Raby Pack:
The Death (?1804-5)
Oc:711x914:signed:Presented by Paul Mellon through the
British Sporting Art Trust 1979

SAUNDERS, Helen 1885-1963
Modern Collection
Tate Gallery Archive holds material concerning this artist

T00622 Monochrome Abstract Composition (circa 1915)
DWπ:289x184:Presented by Miss Ethel M. Saunders in
memory of her sister 1963

T00623 Abstract Composition in Blue and Yellow (circa 1915)
DWVπ:276x171:Presented by Miss Ethel M. Saunders in
memory of her sister 1963

T00624 Abstract Multicoloured Design (circa 1915)
GWDπ:359x257:Presented by Miss Ethel M. Saunders in
memory of her sister 1963

SAURA, Antonio born 1930
Modern Collection

T00866 Imaginary Portrait of Goya (1966)
Oc:1295x965:signed:Purchased 1966

For Jorn (P03241-P03255; complete group; mixed group)
Pour Jorn
P03251 [no title] (1975-6)
CLπ:606x425:signed:Presented by the Asger Jorn
Foundation 1978

SCARFE, Gerald born 1936
Modern Collection
Tate Gallery Archive holds material concerning this artist

P06536 Another Successful Transplant (1969)
CLπ:765x559:Presented by Curwen Studio through the
Institute of Contemporary Prints 1975

P06537 Hugh Hefner (the Play Boy) (1969)
CLπ:740x533:Presented by Curwen Studio through the
Institute of Contemporary Prints 1975

P06538 Investiture Souvenir (1969)
CLπ:768x584:Presented by Curwen Studio through the
Institute of Contemporary Prints 1975

P06539 Jackie and the Shower of Gold (1969)
CLπ:759x562:Presented by Curwen Studio through the
Institute of Contemporary Prints 1975

P06540 Ted Kennedy (1969)
CLπ:752x540:Presented by Curwen Studio through the
Institute of Contemporary Prints 1975

P06541 Marquis de Gaulle (1969)
CLπ:772x584:Presented by Curwen Studio through the
Institute of Contemporary Prints 1975

P06542 Tricky Dick (1969)
CLπ:772x581:Presented by Curwen Studio through the
Institute of Contemporary Prints 1975

P06543 Students of the Revolution (1969)
CLπ:765x559:Presented by Curwen Studio through the
Institute of Contemporary Prints 1975

P06544 Ian Fleming as James Bond (1970)
CLπ:737x546:Presented by Curwen Studio through the
Institute of Contemporary Prints 1975

P06545 Lennon and Ono (1970)
CLπ:746x562:Presented by Curwen Studio through the
Institute of Contemporary Prints 1975

P06546 Pope and the Pill (1970)
CLπ:752x562:Presented by Curwen Studio through the
Institute of Contemporary Prints 1975

P06547 The Queen (1970)
CLπ:746x521:Presented by Curwen Studio through the
Institute of Contemporary Prints 1975

P06548 Spiro Agnew (1970)
CLπ:778x587:Presented by Curwen Studio through the
Institute of Contemporary Prints 1975

SCARFE, Laurence born 1914

Modern Collection
Tate Gallery Archive holds material concerning this artist

P06750 Apparition, Venice (1965)
CLπ:673x429:signed:Presented by Curwen Studio
through the Institute of Contemporary Prints 1976

P06751 Battersea Night (1965)
CLπ:416x619:signed:Presented by Curwen Studio
through the Institute of Contemporary Prints 1976

P06752 Quatrefoil Garden (1965)
CLπ:610x416:signed:Presented by Curwen Studio
through the Institute of Contemporary Prints 1976

SCHETKY, John Christian 1778-1874

British Collection

N01191 Loss of the 'Royal George' (exhibited 1840)
Oc:1060x1829:Presented by the Misses Trevenen 1885

SCHMIDT, Peter born 1931

Modern Collection
Tate Gallery Archive holds material concerning this artist

Europaeische Graphik VII (P06244, P06289-P06291,
P06319, P06340-P06341, P06549; incomplete group;
mixed group)

P06549 Flowing in the Right Direction (1971)
CLπ:521x321:Presented by Curwen Studio through the
Institute of Contemporary Prints 1975

P06550 Flowing in the Right Direction (1971)
CLπ:521x321:signed:Presented by Curwen Studio
through the Institute of Contemporary Prints 1975

SCHMIDT-ROTTLUFF, Karl 1884-1976

Modern Collection

N05953 Woman with a Bag (1915)
Frau mit Tasche
Oc:952x873:signed:Presented by Dr Rosa Shapire 1950

N06248 Dr Rosa Schapire (1919)
Bildnis Rosa Schapire
Oc:1006x873:signed:Presented by the executors of Dr
Rosa Shapire 1954

N06249 Two Women (1912)
Zwei Frauen
Oc:765x845:signed:Presented by the executors of Dr
Rosa Shapire 1954

N06250 Male Head (1917)
Männlicher Kopf
Sw:343x133x165:signed:Presented by the executors of Dr
Rosa Shapire 1954

SCHNABEL, Julian born 1951

Modern Collection
Tate Gallery Archive holds material concerning this artist

T03441 Humanity Asleep (1982)
RVw:2743x3656x280:Purchased 1982

SCHNEIDER, Gerard born 1896

Modern Collection

P08174 Untitled from 'Poèmes d'Eugenio Montale', Milan (1964)
CLπ:35x65:signed:Transferred from the Library 1980

SCHOONHOVEN, Jan born 1914

Modern Collection

T01499 R69-26 (1969)
RAw:1238x838x38:Purchased 1972

SCHORR, Raoh born 1901

Modern Collection
Tate Gallery Archive holds material concerning this artist

N04869 Bengal Tiger (1927)
Sz:210x416x133:signed:Presented by the artist 1937

SCHUFFENECKER, Emile 1851-1934

Modern Collection

T03639 Spring-like Morning (circa 1896)
Matin printanier
Pπ:330x452:Presented anonymously in memory of Sir
Terence Rattigan 1983

T03640 Seascape (Cliffs) (circa 1895)
Marine
Pπ:135x209:Presented anonymously in memory of Sir
Terence Rattigan 1983

T03641 Cliffs and the Sea (circa 1895)
Pπ:140x210:Presented anonymously in memory of Sir
Terence Rattigan 1983

T03642 Cliff, Grey Weather (circa 1895)
Falaise, temps gris
Pπ:222x275:Presented anonymously in memory of Sir
Terence Rattigan 1983

SCHULZE, Alfred Otto Wolfgang - see WOLS

SCHUMACHER, Emil born 1912
Modern Collection

P77173 Composition (1961)
Komposition
Lπ:446x305:signed:Purchased 1986

SCHWABE, Randolph 1885-1948
Modern Collection
Tate Gallery Archive holds material concerning this artist

N04481 High Street, Hampstead (1928)
DWπ:340x337:signed:Purchased 1929

N05207 The Tate Gallery (1940)
DWπ:330x438:signed:Purchased 1940

N05371 The Radcliffe Observatory, Oxford (1942)
Wπ:565x387:signed:Purchased 1942

SCHWITTERS, Kurt 1887-1948
Modern Collection
Tate Gallery Archive holds material concerning this artist

T00214 Opened by Customs (1937-8)
Zollamtlich geöffnet
Vπ:330x254:Purchased 1958

T01259 (Relief in Relief) (circa 1942-5)
ORpw:495x413x102:Purchased 1970

T03766 The Autumn Crocus (1926-8, reconstructed 1958)
Die Herbstzeitlose
Sp:810x293x293:Transferred from the Victoria & Albert Museum 1983

T03863 Picture of Spatial Growths - Picture with Two Small Dogs (1939)
Bild mit Raumgewächsen-Bild mit 2 kleinen Hunden
Vb:970x690:signed:Purchased 1984

SCOTT, Campbell
Modern Collection

P06551 Untitled (1969)
CLπ:794x581:Presented by Curwen Studio through the Institute of Contemporary Prints 1975

SCOTT, David 1806-1849
British Collection

N02405 The By-Way to Hell
Lπ:168x127:Presented by Edmund Houghton 1898

SCOTT, Lady Kathleen - see KENNET, Lady

SCOTT, Robert born 1926
Modern Collection
Tate Gallery Archive holds material concerning this artist

P06753 Peruvian Night (1965)
CLπ:622x460:signed:Presented by Curwen Studio through the Institute of Contemporary Prints 1976

SCOTT, Samuel circa 1702-1772
British Collection

N00313 A View of London Bridge before the Late Alterations (engraved 1758)
Oc:286x546:Presented by Robert Vernon 1847

N00314 A View of Westminster Bridge and Parts Adjacent (engraved 1758)
Oc:298x540:Presented by Robert Vernon 1847

N01223 An Arch of Old Westminster Bridge (circa 1750)
Oc:270x397:Purchased 1886

N05450 A Morning, with a View of Cuckold's Point (circa 1750-60)
Oc:521x959:Presented by H.F. Tomalin 1944

T00202 Admiral Anson's Action off Cape Finisterre 1747 (circa 1749-50)
Oc:1645x2970:Purchased 1958

T01193 An Arch of Westminster Bridge (circa 1750)
Oc:1357x1638:Purchased 1970

T01235 A Sunset, with a View of Nine Elms (circa 1750-60)
Oc:515x959:Presented by the Friends of the Tate Gallery 1970

after
SCOTT, Samuel circa 1702-1772
British Collection

N01328 A View of the Thames with the York Buildings Water Tower (?circa 1760-70)
Oc:603x1095:Purchased 1891

SCOTT, Tim born 1937
Modern Collection
Tate Gallery Archive holds material concerning this artist

T01212 Dulcimer (1961)
Sv:914x3048x914:Purchased 1970

T01215 Peach Wheels (1961-2)
Sv:1219x1372x914:Presented by Alistair McAlpine (later Lord McAlpine of West Green) 1970

T01362 Curlicue (1963)
SAgg:965x718x718:Presented by Alistair McAlpine (later Lord McAlpine of West Green) 1970

T01363 Agrippa (1964)
SAag:1886x1130x1130:Presented by Alistair McAlpine (later Lord McAlpine of West Green) 1970

T01364 Quantic of Giza (1966)
SAwma:2121x2032x2794:Presented by Alistair McAlpine (later Lord McAlpine of West Green) 1970

T01365 Quadreme (1966)
SAma:1099x5245x2159:Presented by Alistair McAlpine (later Lord McAlpine of West Green) 1970

T01366 Quinquereme (1966)
SAwa:2153x6109x2159:Presented by Alistair McAlpine (later Lord McAlpine of West Green) 1970

T01367 Trireme (1968)
SAma:1587x5061x3823:Presented by Alistair McAlpine (later Lord McAlpine of West Green) 1970

T01368 Wine (1969)
SAma:1613x5359x4369:Presented by Alistair McAlpine (later Lord McAlpine of West Green) 1970

T01369 Bird in Arras IV (1969)
SAma:2800x6655x2489:Presented by Alistair McAlpine (later Lord McAlpine of West Green) 1970

T01370 Bird in Arras VI (1969)
SAma:2699x2915x2178:Presented by Alistair McAlpine (later Lord McAlpine of West Green) 1970

T01371 Pool V (1971)
Sma:940x1994x686:Presented by Alistair McAlpine (later Lord McAlpine of West Green) 1970

SCOTT, William 1913-1989
Modern Collection
Tate Gallery Archive holds material concerning this artist

N06245 Mackerel on a Plate (1951-2)
Oc:559x762:Purchased 1954

T00119 Winter Still Life (1956)
Oc:914x1524:signed:Presented by the Contemporary Art
Society 1957

T00415 White, Sand and Ochre (1960-1)
Oc:1600x1727:signed:Purchased 1961

T00505 Ochre Still Life (1958)
Oc:864x1118:Purchased 1962

T00795 Berlin Blues 4 (1965)
Oc:1530x1835:signed:Presented anonymously 1965

T00811 Reclining Nude (Red Nude) (1956)
Oc:914x1524:Purchased 1965

T00831 Orange, Black and White Composition (1953)
Oc:1219x1219:signed:Presented by the Trustees of the
Chantrey Bequest 1966

T01096 Seated Nude (1939)
Oc:507x400:signed:Presented by Mr and Mrs Eugene
Rosenberg through the Friends of the Tate Gallery 1968

P01071 The Harbour (1948-9)
CLπ:333x413:Presented by Robert Simon 1975

P01891 Summer Suite: Brown Predominating (1976)
CLπ:559x762:signed:Presented by Editions Alecto 1979

P05103 Black Bottle, Beige Cup on Brown (1970)
CNπ:597x787:signed:Presented by Rose and Chris Prater
through the Institute of Contemporary Prints 1975

P05104 Bottle and Bowl, Blues on Green (1970)
CNπ:594x778:signed:Presented by Rose and Chris Prater
through the Institute of Contemporary Prints 1975

P05105 Cup and Pan Blues (1970)
CNπ:594x883:signed:Presented by Rose and Chris Prater
through the Institute of Contemporary Prints 1975

P05106 Cup, Bowl, Pan, Browns and Ochres (1970)
CNπ:597x886:signed:Presented by Rose and Chris Prater
through the Institute of Contemporary Prints 1975

P05107 White Bowl, Black Pan on Brown (1970)
CNπ:594x778:signed:Presented by Rose and Chris Prater
through the Institute of Contemporary Prints 1975

A Poem for Alexander (P05108-P05124; complete group)
P05108 Angles Equal (1972)
CNπ:576x774:signed:Presented by Rose and Chris Prater
through the Institute of Contemporary Prints 1975

P05109 Areas Contrasted (1972)
CNπ:578x776:signed:Presented by Rose and Chris Prater
through the Institute of Contemporary Prints 1975

P05110 Blue Field (1972)
CNπ:581x775:signed:Presented by Rose and Chris Prater
through the Institute of Contemporary Prints 1975

P05111 Blue and White Related (1972)
CNπ:581x391:signed:Presented by Rose and Chris Prater
through the Institute of Contemporary Prints 1975

P05112 Brown Field Defined (1972)
CNπ:582x787:signed:Presented by Rose and Chris Prater
through the Institute of Contemporary Prints 1975

P05113 Cobalt Predominates (1972)
CNπ:580x388:signed:Presented by Rose and Chris Prater
through the Institute of Contemporary Prints 1975

P05114 Divided Counterchange (1972)
CNπ:590x774:signed:Presented by Rose and Chris Prater
through the Institute of Contemporary Prints 1975

P05115 Equals (1972)
CNπ:586x777:signed:Presented by Rose and Chris Prater
through the Institute of Contemporary Prints 1975

P05116 Estate Landscape (1972)
CNπ:577x392:signed:Presented by Rose and Chris Prater
through the Institute of Contemporary Prints 1975

P05117 Fire on the Rectangle (1972)
CNπ:579x388:signed:Presented by Rose and Chris Prater
through the Institute of Contemporary Prints 1975

P05118 First Triangles (1972)
CNπ:581x779:signed:Presented by Rose and Chris Prater
through the Institute of Contemporary Prints 1975

P05119 Forms Encaged (1972)
CNπ:580x394:signed:Presented by Rose and Chris Prater
through the Institute of Contemporary Prints 1975

P05120 Lines with Breadth Supercede (1972)
CNπ:581x395:signed:Presented by Rose and Chris Prater
through the Institute of Contemporary Prints 1975

P05121 A Poem for Alexander (1972)
CNπ:586x393:signed:Presented by Rose and Chris Prater
through the Institute of Contemporary Prints 1975

P05122 Second Triangles (1972)
CNπ:579x776:signed:Presented by Rose and Chris Prater
through the Institute of Contemporary Prints 1975

P05123 White Predominates (1972)
CNπ:585x779:signed:Presented by Rose and Chris Prater
through the Institute of Contemporary Prints 1975

P05124 Yellow Square plus Quarter Blue (1972)
CNπ:583x778:signed:Presented by Rose and Chris Prater
through the Institute of Contemporary Prints 1975

P05125 Still Life (1973)
CNπ:673x889:signed:Presented by Rose and Chris Prater
through the Institute of Contemporary Prints 1975

P06552 Arran (1960)
CLπ:527x648:Presented by Curwen Studio through the
Institute of Contemporary Prints 1975

P06553 Benbecula (1961-2)
CLπ:502x625:Presented by Curwen Studio through the
Institute of Contemporary Prints 1975

P06554 Jura (1961-2)
CLπ:498x591:Presented by Curwen Studio through the
Institute of Contemporary Prints 1975

P06555 Barra (1962)
CLπ:502x600:Presented by Curwen Studio through the
Institute of Contemporary Prints 1975

P06556 Mingulay (1962)
CLπ:505x619:Presented by Curwen Studio through the
Institute of Contemporary Prints 1975

P06557 Scalpay (1963)
CLπ:505x657:signed:Presented by Curwen Studio
through the Institute of Contemporary Prints 1975

P06687 Summer Suite with Blue (1976)
CLπ:571x768:signed:Presented by Curwen Studio 1976

P06688 Summer Suite: Green Predominating (1976)
CLπ:568x772:signed:Presented by Curwen Studio 1976

P06822 Grapes (1979)
CLπ:498x645:Presented by Curwen Studio 1980

P06823 Pears (1979)
CLπ:498x651:Presented by Curwen Studio 1980

SCOTT, William Bell 1811-1890
British Collection

N01322 The Eve of the Deluge (1865)
Oc:324x445:signed:Presented by Miss Alice Boyd 1891

N04630 Rossetti's Wombat Seated in his Master's Lap (1871)
Dπ:178x111:signed:Bequeathed by H.F. Stephens 1932

SCULLY, Sean born 1945
Modern Collection
Tate Gallery Archive holds material concerning this artist

T04138 Paul (1984)
3 Oc:2590x3200x240:signed:Presented by the Patrons of
New Art through the Friends of the Tate Gallery 1986

T05724 White Window (1988)
Oc:2455x3725:signed:Purchased 1989

T05731 3.24.89 (1989)
Pπ:569x769:signed:Presented by the artist 1990

T05732 5.12.89 (1989)
Pπ:762x982:signed:Presented by the artist 1990

T05733 3.14.89 (1989)
Pπ:568x770:signed:Presented by the artist 1990

T05736 4.10.84 (1984)
Pπ:591x773:signed:Purchased 1990

T05737 11.10.84 (1984)
Pπ:592x772:signed:Purchased 1990

P02953 Union (1984)
Lπ:376x452:Presented by the artist 1989

P02954 The Fall (1983)
Lπ:554x365:Presented by the artist 1989

P02955 Desire (1985)
Lπ:449x605:Presented by the artist 1989

P02956 Burnt Norton No 1 (1984)
Lπ:749x912:Presented by the artist 1989

P02957 Square Light 1 (1988)
Lπ:528x528:signed:Presented by the artist 1990

P02958 Square Light 2 (1988)
Lπ:528x528:signed:Presented by the artist 1990

P11202 Santa Barbara 3 (1987)
Jπ:1110x830:signed:Presented by Garner H. Tullis and
Pamela Auchincloss 1988

P11218 With (1988)
Jπ:762x761:Presented by the artist and Garner H. Tullis
1989

P11219 With In (1988)
Jπ:758x758:Presented by the artist and Garner H. Tullis
1989

P77287 Sotto Voce (1988)
Lπ:699x1059:signed:Purchased 1989

P77331 Conversation (1986)
Jπ:765x1140:Purchased 1989

SEABROOKE, Elliott 1886-1950
Modern Collection
Tate Gallery Archive holds material concerning this artist

N05944 Evening at Zandvoort (1949)
Oc:641x914:signed:Purchased 1950

N05945 Old Shipping in Heybridge Basin (1947)
Oc:813x813:signed:Purchased 1950

T01999 Near Pourville (1920)
Oc:632x759:signed:Bequeathed by Miss Winifred Elliot
Seabrooke 1975

SEDDON, John Pollard 1827-1906
British Collection

N02407 Recess with Staircase, St Sauveur, Caen (published 1852)
Lπ:213x133:Presented by Edmund Houghton 1898

SEDDON, Thomas 1821-1856
British Collection

N00563 Jerusalem and the Valley of Jehoshaphat from the Hill of
Evil Counsel (1854-5)
Oc:673x832:Presented by subscribers 1857

N05922 The Mountains of Moab
Wπ:251x352:Bequeathed by Miss E.K. Virtue Tebbs 1949

SEDGLEY, Peter born 1930
Modern Collection
Tate Gallery Archive holds material concerning this artist

T00739 Yellow Attenuation (1965)
Ab:1219x1219:signed:Purchased 1965

T01237 Colour Cycle III (1970)
KAc:1841x1829:Purchased 1970

P05126 Blue and Violet Study (1965)
CNπ:508x508:signed:Presented by Rose and Chris Prater
through the Institute of Contemporary Prints 1975

P05127 Blue Green Modulation (1965)
CNπ:318x486:signed:Presented by Rose and Chris Prater
through the Institute of Contemporary Prints 1975

P05128 Blue Scale (1965)
CNπ:483x483:signed:Presented by Rose and Chris Prater
through the Institute of Contemporary Prints 1975

Looking Glass Suite (P05129-P05137; complete group)
P05129 Looking Glass No. 1 (1966)
CNπ:494x495:signed:Presented by Rose and Chris Prater
through the Institute of Contemporary Prints 1975

P05130 Looking Glass No. 2 (1966)
CNπ:495x494:signed:Presented by Rose and Chris Prater
through the Institute of Contemporary Prints 1975

P05131 Looking Glass No. 3 (1966)
CNπ:494x495:signed:Presented by Rose and Chris Prater
through the Institute of Contemporary Prints 1975

P05132 Looking Glass No. 4 (1966)
CNπ:494x494:signed:Presented by Rose and Chris Prater
through the Institute of Contemporary Prints 1975

P05133 Looking Glass No. 5 (1966)
CNπ:493x493:signed:Presented by Rose and Chris Prater
through the Institute of Contemporary Prints 1975

P05134 Looking Glass No. 6 (1966)
CNπ:495x494:signed:Presented by Rose and Chris Prater
through the Institute of Contemporary Prints 1975

P05135 Looking Glass No. 7 (1966)
CNπ:494x494:signed:Presented by Rose and Chris Prater
through the Institute of Contemporary Prints 1975

P05136 Looking Glass No. 8 (1966)
CNπ:494x493:signed:Presented by Rose and Chris Prater
through the Institute of Contemporary Prints 1975

P05137 Looking Glass No. 9 (1966)
CNπ:495x494:signed:Presented by Rose and Chris Prater
through the Institute of Contemporary Prints 1975

SEFRAN, Gorazd born 1945
Modern Collection

P07591 Sindon III (1979)
CLπ:532x690:signed:Purchased 1981

SEGAL, Arthur 1875-1944
Modern Collection
Tate Gallery Archive holds material concerning this artist

T01243 Harbour on Bornholm (1928)
Hafen von Bornholm
Ob:603x816:signed:Presented by Miss Marianne Segal
1970

attributed to
SEGAR, Sir William active 1580 or 5 - 1633
British Collection

T03576 Portrait of a Man in a Slashed Black Doublet (circa 1605)
Ow:1000x806:Purchased 1983

SEGONZAC, André Dunoyer de - see
DUNOYER de SEGONZAC, André

**SELBY-BIGGE, Sir John Amherst, Bt see
BIGGE, John**

SELF, Colin born 1941
Modern Collection
Tate Gallery Archive holds material concerning this artist

T01580 Corvette Engine and Model (1965)
Db:562x391:signed:Purchased 1972

T01850 Guard Dog on a Missile Base, No. 1 (1965)
Db:556x762:Purchased 1974

T02398 Garden (All May 66) (1966)
Dπ:511x349:Presented by the artist 1979

T02399 Gardens with Green Garden Sculpture (1966-9)
Dπ:257x286:Presented by the artist 1979

T02400 The Gardens - with Four Eagles (1972)
Dπ:187x349:Presented by the artist 1979

T03941 'Muckspreading again . . .' (Looking West - Evening.
Fields and Farm in a Spinney - from South of Walcott
near Happisburgh - towards Riddlington, Norfolk), 25
September 1983 (1983)
DPπ:556x756:signed:Purchased 1985

T03942 Late Hay? (Field between the Yarmouth Road and
Plumstead, Norfolk), 19 October 1983 (1983)
DPπ:547x764:signed:Purchased 1985

T03943 Whitlingham Level Crossing at Midnight 1984 (towards
Norwich) - Snow on the Line, 25 January 1984 (1984)
DPπ:563x768:signed:Purchased 1985

T03944 The London Train (Late Night at Norwich (Thorpe)
Station), 26 January 1984 (1984)
DPπ:556x713:signed:Purchased 1985

T03972 Shepherd with Lantern (1983)
DPVπ:784x521:signed:Presented by the artist 1985

T03973 Moneyman No. 2 (1983)
PVπ:795x570:signed:Presented by the artist 1985

T03974 Fantail Pigeon on Nest (1983)
DVπ:601x460:signed:Presented by the artist 1985

T03975 Blue Period No. 2 (1983)
WVπ:760x570:signed:Presented by the artist 1985

T03976 Study for Rose Period No. 3 (1983)
WVπ:767x570:signed:Presented by the artist 1985

Power and Beauty (P07744-P07746; incomplete group)
P07744 Power and Beauty No. 7 (1968)
CNπ:728x993:signed:Purchased 1983

P07745 Power and Beauty No. 6 (1968)
CNπ:707x985:signed:Purchased 1983

P07746 Power and Beauty No. 3 (1968)
CLπ:676x1032:signed:Purchased 1983

P07747 Bomber No. 1 (1963)
CIVπ:396x576:signed:Purchased 1983

P07748 Lonewolf (1981)
CJπ:704x500:signed:Purchased 1983

P07941 Margaret in a Chair (1963)
MIπ:193x147:signed:Purchased 1983

P07942 Monument (1964)
MIπ:778x575:signed:Purchased 1983

P07943 Pluto (circa 1964-5)
MHJπ:426x603:Purchased 1983

P07944 Out of Focus Objects and Flowers (1968)
MIπ:280x251:signed:Purchased 1983

P07945 Picasso's Guernica and the Nazis (1968)
CLπ:188x311:signed:Purchased 1983

P07946 A Letter to Christopher Logue (1980)
CLVπ:148x245, 210x298:signed:Purchased 1983

SERRA, Richard born 1939
Modern Collection
Tate Gallery Archive holds material concerning this artist

T01728 Shovel Plate Prop (1969)
Rm:2502x2000x800:Purchased 1973

P77174 Patience (1984)
VNπ:1571x1335:signed:Purchased 1986

SERRES, John Thomas 1759-1825
British Collection

T01016 Whitby
Wπ:210x416:signed:Presented by the National Art
Collections Fund (Herbert Powell Bequest) 1967

SERUSIER, Paul 1863-1927
Modern Collection
Tate Gallery Archive holds material concerning this artist

T00231 Roof Tops in Paris
Oc:381x457:signed:Presented by the Friends of the Tate
Gallery 1959

SETCH, Terry born 1936
Modern Collection
Tate Gallery Archive holds material concerning this artist

T03591 Once upon a Time there was Oil III, Panel I (1981-2)
OTπc:2600x4360:Purchased 1983

T05549 Once Upon a Time There Was Oil III (1982)
Pπ:565x770:signed:Presented by the artist 1989

T05550 Once Upon a Time There Was Oil II (1982)
Pπ:550x765:signed:Presented by the artist 1989

T05551 Once Upon a Time There Was Oil I (1982)
Pπ:558x765:signed:Presented by the artist 1989

T05552 Once Upon a Time There Was Oil (Raft) (1981)
Pπ:550x764:signed:Presented by the artist 1989

T05553 Once Upon a Time There Was Oil (Beach) (1981)
Pπ:555x765:signed:Presented by the artist 1989

T05554 Once Upon a Time There was Oil (Car on Beach II)
(1981)
PDπ:565x775:signed:Presented by the artist 1989

T05555 Once Upon a Time There Was Oil (Car on Beach) (1981)
PDπ:565x675:signed:Presented by the artist 1989

P03094 Wall Split (1967-8)
CNπ:3048x1829:Presented by the Welsh Arts Council 1975

SEURAT, Georges 1859-1891
Modern Collection

N04203 Clothes on the Grass (1883)
Vêtements sur l'herbe
Ow:162x248:Presented by Alex Reid and Lefevre 1926

N06067 Le Bec du Hoc, Grandcamp (1885)
Oc:648x816:signed:Purchased 1952

SEVERINI, Gino 1883-1966
Modern Collection
Tate Gallery Archive holds material concerning this artist

T01070 Suburban Train Arriving in Paris (1915)
Train de banlieue arrivant à Paris
Oc:886x1156:Purchased with assistance from a member of the National Art Collections Fund 1968

SEVERN, Joseph 1793-1879
British Collection

T03357 The Infant of the Apocalypse Saved from the Dragon (circa 1827-31/1843)
Oc:2235x1270:Purchased 1982

SEYMOUR, James ?1702-1752
British Collection

T01115 A Kill at Ashdown Park (1743)
Oc:1803x2388:signed:Purchased with assistance from the Friends of the Tate Gallery and subscribers 1969

T02265 Chestnut Horse with a Groom near Newmarket (circa 1730-40)
Oc:660x1045:Bequeathed by Miss Agnes Clarke 1978

T02372 Mr Russell on his Bay Hunter (circa 1740)
Oc:876x1108:Presented by Paul Mellon through the British Sporting Art Trust 1979

attributed to
SEYMOUR, James ?1702-1752
British Collection

T02264 Pointer Bitch (circa 1740)
Oc:921x1146:Bequeathed by Miss Agnes Clarke 1978

SHACKLETON, William 1872-1933
British Collection
Tate Gallery Archive holds material concerning this artist

N03820 The Mackerel Nets (1912-3)
Oc:1022x1168:signed:Presented by Professor Frederick Brown 1923

N04676 Line of Life (1915)
Oc:952x1016:signed:Bequeathed by the artist 1933

SHADBOLT, Jack born 1909
Modern Collection

Centennial Suite (P03217-P03225, P03228-P03229; complete group; mixed group)
P03226 Begetting Green (1967-8)
CNπ:476x352:signed:Presented by Simon Fraser University, British Columbia 1977

SHAHN, Ben 1898-1969
Modern Collection

T00314 Lute and Molecules (1958)
MWπ:689x1022:signed:Purchased 1959

SHANNON, Charles 1863-1937
British Collection
Tate Gallery Archive holds material concerning this artist

N02995 Mrs Patrick Campbell (1907)
Oc:1226x1086:signed:Presented by Francis Howard through the National Loans Exhibition Committee 1914

N03152 The Lady with the Amethyst (1915)
Oc:610x597:signed:Presented by the Trustees of the Chantrey Bequest 1916

N05030 Hermes and the Infant Bacchus (1902-6)
Oc:1073x1073:signed:Presented by Francis Howard 1939

N05160 The Bath of Venus (1898-1904)
Oc:1460x978:signed:Presented by Francis Howard 1940

N05363 Les Marmitons (1897)
Oc:381x362:signed:Purchased 1942

P01050 The Ruffled Sea (1893)
MLπ:254x321:signed:Presented by Edward Marsh 1909

P01051 The Modeller (1891)
MLπ:178x489:signed:Presented by Edward Marsh 1909

P03082 The Rebirth of the Arts (1917)
CLπ:743x489:signed:Presented by the Ministry of Information 1918

SHANNON, Sir James 1862-1923
British Collection

N01901 The Flower Girl (1900)
Oc:838x660:signed:Presented by the Trustees of the Chantrey Bequest 1901

N03825 Phil May (1902)
Oc:1333x921:signed:Presented by the Trustees of the Chantrey Bequest 1923

N04263 Madame Patey (1884)
Oc:1270x889:signed:Presented by Ethel Jackson 1927

SHAPINSKY, Harold born 1925
Modern Collection

T04126 Untitled (1949)
OEπb:616x749:signed:Presented anonymously through the Mayor Gallery in honour of Ronald Alley 1985

SHAPIRO, Joel born 1941
Modern Collection
Tate Gallery Archive holds material concerning this artist

T03697 Untitled (1978)
Sz:157x553x337:signed:Purchased 1983

SHAPIRO, Shmuel born 1924
Modern Collection

Gates of Death (P06558-P06567; complete group)
Tor des Todes
P06558 Woman Shielding her Child (1966-7)
MLπ:570x796:signed:Presented by Curwen Studio through the Institute of Contemporary Prints 1975

P06559 Brother and Sister (1966-7)
MLπ:576x808:signed:Presented by Curwen Studio through the Institute of Contemporary Prints 1975

P06560 Adonai (1966-7)
MLπ:800x571:signed:Presented by Curwen Studio through the Institute of Contemporary Prints 1975

P06561 Dying Mother and Child (1966-7)
MLπ:802x570:signed:Presented by Curwen Studio through the Institute of Contemporary Prints 1975

P06562 Man Mad with Fear (1966-7)
MLπ:805x570:signed:Presented by Curwen Studio through the Institute of Contemporary Prints 1975

P06563 Gas Chamber (1966-7)
MLπ:805x570:signed:Presented by Curwen Studio through the Institute of Contemporary Prints 1975

P06564 Burning Woman (1966-7)
MLπ:805x574:signed:Presented by Curwen Studio through the Institute of Contemporary Prints 1975

P06565 Resigned Woman (1966-7)
MLπ:796x570:signed:Presented by Curwen Studio through the Institute of Contemporary Prints 1975

P06566 Dying Man (1966-7)
MLπ:560x798:signed:Presented by Curwen Studio through the Institute of Contemporary Prints 1975

P06567 Woman Crying over Dead Child (1966-7)
MLπ:800x577:signed:Presented by Curwen Studio through the Institute of Contemporary Prints 1975

P06720 Two Lovers (1966-7)
CLπ:349x448:Presented by Curwen Studio 1976

SHAYER, William, Senior 1787-1879
British Collection

T00018 A Village Festival (exhibited 1843)
Oc:902x1086:signed:Presented by the executors of C.F. Dendy Marshall 1955

SHEE, Sir Martin Archer 1769-1850
British Collection
Tate Gallery Archive holds material concerning this artist

N00367 Infant Bacchus (exhibited 1824)
Oc:705x905:Presented by Robert Vernon 1847

N00368 Thomas Morton, Dramatist (exhibited 1835)
Oc:762x635:Presented by Robert Vernon 1847

T04368 Two Rustic Figures (circa 1817)
Wπ:133x111:signed:Presented by Miss Marjorie Ball 1986

attributed to
SHEE, Sir Martin Archer 1769-1850
British Collection

N01480 Gilbert Stuart (?1788)
Oc:730x597:Purchased 1896

SHEFFIELD, George 1839-1892
British Collection

N04973 Churchyard at Bettws-y-Coed (1865)
Wπ:200x298:signed:Bequeathed by Sir Arthur Crosfield 1938

SHELLEY, John born 1938
Modern Collection

T01125 Annunciation (1968)
Ob:959x1568:Presented by the Trustees of the Chantrey Bequest 1969

SHEPPERSON, Claude 1867-1921
British Collection

Tending the Wounded, from 'Britain's Efforts and Ideals' (P03083-P03088; complete group)

P03083 Advanced Dressing Station in France (circa 1917)
MLπ:345x463:signed:Presented by the Ministry of Information 1918

P03084 Casualty Clearing Station in France (circa 1917)
MLπ:355x457:signed:Presented by the Ministry of Information 1918

P03085 On Board a Hospital Transport (circa 1917)
MLπ:362x467:signed:Presented by the Ministry of Information 1918

P03086 Detraining in England (circa 1917)
MLπ:347x461:signed:Presented by the Ministry of Information 1918

P03087 In Hospital, England (circa 1917)
MLπ:346x465:signed:Presented by the Ministry of Information 1918

P03088 Convalescence in England (circa 1917)
MLπ:352x457:signed:Presented by the Ministry of Information 1918

SHERINGHAM, George 1884-1937
Modern Collection
Tate Gallery Archive holds material concerning this artist

N04918 Sketch for Donna Clara in 'The Duenna' (1924)
DWπ:362x248:signed:Presented by Mrs George Sheringham 1938

SHERMAN, Cindy born 1954
Modern Collection

P07804 Untitled (1982)
CFπ:1143x762:Purchased 1983

SHORT, Sir Frank 1857-1945
British Collection

Prints after J.M.W. Turner (T04873, T05042-T05074; complete group)

T04873 The Temple of Jupiter in the Island of Aegina (published 1920)
Iπ:189x269:signed:Presented by Miss Beatrice Haggis 1987

T05042 Liber Studiorum - Frontispiece (1885)
Iπ:124x185:signed:Purchased 1988

T05043 Little Devil's Bridge, over the Russ above Altdorft, Switzerland (1885)
Iπ:178x254:signed:Purchased 1988

T05044 Water Mill (1885)
Iπ:179x258:signed:Purchased 1988

T05045 Water Mill (1885)
Iπ:179x258:signed:Purchased 1988

T05046 Scene in the Campagna (1886)
Iπ:182x258:signed:Purchased 1988

T05047 Procris and Cephalus (1885)
Iπ:188x257:signed:Purchased 1988

T05048 Chain of Alps from Grenoble to Chamberi (1887)
Iπ:178x259:signed:Purchased 1988

T05049 Mill near the Grand Chartreuse - Dauphiny (1885)
Iπ:187x256:signed:Purchased 1988

T05050 Berry Pomeroy Castle (1885)
Iπ:194x270:signed:Purchased 1988

T05051 Berry Pomeroy Castle (1885)
Lπ:194x270:signed:Purchased 1988

T05052 The Source of the Arveron, in the Valley of Chamouni, Savoy (1886)
Lπ:188x264:signed:Purchased 1988

T05053 Bonneville, Savoy (1887)
Lπ:187x270:signed:Purchased 1988

T05054 Ben Arthur, Scotland (1888)
Lπ:181x264:signed:Purchased 1988

T05055 Mount St Gothard (1907)
Lπ:176x255:signed:Purchased 1988

T05056 St Gothard (published 1920)
Lπ:175x265:signed:Purchased 1988

T05057 Peat Bog, Scotland (circa 1936)
Lπ:179x255:signed:Purchased 1988

T05058 Aesacus and Hesperie (published 1896)
Lπ:176x256:signed:Purchased 1988

T05059 Apuleia in Search of Apuleius (1937)
Lπ:181x264:signed:Purchased 1988

T05060 Sheep-Washing, Windsor, or Windsor Castle from Salt Hill (published 1920)
Lπ:181x256:signed:Purchased 1988

T05061 Dumbarton Rock (circa 1937)
Lπ:201x276:signed:Purchased 1988

T05062 The Temple of Jupiter in the Island of Aegina (1920)
Lπ:191x269:signed:Purchased 1988

T05063 The Temple of Jupiter in the Island of Aegina (published 1920)
Lπ:189x267:signed:Purchased 1988

T05064 Via Mala (circa 1895)
Lπ:187x262:signed:Purchased 1988

T05065 Pan and Syrinx (1896)
Lπ:200x265:signed:Purchased 1988

T05066 The Stork and Aqueduct ('The Heron's Pool') (circa 1896)
Lπ:182x247:signed:Purchased 1988

T05067 The Lost Sailor ('Storm over the Lizard') (published 1896)
Lπ:186x263:signed:Purchased 1988

T05068 Moonlight on the Medway (published 1920)
Lπ:186x253:signed:Purchased 1988

T05069 Narcissus and Echo (1896)
Lπ:177x260:signed:Purchased 1988

T05070 View of a River from a Terrace ('Macon') (published 1896)
Lπ:192x274:signed:Purchased 1988

T05071 Falls of the Rhine, Schaffhaussen (1891)
Lπ:212x276:signed:Purchased 1988

T05072 Falls of the Rhine, Schaffhaussen (published 1896)
MLπ:311x436:signed:Purchased 1988

T05073 Sion House, Isleworth (circa 1937)
Lπ:200x257:signed:Purchased 1988

T05074 A Pastoral (1893)
Lπ:180x255:signed:Purchased 1988

P01052 Low Tide and the Evening Star and Rye's Long Pier Deserted (1883)
Lπ:187x264:signed:Presented by Ernest Marsh 1909

SIBERECHTS, Jan 1627 - circa 1700
British Collection

T00899 Landscape with Rainbow, Henley-on-Thames (circa 1690)
Oc:819x1029:Presented by the Friends of the Tate Gallery 1967

SICHEL, Ernest Leopold 1862-1941
British Collection

N04677 Musical Instruments (1895-1905)
Oc:533x1181:signed:Purchased 1933

SICKERT, Bernard 1862 or 63 - 1932
British Collection

N05102 Old Curiosity Shop, Dieppe (circa 1895)
Ob:324x400:signed:Bequeathed by Mrs H.M. Swanwick 1940

SICKERT, Walter Richard 1860-1942
British Collection
Tate Gallery Archive holds material concerning this artist

N03181 George Moore (1890-1)
Oc:603x502:signed:Presented by the Contemporary Art Society 1917

N03182 Café des Tribunaux, Dieppe (circa 1890)
Oc:603x730:Presented by Miss Sylvia Gosse 1917

N03183 Despair (circa 1908-9)
Dπ:270x200:signed:Presented by the Contemporary Art Society 1917

N03621 A Marengo (circa 1903)
Oc:381x457:signed:Purchased 1922

N03810 The Piazzetta and the Old Campanile, Venice (circa 1901)
PWπ:495x330:signed:Purchased 1923

N03846 Ennui (circa 1914)
Oc:1524x1124:signed:Presented by the Contemporary Art Society 1924

N03847 Roquefort (?1918-20)
Oc:410x324:signed:Presented by the Contemporary Art Society 1924

N04651 The Front at Hove (Turpe Senex Miles Turpe Senilis Amor) (1930)
Oc:635x762:signed:Purchased 1932

N04655 Aubrey Beardsley (1894)
Oc:762x311:signed:Purchased with assistance from the National Art Collections Fund 1932

N04673 Miss Gwen Ffrangcon-Davies as Isabella of France (1932)
Oc:2451x921:Presented by the National Art Collections Fund, the Contemporary Art Society and C. Frank Stoop through the Contemporary Art Society 1932

N04912 Jacques-Emile Blanche (circa 1910)
Oc:610x508:Purchased 1932

N05045 Les Arcades de la Poisonnnerie, Dieppe (circa 1900)
Oc:610x502:signed:Presented by the Contemporary Art Society 1939

N05086 The Tottenham Distillery (circa 1924)
Oc:508x610:signed:Bequeathed by Lady Henry Cavendish-Bentinck 1940

N05087 Belvedere, Bath (circa 1917)
Oc:711x711:Bequeathed by Lady Henry Cavendish-Bentinck 1940

N05088 Rowlandson House - Sunset (1910-12)
Oc:610x502:signed:Bequeathed by Lady Henry
Cavendish-Bentinck 1940

N05089 Baccarat - the Fur Cape (1920)
Oc:591x419:signed:Bequeathed by Lady Henry
Cavendish-Bentinck 1940

N05090 L'Américaine (1908)
Oc:508x406:signed:Bequeathed by Lady Henry
Cavendish-Bentinck 1940

N05091 Woman Washing her Hair (circa 1905-6)
Oc:457x381:signed:Bequeathed by Lady Henry
Cavendish-Bentinck 1940

N05092 Tipperary (1914)
Oc:508x406:Bequeathed by Lady Henry
Cavendish-Bentinck 1940

N05093 Venice, la Salute (circa 1901-3)
Oc:451x692:signed:Bequeathed by Lady Henry
Cavendish-Bentinck 1940

N05094 Dieppe, Study No. 2; Facade of St Jacques (circa 1899)
DWπ:321x232:signed:Bequeathed by Lady Henry
Cavendish-Bentinck 1940

N05095 Pierrot and Woman Embracing (1903-4)
DWπ:410x311:signed:Bequeathed by Lady Henry
Cavendish-Bentinck 1940

N05096 Sketch for 'The Statue of Duquesne, Dieppe' (circa 1902)
PWπ:324x235:signed:Bequeathed by Lady Henry
Cavendish-Bentinck 1940

N05127 Mrs Barrett (circa 1908)
Pb:540x711:signed:Presented by the Contemporary Art
Society 1940

N05288 The Little Tea Party: Nina Hamnett and Roald Kristian (1915-16)
Oc:254x356:signed:Purchased 1941

N05296 Two Women on a Sofa - Le Tose (circa 1903-4)
Oc:457x533:signed:Bequeathed by Sir Hugh Walpole
1941

N05312 Study for 'L'Armoire à Glace' (1922)
DWπ:260x187:signed:Purchased 1941

N05313 L'Armoire à Glace (1924)
Oc:610x381:signed:Purchased 1941

N05314 Interior of St Mark's, Venice (1896)
Oc:698x492:signed:Purchased 1941

N05430 Off to the Pub (circa 1912)
Oc:508x406:signed:Presented by Howard Bliss 1943

N05619 Study for 'The Little Tea Party' (1915-16)
Dπ:232x356:Purchased 1945

N05914 St Mark's, Venice (Pax Tibi Marce Evangelista Meus)
(1895-6)
Oc:908x1200:signed:Bequeathed by General Sir Ian
Hamilton, GCB, GCMG, DSO 1949

N06087 Study for 'L'Armoire à Glace' (circa 1922)
DWπ:279x130:signed:Presented by Roland, Browse and
Delbanco 1952

N06142 Mrs Anna Knight (1941-2)
Oc:1524x762:Bequeathed by Mrs Anna Knight 1953

N06174 The New Bedford (1915-6)
Oc:914x356:signed:Bequeathed by Sir Edward Marsh
through the Contemporary Art Society 1953

T00164 Harold Gilman (circa 1912)
Oc:610x457:Presented by the Trustees of the Chantrey
Bequest 1957

T00221 Sir Alec Martin, KBE (1935)
Oc:1397x1079:signed:Presented by Sir Alec Martin, KBE
through the National Art Collections Fund 1958

T00222 Lady Martin (1935)
Oc:1397x1079:signed:Presented by Sir Alec Martin, KBE
through the National Art Collections Fund 1958

T00223 Claude Phillip Martin (1935)
Oc:1270x1016:signed:Presented by Sir Alec Martin, KBE
through the National Art Collections Fund 1958

T00259 The Servant of Abraham (1929)
Oc:610x508:signed:Presented by the Friends of the Tate
Gallery 1959

T00350 Study for 'Ennui' (1913-4)
Dπ:419x340:signed:Presented by the Friends of the Tate
Gallery 1960

T02039 Minnie Cunningham at the Old Bedford (circa 1889)
Oc:765x638:signed:Purchased 1976

T03360 Miss Earhart's Arrival (1932)
Oc:717x1832:Purchased 1982

T03548 La Hollandaise (circa 1906)
Oc:511x406:signed:Purchased 1983

T05529 The Seducer (circa 1929-30)
Oc:425x625:Purchased 1989

P11050 Ennui (circa 1916-8)
MIπ:226x162:Bequeathed by Mrs E. West 1982

follower of
SICKERT, Walter Richard 1860-1942
British Collection

N05309 The Straw Hat (circa 1911)
Dπ:279x190:Presented by the Contemporary Art Society
1941

SIDANER, Henri Le - see LE SIDANER, Henri

SIDDAL, Elizabeth Eleanor 1829-1862
British Collection
Tate Gallery Archive holds material concerning this artist

N03202 Lady Affixing Pennant to a Knight's Spear
Wπ:137x137:Bequeathed by W.C. Alexander 1917

N03471 Sir Patrick Spens (1856)
Wπ:241x229:signed:Purchased 1919

SILVA, Maria Helena Vieira da - see VIEIRA da SILVA, Maria Helena

SIMMONDS, William G. 1876-1968
British Collection
Tate Gallery Archive holds material concerning this artist

N02139 The Seeds of Love (1906)
Wπ:591x464:signed:Presented by the Trustees of the
Chantrey Bequest 1907

N04432 The Farm Team (circa 1924-8)
Sw:740x1525x405:signed:Purchased 1929

N04900 Old Horse (1936-7)
Sw:200x570x325:Presented by the Trustees of the
Chantrey Bequest 1937

SIMMONS, William Henry - see prints after SOLOMON, Abraham

SIMPSON, John 1782-1847
British Collection
Tate Gallery Archive holds material concerning this artist

N00382   Head of a Negro
Oc:559x559:Presented by Robert Vernon 1847

SIMS, Charles 1873-1928
British Collection
Tate Gallery Archive holds material concerning this artist

N02260   The Fountain (1907-8)
Oc:1022x1276:signed:Presented by the Trustees of the
Chantrey Bequest 1908

N02933   The Wood beyond the World (1913)
Oc:1016x1441:signed:Presented by the Trustees of the
Chantrey Bequest 1913

N04396   I Am the Abyss and I Am Light (1928)
Tc:711x914:signed:Presented by Henry M. Andrews
through the National Art Collections Fund 1928

N05348   The Sands at Dymchurch (circa 1920-2)
TOc:432x889:signed:Purchased 1942

SINGIER, Gustave born 1909
Modern Collection

T00181   Provence I (1957)
Oc:997x806:signed:Purchased 1958

SINGLETON, Henry 1766-1839
British Collection

N01027   Ariel on a Bat's Back (exhibited 1819)
Oc:1003x1257:Bequeathed by the artist 1840

N01028   Manto and Tiresias (exhibited 1792)
Oc:2413x1321:Bequeathed by the artist 1840

T01926   Palemon and Lavinia (circa 1792)
Oc:371x321:Presented by Mrs M. Bernard 1974

SINTENIS, Renée 1888-1965
Modern Collection

N04650   Self-Portrait (1931)
Sp:337x159x171:Presented by Sir Thomas D. Barlow 1932

SIRONI, Mario 1885-1961
Modern Collection
Tate Gallery Archive holds material concerning this artist

N06041   Five Figures (circa 1936)
Cinque figure
Tc:451x603:signed:Presented by Mr and Mrs Eric
Estorick 1952

N06042   The Syphon (1916)
GVπ:457x419:signed:Presented by Mr and Mrs Eric
Estorick 1952

T03114   Mountains (circa 1928)
Montagne
Oc:819x1079:signed:Presented by Signora Aglae Sironi
1980

T03312   Compositions (circa 1950-3)
Composizione
DGπ:527x692:signed:Presented by Signora Aglae Sironi
1981

SISLEY, Alfred 1839-1899
Modern Collection

N04249   The Bridge at Sèvres (1877)
Le Pont de Sèvres
Oc:381x460:signed:Purchased 1927

N04843   The Small Meadows in Spring (1880)
Les Petits prés au printemps
Oc:543x730:signed:Presented by a body of subscribers in
memory of Roger Fry 1936

N05144   The Path to the Old Ferry at By (1880)
Le Chemin du vieux bac à By
Oc:498x651:signed:Bequeathed by Montague Shearman
through the Contemporary Art Society 1940

SKEAPING, John 1901-1980
Modern Collection
Tate Gallery Archive holds material concerning this artist

N05455   Blood Horse (1929)
Sw:692x746x356:signed:Purchased 1944

N06129   Horse (exhibited 1934)
Sw:1816x3886x673:Presented by the Zoological Society
of London 1945

T03767   Buffalo (1930)
Ss:100x180x110:signed:Transferred from the Victoria &
Albert Museum 1983

T03768   Burmese Dancer (1928)
Ss:470x170x140:signed:Transferred from the Victoria &
Albert Museum 1983

     School Prints (P01698-P01727; complete group; mixed
group)

P01722   Mare and Foal (1946-9)
CLπ:492x762:signed:Presented by Patrick Seale Prints
1975

SKELTON, Jonathan circa 1735-1759
British Collection

T01017   Tivoli (1758)
DWπ:260x375:signed:Presented by the National Art
Collections Fund (Herbert Powell Bequest) 1967

SKIOLD, Birgit 1923-1982
Modern Collection
Tate Gallery Archive holds material concerning this artist

P01591   Mururoa (1973)
CLπ:597x543:signed:Presented by Editions Alecto
through the Institute of Contemporary Prints 1975

P01592   Shisen-do (1973)
CILπ:530x619:signed:Presented by Editions Alecto
through the Institute of Contemporary Prints 1975

P06569   Sea Image (1968)
CLπ:591x791:signed:Presented by Curwen Studio
through the Institute of Contemporary Prints 1975

SLAUGHTER, Stephen 1697-1765
British Collection

N01982   The Betts Family (circa 1746)
Oc:737x616:Bequeathed by Mrs A. Sealy 1905

T00674   Sir George Lee (1753)
Oc:762x635:signed:Presented by Leggatt Bros through
the National Art Collections Fund 1964

SLAWIK, Bernard born 1904
Modern Collection

P06754 Pre-Historic Subject (1976)
MLπ:292x362:Presented by Curwen Studio 1976

SLEAP, Joseph Axe 1808-1859
British Collection

N00676 St Paul's Wharf, Thames
Wπ:381x381:Bequeathed by Richard Frankum 1861

SLETER, Francesco 1685-1775
British Collection

T03465 A Representation of the Liberal Arts: Ceiling Design for
the State Dining Room at Grimsthorpe Castle (circa
1724)
Oc:613x762:Purchased 1982

SMALL, William 1843-1931
British Collection

N01595 The Last Match (1887)
Oc:1308x1003:signed:Presented by the Trustees of the
Chantrey Bequest 1887

SMART, Edgar Rowley 1887-1934
Modern Collection

N05457 Pinewoods under the Snow (1934)
DWπ:571x397:signed:Presented by Dr Barnett Stross
1944

SMETHAM, James 1821-1889
British Collection

N02394 Forsake Not the Law of Thy Mother
Lπ:165x111:Presented by Edmund Houghton 1898

N02395 The Last Sleep
Lπ:48x29:Presented by Edmund Houghton 1898

N02396 Hugh Miller (1860)
Lπ:229x305:Presented by Edmund Houghton 1898

N02397 Midsummer
Lπ:229x305:Presented by Edmund Houghton 1898

N02398 Mr Robert Levett (1861)
Lπ:305x229:Presented by Edmund Houghton 1898

N02399 The Lord of the Sabbath (1861)
Lπ:229x305:Presented by Edmund Houghton 1898

N02400 The Resurrection of the Daisy (1861)
Lπ:190x222:Presented by Edmund Houghton 1898

N02401 The Death of Earl Siward (1861)
Lπ:225x168:Presented by Edmund Houghton 1898

N02402 The Moorland Edge
Lπ:178x229:Presented by Edmund Houghton 1898

N02403 The Dell
Lπ:229x178:Presented by Edmund Houghton 1898

N02404 The Water-Lily
Lπ:181x229:Presented by Edmund Houghton 1898

N02916 The Days of Noah (1860)
Lπ:140x105:Presented by J. Fairhurst 1912

N03203 Naboth's Vineyard (1856)
Ow:222x171:signed:Bequeathed by W.C. Alexander 1917

N03204 The Eve of St Agnes (1858)
DWπ:83x102:Bequeathed by W.C. Alexander 1917

SMIRKE, Robert 1752-1845
British Collection

N00762 The Order of Knighthood Conferred on Don Quixote by
the Inn Keeper
Oc:546x457:Presented by Capt. Thomas Lambert and
Mrs Lambert 1867

N00763 Don Quixote at Home, after the Termination of his
Second Sally
Oc:546x457:Presented by Capt. Thomas Lambert and
Mrs Lambert 1867

N00765 Scene from Bickerstaffe's Play 'The Hypocrite', Adapted
from Colly Cibber's 'Non Juror'
Oc:495x445:Presented by Capt. Thomas Lambert and
Mrs Lambert 1867

N01777 The Afflicted Matron, the Countess Trifaldi, from 'Don
Quixote'
Oc:578x800:Bequeathed by H.S. Ashbee 1900

N01778 Sancho Panza and the Duchess
Oc:584x806:Bequeathed by H.S. Ashbee 1900

Illustrations to 'Don Quixote' (A00852-A00863;
complete group)
A00852 [title not known] (published 1818)
Ow:241x203:Presented by Capt. Thomas Lambert and
Mrs Lambert 1867

A00853 [title not known] (published 1818)
Ow:241x203:Presented by Capt. Thomas Lambert and
Mrs Lambert 1867

A00854 [title not known] (published 1818)
Ow:241x203:Presented by Capt. Thomas Lambert and
Mrs Lambert 1867

A00855 [title not known] (published 1818)
Ow:241x203:Presented by Capt. Thomas Lambert and
Mrs Lambert 1867

A00856 [title not known] (published 1818)
Ow:241x203:Presented by Capt. Thomas Lambert and
Mrs Lambert 1867

A00857 [title not known] (published 1818)
Ow:241x203:Presented by Capt. Thomas Lambert and
Mrs Lambert 1867

A00858 [title not known] (published 1818)
Ow:241x203:Presented by Capt. Thomas Lambert and
Mrs Lambert 1867

A00859 [title not known] (published 1818)
Ow:241x203:Presented by Capt. Thomas Lambert and
Mrs Lambert 1867

A00860 [title not known] (published 1818)
Ow:241x203:Presented by Capt. Thomas Lambert and
Mrs Lambert 1867

A00861 [title not known] (published 1818)
Ow:241x203:Presented by Capt. Thomas Lambert and
Mrs Lambert 1867

A00862 [title not known] (published 1818)
Ow:241x203:Presented by Capt. Thomas Lambert and
Mrs Lambert 1867

A00863 [title not known] (published 1818)
Ow:241x203:Presented by Capt. Thomas Lambert and
Mrs Lambert 1867

SMITH, David 1906-1965
Modern Collection
Tate Gallery Archive holds material concerning this artist

T00891 Cubi XIX (1964)
Sm:2864x1480x1016:signed:Purchased 1966

T00931   Painting 1964 (1964)
DWπ:1397x451:signed:Presented anonymously 1967

SMITH, Frederick William 1797-1835
British Collection

N02441   Sir Francis Chantrey, R.A. (1824)
Sp:610x349x267:signed:Presented by William White 1909

SMITH, George, of Chichester 1714-1776
British Collection

N02287   Classical Landscape (circa 1760-70)
Oc:305x432:signed:Bequeathed by George Derwent
Radclyffe 1908

N04512   Landscape
Oc:737x1130:Presented by C.H. Eldridge 1930

SMITH, Gordon born 1919
Modern Collection

Centennial Suite (P03217-P03225, P03228-P03229;
complete group; mixed group)
P03227   Special Green (1967-8)
CNπ:381x511:signed:Presented by Simon Fraser
University, British Columbia 1977

SMITH, Hassel born 1915
Modern Collection

T00383   Untitled (1959)
OEc:1803x1245:signed:Presented by Allan D. Emil
through the American Friends of the Tate Gallery 1960

SMITH, Jack born 1928
Modern Collection
Tate Gallery Archive holds material concerning this artist

T00005   Mother Bathing Child (1953)
Ob:1829x1219:signed:Purchased 1955

T00286   Bottles in Light and Shadow (1959)
Oc:1829x1219:Purchased 1959

T00570   Black, White and Grey Movement No. 2 (1962)
Oc:1067x1067:signed:Purchased 1963

T00754   Figure in a Room I (1959)
Oc:1524x1524:signed:Presented by Mr and Mrs Kenneth
Levy through the Friends of the Tate Gallery 1965

T01917   Hazard Collage, 32 Elements (1971)
VDπ:556x730:signed:Purchased 1974

T02259   Sounds and Silences (to the Left of Red) (1975)
Ob:610x610:signed:Purchased 1978

T03812   Written Activity No. 7 (1969)
Oc:1530x1530:signed:Purchased 1983

T03813   Activities, Major and Minor (1972)
Ow:1222x1219:signed:Purchased 1983

T03814   Inside, Outside 3 (1980)
Ob:920x920:signed:Purchased 1983

SMITH, Joel born 1929
Modern Collection

Centennial Suite (P03217-P03225, P03228-P03229;
complete group; mixed group)
P03228   The Red Queen (1967-8)
CNπ:486x359:signed:Presented by Simon Fraser
University, British Columbia 1977

SMITH, John Thomas 1766-1833
British Collection

N02728   Portrait of J.M.W. Turner, R.A.
Oc:486x391:Presented by Lord Duveen 1910

SMITH, John 'Warwick' 1749-1831
British Collection

T01018   St Peter's from the Villa Milleni near Rome (1806)
Wπ:244x349:Presented by the National Art Collections
Fund (Herbert Powell Bequest) 1967

SMITH, Sir Matthew 1879-1959
British Collection
Tate Gallery Archive holds material concerning this artist

N04410   Peonies (exhibited 1928)
Oc:762x635:Purchased 1928

N04782   Cyclamen (circa 1920)
Oc:610x508:Purchased 1935

N04852   Model Turning (circa 1924)
Oc:648x806:signed:Purchased 1936

N05266   Peaches (1937)
Oc:603x730:signed:Purchased 1941

N05401   Still Life (circa 1936)
Oc:806x997:Presented by the artist and Lady Smith 1943

N05440   The Young Actress (1943)
Oc:756x635:signed:Purchased 1943

N05760   Apples (1919-20)
Oc:460x546:signed:Purchased 1947

N05903   Cornish Church (1920)
Oc:533x648:signed:Purchased 1949

N06086   Nude, Fitzroy Street, No. 1 (1916)
Oc:864x762:signed:Presented by the Trustees of the
Chantrey Bequest 1952

N06152   Woman Reclining (circa 1925-6)
Oc:597x730:signed:Bequeathed by Sir Edward Marsh
through the Contemporary Art Society 1953

T01994   Fruit in a Dish (circa 1915)
Oc:305x356:Purchased 1975

T02101   Still Life with Clay Figure, I (1939)
Oc:730x1162:Bequeathed by Mr Francis Halliday 1976

T03351   Winter in Provence (circa 1937)
Oc:540x654:Presented anonymously through the Friends
of the Tate Gallery 1982

SMITH, Richard born 1931
Modern Collection
Tate Gallery Archive holds material concerning this artist

T00822   Tailspin (1965)
Aw:1200x2127x902:Purchased 1966

T00855   Vista (1963)
Oc:1956x2978:signed:Purchased 1966

T01161   Riverfall (1969)
ROc:2286x6858x356:signed:Presented by the Friends of
the Tate Gallery 1969

T01199   Panatella (1961)
Oc:2286x3048:signed:Purchased 1970

T01588   Painting (1958)
Oc:1524x1213:signed:Purchased 1972

T01807   Mandarino (1973)
Acvm:2083x1016:Purchased 1973

T01808   Double Blue Drawing (1973)
ODPVπ:1283x686:signed:Purchased 1973

T02003 Piano (1963)
ROc:1826x2772x1140:Purchased 1975

T02004 Gift Wrap (1963)
ROc:2019x5290x800:signed:Purchased 1975

T02005 Early Reply (1972)
Acmf:1359x2972:Purchased 1975

T03060 Cartouche II -10 (1979)
Acmf:1359x2972:signed:Purchased 1980

T03115 Triangular (1970-1)
Ac:2032x3810x241:Presented anonymously 1980

T04886 The Typographer (1986)
AVc:2972x2020x673:signed:Presented by the artist in memory of his father 1987

T05528 Slot Machine (1962)
ROcwπ:569x505x85:Presented by Henry Geldzahler through the American Fund/Tate Gallery Charitable Trust 1989

Proscenium Suite (P01275-P01281; complete group)
P01275 I (1971)
MIπ:793x594:signed:Presented by Waddington Galleries through the Institute of Contemporary Prints 1975

P01276 II (1971)
MIπ:780x590:signed:Presented by Waddington Galleries through the Institute of Contemporary Prints 1975

P01277 III (1971)
MIπ:793x587:signed:Presented by Waddington Galleries through the Institute of Contemporary Prints 1975

P01278 IV (1971)
MIπ:794x583:signed:Presented by Waddington Galleries through the Institute of Contemporary Prints 1975

P01279 V (1971)
MIπ:585x587:signed:Presented by Waddington Galleries through the Institute of Contemporary Prints 1975

P01280 VI (1971)
MIπ:585x587:signed:Presented by Waddington Galleries through the Institute of Contemporary Prints 1975

P01281 VII (1971)
MIπ:585x588:signed:Presented by Waddington Galleries through the Institute of Contemporary Prints 1975

Butterfly Suite (P01282-P01290; complete group)
P01282 Frontispiece (1972)
CIπ:641x928:signed:Presented by Waddington Galleries through the Institute of Contemporary Prints 1975

P01283 I (1972)
CIπ:639x930:signed:Presented by Waddington Galleries through the Institute of Contemporary Prints 1975

P01284 II (1972)
CIπ:638x930:signed:Presented by Waddington Galleries through the Institute of Contemporary Prints 1975

P01285 III (1972)
CIπ:640x930:signed:Presented by Waddington Galleries through the Institute of Contemporary Prints 1975

P01286 IV (1972)
CIπ:640x930:signed:Presented by Waddington Galleries through the Institute of Contemporary Prints 1975

P01287 V (1972)
CIπ:637x928:signed:Presented by Waddington Galleries through the Institute of Contemporary Prints 1975

P01288 VI (1972)
CIπ:640x933:signed:Presented by Waddington Galleries through the Institute of Contemporary Prints 1975

P01289 VII (1972)
CIπ:645x932:signed:Presented by Waddington Galleries through the Institute of Contemporary Prints 1975

P01290 VIII (1972)
CIπ:640x930:signed:Presented by Waddington Galleries through the Institute of Contemporary Prints 1975

Paper Clip Suite I (P01291-P01295; complete group)
P01291 Print 1 (1974)
CIVπ:439x440:signed:Presented by Waddington Galleries through the Institute of Contemporary Prints 1975

P01292 Print 2 (1974)
CIVπ:443x440:signed:Presented by Waddington Galleries through the Institute of Contemporary Prints 1975

P01293 Print 3 (1974)
CIVπ:445x442:signed:Presented by Waddington Galleries through the Institute of Contemporary Prints 1975

P01294 Print 4 (1974)
CIVπ:446x442:signed:Presented by Waddington Galleries through the Institute of Contemporary Prints 1975

P01295 Print 5 (1974)
CIVπ:441x445:signed:Presented by Waddington Galleries through the Institute of Contemporary Prints 1975

Paper Clip Suite II (P01296-P01300; complete group)
P01296 Print 1 (1974)
CIVπ:438x442:signed:Presented by Waddington Galleries through the Institute of Contemporary Prints 1975

P01297 Print 2 (1974)
CIVπ:443x442:signed:Presented by Waddington Galleries through the Institute of Contemporary Prints 1975

P01298 Print 3 (1974)
CIVπ:441x442:signed:Presented by Waddington Galleries through the Institute of Contemporary Prints 1975

P01299 Print 4 (1974)
CIVπ:442x442:signed:Presented by Waddington Galleries through the Institute of Contemporary Prints 1975

P01300 Print 5 (1974)
CIVπ:442x442:signed:Presented by Waddington Galleries through the Institute of Contemporary Prints 1975

Folded Paper Clip Suite (P01301-P01303; complete group)
P01301 Folded Paper Clip I (1975)
CLVπ:713x717:signed:Presented by Waddington Galleries through the Institute of Contemporary Prints 1975

P01302 Folded Paper Clip II (1975)
CLVπ:707x718:signed:Presented by Waddington Galleries through the Institute of Contemporary Prints 1975

P01303 Folded Paper Clip III (1975)
CLVπ:691x717:signed:Presented by Waddington Galleries through the Institute of Contemporary Prints 1975

P02303 Untitled (1964)
CNπ:651x651:signed:Presented by the artist 1976

P02304 Edward Gordon Craig I (1968)
CLπ:371x711:signed:Presented by the artist 1976

P02305 Edward Gordon Craig II (1968)
CLπ:403x546:signed:Presented by the artist 1976

P02306 Second Time Around (1969)
CLπ:797x137:signed:Presented by the artist 1976

Sixteen Pieces of Paper (P02307-P02310; complete group)
P02307 Drop (1969)
CNπ:391x376:signed:Presented by the artist 1976

P02308 Exit (1969)
CNπ:391x371:signed:Presented by the artist 1976

P02309 Interval (1969)
CNπ:392x372:signed:Presented by the artist 1976

P02310 Proscenium (1969)
CNπ:388x371:signed:Presented by the artist 1976

Eighteen Small Prints (P02311; incomplete group)
P02311 Untitled (1973)
CIVπ:210x416:signed:Presented by the artist 1976

Florentine Set (P02312-P02313; complete group)
P02312 1 (1973)
CLVπ:505x703:signed:Presented by the artist 1976
P02313 2 (1973)
CLVπ:505x707:signed:Presented by the artist 1976

Lawson Set (P02314-P02315; complete group)
P02314 [no title] (1973)
CLVπ:598x802:signed:Presented by the artist 1976
P02315 [no title] (1973)
CLVπ:590x798:signed:Presented by the artist 1976

Times Square Remembered Times Five
(P02316-P02320; complete group)
P02316 1 (1973)
CLVπ:900x600:signed:Presented by the artist 1976
P02317 2 (1973)
CLVπ:900x600:signed:Presented by the artist 1976
P02318 3 (1973)
CLVπ:902x599:signed:Presented by the artist 1976
P02319 4 (1973)
CLVπ:900x600:signed:Presented by the artist 1976
P02320 5 (1973)
CLVπ:899x599:signed:Presented by the artist 1976

P02321 Diary (1975)
CNVπ:1118x1829x51:signed:Presented by the artist 1976

P02322 Nosegay Green (1975)
CNVπ:914x787:signed:Presented by the artist 1976

P02323 Par Terre (1975)
CNVπ:914x787:signed:Presented by the artist 1976

P02324 Russian I (1975)
CIVπ:914x787:signed:Presented by the artist 1976

P02325 Russian II (1975)
CIVπ:914x787:signed:Presented by the artist 1976

For John Constable (P03149-P03157, P03159-P03161,
P03180-P03185; complete group; mixed group)
P03160 [no title] (1976)
CLVπ:470x679:signed:Presented by Bernard Jacobson
Gallery 1976

The Institute of Contemporary Arts Portfolio (P04016,
P04038, P04053, P04076, P04115, P04125, P04166,
P04248, P04256, P04315-P04316, P04334,
P04378-P04380, P04419, P04635, P04752, P04938,
P05138, P05155, P05248; complete group; mixed group)
P05138 PM Zoom (1963)
CNπ:483x762:signed:Presented by Rose and Chris Prater
through the Institute of Contemporary Prints 1975

P05139 P.T.O. Apollinaire (1968)
CNπ:508x445:signed:Presented by Rose and Chris Prater
through the Institute of Contemporary Prints 1975

P05140 Untitled (1972)
CNπ:752x552:signed:Presented by Rose and Chris Prater
through the Institute of Contemporary Prints 1975

LOGO (P07220-P07229; complete group)
P07220 A. Mauve (1971)
CNRa:603x502x51:signed:Purchased 1972

P07221 B. Green (1971)
CNRa:600x500x50:signed:Purchased 1972

P07222 C. Grey (1971)
CNRa:600x500x50:signed:Purchased 1972

P07223 D. Beige (1971)
CNRa:600x500x50:signed:Purchased 1972

P07224 E. Blue-Pink (1971)
CNRa:600x500x50:signed:Purchased 1972

P07225 F. Blue-Orange (1971)
CNRa:600x500x50:signed:Purchased 1972

P07226 G. Pink (1971)
CNRa:600x500x50:signed:Purchased 1972

P07227 H. Cream (1971)
CNRa:600x500x50:signed:Purchased 1972

P07228 J. Turquoise (1971)
CNRa:600x500x50:signed:Purchased 1972

P07229 K. Magenta (1971)
CNRa:600x500x50:signed:Purchased 1972

P07400 Four Knots (1976)
CLVπ:705x765:signed:Purchased 1980

Two of a Kind, Three of a Kind (P07401-P07403;
incomplete group)
P07401 Triangles (1978)
CLVπ:705x905:signed:Purchased 1980
P07402 Triangles (1978)
CLVπ:708x793:signed:Purchased 1980
P07403 Triangles (1978)
CLVπ:706x775:signed:Purchased 1980

Drawing Boards I (P07509-P07510; incomplete group)
P07509 [no title] (1980)
CIπ:450x435:signed:Purchased 1980
P07510 [no title] (1980)
CIπ:520x420:signed:Purchased 1980

Drawing Boards II (P07511-P07512; incomplete group)
P07511 [no title] (1981)
CIπ:542x340:signed:Purchased 1981
P07512 [no title] (1981)
CIπ:450x372:signed:Purchased 1981

SMITH, Sydney Robert James 1857-1913
British Collection

A00864 Project for the Facade of the Tate Gallery (circa 1893)
Dπ:457x695:Presented by the artist 1900

A00865 Project for the Facade of the Tate Gallery (circa 1893)
Dπ:305x683:signed:Presented by the artist 1900

SMITH, Thomas active 1780-1822
British Collection

T05480 Lake of Como from Cadanabbia, near Bellagio
Dπ:152x279:Presented by Miss Marjorie Ball 1988

SMYTHE, Lionel Percy 1840-1918
British Collection

N01709 Germinal (1889)
Wπ:584x445:signed:Presented by the Trustees of the
Chantrey Bequest 1889

SOBRINO, Francisco born 1932
Modern Collection

T00715 Indefinite Spaces S (1963)
Espaces indéfinis S
Ss:559x337x222:Purchased 1964

SOEST, Gerard circa 1600-1681
British Collection

T00746 Henry Howard, 6th Duke of Norfolk (circa 1669)
Oc:1270x1073:Purchased 1965

T04162 Portrait of Mr Tipping (circa 1665)
Oc:939x1149:Presented by the Friends of the Tate
Gallery 1986

SOLOMON, Abraham 1824-1862
British Collection

T03614 Waiting for the Verdict (1857)
Oc:1019x1273:signed:Purchased with assistance from the
National Art Collections Fund and the Sue Hammerson
Charitable Trust 1983

T03615 Not Guilty (The Acquittal) (exhibited 1857)
Oc:1016x1270:signed:Purchased with assistance from the
National Art Collections Fund and the Sue Hammerson
Charitable Trust 1983

prints after
SOLOMON, Abraham 1824-1862
British Collection

T03616 Waiting for the Verdict, engraved by W.H. Simmons
(1866)
Lπ:555x700:Presented anonymously 1983

T03617 The Acquittal, engraved by W.H. Simmons (1866)
Lπ:552x720:Presented anonymously 1983

SOLOMON, Simeon 1840-1905
British Collection

N03409 Meeting of Dante and Beatrice (1859-63)
Dπ:194x229:signed:Bequeathed by Robert Ross through
the National Art Collections Fund 1919

N03410 Self-Portrait (1859)
Dπ:165x146:signed:Presented anonymously 1919

N04013 Hosannah, engraved by the Brothers Dalziel (published
1881)
Mπ:165x121:Presented by Gilbert Dalziel 1924

T01719 The Moon and Sleep (1894)
Oc:514x762:signed:Presented by Miss Margery
Abrahams in memory of Dr Bertram L. Abrahams and
Jane Abrahams 1973

T03063 Sappho and Erinna in a Garden at Mytilene (1864)
Wπ:330x381:signed:Purchased 1980

T03104 Study of Sappho (1862)
Dπ:267x209:signed:Purchased 1980

T03702 A Youth Relating Tales to Ladies (1870)
Oc:355x534:signed:Presented by the Kretschmer family
in accordance with the wishes of William Kretschmer 1983

SOLOMON, Solomon J. 1860-1927
British Collection
Tate Gallery Archive holds material concerning this artist

N04916 A Family Group: The Artist's Wife and Children: 'Papa
Painting!' (1905)
Oc:1613x1753:signed:Presented by the artist's widow 1938

SOMER, Paul van - see VAN SOMER, Paul

SOMERSCALES, Thomas J. 1842-1927
British Collection

N01773 Off Valparaiso (1899)
Oc:965x1803:signed:Presented by the Trustees of the
Chantrey Bequest 1899

SOMOV, Konstantin 1869-1939
Modern Collection

T00654 River Scene (1929)
Gb:362x448:signed:Bequeathed by Peter Provatoroff 1964

SOREL, Agathe born 1935
Modern Collection
Tate Gallery Archive holds material concerning this artist

P02335 Of Biplanes and Catamarans (1976)
CIπ:565x737:signed:Presented by the artist 1976

P02336 The Wise and Foolish Virgin (1966)
CIπ:565x489:signed:Presented by the artist 1976

SORRELL, Alan 1904-1974
Modern Collection

N05730 Up in the Morning Early: RAF Camp 1941 (1942)
Tπ:349x381:signed:Presented by the War Artists'
Advisory Committee 1946

N05731 Southampton Dock (1944)
WDπ:521x625:signed:Presented by the War Artists'
Advisory Committee 1946

SORRELL, Elizabeth born 1916
Modern Collection

N05928 Ferns in the Conservatory (1945)
WTπ:559x375:signed:Presented by the Trustees of the
Chantrey Bequest 1949

SOTO, Jesus-Raphael born 1923
Modern Collection
Tate Gallery Archive holds material concerning this artist

T00649 Horizontal Movement (1963)
Mouvement horizontal
Rv:625x276x165:Purchased 1964

T00793 Cardinal (1965)
Cardenal
Rv:1562x1060x254:signed:Purchased 1965

T00806 Relationships of Contrasting Elements (1965)
Relations éléments opposés
Rv:1581x1073x152:signed:Purchased 1965

T03769 Twelve Blacks and Four Silvers (1965)
12 noirs et 4 argentés
Rwm:1060x1060x162:signed:Transferred from the
Victoria & Albert Museum 1983

T03770 Light Trap (1965)
Piège de lumière
Rwv:470x298x131:Transferred from the Victoria &
Albert Museum 1983

SOUCH, John active 1616-1636
British Collection

N06247 George Puleston (?) (circa 1625-35)
Oc:762x635:signed:Purchased 1954

SOUKOP, Willi born 1907
Modern Collection
Tate Gallery Archive holds material concerning this artist

T00594   Owl (1961-2)
Ss:419x305x305:Presented by the Trustees of the
Chantrey Bequest 1963

SOULAGES, Pierre born 1919
Modern Collection
Tate Gallery Archive holds material concerning this artist

N06199   Painting, 23 May 1953 (1953)
Peinture, 23 mai 1953
Oc:1949x1302:signed:Purchased 1953

P08219   [no title] (1956)
Lπ:245x170:signed:Transferred from the Library 1989

P77116   Etching No. 2 (1952)
CIπ:380x553:signed:Purchased 1985

SOUTHALL, Derek born 1930
Modern Collection
Tate Gallery Archive holds material concerning this artist

T01562   2 HWP 2 Al'Entrada del Temps Clar (1972)
OAc:2527x3150:Purchased 1972

SOUTHALL, Joseph Edward 1861-1944
British Collection
Tate Gallery Archive holds material concerning this artist

T01930   Cinderella (1893-5)
Wπ:543x384:signed:Purchased 1974

T03699   Belgium Supported by Hope (1918)
Tc:318x410:Purchased 1983

SOUTINE, Chaim 1893-1943
Modern Collection

T00315   The Road up the Hill (circa 1924)
La Route de la colline (Vence)
Oc:724x600:signed:Bequeathed by Miss Helen Drysdale
1959

T00692   Landscape at Ceret (circa 1920-1)
Paysage à Céret
Oc:559x838:signed:Purchased 1964

T02132   Cagnes Landscape with Tree (circa 1925-6)
Paysage de Cagnes
Oc:600x727:signed:Bequeathed by John Levy 1977

SOUZA, F.N. born 1924
Modern Collection
Tate Gallery Archive holds material concerning this artist

T00725   Two Saints in a Landscape (1961)
Ac:1283x959:signed:Presented by A.J. Muirhead 1965

SPEAR, Ruskin 1911-1990
Modern Collection
Tate Gallery Archive holds material concerning this artist

N05772   Snow Scene (1946)
Ob:451x629:Presented by the Trustees of the Chantrey
Bequest 1947

N06011   Mr Hollingbery's Canary (1950)
Oc:1829x1067:Presented by the Trustees of the Chantrey
Bequest 1951

T00527   Professor Carel Weight (1961)
Ob:1441x1162:Presented by the Trustees of the Chantrey
Bequest 1962

SPEED, Harold 1872-1957
British Collection
Tate Gallery Archive holds material concerning this artist

N01964   The Alcantara, Toledo, by Moonlight (1894)
Oc:635x914:signed:Presented by the Trustees of the
Chantrey Bequest 1905

SPENCELAYH, Charles 1865-1958
British Collection
Tate Gallery Archive holds material concerning this artist

N05272   Rochester Castle (1895)
Oc:225x610:signed:Purchased 1941

SPENCER, Gilbert 1892-1979
Modern Collection
Tate Gallery Archive holds material concerning this artist

N04670   A Cotswold Farm (1930-1)
Oc:1410x1841:signed:Presented by the Trustees of the
Chantrey Bequest 1932

N05550   The Beginning of an Event in History: The Tolpuddle
Martyrs (circa 1937)
Wπ:559x800:Presented by the Contemporary Art Society
1944

N05554   Blackmore Vale from Compton Abbas (1942)
Oc:660x1016:signed:Presented by the Trustees of the
Chantrey Bequest 1944

N06021   Sashes Meadow, Cookham (1914-19)
Oc:464x616:signed:Purchased 1951

T01903   The Crucifixion (1915)
Oc:864x991:signed:Purchased 1974

T02012   Self-Portrait (1928)
Oc:356x305:Presented by the Trustees of the Chantrey
Bequest 1975

T03224   The Progress of Husbandry (circa 1964)
Of:914x1816:Presented by the Trustees of the Chantrey
Bequest 1981

SPENCER, Sir Stanley 1891-1959
Modern Collection
Tate Gallery Archive holds material concerning this artist

N04117   Christ Carrying the Cross (1920)
Oc:1530x1429:Presented by the Contemporary Art
Society 1925

N04239   The Resurrection, Cookham (1923-7)
Oc:2743x5486:Presented by Lord Duveen 1927

N04245   Camouflaged Grenadier. Verso: Two Composition
Studies for Burghclere Chapel (1922-3)
DWπ:505x371:Purchased 1927

N04678   Terry's Lane, Cookham (circa 1932)
Oc:508x762:Purchased 1933

N04800   Turkeys (1925)
Oc:508x762:Presented by the Contemporary Art Society
1935

N04925   The Robing of Christ (1922)
Ow:352x594:Presented by the Contemporary Art Society
1938

N04926   The Disrobing of Christ (1922)
Ow:359x635:Presented by the Contemporary Art Society
1938

N04942 Rickett's Farm, Cookham Dene (1938)
Oc:660x1168:Purchased 1938

N05148 Daphne (1940)
Oc:610x508:Purchased 1940

N05321 The Sword of the Lord and of Gideon (1922-3)
Oπ:622x559:Presented by the Contemporary Art Society 1942

N05393 The Bridge (1920)
Oc:1213x1226:Presented by the National Art Collections Fund 1942

N05556 The Roundabout (1923)
Oc:521x457:Presented by the Trustees of the Chantrey Bequest 1944

N05607 P.J. Spencer (circa 1932)
Dπ:356x254:Purchased 1945

N05608 'Man Goeth to his Long Home' (1911)
DWπ:432x318:Purchased 1945

N05663 Apple Gatherers (1912-3)
Oc:714x924:Presented by Sir Edward Marsh 1946

N05732 Mr Joe Buchanan, Charge Hand Blacksmith (1943-4)
Dπ:502x416:signed:Presented by the War Artists' Advisory Committee 1946

N05733 William McBrearty, Sawyer (1943-4)
Dπ:489x394:Presented by the War Artists' Advisory Committee 1946

N05775 Study for 'The Bridge' and other works (1912-20)
DWπ:356x508:Presented anonymously 1947

N05961 The Resurrection: Port Glasgow (1947-50)
Oc:2146x6655:Presented by the Trustees of the Chantrey Bequest 1950

N06150 Tree and Chicken Coops, Wangford (1925)
Oc:457x762:Bequeathed by Sir Edward Marsh through the Contemporary Art Society 1953

N06188 Self-Portrait (1913)
Oc:629x508:Bequeathed by Sir Edward Marsh through the Contemporary Art Society 1953

N06233 Study for 'The Apple Gatherers' (circa 1912)
DWπ:276x321:Bequeathed by Sir Edward Marsh through the Contemporary Art Society 1954

T00048 Study for 'Joachim among the Shepherds' (1912)
DWπ:406x371:signed:Presented by the Trustees of the Chantrey Bequest 1955

T00141 Dinner on the Hotel Lawn (1956-7)
Oc:949x1359:Presented by the Trustees of the Chantrey Bequest 1957

T00359 The Centurion's Servant (1914)
Oc:1143x1143:signed:Presented by the Trustees of the Chantrey Bequest 1960

T00525 Swan Upping at Cookham (1914-19)
Oc:1480x1162:signed:Presented by the Friends of the Tate Gallery 1962

T00530 Mending Cowls, Cookham (1914)
Oc:1092x1092:Presented by the Trustees of the Chantrey Bequest 1962

T00961 St Francis and the Birds (1935)
Oc:660x584:Presented by the Trustees of the Chantrey Bequest 1967

T01207 Turk's Boatyard Cookham (circa 1931)
Oc:635x765:Bequeathed by Mrs I.M. Andrews 1970

T01769 Jacob and Esau (1910-11)
Dπ:343x241:Bequeathed by Lady Ruth Gollancz 1973

T01863 Double Nude Portrait: The Artist and his Second Wife (1937)
Oc:838x937:Purchased 1974

Drawings for the Port Glasgow Resurrection Series (T03035-T03050; complete group)

T03035 Early Sketch for 'Resurrection: Rejoicing'
Dπ:121x413:Purchased 1980

T03036 Drawing for the Left Panel of 'Resurrection: Rejoicing'
Dπ:403x267:Purchased 1980

T03037 Drawing for Centre Panel of 'Resurrection: Rejoicing'
Dπ:403x267:Purchased 1980

T03038 Drawing for Right Panel of 'Resurrection: Rejoicing'
Dπ:403x267:Purchased 1980

T03039 Drawing for the Right Hand Section of 'Resurrection: Port Glasgow'
Dπ:403x267:Purchased 1980

T03040 Drawing for Left Section of 'Resurrection: Port Glasgow'
Dπ:403x267:Purchased 1980

T03041 Drawing for Centre Section of 'Resurrection: Port Glasgow'
Dπ:403x267:Purchased 1980

T03042 Drawing for Right Section of 'Resurrection: Port Glasgow'
Dπ:403x267:Purchased 1980

T03043 Drawing for Left Panel of 'Resurrection: Waking Up'
Dπ:403x267:Purchased 1980

T03044 Drawing for Right Panel of 'Resurrection: Waking Up'
Dπ:276x403:Purchased 1980

T03045 Drawing for Left Panel of 'Resurrection: Reunion'
Dπ:403x267:Purchased 1980

T03046 Drawing for Centre Panel of 'Resurrection: Reunion'
Dπ:403x267:Purchased 1980

T03047 Drawing for Right Panel of 'Resurrection: Reunion'
Dπ:403x267:Purchased 1980

T03048 Drawing for Left Panel of 'Resurrection: Tidying'
Dπ:403x267:Purchased 1980

T03049 Drawing for Right Panel of 'Resurrection: Tidying'
Dπ:403x267:Purchased 1980

T03050 Mother and Children
Dπ:403x267:Purchased 1980

T03061 Figures on Either Side of a Window
Dπ:403x267:[uncovered during remounting of T03043] 1980

T03062 Trumpet Player with other figures
Dπ:403x267:[uncovered during remounting of T03048] 1980

T03335 Self-Portrait (1959)
Oc:508x406:Presented by the Friends of the Tate Gallery 1982

T03336 Study for 'Christ Carrying the Cross' (1920)
DWπ:441x356:Presented by Mrs Nancy Carline in memory of her husband Richard Carline 1982

T03337 Portrait of Louis Behrend
DWπ:292x225:Presented by Mrs Nancy Carline in memory of her husband Richard Carline 1982

T05525 Study for Double Nude Portrait: the Artist and his Second Wife (circa 1937)
WDGπ:177x223:Presented by Mr Robert Littman through the American Fund/Tate Gallery Charitable Trust in honour of the Director 1989

T05526 Study for the Resurrection of Soldiers: Burghclere Chapel (1927-8)
Dπ:304x230:Presented by Mr Robert Littman through the American Fund/Tate Gallery Charitable Trust in honour of the Director 1989

T05527 Study for Double Nude Portrait: the Artist and his
Second Wife (circa 1937)
Dπ:175x229:Presented by Mr Robert Littman through
the American Fund/Tate Gallery Charitable Trust 1989

T05762 Farm Pond, Leonard Stanley (1940)
Oc:610x914:Bequeathed by Helena and Kenneth Levy
1990

P11032 Retrieving a Ball (1954)
CLπ:425x559:Presented by Mrs Nancy Carline in
memory of her husband Richard Carline 1981

SPENCER, Thomas active 1740-1756
British Collection

T02373 A Bay Hunter Held by a Groom, with a Stag-Hunt in the
Background (circa 1750)
Oc:1149x1356:Presented by Paul Mellon through the
British Sporting Art Trust 1979

SPENDER, Humphrey born 1910
Modern Collection
Tate Gallery Archive holds material concerning this artist

P06570 Gravel Pit (1968)
CLπ:486x692:signed:Presented by Curwen Studio
through the Institute of Contemporary Prints 1975

P06571 Cornish Tin Mines (1969)
CLπ:422x670:Presented by Curwen Studio through the
Institute of Contemporary Prints 1975

P06572 Donegal Coastscape (1969)
CLπ:400x556:signed:Presented by Curwen Studio
through the Institute of Contemporary Prints 1975

P06573 Donegal Landscape (1969)
CLπ:413x568:Presented by Curwen Studio through the
Institute of Contemporary Prints 1975

P06574 Reedy Pool, Essex (1969)
CLπ:441x641:Presented by Curwen Studio through the
Institute of Contemporary Prints 1975

P06575 Walled Landscape, Kerry (1969)
CLπ:384x597:Presented by Curwen Studio through the
Institute of Contemporary Prints 1975

P06576 Cornish Tin Mines (1971)
CLπ:384x597:signed:Presented by Curwen Studio
through the Institute of Contemporary Prints 1975

SPILSBURY, Maria 1777 - circa 1823
British Collection

N04880 The Schoolmistress (circa 1803)
Oc:762x914:Presented by Miss Ruth Young 1937

SPOERRI, Daniel born 1930
Modern Collection

T03382 Prose Poems (1959-60)
Poèmes en prose
Vw:690x542x361:signed:Purchased 1982

P07569 Daniel Isaac Spoerri-Feinstein (1977)
CLπ:890x596:signed:Purchased 1981

SPRUANCE, Benton born 1904
Modern Collection

P06577 Icarus I (1963)
CLπ:425x546:Presented by Curwen Studio through the
Institute of Contemporary Prints 1975

P06578 Icarus III (1963)
CLπ:451x610:signed:Presented by Curwen Studio
through the Institute of Contemporary Prints 1975

P06579 Bestiary (1967)
MLπ:600x483:Presented by Curwen Studio through the
Institute of Contemporary Prints 1975

SPURRIER, Steven 1878-1961
British Collection
Tate Gallery Archive holds material concerning this artist

N05339 Yellow Wash-stand (circa 1939)
Oc:546x654:signed:Presented by the Trustees of the
Chantrey Bequest 1940

STAEL, Nicolas de 1914-1955
Modern Collection

T00136 Marathon (1948)
Oc:803x648:signed:Purchased 1957

T00607 Landscape Study (1952)
Etude de paysage
Ob:327x460:signed:Purchased 1963

T03084 Composition 1950 (1950)
Ob:1248x794:signed:Purchased 1980

STAHLY, François born 1911
Modern Collection

T00940 Growth (1963)
Croissance
Sz:1184x441x349:signed:Presented anonymously 1967

STAMOS, Theodorus born 1922
Modern Collection

P05141 Delphic Sun Box I (1971)
CNπ:657x606:signed:Presented by Rose and Chris Prater
through the Institute of Contemporary Prints 1975

P05142 Green Sun Box (1971)
CNπ:606x657:signed:Presented by Rose and Chris Prater
through the Institute of Contemporary Prints 1975

P05143 Spartan Sun Box I (1971)
CNπ:606x657:signed:Presented by Rose and Chris Prater
through the Institute of Contemporary Prints 1975

STANFIELD, William Clarkson 1793-1867
British Collection
Tate Gallery Archive holds material concerning this artist

N00404 Entrance to the Zuyder Zee, Texel Island (exhibited
1844)
Oc:1003x1257:Presented by Robert Vernon 1847

N00405 Sketch for the Battle of Trafalgar, and the Victory of
Lord Nelson over the Combined French and Spanish
Fleets, October 21, 1805 (1833)
Ow:387x803:Presented by Robert Vernon 1847

N00406 Lake Como (1825)
Ow:470x768:Presented by Robert Vernon 1847

N00407 The Canal of the Guidecca, and Church of the Gesuati,
Venice (1836)
Oc:610x902:Presented by Robert Vernon 1847

N03531 View of Saintes (1851)
WDπ:330x495:signed:Presented by J. Kerr Lawson
through the National Art Collections Fund 1920

T05627 Falmouth from the Mills (1836)
Lπ:133x104:Transferred from the Library 1989

T05628 Falmouth from the Mills (1836)
Iπ:135x104:Transferred from the Library 1989

T05629 Treport (Vignette) (1836)
Iπ:125x100:Transferred from the Library 1989

T05630 Treport (Vignette) (1836)
Iπ:118x100:Transferred from the Library 1989

T05631 St Michael's Mount, Cornwall (1836)
Iπ:87x140:signed:Transferred from the Library 1989

T05632 St Michael's Mount, Normandy from the West (1836)
Iπ:86x140:signed:Transferred from the Library 1989

T05633 St Michael's Mount, Normandy, from the West (1836)
Iπ:86x140:Transferred from the Library 1989

T05634 The Greves from the Summit of Mount St Michael (1836)
Iπ:95x139:Transferred from the Library 1989

T05635 The Greves from the Summit of Mount St Michael (1836)
Iπ:95x140:signed:Transferred from the Library 1989

T05636 Botallack Mine, Cornwall (1836)
Iπ:90x140:Transferred from the Library 1989

T05637 Land's End, Cornwall (1836)
Iπ:95x140:Transferred from the Library 1989

T05638 Land's End, Cornwall (1836)
Iπ:51x146:Transferred from the Library 1989

T05639 Dartmouth (1836)
Iπ:93x143:Transferred from the Library 1989

T05640 Dartmouth (1836)
Iπ:93x143:Transferred from the Library 1989

T05641 Dartmouth Castle (1836)
Iπ:87x140:Transferred from the Library 1989

T05642 Dartmouth Castle (1836)
Iπ:90x140:Transferred from the Library 1989

T05643 St Malo (1836)
Iπ:92x142:Transferred from the Library 1989

T05644 St Malo (1836)
Iπ:92x142:Transferred from the Library 1989

T05645 The Approach to St Malo (1836)
Iπ:92x140:Transferred from the Library 1989

T05646 The Approach to St Malo (1836)
Iπ:92x140:Transferred from the Library 1989

T05647 The Coast of Britany, near Doll (1836)
Iπ:91x140:Transferred from the Library 1989

T05648 The Coast of Britany, near Doll (1836)
Iπ:91x140:Transferred from the Library 1989

T05649 Portsmouth Harbour (1836)
Iπ:91x142:Transferred from the Library 1989

T05650 Portsmouth Harbour (1836)
Iπ:91x142:Transferred from the Library 1989

T05651 The Semaphore, Portsmouth (1836)
Iπ:95x140:Transferred from the Library 1989

T05652 The Semaphore, Portsmouth (1836)
Iπ:95x140:Transferred from the Library 1989

T05653 Porchester Castle (1836)
Iπ:143x102:Transferred from the Library 1989

T05654 Porchester Castle (1836)
Iπ:143x102:Transferred from the Library 1989

T05655 The Needles (1836)
Iπ:96x141:Transferred from the Library 1989

T05656 The Needles (1836)
Iπ:96x141:Transferred from the Library 1989

T05657 Brading Harbour, Isle of Wight (1836)
Iπ:97x139:Transferred from the Library 1989

T05658 Brading Harbour, Isle of Wight (1836)
Iπ:96x139:Transferred from the Library 1989

T05659 Arched Rock, Isle of Wight (1836)
Iπ:95x138:Transferred from the Library 1989

T05660 Arched Rock, Isle of Wight (1836)
Iπ:66x138:Transferred from the Library 1989

T05661 Powderham Park, Exmouth (1836)
Iπ:94x140:Transferred from the Library 1989

T05662 Powderham Park, Exmouth (1836)
Iπ:94x140:Transferred from the Library 1989

T05663 The Hamoaze, Plymouth (1836)
Iπ:97x151:Transferred from the Library 1989

T05664 The Hamoaze, Plymouth (1836)
Iπ:97x151:Transferred from the Library 1989

T05665 Stonehouse Bridge, Plymouth (1836)
Iπ:93x140:Transferred from the Library 1989

T05666 Stonehouse Bridge, Plymouth (1836)
Iπ:93x140:Transferred from the Library 1989

T05667 Rye Old Harbour, Blockade Station (1836)
Iπ:90x138:Transferred from the Library 1989

T05668 Rye Old Harbour, Blockade Station (1836)
Iπ:90x135:Transferred from the Library 1989

T05669 Hastings from the Sea (1836)
Iπ:93x140:Transferred from the Library 1989

T05670 Hastings from the Sea (1836)
Iπ::Transferred from the Library 1989

T05671 Martello Tower (1836)
Iπ:92x144:Transferred from the Library 1989

T05672 Martello Tower (1836)
Iπ:92x142:Transferred from the Library 1989

T05673 East Cliff, Hastings (1836)
Iπ:91x141:Transferred from the Library 1989

T05674 East Cliff, Hastings (1836)
Iπ:75x141:Transferred from the Library 1989

T05675 Havre de Grace (1836)
Iπ:92x140:Transferred from the Library 1989

T05676 Havre de Grace (1836)
Iπ:92x140:Transferred from the Library 1989

T05677 Dieppe (1836)
Iπ:95x140:Transferred from the Library 1989

T05678 Dieppe (1836)
Iπ:95x140:Transferred from the Library 1989

T05679 Boulogne, Upper Harbour (1836)
Iπ:95x141:Transferred from the Library 1989

T05680 Boulogne, Upper Harbour (1836)
Iπ:94x141:Transferred from the Library 1989

T05681 Boulogne, Old Pier (1836)
Iπ:95x138:Transferred from the Library 1989

T05682 Boulogne, Old Pier (1836)
Iπ:95x138:Transferred from the Library 1989

T05683 Boulogne, Wreck on the Coast (1836)
Iπ:89x141:Transferred from the Library 1989

T05684 Boulogne, Wreck on the Coast (1836)
Iπ:88x141:Transferred from the Library 1989

T05685 Calais (1836)
Iπ::Transferred from the Library 1989

T05686 Calais (1836)
Iπ:94x139:Transferred from the Library 1989

T05687 Roque de Guet, Guernsey (1836)
Iπ:97x153:Transferred from the Library 1989

T05688 Roque de Guet, Guernsey (1836)
Iπ:97x154:Transferred from the Library 1989

T05689 St Pierre Port (1836)
Lπ::Transferred from the Library 1989

T05690 Dover Pier (1836)
Lπ:92x140:Transferred from the Library 1989

T05691 Dover Pier (1836)
Lπ::Transferred from the Library 1989

T05692 Ramsgate (1836)
Lπ:99x142:Transferred from the Library 1989

T05693 Ramsgate (1836)
Lπ:97x142:Transferred from the Library 1989

T05694 Broadstairs (1836)
Lπ:93x139:Transferred from the Library 1989

T05695 Broadstairs (1836)
Lπ:91x138:Transferred from the Library 1989

T05696 Eddystone Lighthouse (1836)
Lπ:95x141:Transferred from the Library 1989

T05697 Eddystone Lighthouse (1836)
Lπ:94x141:Transferred from the Library 1989

T05698 Worthbarrow Bay, Dorsetshire (1836)
Lπ:95x141:Transferred from the Library 1989

T05699 Worthbarrow Bay, Dorsetshire (1836)
Lπ:93x141:Transferred from the Library 1989

STANHOPE, John Roddam Spencer 1829-1908
British Collection

N03232 Study for 'Thoughts of the Past' (circa 1859)
Dπ:610x318:Presented by Mrs Evelyn de Morgan 1917

N03338 Thoughts of the Past (exhibited 1859)
Oc:864x508:signed:Presented by Mrs F. Evans 1918

N04493 The Wine Press
Oc:940x667:Presented by Sir Henry Grayson Bt 1930

STANLEY, Lady Dorothy 1855-1926
British Collection

N01567 His First Offence (1896)
Oc:629x343:signed:Presented by Sir Henry Tate 1897

STARCZEWSKI, Antoni born 1924
Modern Collection

P02433 I/MFI (1971)
MJπ:435x416:signed:Presented by the artist 1977

P02434 MF30 (circa 1974)
MJπ:391x403:Presented by the artist 1977

P02526 O/ab+cd (1969)
MIπ:384x384:signed:Presented by the artist 1979

P02527 ML/G2/I/T. CH (1974)
MJVπ:410x397:Presented by the artist 1979

P11091 G R 2 (1975-6)
MIπ:493x385:signed:Presented by Professor Akumal Ramachander 1985

P11092 a+b/a+b (1971)
MIπ:495x370:signed:Presented by Professor Akumal Ramachander 1985

STARK, James 1794-1859
British Collection
Tate Gallery Archive holds material concerning this artist

N02164 Woody Landscape
Oc:521x813:Bequeathed by Henry Callcott Brunning 1907

STARK, Robert 1853-1931
British Collection

N01760 Indian Rinoceros (1887)
Sz:432x781x276:signed:Presented by the Trustees of the Chantrey Bequest 1892

STARR, Sydney 1857-1925
British Collection

N04766 Study in Blue and Grey (1891)
Oc:1905x1073:signed:Presented by F. Howard 1934

T03643 A Study (circa 1887)
Oc:455x355:signed:Presented anonymously in memory of Sir Terence Rattigan 1983

STARTUP, Peter 1921-1976
Modern Collection
Tate Gallery Archive holds material concerning this artist

T00612 Up-Ended Figure (1961)
Sw:2629x737x457:Purchased 1963

STAZEWSKI, Henryk 1894-1988
Modern Collection
Tate Gallery Archive holds material concerning this artist

T00576 White-Black Relief No. 6 (1962)
Biato - Czarny relief
Ow:378x375:signed:Purchased 1963

STEADMAN, Ralph born 1936
Modern Collection
Tate Gallery Archive holds material concerning this artist

P06580 Courtroom Scene from Alice in Wonderland (1967)
MLπ:571x797:Presented by Curwen Studio through the Institute of Contemporary Prints 1975

STEELE, Jeffrey born 1931
Modern Collection
Tate Gallery Archive holds material concerning this artist

P03095 Domenico (1967-8)
CNπ:3048x6096:Presented by the Welsh Arts Council 1975

P07429 Rational Concepts (1977)
CNπ:597x597:signed:Purchased 1981

STEER, Philip Wilson 1860-1942
British Collection
Tate Gallery Archive holds material concerning this artist

N02473 Chepstow Castle (1905)
Oc:765x918:signed:Presented by Miss Mary Hoadley Dodge 1909

N02872 The Music Room (1905-6)
Oc:1022x1270:signed:Presented by the National Art Collections Fund 1912

N03019 Chepstow (1905)
WDπ:251x362:signed:Presented by Geoffrey Blackwell through the National Art Collections Fund 1915

N03193 Richmond Castle (1903)
Oc:768x1022:signed:Presented by Sir Michael Sadler through the National Art Collections Fund 1917

N03321 Yorkshire Moorland (1906)
WGπ:254x375:signed:Presented by Viscount Bearsted through the National Art Collections Fund 1923

N03508 Farmyard (1919)
Wπ:241x349:signed:Presented by Lord Duveen 1920

N03668 A Procession of Yachts (1892-3)
Oc:629x762:Purchased 1922

N03715 Elm Trees (1922)
Wπ:232x327:signed:Presented by A.E. Anderson through
the National Art Collections Fund 1923

N03803 Mrs Raynes (1922)
Oc:686x559:Presented by the Trustees of the Chantrey
Bequest 1922

N03884 Painswick Beacon (1915)
Oc:610x914:signed:Purchased 1924

N04264 Sleep (exhibited 1898)
Oc:895x1321:signed:Presented by Lord Ivor Spencer
Churchill 1927

N04272 The Toilet of Venus (1898)
Oc:2553x1835:Presented by Frank Lycett Green 1927

N04422 Mrs Cyprian Williams and her Two Little Girls (1891)
Oc:762x1022:Purchased with assistance from anonymous
subscribers 1928

N04462 Bathsheba (circa 1919-21)
Oc:660x508:Bequeathed by H.B. Harris 1929

N04463 Stroud: An Upland Landscape (1902)
Oc:514x692:signed:Bequeathed by H.B. Harris 1929

N04546 Paddlers (1929)
Wπ:235x340:signed:Presented by the Trustees of the
Chantrey Bequest 1930

N04561 David Croal Thomson (1895)
Oc:765x635:signed:Bequeathed by David Croal Thomson
1930

N04955 Bird-nesting, Ludlow (1898)
Oc:571x927:signed:Presented by the Trustees of the
Chantrey Bequest 1937

N05256 The Bridge (1887-8)
Oc:495x654:signed:Purchased 1941

N05261 Seated Nude: The Black Hat (circa 1900)
Oc:508x406:signed:Presented by the Contemporary Art
Society 1941

N05290 Nutting (1905)
Oc:689x921:signed:Bequeathed by Sir Hugh Walpole
1941

N05295 Girl in a Blue Dress (circa 1891)
Ow:273x210:signed:Bequeathed by Sir Hugh Walpole
1941

N05351 The Beach at Walberswick (?circa 1889)
Oc:603x762:signed:Purchased 1942

N05374 Southwold (circa 1889)
Oc:508x610:Purchased 1942

N05375 The Swiss Alps at the Earl's Court Exhibition (1887)
Oc:641x762:Purchased 1942

N05439 Boulogne Sands (1888-91)
Oc:610x765:signed:Presented by the National Art
Collections Fund 1943

N05618 What of the War? (circa 1881)
Oc:914x705:signed:Purchased 1945

N05766 Figures on the Beach, Walberswick (circa 1888-9)
Oc:610x610:Purchased 1947

N05890 On the River Blackwater, Maldon (1933)
Wπ:225x308:signed:Bequeathed by Harwood C.
Laurence through the National Art Collections Fund
1949

N05891 The Landing Stage, Greenhithe (1932)
Wπ:241x311:signed:Bequeathed by Harwood C.
Laurence through the National Art Collections Fund
1949

N06008 Girls Running, Walberswick Pier (1888-94)
Oc:629x927:signed:Presented by Lady Augustus Daniel
1951

N06141 The Church at Montreuil (1907)
Oc:502x610:signed:Presented by Owen Fleming 1953

N06184 The Outskirts of Montreuil (1907)
Oc:965x1219:signed:Bequeathed by George E. Healing
1953

N06185 The White Yacht (1912)
Oc:610x921:signed:Bequeathed by George E. Healing
1953

N06186 The River, Ironbridge (1910)
Wπ:232x352:signed:Bequeathed by George E. Healing
1953

N06187 Morning, Ironbridge (1910)
Wπ:232x356:signed:Bequeathed by George E. Healing
1953

T00126 Low Tide, Greenhithe (1932)
Wπ:222x305:signed:Bequeathed by Miss Grace English
1957

STEIN, Ronald born 1930
Modern Collection

P05144 Lessons of the Camp (1967)
CNπ:622x940:signed:Presented by Rose and Chris Prater
through the Institute of Contemporary Prints 1975

STEINLEN, Théophile-Alexandre 1859-1923
Modern Collection

T03771 A Cat
Chat
Sz:130x50x65:signed:Transferred from the Victoria &
Albert Museum 1983

STEIR, Pat born 1940
Modern Collection

P02952 Waterfall Night (1988)
Iπ:1135x909:signed:Presented by the artist 1988

P11207 Kyoto Chrysanthemum (1982)
Jπ:363x514:signed:Presented by Karen McCready, New
York 1988

P77193 The Wave - From the Sea - After Leonardo, Hokusai and
Courbet (1985)
VIπ:895x1137:signed:Purchased 1987

STELLA, Frank born 1936
Modern Collection
Tate Gallery Archive holds material concerning this artist

T00730 Hyena Stomp (1962)
Ac:1956x1956:Purchased 1965

T01552 Six Mile Bottom (1960)
Ac:3000x1822:Purchased 1972

T03058 Guadalupe Island, Caracara (1979)
Rvm:2381x3073x457:Purchased 1980

P07404 Polar Coordinates I (1980)
CNLπ:978x965:signed:Purchased 1980

P07405 Polar Coordinates II (1980)
CNLπ:978x965:signed:Purchased 1980

P07735 Estoril Five II (1982)
CIRπ:1695x1315:signed:Purchased 1982

STEPHENS, Frederic George 1828-1907
British Collection
Tate Gallery Archive holds material concerning this artist

N04632 The Artist's Mother (circa 1850)
Dπ:194x175:Bequeathed by H.F. Stephens 1932

N04633 The Proposal (The Marquis and Griselda) (circa 1850)
Oc:806x648:signed:Bequeathed by H.F. Stephens 1932

N04634 Mother and Child (circa 1854)
Oc:470x641:signed:Bequeathed by H.F. Stephens 1932

N04635 Morte d'Arthur (circa 1850-55)
Oc:349x730:signed:Bequeathed by H.F. Stephens 1932

STEPHENSON, Ian born 1934
Modern Collection

T00523 Polychromatic G (1961)
Oc:1270x1270:Purchased 1962

T00706 Parachrome (1964)
Oc:2134x2134:Purchased 1964

T01688 Quadrama IV (1969)
OEc:3353x4572:Purchased 1972

T01689 Parental Palette (1959)
Ow:419x356:signed:Purchased 1972

T01690 Sideboard Abstraction (1957)
OEw:502x425:signed:Purchased 1972

Sandsend Series from Beyond the World's End
(T01941-T01944; complete group)

T01941 Chelsea Reach: Understudy (1972)
OEVπ:559x759:signed:Purchased 1975

T01942 Chelsea Reach: Understudy (1972)
ODEπ:762x1016:signed:Purchased 1975

T01943 Flaxman: Understudy (1972)
OEVπ:559x762:signed:Purchased 1975

T01944 Flaxman: Understudy (1972)
ODEπ:762x1016:signed:Purchased 1975

Phoenix (P11010-P11015; complete group)

P11010 53/540 (1980)
CNVπ:560x712:signed:Presented by the Contemporary
Art Society 1981

P11011 143/540 (1980)
CNVπ:560x714:signed:Presented by the Contemporary
Art Society 1981

P11012 233/540 (1980)
CNVπ:560x714:signed:Presented by the Contemporary
Art Society 1981

P11013 323/540 (1980)
CNVπ:560x714:signed:Presented by the Contemporary
Art Society 1981

P11014 413/540 (1980)
CNVπ:560x713:signed:Presented by the Contemporary
Art Society 1981

P11015 503/540 (1980)
CNVπ:560x713:signed:Presented by the Contemporary
Art Society 1981

STEPHENSON, John Cecil 1889-1965
Modern Collection
Tate Gallery Archive holds material concerning this artist

T00617 Painting (1937)
Tc:711x914:signed:Purchased 1963

STERNE, Maurice 1878-1957
Modern Collection

N05609 Mexican Church Interior (1934-5)
Oc:1283x1022:signed:Presented by Marshall Field 1945

STEVENS, Alfred 1817-1875
British Collection
Tate Gallery Archive holds material concerning this artist

N01775 Mary Ann, Wife of Leonard Collman (circa 1854)
Oc:705x552:Purchased 1900

N01846 Isaiah (1862)
Oπ:4572x7925:Presented by C.J. Knowles 1897

N01922 Judith (circa 1848)
Ow:229x178:Purchased 1903

N01923 King Alfred and his Mother (circa 1848)
Ow:343x343:Purchased 1903

N01957 The Angel Announcing the Birth of Our Lord to the
Shepherds (circa 1860)
Ob:397x1019:Purchased 1905

N02003 Study for Amoret Bound in the House of Busirane
(?circa 1855)
Dπ:305x248:Purchased 1905

N02028 The Hon. and Rev. Samuel Best (circa 1833)
Dπ:422x286:Purchased 1905

N02039 Study of the End of a Room Including a Bust of Raphael
and his Fresco 'Jurisprudence' (?circa 1859)
DWπ:302x391:Purchased 1905

N02040 Design for Two-Handled Majolica Vase (1861)
DWπ:327x178:Purchased 1905

N02047 Design in Perspective for the Decoration of a Vaulted
Corridor
DWπ:321x470:Purchased 1905

N02048 Study for 'Mutability', Probably for Deysbrook House,
Liverpool (?1847)
Dπ:216x584:Purchased 1905

N02051 Design for 'The Angel Announcing the Birth of Our
Lord to the Shepherds' (N01957) (circa 1860)
DWπ:156x527:Purchased 1905

N02132 John Morris Moore (circa 1840)
Oc:597x476:Presented by Sir Joseph Duveen and
subscribers through the National Art Collections Fund
1907

N02212 An Artist in his Studio (circa 1840-2)
Oc:600x476:Purchased 1908

N02213 Portrait of a Man (circa 1839-40)
Oc:416x454:Purchased 1908

N02270 Truth and Falsehood: Study for the Wellington
Monument, St Paul's (circa 1863)
Sp:603x292x432:Presented by Sir Herbert Cook Bt in
memory of Sir James Knowles KCVO 1908

N02931 Herbert Collman (circa 1860)
Sz:445x210x203:Presented by Alfred A. de Pass 1913

N02932 Leonard Collman (circa 1860)
Sz:438x216x210:Presented by Alfred A. de Pass 1913

N02939 William Blundell Spence (circa 1851)
Oc:613x508:Presented by Alfred A. de Pass 1913

N03009 Design for Roundel of a Door at Dorchester House
(circa 1864)
WDπ::Presented by W.C. Alexander 1914

N03392 The Hon. and Rev. Samuel Best (?1840)
Oc:514x483:Presented by Lady Holroyd in accordance
with the wishes of the late Sir Charles Holroyd 1919

N03467 Mrs Elizabeth Young Mitchell and her Baby (1851)
Oc:635x762:Purchased 1919

N03762 Study for a Seated Woman Gazing at 'Magog Thrown into the Sea', for Dorchester House (circa 1860)
Dπ:333x270:Presented by the Trustees of the Chantrey Bequest 1923

N03774 Study of a Kneeling Boy Bending a Bow, for Dorchester House (circa 1860)
Dπ:321x257:Presented by the Trustees of the Chantrey Bequest 1923

N03778 Study for 'Aeneas Bearing Anchises on his Shoulders', for Dorchester House (1860)
Dπ:333x260:Presented by the Trustees of the Chantrey Bequest 1923

N03786 Design for the Top Panel of the Overmantel of the Fireplace for Dorchester House (circa 1863-5)
WDπ:140x470:Presented by the Trustees of the Chantrey Bequest 1923

N03805 Self-Portrait at the Age of 14 (1832)
Oc:308x248:Purchased 1923

N04220 Samuel Pegler (1832)
Oc:460x381:Purchased 1926

N04379 Miss Emma Pegler (circa 1832)
Oc:533x432:Presented by Mrs Sigismund Goetze through the National Art Collections Fund 1928

A00866 Studies of Angels etc. for the Dome of St Paul's (circa 1862-7)
Dπ:308x257:Purchased 1905

STEVENS, Norman 1937-1988
Modern Collection
Tate Gallery Archive holds material concerning this artist

T01453 Porch (1971)
Ac:1238x1222:Presented by the Trustees of the Chantrey Bequest 1971

P01593 Clapboard House in Moonlight (1975)
CIπ:381x546:signed:Presented by Christie's Contemporary Art through the Institute of Contemporary Prints 1975

P01594 Dusk (1973)
CIπ:403x305:signed:Presented by Editions Alecto through the Institute of Contemporary Prints 1975

P01595 Clapboard House with Fronds and Architectural French Curve (1974)
CIπ:273x346:signed:Presented by Editions Alecto through the Institute of Contemporary Prints 1975

P01596 Courtyard (1974)
CIπ:327x632:signed:Presented by Editions Alecto through the Institute of Contemporary Prints 1975

P01597 Covered Walk (1974)
CIπ:254x365:signed:Presented by Editions Alecto through the Institute of Contemporary Prints 1975

P01598 Flight of Steps (1974)
CIπ:305x270:signed:Presented by Editions Alecto through the Institute of Contemporary Prints 1975

P01599 Morning (1974)
CIπ:543x391:signed:Presented by Editions Alecto through the Institute of Contemporary Prints 1975

P01600 Path (1974)
CIπ:330x632:signed:Presented by Editions Alecto through the Institute of Contemporary Prints 1975

P01601 Stone Circle (1974)
CIπ:254x435:signed:Presented by Editions Alecto through the Institute of Contemporary Prints 1975

P01602 Stonehenge (1974)
CIπ:445x467:signed:Presented by Editions Alecto through the Institute of Contemporary Prints 1975

P01870 Lane (1976)
CIπ:340x311:signed:Presented by Christie's Contemporary Art 1979

P01871 Darkling Thrush (1977-8)
CIπ:435x546:signed:Presented by Christie's Contemporary Art 1979

For John Constable (P03149-P03157, P03159-P03161, P03180-P03185; complete group; mixed group)

P03161 [no title] (1976)
WMIπ:102x152:signed:Presented by Bernard Jacobson Gallery 1976

Lower Wessex Lane (P06689-P06692; complete group)

P06689 Spring (1976)
CLπ:445x507:signed:Presented by Curwen Studio 1976

P06690 Summer (1976)
CLπ:445x507:signed:Presented by Curwen Studio 1976

P06691 Autumn (1976)
CLπ:444x508:signed:Presented by Curwen Studio 1976

P06692 Winter (1976)
CLπ:445x510:signed:Presented by Curwen Studio 1976

STEVENSON, James 1881-1937
Modern Collection

N03032 Imperator (1915)
Sz:368x368x267:signed:Presented by W.J. Barwick 1915

STEVENSON, Robert Alan Mowbray 1847-1900
British Collection

N04204 Houses in Snow
Oc:610x464:Presented anonymously 1926

STEZAKER, John born 1949
Modern Collection

Jam Press Phase One (P08006-P08014; complete group; mixed group)

P08014 1. 10 and 1. 11 (1973-4)
MLπ:559x441:Transferred from the Library 1977

STILL, Clyfford 1904-1980
Modern Collection

T01498 1953 (1953)
Oc:2359x1740:signed:Purchased 1971

STOKES, Adrian 1854-1935
British Collection

N01623 Uplands and Sky (1886-8)
Oc:1492x2089:signed:Presented by the Trustees of the Chantrey Bequest 1888

N01927 Autumn in the Mountains (exhibited 1903)
Tc:800x1067:Presented by the Trustees of the Chantrey Bequest 1903

STOKES, Adrian 1902-1972
Modern Collection
Tate Gallery Archive holds material concerning this artist

T00215 Piazza Sant 'Eustachio, Rome (1955)
Oc:546x457:Purchased 1958

T00216 Olive Trees (1958)
Oc:762x635:signed:Purchased 1958

T00720 Still Life (1963)
Oc:457x457:signed:Purchased 1965

T00721 Olive Terraces (1938 and circa 1952)
Oc:762x559:signed:Purchased 1965

T03579 Still Life: Last Eleven (No. 4) (1972)
Oc:328x410:Purchased 1983

T03580 Still Life: Last Eleven (No. 6) (1972)
Oc:356x457:signed:Purchased 1983

T03581 Still Life: Last Eleven (No. 11) (1972)
Oc:356x457:Purchased 1983

T03582 Still Life: Last Eleven (No. 5) (1972)
Oc:356x457:signed:Purchased 1983

T03583 Still Life: Last Eleven (No. 8) (1972)
Oc:508x407:signed:Purchased 1983

T03584 Still Life: Last Eleven (No. 7) (1972)
Oc:356x457:signed:Purchased 1983

T03585 Still Life: Last Eleven (No. 10) (1972)
Oc:559x759:signed:Purchased 1983

T03586 Still Life: Last Eleven (No. 9) (1972)
Oc:508x534:signed:Purchased 1983

T03587 Still Life: Last Eleven (No. 3) (1972)
Oc:508x610:Purchased 1983

T04123 Landscape, West Penwith Moor (1937)
Oc:609x508:Purchased 1985

STOKES, Marianne 1855-1927
British Collection

T02108 Candlemas Day (circa 1901)
Tw:416x340:signed:Presented by the Trustees of the Chantrey Bequest 1977

STONE, Marcus 1840-1921
British Collection

N01583 Il y en a toujours un autre (1882)
Oc:1537x705:signed:Presented by the Trustees of the Chantrey Bequest 1882

STOREY, George Adolphus 1834-1919
British Collection

N02861 My Mother (1874)
Oc:914x711:Presented by the National Art Collections Fund 1912

N02993 My Father (1868)
Oc:584x495:signed:Presented by the Contemporary Art Society 1914

N04109 Sketch for 'The Bride's Burial' (circa 1859)
Wπ:222x184:signed:Presented in memory of Lord Leverhulme by his executors through the National Art Collections Fund 1925

STOTHARD, Thomas 1755-1834
British Collection
Tate Gallery Archive holds material concerning this artist

N00317 A Greek Vintage (exhibited 1821)
Oc:1048x1321:Presented by Robert Vernon 1847

N00318 A Woodland Dance
Oc:638x470:Presented by Robert Vernon 1847

N00319 Cupid Bound by Nymphs (exhibited 1814)
Ow:394x305:Presented by Robert Vernon 1847

N00320 Diana and her Nymphs Bathing (exhibited 1816)
Oc:508x610:Presented by Robert Vernon 1847

N00321 Intemperance: Mark Antony and Cleopatra (circa 1802)
Oc:495x749:Presented by Robert Vernon 1847

N00322 A Battle
Oc:610x686:Presented by Robert Vernon 1847

N01069 Nymphs Discover the Narcissus (exhibited 1793)
Oc:305x343:Purchased 1879

N01070 Cupids Preparing for the Chase
Oc:457x330:Purchased 1879

N01163 The Pilgrimage to Canterbury (1806-7)
Ow:318x952:Purchased 1884

N01185 Nymphs and Satyrs
Ow:311x229:Bequeathed by Mrs Elizabeth Vaughan 1885

N01827 A Nymph Sleeping
Ow:127x184:Bequeathed by Henry Vaughan 1900

N01829 Sans Souci (exhibited 1817)
Ow:787x508:Bequeathed by Henry Vaughan 1900

N01830 Shekespearean Characters (exhibited 1813)
Oπ:267x930:Bequeathed by Henry Vaughan 1900

N01832 Cupid Bound to a Tree
Ow:394x292:Bequeathed by Henry Vaughan 1900

N01833 Lord William Russell Taking Leave of his Children
Oc:292x381:Bequeathed by Henry Vaughan 1900

N01835 Scene from 'Romeo and Juliet'
Oπ:152x117:Bequeathed by Henry Vaughan 1900

N01836 Lady Reclining
Oc:152x190:Bequeathed by Henry Vaughan 1900

N02219 Peace Came Down upon the Earth
Oc:508x762:Presented by the Misses Sharpe 1908

N04318 Study of Female Figures
DWπ:152x102:Bequeathed by J.R. Holliday 1927

N05191 Classical Female Figures
DWπ:63x86:Bequeathed by Miss Alice G.E. Carthew 1940

N05194 Religion Teaching her Children
WDπ:254x356:Bequeathed by Miss Alice G.E. Carthew 1940

Studies for 'The Pilgrimage to Canterbury' (N01163).
A00868-A00877 studies of groups, figures, heads etc.
(A00867-A00878; complete group)

A00867 The First Drawing . . . made for Ritson (circa 1806-7)
Dπ:89x121:Presented by Henry Vaughan 1891

A00868 [title not known] (circa 1806-7)
Dπ:114x190:Presented by Henry Vaughan 1891

A00869 [title not known] (1806-7)
Dπ:114x190:Presented by Henry Vaughan 1891

A00870 [title not known] (1806-7)
Dπ:114x190:Presented by Henry Vaughan 1891

A00871 [title not known] (1806-7)
Dπ:114x190:Presented by Henry Vaughan 1891

A00872 [title not known] (1806-7)
Dπ:114x190:Presented by Henry Vaughan 1891

A00873 [title not known] (1806-7)
Dπ:114x190:Presented by Henry Vaughan 1891

A00874 [title not known] (1806-7)
Dπ:114x190:Presented by Henry Vaughan 1891

A00875 [title not known] (1806-7)
Dπ:114x190:Presented by Henry Vaughan 1891

A00876 [title not known] (1806-7)
Dπ:114x190:Presented by Henry Vaughan 1891

A00877 [title not known] (1806-7)
Dπ:114x190:Presented by Henry Vaughan 1891

A00878 Preliminary Version (?or Later Replica) of Finished
Composition (N01163)
Wπ:133x460:Presented by Henry Vaughan 1891

STOTT, Edward 1859-1918
British Collection

N03670 Changing Pastures (1893)
Oc:705x876:signed:Presented by the Trustees of the
Chantrey Bequest 1922

STOTT, William 1857-1900
British Collection

N05031 Girl in a Meadow (1880)
Oc:718x578:signed:Presented by R. Temperley through
the National Art Collections Fund 1939

STRANG, Ian 1886-1952
Modern Collection

N05285 Chateau Fort, Foix (1934)
Dπ:470x403:signed:Presented by Mrs R.M. Bateman, the
artist's mother-in-law 1941

N05286 Craig-y-Bere (1939)
Dπ:378x533:signed:Presented by Mrs R.M. Bateman, the
artist's mother-in-law 1941

STRANG, William 1859-1921
British Collection

N02079 Sir Henry Newbolt (1897)
Dπ:305x190:signed:Presented by James MacLehose
through the National Art Collections Fund 1906

N03036 Bank Holiday (1912)
Oc:1527x1226:signed:Presented by F. Howard through
the National Loan Exhibition Committee 1922

N03606 Self-Portrait (1912)
Oc:610x508:signed:Presented by Mrs Strang 1922

N03607 Jacob Wrestling with the Angel (1894 or 1904)
DWπ:254x289:signed:Presented by Sir Charles Holmes
1922

N03629 Self-Portrait (1919)
Oc:1168x1118:signed:Presented by the Trustees of the
Chantrey Bequest 1921

N03675 Landscape (circa 1912-21)
Ow:210x260:Purchased 1922

N04431 Mrs James MacLehose (1903)
Dπ:416x273:signed:Presented by J. MacLehose 1929

P07115 Portrait of a Man (1899)
Iπ:190x140:Purchased 1924

P07116 Salvation Army (1889)
Iπ:333x483:Purchased 1924

STREATFEILD, Robert 1786-1852
British Collection

T05469 A Man Gazing over a Wide View of Laurensburg (circa
1845)
DWπ:127x175:Presented by William Drummond 1988

STRINGER, Daniel 1754-1806
British Collection

N03137 Portrait of the Artist (1776)
Oc:845x683:signed:Purchased 1916

STROUD, Peter born 1921
Modern Collection
Tate Gallery Archive holds material concerning this artist

T00508 Six Thin Reds (1960)
ARwb:2134x1340x19:Presented by E.J. Power through
the Friends of the Tate Gallery 1962

The Clifford Suite (P05145-P05150; complete group)
P05145 [no title] (1972)
CNπ:305x343:signed:Presented by Rose and Chris Prater
through the Institute of Contemporary Prints 1975

P05146 [no title] (1972)
CNπ:306x343:signed:Presented by Rose and Chris Prater
through the Institute of Contemporary Prints 1975

P05147 [no title] (1972)
CNπ:305x344:signed:Presented by Rose and Chris Prater
through the Institute of Contemporary Prints 1975

P05148 [no title] (1972)
CNπ:306x344:signed:Presented by Rose and Chris Prater
through the Institute of Contemporary Prints 1975

P05149 [no title] (1972)
CNπ:306x345:signed:Presented by Rose and Chris Prater
through the Institute of Contemporary Prints 1975

P05150 [no title] (1972)
CNπ:305x344:signed:Presented by Rose and Chris Prater
through the Institute of Contemporary Prints 1975

P05151 Extended Yellow (1966)
CNπ:368x737:signed:Presented by Rose and Chris Prater
through the Institute of Contemporary Prints 1975

P05152 Four at the Centre (1966)
CNπ:381x381:signed:Presented by Rose and Chris Prater
through the Institute of Contemporary Prints 1975

P05153 Tall One (1966)
CNπ:813x168:signed:Presented by Rose and Chris Prater
through the Institute of Contemporary Prints 1975

P05154 Untitled (1967)
CNπ:384x381:signed:Presented by Rose and Chris Prater
through the Institute of Contemporary Prints 1975

STRUDWICK, John Melhuish 1849-1935
British Collection

N01625 A Golden Thread (exhibited 1885)
Oc:724x425:Presented by the Trustees of the Chantrey
Bequest 1885

STRUNKE, Niklavs 1894-1966
Modern Collection

N05033 The Tower of Kraslava (1937-8)
Oc:540x679:signed:Purchased 1939

STUART, Gilbert 1755-1828
British Collection

N00217 William Woollet the Engraver (exhibited 1783)
Oc:902x705:Presented by Henry Farrer 1849

N00229 Benjamin West, P.R.A. (?exhibited 1781)
Oc:914x1219:Presented by J.H. Anderdon 1853

N05612 Self-Portrait (circa 1785)
Oc:724x597:Bequeathed by Hon. Clare Stuart Wortley
1945

STUBBING, Tony 1921-1983
Modern Collection
Tate Gallery Archive holds material concerning this artist

T04874 Christian Ritual (1958)
Oc:1325x1095:Presented by Mrs Yvonne Hagen
Stubbing, the artist's widow 1986

STUBBS, George 1724-1806
British Collection

N01452 A Grey Hunter with a Groom and a Greyhound at
Creswell Crags (circa 1762-4)
Oc:445x679:Purchased 1895

N04696 Horse in the Shade of a Wood (1780)
Oc:597x762:signed:Purchased 1933

T00295 Mares and Foals in a River Landscape (circa 1763-8)
Oc:1016x1619:Purchased with assistance from the
Pilgrim Trust 1959

T00785 Mother and Child (1774)
Em:305x305:signed:Presented by Sabin Galleries 1965

T01192 Horse Attacked by a Lion (1769)
Em:241x283:signed:Purchased with assistance from the
Friends of the Tate Gallery 1970

T01705 A Couple of Foxhounds (1792)
Oc:1016x1270:signed:Purchased with assistance from the
Friends of the Tate Gallery 1973

T01985 Leopards at Play (?1780)
Bπ:381x483:Purchased 1975

T01986 Leopards at Play (? 1780, reprinted 1974)
Iπ:356x467:Purchased 1975

T02058 Horse Devoured by a Lion (?exhibited 1763)
Oc:692x1035:Purchased 1976

T02256 Haymakers (1785)
Ow:895x1353:signed:Purchased with assistance from the
Friends of the Tate Gallery, the National Art Collections
Fund, the Pilgrim Trust and subscribers 1977

T02257 Reapers (1785)
Ow:899x1368:signed:Purchased with assistance from the
Friends of the Tate Gallery, the National Art Collections
Fund, the Pilgrim Trust and subscribers 1977

T02374 Bay Hunter by a Lake (1787)
Ow:905x1372:signed:Presented by Paul Mellon through
the British Sporting Art Trust 1979

T02375 Otho, with John Larkin up (1768)
Oc:1013x1270:signed:Presented by Paul Mellon through
the British Sporting Art Trust 1979

T02388 Newmarket Heath, with a Rubbing-Down House (circa
1765)
Oc:302x419:Purchased 1979

T03778 Reapers (published 1791)
Iπ:482x685:signed:Transferred from the British Museum
1983

T03779 Labourers (published 1789)
Iπ:530x707:signed:Transferred from the British Museum
1983

T03780 A Foxhound (published 1788)
MIπ:92x115:signed:Transferred from the British Museum
1983

T03781 A Foxhound Viewed from Behind (published 1788)
Iπ:84x107:signed:Transferred from the British Museum
1983

T03843 A Horse Attacked by a Lion (A Lion Devouring a Horse)
(published 1788)
Iπ:250x335:signed:Transferred from the British Museum
1984

T03844 A Lion Resting on a Rock (published 1788)
Iπ:227x314:signed:Transferred from the British Museum
1984

T05204 Portrait of a Young Gentleman Out Shooting (1781)
Ep:457x622:Purchased with assistance from the National
Heritage Memorial Fund and the National Art
Collections Fund 1988

STUDD, Arthur 1863-1919
British Collection
Tate Gallery Archive holds material concerning this artist

N03275 A Venetian Lyric (?1900-10)
Ow:241x400:signed:Presented by Mrs Frank Gibson 1918

N03276 Breton Woman and Child (circa 1890)
Dπ:368x495:Presented by R. Thomas 1918

N03277 Pacific Island Subject (1898)
DPπ:235x381:Presented by R. Thomas 1918

T03644 The Mauve Hat (?) (circa 1900-10)
Ow:220x157:Presented anonymously in memory of Sir
Terence Rattigan 1983

T03645 Venetian Lyric (San Giorgio)(?) (circa 1900-10)
Ow:127x217:signed:Presented anonymously in memory of
Sir Terence Rattigan 1983

T03646 Venetian Lyric (Santa Maria della Salute)(?) (circa
1900-10)
Ow:127x217:signed:Presented anonymously in memory of
Sir Terence Rattigan 1983

STUDIN, Marin 1895-1960
Modern Collection

N06170 War (1944)
Rw:799x1178x88:signed:Presented anonymously 1953

SULLIVAN, Edmund J. 1869-1933
British Collection
Tate Gallery Archive holds material concerning this artist

P03089 Reign of Justice (1917)
CLπ:689x438:signed:Presented by the Ministry of
Information 1918

SULLIVAN, Luke - see HOGARTH, William and SULLIVAN, Luke

SUMMERS, Carol born 1925
Modern Collection
Tate Gallery Archive holds material concerning this artist

P01799 Stromboli Dark (1965)
CJπ:540x743:signed:Presented by the Museum of
Modern Art, New York 1976

SUTEJ, Miroslav born 1936
Modern Collection

P02552 Large Print III (1978)
CNπ:654x984:signed:Presented by the artist 1981

P07592 Print 2 (1976)
CNπ:670x924:signed:Purchased 1981

SUTHERLAND, Graham, OM 1903-1980
Modern Collection
Tate Gallery Archive holds material concerning this artist

N05139 Green Tree Form: Interior of Woods (1940)
Oc:787x1079:Purchased 1940

N05666 Welsh Landscape with Roads (1936)
Oc:610x914:signed:Presented by the Contemporary Art
Society 1946

N05734 Devastation, 1940: A House on the Welsh Border (1940)
WGDπ:800x546:signed:Presented by the War Artists'
Advisory Committee 1946

N05735 Devastation, 1941: East End, Wrecked Public House
(1941)
GDπ:673x476:signed:Presented by the War Artists'
Advisory Committee 1946

N05736 Devastation, 1941: An East End Street (1941)
WGDπ:648x1137:signed:Presented by the War Artists'
Advisory Committee 1946

N05737 Devastation, 1941: East End, Burnt Paper Warehouse
(1941)
OWDπ:673x1137:signed:Presented by the War Artists'
Advisory Committee 1946

N05738 Feeding a Steel Furnace (circa 1941)
Oc:902x864:Presented by the War Artists' Advisory
Committee 1946

N05739 A Foundry: Hot Metal has been Poured into a Mould and
Inflammable Gas is Rising (circa 1941)
WGπ:918x1092:Presented by the War Artists' Advisory
Committee 1946

N05740 Tapping a Blast Furnace (1941)
Oc:921x860:signed:Presented by the War Artists'
Advisory Committee 1946

N05741 Miner Probing a Drill Hole (circa 1942)
GDπ:559x508:signed:Presented by the War Artists'
Advisory Committee 1946

N05743 Furnaces (1944)
WGDπ:689x1524:signed:Presented by the War Artists'
Advisory Committee 1946

N05774 Crucifixion (1946)
Ob:908x1016:Purchased 1947

N06034 Somerset Maugham (1949)
Oc:1372x635:signed:Presented by Lady John Hope 1951

N06085 The Origins of the Land (1950-1)
Oc:4255x3277:Presented by the Arts Council of Great
Britain 1952

N06183 Head III (1953)
Oc:1143x883:Purchased 1953

N06190 Entrance to a Lane (1939)
Oc:1454x1232:signed:Purchased 1953

T00536 The Scales (1961-2)
Oc:1454x1232:signed:Purchased 1962

T00834 Horned Forms (1944)
Ob:813x641:Presented by the Friends of the Tate Gallery
1966

T01217 Hydrant II (1954)
Oc:1118x905:signed:Presented anonymously 1970

T01396 Study for 'Horned Forms' (1944)
Gπ:159x133:Presented by the artist 1971

T01726 Form over River (1971-2)
Oc:1797x1737:Presented by Alistair McAlpine (later
Lord McAlpine of West Green) through the Friends of
the Tate Gallery 1973

T01880 Lord Goodman (1973-4)
Oc:959x959:Presented anonymously through the Friends
of the Tate Gallery 1974

T02381 Working Drawing for 'Origins of the Land' (1951)
DTOπ:635x505:signed:Presented by Sir Kenneth Clark
(later Lord Clark of Saltwood) 1979

T03085 Black Landscape (1939-40)
Oc:810x1321:signed:Purchased 1980

T03113 Standing Forms II (1952)
Oc:1800x1410:Presented by Mrs Kathleen Sutherland,
the artist's widow 1980

La Foresta, Il Fiume, La Roccia (P01603-P01608;
complete group)
P01603 La Foresta I (1971-2)
CLπ:630x481:signed:Presented by the Institute of
Contemporary Prints 1975

P01604 La Foresta II (1971-2)
CLπ:634x478:signed:Presented by the Institute of
Contemporary Prints 1975

P01605 Il Fiume I (1971-2)
CLπ:630x481:signed:Presented by the Institute of
Contemporary Prints 1975

P01606 Il Fiume II (1971-2)
CLπ:636x483:signed:Presented by the Institute of
Contemporary Prints 1975

P01607 La Roccia (1971-2)
CLπ:631x481:signed:Presented by the Institute of
Contemporary Prints 1975

P01608 La Roccia (1971-2)
CLπ:632x480:signed:Presented by the Institute of
Contemporary Prints 1975

P02066 Pecken Wood (1925)
MIπ:137x184:signed:Presented by the artist 1970

P02067 Cray Fields (1925)
MIπ:117x124:signed:Presented by the artist 1970

P02068 Clegyr Boia (1938)
MIπ:197x146:signed:Presented by the artist 1970

P06581 Portrait of Aloys Senefelder (1971-2)
MLπ:657x492:signed:Presented by Curwen Studio
through the Institute of Contemporary Prints 1975

P07117 Pastoral (1930)
MIπ:130x190:signed:Purchased 1970

P11009 Portrait of Somerset Maugham I (1953)
MLπ:232x154:Presented by Mrs Kathleen Sutherland,
the artist's widow 1981

The Bestiary or the Procession of Orpheus
(P77085-P77102; complete group)
P77085 [no title: frontispiece] (1978-9)
CIπ:82x73:signed:Purchased 1985

P77086 1. Orpheus (1978-9)
CIπ:216x234:signed:Purchased 1985

P77087 2. The Tortoise (1978-9)
CIπ:451x736:signed:Purchased 1985

P77088 3. The Lion (1978-9)
CIπ:182x218:signed:Purchased 1985

P77089 4. The Snake (1978-9)
CIπ:491x362:signed:Purchased 1985

P77090 5. The Mouse (1978-9)
CIπ:482x389:signed:Purchased 1985

P77091 6. The Elephant (1978-9)
CIπ:486x393:signed:Purchased 1985

P77092 7. Orpheus (1978-9)
CIπ:146x140:signed:Purchased 1985

P77093 8. The Caterpillar (1978-9)
Clπ:188x167:signed:Purchased 1985

P77094 9. The Fly (1978-9)
Clπ:481x739:signed:Purchased 1985

P77095 10. The Flea (1978-9)
Clπ:472x363:signed:Purchased 1985

P77096 11. The Grasshopper (1978-9)
Clπ:219x216:signed:Purchased 1985

P77097 12. Orpheus (1978-9)
Clπ:484x755:signed:Purchased 1985

P77098 13. The Octopus (1978-9)
Clπ:488x394:signed:Purchased 1985

P77099 14. The Sirens (1978-9)
Clπ:493x767:signed:Purchased 1985

P77100 15. Ibis (1978-9)
Clπ:378x638:signed:Purchased 1985

P77101 16. The Ox (1978-9)
Clπ:483x378:signed:Purchased 1985

P77102 17. The Pyre (1978-9)
Clπ:220x259:signed:Purchased 1985

SUTTON, Philip born 1928
Modern Collection
Tate Gallery Archive holds material concerning this artist

T00112 Autumn Flowers (1955)
Oc:1016x1270:signed:Purchased 1956

T00330 The Tree (1958)
Oc:1372x1372:signed:Purchased 1960

P06582 Great Australian Bight (1966)
CLπ:502x508:signed:Presented by Curwen Studio
through the Institute of Contemporary Prints 1975

P06583 Hawaii (1966)
CLπ:511x511:Presented by Curwen Studio through the
Institute of Contemporary Prints 1975

P06584 Pacific (1966)
CLπ:505x511:signed:Presented by Curwen Studio
through the Institute of Contemporary Prints 1975

P06585 Samoa (1966)
CLπ:508x508:signed:Presented by Curwen Studio
through the Institute of Contemporary Prints 1975

P06586 San Francisco (1966)
CLπ:511x514:signed:Presented by Curwen Studio
through the Institute of Contemporary Prints 1975

P06587 Vancouver (1966)
CLπ:511x514:signed:Presented by Curwen Studio
through the Institute of Contemporary Prints 1975

SUTTON, Trevor born 1948
Modern Collection

P11214 Untitled (1988)
Jπ:650x509:Presented by Garner H. Tullis and Pamela
Auchincloss 1989

SWAN, John Macallan 1847-1910
British Collection

N01569 The Prodigal Son (1888)
Oc:1118x1575:signed:Presented by the Trustees of the
Chantrey Bequest 1889

N02708 Panthers Resting
Pπ:279x451:signed:Presented anonymously through the
National Art Collections Fund 1910

N02766 The Gladiators
Dπ:375x870:Presented by the John M. Swan Memorial
Fund 1911

N02768 Head of a Lion and Lion Lying Down
Dπ:178x286:signed:Presented by the John M. Swan
Memorial Fund 1911

N02769 Tiger Lying Down
Dπ:368x267:Presented by the John M. Swan Memorial
Fund 1911

N02770 Two Lionesses and Two Heads of Lionesses
Dπ:254x333:Presented by the John M. Swan Memorial
Fund 1911

N02771 Tiger Lying Down with Head Raised
Dπ:273x419:Presented by the John M. Swan Memorial
Fund 1911

N02772 Leopard Bending Down to Drink
Dπ:178x292:Presented by the John M. Swan Memorial
Fund 1911

N02773 Back View of a Leopard Lying Down
Dπ:235x349:Presented by the John M. Swan Memorial
Fund 1911

N02774 Head of a Tiger
Dπ:184x152:signed:Presented by the John M. Swan
Memorial Fund 1911

N02775 Head of a Lioness
Dπ:127x197:signed:Presented by the John M. Swan
Memorial Fund 1911

N02776 Leopard Drinking
Dπ:140x305:signed:Presented by the John M. Swan
Memorial Fund 1911

N02777 Lioness Walking
Dπ:152x283:Presented by the John M. Swan Memorial
Fund 1911

N02778 Head and Forepart of a Tiger
Dπ:222x346:Presented by the John M. Swan Memorial
Fund 1911

N02779 Leopard Gnawing a Bone
Dπ:190x343:signed:Presented by the John M. Swan
Memorial Fund 1911

N02780 Leopard Lying Down
Dπ:260x391:Presented by the John M. Swan Memorial
Fund 1911

N02781 Back of a Leopard Lying Down
Dπ:184x340:Presented by the John M. Swan Memorial
Fund 1911

N04729 Boy and Bear Cubs (exhibited 1902)
Sz:1638x889:Presented by Sir Paul Makins Bt 1934

N05277 Young Indian Leopard and Tortoise (exhibited 1897)
Sm:159x330x140:Bequeathed by Ernest L. Sichel 1941

SWANSON, John born 1938
Modern Collection

P02326 The Restaurant (1974)
CNπ:359x597:signed:Presented by the artist 1976

P02327 The Carousel (1975)
CNπ:679x791:signed:Presented by the artist 1976

SWYNNERTON, Annie Louisa 1844-1933
British Collection
Tate Gallery Archive holds material concerning this artist

N03619 Oreads (exhibited 1907)
Oc:1778x1778:Presented by John Singer Sargent 1922

N03952 New Risen Hope (1904)
Oc:559x508:signed:Presented by the Trustees of the
Chantrey Bequest 1924

N04473 The Convalescent (exhibited 1929)
Oc:571x635:Presented by the Trustees of the Chantrey
Bequest 1929

N04545 Dame Millicent Fawcett, C.B.E., LL.D. (exhibited 1930)
Oc:813x737:Presented by the Trustees of the Chantrey
Bequest 1930

N04656 Count Zouboff (exhibited 1931)
Oc:1905x1524:signed:Presented by Messrs Wallis and
Son 1932

N05019 Miss Elizabeth Williamson on a Pony (1906)
Oc:1676x1308:signed:Presented by F. Howard 1939

SYDNEY, Berenice 1944-1983
Modern Collection
Tate Gallery Archive holds material concerning this artist

P01609 Little Squares (1969)
CIπ:200x152:signed:Presented by the artist through the
Institute of Contemporary Prints 1975

P01610 Small Garden (1969)
CIπ:178x178:signed:Presented by the artist through the
Institute of Contemporary Prints 1975

P01611 Fast Rhythm (1972)
CIπ:505x406:signed:Presented by the artist through the
Institute of Contemporary Prints 1975

P01612 The Young Moon's Arms (1972)
MIπ:483x400:signed:Presented by the artist through the
Institute of Contemporary Prints 1975

P01613 Monoprint with Red Hand (1973)
CJπ:794x587:signed:Presented by the artist through the
Institute of Contemporary Prints 1975

P01614 Monoprint with Round Puff (1973)
CJπ:781x587:signed:Presented by the artist through the
Institute of Contemporary Prints 1975

P02280 Screenprint with Balance (1974)
CNπ:800x584:Presented by the artist 1976

P02281 Etching with Brother Dog (1975)
CIπ:203x254:Presented by the artist 1976

P02282 Etching with Evil Spirits (1975)
MIπ:267x190:Presented by the artist 1976

SYMONS, Patrick born 1925
Modern Collection
Tate Gallery Archive holds material concerning this artist

T03552 Oak Arch Grey (Wimbledon Common) (1977-81)
Oc:892x795:signed:Purchased 1983

TAKIS born 1925
Modern Collection

T00731 Signal 'Insect-Animal of Space' (1956)
Signal 'insecte-animal de l'espace'
Sm:2080x229x241:Presented by Mrs Peggy Guggenheim
through the Contemporary Art Society 1965

TALMAGE, Algernon 1871-1939
British Collection
Tate Gallery Archive holds material concerning this artist

N04877 The Founding of Australia 1788 (1937)
Oc:2261x3188:signed:Presented by Frank Albert 1937

TAMAYO, Rufino born 1899
Modern Collection

T03370 Man and Woman (1981)
Hombre y muser
Oc:1247x1800:signed:Purchased 1982

P01800 Dream Figure (circa 1960)
CLπ:660x498:signed:Presented by the Museum of
Modern Art, New York 1976

P11030 [Title not known] (1981)
CLπ:238x171:signed:Presented by the Rufino Tamayo
Museum, Mexico 1981

TANABE, Takao born 1926
Modern Collection
Tate Gallery Archive holds material concerning this artist

Centennial Suite (P03217-P03225, P03228-P03229;
complete group; mixed group)
P03229 Envelope Sketch (1967)
CNπ:333x435:signed:Presented by Simon Fraser
University, British Columbia 1977

TANGUY, Yves 1900-1955
Modern Collection
Tate Gallery Archive holds material concerning this artist

T00657 The Invisibles (1951)
Les Transparents
Oc:987x810:signed:Purchased 1964

TANNING, Dorothea born 1910
Modern Collection

T00298 A Mi-Voix (1958)
Oc:1302x972:signed:Presented by William N. Copley 1959

TAPIES, Antoni born 1923
Modern Collection
Tate Gallery Archive holds material concerning this artist

T00471 Grey and Green Painting (1957)
Peinture grise et verte
OVc:1140x1613:signed:Presented by the Friends of the
Tate Gallery 1962

T00927 Grey Ochre (1958)
Ochre gris
Oc:2603x1943:signed:Purchased 1967

P07570 The Sieve (1972)
Le Tamis
CLπ:654x892:signed:Purchased 1981

P07571 Cartography (1976)
Cartographie
CLπ:560x843:signed:Purchased 1981

P07572 Pasted Cloth (1976)
Tissu collé
CIVπ:632x908:signed:Purchased 1981

TAYLER, Frederick 1802-1889
British Collection

N01979 Dragoons on the March
Wπ:584x914:signed:Bequeathed by C. Fraser 1905

attributed to
TAYLOR, John, of Bath 1735-1806
British Collection

N02983 Paddlers among Ruins
Oc:305x349:Bequeathed by Richard and Catherine
Garnons 1854

TAYLOR, Leonard Campbell 1874-1969
British Collection

N02137 The Rehearsal (1907)
Oc:2165x3054:signed:Presented by the Trustees of the
Chantrey Bequest 1907

TAYLOR, Walter 1860-1943
British Collection
Tate Gallery Archive holds material concerning this artist

N03716 Boodle's Club (?circa 1914-15)
DWπ:387x318:signed:Presented by the artist 1923

TCHELITCHEW, Pavel 1898-1957
Modern Collection

N06236 Mrs R.A. Gorer (1930)
Gπ:1010x686:signed:Presented by Geoffrey, Peter and
Richard Gorer in memory of Rée Alice Gorer 1954

TENNIEL, Sir John 1820-1914
British Collection

N04127 The Lady Shows Alnaschar the Hidden Treasure,
engraved by the Dalziel Brothers (published 1864)
Jπ:127x76:Presented by Gilbert Dalziel 1925

TESHIGAHARA, Sofu 1900-1979
Modern Collection

T00546 White Cloud (1960)
Haku-Un
Df:1683x908:signed:Purchased 1962

THANGUE, Henry Herbert la - see LA
THANGUE, Henry Herbert

THARRATS, Joan-Josep born 1918
Modern Collection

T00507 Who Looks . . . (1961)
Quien mira . . .
Oc:1299x1619:signed:Presented by the Directorate
General of Cultural Relations, Spanish Foreign Ministry
1962

THIEBAUD, Wayne born 1920
Modern Collection

P07724 Chocolate Cake (1971)
MLπ:445x330:signed:Purchased 1982

THIRSK, John born 1945
Modern Collection

Follies (P06025, P06028-P06029, P06315-P06316,
P06518, P06588-P06589; complete group; mixed group)

P06588 Deer House, Bishop Auckland (1971)
CLπ:445x651:signed:Presented by Curwen Studio
through the Institute of Contemporary Prints 1975

P06589 Wainhouse Tower, Halifax (1971)
CLπ:445x651:signed:Presented by Curwen Studio
through the Institute of Contemporary Prints 1975

P06590 Dr W.G. Grace (1972)
CLπ:575x384:signed:Presented by Curwen Studio
through the Institute of Contemporary Prints 1975

THIRTLE, John 1777-1839
British Collection
Tate Gallery Archive holds material concerning this artist

N04380 Old Lynn
Wπ:359x530:Presented by Sir William Lancaster 1928

THOMAS, George Houston 1824-1868
British Collection

N04330 Three Drawings for Illustration. i) A Cab for Two Men
ii) Dictating the Will iii) Scene on a Ship
WGπ:149x190, 111x175, 102x159:Bequeathed by J.R.
Holliday 1927

THOMAS, George Havard 1893-1933
Modern Collection

N04767 Aphrodite (circa 1928-30)
Ss:883x273x241:signed:Purchased 1934

THOMAS, James Havard 1854-1921
British Collection

N02268 Mrs Asher Wertheimer (1907)
Ss:775x565x381:signed:Presented by Asher Wertheimer
1908

N02763 Lycidas (1902-8)
Sz:1613x832x521:signed:Presented by Sir Michael and
Lady Sadler through the National Art Collections Fund
1911

N03184 The Offering (circa 1908)
Dπ:660x571:signed:Presented by the Contemporary Art
Society 1917

N03639 Cow and Calf (1897)
Rs:295x394:signed:Purchased 1922

N03640 Irrigators, Southern Italy (circa 1899-1906)
Dπ:549x813:Purchased 1922

N03674 Cardinal Manning (1876-86)
Sz:571x235x244:signed:Presented by the Trustees of the
Chantrey Bequest 1922

N04202 Thyrsis (1912)
Spw:1683x702:signed:Presented by the National Art
Collections Fund, Lord Duveen and Vernon Wethered
1926

N04739 Castagnettes No. 2 (1900)
Sz:337x244x127:signed:Bequeathed by Dr Bluett Duncan
1934

N05958 Thyrsis (1912)
Sz:1683x702x397:signed:Purchased 1948

N06031 Cassandra (1912-21)
Sp:1613x552x600:Purchased 1949

N06082 Cassandra (circa 1912-21)
Sz:1613x552x600:Purchased 1951

T00229 Dr P.H. Emerson (1888)
Rs:254x175x19:Purchased 1959

THOMAS, John 1813-1862
British Collection

N02061 W.P. Frith (1859)
Ss:800x495x305:signed:Presented by L. Loewenthal 1906

THOMKINS, André 1930-1985
Modern Collection

P08175 Fugger (1978)
MJπ:178x122:Transferred from the Library 1980

THOMSON, Alfred R. 1894-1979
Modern Collection

N05107 Sister Fry (1939)
Oc:762x635:signed:Presented by the Trustees of the
Chantrey Bequest 1940

THOMSON, George 1860-1939
British Collection

N03506 St Paul's (circa 1897)
Oc:635x762:signed:Purchased 1920

THOMSON, Rev. John, of Duddingston
1778-1840
British Collection

N00731 Loch-an-Eilean, Rothiemurchus, Inverness-shire (1835)
Oc:857x1327:Bequeathed by Mrs Anne Thomson 1864

THORNHILL, Sir James 1675 or 76 - 1734
British Collection

N06200 The Apotheosis of Romulus: Sketch for a Ceiling
Decoration, Possibly for Hewell Grange, Worcestershire
(circa 1710)
Oc:457x521:Purchased 1953

T00814 Thetis Accepting the Shield of Achilles from Vulcan
(circa 1710)
Ow:489x498:Purchased 1965

T01551 Three Studies for 'Thetis in the Forge of Vulcan
Watching the Making of Achilles' Armour' (circa 1710)
Dπ:254x400:Purchased 1972

THORNTON, Alfred 1863-1939
British Collection
Tate Gallery Archive holds material concerning this artist

N04539 St Germans (circa 1897)
Oc:762x1016:signed:Presented by the Trustees of the
Chantrey Bequest 1930

THORNTON, Valerie 1931-1991
Modern Collection
Tate Gallery Archive holds material concerning this artist

P01615 Amboise (1973)
CLπ:403x575:Presented by the Contemporary Art Society through the Institute of Contemporary Prints 1975

P01616 Boxford Church, Suffolk (1974)
CLπ:400x625:Presented by Christie's Contemporary Art through the Institute of Contemporary Prints 1975

P02638 Monterde (1980)
CLπ:495x692:signed:Presented by the artist 1983

P02639 Sangüesa (1982)
CLπ:648x416:signed:Presented by the artist 1983

P06815 Norfolk Farm (1977)
CLπ:410x635:signed:Presented by Curwen Studio 1978

THORNYCROFT, Sir Hamo 1850-1925
British Collection

N01751 Teucer (1881)
Sz:2407x1511x660:signed:Presented by the Trustees of the Chantrey Bequest 1882

N03153 The Kiss (1916)
Ss:1778x597x864:signed:Presented by the Trustees of the Chantrey Bequest 1916

N04214 Sketch for 'The Mower' (1882)
Sp:216x121x83:signed:Presented by Lady Thornycroft 1926

N04215 Sketch for 'Artemis' (1880)
Sp:184x70x181:signed:Presented by Lady Thornycroft 1926

N04216 Mother and Child (1894)
Sp:152x83x114:signed:Presented by Lady Thornycroft 1926

N04217 Study for the Statue of Cecil Rhodes (1904)
Sp:248x89x254:signed:Presented by Lady Thornycroft 1926

T03963 The Mower (1888-90)
Sz:585x330x185:signed:Presented by Arthur Grogan 1985

THRALL, Arthur born 1926
Modern Collection

P01617 Translation (1965)
CLπ:505x403:signed:Presented by the artist through the Institute of Contemporary Prints 1975

P01618 Proclamation (1970)
CLπ:603x451:signed:Presented by the artist through the Institute of Contemporary Prints 1975

P01619 Notes (1974)
CLπ:267x200:signed:Presented by the artist through the Institute of Contemporary Prints 1975

P01620 Three Variations (1974)
MIπ:165x102:signed:Presented by the artist through the Institute of Contemporary Prints 1975

P01621 Nine (1975)
CLπ:543x343:signed:Presented by the artist through the Institute of Contemporary Prints 1975

TIBBLE, Geoffrey 1909-1952
Modern Collection
Tate Gallery Archive holds material concerning this artist

T00946 Still Life (1929)
Oc:559x762:Presented by A.C. Sewter 1967

T03655 Three Women (1930)
Oc:305x406:signed:Presented anonymously in memory of Sir Terence Rattigan 1983

T03656 The Mug (1948)
Oc:370x445:signed:Presented anonymously in memory of Sir Terence Rattigan 1983

T03657 Interior with Self Portrait and Two Women (circa 1944)
Dπ:425x320:Presented anonymously in memory of Sir Terence Rattigan 1983

T03658 Dressing (1944)
Oc:762x990:signed:Presented anonymously in memory of Sir Terence Rattigan 1983

TILLEMANS, Peter circa 1684-1734
British Collection

T02376 Foxhunting in Wooded Country (circa 1720-30)
Oc:1022x1172:Presented by Paul Mellon through the British Sporting Art Trust 1979

TILLYER, William born 1938
Modern Collection
Tate Gallery Archive holds material concerning this artist

For John Constable (P03149-P03157, P03159-P03161, P03180-P03185; complete group; mixed group)
P03183 [no title] (1976)
CLπ:708x251:signed:Presented by Bernard Jacobson Gallery 1976

P07336 Mill Wood (1972)
MIπ:759x489:signed:Purchased 1979

P07337 Night Rain (1972)
MIπ:454x356:signed:Purchased 1979

A Furnished Landscape (P07338-P07342; incomplete group)
P07338 Gateway (1974)
CLπ:480x382:signed:Purchased 1979

P07339 High Force (1974)
CNπ:800x623:signed:Purchased 1979

P07340 Landscape (1974)
CNπ:805x615:signed:Purchased 1979

P07341 Opening (1974)
CNπ:795x622:signed:Purchased 1979

P07342 Valley (1974)
CLπ:775x595:signed:Purchased 1979

Bel Air Series (P07343-P07345; incomplete group)
P07343 [no title] (1975)
CLπ:410x960:signed:Purchased 1979

P07344 [no title] (1975)
CLπ:405x952:signed:Purchased 1979

P07345 [no title] (1975)
CLπ:417x965:signed:Purchased 1979

The Providence Suite (P07346-P07348; incomplete group)
P07346 [no title] (1976)
MJπ:915x305:signed:Purchased 1979

P07347 [no title] (1976)
MJπ:920x305:signed:Purchased 1979

P07348 [no title] (1976)
MJπ:915x300:signed:Purchased 1979

Florist Set: One Theme, Four Works (P07349; incomplete group)
P07349 The Print. The Fragment (1978)
CNπ:1090x1308:signed:Purchased 1979

TILSON, Joe born 1928
Modern Collection
Tate Gallery Archive holds material concerning this artist

T00480 Wood Relief No. 17 (1961)
Rw:1257x956x80:Purchased 1962

T02026 Vox Box (1963)
ROw:1524x1219x70:Purchased 1976

T03772 Ziglical Column (1966)
NEm:820x305x155:Transferred from the Victoria & Albert Museum 1983

T05465 Liknon 3 (1987)
Ocw:1966x1975:Presented by the Trustees of the Chantrey Bequest 1988

P01053 Transparency Clip-o-Matic Lips (1967-8)
CNπ:883x657:signed:Presented by John Piper 1970

P01622 Bela Lugosi Journal II (1970)
MIπ:787x518:signed:Presented by Marlborough Graphics through the Institute of Contemporary Prints 1975

P01623 Che Guevara (page 39) (1970)
MIπ:781x508:signed:Presented by Marlborough Graphics through the Institute of Contemporary Prints 1975

P01624 He She and It I (1970)
MIπ:788x510:signed:Presented by Marlborough Graphics through the Institute of Contemporary Prints 1975

P01625 He She and It II (1970)
MIπ:783x512:signed:Presented by Marlborough Graphics through the Institute of Contemporary Prints 1975

P01626 He She and It III (1970)
MIπ:790x516:signed:Presented by Marlborough Graphics through the Institute of Contemporary Prints 1975

P01627 Muhammad Speaks (1970)
MIπ:797x530:signed:Presented by Marlborough Graphics through the Institute of Contemporary Prints 1975

P01628 Snow White and the Black Dwarf (1970)
MIπ:781x511:signed:Presented by Marlborough Graphics through the Institute of Contemporary Prints 1975

P02328 Transparency, Astronaut Seat C (1968)
CNRVa:1219x1219x51:Presented by the artist 1976

P02329 Transparency, Che Guevara D (1968)
CNRVa:1219x1219x51:signed:Presented by the artist 1976

P02330 Transparency I: Yuri Gagarin 12 April 1961 (1968)
CNRVa:1219x1219x51:Presented by the artist 1976

P02331 Transparency, the Five Senses, Hearing (1969)
CNVRa:2030x2030x75:signed:Presented by the artist 1976

P02332 Transparency, the Five Senses, Sight (1969)
CNVRa:2030x2030x75:signed:Presented by the artist 1976

P02333 Transparency, the Five Senses, Smell (1969)
CNVRa:2030x2030x75:signed:Presented by the artist 1976

P02334 Transparency, the Five Senses, Touch (1969)
CNVRa:2030x2030x75:signed:Presented by the artist 1976

A-Z Box (P05190-P05214, P02436; complete group)
P02436 H - Ho Chi Minh (1969-70)
CNπ:750x502:signed:Presented by the artist 1977

P02437 Origins (1976)
CIπ:495x587:signed:Presented by the artist 1977

P02438 Pool Mantra (1976)
CIVπ:892x664:signed:Presented by the artist 1977

P02439 Six Labyrinths (1976)
CNπ:737x683:signed:Presented by the artist 1977

P02451 Alchera (1970-4)
CNπ:737x683:signed:Presented by the artist 1978

P02452 Earth Mantra (1977)
CIVπ:876x648:signed:Presented by the artist 1978

Wessex Portfolio (P02453-P02459; complete group)
P02453 [no title] (1976-7)
:385x185:signed:Presented by the artist 1978

P02454 [no title] (1976-7)
:386x189:signed:Presented by the artist 1978

P02455 [no title] (1976-7)
:388x185:signed:Presented by the artist 1978

P02456 [no title] (1976-7)
:388x185:signed:Presented by the artist 1978

P02457 [no title] (1976-7)
:387x185:signed:Presented by the artist 1978

P02458 [no title] (1976-7)
:385x184:signed:Presented by the artist 1978

P02459 [no title] (1976-7)
:287x382:signed:Presented by the artist 1978

P03148 Labrinth (1975)
MIπ:279x270:signed:Presented by Marlborough Graphics 1976

P03256 Seed Mantra (1977-78)
CIVπ:876x651:signed:Presented by Waddington Galleries 1978

P03257 Demetrius' Ladder (1978)
CIπ:873x406:signed:Presented by Waddington Galleries 1978

P03258 Proscinemi, Tyrins (1978)
CIVπ:889x591:signed:Presented by Waddington Galleries 1978

P03259 Proscinemi, Dodona, Oracle of Zeus (1978)
CINLπ:778x524:signed:Presented by Waddington Galleries 1978

P03261 Transparency, the Five Senses: Taste (1969)
CNVRa:1470x1470x50:signed:Presented by Marlborough Graphics through the Institute of Contemporary Prints 1970

The Institute of Contemporary Arts Portfolio (P04016, P04038, P04053, P04076, P04115, P04125, P04166, P04248, P04256, P04315-P04316, P04334, P04378-P04380, P04419, P04635, P04752, P04938, P05138, P05155, P05248; complete group; mixed group)
P05155 Lufbery and Rickenbacker (1963)
CNπ:689x495:signed:Presented by Rose and Chris Prater through the Institute of Contemporary Prints 1975

P05156 10th Sonnet (1964)
CNπ:695x1003:signed:Presented by Rose and Chris Prater through the Institute of Contemporary Prints 1975

P05157 21st (1964)
CNVπ:825x610:signed:Presented by Rose and Chris Prater through the Institute of Contemporary Prints 1975

P05158 Ziggurat (1964)
CNπ:743x549:signed:Presented by Rose and Chris Prater through the Institute of Contemporary Prints 1975

P05159 Geometry? (1965)
CNπ:552x546:signed:Presented by Rose and Chris Prater through the Institute of Contemporary Prints 1975

P05160 1/2 Ziggurat (1965)
CNπ:578x841:signed:Presented by Rose and Chris Prater through the Institute of Contemporary Prints 1975

P05161 PC from NYC (1965)
CNπ:1984x657:signed:Presented by Rose and Chris Prater through the Institute of Contemporary Prints 1975

P05162 Rainbow Grill (1965)
CNVπ:610x603:signed:Presented by Rose and Chris Prater through the Institute of Contemporary Prints 1975

P05163 Six Small Prints (1965)
CNπ:559x838:signed:Presented by Rose and Chris Prater through the Institute of Contemporary Prints 1975

P05164 3D Geometry (1965)
CNπ:822x508:Presented by Rose and Chris Prater through the Institute of Contemporary Prints 1975

P05165 Three Wrist Watches (1965)
CNπ:559x845:signed:Presented by Rose and Chris Prater through the Institute of Contemporary Prints 1975

P05166 5 Objects in Space (1965-6)
CNπ:584x941:signed:Presented by Rose and Chris Prater through the Institute of Contemporary Prints 1975

P05167 Ziggurat 5 (1966)
CNπ::signed:Presented by Rose and Chris Prater through the Institute of Contemporary Prints 1975

P05168 Ziggurat 6 (1966)
CNπ::signed:Presented by Rose and Chris Prater through the Institute of Contemporary Prints 1975

P05169 Ziggurat 7 (1966)
CNπ::signed:Presented by Rose and Chris Prater through the Institute of Contemporary Prints 1975

P05170 New York Decals 1 and 2 (1967)
CNVπ:905x1013:signed:Presented by Rose and Chris Prater through the Institute of Contemporary Prints 1975

P05171 New York Decals 3 and 4 (1967)
CNVπ:905x1013:signed:Presented by Rose and Chris Prater through the Institute of Contemporary Prints 1975

P05172 Rank 1 (1967)
CNπ:495x441:signed:Presented by Rose and Chris Prater through the Institute of Contemporary Prints 1975

P05173 Rank 2 (1967)
CNπ:496x440:signed:Presented by Rose and Chris Prater through the Institute of Contemporary Prints 1975

P05174 Rank 3 (1967)
CNπ:495x438:signed:Presented by Rose and Chris Prater through the Institute of Contemporary Prints 1975

P05175 Sky 1 (1967)
CNVπ:1196x683:signed:Presented by Rose and Chris Prater through the Institute of Contemporary Prints 1975

P05176 Sky 2 (1967)
CNVπ:1202x685:signed:Presented by Rose and Chris Prater through the Institute of Contemporary Prints 1975

P05177 Sky 3 (1967)
CNVπ:978x607:signed:Presented by Rose and Chris Prater through the Institute of Contemporary Prints 1975

P05178 Transparency, Clip-o-Matic Lips (1967)
CNπ:711x511:signed:Presented by Rose and Chris Prater through the Institute of Contemporary Prints 1975

P05179 Transparency, Empire State Building (1967)
CNπ:711x511:signed:Presented by Rose and Chris Prater through the Institute of Contemporary Prints 1975

P05180 Cut Out and Send (1968)
CNVπ:1016x686:signed:Presented by Rose and Chris Prater through the Institute of Contemporary Prints 1975

P05181 Cut Out and Send II (1968)
CNπ:1013x686:signed:Presented by Rose and Chris Prater through the Institute of Contemporary Prints 1975

P05182 Software Chart (1968)
CNπ:651x1273:signed:Presented by Rose and Chris Prater through the Institute of Contemporary Prints 1975

P05183 Bela Lugosi Journal A (1969)
CNπ:810x597:signed:Presented by Rose and Chris Prater through the Institute of Contemporary Prints 1975

P05184 Bela Lugosi Journal B (1969)
CNπ:978x638:signed:Presented by Rose and Chris Prater through the Institute of Contemporary Prints 1975

P05185 Is This Che Guevara? (1969)
CNVπ:1016x6896:signed:Presented by Rose and Chris Prater through the Institute of Contemporary Prints 1975

P05186 Jan Palach (1969)
CNVπ:660x533:signed:Presented by Rose and Chris Prater through the Institute of Contemporary Prints 1975

P05187 Letter from Che (1969)
CNVπ:1010x603:signed:Presented by Rose and Chris Prater through the Institute of Contemporary Prints 1975

P05188 Transparency, Clip-O-Matic Eye (1969)
CNπ:711x511:signed:Presented by Rose and Chris Prater through the Institute of Contemporary Prints 1975

P05189 Transparency, Vellegrande Bolivia, October 10th (1969)
CNπ:711x508:signed:Presented by Rose and Chris Prater through the Institute of Contemporary Prints 1975

A-Z Box (P05190-P05214, P02436; complete group)

P05190 A - Aperture Card (1969-70)
CNπ:747x502:signed:Presented by Rose and Chris Prater through the Institute of Contemporary Prints 1975

P05191 B - Snow White and the Black Dwarf (1969-70)
CNπ:750x499:signed:Presented by Rose and Chris Prater through the Institute of Contemporary Prints 1975

P05192 C - Deaf and Dumb Alphabet (1969-70)
CNπ:749x501:signed:Presented by Rose and Chris Prater through the Institute of Contemporary Prints 1975

P05193 D - Desire (1969-70)
CNπ:750x500:signed:Presented by Rose and Chris Prater through the Institute of Contemporary Prints 1975

P05194 E - Erotic - Earth - Eyes (1969-70)
CNπ:747x499:signed:Presented by Rose and Chris Prater through the Institute of Contemporary Prints 1975

P05195 F - Front Page (1969-70)
CNπ:750x500:signed:Presented by Rose and Chris Prater through the Institute of Contemporary Prints 1975

P05196 G - Guillaume Apollinaire (1969-70)
CNπ:747x495:signed:Presented by Rose and Chris Prater through the Institute of Contemporary Prints 1975

P05197 I - He, She and It (1969-70)
CNπ:741x500:signed:Presented by Rose and Chris Prater through the Institute of Contemporary Prints 1975

P05198 J - James Joyce and Others (1969-70)
CNπ:749x502:signed:Presented by Rose and Chris Prater through the Institute of Contemporary Prints 1975

P05199 K - The Death of Martin Luther King (1969-70)
CNπ:747x502:signed:Presented by Rose and Chris Prater through the Institute of Contemporary Prints 1975

P05200 L - Letter from Jonathan Williams (1969-70)
CNπ:746x420:signed:Presented by Rose and Chris Prater through the Institute of Contemporary Prints 1975

P05201 M - Memorial Issue (1969-70)
CNπ:742x494:signed:Presented by Rose and Chris Prater through the Institute of Contemporary Prints 1975

P05202 N - Newsletter (1969-70)
CNπ:737x500:signed:Presented by Rose and Chris Prater through the Institute of Contemporary Prints 1975

P05203 O - Oracle (1969-70)
CNπ:740x500:signed:Presented by Rose and Chris Prater through the Institute of Contemporary Prints 1975

P05204 P - Prague Postcard (1969-70)
CNπ:680x4187:signed:Presented by Rose and Chris Prater through the Institute of Contemporary Prints 1975

P05205 Q - Questions (1969-70)
CNπ:750x501:signed:Presented by Rose and Chris Prater through the Institute of Contemporary Prints 1975

P05206 R - Rhyme and Ritual (1969-70)
CNπ:745x500:signed:Presented by Rose and Chris Prater through the Institute of Contemporary Prints 1975

P05207 S - Semiologie (1969-70)
CNπ:750x502:signed:Presented by Rose and Chris Prater through the Institute of Contemporary Prints 1975

P05208 T - Tania la Guerillera (1969-70)
CNπ:747x502:signed:Presented by Rose and Chris Prater through the Institute of Contemporary Prints 1975

P05209 U - Unknown Systems (1969-70)
CNπ:746x500:signed:Presented by Rose and Chris Prater through the Institute of Contemporary Prints 1975

P05210 V - Vietnam Courier (1969-70)
CNπ:750x501:signed:Presented by Rose and Chris Prater through the Institute of Contemporary Prints 1975

P05211 W - Wittgenstein and Muhammed (1969-70)
CNπ:749x500:signed:Presented by Rose and Chris Prater through the Institute of Contemporary Prints 1975

P05212 X - Malcolm X (1969-70)
CNπ:749x500:signed:Presented by Rose and Chris Prater through the Institute of Contemporary Prints 1975

P05213 Y - Yes (1969-70)
CNπ:748x499:signed:Presented by Rose and Chris Prater through the Institute of Contemporary Prints 1975

P05214 Z - Ziggurat (1969-70)
CNπ:756x510:signed:Presented by Rose and Chris Prater through the Institute of Contemporary Prints 1975

P05215 A E I O U (1970)
CNVπ:740x489:signed:Presented by Rose and Chris Prater through the Institute of Contemporary Prints 1975

P05216 Ho Chi Minh (1970)
CNVπ:1032x702:signed:Presented by Rose and Chris Prater through the Institute of Contemporary Prints 1975

P05217 Jan Palach (1970)
CNVπ:1029x698:Presented by Rose and Chris Prater through the Institute of Contemporary Prints 1975

Alcheringa (P05218-P05220, P05224; complete group)
P05218 Alcheringa 1 - Fire (1971)
CNVπ:978x679:signed:Presented by Rose and Chris Prater 1975

P05219 Alcheringa 2 - Air (1971)
CNVπ:978x679:signed:Presented by Rose and Chris Prater 1975

P05220 Alcheringa 4 - Earth (1971)
CNVπ:978x679:signed:Presented by Rose and Chris Prater 1975

P05221 Let a Thousand Parks Bloom (1971)
CNπ:952x654:signed:Presented by Rose and Chris Prater through the Institute of Contemporary Prints 1975

P05222 Transparency, Clip-o-Matic Breast (1971)
CNπ:711x508:signed:Presented by Rose and Chris Prater through the Institute of Contemporary Prints 1975

P05223 Transparency, Snapshot (1971)
CNπ:698x549:signed:Presented by Rose and Chris Prater through the Institute of Contemporary Prints 1975

Alcheringa (P05218-P05220, P05224; complete group)
P05224 Alcheringa 3 - Water (1971)
:978x679:signed:Presented by Rose and Chris Prater 1975

P05225 Earth Ritual (1972)
CNπ:1026x702:signed:Presented by Rose and Chris Prater through the Institute of Contemporary Prints 1975

P05226 Four Elements - Mudra (1972)
CNVπ:454x562:signed:Presented by Rose and Chris Prater through the Institute of Contemporary Prints 1975

P05227 Mother Earth (1972)
CNVπ:613x921:signed:Presented by Rose and Chris Prater through the Institute of Contemporary Prints 1975

P05228 Tools of the Shaman (1972)
CNVπ:1022x695:signed:Presented by Rose and Chris Prater through the Institute of Contemporary Prints 1975

P05229 Mysterious Principles of the Blue Bag (1973)
CNVπ:1013x705:signed:Presented by Rose and Chris Prater through the Institute of Contemporary Prints 1975

P05230 Namings and Origins (1973)
CNπ:1019x714:signed:Presented by Rose and Chris Prater through the Institute of Contemporary Prints 1975

P05231 Oceanus / Tethys (1973)
CNVπ:1016x702:signed:Presented by Rose and Chris Prater through the Institute of Contemporary Prints 1975

P05232 Moon Signatures (1975)
CNVπ:918x616:signed:Presented by Rose and Chris Prater through the Institute of Contemporary Prints 1975

P05233 Sun Signatures (1975)
CNVπ:978x686:signed:Presented by Rose and Chris Prater through the Institute of Contemporary Prints 1975

P05383 New Coloured Fire from the Vast Strange Country (1968)
CNVπ:1016x686:signed:Presented by Rose and Chris Prater 1976

P05538 Proscinemi, Delphi (1979)
CIπ:800x578:Presented by Rose and Chris Prater 1979

P05539 Proscinemi, Olympia (1979)
CIπ:800x581:Presented by Rose and Chris Prater 1979

P05554 Oak Oracle (1980)
CIπ:803x571:Presented by Rose and Chris Prater through the Institute of Contemporary Prints 1980

P05565 Delphic Oracle (1980)
CNVπ:737x641:signed:Presented by Rose and Chris Prater 1980

P07364 Alchera: Notes for Country Works 1970-1974 (1976-77)
CNπ:502x698:signed:Purchased 1980

P77058 The Arrival of Demeter (1982)
CIπ:552x464:signed:Purchased 1984

P77059 The Arrival of Dionysos (1982)
CIπ:552x464:signed:Purchased 1984

P77060 The Arrival of Kore (1982)
CIπ:552x464:signed:Purchased 1984

TINDLE, David born 1932
Modern Collection
Tate Gallery Archive holds material concerning this artist

T03225 Still Life with Plastic Cup and Spoon (1974)
Tb:505x711:signed:Presented by the Trustees of the Chantrey Bequest 1981

P06816 Moth (1978)
CLπ:311x486:signed:Presented by Curwen Studio 1978

TING, Walasse born 1929
Modern Collection

For Jorn (P03241-P03255; complete group; mixed group)
Pour Jorn
P03252 [no title] (1975-6)
MLπ:543x752:signed:Presented by the Asger Jorn Foundation 1978

TINGUELY, Jean born 1925
Modern Collection
Tate Gallery Archive holds material concerning this artist

T03822 Débricollage (1970)
SKVm:508x762x648:signed:Purchased with assistance from the Friends of the Tate Gallery 1984

T03823 Metamechanical Sculpture with Tripod (1954)
Méta-mécanique à trépied
SKbm:2360x815x915:Purchased 1984

P77175 Chaos I (1972)
Iπ:350x480:signed:Purchased 1986

TIRTOFF, Romain de - see ERTÉ

TISDALL, Hans born 1925
Modern Collection
Tate Gallery Archive holds material concerning this artist

School Prints (P01698-P01727; complete group; mixed group)
P01723 Fisherman's Hut (1946-9)
CLπ:495x762:signed:Presented by Patrick Seale Prints 1975

TISSOT, James 1836-1902
Modern Collection

N04271 Portrait (1876)
Oc:914x508:signed:Purchased 1927

N04292 Studies of a Kneeling Woman (circa 1872-3)
Dπ:333x489:Bequeathed by J.R. Holliday 1927

N04293 Study of a Girl in a Mob Cap (circa 1872)
Dπ:311x206:Bequeathed by J.R. Holliday 1927

N04294 Study after Reynolds' Portrait of Mrs Williams Hope (circa 1872)
Dπ:121x67:Bequeathed by J.R. Holliday 1927

N04295 Ramsgate (circa 1876)
Dπ:251x352:Bequeathed by J.R. Holliday 1927

N04413 Holyday (circa 1876)
Oc:762x994:Purchased 1928

N04847 The Gallery of HMS Calcutta (Portsmouth) (circa 1876)
Oc:686x918:signed:Presented by Samuel Courtauld 1936

N04892 The Ball on Shipboard (circa 1874)
Oc:841x1295:signed:Presented by the Trustees of the Chantrey Bequest 1937

N05302 Portsmouth Dockyard (circa 1877)
Oc:381x546:signed:Bequeathed by Sir Hugh Walpole 1941

TOBEY, Mark 1890-1976
Modern Collection
Tate Gallery Archive holds material concerning this artist

T00463 Northwest Drift (1958)
TGπ:1135x905:Presented by the American Friends of the Tate Gallery 1961

TODD, A.R. Middleton 1891-1966
Modern Collection
Tate Gallery Archive holds material concerning this artist

N05111 The Picture Book (1939)
Ow:356x454:signed:Presented by the Trustees of the Chantrey Bequest 1940

TOFT, Albert 1862-1949
British Collection

N03030 The Bather (1915)
Ss:1930x667x724:signed:Presented by the Trustees of the Chantrey Bequest 1915

TOLEDANO, Edward born 1919
Modern Collection

P06817 Single Image (1977)
MLπ:502x641:signed:Presented by Curwen Studio 1978

TOMLIN, Stephen 1901-1937
Modern Collection
Tate Gallery Archive holds material concerning this artist

N04616 Lytton Strachey (1928-30)
Sz:457x254x276:Presented by Brinsley Ford (later Sir Brinsley Ford) 1932

TONKS, Henry 1862-1937
British Collection
Tate Gallery Archive holds material concerning this artist

N03016 The Toilet (exhibited 1914)
Pπ:330x441:Presented by Geoffrey Blackwell through the Contemporary Art Society 1915

N03017 Auguste Rodin (1914)
Pπ:537x400:Presented by Viscount D'Abernon through the Contemporary Art Society 1915

N03018 Madame Rodin (1914)
Pπ:375x286:signed:Presented by subscribers through the Contemporary Art Society 1917

N03185 A Girl's Head (exhibited 1903)
Oc:622x508:signed:Presented by the Contemporary Art Society 1917

N03186 A Girl with a Parrot (circa 1893)
Oc:457x311:Presented by W.C. Alexander through the Contemporary Art Society 1917

N03231 Portrait of the Artist (1909)
Oc:806x597:signed:Presented by Hugh Hammersley through the National Art Collections Fund 1917

N03717 Rosamund and the Purple Jar (exhibited 1900)
Ow:527x375:Purchased 1923

N04565 Summer (1908)
Oc:940x940:signed:Presented by Mrs F.J. Weldon 1931

N04600 Spring Days (1928)
Oc:864x813:signed:Presented by the Trustees of the Chantrey Bequest 1931

N04614 Saturday Night in the Vale (1928-9)
Oc:514x610:signed:Bequeathed by Sir William Orpen 1932

T00040 Sodales - Mr Steer and Mr Sickert (1930)
Oc:349x460:signed:Bequeathed by Mrs Violet Ormond 1955

TOPOLSKI, Feliks 1907-1989
Modern Collection
Tate Gallery Archive holds material concerning this artist

N05136 Goodwood, 25-28 July 1939 (1939)
DWPπ:419x533:signed:Purchased 1940

N05137 The Royal Academy: Varnishing Day (1939)
DWπ:381x391:signed:Purchased 1940

N05138 The Royal Academy: Private View Day (1929)
DWπ:330x391:signed:Purchased 1940

P01629 Autobiography (1973)
CNπ:1000x391:signed:Presented by Christie's Contemporary Art through the Institute of Contemporary Prints 1975

P01630 Westminster (1973)
CNπ:489x625:signed:Presented by Christie's Contemporary Art through the Institute of Contemporary Prints 1975

School Prints (P01698-P01727; complete group; mixed group)
P01724 This England (1946-9)
CLπ:498x762:signed:Presented by Patrick Seale Prints 1975

London Suite (P06591-P06596; complete group)
P06591 City (1973)
CLπ:334x507:signed:Presented by Curwen Studio through the Institute of Contemporary Prints 1975

P06592 Piccadilly Circus (1973)
CLπ:359x422:signed:Presented by Curwen Studio through the Institute of Contemporary Prints 1975

P06593 Westminster (1973)
CLπ:429x383:signed:Presented by Curwen Studio through the Institute of Contemporary Prints 1975

P06594 Speakers' Corner (1973)
CLπ:298x454:signed:Presented by Curwen Studio through the Institute of Contemporary Prints 1975

P06595 Trafalgar Square (1973)
CLπ:460x359:signed:Presented by Curwen Studio through the Institute of Contemporary Prints 1975

P06596 Trooping the Colour (1973)
CLπ:354x499:signed:Presented by Curwen Studio through the Institute of Contemporary Prints 1975

TORNER, Gustavo born 1925
Modern Collection

T00483 Composition 1961 (1961)
RmOc:1949x1619:signed:Purchased 1962

TOULOUSE-LAUTREC, Henri de 1864-1901
Modern Collection

N05142 The Two Friends (1894)
Les Deux Amies
Ob:479x340:signed:Bequeathed by Montague Shearman through the Contemporary Art Society 1940

T00465 Emile Bernard (1885)
Oc:540x445:signed:Bequeathed by Arthur Jeffress 1961

T03575 Amazon (1899)
Amazone
OGb:555x425:signed:Bequeathed by Mrs A.F. Kessler 1983

TOUSIGNANT, Serge born 1942
Modern Collection

Homage to Albert Dumouchel (P03166-P03178; complete group; mixed group)
Hommage à Albert Dumouchel
P03176 At Sea Somewhere Between Lisbon and Southampton (1972)
Quelque part en mer entre Lisbonne et Southampton
CFVπ:765x568:signed:Presented by the University of Quebec 1976

TOWN, Harold 1924-1990
Modern Collection

T00563 Tyranny of the Corner, Persian Set (1962)
Oc:2038x1626:Presented by Mr and Mrs Samuel Zacks 1963

TOWNE, Francis 1739 or 40 - 1816
British Collection

T01019 A View at Ambleside (1786)
WDπ:156x473:signed:Presented by the National Art Collections Fund (Herbert Powell Bequest) 1967

T01155 Haldon Hall, near Exeter (1780)
Oc:800x1257:signed:Purchased 1969

TOWNROE, Reuben 1835-1911
British Collection

Thirty copies in miniature of Alfred Stevens's figure compositions for the cupola of the British Museum (A00879-A00908; complete group)
A00879 [title not known] (circa 1858)
Wπ::Purchased 1905

A00880 [title not known] (circa 1858)
Wπ::Purchased 1905

A00881 [title not known] (circa 1858)
Wπ::Purchased 1905

A00882 [title not known] (circa 1858)
Wπ::Purchased 1905

A00883 [title not known] (circa 1858)
Wπ::Purchased 1905

A00884 [title not known] (circa 1858)
Wπ::Purchased 1905

A00885 [title not known] (circa 1858)
Wπ::Purchased 1905

A00886 [title not known] (circa 1858)
Wπ::Purchased 1905

A00887 [title not known] (circa 1858)
Wπ::Purchased 1905

A00888 [title not known] (circa 1858)
Wπ::Purchased 1905

A00889 [title not known] (circa 1858)
Wπ::Purchased 1905

A00890 [title not known] (circa 1858)
Wπ::Purchased 1905

A00891 [title not known] (circa 1858)
Wπ::Purchased 1905

A00892 [title not known] (circa 1858)
Wπ::Purchased 1905

A00893 [title not known] (circa 1858)
Wπ::Purchased 1905

A00894 [title not known] (circa 1858)
Wπ::Purchased 1905

A00895 [title not known] (circa 1858)
Wπ::Purchased 1905

A00896 [title not known] (circa 1858)
Wπ::Purchased 1905

A00897 [title not known] (circa 1858)
Wπ::Purchased 1905

A00898 [title not known] (circa 1858)
Wπ::Purchased 1905

A00899 [title not known] (circa 1858)
Wπ::Purchased 1905

A00900 [title not known] (circa 1858)
Wπ::Purchased 1905

A00901 [title not known] (circa 1858)
Wπ::Purchased 1905

A00902 [title not known] (circa 1858)
Wπ::Purchased 1905

A00903 [title not known] (circa 1858)
Wπ::Purchased 1905

A00904 [title not known] (circa 1858)
Wπ::Purchased 1905

A00905 [title not known] (circa 1858)
Wπ::Purchased 1905

A00906 [title not known] (circa 1858)
Wπ::Purchased 1905

A00907 [title not known] (circa 1858)
Wπ::Purchased 1905

A00908 [title not known] (circa 1858)
Wπ::Purchased 1905

TOWNSEND, William 1909-1973
Modern Collection
Tate Gallery Archive holds material concerning this artist

N06148 Hop Alleys (1951-2)
Oc:762x508:signed:Purchased 1953

T00486 Dungeon Ghyll (1956)
Oc:1372x762:signed:Purchased 1962

TRAVIS, Ann born 1931
Modern Collection

P06597 Bloomsbury Pie (1974)
CLπ:359x391:signed:Presented by Curwen Studio
through the Institute of Contemporary Prints 1975

TREMBLAY, Gerard born 1928
Modern Collection

Homage to Albert Dumouchel (P03166-P03178;
complete group; mixed group)
Hommage à Albert Dumouchel
P03177 The Sun Turns Square (1971)
Le Soleil Tourne Carré
CLπ:508x406:signed:Presented by the University of
Quebec 1976

TREMLETT, David born 1945
Modern Collection

T01742 The Spring Recordings (1972)
RVπ:381x6096x222:Purchased 1973

T01743 Green (1972)
81 F::Purchased 1973

T03689 The Cards (1972)
81 Hb:88x140:Purchased 1983

T03860 Africa No. 6 (1983)
DPπ:2307x2025:signed:Purchased 1984

TREVELYAN, Julian 1910-1988
Modern Collection
Tate Gallery Archive holds material concerning this artist

T00034 Oxen (1955)
Oc:762x1016:signed:Presented by the Trustees of the
Chantrey Bequest 1955

T00887 A Symposium (1936)
ROb:660x918:signed:Presented by the Friends of the Tate
Gallery 1966

T01921 Ombla (1931-2)
Dπ:270x349:signed:Purchased 1974

T03226 Interior, Hammersmith (1946)
Oc:603x813:signed:Presented by the Trustees of the
Chantrey Bequest 1981

P01304 During the Night (1935-71)
MIπ:114x152:signed:Presented by Waddington Galleries
through the Institute of Contemporary Prints 1975

P01305 The Bat (1936-72)
GMIπ:203x356:signed:Presented by Waddington
Galleries through the Institute of Contemporary Prints
1975

P01306 Dream Scaffold (1936-71)
GMIπ:203x352:signed:Presented by Waddington
Galleries through the Institute of Contemporary Prints
1975

P01307 Hungry People (1936-72)
GMIπ:159x254:signed:Presented by Waddington
Galleries through the Institute of Contemporary Prints
1975

P01308 Seaside (1936-72)
GMIπ:178x254:signed:Presented by Waddington
Galleries through the Institute of Contemporary Prints
1975

P01309 Spain (1936-72)
GMIπ:156x254:signed:Presented by Waddington
Galleries through the Institute of Contemporary Prints
1975

P01310 Valentine (1936-72)
GMIπ:203x254:signed:Presented by Waddington
Galleries through the Institute of Contemporary Prints
1975

P01311 Bicycle Shop (1937-72)
GMIπ:203x254:signed:Presented by Waddington
Galleries through the Institute of Contemporary Prints
1975

P01312 Figures (1937-71)
GMIπ:105x178:signed:Presented by Waddington
Galleries through the Institute of Contemporary Prints
1975

P01313 Somnambulist I (1937-71)
GMIπ:156x254:signed:Presented by Waddington
Galleries through the Institute of Contemporary Prints
1975

P01314 Somnambulist II (1937-71)
GMIπ:156x254:signed:Presented by Waddington Galleries through the Institute of Contemporary Prints 1975

P01315 Green Oxen (1968)
CLπ:384x508:signed:Presented by Waddington Galleries through the Institute of Contemporary Prints 1975

P01316 Activated Sludge (1971)
CLπ:356x483:signed:Presented by Waddington Galleries through the Institute of Contemporary Prints 1975

P01317 Chiswick Eyot (1971)
CLπ:352x483:signed:Presented by Waddington Galleries through the Institute of Contemporary Prints 1975

P01318 Durham Wharf (1971)
CLπ:352x479:signed:Presented by Waddington Galleries through the Institute of Contemporary Prints 1975

P01319 Home Waters (1971)
CLπ:352x483:signed:Presented by Waddington Galleries through the Institute of Contemporary Prints 1975

P01320 Aix-en-Provence (1972)
CLπ:352x483:signed:Presented by Waddington Galleries through the Institute of Contemporary Prints 1975

P01321 Arles (1972)
CLπ:483x352:signed:Presented by Waddington Galleries through the Institute of Contemporary Prints 1975

P01322 Avignon (1972)
CLπ:483x352:signed:Presented by Waddington Galleries through the Institute of Contemporary Prints 1975

P01323 Camels (1972)
CLπ:352x483:signed:Presented by Waddington Galleries through the Institute of Contemporary Prints 1975

P01324 Fontaine de Vaucluse (1972)
CLπ:356x483:signed:Presented by Waddington Galleries through the Institute of Contemporary Prints 1975

P01325 Hammersmith Bridge (1972)
CLπ:479x352:signed:Presented by Waddington Galleries through the Institute of Contemporary Prints 1975

P01326 Hay-Cart (1972)
CLπ:356x483:signed:Presented by Waddington Galleries through the Institute of Contemporary Prints 1975

P01327 Nimes (1972)
CLπ:352x479:signed:Presented by Waddington Galleries through the Institute of Contemporary Prints 1975

P01328 Rowers (1972)
CLπ:356x479:signed:Presented by Waddington Galleries through the Institute of Contemporary Prints 1975

P01329 Souk (1972)
CLπ:483x359:signed:Presented by Waddington Galleries through the Institute of Contemporary Prints 1975

P01330 Spinnakers (1972)
CLπ:479x352:signed:Presented by Waddington Galleries through the Institute of Contemporary Prints 1975

P01331 Airport (1972)
CLπ:352x483:signed:Presented by Waddington Galleries through the Institute of Contemporary Prints 1975

P01332 Athletes (1973)
CLπ:479x352:signed:Presented by Waddington Galleries through the Institute of Contemporary Prints 1975

P01333 Bulldozer (1973)
CLπ:352x483:signed:Presented by Waddington Galleries through the Institute of Contemporary Prints 1975

P01334 The Etching Class (1973)
CLπ:352x479:signed:Presented by Waddington Galleries through the Institute of Contemporary Prints 1975

P01335 Hangars (1973)
CLπ:352x483:signed:Presented by Waddington Galleries through the Institute of Contemporary Prints 1975

P01336 Heathrow (1973)
CLπ:352x483:signed:Presented by Waddington Galleries through the Institute of Contemporary Prints 1975

P01337 Islam (1973)
CLπ:352x479:signed:Presented by Waddington Galleries through the Institute of Contemporary Prints 1975

P01338 Kasbah (1973)
CLπ:479x356:signed:Presented by Waddington Galleries through the Institute of Contemporary Prints 1975

P01339 La Turbie (1973)
CLπ:479x356:signed:Presented by Waddington Galleries through the Institute of Contemporary Prints 1975

P01340 Marakesh (1973)
CLπ:352x483:signed:Presented by Waddington Galleries through the Institute of Contemporary Prints 1975

P01341 Near Miss (1973)
CLπ:479x352:signed:Presented by Waddington Galleries through the Institute of Contemporary Prints 1975

P01342 Sahara (1973)
CLπ:352x479:signed:Presented by Waddington Galleries through the Institute of Contemporary Prints 1975

P01343 Sleeping Tom (1973)
CLπ:479x352:signed:Presented by Waddington Galleries through the Institute of Contemporary Prints 1975

P01344 Amsterdam (1974)
CLπ:352x483:signed:Presented by Waddington Galleries through the Institute of Contemporary Prints 1975

P01345 Chiswick Mall (1974)
CLπ:352x479:signed:Presented by Waddington Galleries through the Institute of Contemporary Prints 1975

P01346 Holland (1974)
CLπ:479x352:signed:Presented by Waddington Galleries through the Institute of Contemporary Prints 1975

P01347 Low Tide (1974)
CLπ:352x479:signed:Presented by Waddington Galleries through the Institute of Contemporary Prints 1975

P01348 Winter (1974)
CLπ:349x479:signed:Presented by Waddington Galleries through the Institute of Contemporary Prints 1975

P01349 Wallington (1975)
CLπ:349x479:signed:Presented by Waddington Galleries through the Institute of Contemporary Prints 1975

P01350 Wallington, Clock Tower (1975)
CLπ:352x483:signed:Presented by Waddington Galleries through the Institute of Contemporary Prints 1975

P01631 Camel Corps (1972)
CLπ:352x479:signed:Presented by Christie's Contemporary Art through the Institute of Contemporary Prints 1975

School Prints (P01698-P01727; complete group; mixed group)

P01725 Harbour (1946)
CLπ:495x762:signed:Presented by Patrick Seale Prints 1975

P03208 Les Baux (1975)
CLπ:340x479:signed:Presented by Waddington Galleries 1977

P03209 My Garden (1975)
CLπ:340x479:signed:Presented by Waddington Galleries 1977

P03210 Mont Ventoux (1975)
Clπ:479x352:signed:Presented by Waddington Galleries 1977

P03211 Marseilles (1975)
Clπ:479x352:signed:Presented by Waddington Galleries 1977

P03212 Aigues Mortes (1975)
Clπ:356x479:signed:Presented by Waddington Galleries 1977

P06598 Thames Boat (1968)
CLπ:492x359:signed:Presented by Curwen Studio through the Institute of Contemporary Prints 1975

P06599 Tower Bridge (1968)
CLπ:489x362:signed:Presented by Curwen Studio through the Institute of Contemporary Prints 1975

P06693 Grand Union Canal at Brentford (1975)
CLπ:511x385:signed:Presented by Curwen Studio 1976

P06694 Camden Lock (1975)
CLπ:382x513:signed:Presented by Curwen Studio 1976

P06695 Canal Holidays (1975)
CLπ:382x513:signed:Presented by Curwen Studio 1976

P06696 The Lock Keeper's Cottage (1975)
CLπ:512x382:signed:Presented by Curwen Studio 1976

P11004 Leningrad (1961)
Clπ:492x394:signed:Bequeathed by Mrs Cynthia Shepley 1980

P11230 Love and Friendship (1932)
Iπ:179x236:signed:Presented by Mrs Mary Trevelyan, the artist's widow 1989

P11231 The Cow (1933)
Iπ:175x237:signed:Presented by Mrs Mary Trevelyan, the artist's widow 1989

P11232 Christmas Card (1935)
Iπ:54x101:signed:Presented by Mrs Mary Trevelyan, the artist's widow 1989

P11233 Abstract (1937)
Iπ:59x100:signed:Presented by Mrs Mary Trevelyan, the artist's widow 1989

P11234 Helicopter (1936)
Iπ:105x151:signed:Presented by Mrs Mary Trevelyan, the artist's widow 1989

P11235 Symbols of Growth (1936)
Iπ:100x176:signed:Presented by Mrs Mary Trevelyan, the artist's widow 1989

P11236 Pie in the Sky (1936)
Iπ:100x178:signed:Presented by Mrs Mary Trevelyan, the artist's widow 1989

P11237 Thames Regatta (1951)
Lπ:492x759:signed:Presented by Mrs Mary Trevelyan, the artist's widow 1989

P11238 Chiswick Eyot (1953)
Iπ:375x490:signed:Presented by Mrs Mary Trevelyan, the artist's widow 1989

P11239 Oxen (1955)
Iπ:200x252:signed:Presented by Mrs Mary Trevelyan, the artist's widow 1989

P11240 [no title] (1958)
Iπ:375x490:signed:Presented by Mrs Mary Trevelyan, the artist's widow 1989

P11241 Cretan Witches Fighting (1964)
Iπ:350x476:signed:Presented by Mrs Mary Trevelyan, the artist's widow 1989

P11242 Market, Bolton (1964)
Iπ:427x550:signed:Presented by Mrs Mary Trevelyan, the artist's widow 1989

P11243 Palazzo Pitti (1965)
Iπ:350x475:signed:Presented by Mrs Mary Trevelyan, the artist's widow 1989

P11244 Outside Kampala (1966)
Iπ:350x473:signed:Presented by Mrs Mary Trevelyan, the artist's widow 1989

P11245 Equilibrium (1974)
Iπ:237x177:signed:Presented by Mrs Mary Trevelyan, the artist's widow 1989

P11246 Etruria (1976)
Iπ:352x476:signed:Presented by Mrs Mary Trevelyan, the artist's widow 1989

P11247 Ram (1978)
Iπ:351x473:signed:Presented by Mrs Mary Trevelyan, the artist's widow 1989

P11248 Solent (1978)
Iπ:155x475:signed:Presented by Mrs Mary Trevelyan, the artist's widow 1989

P11249 Before the Race (1978)
Iπ:349x477:signed:Presented by Mrs Mary Trevelyan, the artist's widow 1989

P11250 Kilns (1979)
Iπ:154x472:signed:Presented by Mrs Mary Trevelyan, the artist's widow 1989

P11251 Entre deux Mers (1980)
Iπ:349x475:signed:Presented by Mrs Mary Trevelyan, the artist's widow 1989

P11252 Building the Thames Barrage (1980)
Iπ:477x349:signed:Presented by Mrs Mary Trevelyan, the artist's widow 1989

P11253 Avenue of the Americas (1982)
Iπ:480x350:signed:Presented by Mrs Mary Trevelyan, the artist's widow 1989

P11254 West Wind (1983)
Iπ:348x476:signed:Presented by Mrs Mary Trevelyan, the artist's widow 1989

P11255 Wings of a Dove (1984)
Iπ:296x244:signed:Presented by Mrs Mary Trevelyan, the artist's widow 1989

P11256 The Watchers (1984)
Iπ:219x470:signed:Presented by Mrs Mary Trevelyan, the artist's widow 1989

P11257 Soldier (1942)
Iπ:75x100:signed:Presented by Mrs Mary Trevelyan, the artist's widow 1989

P11258 [no title]
Iπ:106x150:Presented by Mrs Mary Trevelyan, the artist's widow 1989

P11259 [no title]
Iπ:375x490:signed:Presented by Mrs Mary Trevelyan, the artist's widow 1989

P11260 Cross Patch
Iπ:476x351:signed:Presented by Mrs Mary Trevelyan, the artist's widow 1989

P11261 [no title]
Iπ:498x375:signed:Presented by Mrs Mary Trevelyan, the artist's widow 1989

P11262 [no title]
Iπ:266x266:Presented by Mrs Mary Trevelyan, the artist's widow 1989

P11263 [no title]
Lπ:74x101:Presented by Mrs Mary Trevelyan, the artist's widow 1989

P11264 [no title]
Lπ:353x473:signed:Presented by Mrs Mary Trevelyan, the artist's widow 1989

TROCKEL, Rosemarie born 1952
Modern Collection

T04931 Untitled (1986)
Sfw:2200x1505:Purchased 1987

TROOSTWYK, David born 1929
Modern Collection
Tate Gallery Archive holds material concerning this artist

P07237 Wood X Square (1974)
MFπ:914x914:signed:Purchased 1975

TROUBETZKOY, Paul 1866-1938
Modern Collection

N04274 George Bernard Shaw (1926)
Sz:594x365x267:signed:Presented by Mrs George Bernard Shaw 1927

TROVA, Ernest born 1927
Modern Collection

T00666 Falling Man 80 (1963)
Ac:1372x1372:signed:Presented anonymously through the Friends of the Tate Gallery 1964

P01801 Grid with Multiple Figures (1966)
CNπ:664x1016:signed:Presented by the Museum of Modern Art, New York 1976

TRYON, Wyndham 1883-1942
Modern Collection

N04442 Fraga (circa 1925-9)
Dπ:314x464:Purchased 1929

N05408 Castle in Spain (circa 1925-9)
Dπ:330x495:Presented by Sir Edward Marsh 1943

TSAI, Wen-Ying born 1928
Modern Collection

T01521 Umbrella (1971)
SKm:2654x1803x1803:Purchased 1972

TSAPLINE, Dmitri 1890-1967
Modern Collection

N04793 Bird (1934)
Ss:514x114x305:signed:Purchased 1935

TUCKER, William born 1935
Modern Collection
Tate Gallery Archive holds material concerning this artist

T00856 Memphis (1965-6)
Sp:768x1759x1397:Purchased 1966

T01060 Meru I (1964)
OSm:749x1930x1397:Presented by the Contemporary Art Society 1968

T01200 Anabasis I (1964)
Sa:1492x1099x213:Purchased 1970

T01372 Margin I (1962)
SAma:1124x781x413:Presented by Alistair McAlpine (later Lord McAlpine of West Green) 1970

T01373 Margin II (1963)
SAm:1327x1575x578:Presented by Alistair McAlpine (later Lord McAlpine of West Green) 1970

T01374 Unfold (1963)
SAm:711x1172x1340:Presented by Alistair McAlpine (later Lord McAlpine of West Green) 1970

T01375 Meru II (1964)
SAm:962x2324x410:Presented by Alistair McAlpine (later Lord McAlpine of West Green) 1970

T01376 Meru III (1964)
SAma:933x1778x343:Presented by Alistair McAlpine (later Lord McAlpine of West Green) 1970

T01377 Orpheus 2 (1965)
SAm:768x2007x2007:signed:Presented by Alistair McAlpine (later Lord McAlpine of West Green) 1970

T01378 Karnak (1965)
SAa:546x1368x1321:Presented by Alistair McAlpine (later Lord McAlpine of West Green) 1970

T01379 Meru/Union (1966)
SAma:914x1524x1524:Presented by Alistair McAlpine (later Lord McAlpine of West Green) 1970

T01380 Series A No. 1 (1968-9)
SAa:552x2311x1861:Presented by Alistair McAlpine (later Lord McAlpine of West Green) 1970

T01816 Shuttler B (1970)
Sw:1968x2000x1810:Purchased 1973

T01817 Cats Cradle 3 (1971)
Sm:1632x2610x1499:Purchased 1973

T01818 Beulah i (1971)
Sm:1511x2661x1499:Purchased 1973

T05560 Tunnel (1972-5)
Sbm:2130x3840x3270:Presented by the artist through the Contemporary Art Society 1989

[no title] (P01351, P05234-P05237; complete group)

P01351 [no title] (1968)
CNVπ:760x974:signed:Presented by Waddington Galleries through the Institute of Contemporary Prints 1975

P05234 [no title] (1968)
CNVπ:759x977:signed:Presented by Rose and Chris Prater through the Institute of Contemporary Prints 1975

P05235 [no title] (1968)
CNVπ:760x865:signed:Presented by Rose and Chris Prater through the Institute of Contemporary Prints 1975

P05236 [no title] (1968)
CNVπ:759x978:signed:Presented by Rose and Chris Prater through the Institute of Contemporary Prints 1975

P05237 [no title] (1968)
CNVπ:760x957:signed:Presented by Rose and Chris Prater through the Institute of Contemporary Prints 1975

Ten Variations (P05238-P05247; complete group)

P05238 [no title] (1969)
CNVπ:2554x202:signed:Presented by Rose and Chris Prater through the Institute of Contemporary Prints 1975

P05239 [no title] (1969)
CNVπ:203x255:signed:Presented by Rose and Chris Prater through the Institute of Contemporary Prints 1975

P05240 [no title] (1969)
CNVπ:202x255:signed:Presented by Rose and Chris Prater through the Institute of Contemporary Prints 1975

P05241 [no title] (1969)
CNVπ:205x255:signed:Presented by Rose and Chris Prater through the Institute of Contemporary Prints 1975

P05242 [no title] (1969)
CNVπ:204x255:signed:Presented by Rose and Chris Prater through the Institute of Contemporary Prints 1975

P05243 [no title] (1969)
CNVπ:254x203:signed:Presented by Rose and Chris Prater through the Institute of Contemporary Prints 1975

P05244 [no title] (1969)
CNVπ:205x255:signed:Presented by Rose and Chris Prater through the Institute of Contemporary Prints 1975

P05245 [no title] (1969)
CNVπ:205x253:signed:Presented by Rose and Chris Prater through the Institute of Contemporary Prints 1975

P05246 [no title] (1969)
CNVπ:205x255:signed:Presented by Rose and Chris Prater through the Institute of Contemporary Prints 1975

P05247 [no title] (1969)
CNVπ:255x203:signed:Presented by Rose and Chris Prater through the Institute of Contemporary Prints 1975

P11201 Kronos (1985)
Jπ:1540x1115:Presented by Garner H. Tullis and Pamela Auchincloss 1988

P11213 Untitled (1987)
Jπ:511x384:Presented by Garner H. Tullis and Pamela Auchincloss 1989

TUDOR, Thomas 1785-1855
British Collection

T05481 Evening Landscape, with a View over a Bay
Wπ:125x246:Presented by Miss Marjorie Ball 1988

TUKE, Henry Scott 1858-1929
British Collection

N01613 August Blue (1893-4)
Oc:1219x1829:signed:Presented by the Trustees of the Chantrey Bequest 1894

N01618 All Hands to the Pumps (1888-9)
Oc:1854x1397:signed:Presented by the Trustees of the Chantrey Bequest 1889

N04470 Mrs Florence Humphris (1892)
Ow:400x318:signed:Bequeathed by Mrs Humphris 1929

TUNNARD, John 1900-1971
Modern Collection
Tate Gallery Archive holds material concerning this artist

N05373 Construction (1942)
WOπ:384x559:signed:Purchased 1942

N05624 Reclamation (1944)
OGb:559x714:signed:Purchased 1945

T00832 Composition (1942)
Ob:454x705:signed:Presented by the Trustees of the Chantrey Bequest 1966

T01216 Transition (1966)
Ob:1219x914:signed:Presented by the artist 1970

T02327 Fulcrum (1939)
Ob:445x813:signed:Presented by the Trustees of the Chantrey Bequest 1978

T03227 Tolpen (1942)
ODb:733x641:signed:Presented by the Trustees of the Chantrey Bequest 1981

School Prints (P01698-P01727; complete group; mixed group)

P01726 Holiday (1947)
CLπ:495x762:signed:Presented by Patrick Seale Prints 1975

TURNBULL, William born 1922
Modern Collection
Tate Gallery Archive holds material concerning this artist

T00424 Head (1960)
Szsw:1162x540x305:signed:Purchased 1961

T00515 No. 1 (1962)
Oc:2540x3759:signed:Presented by E.J. Power through the Friends of the Tate Gallery 1962

T00903 Mobile Stabile (1949)
Sz:384x689x508:Purchased 1967

T01150 No. 3 (1964)
Sm:2578x457x387:Presented by Alistair McAlpine (later Lord McAlpine of West Green) 1969

T01381 Horse (1954)
Szws:1130x718x270:Presented by Alistair McAlpine (later Lord McAlpine of West Green) 1970

T01382 Janus 2 (1959)
Sws:1524x625x375:Presented by Alistair McAlpine (later Lord McAlpine of West Green) 1970

T01383 Spring Totem (1962-3)
Swz:895x1480x432:Presented by Alistair McAlpine (later Lord McAlpine of West Green) 1970

T01384 No. 2 (1963)
SAm:2140x378x378:Presented by Alistair McAlpine (later Lord McAlpine of West Green) 1970

T01385 Two (1965)
SAm:1651x762x559:Presented by Alistair McAlpine (later Lord McAlpine of West Green) 1970

T01386 No. 7 (1965)
SAm:2346x451x451:Presented by Alistair McAlpine (later Lord McAlpine of West Green) 1970

T01387 No. 9 (1965)
SAm:2356x406x406:Presented by Alistair McAlpine (later Lord McAlpine of West Green) 1970

T01388 3/4/5 (1966)
SAm:2456x2626x787:Presented by Alistair McAlpine (later Lord McAlpine of West Green) 1970

T01389 Butt (1966)
SAm:559x1845x540:Presented by Alistair McAlpine (later Lord McAlpine of West Green) 1970

T01390 5 x 1 (1966)
SAm:1841x533x559:Presented by Alistair McAlpine (later Lord McAlpine of West Green) 1970

T01391 Parallels (1967)
SAm:51x2743x102:Presented by Alistair McAlpine (later Lord McAlpine of West Green) 1970

T01524 No. 1 1959 (1958-9)
Oc:1778x1778:signed:Purchased 1972

T01525 No. 7 1959 (1959)
Oc:1981x1486:Purchased 1972

T01788 Trestle (1971)
Sw:1048x1219x1524:Purchased 1973

T03270 Metamorphosis 2 (1980)
Sz:400x413x48:signed:Presented by the Sainsbury Charitable Fund through the Friends of the Tate Gallery 1981

T03271 Axe-Head Torso (1979)
Sz:333x302x67:signed:Presented by the Sainsbury Charitable Fund through the Friends of the Tate Gallery 1981

T03272 Tragic Mask (1979)
Sz:162x149x41:signed:Presented by the Sainsbury Charitable Fund through the Friends of the Tate Gallery 1981

T03773 Mask I (1953)
Sz:230x205x70:Transferred from the Victoria & Albert Museum 1983

T05211 Head (1954)
Sz:160x242x155:Purchased 1988

P01352 Black Leaf Form (1967)
MLπ:794x587:signed:Presented by Waddington Galleries through the Institute of Contemporary Prints 1975

P01353 Leaves, Blue (1967)
CLπ:800x591:signed:Presented by Waddington Galleries through the Institute of Contemporary Prints 1975

P01354 Leaves, Red (1967)
CLπ:803x591:signed:Presented by Waddington Galleries through the Institute of Contemporary Prints 1975

P01355 Yellow Leaf Form (1967)
CLπ:797x597:signed:Presented by Waddington Galleries through the Institute of Contemporary Prints 1975

P01818 Untitled Aquatint (1976)
CLπ:273x222:signed:Presented by White Ink 1977

P02339 Sitting Figure - Etching XIV (1971)
MIπ:279x152:signed:Presented by the artist 1976

P02340 Leaves - Drypoint I (1972)
MIπ:348x272:signed:Presented by the artist 1976

P02341 Leaves - Drypoint II (1972)
MIπ:346x271:signed:Presented by the artist 1976

P02342 Leaves - Drypoint III (1972)
MIπ:350x272:signed:Presented by the artist 1976

P02343 Leaves - Drypoint IV (1972)
MIπ:348x273:signed:Presented by the artist 1976

P02344 Leaves - Drypoint V (1972)
MIπ:346x273:signed:Presented by the artist 1976

P02345 Leaves - Drypoint VI (1972)
MIπ:353x273:signed:Presented by the artist 1976

P02346 Leaves - Drypoint VII (1972)
MIπ:348x272:signed:Presented by the artist 1976

P02347 Leaves - Drypoint VIII (1972)
MIπ:350x271:signed:Presented by the artist 1976

P02348 Leaves - Drypoint XV (1971)
MIπ:355x275:Presented by the artist 1976

P02349 Standing Figure - Drypoint IX (1972)
MIπ:347x252:signed:Presented by the artist 1976

P02350 Standing Figure - Drypoint X (1972)
MIπ:349x252:signed:Presented by the artist 1976

P02351 Standing Figure - Drypoint XI (1972)
MIπ:252x165:signed:Presented by the artist 1976

P02352 Standing Figure - Drypoint XII (1972)
MIπ:252x99:signed:Presented by the artist 1976

The Institute of Contemporary Arts Portfolio (P04016, P04038, P04053, P04076, P04115, P04125, P04166, P04248, P04256, P04315-P04316, P04334, P04378-P04380, P04419, P04635, P04752, P04938, P05138, P05155, P05248; complete group; mixed group)

P05248 Untitled (1964)
CNπ:505x711:signed:Presented by Rose and Chris Prater through the Institute of Contemporary Prints 1975

Fugue (P05249-P05257; complete group)

P05249 1 (1971)
CNπ:597x802:signed:Presented by Rose and Chris Prater through the Institute of Contemporary Prints 1975

P05250 2 (1971)
CNπ:593x799:signed:Presented by Rose and Chris Prater through the Institute of Contemporary Prints 1975

P05251 3 (1971)
CNπ:800x598:signed:Presented by Rose and Chris Prater through the Institute of Contemporary Prints 1975

P05252 4 (1971)
CNπ:591x800:signed:Presented by Rose and Chris Prater through the Institute of Contemporary Prints 1975

P05253 5 (1971)
CNπ:594x800:signed:Presented by Rose and Chris Prater through the Institute of Contemporary Prints 1975

P05254 6 (1971)
CNπ:592x801:signed:Presented by Rose and Chris Prater through the Institute of Contemporary Prints 1975

P05255 7 (1971)
CNπ:594x800:signed:Presented by Rose and Chris Prater through the Institute of Contemporary Prints 1975

P05256 8 (1971)
CNπ:593x800:signed:Presented by Rose and Chris Prater through the Institute of Contemporary Prints 1975

P05257 9 (1971)
CNπ:800x590:signed:Presented by Rose and Chris Prater through the Institute of Contemporary Prints 1975

P07205 Head Black/White (1956)
MNπ:765x562:signed:Purchased 1976

P07206 Head (proofs) (1956)
CNπ:765x562:signed:Purchased 1976

P07207 Head Blue/Yellow (1956)
CNπ:765x562:signed:Purchased 1976

TURNER, Alfred 1874-1940
British Collection
Tate Gallery Archive holds material concerning this artist

N03630 Psyche (circa 1918-9)
Ss:1702x546x483:signed:Presented by the Trustees of the Chantrey Bequest 1922

N04841 The Hand (1936)
Ss:940x838x457:Presented by the Trustees of the Chantrey Bequest 1936

TURNER, Charles 1773-1857
British Collection

N02301 J.M.W. Turner (1851)
Gπ:89x63:Presented by Sir Sydney Cockerell 1908

T04842 Portrait of J.M.W. Turner (1852)
Iπ:172x120:Purchased 1987

TURNER, Daniel active 1782-1801
British Collection

N01681 View of St Paul's from the Thames (?circa 1790)
Oc:591x749:Purchased 1899

N05784 Old London Bridge (after Samuel Scott, N00313)
Oc:559x1118:Purchased 1947

N05785 Westminster Bridge
Ow:203x305:signed:Purchased 1947

after

TURNER, F.C. active 1810-1846
British Collection

T05203 Damon and Pythias, from 'The Book of Gems' (1837)
Lπ:76x95:Purchased 1986

TURNER, Joseph Mallord William
1775-1851
British Collection
Tate Gallery Archive holds material concerning this artist

N00369 The Prince of Orange, William III, Embarked from
Holland, and Landed at Torbay, November 4th, 1688,
after a Stormy Passage (exhibited 1832)
Oc:902x1200:Presented by Robert Vernon 1847

N00370 Bridge of Sighs, Ducal Palace and Custom-House,
Venice: Canaletti Painting (exhibited 1833)
Oc:511x816:Presented by Robert Vernon 1847

N00371 The Golden Bough (exhibited 1834)
Oc:1041x1638:Presented by Robert Vernon 1847

N00372 The Dogana, San Giorgio, Citella, from the Steps of the
Dogana (exhibited 1842)
Oc:616x927:Presented by Robert Vernon 1847

N00458 Self-Portrait (circa 1800)
Oc:743x584:Bequeathed by the artist 1856

N00459 Moonlight, a Study at Millbank (exhibited 1797)
Oc:314x403:Bequeathed by the artist 1856

N00460 Buttermere Lake, with Part of Cromackwater,
Cumberland, a Shower (exhibited 1798)
Oc:889x1194:Bequeathed by the artist 1856

N00461 Morning amongst the Coniston Fells, Cumberland
(exhibited 1798)
Oc:1229x899:Bequeathed by the artist 1856

N00462 Union of the Thames and Isis (exhibited 1808)
Oc:908x1213:Bequeathed by the artist 1856

N00463 Aeneas and the Sibyl, Lake Avernus (circa 1798)
Oc:765x984:Bequeathed by the artist 1856

N00464 A Subject from the Runic Superstitions . . . (exhibited
1808)
Oc:921x1219:Bequeathed by the artist 1856

N00465 Mountain Scene with Castle, Probably Martigny (circa
1802-3)
Oc:438x540:Bequeathed by the artist 1856

N00466 View in Wales: Mountain Scene with Village and Castle -
Evening (circa 1799-1800)
Oc:581x727:Bequeathed by the artist 1856

N00467 Sketch of a Bank, with Gipsies (? exhibited 1809)
Oc:613x838:Bequeathed by the artist 1856

N00468 View on Clapham Common (circa 1800-05)
Ow:321x445:Bequeathed by the artist 1856

N00469 Shipping by a Breakwater (circa 1798)
Ow:302x194:Bequeathed by the artist 1856

N00470 The Tenth Plague of Egypt (exhibited 1802)
Oc:1435x2362:Bequeathed by the artist 1856

N00471 Jason (exhibited 1802)
Oc:902x1197:Bequeathed by the artist 1856

N00473 Holy Family (exhibited 1803)
Oc:1022x1416:Bequeathed by the artist 1856

N00474 The Destruction of Sodom (? exhibited 1805)
Oc:1460x2375:Bequeathed by the artist 1856

N00475 View of a Town (circa 1798)
Oc:241x324:Bequeathed by the artist 1856

N00476 The Shipwreck (exhibited 1805)
Oc:1705x2416:Bequeathed by the artist 1856

N00477 The Goddess of Discord Choosing the Apple of
Contention in the Garden of the Hesperides (exhibited
1806)
Oc:1553x2184:Bequeathed by the artist 1856

N00478 A Country Blacksmith Disputing upon the Price of Iron,
and the Price Charged to the Butcher for Shoeing his
Poney (exhibited 1807)
Ow:549x778:Bequeathed by the artist 1856

N00480 The Battle of Trafalgar, as Seen from the Mizen
Starboard Shrouds of the Victory (1806-8)
Oc:1708x2388:Bequeathed by the artist 1856

N00481 Spithead: Two Captured Danish Ships Entering
Portsmouth Harbour (1807-9)
Oc:1714x2337:Bequeathed by the artist 1856

N00482 The Garreteer's Petition (exhibited 1809)
Ow:552x791:Bequeathed by the artist 1856

N00483 London (exhibited 1809)
Oc:902x1200:Bequeathed by the artist 1856

N00484 St Mawes at the Pilchard Season (exhibited 1812)
Oc:911x1206:Bequeathed by the artist 1856

N00485 Dorchester Mead, Oxfordshire ('Abingdon') (exhibited
1810)
Oc:1016x1302:Bequeathed by the artist 1856

N00486 Ploughing Up Turnips, near Slough ('Windsor')
(exhibited 1809)
Oc:1019x1302:Bequeathed by the artist 1856

N00487 The Quiet Ruin, Cattle in Water; A Sketch, Evening
(?exhibited 1809)
Ow:612x765:Bequeathed by the artist 1856

N00488 Apollo and Python (exhibited 1811)
Oc:1454x2375:Bequeathed by the artist 1856

N00489 The Fall of an Avalanche in the Grisons (exhibited 1810)
Oc:902x1200:Bequeathed by the artist 1856

N00490 Snow Storm: Hannibal and his Army Crossing the Alps
(exhibited 1812)
Oc:1460x2375:Bequeathed by the artist 1856

N00491 Harvest Dinner, Kingston Bank (exhibited 1809)
Oc:902x1210:Bequeathed by the artist 1856

N00492 Frosty Morning (exhibited 1813)
Oc:1137x1746:Bequeathed by the artist 1856

N00493 The Deluge (?exhibited 1805)
Oc:1429x2356:Bequeathed by the artist 1856

N00494 Dido and Aeneas (exhibited 1814)
Oc:1460x2372:Bequeathed by the artist 1856

N00495 Apullia in Search of Appullus (exhibited 1814)
Oc:1448x2362:Bequeathed by the artist 1856

N00496 Fishing upon the Blythe-Sand, Tide Setting In (exhibited
1809)
Oc:889x1194:Bequeathed by the artist 1856

N00497 Crossing the Brook (exhibited 1815)
Oc:1930x1651:Bequeathed by the artist 1856

N00499 The Decline of the Carthaginian Empire . . . (exhibited
1817)
Oc:1702x2388:Bequeathed by the artist 1856

N00500 The Field of Waterloo (exhibited 1818)
Oc:1473x2388:Bequeathed by the artist 1856

N00501 Entrance of the Meuse: Orange Merchant on the Bar,
Going to Pieces . . . (exhibited 1819)
Oc:1753x2464:signed:Bequeathed by the artist 1856

N00502 England: Richmond Hill, on the Prince Regent's Birthday
(exhibited 1819)
Oc:1800x3346:Bequeathed by the artist 1856

N00503 Rome, from the Vatican. Raffaelle, Accompanied by La
Fornarina. . . (exhibited 1820)
Oc:1772x3353:Bequeathed by the artist 1856

N00504 Forum Romanum, for Mr Soane's Museum (exhibited 1826)
Oc:1457x2363:Bequeathed by the artist 1856

N00505 The Bay of Baiae, with Apollo and the Sibyl (exhibited 1823)
Oc:1454x2375:Bequeathed by the artist 1856

N00506 Dido Directing the Equipment of the Fleet, or the Morning of the Carthaginian Empire (exhibited 1828)
Oc:1473x2261:Bequeathed by the artist 1856

N00507 Boccaccio Relating the Tale of the Bird-Cage (exhibited 1828)
Oc:1219x899:Bequeathed by the artist 1856

N00509 The Loretto Necklace (1829)
Oc:1308x1749:Bequeathed by the artist 1856

N00510 Pilate Washing his Hands (exhibited 1830)
Oc:914x1219:Bequeathed by the artist 1856

N00511 View of Orvieto, Painted in Rome (1828, reworked 1830)
Oc:914x1232:Bequeathed by the artist 1856

N00512 Caligula's Palace and Bridge (exhibited 1831)
Oc:1372x2464:Bequeathed by the artist 1856

N00513 Vision of Medea (1828)
Oc:1737x2489:Bequeathed by the artist 1856

N00514 Watteau Study by Fresnoy's Rules (exhibited 1831)
Ow:400x692:Bequeathed by the artist 1856

N00515 Lucy, Countess of Carlisle, and Dorothy Percy's Visit to their Father Lord Percy, when under Attainder . . . (exhibited 1831)
Ow:400x692:Bequeathed by the artist 1856

N00516 Childe Harold's Pilgrimage - Italy (exhibited 1832)
Oc:1422x2483:Bequeathed by the artist 1856

N00517 Shadrach, Meshach and Abednego in the Burning Fiery Furnace (exhibited 1832)
Ow:918x708:Bequeathed by the artist 1856

N00518 Heidelberg (circa 1840-5)
Oc:1321x2019:Bequeathed by the artist 1856

N00519 Regulus (1828, reworked 1837)
Oc:895x1238:Bequeathed by the artist 1856

N00520 Story of Apollo and Daphne (exhibited 1837)
Ow:1099x1988:Bequeathed by the artist 1856

N00522 Phryne Going to the Public Baths as Venus: Demosthenes Taunted by Aeschines (exhibited 1838)
Oc:1930x1651:Bequeathed by the artist 1856

N00523 Ancient Rome; Agrippina Landing with the Ashes of Germanicus (exhibited 1839)
Oc:914x1219:Bequeathed by the artist 1856

N00525 Bacchus and Ariadne (exhibited 1840)
Oc:787x787:Bequeathed by the artist 1856

N00526 The New Moon (exhibited 1840)
Ow:654x813:Bequeathed by the artist 1856

N00527 Venice, the Bridge of Sighs (exhibited 1840)
Oc:686x914:Bequeathed by the artist 1856

N00528 Peace - Burial at Sea (1841, exhibited 1842)
Oc:870x867:Bequeathed by the artist 1856

N00529 War. The Exile and the Rock Limpet (exhibited 1842)
Oc:794x794:Bequeathed by the artist 1856

N00530 Snow Storm - Steam-Boat off a Harbour's Mouth (exhibited 1842)
Oc:914x1219:Bequeathed by the artist 1856

N00531 Shade and Darkness - the Evening of the Deluge (exhibited 1843)
Oc:787x781:Bequeathed by the artist 1856

N00532 Light and Colour (Goethe's Theory) - the Morning after the Deluge - Moses Writing the Book of Genesis (exhibited 1843)
Oc:787x787:Bequeathed by the artist 1856

N00533 The Opening of the Wallhalla (exhibited 1843)
Ow:1127x2007:Bequeathed by the artist 1856

N00534 St Benedetto, Looking towards Fusina (exhibited 1843)
Oc:622x927:Bequeathed by the artist 1856

N00535 The Sun of Venice Going to Sea (exhibited 1843)
Oc:616x921:Bequeathed by the artist 1856

N00536 Fishing Boats Bringing a Disabled Ship into Port Ruysdael (exhibited 1844)
Oc:914x1232:Bequeathed by the artist 1856

N00537 Van Tromp Returning after the Battle off the Dogger Bank (exhibited 1833)
Oc:905x1206:Bequeathed by the artist 1856

N00539 Venice - Maria della Salute (exhibited 1844)
Oc:613x921:Bequeathed by the artist 1856

N00540 Venice Quay, Ducal Palace (exhibited 1844)
Oc:622x927:Bequeathed by the artist 1856

N00541 Venice - Noon (exhibited 1845)
Oc:610x918:Bequeathed by the artist 1856

N00542 Venice - Sunset, a Fisher (exhibited 1845)
Oc:613x921:Bequeathed by the artist 1856

N00543 Venice, Evening, Going to the Ball (exhibited 1845)
Oc:616x924:Bequeathed by the artist 1856

N00544 Morning, Returning from the Ball, St Martino (exhibited 1845)
Oc:616x924:Bequeathed by the artist 1856

N00545 Whalers (exhibited 1845)
Oc:911x1219:Bequeathed by the artist 1856

N00546 'Hurrah! for the Whaler Erebus! Another Fish!' (exhibited 1846)
Oc:902x1206:Bequeathed by the artist 1856

N00547 Whalers (Boiling Blubber) Entangled in Flaw Ice, Endeavouring to Extricate Themselves (exhibited 1846)
Oc:899x1200:Bequeathed by the artist 1856

N00548 Queen Mab's Cave (exhibited 1846)
Oc:921x1226:Bequeathed by the artist 1856

N00549 Undine Giving the Ring to Massaniello, Fisherman of Naples (exhibited 1846)
Oc:791x791:Bequeathed by the artist 1856

N00550 The Angel Standing in the Sun (exhibited 1846)
Oc:787x787:Bequeathed by the artist 1856

N00551 The Hero of a Hundred Fights (circa 1800-10, reworked and exhibited 1847)
Oc:908x1213:Bequeathed by the artist 1856

N00553 Mercury Sent to Admonish Aeneas (exhibited 1850)
Oc:902x1206:Bequeathed by the artist 1856

N00554 The Departure of the Fleet (exhibited 1850)
Oc:899x1203:Bequeathed by the artist 1856

N00555 The Visit to the Tomb (exhibited 1850)
Oc:914x1219:Bequeathed by the artist 1856

N00556 Second Sketch for 'The Battle of Trafalgar' (circa 1823)
Oc:902x1213:Bequeathed by the artist 1856

N00557 View of Richmond Hill and Bridge (exhibited 1808)
Oc:914x1219:Bequeathed by the artist 1856

N00558 A Fire at Sea (?circa 1835)
Oc:1714x2203:Bequeathed by the artist 1856

N00559 Petworth Park; Tillington Church in the Distance (circa 1828)
Oc:600x1457:Bequeathed by the artist 1856

N00560 Chichester Canal (circa 1828)
Oc:654x1346:Bequeathed by the artist 1856

N00562 Harvest Home (circa 1809)
Ow:905x1203:Bequeathed by the artist 1856

N01180 Cliveden on Thames (?exhibited 1807)
Oc:284x584:Bequeathed by Mrs Elizabeth Vaughan 1885

N01857 River Scene with Cattle (circa 1810)
Oc:1283x1740:Bequeathed by the artist 1856

N01867 Caernarvon Castle (circa 1798)
Ow:152x232:Bequeathed by the artist 1856

N01875 Landscape: Christ and the Woman of Samaria (?circa 1825)
Oc:1473x2388:Bequeathed by the artist 1856

N01876 Sunset (?circa 1830-5)
Oc:667x819:Bequeathed by the artist 1856

N01980 Rough Sea with Wreckage (circa 1830-5)
Oc:921x1226:Bequeathed by the artist 1856

N01981 Norham Castle, Sunrise (circa 1845)
Oc:908x1219:Bequeathed by the artist 1856

N01985 Sunrise, a Castle on a Bay: 'Solitude' (circa 1840-5)
Oc:908x1219:Bequeathed by the artist 1856

N01986 Hastings (circa 1830-5)
Oc:902x1219:Bequeathed by the artist 1856

N01987 Breakers on a Flat Beach (circa 1830-5)
Oc:902x1210:Bequeathed by the artist 1856

N01988 Interior at Petworth (circa 1837)
Oc:908x1219:Bequeathed by the artist 1856

N01989 Rocky Bay with Figures (circa 1830)
Oc:902x1232:Bequeathed by the artist 1856

N01990 Sunrise with Sea Monsters (circa 1845)
Oc:914x1219:Bequeathed by the artist 1856

N01992 The Thames above Waterloo Bridge (circa 1830-5)
Oc:905x1210:Bequeathed by the artist 1856

N01993 Sketch for 'East Cowes Castle, the Regatta Beating to Windward' No. 3 (1827)
Oc:464x724:Bequeathed by the artist 1856

N01994 Sketch for 'East Cowes Castle, the Regatta Beating to Windward' No. 2 (1827)
Oc:457x610:Bequeathed by the artist 1856

N01995 Sketch for 'East Cowes Castle, the Regatta Beating to Windward' No. 1 (1827)
Oc:298x489:Bequeathed by the artist 1856

N01996 Between Decks (1827)
Oc:305x486:Bequeathed by the artist 1856

N01997 Sketch for 'East Cowes Castle, the Regatta Starting for Their Moorings' No. 3 (1827)
Oc:451x610:Bequeathed by the artist 1856

N01998 Sketch for 'East Cowes Castle, the Regatta Starting for Their Moorings' No. 1 (1827)
Oc:464x616:Bequeathed by the artist 1856

N01999 Shipping off East Cowes Headland (1827)
Oc:460x603:Bequeathed by the artist 1856

N02000 Sketch for 'East Cowes Castle, the Regatta Starting for Their Moorings' No. 2 (1827)
Oc:445x737:Bequeathed by the artist 1856

N02001 Study of Sea and Sky, Isle of Wight (1827)
Oc:305x486:Bequeathed by the artist 1856

N02002 Sunrise, with a Boat between Headlands (circa 1840-5)
Oc:914x1219:Bequeathed by the artist 1856

N02055 The Cobbler's Home (circa 1825)
Oc:597x800:Bequeathed by the artist 1856

N02064 The Chain Pier, Brighton (circa 1828)
Oc:711x1365:Bequeathed by the artist 1856

N02065 A Ship Aground (circa 1828)
Oc:698x1359:Bequeathed by the artist 1856

N02066 The Arch of Constantine, Rome (circa 1835)
Oc:914x1219:Bequeathed by the artist 1856

N02067 Tivoli: Tobias and the Angel (circa 1835)
Oc:905x1210:Bequeathed by the artist 1856

N02068 Procession of Boats with Distant Smoke, Venice (circa 1845)
Oc:902x1206:Bequeathed by the artist 1856

N02302 Newark Abbey (circa 1807)
Ow:295x352:Bequeathed by the artist 1856

N02303 A Narrow Valley (circa 1807)
Ow:206x165:Bequeathed by the artist 1856

N02304 Godalming from the South (circa 1807)
Ow:203x349:Bequeathed by the artist 1856

N02305 The Thames near Windsor (circa 1807)
Ow:187x260:Bequeathed by the artist 1856

N02306 Windsor Castle from the River (circa 1807)
Ow:200x368:Bequeathed by the artist 1856

N02307 On the Thames (?) (circa 1807)
Ow:298x349:Bequeathed by the artist 1856

N02308 Windsor Castle from the Meadows (circa 1807)
Ow:222x556:Bequeathed by the artist 1856

N02309 Tree Tops and Sky, Guildford Castle(?), Evening (?1807)
Ow:276x737:Bequeathed by the artist 1856

N02310 Guildford from the Banks of the Wey (circa 1807)
Ow:254x197:Bequeathed by the artist 1856

N02311 Sunset on the River (circa 1807)
Ow:156x187:Bequeathed by the artist 1856

N02312 Windsor Castle from Salt Hill (circa 1807)
Ow:276x737:Bequeathed by the artist 1856

N02313 Eton, from the River (?1807)
Ow:356x660:Bequeathed by the artist 1856

N02424 The Ponte Delle Torri, Spoleto (circa 1840-5)
Oc:914x1219:Bequeathed by the artist 1856

N02425 A Wreck, with Fishing Boats (circa 1840-5)
Oc:914x1222:Bequeathed by the artist 1856

N02676 St Catherine's Hill, Guildford (circa 1807)
Ow:365x737:Bequeathed by the artist 1856

N02677 Newark Abbey on the Wey (circa 1807)
Ow:368x737:Bequeathed by the artist 1856

N02678 Windsor from Lower Hope (circa 1807)
Ow:321x737:Bequeathed by the artist 1856

N02679 The Ford (circa 1807)
Ow:371x737:Bequeathed by the artist 1856

N02680 The Thames near Walton Bridges (circa 1807)
Ow:371x737:Bequeathed by the artist 1856

N02681 Walton Reach (circa 1807)
Ow:368x737:Bequeathed by the artist 1856

N02691 A Thames Backwater with Windsor Castle in the Distance (circa 1806-07)
Oc:867x1210:Bequeathed by the artist 1856

N02692 Trees beside the River, with Bridge in the Middle Distance (circa 1806-7)
Oc:879x1206:Bequeathed by the artist 1856

N02693 Hampton Court from the Thames (circa 1806-7)
Oc:857x1200:Bequeathed by the artist 1856

N02694 House beside the River, with Trees and Sheep (circa 1806-7)
Oc:905x1165:Bequeathed by the artist 1856

N02695 Men with Horses Crossing a River (circa 1806-7)
Oc:879x1184:Bequeathed by the artist 1856

N02696 Sketch for 'Harvest Dinner, Kingston Bank' (circa 1806-7)
Oc:610x914:Bequeathed by the artist 1856

N02697 Caversham Bridge with Cattle in the Water (circa 1806-7)
Oc:854x1158:Bequeathed by the artist 1856

N02698 Coast Scene with Fishermen and Boats (circa 1806-7)
Oc:857x1162:Bequeathed by the artist 1856

N02699 Washing Sheep (circa 1806-7)
Oc:845x1165:Bequeathed by the artist 1856

N02700 Margate (circa 1806-7)
Oc:857x1162:Bequeathed by the artist 1856

N02701 The Lake, Petworth, Sunset (circa 1828)
Oc:635x1397:Bequeathed by the artist 1856

N02702 Shipping at the Mouth of the Thames (circa 1806-7)
Oc:857x1168:Bequeathed by the artist 1856

N02703 River Scene with Weir in Middle Distance (circa 1806-7)
Oc:854x1156:Bequeathed by the artist 1856

N02704 Goring Mill and Church (circa 1806-7)
Oc:857x1162:Bequeathed by the artist 1856

N02705 Weir and Cattle (circa 1806-7)
Oc:883x1200:Bequeathed by the artist 1856

N02706 Willows beside a Stream (circa 1806-7)
Oc:860x1162:Bequeathed by the artist 1856

N02707 Barge on the River, Sunset (circa 1806-7)
Oc:851x1162:Bequeathed by the artist 1856

N02857 George IV at St Giles's, Edinburgh (circa 1822)
Ow:746x918:Bequeathed by the artist 1856

N02858 George IV at the Provost's Banquet in the Parliament
House, Edinburgh (circa 1822)
Ow:686x918:Bequeathed by the artist 1856

N02879 Shipping (circa 1825-30?)
Ow:679x918:Bequeathed by the artist 1856

N02880 Shipping, with a Flag (circa 1825-30?)
Ow:752x921:Bequeathed by the artist 1856

N02881 Waves Breaking against the Wind (circa 1835)
Oc:584x889:Bequeathed by the artist 1856

N02882 Waves Breaking on a Lee Shore (circa 1835)
Oc:597x952:Bequeathed by the artist 1856

Etchings and Engravings for the 'Liber Studiorum'
(N02941, A00911-A01015, A01112-A01159; complete
group)

N02941 Windmill and Lock (1811)
IWπ:177x258:Presented by W.G. Rawlinson 1913

N02942 Shipping at the Entrance of the Medway (circa 1816)
Wπ:216x286:Presented by W.G. Rawlinson 1913

N02958 Sketch for 'Ulysses Deriding Polyphemus' (?1828)
Oc:600x892:Bequeathed by the artist 1856

N02959 Italian Bay (?1828)
Oc:603x1022:Bequeathed by the artist 1856

N02988 Grenoble Seen from the River Drac with Mont Blanc in
the Distance (circa 1802)
Oc:362x641:Bequeathed by the artist 1856

N02990 Ariccia (?): Sunset (?1828)
Oc:606x794:Bequeathed by the artist 1856

N02991 Overlooking the Coast, with Classical Building (?1828)
Oc:603x845:Bequeathed by the artist 1856

N02992 Italian Landscape with Tower, Trees and Figures (?1828)
Oc:600x886:Bequeathed by the artist 1856

N03026 Classical Harbour Scene (?1828)
Oc:603x1019:Bequeathed by the artist 1856

N03027 Lake Nemi (?1828)
Oc:603x997:Bequeathed by the artist 1856

N03048 Gipsy Camp (circa 1807)
Ow:1219x914:Bequeathed by the artist 1856

N03133 Tynemouth Priory (?circa 1820-5)
Oc:318x610:Bequeathed by the artist 1856

N03380 Rocky Bay (?1828)
Oc:603x921:Bequeathed by the artist 1856

N03381 Archway with Trees by the Sea (?1828)
Oc:594x870:Bequeathed by the artist 1856

N03382 Claudian Harbour Scene (?1828)
Oc:600x937:Bequeathed by the artist 1856

N03383 Stack and Fire? (?1828)
Oc:600x848:Bequeathed by the artist 1856

N03384 A Park (?1828)
Oc:603x987:Bequeathed by the artist 1856

N03385 Scene on the Banks of a River (?1828)
Oc:603x892:Bequeathed by the artist 1856

N03386 Fishing Boat in a Mist (?1828)
Oc:603x908:Bequeathed by the artist 1856

N03387 Italian Landscape with Bridge and Tower (?1828)
Oc:603x981:Bequeathed by the artist 1856

N03388 Tivoli, the Cascatelle (?1828)
Oc:607x777:Bequeathed by the artist 1856

N03550 Music Party, East Cowes Castle (circa 1835)
Oc:1213x905:Bequeathed by the artist 1856

N03557 Landscape with Lake and Fallen Tree (?circa 1800)
Oc:391x606:Bequeathed by the artist 1856

N03631 Via Mala
Wπ:216x254:Bequeathed by the artist 1856

N04445 Seascape with Storm Coming On (circa 1840)
Oc:914x1216:Bequeathed by the artist 1856

N04446 Venice, the Piazzetta with the Ceremony of the Doge
Marrying the Sea (circa 1835)
Oc:914x1219:Bequeathed by the artist 1856

N04657 Cows in a Landscape with a Footbridge (circa 1805-7)
Oc:479x711:Bequeathed by the artist 1856

N04658 Stormy Sea with Blazing Wreck (circa 1835-40)
Oc:994x1416:Bequeathed by the artist 1856

N04659 Venetian Festival (circa 1845)
Oc:724x1133:Bequeathed by the artist 1856

N04660 Festive Lagoon Scene, Venice? (circa 1840-5)
Oc:908x1213:Bequeathed by the artist 1856

N04661 Riva degli Schiavone, Venice: Water Fête (circa 1845)
Oc:724x1130:Bequeathed by the artist 1856

N04662 Yacht Approaching the Coast (circa 1835-40)
Oc:1022x1422:Bequeathed by the artist 1856

N04663 Cassiobury Park: Reaping (circa 1807)
Ow:902x1219:Bequeathed by the artist 1856

N04664 Stormy Sea with Dolphins (circa 1835-40)
Oc:908x1219:Bequeathed by the artist 1856

N04665 Sun Setting over a Lake (circa 1840)
Oc:911x1226:Bequeathed by the artist 1856

N04953 Edinburgh Castle: March of the Highlanders (engraved
1836)
Wπ:86x140:Bequeathed by R.H. Williamson 1938

N05236 Aldborough, Suffolk (circa 1826)
Wπ:280x400:Bequeathed by Beresford Rimington
Heaton 1940

N05237 Luxembourg (circa 1826 or 1834)
Wπ:137x187:Bequeathed by Beresford Rimington
Heaton 1940

N05238 Parnassus and Castalian Spring (engraved 1833)
Wπ:184x140:Bequeathed by Beresford Rimington
Heaton 1940

N05239 Yarmouth, from near the Harbour's Mouth (circa 1840)
Wπ:244x368:Bequeathed by Beresford Rimington
Heaton 1940

N05240 Luxembourg (circa 1826 or circa 1834)
Wπ:140x187:Bequeathed by Beresford Rimington
Heaton 1940

N05241 Dryburgh Abbey (engraved 1834)
Wπ:79x149:Bequeathed by Beresford Rimington Heaton
1940

N05242 The Walls of Rome with the Tomb of Caius Sestus
(engraved 1833)
Wπ:146x197:Bequeathed by Beresford Rimington
Heaton 1940

N05243 The Castle of St Angelo (engraved 1832)
Wπ:171x210:Bequeathed by Beresford Rimington
Heaton 1940

N05473 Italian Landscape, probably Civita di Bagnoregio (?1828)
Oc:1499x2496:Bequeathed by the artist 1856

N05474 Christ Driving the Traders from the Temple (circa 1832)
Ow:921x705:Bequeathed by the artist 1856

N05475 A River Seen from a Hill (circa 1840-5)
Oc:787x794:Bequeathed by the artist 1856

N05476 Mountain Scene with Lake and Hut (circa 1840-5)
Oc:711x965:Bequeathed by the artist 1856

N05477 Seascape with Buoy (circa 1840)
Oc:914x1219:Bequeathed by the artist 1856

N05478 Steamer and Lightship (circa 1825-30)
Oc:914x1197:Bequeathed by the artist 1856

N05479 Rough Sea (circa 1840-5)
Oc:914x1219:Bequeathed by the artist 1856

N05480 First Sketch for 'The Battle of Trafalgar' (circa 1823)
Oc:902x1213:Bequeathed by the artist 1856

N05481 Seascape (?1828)
Ob:419x521:Bequeathed by the artist 1856

N05482 Venetian Scene (circa 1840-5)
Oc:794x787:Bequeathed by the artist 1856

N05483 An Avenue of Trees (?circa 1822)
Oc:495x537:Bequeathed by the artist 1856

N05484 Landscape with Castle on a Promontory (?circa 1820-30)
Oc:489x403:Bequeathed by the artist 1856

N05485 Seascape with a Yacht (?) (circa 1825-30)
Oc:502x660:Bequeathed by the artist 1856

N05486 Mountain Landscape (circa 1840-5)
Oc:711x965:Bequeathed by the artist 1856

N05487 Venice with the Salute (circa 1840-5)
Oc:622x927:Bequeathed by the artist 1856

N05488 Scene in Venice (circa 1840-5)
Oc:622x927:Bequeathed by the artist 1856

N05491 Three Seascapes (circa 1827)
Oc:908x603:Bequeathed by the artist 1856

N05492 Scene in a Church or Vaulted Hall (circa 1830)
Oc:749x991:Bequeathed by the artist 1856

N05493 Venus and the Dead Adonis (?circa 1805)
Oc:318x451:Bequeathed by the artist 1856

N05494 Head of a Person Asleep (circa 1835)
Oc:244x302:Bequeathed by the artist 1856

N05495 Waves Breaking on a Shore (circa 1835)
Oc:464x606:Bequeathed by the artist 1856

N05496 Figures in a Building (circa 1830-5)
Oc:914x1219:Bequeathed by the artist 1856

N05497 The Finding of Moses (circa 1805)
Oc:1505x1118:Bequeathed by the artist 1856

N05498 Reclining Venus (1828)
Oc:1753x2489:Bequeathed by the artist 1856

N05499 Rocky Coast (circa 1825-30)
Oc:502x657:Bequeathed by the artist 1856

N05500 The Procuress (?) (?circa 1805)
Oc:1241x914:Bequeathed by the artist 1856

N05501 Two Women and a Letter (circa 1835)
Oc:1219x914:Bequeathed by the artist 1856

N05502 Dinner in a Great Room with Figures in Costume (circa
1830-5)
Oc:908x1219:Bequeathed by the artist 1856

N05503 An Artists' Colourman's Workshop (circa 1807)
Ow:622x914:Bequeathed by the artist 1856

N05504 Death on a Pale Horse (?) (circa 1825-30)
Oc:597x756:Bequeathed by the artist 1856

N05505 Valley with a Distant Bridge and Tower (circa 1825)
Oc:911x1222:Bequeathed by the artist 1856

N05506 Southern Landscape with an Aqueduct and Waterfall
(?1828)
Oc:1502x2492:Bequeathed by the artist 1856

N05507 The Vision of Jacob's Ladder (?) (circa 1830)
Oc:1232x1880:Bequeathed by the artist 1856

N05508 Studies for 'Dawn of Christianity' (circa 1841)
Oc:1337x651:Bequeathed by the artist 1856

N05509 Outline of a Venus Pudica (1828)
Oc:1356x981:Bequeathed by the artist 1856

N05510 Southern Landscape (1828)
Oc:1765x2518:Bequeathed by the artist 1856

N05511 A Lady in a Van Dyck Costume (circa 1830-5)
Oc:1213x911:Bequeathed by the artist 1856

N05513 Landscape with Water (circa 1840-5)
Oc:1219x1822:Bequeathed by the artist 1856

N05514 Harbour with Town and Fortress (?circa 1830)
Oc:1727x2235:Bequeathed by the artist 1856

N05515 Seascape (circa 1835-40)
Oc:902x1210:Bequeathed by the artist 1856

N05516 Seascape with Distant Coast (circa 1840)
Oc:914x1219:Bequeathed by the artist 1856

N05517 Two Recumbent Nude Figures (1828)
Oc:1746x2492:Bequeathed by the artist 1856

N05518 Estuary with Rocks and Buildings (circa 1830-40)
Oc:1727x2432:Bequeathed by the artist 1856

N05519 The Thames Glimpsed between Trees, possibly at Kew
Bridge (circa 1806-7)
Oc:911x1216:Bequeathed by the artist 1856

N05520 Seascape with a Sailing Boat and a Ship (circa 1825-30)
Oc:467x610:Bequeathed by the artist 1856

N05521 A Sandy Beach (circa 1825-30)
Oc:600x914:Bequeathed by the artist 1856

N05522 The Cave of Despair (circa 1835)
Ow:508x813:Bequeathed by the artist 1856

N05523 Landscape Composition (circa 1820-30)
Oc:519x749:Bequeathed by the artist 1856

N05524 A Seashore (?1828)
Of:416x521:Bequeathed by the artist 1856

N05525 Lake or River with Trees on the Right (circa 1825-30)
Ob:413x597:Bequeathed by the artist 1856

N05526 Hilltown on the Edge of the Campagna (?1828)
Ob:410x594:Bequeathed by the artist 1856

N05527 Coast Scene near Naples (?1828)
Ob:410x597:Bequeathed by the artist 1856

N05528 Landscape with Trees and a Castle (?1828)
Ob:416x600:Bequeathed by the artist 1856

N05529 Interior of a Romanesque Church (circa 1795-1800)
Ow:610x502:Bequeathed by the artist 1856

N05530 Seacoast with Ruin, probably the Bay of Baiae (?1828)
Of:413x603:Bequeathed by the artist 1856

N05531 Mountainous Landscape (?1828)
Of:413x597:Bequeathed by the artist 1856

N05532 Hilly Landscape with Tower (?1828)
Of:422x524:Bequeathed by the artist 1856

N05533 Two Compositions: A Claudian Seaport and an Open
Landscape (circa 1825-30)
Oc:337x603:Bequeathed by the artist 1856

N05534 Cattle in a Stream under a Bridge (circa 1805-7)
Ow:314x394:Bequeathed by the artist 1856

N05535 Seascape with Burning Hulk (?1828)
Of:241x416:Bequeathed by the artist 1856

N05536 Interior of a Gothic Church (circa 1797)
Ow:279x406:Bequeathed by the artist 1856

N05539 The Long Cellar at Petworth (circa 1835)
Ow:749x914:Bequeathed by the artist 1856

N05540 Italian Landscape with a Tower (circa 1825-30)
Oc:584x762:Bequeathed by the artist 1856

N05541 Windsor Castle: Cows in a Woody Landscape (circa
1805-7)
Oc:476x718:Bequeathed by the artist 1856

N05542 Extensive Landscape with River or Estuary and a Distant
Mountain (?circa 1830-40)
Oc:1410x2515:Bequeathed by the artist 1856

N05543 The Rialto, Venice (circa 1820)
Oc:1775x3353:Bequeathed by the artist 1856

N05544 Seaport in the Grand Style (?circa 1830-40)
Oc:1727x2432:Bequeathed by the artist 1856

N05545 Landscape with a Tree on the Right (?1828)
Ob:279x416:Bequeathed by the artist 1856

N05546 Richmond Hill with Girls Carrying Corn (circa 1819)
Oc:1473x2381:Bequeathed by the artist 1856

N05563 Evening Landscape, probably Chichester Canal (circa
1825)
Oc:648x1257:Presented by Miss M.H. Turner 1944

N05615 Rievaulx Abbey (engraved 1836)
Wπ:121x206:Bequeathed by Travers Buxton 1945

N06283 Palestrina (1828, exhibited 1830)
Oc:1403x2489:Bequeathed by C.W. Dyson Perrins 1958

T01020 The Radcliffe Library, Oxford (circa 1792)
Dπ:273x206:Presented by the National Art Collections
Fund (Herbert Powell Bequest) 1967

T01021 Warwick Castle (circa 1820-30)
Wπ:229x353:Presented by the National Art Collections
Fund (Herbert Powell Bequest) 1967

T01022 The Falls of the Rhine at Schaffhausen (circa 1841-4)
DWπ:232x295:Presented by the National Art Collections
Fund (Herbert Powell Bequest) 1967

T01585 Fishermen at Sea (exhibited 1796)
Oc:914x1222:Purchased 1972

T03868 Ships Bearing up for Anchorage ('The Egremont
Seapiece') (exhibited 1802)
Oc:1120x1830:signed:Presented by H.M. Treasury 1984

T03869 Narcissus and Echo (exhibited 1804)
Oc:865x1170:Presented by H.M. Treasury 1984

T03870 Windsor Castle from the Thames (circa 1805)
Oc:910x1220:signed:Presented by H.M. Treasury 1984

T03871 The Thames near Windsor (?exhibited 1807)
Oc:890x1195:Presented by H.M. Treasury 1984

T03872 The Thames at Weybridge (circa 1805-6)
Oc:905x1217:Presented by H.M. Treasury 1984

T03873 The Thames at Eton (exhibited 1808)
Oc:595x900:Presented by H.M. Treasury 1984

T03874 The Confluence of the Thames and the Medway
(exhibited 1808)
Oc:910x1220:signed:Presented by H.M. Treasury 1984

T03875 The Forest of Bere (exhibited 1808)
Oc:890x1195:signed:Presented by H.M. Treasury 1984

T03876 Margate (exhibited 1808)
Oc:900x1205:Presented by H.M. Treasury 1984

T03877 Near the Thames' Lock, Windsor (exhibited 1809)
Oc:890x1180:signed:Presented by H.M. Treasury 1984

T03878 Tabley, Cheshire, the Seat of Sir J.F. Leicester, Bart.:
Calm Morning (exhibited 1809)
Oc:910x1215:signed:Presented by H.M. Treasury 1984

T03879 Cockermouth Castle (exhibited 1810)
Oc:605x900:Presented by H.M. Treasury 1984

T03880 Petworth, Sussex, the Seat of the Earl of Egremont: Dewy
Morning (exhibited 1810)
Oc:915x1205:signed:Presented by H.M. Treasury 1984

T03881 Hulks on the Tamar (?exhibited 1812)
Oc:900x1205:signed:Presented by H.M. Treasury 1984

T03882 Teignmouth (exhibited 1812)
Oc:900x1205:signed:Presented by H.M. Treasury 1984

T03883 The Lake, Petworth: Sunset, Fighting Bucks (circa 1829)
Oc:620x1460:Presented by H.M. Treasury 1984

T03884 The Lake, Petworth: Sunset, a Stag Drinking (circa 1829)
Oc:635x1320:Presented by H.M. Treasury 1984

T03885 Chichester Canal (circa 1829)
Oc:635x1320:Presented by H.M. Treasury 1984

T03886 Brighton from the Sea (circa 1829)
Oc:635x1320:Presented by H.M. Treasury 1984

T03887 Jessica (exhibited 1830)
Oc:1220x915:Presented by H.M. Treasury 1984

T04160 The Siege of Seringapatam (circa 1800)
DGWπ:421x654:Purchased 1986

Sequels to the Liber Studiorum ('Little Liber')
(T04914-T04916; complete group)

T04914 Paestum (circa 1825)
Lπ:154x216:Purchased 1987

T04915 Shields Lighthouse (circa 1825)
Lπ:150x211:Purchased 1987

T04916 Bridge and Monument (circa 1825)
Lπ:151x212:Purchased 1987

T04918 Trial Print (?circa 1812)
Lπ:192x267:Purchased 1987

T05201 Trial Print (?circa 1812)
Lπ:194x266:Purchased 1988

T05202 Catania, Sicily, for the 'Sequels to the Liber Studiorum'
(circa 1825)
Lπ:154x216:Purchased 1988

T05482 A Ruined Gateway
Dπ:248x251:Presented by Miss Marjorie Ball 1988

T05568 Catania, Sicily (circa 1825)
Lπ:152x214:Purchased 1989

T05569 Study of Sea and Sky (circa 1825)
Lπ:154x214:Purchased 1989

T05570 Ship and Cutter (circa 1825)
Lπ:154x222:Purchased 1989

T05571 Gloucester Cathedral (circa 1825)
Lπ:151x213:Purchased 1989

T05726 Ship in a Storm (circa 1826)
Lπ:151x213:Transferred from the British Museum 1990

A00909 Mountain Glen, Perhaps with Diana and Actaeon (circa
1835-40)
Oc:1492x1111:Bequeathed by the artist 1856

A00910 Mountain Stream (circa 1810-15)
ODπ:448x591:Bequeathed by the artist 1856

Etchings and Engravings for the 'Liber Studiorum'
(N02941, A00911-A01015, A01112-A01159; complete group)

A00911 Frontispiece (1812)
Iπ:187x263:Presented by A. Acland Allen through the National Art Collections Fund 1925

A00912 Frontispiece (1812)
Iπ:188x265:Presented by A. Acland Allen through the National Art Collections Fund 1925

A00913 Bridge and Cows (1807)
Iπ:180x260:Presented by A. Acland Allen through the National Art Collections Fund 1925

A00914 Bridge and Cows (1807)
Iπ:182x264:Presented by A. Acland Allen through the National Art Collections Fund 1925

A00915 Woman and Tambourine (1807)
Iπ:182x262:Presented by A. Acland Allen through the National Art Collections Fund 1925

A00916 Woman and Tambourine (1807)
Iπ:184x267:Presented by A. Acland Allen through the National Art Collections Fund 1925

A00917 Scene on the French Coast (1807)
Iπ:180x254:Presented by A. Acland Allen through the National Art Collections Fund 1925

A00918 Scene on the French Coast (1807)
Iπ:183x259:Presented by A. Acland Allen through the National Art Collections Fund 1925

A00919 Basle (1807)
Iπ:185x258:Presented by A. Acland Allen through the National Art Collections Fund 1925

A00920 Basle (1807)
Iπ:185x260:Presented by A. Acland Allen through the National Art Collections Fund 1925

A00921 Jason (1807)
Iπ:180x254:Presented by A. Acland Allen through the National Art Collections Fund 1925

A00922 Jason (1807)
Iπ:183x258:Presented by A. Acland Allen through the National Art Collections Fund 1925

A00923 The Strawyard (1808)
Iπ:180x248:Presented by A. Acland Allen through the National Art Collections Fund 1925

A00924 The Strawyard (1808)
Iπ:183x254:Presented by A. Acland Allen through the National Art Collections Fund 1925

A00925 The Castle above the Meadows (1808)
Iπ:176x259:Presented by A. Acland Allen through the National Art Collections Fund 1925

A00926 The Castle above the Meadows (1808)
Iπ:177x261:Presented by A. Acland Allen through the National Art Collections Fund 1925

A00927 Mount St Gothard (1808)
Iπ:175x255:Presented by A. Acland Allen through the National Art Collections Fund 1925

A00928 Mount St Gothard (1808)
Iπ:177x259:Presented by A. Acland Allen through the National Art Collections Fund 1925

A00929 Ships in a Breeze (1808)
Iπ:180x254:Presented by A. Acland Allen through the National Art Collections Fund 1925

A00930 Ships in a Breeze (1808)
Iπ:180x258:Presented by A. Acland Allen through the National Art Collections Fund 1925

A00931 Holy Island Cathedral (1808)
Iπ:179x257:Presented by A. Acland Allen through the National Art Collections Fund 1925

A00932 Holy Island Cathedral (1808)
Iπ:181x259:Presented by A. Acland Allen through the National Art Collections Fund 1925

A00933 Pembury Mill, Kent (1808)
Iπ:179x261:Presented by A. Acland Allen through the National Art Collections Fund 1925

A00934 Pembury Mill, Kent (1808)
Iπ:182x264:Presented by A. Acland Allen through the National Art Collections Fund 1925

A00935 The Bridge in Middle Distance (1808)
Iπ:177x257:Presented by A. Acland Allen through the National Art Collections Fund 1925

A00936 The Bridge in Middle Distance (1808)
Iπ:181x262:Presented by A. Acland Allen through the National Art Collections Fund 1925

A00937 Dunstanborough Castle (1808)
Iπ:182x263:Presented by A. Acland Allen through the National Art Collections Fund 1925

A00938 Dunstanborough Castle (1808)
Iπ:182x263:Presented by A. Acland Allen through the National Art Collections Fund 1925

A00939 Lake Thun, Switzerland (1808)
Iπ:177x261:Presented by A. Acland Allen through the National Art Collections Fund 1925

A00940 Lake Thun, Switzerland (1808)
Iπ:181x264:Presented by A. Acland Allen through the National Art Collections Fund 1925

A00941 The Fifth Plague of Egypt (1808)
Iπ:176x255:Presented by A. Acland Allen through the National Art Collections Fund 1925

A00942 The Fifth Plague of Egypt (1808)
Iπ:180x260:Presented by A. Acland Allen through the National Art Collections Fund 1925

A00943 The Farmyard with the Cock (1809)
Iπ:179x258:Presented by A. Acland Allen through the National Art Collections Fund 1925

A00944 The Farmyard with the Cock (1809)
Iπ:179x260:Presented by A. Acland Allen through the National Art Collections Fund 1925

A00945 The Fall of the Clyde (1809)
Iπ:179x261:Presented by A. Acland Allen through the National Art Collections Fund 1925

A00946 The Fall of the Clyde (1809)
Iπ:182x265:Presented by A. Acland Allen through the National Art Collections Fund 1925

A00947 Little Devil's Bridge (1809)
Iπ:177x256:Presented by A. Acland Allen through the National Art Collections Fund 1925

A00948 Little Devil's Bridge (1809)
Iπ:178x258:Presented by A. Acland Allen through the National Art Collections Fund 1925

A00949 Little Devil's Bridge (1809)
Iπ:179x259:Presented by A. Acland Allen through the National Art Collections Fund 1925

A00950 The Leader Sea-piece (1809)
Iπ:175x256:Presented by A. Acland Allen through the National Art Collections Fund 1925

A00951 The Leader Sea-piece (1809)
Lπ:177x258:Presented by A. Acland Allen through the
National Art Collections Fund 1925

A00952 Morpeth, Northumberland (1809)
Lπ:176x255:Presented by A. Acland Allen through the
National Art Collections Fund 1925

A00953 Morpeth, Northumberland (1809)
Lπ:177x259:Presented by A. Acland Allen through the
National Art Collections Fund 1925

A00954 Juvenile Tricks (1811)
Lπ:177x259:Presented by A. Acland Allen through the
National Art Collections Fund 1925

A00955 Juvenile Tricks (1811)
Lπ:178x260:Presented by A. Acland Allen through the
National Art Collections Fund 1925

A00956 Temple of Minerva Medica (1811)
Mπ:181x265:Presented by A. Acland Allen through the
National Art Collections Fund 1925

A00957 Temple of Minerva Medica (1811)
Lπ:183x266:Presented by A. Acland Allen through the
National Art Collections Fund 1925

A00958 Coast of Yorkshire, near Whitby (1811)
Lπ:178x261:Presented by A. Acland Allen through the
National Art Collections Fund 1925

A00959 Coast of Yorkshire, near Whitby (1811)
Lπ:181x265:Presented by A. Acland Allen through the
National Art Collections Fund 1925

A00960 Hindhead Hill (1811)
Lπ:176x257:Presented by A. Acland Allen through the
National Art Collections Fund 1925

A00961 Hindhead Hill (1811)
Lπ:178x260:Presented by A. Acland Allen through the
National Art Collections Fund 1925

A00962 London from Greenwich (1811)
Lπ:176x264:Presented by A. Acland Allen through the
National Art Collections Fund 1925

A00963 London from Greenwich (1811)
Lπ:178x266:Presented by A. Acland Allen through the
National Art Collections Fund 1925

A00964 Windmill and Lock (1811)
Lπ:176x256:Presented by A. Acland Allen through the
National Art Collections Fund 1925

A00965 Windmill and Lock (1811)
Lπ:178x259:Presented by A. Acland Allen through the
National Art Collections Fund 1925

A00966 Junction of Severn and Wye (1811)
Lπ:180x261:Presented by A. Acland Allen through the
National Art Collections Fund 1925

A00967 Junction of Severn and Wye (1811)
Lπ:181x263:Presented by A. Acland Allen through the
National Art Collections Fund 1925

A00968 Marine Dabblers (1811)
Lπ:177x258:Presented by A. Acland Allen through the
National Art Collections Fund 1925

A00969 Marine Dabblers (1811)
Lπ:179x262:Presented by A. Acland Allen through the
National Art Collections Fund 1925

A00970 Near Blair Athol, Scotland (1811)
Lπ:179x261:Presented by A. Acland Allen through the
National Art Collections Fund 1925

A00971 Near Blair Athol, Scotland (1811)
Mπ:181x264:Presented by A. Acland Allen through the
National Art Collections Fund 1925

A00972 Lauffenburgh on the Rhine (1811)
Lπ:175x257:Presented by A. Acland Allen through the
National Art Collections Fund 1925

A00973 Lauffenburgh on the Rhine (1811)
Lπ:175x258:Presented by A. Acland Allen through the
National Art Collections Fund 1925

A00974 Young Anglers (1811)
Lπ:177x259:Presented by A. Acland Allen through the
National Art Collections Fund 1925

A00975 Young Anglers (1811)
Lπ:179x262:Presented by A. Acland Allen through the
National Art Collections Fund 1925

A00976 St Catherine's Hill, near Guildford (1811)
Lπ:184x260:Presented by A. Acland Allen through the
National Art Collections Fund 1925

A00977 St Catherine's Hill, near Guildford (1811)
Lπ:186x262:Presented by A. Acland Allen through the
National Art Collections Fund 1925

A00978 Martello Towers, nr Bexhill, Sussex (1811)
Lπ:176x257:Presented by A. Acland Allen through the
National Art Collections Fund 1925

A00979 Martello Towers, nr Bexhill, Sussex (1811)
Lπ:179x261:Presented by A. Acland Allen through the
National Art Collections Fund 1925

A00980 Inverary Pier (1811)
Lπ:177x260:Presented by A. Acland Allen through the
National Art Collections Fund 1925

A00981 Inverary Pier (1811)
Lπ:179x261:Presented by A. Acland Allen through the
National Art Collections Fund 1925

A00982 From Spenser's Fairy Queen (1811)
Lπ:180x260:Presented by A. Acland Allen through the
National Art Collections Fund 1925

A00983 From Spenser's Fairy Queen (1811)
Lπ:182x265:Presented by A. Acland Allen through the
National Art Collections Fund 1925

A00984 Water-Mill (1812)
Lπ:181x259:Presented by A. Acland Allen through the
National Art Collections Fund 1925

A00985 Water-Mill (1812)
Lπ:182x262:Presented by A. Acland Allen through the
National Art Collections Fund 1925

A00986 Scene in the Campagna (1812)
Lπ:180x260:Presented by A. Acland Allen through the
National Art Collections Fund 1925

A00987 Scene in the Campagna (1812)
Lπ:182x264:Presented by A. Acland Allen through the
National Art Collections Fund 1925

A00988 Crypt of Kirkstall Abbey (1812)
Lπ:180x264:Presented by A. Acland Allen through the
National Art Collections Fund 1925

A00989 Crypt of Kirkstall Abbey (1812)
Lπ:180x264:Presented by A. Acland Allen through the
National Art Collections Fund 1925

A00990 The Mildmay Sea-piece (1812)
Lπ:180x261:Presented by A. Acland Allen through the
National Art Collections Fund 1925

A00991 The Mildmay Sea-piece (1812)
Lπ:181x264:Presented by A. Acland Allen through the
National Art Collections Fund 1925

A00992 Procris and Cephalus (1812)
Lπ:185x262:Presented by A. Acland Allen through the
National Art Collections Fund 1925

A00993 Procris and Cephalus (1812)
Iπ:187x265:Presented by A. Acland Allen through the
National Art Collections Fund 1925

A00994 Winchelsea, Sussex (1812)
Iπ:180x258:Presented by A. Acland Allen through the
National Art Collections Fund 1925

A00995 Winchelsea, Sussex (1812)
Iπ:181x262:Presented by A. Acland Allen through the
National Art Collections Fund 1925

A00996 The Bridge and Goats (1812)
Iπ:181x252:Presented by A. Acland Allen through the
National Art Collections Fund 1925

A00997 The Bridge and Goats (1812)
Iπ:182x255:Presented by A. Acland Allen through the
National Art Collections Fund 1925

A00998 Calm (1812)
Mπ:184x260:Presented by A. Acland Allen through the
National Art Collections Fund 1925

A00999 Calm (1812)
Iπ:178x267:Presented by A. Acland Allen through the
National Art Collections Fund 1925

A01000 Peat Bog, Scotland (1812)
Iπ:178x258:Presented by A. Acland Allen through the
National Art Collections Fund 1925

A01001 Peat Bog, Scotland (1812)
Iπ:179x260:Presented by A. Acland Allen through the
National Art Collections Fund 1925

A01002 Rispah (1812)
Iπ:179x262:Presented by A. Acland Allen through the
National Art Collections Fund 1925

A01003 Rispah (1812)
Iπ:180x263:Presented by A. Acland Allen through the
National Art Collections Fund 1925

A01004 Hedging and Ditching (1812)
Iπ:184x259:Presented by A. Acland Allen through the
National Art Collections Fund 1925

A01005 Hedging and Ditching (1812)
Iπ:186x262:Presented by A. Acland Allen through the
National Art Collections Fund 1925

A01006 River Wye (1812)
Mπ:183x264:Presented by A. Acland Allen through the
National Art Collections Fund 1925

A01007 River Wye (1812)
Iπ:184x265:Presented by A. Acland Allen through the
National Art Collections Fund 1925

A01008 Chain of Alps from Grenoble to Chamberi (1812)
Iπ:178x259:Presented by A. Acland Allen through the
National Art Collections Fund 1925

A01009 Chain of Alps from Grenoble to Chamberi (1812)
Iπ:178x261:Presented by A. Acland Allen through the
National Art Collections Fund 1925

A01010 Mer de Glace (1812)
Iπ:178x253:Presented by A. Acland Allen through the
National Art Collections Fund 1925

A01011 Mer de Glace (1812)
Iπ:179x257:Presented by A. Acland Allen through the
National Art Collections Fund 1925

A01012 Rivaux Abbey, Yorkshire (1812)
Iπ:182x265:Presented by A. Acland Allen through the
National Art Collections Fund 1925

A01013 Rivaux Abbey, Yorkshire (1812)
Iπ:183x266:Presented by A. Acland Allen through the
National Art Collections Fund 1925

A01014 Rivaux Abbey, Yorkshire (1812)
Iπ:183x267:Presented by A. Acland Allen through the
National Art Collections Fund 1925

A01015 Solway Moss (1816)
Iπ:184x267:Presented by A. Acland Allen through the
National Art Collections Fund 1925

A01112 Solitude (1814)
Iπ:176x256:Presented by A. Acland Allen through the
National Art Collections Fund 1925

A01113 Solitude (1814)
Iπ:177x257:Presented by A. Acland Allen through the
National Art Collections Fund 1925

A01114 Mill near the Grand Chartreuse (1816)
Iπ:187x257:Presented by A. Acland Allen through the
National Art Collections Fund 1925

A01115 Mill near the Grand Chartreuse (1816)
Iπ:188x257:Presented by A. Acland Allen through the
National Art Collections Fund 1925

A01116 Entrance of Calais Harbour (1816)
MIπ:179x267:Presented by A. Acland Allen through the
National Art Collections Fund 1925

A01117 Dunblane Abbey, Scotland (1816)
Iπ:186x266:Presented by A. Acland Allen through the
National Art Collections Fund 1925

A01118 Dunblane Abbey, Scotland (1816)
Iπ:187x267:Presented by A. Acland Allen through the
National Art Collections Fund 1925

A01119 Norham Castle on the Tweed (1816)
Iπ::Presented by A. Acland Allen through the National
Art Collections Fund 1925

A01120 Norham Castle on the Tweed (1816)
MIπ::Presented by A. Acland Allen through the National
Art Collections Fund 1925

A01121 Berry Pomeroy Castle (1816)
Fπ::Presented by A. Acland Allen through the National
Art Collections Fund 1925

A01122 Berry Pomeroy Castle (1816)
Iπ::Presented by A. Acland Allen through the National
Art Collections Fund 1925

A01123 Ville de Thun, Switzerland (1816)
Iπ:178x263:Presented by A. Acland Allen through the
National Art Collections Fund 1925

A01124 Ville de Thun, Switzerland (1816)
Iπ:178x264:Presented by A. Acland Allen through the
National Art Collections Fund 1925

A01125 The Source of the Arveron (1816)
Fπ::Presented by A. Acland Allen through the National
Art Collections Fund 1925

A01126 The Source of the Arveron (1816)
Iπ:189x268:Presented by A. Acland Allen through the
National Art Collections Fund 1925

A01127 The Tenth Plague of Egypt (1816)
Iπ:178x258:Presented by A. Acland Allen through the
National Art Collections Fund 1925

A01128 The Tenth Plague of Egypt (1816)
Iπ:179x261:Presented by A. Acland Allen through the
National Art Collections Fund 1925

A01129 The Watercress Gatherers (1819)
Iπ:187x264:Presented by A. Acland Allen through the
National Art Collections Fund 1925

A01130 The Watercress Gatherers (1819)
Iπ:188x265:Presented by A. Acland Allen through the
National Art Collections Fund 1925

A01131 The Alcove, Isleworth (1819)
Lπ:181x259:Presented by A. Acland Allen through the National Art Collections Fund 1925

A01132 The Alcove, Isleworth (1819)
Lπ:182x262:Presented by A. Acland Allen through the National Art Collections Fund 1925

A01133 The Alcove, Isleworth (1819)
Lπ:183x262:Presented by A. Acland Allen through the National Art Collections Fund 1925

A01134 Bonneville, Savoy (1816)
Lπ:189x272:Presented by A. Acland Allen through the National Art Collections Fund 1925

A01135 Bonneville, Savoy (1816)
Lπ:190x275:Presented by A. Acland Allen through the National Art Collections Fund 1925

A01136 Inverary Castle and Town (1816)
Lπ:180x256:Presented by A. Acland Allen through the National Art Collections Fund 1925

A01137 Inverary Castle and Town (1816)
Lπ:181x258:Presented by A. Acland Allen through the National Art Collections Fund 1925

A01138 Aesacus and Hesperie (1819)
Lπ:177x257:Presented by A. Acland Allen through the National Art Collections Fund 1925

A01139 Aesacus and Hesperie (1819)
Lπ:177x257:Presented by A. Acland Allen through the National Art Collections Fund 1925

A01140 East Gate, Winchelsea, Sussex (1819)
Lπ:175x258:Presented by A. Acland Allen through the National Art Collections Fund 1925

A01141 East Gate, Winchelsea, Sussex (1819)
Lπ:175x259:Presented by A. Acland Allen through the National Art Collections Fund 1925

A01142 Isis (1819)
Lπ:179x260:Presented by A. Acland Allen through the National Art Collections Fund 1925

A01143 Isis (1819)
Lπ:180x261:Presented by A. Acland Allen through the National Art Collections Fund 1925

A01144 Ben Arthur, Scotland (1819)
Lπ:182x265:Presented by A. Acland Allen through the National Art Collections Fund 1925

A01145 Ben Arthur, Scotland (1819)
Lπ:180x261:Presented by A. Acland Allen through the National Art Collections Fund 1925

A01146 Interior of a Church (1819)
Lπ:172x267:Presented by A. Acland Allen through the National Art Collections Fund 1925

A01147 Interior of a Church (1819)
Lπ:176x269:Presented by A. Acland Allen through the National Art Collections Fund 1925

A01148 Christ and the Woman of Samaria (1819)
Lπ:181x260:Presented by A. Acland Allen through the National Art Collections Fund 1925

A01149 Christ and the Woman of Samaria (1819)
Lπ:182x260:Presented by A. Acland Allen through the National Art Collections Fund 1925

A01150 Glaucus and Scylla
Fπ::Presented by A. Acland Allen through the National Art Collections Fund 1925

A01151 Pam and Syrinx
Fπ::Presented by A. Acland Allen through the National Art Collections Fund 1925

A01152 The Stork and Aqueduct
Fπ::Presented by A. Acland Allen through the National Art Collections Fund 1925

A01153 Moonlight at Sea
Fπ::Presented by A. Acland Allen through the National Art Collections Fund 1925

A01154 Moonlight at Sea
Lπ:188x264:Presented by A. Acland Allen through the National Art Collections Fund 1925

A01155 The Deluge
Lπ:211x276:Presented by A. Acland Allen through the National Art Collections Fund 1925

A01156 Flounder Fishing, Battersea
Fπ::Presented by A. Acland Allen through the National Art Collections Fund 1925

A01157 Flounder Fishing, Battersea
Lπ:179x253:Presented by A. Acland Allen through the National Art Collections Fund 1925

A01158 Narcissus and Echo
Fπ::Presented by A. Acland Allen through the National Art Collections Fund 1925

A01159 Sandbank and Gypsies
Fπ::Presented by A. Acland Allen through the National Art Collections Fund 1925

attributed to
TURNER, Joseph Mallord William
1775-1851
British Collection

N05489 Landscape with Windmill and Rainbow (partly after Gainsborough) (circa 1795-1800)
Oc:705x902:Bequeathed by the artist 1856

N05490 Diana and Callisto (after Wilson) (circa 1796)
Oc:565x914:Bequeathed by the artist 1856

N05512 Tivoli and the Roman Campagna (after Wilson) (circa 1798)
Oc:724x965:Bequeathed by the artist 1856

after
TURNER, Joseph Mallord William
1775-1851
British Collection

N02642 A Fresh Breeze (after 'Sheerness and the Isle of Sheppey')
Oc:394x483:Bequeathed by George Salting 1910

Picturesque Views on the Southern Coast of England (T04370-T04427; complete group)

T04370 St Michael's Mount, Cornwall (1814)
Lπ:148x224:Purchased 1986

T04371 St Michael's Mount, Cornwall (1814)
Lπ:148x224:Purchased 1986

T04372 Poole, Dorsetshire (1814)
Lπ:149x222:Purchased 1986

T04373 Land's End, Cornwall (1814)
Lπ:141x219:Purchased 1986

T04374 Land's End, Cornwall (1814)
Lπ:142x220:Purchased 1986

T04375 Weymouth, Dorsetshire (1814)
Lπ:147x219:Purchased 1986

T04376 Lulworth Cove, Dorsetshire (1814)
Lπ:146x218:Purchased 1986

T04377 Corfe Castle, Dorsetshire (1814)
Lπ:144x216:Purchased 1986

T04378 Lyme Regis, Dorsetshire (1814)
Iπ:148x225:Purchased 1986

T04379 Lyme Regis, Dorsetshire (1814)
Iπ:148x223:Purchased 1986

T04380 Teignmouth, Devonshire (1815)
Iπ:154x228:Purchased 1986

T04381 Dartmouth, Devonshire (1815)
Iπ:146x216:Purchased 1986

T04382 Dartmouth, Devonshire (1815)
Iπ:146x217:Purchased 1986

T04383 The Mew Stone at the Entrance of Plymouth Sound,
Devonshire (1816)
Iπ:160x240:Purchased 1986

T04384 The Mew Stone at the Entrance of Plymouth Sound,
Devonshire (1816)
Iπ:159x240:Purchased 1986

T04385 The Mew Stone at the Entrance of Plymouth Sound,
Devonshire (1816)
Iπ:160x240:Purchased 1986

T04386 Falmouth Harbour, Cornwall (1816)
Iπ:156x239:Purchased 1986

T04387 Plymouth Dock seen from Mount Edgecomb, Devonshire
(1816)
Iπ:160x245:Purchased 1986

T04388 Plymouth with Mount Batten (1817)
Iπ:162x242:Purchased 1986

T04389 Pendennis Castle and Entrance of Falmouth Harbour,
Cornwall (1817)
Iπ:159x239:Purchased 1986

T04390 Pendennis Castle and Entrance of Falmouth Harbour,
Cornwall (1817)
Iπ:158x238:Purchased 1986

T04391 Bow and Arrow Castle, Isle of Portland, Dorsetshire
(1817)
Iπ:160x243:Purchased 1986

T04392 Martello Tower at Bexhill (1817)
Iπ:152x214:Purchased 1986

T04393 East and West Looe, Cornwall (1818)
Iπ:157x238:Purchased 1986

T04394 East and West Looe, Cornwall (1818)
Iπ:157x239:Purchased 1986

T04395 Ilfracomb, North Devon (1818)
Iπ:158x239:Purchased 1986

T04396 Ilfracomb, North Devon (1818)
Iπ:159x241:Purchased 1986

T04397 Watchet, Somersetshire (1820)
Iπ:157x238:Purchased 1986

T04398 Bridport, Dorsetshire (1820)
Iπ:166x243:Purchased 1986

T04399 Bridport, Dorsetshire (1820)
Iπ:166x244:Purchased 1986

T04400 Lulworth Castle, Dorsetshire (1821)
Iπ:158x241:Purchased 1986

T04401 Lulworth Castle, Dorsetshire (1821)
Iπ:158x240:Purchased 1986

T04402 Torbay from Brixham (1821)
Iπ:158x242:Purchased 1986

T04403 Torbay from Brixham (1821)
Iπ:159x240:Purchased 1986

T04404 Minehead and Dunster Castle, Somersetshire (1821)
Iπ:157x225:Purchased 1986

T04405 Margate, Kent (1824)
Iπ:158x240:Purchased 1986

T04406 Margate, Kent (1824)
Iπ:159x240:Purchased 1986

T04407 Rye, Sussex (1824)
Iπ:149x233:Purchased 1986

T04408 Rye, Sussex (1824)
Iπ:148x234:Purchased 1986

T04409 St Mawes, Cornwall (1824)
Iπ:145x221:Purchased 1986

T04410 St Mawes, Cornwall (1824)
Iπ:146x223:Purchased 1986

T04411 St Mawes, Cornwall (1824)
Iπ:146x222:Purchased 1986

T04412 Ramsgate, Kent (1824)
Iπ:150x241:Purchased 1986

T04413 Ramsgate, Kent (1824)
Iπ:151x240:Purchased 1986

T04414 Hythe, Kent (1824)
Iπ:151x235:Purchased 1986

T04415 Hythe, Kent (1824)
Iπ:151x233:Purchased 1986

T04416 Combe Martin (1825)
Iπ:151x240:Purchased 1986

T04417 Combe Martin (1825)
Iπ:151x239:Purchased 1986

T04418 Combe Martin (1825)
Iπ:151x240:Purchased 1986

T04419 Portsmouth, Hampshire (1825)
Iπ:159x237:Purchased 1986

T04420 Brighthelmstone (1825)
Iπ:154x230:Purchased 1986

T04421 Brighthelmstone (1825)
Iπ:154x231:Purchased 1986

T04422 Deal, Kent (1826)
Iπ:147x274:Purchased 1986

T04423 Mount Edgecomb, Devonshire (1826)
Iπ:162x240:Purchased 1986

T04424 Dover from Shakespeare's Cliff (1826)
Iπ:163x243:Purchased 1986

T04425 Whitstable, Kent (1826)
Iπ:166x250:Purchased 1986

T04426 Whitstable, Kent (1826)
Iπ:166x249:Purchased 1986

T04427 Whitstable, Kent (1826)
Iπ:167x249:Purchased 1986

Views in Sussex (T04428-T04438; complete group)
T04428 Battle Abbey, the Spot Where Harold Fell (1819)
Iπ:162x243:Purchased 1986

T04429 Battle Abbey, the Spot Where Harold Fell (1819)
Iπ:164x244:Purchased 1986

T04430 Battle Abbey, the Spot Where Harold Fell (1819)
Iπ:163x243:Purchased 1986

T04431 Brightling Observatory Seen from Rose-Hill Park (1819)
Iπ:191x278:Purchased 1986

T04432 Brightling Observatory Seen from Rose-Hill Park (1819)
Iπ:191x281:Purchased 1986

T04433 Pevensey Bay from Crowhurst Park (1816)
Iπ:192x284:Purchased 1986

T04434 Pevensey Bay from Crowhurst Park (1816)
Iπ:191x283:Purchased 1986

T04435 The Vale of Heathfield (1818)
Iπ:191x284:Purchased 1986

T04436 The Vale of Heathfield (1818)
Iπ:191x282:Purchased 1986

T04437 Bodiham Castle, Sussex (1817)
Iπ:193x284:Purchased 1986

T04438 Hurstmonceux Castle (1820)
Iπ:191x282:Purchased 1986

History of Richmondshire (T04439-T04484; complete group)

T04439 Richmond, Yorkshire (1819)
Iπ:191x272:Purchased 1986

T04440 Richmond, Yorkshire (1819)
Iπ:191x272:Purchased 1986

T04441 Richmond, Yorkshire (1819)
Iπ:190x272:Purchased 1986

T04442 Richmond Castle and Town (1820)
Iπ:191x276:Purchased 1986

T04443 St Agatha's Abbey, Easby (1822)
Iπ:203x283:Purchased 1986

T04444 St Agatha's Abbey, Easby (1822)
Iπ:202x286:Purchased 1986

T04445 Aske Hall (1820)
Iπ:192x278:Purchased 1986

T04446 Aske Hall (1820)
Iπ:192x279:Purchased 1986

T04447 High Force or Fall of Tees (1822)
Iπ:194x272:Purchased 1986

T04448 High Force or Fall of Tees (1822)
Iπ:194x273:Purchased 1986

T04449 Egglestone Abbey, near Barnard Castle (1822)
Iπ:186x270:Purchased 1986

T04450 Egglestone Abbey, near Barnard Castle (1822)
Iπ:186x271:Purchased 1986

T04451 Junction of the Greta and Tees at Rokeby (1819)
Iπ:184x268:Purchased 1986

T04452 Junction of the Greta and Tees at Rokeby (1819)
Iπ:183x270:Purchased 1986

T04453 Brignall Church (1822)
Iπ:190x270:Purchased 1986

T04454 Brignall Church (1822)
Iπ:188x272:Purchased 1986

T04455 Wycliffe, near Rokeby (1823)
Iπ:188x271:Purchased 1986

T04456 Wycliffe, near Rokeby (1823)
Iπ:188x271:Purchased 1986

T04457 Wycliffe, near Rokeby (1823)
Iπ:189x270:Purchased 1986

T04458 Merrick Abbey, Swaledale (1822)
Iπ:189x270:Purchased 1986

T04459 Merrick Abbey, Swaledale (1822)
Iπ:193x275:Purchased 1986

T04460 Merrick Abbey, Swaledale (1822)
Iπ:193x278:Purchased 1986

T04461 Aysgarth Force (1820)
Iπ:192x278:Purchased 1986

T04462 Aysgarth Force (1820)
Iπ:191x279:Purchased 1986

T04463 Simmer Lake, near Askrigg (circa 1822)
Iπ:191x267:Purchased 1986

T04464 Simmer Lake, near Askrigg (circa 1822)
Iπ:191x267:Purchased 1986

T04465 Simmer Lake, near Askrigg (circa 1822)
Iπ:191x266:Purchased 1986

T04466 Moss Dale Fall (1822)
Iπ:191x268:Purchased 1986

T04467 Moss Dale Fall (1822)
Iπ:190x270:Purchased 1986

T04468 Hardraw Fall (1818)
Iπ:190x273:Purchased 1986

T04469 Hardraw Fall (1818)
Iπ:190x273:Purchased 1986

T04470 Hardraw Fall (1818)
Iπ:189x270:Purchased 1986

T04471 Crook of Lune Looking towards Hornby Castle (1821)
Iπ:191x278:Purchased 1986

T04472 Crook of Lune Looking towards Hornby Castle (1821)
Iπ:190x280:Purchased 1986

T04473 Ingleborough from Hornby Castle Terrace (1822)
Iπ:191x270:Purchased 1986

T04474 Ingleborough from Hornby Castle Terrace (1822)
Iπ:190x276:Purchased 1986

T04475 Hornby Castle from Tatham Church (1822)
Iπ:189x277:Purchased 1986

T04476 Hornby Castle from Tatham Church (1822)
Iπ:190x270:Purchased 1986

T04477 Hornby Castle from Tatham Church (1822)
Iπ:189x271:Purchased 1986

T04478 Kirby Lonsdale Churchyard (1822)
Iπ:195x277:Purchased 1986

T04479 Kirby Lonsdale Churchyard (1822)
Iπ:194x280:Purchased 1986

T04480 Heysham and Cumberland Mountains (1822)
Iπ:189x272:Purchased 1986

T04481 Heysham and Cumberland Mountains (1822)
Iπ:188x270:Purchased 1986

T04482 Heysham and Cumberland Mountains (1822)
Iπ:188x272:Purchased 1986

T04483 Weathercote Cave (1822)
Iπ:193x269:Purchased 1986

T04484 Weathercote Cave (1822)
Iπ:193x271:Purchased 1986

The Provincial Antiquities of Scotland (T04485-T04501; complete group)

T04485 Crichton Castle (1819)
Iπ:164x248:Purchased 1986

T04486 Crichton Castle (1819)
Iπ:163x247:Purchased 1986

T04487 Crichton Castle (1819)
Iπ:163x248:Purchased 1986

T04488 Crichton Castle (1819)
Iπ:163x248:Purchased 1986

T04489 Borthwick Castle (1819)
Iπ:161x245:Purchased 1986

T04490 Edinburgh from the Calton Hill (1820)
Iπ:172x251:Purchased 1986

T04491 Edinburgh from the Calton Hill (1820)
Iπ:172x254:Purchased 1986

T04492 Heriot's Hospital (1822)
Iπ:164x244:Purchased 1986

T04493 Roslyn Castle (1822)
Iπ:161x239:Purchased 1986

T04494 Dunbar (1824)
Iπ:171x256:Purchased 1986

T04495 Dunbar (1824)
Iπ:170x257:Purchased 1986

T04496 Tantallon Castle (1822)
Ln:162x241:Purchased 1986

T04497 Tantallon Castle (1822)
Ln:164x243:Purchased 1986

T04498 Linlithgow Palace (1822)
Ln:167x246:Purchased 1986

T04499 Bass Rock (1826)
Ln:171x253:Purchased 1986

T04500 Bass Rock (1826)
Ln:171x253:Purchased 1986

T04501 Bass Rock, engraved by William Miller (1826)
Ln:171x254:Purchased 1986

T04502 Tivoli, a Composition (1827)
Ln:404x605:Purchased 1986

Picturesque Views in England and Wales
(T04503-T04612, T05081-T05104, T05873; complete group)

T04503 Rivaulx Abbey, Yorkshire (1827)
Ln:165x236:Purchased 1986

T04504 Rivaulx Abbey, Yorkshire (1827)
Ln:165x236:Purchased 1986

T04505 Lancaster from the Aqueduct Bridge (1827)
Ln:165x233:Purchased 1986

T04506 Lancaster from the Aqueduct Bridge (1827)
Ln:165x232:Purchased 1986

T04507 Dartmouth Cove (1827)
Ln:147x230:Purchased 1986

T04508 Dartmouth Cove (1827)
Ln:165x232:Purchased 1986

T04509 Bolton Abbey, Yorkshire (1827)
Ln:163x230:Purchased 1986

T04510 Bolton Abbey, Yorkshire (1827)
Ln:163x231:Purchased 1986

T04511 Colchester, Essex (1827)
Ln:168x231:Purchased 1986

T04512 Colchester, Essex (1827)
Ln:166x230:Purchased 1986

T04513 Richmond Yorkshire (1827)
Ln:169x240:Purchased 1986

T04514 Richmond Yorkshire (1827)
Ln:169x240:Purchased 1986

T04515 Launceston, Cornwall (1827)
Ln:167x237:Purchased 1986

T04516 Launceston, Cornwall (1827)
Ln:169x238:Purchased 1986

T04517 Barnard Castle, Durham (1827)
Ln:168x232:Purchased 1986

T04518 Barnard Castle, Durham (1827)
Ln:167x234:Purchased 1986

T04519 Saltash, Cornwall (1827)
Ln:163x232:Purchased 1986

T04520 Saltash, Cornwall (1827)
Ln:164x233:Purchased 1986

T04521 Aldborough, Suffolk (1827)
Ln:164x232:Purchased 1986

T04522 Aldborough, Suffolk (1827)
Ln:163x233:Purchased 1986

T04523 Orford, Suffolk (1827)
Ln:165x238:Purchased 1986

T04524 Orford, Suffolk (1827)
Ln:165x237:Purchased 1986

T04525 Prudhoe Castle, Northumberland (1828)
Ln:166x234:Purchased 1986

T04526 Prudhoe Castle, Northumberland (1828)
Ln:166x235:Purchased 1986

T04527 Valle Crucis Abbey, Denbighshire (1828)
Ln:159x233:Purchased 1986

T04528 Buckfastleigh Abbey, Devonshire (1828)
Ln:165x233:Purchased 1986

T04529 Buckfastleigh Abbey, Devonshire (1828)
Ln:165x234:Purchased 1986

T04530 Entrance to Fowey Harbour, Cornwall (1829)
Ln:162x230:Purchased 1986

T04531 Entrance to Fowey Harbour, Cornwall (1829)
Ln:163x230:Purchased 1986

T04532 Okehampton, Devonshire (1828)
Ln:167x241:Purchased 1986

T04533 Okehampton, Devonshire (1828)
Ln:167x241:Purchased 1986

T04534 Lancaster Sands (1828)
Ln:164x236:Purchased 1986

T04535 Lancaster Sands (1828)
Ln:164x236:Purchased 1986

T04536 Knaresborough, Yorkshire (1828)
Ln:168x230:Purchased 1986

T04537 Knaresborough, Yorkshire (1828)
Ln:166x230:Purchased 1986

T04538 Malmsbury, Wiltshire (1829)
Ln:160x232:Purchased 1986

T04539 Malmsbury, Wiltshire (1829)
Ln:161x233:Purchased 1986

T04540 Kilgarren Castle, Pembroke (1829)
Ln:166x240:Purchased 1986

T04541 Exeter (1829)
Ln:164x232:Purchased 1986

T04542 Richmond, Yorkshire (from the Moors) (1828)
Ln:166x236:Purchased 1986

T04543 Richmond, Yorkshire (from the Moors) (1828)
Ln:166x236:Purchased 1986

T04544 Louth, Lincolnshire (1829)
Ln:166x240:Purchased 1986

T04545 Louth, Lincolnshire (1829)
Ln:167x242:Purchased 1986

T04546 Great Yarmouth, Norfolk (1829)
Ln:179x254:Purchased 1986

T04547 Great Yarmouth, Norfolk (1829)
Ln:178x253:Purchased 1986

T04548 Stonehenge, Wiltshire (1829)
Ln:165x235:Purchased 1986

T04549 Stone Henge, engraved by R. Wallis (1829)
Ln:166x234:Purchased 1986

T04550 Hampton Court Palace (?1829)
Ln:164x231:Purchased 1986

T04551 Devonport and Dockyard, Devonshire (1830)
Ln:162x244:Purchased 1986

T04552 Devonport and Dockyard, Devonshire (1830)
Ln:162x244:Purchased 1986

T04553 Dunstanborough Castle, Northumberland (1830)
Ln:165x235:Purchased 1986

T04554 Carisbrook Castle, Isle of Wight (1830)
Ln:166x235:Purchased 1986

T04555 Carisbrook Castle, Isle of Wight (1830)
Ln:166x235:Purchased 1986

T04556 Cowes, Isle of Wight (1830)
In:165x238:Purchased 1986

T04557 Stamford, Lincolnshire (1830)
In:164x231:Purchased 1986

T04558 Holy Island, Northumberland (1830)
In:166x247:Purchased 1986

T04559 Holy Island, Northumberland (1830)
In:166x246:Purchased 1986

T04560 Stoneyhurst, Lancashire (1830)
In:161x235:Purchased 1986

T04561 Winchelsea, Sussex (1830)
In:166x231:Purchased 1986

T04562 Winchelsea, Sussex (1830)
In:164x232:Purchased 1986

T04563 Trematon Castle, Cornwall (1830)
In:168x235:Purchased 1986

T04564 Trematon Castle, Cornwall (1830)
In:168x236:Purchased 1986

T04565 St Mawes, Cornwall (1830)
In:166x238:Purchased 1986

T04566 St Mawes, Cornwall (1830)
In:163x238:Purchased 1986

T04567 Walton Bridge on Thames, Surrey (1830)
In:163x251:Purchased 1986

T04568 Ludlow Castle, Shropshire (1831)
In:158x239:Purchased 1986

T04569 Ludlow Castle, Shropshire (1831)
In:156x241:Purchased 1986

T04570 Folkestone Harbour and Coast to Dover (1831)
In:155x235:Purchased 1986

T04571 Folkestone Harbour and Coast to Dover (1831)
In:155x235:Purchased 1986

T04572 Tynemouth, Northumberland (1831)
In:167x229:Purchased 1986

T04573 Tynemouth, Northumberland (1831)
In:166x229:Purchased 1986

T04574 Gosport, Entrance to Portsmouth Harbour (1831)
In:162x234:Purchased 1986

T04575 Gosport, Entrance to Portsmouth Harbour (1831)
In:162x232:Purchased 1986

T04576 Eton College, Berkshire (1831)
In:161x240:Purchased 1986

T04577 Eton College, Berkshire (1831)
In:162x238:Purchased 1986

T04578 Bedford, Bedfordshire (1831)
In:163x228:Purchased 1986

T04579 Pembroke Castle, Wales (1831)
In:161x233:Purchased 1986

T04580 Pembroke Castle, Wales (1831)
In:160x232:Purchased 1986

T04581 Richmond Hill and Bridge, Surrey (1832)
In:161x228:Purchased 1986

T04582 Richmond Hill and Bridge, Surrey (1832)
In:161x229:Purchased 1986

T04583 Malvern Abbey and Gate, Worcestershire (1832)
In:168x238:Purchased 1986

T04584 Plymouth, Devonshire (1832)
In:164x234:Purchased 1986

T04585 Plymouth, Devonshire (1832)
In:162x234:Purchased 1986

T04586 Salisbury, Wiltshire (1830)
In:167x239:Purchased 1986

T04587 St Catherine's Hill, Near Guildford, Surrey (1832)
In:159x243:Purchased 1986

T04588 Chatham, Kent (1832)
In:148x235:Purchased 1986

T04589 Chatham, Kent (1832)
In:149x233:Purchased 1986

T04590 Margate, Kent (1832)
In:160x244:Purchased 1986

T04591 Margate, Kent (1832)
In:162x241:Purchased 1986

T04592 Margate, Kent (1832)
In:162x240:Purchased 1986

T04593 Ashby de la Zouch, Leicestershire (1832)
In:167x244:Purchased 1986

T04594 Warwick Castle, Warwickshire (1832)
In:165x241:Purchased 1986

T04595 Warwick Castle, Warwickshire (1832)
In:164x242:Purchased 1986

T04596 Kenilworth Castle, Warwickshire (1832)
In:165x252:Purchased 1986

T04597 Brinkburn Priory, Northumberland (1832)
In:154x237:Purchased 1986

T04598 Tamworth Castle, Staffordshire (1832)
In:165x246:Purchased 1986

T04599 Blenheim, Oxfordshire (1833)
In:153x241:Purchased 1986

T04600 Blenheim, Oxfordshire (1833)
In:152x242:Purchased 1986

T04601 Penmaen-Mawr, Caernarvonshire (1834)
In:165x228:Purchased 1986

T04602 Arundel Castle and Town, Sussex (1834)
In:269x242:Purchased 1986

T04603 Caernarvon Castle, Wales (1835)
In:165x241:Purchased 1986

T04604 Beaumaris, Isle of Anglesea (1836)
In:163x251:Purchased 1986

T04605 Lyme Regis (1836)
In:166x256, 257x329:Purchased 1986

T04606 Harlech Castle, North Wales (1836)
In:162x244:Purchased 1986

T04607 Kidwelly Castle, South Wales (1837)
In:163x251:Purchased 1986

T04608 Keswick Lake, Cumberland (1837)
In:152x244:Purchased 1986

T04609 Llangollen, North Wales (1837)
In:164x255:Purchased 1986

T04610 Crickieth Castle, North Wales (1837)
In:165x241:Purchased 1986

T04611 Richmond Terrace, Surrey (1838)
In:165x248:Purchased 1986

T04612 Mount St Michael, Cornwall (1838)
In:167x241:Purchased 1986

T04613 Dunwich, for 'East Coast of England'
In:172x255:Purchased 1986

The Keepsake (T04614-T04630, T05105-T05109; complete group)

T04614 Lake Albano (1829)
In:91x134:Purchased 1986

T04615 Lake Albano (1829)
In:91x134:Purchased 1986

T04616 Virginia Water No. 1 (1830)
Iπ:93x139:Purchased 1986

T04617 Virginia Water No. 1 (1830)
Iπ:93x139:Purchased 1986

T04618 Virginia Water No. 2 (1830)
Iπ:92x138:Purchased 1986

T04619 Nantes (1831)
Iπ:87x130:Purchased 1986

T04620 Nantes (1831)
Iπ:87x129:Purchased 1986

T04621 St Germain-en-Laye (1832)
Iπ:92x144:Purchased 1986

T04622 St Germain-en-Laye (1832)
Iπ:92x144:Purchased 1986

T04623 Ehrenbreitstein (1833)
Iπ:99x144:Purchased 1986

T04624 Ehrenbreitstein (1833)
Iπ:99x144:Purchased 1986

T04625 Falls of the Rhine (1833)
Iπ:94x142:Purchased 1986

T04626 Havre (1834)
Iπ:98x140:Purchased 1986

T04627 Palace of La Belle Gabrielle (1834)
Iπ:97x132:Purchased 1986

T04628 Burning of the Houses of Parliament (1835)
Iπ:115x90:Purchased 1986

T04629 Fire at Sea (1835)
Iπ:125x88:Purchased 1986

T04630 The Wreck (1836)
Iπ:110x80:Purchased 1986

Rogers's 'Italy' (T04631-T04670; complete group)
T04631 The Lake of Geneva (1830)
Iπ:241x138:Purchased 1986

T04632 The Lake of Geneva (1830)
Iπ:241x138:Purchased 1986

T04633 William Tell's Chapel (1830)
Iπ:260x142:Purchased 1986

T04634 St Maurice (1830)
Iπ:259x142:Purchased 1986

T04635 Hospice of the Great St Bernard I (1830)
Iπ:261x145:Purchased 1986

T04636 Hospice of the Great St Bernard I (1830)
Iπ:260x144:Purchased 1986

T04637 Hospice of the Great St Bernard II (The Dead-House)
(1830)
Iπ:257x141:Purchased 1986

T04638 Hospice of the Great St Bernard II (The Dead-House)
(1830)
Iπ:258x140:Purchased 1986

T04639 Marengo (1830)
Iπ:259x142:Purchased 1986

T04640 Aosta (1830)
Iπ:260x145:Purchased 1986

T04641 Aosta (1830)
Iπ:261x144:Purchased 1986

T04642 Martigny (1830)
Iπ:253x144:Purchased 1986

T04643 Martigny (1830)
Iπ:254x144:Purchased 1986

T04644 Hannibal Passing the Alps (1830)
Iπ:258x140:Purchased 1986

T04645 Lake of Como I (1830)
Iπ:62x82:Purchased 1986

T04646 Venice (1830)
Iπ:260x141:Purchased 1986

T04647 Florence (1830)
Iπ:258x141:Purchased 1986

T04648 Florence (1830)
Iπ:259x141:Purchased 1986

T04649 Galileo's Villa (1830)
Iπ:286x142:Purchased 1986

T04650 Galileo's Villa (1830)
Iπ:285x142:Purchased 1986

T04651 Villa Madama - Moonlight (1830)
Iπ:259x144:Purchased 1986

T04652 Rome, Castle of St Angelo (1830)
Iπ:260x140:Purchased 1986

T04653 The Forum (1830)
Iπ:259x140:Purchased 1986

T04654 The Forum (1830)
Iπ:260x140:Purchased 1986

T04655 The Campagna of Rome (1830)
Iπ:258x140:Purchased 1986

T04656 The Campagna of Rome (1830)
Iπ:258x140:Purchased 1986

T04657 Tivoli (1830)
Iπ:253x146:Purchased 1986

T04658 Tivoli (1830)
Iπ:254x146:Purchased 1986

T04659 Perugia (1830)
Iπ:262x140:Purchased 1986

T04660 Perugia (1830)
Iπ:260x141:Purchased 1986

T04661 Banditti (1830)
Iπ:261x142:Purchased 1986

T04662 Naples (1830)
Iπ:255x141:Purchased 1986

T04663 Naples (1830)
Iπ:256x139:Purchased 1986

T04664 Paestum (1830)
Iπ:253x144:Purchased 1986

T04665 Paestum (1830)
Iπ:255x144:Purchased 1986

T04666 Amalfi (1830)
Iπ:257x141:Purchased 1986

T04667 Amalfi (1830)
Iπ:256x139:Purchased 1986

T04668 A Villa on the Night of a Festa di Ballo (1830)
Iπ:259x140:Purchased 1986

T04669 A Villa on the Night of a Festa di Ballo (1830)
Iπ:259x140:Purchased 1986

T04670 A Farewell - Lake of Como II (1830)
Iπ:260x141:Purchased 1986

Rogers's 'Poems' (T04671-T04677; complete group)
T04671 A Garden (1834)
Iπ:295x157:Purchased 1986

T04672 Leaving Home (1834)
Iπ:293x151:Purchased 1986

T04673 Greenwich Hospital (1834)
Iπ:292x150:Purchased 1986

T04674 St Herbert's Chapel (1834)
Iπ:281x165:Purchased 1986

T04675 A Village Fair (1834)
MIπ:293x151:Purchased 1986

T04676 St Julienne's Chapel (1834)
Iπ:292x150:Purchased 1986

T04677 A Tempest - Voyage of Columbus (1834)
Iπ:291x151:Purchased 1986

Turner's Annual Tour, 1833: Wanderings by the Loire
(T04678-T04697; complete group)
T04678 Nantes (1833)
Iπ:124x90:Purchased 1986

T04679 Orleans (1833)
Iπ:98x143:Purchased 1986

T04680 Beaugency (1833)
Iπ:92x138:Purchased 1986

T04681 Blois (1833)
Iπ:94x137:Purchased 1986

T04682 Palais at Blois (1833)
Iπ:96x142:Purchased 1986

T04683 Amboise (1833)
Iπ:103x142:Purchased 1986

T04684 Château of Amboise (1833)
Iπ:94x144:Purchased 1986

T04685 Canal of the Loire and Cher, near Tours (1833)
Iπ:96x140:Purchased 1986

T04686 Tours (1833)
Iπ:93x137:Purchased 1986

T04687 St Julian's, Tours (1833)
Iπ:96x145:Purchased 1986

T04688 Tours - Looking Backwards (1833)
Iπ:93x143:Purchased 1986

T04689 Saumur (1833)
Iπ:97x145:Purchased 1986

T04690 Rietz, near Saumur (1833)
Iπ:89x137:Purchased 1986

T04691 Montjen (1833)
Iπ:96x137:Purchased 1986

T04692 Between Clairmont and Mauves (1833)
Iπ:99x134:Purchased 1986

T04693 Château Hamelin (1833)
Iπ:92x131:Purchased 1986

T04694 Scene on the Loire (1833)
Iπ:95x144:Purchased 1986

T04695 Clairmont (1833)
Iπ:98x136:Purchased 1986

T04696 Coteaux de Mauves (1833)
Iπ:97x144:Purchased 1986

T04697 Château de Nantes (1833)
Iπ:95x135:Purchased 1986

Turner's Annual Tour, 1834: Wanderings by the Seine
(T04698-T04707; complete group)
T04698 Havre (1834)
Iπ:98x139:Purchased 1986

T04699 Havre, Tower of Francis I (1834)
Iπ:102x141:Purchased 1986

T04700 Graville (1834)
Iπ:95x141:Purchased 1986

T04701 Château de Tancarville with Town of Quilleboeuf (1834)
Iπ:92x140:Purchased 1986

T04702 Lillebonne, Château and Tower (1834)
Iπ:100x136:Purchased 1986

T04703 Lillebonne, Château (1834)
Iπ:95x138:Purchased 1986

T04704 Rouen, Looking Down the River (1834)
Iπ:98x136:Purchased 1986

T04705 Rouen, from St Catherine's Hill (1834)
Iπ:100x135:Purchased 1986

T04706 Château de la Mailleraie (1834)
Iπ:93x139:Purchased 1986

T04707 Honfleur (1834)
Iπ:95x140:Purchased 1986

Turner's Annual Tour, 1835: Wanderings by the Seine
(T04708-T04726; complete group)
T04708 Château Gaillard, from the South (1835)
Iπ:108x90:Purchased 1986

T04709 Château Gaillard, from the East (1835)
Iπ:103x143:Purchased 1986

T04710 Vernon (1835)
Iπ:102x143:Purchased 1986

T04711 Pont de l'Arche (1835)
Iπ:98x133:Purchased 1986

T04712 Mantes (1835)
Iπ:98x136:Purchased 1986

T04713 Bridge of Meulan (1835)
Iπ:87x134:Purchased 1986

T04714 St Germains (1835)
Iπ:96x136:Purchased 1986

T04715 Saint Denis (1835)
Iπ:100x138:Purchased 1986

T04716 Bridges of St Cloud and Sèvres (1835)
Iπ:100x137:Purchased 1986

T04717 The Lanterne of St Cloud (1835)
Iπ:99x139:Purchased 1986

T04718 Bridge of St Cloud from Sèvres (1835)
Iπ:99x136:Purchased 1986

T04719 Paris from the Barriere de Passy (1835)
Iπ:101x141:Purchased 1986

T04720 Pont-Neuf, Paris (1835)
Iπ:100x133:Purchased 1986

T04721 Marché aux Fleures and Pont-au-Change (1835)
Iπ:99x136:Purchased 1986

T04722 Hôtel de Ville and Pont d'Arcole (1835)
Iπ:100x137:Purchased 1986

T04723 Boulevards, Paris (1835)
Iπ:102x138:Purchased 1986

T04724 Confluence of the Seine and Marne (1835)
Iπ:99x137:Purchased 1986

T04725 Melun (1835)
Iπ:98x134:Purchased 1986

T04726 Troyes (1835)
Iπ:102x138:Purchased 1986

Scott's Prose Works (T04727-T04763; complete group)
T04727 Dryden's Monument (1834-6)
Iπ:210x152:Purchased 1986

T04728 Dumbarton Castle (1834-6)
Iπ:311x154:Purchased 1986

T04729 Brussels - Distant View (1834-6)
Iπ:82x140:Purchased 1986

T04730 Hougoumont (1834-6)
Iπ:210x153:Purchased 1986

T04731 Norham Castle - Moonrise (1834-6)
Iπ:86x140:Purchased 1986

T04732 Jerusalem (1834-6)
Ln:133x81:Purchased 1986

T04733 Hôtel de Ville, Paris (1834-6)
Ln:211x153:Purchased 1986

T04734 Napoleon's Logement, Quai Conti (1834-6)
Ln:210x151:Purchased 1986

T04735 Brienne (1834-6)
Ln:82x145:Purchased 1986

T04736 Venice - The Campanile (1834-6)
Ln:211x154:Purchased 1986

T04737 Placenza (Piacenza) (1834-6)
Ln:82x144:Purchased 1986

T04738 Verona (1834-6)
Ln:87x145:Purchased 1986

T04739 St Cloud (1834-6)
Ln:180x130:Purchased 1986

T04740 Mayence (1834-6)
Ln:210x150:Purchased 1986

T04741 Milan (1834-6)
Ln:84x140:Purchased 1986

T04742 Milan (1834-6)
Ln:84x140:Purchased 1986

T04743 The Simplon (1834-6)
Ln:210x152:Purchased 1986

T04744 Paris from Père-la-Chaise (1834-6)
Ln:80x117:Purchased 1986

T04745 Malmaison (1834-6)
Ln:210x155:Purchased 1986

T04746 Fontainebleau (1834-6)
Ln:210x151:Purchased 1986

T04747 Field of Waterloo (1834-6)
Ln:84x142:Purchased 1986

T04748 Chiefswood Cottage (1834-6)
Ln:211x152:Purchased 1986

T04749 The Rhymer's Glen (1834-6)
Ln:209x151:Purchased 1986

T04750 Edinburgh from St Anthony's Chapel (1834-6)
Ln:301x438:Purchased 1986

T04751 Dunfermline (1834-6)
Ln:208x151:Purchased 1986

T04752 Stirling (1834-6)
Ln:80x144:Purchased 1986

T04753 Craigmillar Castle (1834-6)
Ln:206x151:Purchased 1986

T04754 Dunstaffnage (1834-6)
Ln:85x134:Purchased 1986

T04755 Linlithgow (1834-6)
Ln:210x152:Purchased 1986

T04756 Glencoe (1834-6)
Ln:86x142:Purchased 1986

T04757 Killiecrankie (1834-6)
Ln:229x150:Purchased 1986

T04758 Inverness (1834-6)
Ln:79x138:Purchased 1986

T04759 Fort Augustus (1834-6)
Ln:210x151:Purchased 1986

T04760 Rouen - Distant View (1834-6)
Ln:80x143:Purchased 1986

T04761 Calais (1834-6)
Ln:290x150:Purchased 1986

T04762 Château d'Arc, near Dieppe (1834-6)
Ln:80x126:Purchased 1986

T04763 Abbeville (1834-6)
Ln:210x152:Purchased 1986

Campbell's Poetical Works (T04764-T04785; complete group)

T04764 Summer Eve - the Rainbow (1837)
Ln:82x82:Purchased 1986

T04765 Summer Eve - the Rainbow (1837)
Ln:82x82:Purchased 1986

T04766 The Andes Coast (1837)
Ln:79x72:Purchased 1986

T04767 Prague - Kosciusko (1837)
Ln:84x80:Purchased 1986

T04768 Sinai's Thunder (1837)
Ln:103x74:Purchased 1986

T04769 A Swiss Valley (1837)
Ln:82x69:Purchased 1986

T04770 O'Connor's Child (1837)
Ln:92x68:Purchased 1986

T04771 Lochiel's Warning (1837)
Ln:76x68:Purchased 1986

T04772 Battle of the Baltic (1837)
Ln:83x70:Purchased 1986

T04773 Hohenlinden (1837)
Ln:104x74:Purchased 1986

T04774 Lord Ullin's Daughter (1837)
Ln:101x79:Purchased 1986

T04775 The Soldier's Dream (1837)
Ln:88x59:Purchased 1986

T04776 The Last Man (1837)
Ln:86x63:Purchased 1986

T04777 Gertrude of Wyoming - the Valley (1837)
Ln:85x67:Purchased 1986

T04778 Gertrude of Wyoming - The Waterfall (1837)
Ln:77x70:Purchased 1986

T04779 Rolandseck (1837)
Ln:80x67:Purchased 1986

T04780 The Beech Tree's Petition (1837)
Ln:80x67:Purchased 1986

T04781 Camp Hill, Hastings (1837)
Ln:294x153:Purchased 1986

T04782 Camp Hill, Hastings (1837)
Ln:80x73:Purchased 1986

T04783 The Death-Boat of Heligoland (1837)
Ln:76x72:Purchased 1986

T04784 Ehrenbreitstein (1837)
Ln:78x72:Purchased 1986

T04785 The Dead Eagle - Oran (1837)
Ln:93x81:Purchased 1986

T04786 Tynemouth Priory, from 'Dr Broadley's Poems' (circa 1844)
Ln:67x98:Purchased 1986

The Thames at Mortlake, from 'The Book of Gems' (T04787-T04788; complete group)

T04787 The Thames at Mortlake (1836)
Ln:60x80:Purchased 1986

T04788 The Thames at Mortlake (1836)
Ln:60x80:Purchased 1986

T04789 Caligula's Palace and Bridge (circa 1842)
Ln:394x615:Purchased 1986

The Rivers of England (T04790-T04819; complete group)

T04790 Shields, on the River Tyne (1823)
Lπ:154x217:Purchased 1986

T04791 Newcastle-on-Tyne (1823)
Lπ:156x219:Purchased 1986

T04792 Newcastle-on-Tyne (1823)
Lπ:155x218:Purchased 1986

T04793 Newcastle-on-Tyne (1823)
Lπ:155x220:Purchased 1986

T04794 More Park, near Watford, on the River Colne (1824)
Lπ:156x222:Purchased 1986

T04795 More Park, near Watford, on the River Colne (1824)
Lπ:155x221:Purchased 1986

T04796 Rochester, on the River Medway (1824)
Lπ:152x218:Purchased 1986

T04797 Rochester, on the River Medway (1824)
Lπ:152x217:Purchased 1986

T04798 Rochester, on the River Medway (1824)
Lπ:153x218:Purchased 1986

T04799 Norham Castle, on the River Tweed (1824)
Lπ:153x216:Purchased 1986

T04800 Norham Castle, on the River Tweed (1824)
Lπ:154x218:Purchased 1986

T04801 Norham Castle, on the River Tweed (1824)
Lπ:152x216:Purchased 1986

T04802 Dartmouth Castle, on the River Dart (1824)
Lπ:158x224:Purchased 1986

T04803 Dartmouth Castle, on the River Dart (1824)
Lπ:158x223:Purchased 1986

T04804 Dartmouth Castle, on the River Dart (1824)
Lπ:159x224:Purchased 1986

T04805 Okehampton Castle, on the River Okement (1825)
Lπ:158x227:Purchased 1986

T04806 Okehampton Castle, on the River Okement (1825)
Lπ:158x227:Purchased 1986

T04807 Okehampton Castle, on the River Okement (1825)
Lπ:158x228:Purchased 1986

T04808 Dartmouth, on the River Dart (1825)
Lπ:153x220:Purchased 1986

T04809 Brougham Castle, near the Junction of the Rivers Eamont and Lowther (1825)
Lπ:155x214:Purchased 1986

T04810 Kirkstall Abbey, on the River Aire (1826)
Lπ:161x224:Purchased 1986

T04811 Kirkstall Abbey, on the River Aire (1826)
Lπ:161x224:Purchased 1986

T04812 Warkworth Castle, on the River Coquet (1826)
Lπ:149x212:Purchased 1986

T04813 Mouth of the River Humber (1826)
Lπ:152x222:Purchased 1986

T04814 Mouth of the River Humber (1826)
Lπ:153x222:Purchased 1986

T04815 Arundel Castle, on the River Arun (1827)
Lπ:154x218:Purchased 1986

T04816 Kirkstall Lock, on the River Aire (1827)
Lπ:154x228:Purchased 1986

T04817 Stangate Creek, on the River Medway (1827)
Lπ:160x238:Purchased 1986

T04818 Stangate Creek, on the River Medway (1827)
Lπ:159x238:Purchased 1986

T04819 Totnes, on the Dart (1825)
Lπ:162x227:Purchased 1986

T04820 The Eddystone Lighthouse (1824)
Lπ:210x312:Purchased 1986

T04821 Colebrooke Dale (1825)
Lπ:136x198:Purchased 1986

The Ports of England (T04822-T04837; complete group)

T04822 Naval Design on Wrapper (1826)
Lπ:160x110:Purchased 1986

T04823 Scarborough (1826)
Lπ:158x225:Purchased 1986

T04824 Scarborough (1826)
Lπ:158x225:Purchased 1986

T04825 Whitby (1826)
Lπ:156x221:Purchased 1986

T04826 Whitby (1826)
Lπ:155x219:Purchased 1986

T04827 Whitby (1826)
Lπ:155x221:Purchased 1986

T04828 Dover (1827)
Lπ:161x241:Purchased 1986

T04829 Dover (1827)
Lπ:161x242:Purchased 1986

T04830 Ramsgate (1827)
Lπ:163x233:Purchased 1986

T04831 Ramsgate (1827)
Lπ:164x235:Purchased 1986

T04832 Sheerness (1828)
Lπ:162x241:Purchased 1986

T04833 Portsmouth (1828)
Lπ:160x240:Purchased 1986

T04834 Portsmouth (1828)
Lπ:160x240:Purchased 1986

T04835 Plymouth (published 1856)
Lπ:160x244:Purchased 1986

T04836 Catwater, Plymouth (published 1856)
Lπ:159x235:Purchased 1986

T04837 Falmouth (published 1856)
Lπ:155x219:Purchased 1986

T04838 The Deluge (1828)
Lπ:379x577:Purchased 1986

T04839 Fishing Boats off Calais (The 'Pas de Calais') (1830)
Lπ:391x587:Purchased 1986

History and Description of Cassiobury Park (T04840-T04841; complete group)

T04840 West Front, Cassiobury (1837)
Lπ:237x206:Purchased 1986

T04841 North-West Front, Cassiobury (1816)
Lπ:203x292:Purchased 1986

T04843 Coast Scene with Fishermen Hauling a Boat Ashore (The 'Iveagh Seapiece') (circa 1803-4)
Lπ:127x172:Purchased 1986

T04917 Newcastle-on-Tyne, from 'The Rivers of England' (1823)
Lπ:155x216:Purchased 1987

Scott's Poetical Works (T04947-T04960; complete group)

T04947 Jedburgh Abbey (1834)
Lπ:85x146:Purchased 1987

T04948 Kelso (1834)
Lπ:82x147:Purchased 1987

T04949 Hermitage Castle (1834)
Lπ:105x90:Purchased 1987

T04950 Dryburgh Abbey (1834)
Lπ:80x148:Purchased 1987

T04951 Bemerside Tower (1834)
Lπ:120x90:Purchased 1987

T04952 Edinburgh from Blackford Hill (1834)
Lπ:86x147:Purchased 1987

T04953 Ashestiel (1834)
Lπ:102x82:Purchased 1987

T04954 Loch Achray (1834)
Lπ:90x85:Purchased 1987

T04955 Junction of the Greta and the Tees (1834)
Lπ:83x146:Purchased 1987

T04956 Bowes Tower (1834)
Lπ:130x90:Purchased 1987

T04957 Loch Coriskin (1834)
Lπ:81x130:Purchased 1987

T04958 Fingal's Cave, Staffa (1834)
Lπ:123x80:Purchased 1987

T04959 Mayburgh (1834)
Lπ:90x90:Purchased 1987

T04960 Abbotsford (1834)
Lπ:97x90:Purchased 1987

Scott's Prose Works (T04727-T04763; complete group)

T04961 Dryden's Monument (1834-6)
Lπ:110x75:Purchased 1987

T04962 Dumbarton Castle (1834-6)
Lπ:80x90:Purchased 1987

T04963 Brussels - Distant View (1834-6)
Lπ:83x141:Purchased 1987

T04964 Hougoumont (1834-6)
Lπ:100x90:Purchased 1987

T04965 New Abbey, near Dumfries (1834-6)
Lπ:120x85:Purchased 1987

T04966 Shakespeare's Monument (1834-6)
Lπ:110x75:Purchased 1987

T04967 Hôtel de Ville, Paris (1834-6)
Lπ:105x85:Purchased 1987

T04968 Napoleon's Logement, Quai Conti (1834-6)
Lπ:115x70:Purchased 1987

T04969 Brienne (1834-6)
Lπ:82x145:Purchased 1987

T04970 Venice - The Campanile (1834-6)
Lπ:105x90:Purchased 1987

T04971 Plancenza (1834-6)
(Piacenza)
MIπ:82x144:Purchased 1987

T04972 Verona (1834-6)
Lπ:87x146:Purchased 1987

T04973 Vincennes (1834-6)
Lπ:77x80:Purchased 1987

T04974 St Cloud (1834-6)
Lπ:80x130:Purchased 1987

T04975 Mayence (1834-6)
Lπ:80x85:Purchased 1987

T04976 Milan (1834-6)
Lπ:84x140:Purchased 1987

T04977 The Simplon (1834-6)
Lπ:110x80:Purchased 1987

T04978 Paris from Père-la-Chaise (1834-6)
Lπ:80x117:Purchased 1987

T04979 Malmaison (1834-6)
Lπ:115x85:Purchased 1987

T04980 Fontainebleau (1834-6)
Lπ:95x75:Purchased 1987

T04981 Field of Waterloo (1834-6)
Lπ:85x143:Purchased 1987

T04982 The Bellerophon, Plymouth Sound (1834-6)
Lπ:110x85:Purchased 1987

T04983 Chiefswood Cottage (1834-6)
Lπ:105x70:Purchased 1987

T04984 The Rhymer's Glen (1834-6)
Lπ:120x80:Purchased 1987

T04985 Edinburgh from St Anthony's Chapel (1834-6)
Lπ:85x130:Purchased 1987

T04986 Dunfermline (1834-6)
Lπ:100x90:Purchased 1987

T04987 Craigmillar Castle (1834-6)
Lπ:95x85:Purchased 1987

T04988 Linlithgow (1834-6)
Lπ:85x85:Purchased 1987

T04989 Glencoe (1834-6)
Lπ:86x142:Purchased 1987

T04990 Killiecrankie (1834-6)
Lπ:100x80:Purchased 1987

T04991 Fort Augustus (1834-6)
Lπ:105x80:Purchased 1987

T04992 Rouen - Distant View (1834-6)
Lπ:80x143:Purchased 1987

T04993 Calais (1834-6)
Lπ:105x70:Purchased 1987

T04994 Abbeville (1834-6)
Lπ:95x85:Purchased 1987

T05078 The Vale of Ashburnham, from 'Views in Sussex' (1816)
Lπ:187x282:Purchased 1988

T05079 Bridge at Narni,from Hakewill's 'Picturesque Tour in Italy' (1819)
Lπ:139x221:Purchased 1988

T05080 The Temple of Jupiter Panhellenius in the Island of Aegina (1828)
Lπ:383x580:Purchased 1988

Picturesque Views in England and Wales (T04503-T04612, T05081-T05104, T05873; complete group)

T05081 Fall of the Tees, Yorkshire (1827)
Lπ:163x226:Purchased 1988

T05082 Exeter (1829)
Lπ:164x232:Purchased 1988

T05083 Dunstansborough Castle, Northumberland (1830)
Lπ:164x235:Purchased 1988

T05084 Alnwick Castle, Northumberland, engraved by J.T. Willmore (1830)
Lπ:166x243:Purchased 1988

T05085 Stoneyhurst, Lancashire (1830)
Lπ:67x237:Purchased 1988

T05086 Windsor Castle, Berkshire (1831)
Lπ:156x234:Purchased 1988

T05087 Bedford, Bedfordshire (1831)
Lπ:162x230:Purchased 1988

T05088 St Catherine's Hill, near Guildford, Surrey (1832)
Lπ:160x242:Purchased 1988

T05089 Chatham, Kent (1832)
Lπ:149x235:Purchased 1988

T05090 Ashby de la Zouch, Leicestershire (1832)
Lπ:168x244:Purchased 1988

T05091 Brinkburn Priory, Northumberland (1832)
Iπ:154x237:Purchased 1988

T05092 Ely Cathedral, Cambridgeshire (1833)
Iπ:168x229:Purchased 1988

T05093 Carew Castle, Pembroke (1834)
Iπ:157x240:Purchased 1988

T05094 Christ Church College, Oxford (1834)
Iπ:160x227:Purchased 1988

T05095 Llanberis Lake, Wales (1834)
Iπ:164x243:Purchased 1988

T05096 Leicester Abbey, Leicestershire (1834)
Iπ:148x236:Purchased 1988

T05097 Dudley, Worcestershire (1835)
Iπ:163x239:Purchased 1988

T05098 Powis Castle, Montgomery (1836)
Iπ:165x252:Purchased 1988

T05099 Beaumaris, Isle of Anglesea (1836)
Iπ:164x250:Purchased 1988

T05100 Lowestoffe, Suffolk (1837)
Iπ:167x250:Purchased 1988

T05101 Durham Cathedral (1836)
Iπ:157x234:Purchased 1988

T05102 Winander-mere, Westmorland (1837)
Iπ:167x246:Purchased 1988

T05103 Whitehaven, Cumberland (1837)
Iπ:168x249:Purchased 1988

T05104 Rochester, Stroud and Chatham, Medway, Kent (1838)
Iπ:162x242:Purchased 1988

The Keepsake (T04614-T04630, T05105-T05109; complete group)
T05105 Florence (1828)
Iπ:87x132:Purchased 1988

T05106 Lago Maggiore (1829)
Iπ:87x131:Purchased 1988

T05107 Saumur (1831)
Iπ:94x141:Purchased 1988

T05108 Marly (1832)
Iπ:96x141:Purchased 1988

T05109 The Sea! The Sea! (1837)
Iπ:125x96:Purchased 1988

T05110 Florence from the Chiesa al Monte, from 'The Amulet' (1831)
Iπ:77x117:Purchased 1988

T05111 Fonthill, from 'The Anniversary' (1829)
Iπ:87x129:Purchased 1988

Barnard Castle, from 'The Talisman' (T05112-T05113; complete group)
T05112 Barnard Castle (1831)
Iπ:87x119:Purchased 1988

T05113 Barnard Castle (1831)
Iπ:87x120:Purchased 1988

Rogers's 'Poems' (T04671-T04677; complete group)
T05114 A Village - Evening (1834)
Iπ:75x95:Purchased 1988

T05115 An Old Manor House (1834)
Iπ:98x95:Purchased 1988

T05116 Traitor's Gate, Tower of London (1834)
Iπ:90x87:Purchased 1988

T05117 An Old Oak (1834)
Iπ:82x83:Purchased 1988

T05118 Shipbuilding (An Old Oak Dead) (1834)
Iπ:70x83:Purchased 1988

T05119 Shipbuilding (An Old Oak Dead) (1834)
Iπ:67x90:Purchased 1988

T05120 The Boy of Egremont (1834)
Iπ:75x83:Purchased 1988

T05121 Bolton Abbey (1834)
Iπ:88x83:Purchased 1988

T05122 The Alps at Daybreak (1834)
Iπ:87x92:Purchased 1988

T05123 St Anne's Hill (II) (1834)
Iπ:78x80:Purchased 1988

T05124 Columbus and his Son (1834)
Iπ:82x87:Purchased 1988

T05125 Columbus Setting Sail (1834)
Iπ:77x87:Purchased 1988

T05126 The Vision of Columbus (1834)
Iπ:77x85:Purchased 1988

T05127 Land Discovered by Columbus (1834)
Iπ:90x82:Purchased 1988

T05128 The Landing of Columbus (1834)
Iπ:68x101:Purchased 1988

T05129 The Landing of Columbus (1834)
Iπ:68x101:Purchased 1988

T05130 A Tempest - Voyage of Columbus (1834)
Iπ:88x78:Purchased 1988

T05131 Cortes and Pizarro (1834)
Iπ:105x84:Purchased 1988

T05132 Datur hora quieti (1834)
Iπ:78x94:Purchased 1988

T05133 Datur hora quieti (1834)
Iπ:77x95:Purchased 1988

Scott's Poetical Works (T04947-T04960; complete group)
T05134 Carlisle (1834)
Iπ:83x143:Purchased 1988

T05135 Smailholme Tower (1834)
Iπ:110x91:Purchased 1988

T05136 Johnnie Armstrong's Tower (1834)
Iπ:107x89:Purchased 1988

T05137 Kelso (1834)
Iπ:83x146:Purchased 1988

T05138 Lochmabon Castle (1834)
Iπ:110x94:Purchased 1988

T05139 Caerlaverock Castle (1834)
Iπ:81x143:Purchased 1988

T05140 Hermitage Castle (1834)
Iπ:110x90:Purchased 1988

T05141 Dryburgh Abbey (1834)
Iπ:80x148:Purchased 1988

T05142 Melrose (1834)
Iπ:88x137:Purchased 1988

T05143 Newark Castle (1834)
Iπ:108x89:Purchased 1988

T05144 Loch Katrine (1834)
Iπ:88x137:Purchased 1988

T05145 Berwick-upon-Tweed (1834)
Iπ:83x144:Purchased 1988

Illustrations to Waverley Novels (T05146-T05147; complete group)
T05146 Wolf's Hope (1836)
Iπ:82x133:Purchased 1988

T05147 Loch Leven Castle (1836)
Iπ:83x132:Purchased 1988

T05148 Abbotsford, from 'Scott's Poetical Works' (Library Edition) (1841)
Iπ:122x120:Purchased 1988

The Gallery of Modern British Artists (T05149-T05151; complete group)
T05149 Fish Market, Rotterdam (1834)
Iπ:107x151:Purchased 1988

T05150 Fish Market, Rotterdam (1834)
Iπ:106x148:Purchased 1988

T05151 Rievaulx Abbey (1836)
Iπ:94x155:Purchased 1988

Landscape Illustrations of the Bible (T05152-T05175; complete group)
T05152 The Red Sea and Suez (1836)
Iπ:99x142:Purchased 1988

T05153 Encampment of Israelites, Mount Sinai (1836)
Iπ:88x142:Purchased 1988

T05154 The Desert of Sinai (1836)
Iπ:103x143:Purchased 1988

T05155 Jericho (1836)
Iπ:228x278:Purchased 1988

T05156 Jericho (1836)
Iπ:91x138:Purchased 1988

T05157 The Dead Sea, Jericho and Mouth of Jordan (1836)
Iπ:98x140:Purchased 1988

T05158 Wilderness of Engedi and Convent of Santa Saba (1836)
Iπ:102x142:Purchased 1988

T05159 Joppa (1836)
Iπ:91x144:Purchased 1988

T05160 Solomon's Pools (1836)
Iπ:94x140:Purchased 1988

T05161 Ramah and Rachel's Tomb (1836)
Iπ:98x146:Purchased 1988

T05162 Babylon (1836)
Iπ:98x139:Purchased 1988

T05163 Egypt, the Pyramids of Ghizeh (1836)
Iπ:95x142:Purchased 1988

T05164 Mount Lebanon and Convent of St Antonio (1836)
Iπ:97x140:Purchased 1988

T05165 Ninevah, Moussul on the Tigris (1836)
Iπ:97x139:Purchased 1988

T05166 Lebanon from Tripoli (1836)
Iπ:96x141:Purchased 1988

T05167 Jerusalem from the Mount of Olives (1836)
Iπ:94x141:Purchased 1988

T05168 Bethlehem (1836)
Iπ:229x278:Purchased 1988

T05169 Bethlehem (1836)
Iπ:93x141:Purchased 1988

T05170 Nazareth (1836)
Iπ:92x139:Purchased 1988

T05171 Jerusalem, with the Walls (1836)
Iπ:112x164:Purchased 1988

T05172 Jerusalem, Pool of Bethesda (1836)
Iπ:96x142:Purchased 1988

T05173 Valley of the Brook Kedron (1836)
Iπ:93x135:Purchased 1988

T05174 Corinth (1836)
Iπ:96x142:Purchased 1988

T05175 Assos (1836)
Iπ:92x138:Purchased 1988

Views in India (T05176-T05182; complete group)
T05176 Part of the Ghaut at Hurdwar (1836)
Iπ:124x189:Purchased 1988

T05177 Mussooree and the Dhoon from Landour (1836)
Iπ:126x205:Purchased 1988

T05178 Snowy Range from Tyre or Marma (1836)
Iπ:124x209:Purchased 1988

T05179 View near Jubbera (1836)
Iπ:127x128:Purchased 1988

T05180 Falls near the Source of the Jumna (1836)
Iπ:137x209:Purchased 1988

T05181 Valley of the Dhoon (1836)
Iπ:137x203:Purchased 1988

T05182 Rocks at Colong on the Ganges (1836)
Iπ:133x208:Purchased 1988

Dr Broadley's Poems (T05183-T05186; complete group)
T05183 Whitby (?1844)
Iπ:66x98:Purchased 1988

T05184 The Abbey Pool (?1844)
Iπ:72x99:Purchased 1988

T05185 Tynemouth Priory (?1844)
Iπ:67x98:Purchased 1988

T05186 St Agatha's Abbey (?1844)
Iπ:71x98:Purchased 1988

T05187 Dido and Aeneas; the Morning of the Chase (published 1842)
Iπ:409x614:Purchased 1988

T05188 St Mark's Place, Venice - Juliet and her Nurse (1842)
Iπ:423x564:Purchased 1988

T05189 Ancient Italy (1842)
Iπ:432x600:Purchased 1988

T05190 Heidelberg from the Opposite Bank of the Neckar (1846)
Iπ:364x544, 364x544:Purchased 1988

T05191 Hastings (1851)
Iπ:401x590:Purchased 1988

T05192 Venice - Bellinis's Pictures being Conveyed to the Church of the Redentore (1858)
Iπ:392x610, 392x610:Purchased 1988

T05193 The Approach to Venice (1859)
Iπ:397x595:Purchased 1988

The Turner Gallery (T05194-T05196; complete group)
T05194 Dutch Boats in a Gale (1859)
Iπ:185x263:Purchased 1988

T05195 View of Cologne from the River (1859)
Iπ:192x265:Purchased 1988

T05196 Ancient Rome (1859)
Iπ:199x274:Purchased 1988

T05197 Folkestone (1830)
Iπ:210x309:Purchased 1988

T05198 Tours, Looking Backwards
Iπ:130x189:Purchased 1988

T05199 Chateau de Blois
Iπ:129x180:Purchased 1988

T05200 The Lake of Zug
Iπ:124x197:Purchased 1988

Picturesque Views on the Southern Coast of England (T05218-T05463; complete group; mixed group)
T05218 Whitstable (1826)
Iπ:167x249:Purchased 1988

T05219 Whitstable (1826)
Lπ:167x249:Purchased 1988

T05220 Whitstable (1826)
Lπ:166x249:Purchased 1988

T05223 Margate (1824)
Lπ:158x242:Purchased 1988

T05224 Margate (1824)
Lπ:157x239:Purchased 1988

T05225 Margate (1824)
Lπ:158x242:Purchased 1988

T05226 Margate (1824)
Lπ:158x242:Purchased 1988

T05227 Margate (1824)
Lπ:158x240:Purchased 1988

T05228 Margate (1824)
Lπ:158x239:Purchased 1988

T05229 Margate (1824)
Lπ:158x240:Purchased 1988

T05230 Margate (1824)
Lπ:159x240:Purchased 1988

T05231 Margate (1824)
Lπ:158x241:Purchased 1988

T05232 Ramsgate (1824)
Lπ:151x240:Purchased 1988

T05233 Ramsgate (1824)
Lπ:152x242:Purchased 1988

T05234 Ramsgate (1824)
Lπ:150x241:Purchased 1988

T05235 Ramsgate (1824)
Lπ:150x241:Purchased 1988

T05236 Deal (1826)
Lπ:147x237:Purchased 1988

T05237 Deal (1826)
Lπ:147x238:Purchased 1988

T05246 Dover from Shakespeare's Cliff (1826)
Lπ:162x242:Purchased 1988

T05247 Dover from Shakespeare's Cliff (1826)
Lπ:162x242:Purchased 1988

T05248 Dover from Shakespeare's Cliff (1826)
Lπ:162x241:Purchased 1988

T05249 Dover from Shakespeare's Cliff (1826)
Lπ:161x242:Purchased 1988

T05250 Dover from Shakespeare's Cliff (1826)
Lπ:162x242:Purchased 1988

T05251 Dover from Shakespeare's Cliff (1826)
Lπ:161x242:Purchased 1988

T05254 Folkestone (1826)
Lπ:151x245:Purchased 1988

T05257 Hythe (1824)
Lπ:153x236:Purchased 1988

T05258 Hythe (1824)
Lπ:151x234:Purchased 1988

T05259 Hythe (1824)
Lπ:151x233:Purchased 1988

T05260 Hythe (1824)
Lπ:151x233:Purchased 1988

T05261 Hythe (1824)
Lπ:152x235:Purchased 1988

T05262 Hythe (1824)
Lπ:152x234:Purchased 1988

T05263 Hythe (1824)
Lπ:152x234:Purchased 1988

T05264 Hythe (1824)
Lπ:153x235:Purchased 1988

T05270 Rye (1824)
Lπ:149x234:Purchased 1988

T05271 Rye (1824)
Lπ:150x234:Purchased 1988

T05272 Rye (1824)
Lπ:150x233:Purchased 1988

T05273 Rye (1824)
Lπ:150x233:Purchased 1988

T05280 Bexhill, Martello Tower (1817)
Lπ:153x215:Purchased 1988

T05281 Bexhill, Martello Tower (1817)
Lπ:153x215:Purchased 1988

T05282 Bexhill, Martello Tower (1817)
Lπ:154x215:Purchased 1988

T05288 Brighthelmstone (1825)
Lπ:155x231:Purchased 1988

T05289 Brighthelmstone (1825)
Lπ:155x232:Purchased 1988

T05290 Brighthelmstone (1825)
Lπ:155x232:Purchased 1988

T05291 Brighton with the Pier (1825)
Lπ::Purchased 1988

T05292 Brighthelmstone (1825)
Lπ:154x231:Purchased 1988

T05293 Brighthelmstone (1825)
Lπ:155x231:Purchased 1988

T05294 Brighthelmstone (1825)
Lπ:155x232:Purchased 1988

T05295 Brighthelmstone (1825)
Lπ:155x233:Purchased 1988

T05302 Portsmouth, Hampshire (1825)
Lπ:157x236:Purchased 1988

T05303 Portsmouth, Hampshire (1825)
Lπ:157x235:Purchased 1988

T05304 Portsmouth, Hampshire (1825)
Lπ:158x237:Purchased 1988

T05326 Poole (1814)
Lπ:149x222:Purchased 1988

T05327 Poole (1814)
Lπ:150x220:Purchased 1988

T05328 Poole (1814)
Lπ:150x222:Purchased 1988

T05329 Poole (1814)
Lπ:149x221:Purchased 1988

T05330 Poole (1814)
Lπ:149x222:Purchased 1988

T05331 Poole (1814)
Lπ:149x221:Purchased 1988

T05332 Poole (1814)
Lπ:150x222:Purchased 1988

T05333 Poole (1814)
Lπ:149x221:Purchased 1988

T05334 Poole (1814)
Lπ:150x220:Purchased 1988

T05335 Poole (1814)
Lπ:150x221:Purchased 1988

T05336 Poole (1814)
Lπ:150x222:Purchased 1988

T05337 Poole (1814)
Lπ:150x221:Purchased 1988

T05338 Corfe Castle (1814)
Lπ:144x214:Purchased 1988

T05339 Corfe Castle (1814)
Lπ:144x213:Purchased 1988

T05340 Corfe Castle (1814)
Lπ:144x215:Purchased 1988

T05341 Corfe Castle (1814)
Lπ:144x215:Purchased 1988

T05342 Corfe Castle (1814)
Lπ:144x216:Purchased 1988

T05343 Corfe Castle (1814)
Lπ:145x215:Purchased 1988

T05344 Corfe Castle (1814)
Lπ:145x213:Purchased 1988

T05345 Corfe Castle (1814)
Lπ:145x214:Purchased 1988

T05346 Corfe Castle (1814)
Lπ:145x215:Purchased 1988

T05347 Lulworth Cove (1814)
Lπ:145x218:Purchased 1988

T05348 Lulworth Cove (1814)
Lπ:146x217:Purchased 1988

T05351 Lulworth Castle (1821)
Lπ:158x241:Purchased 1988

T05352 Lulworth Castle (1821)
Lπ:158x241:Purchased 1988

T05353 Lulworth Castle (1821)
Lπ:158x241:Purchased 1988

T05354 Lulworth Castle (1821)
Lπ:158x241:Purchased 1988

T05355 Lulworth Castle (1821)
Lπ:159x241:Purchased 1988

T05356 Lulworth Castle (1821)
Lπ:159x240:Purchased 1988

T05357 Lulworth Castle (1821)
Lπ:158x240:Purchased 1988

T05358 Lulworth Castle (1821)
Lπ:159x241:Purchased 1988

T05359 Lulworth Castle (1821)
Lπ:159x241:Purchased 1988

T05360 Weymouth (1814)
Lπ:147x221:Purchased 1988

T05361 Weymouth (1814)
Lπ:147x221:Purchased 1988

T05362 Weymouth (1821)
Lπ:149x221:Purchased 1988

T05365 Portland Isle, Bow and Arrow Castle (1817)
Lπ:159x243:Purchased 1988

T05366 Portland Isle, Bow and Arrow Castle (1817)
Lπ:160x243:Purchased 1988

T05367 Bridport (1820)
Lπ:165x242:Purchased 1988

T05368 Bridport (1820)
Lπ:165x244:Purchased 1988

T05369 Lyme Regis (1814)
Lπ:149x223:Purchased 1988

T05370 Lyme Regis (1814)
Lπ:148x224:Purchased 1988

T05376 Teignmouth (1815)
Lπ::Purchased 1988

T05377 Teignmouth (1815)
Lπ:153x228:Purchased 1988

T05378 Teignmouth (1815)
Lπ:153x228:Purchased 1988

T05379 Teignmouth (1815)
Lπ:153x227:Purchased 1988

T05380 Teignmouth (1815)
Lπ:152x227:Purchased 1988

T05381 Teignmouth (1815)
Lπ:153x227:Purchased 1988

T05382 Teignmouth (1815)
Lπ:153x226:Purchased 1988

T05383 Teignmouth (1815)
Lπ:154x228:Purchased 1988

T05384 Teignmouth (1815)
Lπ:154x227:Purchased 1988

T05385 Torbay (1821)
Lπ:159x241:Purchased 1988

T05386 Torbay (1821)
Lπ:159x240:Purchased 1988

T05387 Torbay (1821)
Lπ:158x240:Purchased 1988

T05390 Dartmouth (1815)
Lπ:147x217:Purchased 1988

T05391 Dartmouth (1815)
Lπ:147x217:Purchased 1988

T05392 The Mew Stone (1816)
Lπ:160x240:Purchased 1988

T05393 The Mew Stone (1816)
Lπ:161x241:Purchased 1988

T05396 Plymouth (1817)
Lπ:164x241:Purchased 1988

T05397 Plymouth (1817)
Lπ:164x241:Purchased 1988

T05398 Plymouth Dock (1816)
Lπ:161x244:Purchased 1988

T05399 Plymouth Dock (1816)
Lπ:162x245:Purchased 1988

T05400 Plymouth Dock (1816)
Lπ:162x245:Purchased 1988

T05401 Mount Edgecombe (1816)
Lπ:163x240:Purchased 1988

T05404 Looe, East and West (1818)
Lπ:157x238:Purchased 1988

T05405 Looe, East and West (1818)
Lπ:157x238:Purchased 1988

T05406 Fowey (1820)
Lπ:158x238:Purchased 1988

T05407 Fowey (1820)
Lπ:158x238:Purchased 1988

T05408 Fowey (1820)
Lπ:157x238:Purchased 1988

T05409 Falmouth Harbour (1816)
Lπ:157x239:Purchased 1988

T05410 Falmouth Harbour (1816)
Lπ:157x240:Purchased 1988

T05411 Pendennis Castle (1817)
Lπ:159x239:Purchased 1988

T05412 Pendennis Castle (1817)
Lπ:159x240:Purchased 1988

T05413 Pendennis Castle (1817)
Lπ:159x240:Purchased 1988

T05414 Pendennis Castle (1817)
Lπ:159x240:Purchased 1988

T05415 Pendennis Castle (1817)
Lπ:159x240:Purchased 1988

T05416 Pendennis Castle (1817)
Lπ:159x240:Purchased 1988

T05417 Pendennis Castle (1817)
Lπ:159x240:Purchased 1988

T05418 Pendennis Castle (1817)
Lπ:159x240:Purchased 1988

T05419 St Mawes (1824)
Lπ:146x221:Purchased 1988

T05420 St Mawes (1824)
Lπ:146x221:Purchased 1988

T05421 St Mawes (1817)
Lπ:145x221:Purchased 1988

T05422 St Michael's Mount (1814)
Lπ:149x224:Purchased 1988

T05423 St Michael's Mount (1814)
Lπ:149x224:Purchased 1988

T05426 Land's End (1814)
Lπ:143x221:Purchased 1988

T05427 Land's End (1818)
Lπ:142x221:Purchased 1988

T05428 Land's End (1818)
Lπ:142x221:Purchased 1988

T05429 Land's End (1818)
Lπ:142x221:Purchased 1988

T05430 Land's End (1818)
Lπ:142x221:Purchased 1988

T05431 Land's End (1818)
Lπ:142x221:Purchased 1988

T05432 Land's End (1818)
Lπ:142x221:Purchased 1988

T05433 Land's End (1818)
Lπ:142x221:Purchased 1988

T05436 Tintagel Castle (1818)
Lπ:162x241:Purchased 1988

T05437 Tintagel Castle (1818)
Lπ:162x241:Purchased 1988

T05438 Tintagel Castle (1818)
Lπ:162x241:Purchased 1988

T05439 Tintagel Castle (1818)
Lπ:162x241:Purchased 1988

T05440 Tintagel Castle (1818)
Lπ:163x242:Purchased 1988

T05441 Tintagel Castle (1818)
Lπ:161x241:Purchased 1988

T05442 Tintagel Castle (1818)
Lπ:161x241:Purchased 1988

T05443 Tintagel Castle (1818)
Lπ:162x241:Purchased 1988

T05444 Boscastle (1825)
Lπ:149x238:Purchased 1988

T05445 Boscastle (1825)
Lπ:150x237:Purchased 1988

T05446 Clovelly Bay (1824)
Lπ:149x228:Purchased 1988

T05447 Ilfracomb (1818)
Lπ:159x240:Purchased 1988

T05448 Ilfracomb (1818)
Lπ:159x242:Purchased 1988

T05449 Comb Martin (1825)
Lπ:152x240:Purchased 1988

T05453 Minehead and Dunster Castle (1821)
Lπ:156x225:Purchased 1988

T05454 Minehead and Dunster Castle (1821)
Lπ:158x227:Purchased 1988

T05455 Watchet (1820)
Lπ:158x240:Purchased 1988

T05456 Watchet (1820)
Lπ:158x240:Purchased 1988

T05457 Watchet (1820)
Lπ:157x240:Purchased 1988

T05458 Watchet (1820)
Lπ:158x240:Purchased 1988

T05459 Watchet (1820)
Lπ:158x240:Purchased 1988

T05460 Watchet (1820)
Lπ:158x240:Purchased 1988

T05461 Watchet (1820)
Lπ:158x240:Purchased 1988

T05462 Watchet (1820)
Lπ:158x240:Purchased 1988

T05463 Watchet (1820)
Lπ:158x240:Purchased 1988

T05574 Orleans
Lπ::Transferred from the Library 1989

T05575 Beaugency
Lπ::Transferred from the Library 1989

T05576 Blois
Lπ::Transferred from the Library 1989

T05577 Palace at Blois
Lπ::Transferred from the Library 1989

T05578 Amboise
Lπ::Transferred from the Library 1989

T05579 Canal of the Loire and Cher, near Tours
Lπ::Transferred from the Library 1989

T05580 Tours
Lπ::Transferred from the Library 1989

T05581 St Julian's Tours
Lπ::Transferred from the Library 1989

T05582 Tours - Looking Backward
Lπ::Transferred from the Library 1989

T05583 Saumur
Lπ::Transferred from the Library 1989

T05584 Rietz near Saumur
Lπ::Transferred from the Library 1989

T05585 Montjen
Lπ::Transferred from the Library 1989

T05586 St Florent
Lπ::Transferred from the Library 1989

T05587 Between Clairmont and Mauves
Lπ::Transferred from the Library 1989

T05588 Château Hamelin
Lπ::Transferred from the Library 1989

T05589 Scene on the Loire
Lπ::Transferred from the Library 1989

T05590 Clairmont
Lπ::Transferred from the Library 1989

T05591 Coteaux de Mauves
Lπ::Transferred from the Library 1989

T05592 Château de Nantes
Lπ::Transferred from the Library 1989

T05593 Light Towers of the Hève (Vignette Title Page)
Lπ::Transferred from the Library 1989

T05594 Havre
Lπ::Transferred from the Library 1989

T05595 Graville
Lπ::Transferred from the Library 1989

T05596 Harfleur
Lπ::Transferred from the Library 1989

T05597 Tancarville
Lπ::Transferred from the Library 1989

T05598 Château de Tancarville with Town of Quilleboeuf
Lπ::Transferred from the Library 1989

T05599 Lillebonne, Château and Tower
Lπ::Transferred from the Library 1989

T05600 Lillebonne, Château
Lπ::Transferred from the Library 1989

T05601 Caudebec
Lπ::Transferred from the Library 1989

T05602 Jumièges
Lπ::Transferred from the Library 1989

T05603 La Chaise de Gargantua near Duclair
Lπ::Transferred from the Library 1989

T05604 Rouen Looking up the River
Lπ::Transferred from the Library 1989

T05605 Rouen Looking down the River
Lπ::Transferred from the Library 1989

T05606 Rouen Cathedral
Lπ::Transferred from the Library 1989

T05607 Rouen from St Catherine's Hill
Lπ::Transferred from the Library 1989

T05608 Château de la Mailleraie
Lπ::Transferred from the Library 1989

T05609 Between Quilleboeuf and Villequier
Lπ::Transferred from the Library 1989

T05610 Quilleboeuf
Lπ::Transferred from the Library 1989

T05611 Honfleur
Lπ::Transferred from the Library 1989

T05612 Château Gaillard from the South (Vignette Title Page)
Lπ::Transferred from the Library 1989

T05613 Pont de l'Arche
Lπ::Transferred from the Library 1989

T05614 View on the Seine between Mantes and Vernon
Lπ::Transferred from the Library 1989

T05615 Bridge of Meulan
Lπ::Transferred from the Library 1989

T05616 St Germains
Lπ::Transferred from the Library 1989

T05617 St Denis
Lπ::Transferred from the Library 1989

T05618 Bridges of St Cloud and Sèvres
Lπ::Transferred from the Library 1989

T05619 The Lanterne of St Cloud
Lπ::Transferred from the Library 1989

T05620 Bridge of St Cloud from Sèvres
Lπ::Transferred from the Library 1989

T05621 Pont-Neuf, Paris
Lπ::Transferred from the Library 1989

T05622 Marché aux Fleurs and the Pont-au-Change
Lπ::Transferred from the Library 1989

T05623 Hôtel de Ville and Pont d'Arcole
Lπ::Transferred from the Library 1989

T05624 Boulevards, Paris
Lπ::Transferred from the Library 1989

T05625 Confluence of the Seine and the Marne
Lπ::Transferred from the Library 1989

T05626 Troyes
Lπ::Transferred from the Library 1989

T05727 Nantes (1833)
Lπ:125x88:Transferred from the Library 1990

T05728 Havre, Tower of Francis I (1834)
Lπ:102x140:Transferred from the Library 1990

T05730 A Distant View of Chester (1810)
Lπ:151x214:Presented by William Drummond 1990

TURNER, William, of Oxford 1789-1862
British Collection

N02977 A Water Mill
Oc:533x673:signed:Bequeathed by Richard and
Catherine Garnons 1854

N02978 Skating
Oc:508x610:signed:Bequeathed by Richard and
Catherine Garnons 1854

N02979 Peasants outside an Inn
Oc:508x610:signed:Bequeathed by Richard and
Catherine Garnons 1854

TURNER, Winifred 1903-1983
Modern Collection
Tate Gallery Archive holds material concerning this artist

N04708 Thought (exhibited 1933)
Sz:832x775x435:Presented by the Trustees of the
Chantrey Bequest 1933

TWEED, John 1869-1933
British Collection

N04807 Lord Clive (circa 1910-12)
Sz:851x419x311:signed:Presented by the Trustees of the
Chantrey Bequest 1934

N06064 Auguste Rodin (?1902)
Rp:406x330:Bequeathed by Sir C. Phillips 1924

TWOMBLY, Cy born 1929
Modern Collection

P07406 Untitled (1967)
CLπ:597x718:signed:Purchased 1981

Natural History, Part I, Mushrooms (P07573-P07582;
complete group)

P07573 No. I (1974)
CLVπ:758x558:signed:Purchased 1981

P07574 No. II (1974)
CLVπ:758x558:signed:Purchased 1981

P07575 No. III (1974)
CLVπ:758x558:signed:Purchased 1981

P07576 No. IV (1974)
CLVπ:758x558:signed:Purchased 1981

P07577 No. V (1974)
CLVπ:758x558:signed:Purchased 1981

P07578 No. VI (1974)
CLVπ:758x558:signed:Purchased 1981

P07579 No. VII (1974)
CLVπ:758x558:signed:Purchased 1981

P07580 No. VIII (1974)
CLVπ:758x558:signed:Purchased 1981

P07581 No. IX (1974)
CLVπ:758x558:signed:Purchased 1981

P07582 No. X (1974)
CLVπ:758x558:signed:Purchased 1981

TYRWHITT, Ursula 1878-1966
British Collection
Tate Gallery Archive holds material concerning this artist

N04814 Flowers (1912)
Wπ:406x384:signed:Presented by Mrs Mary McEvoy 1935

TYSON, Ian born 1933
Modern Collection
Tate Gallery Archive holds material concerning this artist

The Graves (P01632-P01635; incomplete group)

P01632 The Graves 1 (1972)
CNπ:773x602:signed:Presented by the Institute of
Contemporary Prints 1975

P01633 The Graves 2 (1972)
CNπ:774x603:signed:Presented by the Institute of
Contemporary Prints 1975

P01634 The Graves 3 (1972)
CNπ:773x602:signed:Presented by the Institute of
Contemporary Prints 1975

P01635 The Graves 4 (1972)
CNπ:775x602:signed:Presented by the Institute of
Contemporary Prints 1975

The Instructions for Solo Voice and Percussion
(P01636-P01665; complete group)

P01636 [no title] (1972)
MNπ:73x73:signed:Presented by Tetrad Press through
the Institute of Contemporary Prints 1975

P01637 [no title] (1972)
MNπ:73x73:signed:Presented by Tetrad Press through
the Institute of Contemporary Prints 1975

P01638 [no title] (1972)
MNπ:73x73:signed:Presented by Tetrad Press through
the Institute of Contemporary Prints 1975

P01639 [no title] (1972)
MNπ:73x73:signed:Presented by Tetrad Press through
the Institute of Contemporary Prints 1975

P01640 [no title] (1972)
MNπ:73x73:signed:Presented by Tetrad Press through
the Institute of Contemporary Prints 1975

P01641 [no title] (1972)
MNπ:73x73:signed:Presented by Tetrad Press through
the Institute of Contemporary Prints 1975

P01642 [no title] (1972)
MNπ:73x73:signed:Presented by Tetrad Press through
the Institute of Contemporary Prints 1975

P01643 [no title] (1972)
MNπ:73x73:signed:Presented by Tetrad Press through
the Institute of Contemporary Prints 1975

P01644 [no title] (1972)
MNπ:73x73:signed:Presented by Tetrad Press through
the Institute of Contemporary Prints 1975

P01645 [no title] (1972)
MNπ:73x73:signed:Presented by Tetrad Press through
the Institute of Contemporary Prints 1975

P01646 [no title] (1972)
MNπ:73x73:signed:Presented by Tetrad Press through
the Institute of Contemporary Prints 1975

P01647 [no title] (1972)
MNπ:73x73:signed:Presented by Tetrad Press through
the Institute of Contemporary Prints 1975

P01648 [no title] (1972)
MNπ:73x73:signed:Presented by Tetrad Press through
the Institute of Contemporary Prints 1975

P01649 [no title] (1972)
MNπ:73x73:signed:Presented by Tetrad Press through
the Institute of Contemporary Prints 1975

P01650 [no title] (1972)
MNπ:73x73:signed:Presented by Tetrad Press through
the Institute of Contemporary Prints 1975

P01651 [no title] (1972)
MNπ:73x73:signed:Presented by Tetrad Press through
the Institute of Contemporary Prints 1975

P01652 [no title] (1972)
MNπ:73x73:signed:Presented by Tetrad Press through
the Institute of Contemporary Prints 1975

P01653 [no title] (1972)
MNπ:73x73:signed:Presented by Tetrad Press through
the Institute of Contemporary Prints 1975

P01654 [no title] (1972)
MNπ:73x73:signed:Presented by Tetrad Press through
the Institute of Contemporary Prints 1975

P01655 [no title] (1972)
MNπ:73x73:signed:Presented by Tetrad Press through
the Institute of Contemporary Prints 1975

P01656 [no title] (1972)
MNπ:73x73:signed:Presented by Tetrad Press through
the Institute of Contemporary Prints 1975

P01657 [no title] (1972)
MNπ:73x73:signed:Presented by Tetrad Press through
the Institute of Contemporary Prints 1975

P01658 [no title] (1972)
MNπ:73x73:signed:Presented by Tetrad Press through
the Institute of Contemporary Prints 1975

P01659 [no title] (1972)
MNπ:73x73:signed:Presented by Tetrad Press through
the Institute of Contemporary Prints 1975

P01660 [no title] (1972)
MNπ:73x73:signed:Presented by Tetrad Press through
the Institute of Contemporary Prints 1975

P01661 [no title] (1972)
MNπ:73x73:signed:Presented by Tetrad Press through
the Institute of Contemporary Prints 1975

P01662 [no title] (1972)
MNπ:73x73:signed:Presented by Tetrad Press through
the Institute of Contemporary Prints 1975

P01663 [no title] (1972)
MNπ:73x73:signed:Presented by Tetrad Press through
the Institute of Contemporary Prints 1975

P01664 [no title] (1972)
MNπ:73x73:signed:Presented by Tetrad Press through
the Institute of Contemporary Prints 1975

P01665 [no title] (1972)
MNπ:73x73:signed:Presented by Tetrad Press through
the Institute of Contemporary Prints 1975

Approval Stamp Offer (P01676-P01687; complete group; mixed group)

P01685 Untitled (1972)
MJπ:51x51:signed:Presented by Tetrad Press through the Institute of Contemporary Prints 1975

P01686 Untitled (1972)
MJπ:51x51:signed:Presented by Tetrad Press through the Institute of Contemporary Prints 1975

P01687 Untitled (1972)
MJπ:51x51:signed:Presented by Tetrad Press through the Institute of Contemporary Prints 1975

Tetrad Pamphlets Vol. I Nos. I-X (P01688-P01697; complete group; mixed group)

P01695 Knights Eminence (1970)
CNπ:305x508:Presented by Tetrad Press through the Institute of Contemporary Prints 1975

P01696 Mask Masque (1970)
CNπ:305x508:Presented by Tetrad Press through the Institute of Contemporary Prints 1975

P01697 23rd Light Poem 7th Poem for Larry Eigner 15 January 1969 (1970)
CNπ:305x508:Presented by Tetrad Press through the Institute of Contemporary Prints 1975

P02449 White Rain (1975-6)
CIπ:479x152:signed:Presented by the artist 1978

P02450 Reeded Glass II (1976)
CIπ:486x156:signed:Presented by the artist 1978

P02557 Sign (1981)
MJπ:181x156:signed:Presented by the artist 1982

P03122 Pathway (1974)
CNπ:587x587:signed:Presented by Tetrad Press 1976

P03123 Reeded Glass II (1975-6)
CIπ:489x152:signed:Presented by Tetrad Press 1976

P03124 Untitled (1975)
CNπ:419x419:signed:Presented by Tetrad Press 1976

P03125 Glass Screen (1976)
CIπ:489x156:signed:Presented by Tetrad Press 1976

P03126 A Gift for Eric Satie (1975)
MJπ:327x225:signed:Presented by Tetrad Press 1976

The 17 Horse Songs of Frank Mitchell (P05258-P05261; incomplete group)

P05258 No. X (1969)
CNπ:305x254:signed:Presented by Rose and Chris Prater through the Institute of Contemporary Prints 1975

P05259 No. XI (1969)
CNπ:305x254:signed:Presented by Rose and Chris Prater through the Institute of Contemporary Prints 1975

P05260 No. XII (1969)
CNπ:305x254:signed:Presented by Rose and Chris Prater through the Institute of Contemporary Prints 1975

P05261 No. XIII (1969)
CNπ:305x254:signed:Presented by Rose and Chris Prater through the Institute of Contemporary Prints 1975

P05262 Mid West I (1970)
CNπ:864x152:signed:Presented by Rose and Chris Prater through the Institute of Contemporary Prints 1975

P05263 Mid West II (1970)
CNπ:864x152:signed:Presented by Rose and Chris Prater through the Institute of Contemporary Prints 1975

P05264 Mid West III (1970)
CNπ:864x152:signed:Presented by Rose and Chris Prater through the Institute of Contemporary Prints 1975

Letters from the Black Palace (P05265-P05270; complete group)

P05265 Letters from the Black Palace I-IIIII [title page] (1971)
CNπ:197x257:signed:Presented by Rose and Chris Prater through the Institute of Contemporary Prints 1975

P05266 Letter I [Memoriam Residence] (1971)
CNπ:199x257:signed:Presented by Rose and Chris Prater through the Institute of Contemporary Prints 1975

P05267 Letter II [Fountain Music] (1971)
CNπ:198x256:signed:Presented by Rose and Chris Prater through the Institute of Contemporary Prints 1975

P05268 Letter III [Noh Raid] (1971)
CNπ:198x257:signed:Presented by Rose and Chris Prater through the Institute of Contemporary Prints 1975

P05269 Letter IIII [Charm Furniture] (1971)
CNπ:197x256:signed:Presented by Rose and Chris Prater through the Institute of Contemporary Prints 1975

P05270 Letter IIIII [Li's Ghost] (1971)
CNπ:198x256:signed:Presented by Rose and Chris Prater through the Institute of Contemporary Prints 1975

The Pronouns (P05271-P05279; complete group)

P05271 Enough Red [frontispiece] (1971)
CNπ:406x433:signed:Presented by Rose and Chris Prater through the Institute of Contemporary Prints 1975

P05272 Reacting to Orange Hair [illustration for 'Some Remarks to the Dancers'] (1971)
CNπ:533x434:signed:Presented by Rose and Chris Prater through the Institute of Contemporary Prints 1975

P05273 Smoke [illustration for 'Folio 1, Dances 1-7'] (1971)
CNπ:534x434:signed:Presented by Rose and Chris Prater through the Institute of Contemporary Prints 1975

P05274 Boiling Glass [illustration for 'Folio 2, Dances 8-13'] (1971)
CNπ:533x433:signed:Presented by Rose and Chris Prater through the Institute of Contemporary Prints 1975

P05275 Matching Parcels [illustration for 'Folio 3, Dances 14-19'] (1971)
CNπ:533x432:signed:Presented by Rose and Chris Prater through the Institute of Contemporary Prints 1975

P05276 Roof Structure [illustration for 'Folio 4, Dances 20-23'] (1971)
CNπ:533x433:signed:Presented by Rose and Chris Prater through the Institute of Contemporary Prints 1975

P05277 Making a Bridge [illustration for 'Folio 5, Dances 24-29'] (1971)
CNπ:533x432:signed:Presented by Rose and Chris Prater through the Institute of Contemporary Prints 1975

P05278 Making a Garden [illustration for 'Folio 6, Dances 30-35'] (1971)
CNπ:533x432:signed:Presented by Rose and Chris Prater through the Institute of Contemporary Prints 1975

P05279 Making Something Narrow and Yellow [illustration for 'Folio 7, Dances 36-40'] (1971)
CNπ:533x432:signed:Presented by Rose and Chris Prater through the Institute of Contemporary Prints 1975

A Illiers-Combray (P05280-P05286; complete group)

P05280 [title page] (1973-4)
CNπ:864x660:signed:Presented by Rose and Chris Prater through the Institute of Contemporary Prints 1975

P05281 A Illiers-Combray I (1973-4)
CNπ:865x660:signed:Presented by Rose and Chris Prater through the Institute of Contemporary Prints 1975

P05282   A Illiers-Combray II (1973-4)
CNπ:866x660:signed:Presented by Rose and Chris Prater
through the Institute of Contemporary Prints 1975
P05283   A Illiers-Combray III (1973-4)
CNπ:865x659:signed:Presented by Rose and Chris Prater
through the Institute of Contemporary Prints 1975
P05284   A Illiers-Combray IV (1973-4)
CNπ:865x660:signed:Presented by Rose and Chris Prater
through the Institute of Contemporary Prints 1975
P05285   A Illiers-Combray V (1973-4)
CNπ:866x660:signed:Presented by Rose and Chris Prater
through the Institute of Contemporary Prints 1975
P05286   A Illiers-Combray VI (1973-4)
CNπ:866x661:signed:Presented by Rose and Chris Prater
through the Institute of Contemporary Prints 1975

P05287   Location (1973-4)
CNπ:889x660:Presented by Rose and Chris Prater
through the Institute of Contemporary Prints 1975
P07365   Screens I-XIV (1976-7)
CNπ:502x698:Purchased 1980

TYZACK, Michael born 1933
Modern Collection
Tate Gallery Archive holds material concerning this artist

T01225   Leutgeb (1970)
Ac:2184x1219:signed:Purchased 1970

UECKER, Gunther born 1930
Modern Collection
Tate Gallery Archive holds material concerning this artist

T00684 White Field (1964)
Weisses Feld
Rv:870x870x76:signed:Purchased 1964

UGLOW, Euan born 1930
Modern Collection
Tate Gallery Archive holds material concerning this artist

T00447 Standing Nude (1960-1)
Ow:483x343:signed:Purchased 1961

T00659 Nude (1962-3)
Oc:1632x1168:signed:Presented by the Trustees of the
Chantrey Bequest 1964

T03418 Zagi (1981-2)
Oc:1500x1070:signed:Purchased 1982

UHLIG, Max born 1937
Modern Collection

P07619 Portrait of Mario Calabria (1981)
Bildnis Mario Calabria
MLπ:546x394:Purchased 1982

P07620 Autumn Bouquet (1980-1)
Herbststrauss
MLπ:470x594:Purchased 1982

ULREICH, Buk born circa 1900
Modern Collection

School Prints (P01698-P01727; complete group; mixed
group)
P01727 Arizona Cowboys (1946-9)
CLπ:498x762:signed:Presented by Patrick Seale Prints
1975

UNDERWOOD, Leon 1890-1975
Modern Collection
Tate Gallery Archive holds material concerning this artist

N04975 Torso: The June of Youth (1937)
Sz:610x381x216:Purchased 1938

T00644 Totem to the Artist (1925-30)
Swm:1105x254x273:Presented by the Trustees of the
Chantrey Bequest 1964

T02248 The Fireside (1919)
Tc:460x359:signed:Presented by the Trustees of the
Chantrey Bequest 1977

T02323 Casement to Infinity (1930)
Oc:762x635:signed:Presented by Garth Underwood 1978

T02324 Torso (1930)
Ss:473x203x108:signed:Presented by Garth Underwood
1978

T03775 Herald of New Day (1932-3)
Sp:647x292x317:Transferred from the Victoria & Albert
Museum 1983

UNWIN, Francis 1885-1925
Modern Collection

N03878 Cromer Hotels (1922)
DWπ:445x546:signed:Purchased 1924

N04146 The Ambulatory, Groote Kerke, Dordrecht (exhibited
1907)
DWπ:406x343:signed:Presented by Sir Edward Marsh
through the National Art Collections Fund 1926

UNWIN, Marianne born 1930
Modern Collection

P06818 The Woodyard (1976-7)
CLπ:445x571:signed:Presented by Curwen Studio 1978

UTRILLO, Maurice 1883-1955
Modern Collection

N04139 La Place du Tertre (circa 1910)
Oc:502x730:signed:Presented by the Courtauld Fund
Trustees 1926

N04780 La Porte Saint Martin (circa 1910)
Ob:692x800:signed:Presented by the Sutro Family in
memory of the late Alfred and Esther Sutro 1935

N04943 Church at St Hilaire (circa 1911)
Eglise de St Hilaire
Ob:502x651:signed:Purchased 1938

N05020 Vase de Fleurs (circa 1938-9)
Oc:241x190:signed:Purchased 1939

N05143 Le Passage Cottin (circa 1910)
Oc:540x730:signed:Bequeathed by Montague Shearman
through the Contemporary Art Society 1940

UWINS, Thomas 1782-1857
British Collection

N00387 Vintage (exhibited 1848)
Oc:787x1549:Presented by Robert Vernon 1847

N00388 Le Chapeau de Brigand (1839)
Oc:792x578:Presented by Robert Vernon 1847

VACHER, Charles 1818-1883
British Collection

N01911 Rezzonico and the Splügen Range, Lake Como (1867)
Wπ:813x1410:Bequeathed by George Vacher 1902

VALENTI, Italo born 1912
Modern Collection

T00687 Palestrina (1963)
Vb:470x476:signed:Purchased 1964

VALLOTTON, Félix 1865-1925
Modern Collection

N04232 Road at St Paul (Var) (1922)
Route à St Paul (Var)
Oc:806x645:signed:Presented by Paul Vallotton, the
artist's brother 1927

VALOCH, Jiri born 1946
Modern Collection
Tate Gallery Archive holds material concerning this artist

P08035 Do It Yourself I - Signs (1972)
MJπ:210x149:signed:Transferred from the Library 1979
P08036 Do It Yourself II - Dialogues (1972)
MJπ:206x149:signed:Transferred from the Library 1979
P08037 Study of Identification (1972)
MJπ:149x149:signed:Transferred from the Library 1979
P08038 Symmetrical Concept (1972)
MJπ:206x146:signed:Transferred from the Library 1979

VAN AKEN, Joseph circa 1699-1749
British Collection

N04500 An English Family at Tea (circa 1720)
Oc:994x1162:Presented by Lionel A. Crichton through
the National Art Collections Fund 1930

VANDERBANK, John 1694-1739
British Collection

T00937 Don Quixote Addressing the Goatherds (1730)
Ow:406x295:signed:Purchased 1967
T03539 A Youth of the Lee Family, Probably William Lee of
Totteridge Park (1738)
Oc:1679x1068:signed:Purchased 1982

**VAN DER LECK, Bart - see LECK, Bart van
der**

**VAN DOESBURG, Theo - see DOESBURG,
Theo van**

VAN DYCK, Sir Anthony 1599-1641
British Collection

T02139 A Lady of the Spencer Family (circa 1633-8)
Oc:2076x1276:Purchased 1977

VAN ELK, Ger - see ELK, Ger van

**VAN GOGH, Vincent - see GOGH, Vincent
van**

VAN HEEMSKERK, Egbert, III
British Collection

T00808 The Doctor's Visit (circa 1725)
Oc:759x625:Purchased 1965

VAN LEYDEN, Ernst 1892-1969
Modern Collection

N04859 Girl with Clasped Hands (1931)
Meisje met gevouwen handen
Oc:727x603:signed:Purchased 1937

VAN SOMER, Paul circa 1576 - circa 1621 or
22
British Collection

T00398 Lady Elizabeth Grey, Countess of Kent (circa 1618-20)
Ow:1143x819:Presented by the Friends of the Tate
Gallery 1961

manner of
VAN SOMER, Paul 1576-1621
British Collection

T03033 Anne Wortley, Later Lady Morton (circa 1620)
Oc:2057x1270:Purchased with assistance from the
Friends of the Tate Gallery, the National Art Collections
Fund and the Pilgrim Trust 1980

VANTONGERLOO, Georges 1886-1965
Modern Collection
Tate Gallery Archive holds material concerning this artist

T01574 No. 98 2478 Red/135 Green (1936)
No. 98 2478 rouge/135 vert
Oπ:575x568:signed:Purchased 1972
T02306 Interrelation of Volumes (1919)
Rapport des volumes
Ss:225x137x137:Purchased 1978

VAN VUONG, Ha - see VUONG, Ha van

VARLEY, Cornelius 1781-1873
British Collection

T01023 View near St Albans (1804)
Wπ:241x349:signed:Presented by the National Art
Collections Fund (Herbert Powell Bequest) 1967
T01710 Evening at Llanberis (1805)
Wπ:200x238:signed:Purchased 1973
T01711 West Humble Lane, Dorking (1806)
WDπ:219x340:signed:Purchased 1973
T01712 Millbank (circa 1805)
WDπ:219x337:signed:Purchased 1973
T01713 Canonbury House, Islington (after 1804)
WDπ:213x314:signed:Purchased 1973

VARLEY, John 1778-1842
British Collection
Tate Gallery Archive holds material concerning this artist

N01738 Sea-piece with Fishing Boats in a Calm
Wπ:251x349:Presented by Miss Julia Emily Gordon 1888
N04316 Near Duncombe Park, Yorkshire
Wπ:98x127:Bequeathed by J.R. Holliday 1927
N04317 Holy Island Castle (?1810)
Wπ:105x127:Bequeathed by J.R. Holliday 1927

T01024 View of Bodenham and the Malvern Hills, Herefordshire
(1801)
Wπ:311x521:signed:Presented by the National Art
Collections Fund (Herbert Powell Bequest) 1967

T05483 Classical Landscape Composition
Dπ:152x114:Presented by Miss Marjorie Ball 1988

manner of
VARLEY, John 1778-1842
British Collection

N01737 Dunstanborough Castle (1837)
Wπ:117x190:signed:Presented by Miss Julia Emily
Gordon 1888

VASARELY, Victor born 1908
Modern Collection
Tate Gallery Archive holds material concerning this artist

T00461 Nives II (1949-58)
Oc:1949x1143:signed:Presented by the Friends of the
Tate Gallery 1961

T00676 Supernovae (1959-61)
Oc:2419x1524:signed:Purchased 1964

T00753 Banya (1964)
Gw:597x597:signed:Purchased 1965

P08220 Untitled (1963)
Nπ:220x144:Transferred from the Library 1988

P08221 Untitled (1963)
Nπ:151x137:Transferred from the Library 1988

VAUGHAN, Keith 1912-1977
Modern Collection
Tate Gallery Archive holds material concerning this artist

T00001 Demolished Houses in St John's Wood, No. 2 (1953)
Gπ:165x140:signed:Purchased 1955

T00090 Leaping Figure (1951)
Oc:914x711:signed:Purchased 1956

T00091 Small Assembly of Figures (1951)
Oc:559x610:signed:Purchased 1956

T00501 Rotherhithe (1961)
Oc:762x1219:signed:Purchased 1962

T00502 Bather: August 4th 1961 (1961)
Oc:1022x914:signed:Purchased 1962

T03700 Ninth Assembly of Figures (Eldorado Banal) (1976)
Oc:11501x1530:signed:Purchased 1983

T05703 Communication of Hate (circa 1943)
DWPGπ:368x231:Purchased 1989

T05704 Untitled (Male Figure) (circa 1970)
Dπ:795x575:Purchased 1989

P77176 Figure with a Boat (1949)
Lπ:305x415:signed:Purchased 1986

P77196 Figure in a Churchyard (1948)
Jπ:480x380:signed:Purchased 1987

P77197 Girl by a Row of Cottages (1948)
Jπ:480x382:signed:Purchased 1987

VAUX, Marc born 1932
Modern Collection
Tate Gallery Archive holds material concerning this artist

T01761 B/3L/73 (1973)
Ac:2591x2134:Presented by E.J. Power through the
Friends of the Tate Gallery 1973

VEDOVA, Emilio born 1919
Modern Collection

P11272 [no title] (1989)
Jπ:1075x1424:Presented by Garner H. Tullis and Pamela
Auchincloss 1990

VELDE, Bram van born 1895
Modern Collection

For Jorn (P03241-P03255; complete group; mixed group)
Pour Jorn

P03253 [no title] (1975-6)
CLπ:292x225:signed:Presented by the Asger Jorn
Foundation 1978

VELICKOVIC, Vladimir born 1935
Modern Collection

P07593 Elements and Documents Employed (1979)
Elements et documents utilisés
CNπ:749x1079:signed:Purchased 1981

VENARD, Claude born 1913
Modern Collection

T00256 Still Life (1955-6)
Nature morte
Oc:1003x1003:signed:Presented by Marquis de Bolli 1959

VERHEYEN, Jeff born 1932
Modern Collection

P05288 Untitled (1972)
CNπ:654x651:signed:Presented by Rose and Chris Prater
through the Institute of Contemporary Prints 1975

P05289 Untitled (1972)
CNπ:651x651:signed:Presented by Rose and Chris Prater
through the Institute of Contemporary Prints 1975

VERLON, André born 1917
Modern Collection

T03156 Roads to Eternity (1959)
Oπ:864x622:signed:Presented by the artist 1980

VERRIO, Antonio 1639-1707
British Collection

T00916 Sketch for a Ceiling Decoration: An Assembly of the
Gods (circa 1680-1700)
Oc:1692x829:Purchased 1967

VEZELAY, Paule 1892-1984
Modern Collection
Tate Gallery Archive holds material concerning this artist

T00631 Lines in Space No. 34 (1954)
RV:365x445x38:signed:Purchased 1963

T01725 Construction. Grey Lines on Pink Ground (1938)
Oc:813x1159:signed:Purchased 1973

T01911 Forms (1936)
Dc:730x540:signed:Presented by the artist 1971

T03954 Curves and Circles (1930)
Oc:920x730:signed:Bequeathed by the artist 1985

T03955 Forms on Grey (1935)
Oc:1299x971:signed:Bequeathed by the artist 1985

T03956 Eight Forms and Three Circles (1959)
Oc:730x1160:signed:Bequeathed by the artist 1985

P02069 Le Pont Neuf, Paris (1921)
MLπ:435x552:signed:Presented by the artist 1973

P02070 La Danseuse à la Corde (1923)
MJπ:391x305:signed:Presented by the artist 1973

P02071 The Bathers (1923)
MJπ:267x235:signed:Presented by the artist 1973

P02521 A Circle, a Diamond & Two White Lines (1970)
CNπ:438x279:signed:Presented by the artist 1979

P02522 Contrasted Curves (1970)
CNπ:470x330:signed:Presented by the artist 1979

P02523 Black Silhouettes on Red (1976)
CNπ:432x546:signed:Presented by the artist 1979

P02524 Four Forms and a Black Circle (1976)
MLπ:464x594:signed:Presented by the artist 1979

P02525 Two Forms and Two Dots (1976)
CNπ:384x565:signed:Presented by the artist 1979

VIEIRA da SILVA, Maria Helena born 1908
Modern Collection
Tate Gallery Archive holds material concerning this artist

N06189 The Corridor (1950)
Oc:648x911:signed:Purchased 1953

T00245 Paris (1951)
Oc:327x457:Purchased 1959

VILACASAS, Joan born 1920
Modern Collection

T00482 Planimentary 303 (1961)
Planimetria
Vc:813x1000:signed:Purchased 1962

VILLARD, Antoine 1867-1934
Modern Collection

N03830 Circuit Railway at Grenelle (1922)
Chemin de fer de ceinture à Grenelle
Oc:921x730:signed:Presented by Miss J.M.A. Workman 1923

VILLERS, Dee
Modern Collection

P06600 Kyrenia Harbour (1970)
MLπ:410x619:signed:Presented by Curwen Studio through the Institute of Contemporary Prints 1975

VISSER, Carel born 1928
Modern Collection
Tate Gallery Archive holds material concerning this artist

T01757 Hanging (1966)
Aan elkaar
Sm:902x930x114:Purchased 1973

T02313 Fish Spine (1954)
Ruggegraat
Sm:1372x302x92:Purchased 1978

T02349 Auschwitz (1957)
Sm:606x851x813:Presented by the artist 1979

Untitled (P07435-P07442; complete group)
P07435 [title not known] (1979)
CJπ:622x933:signed:Purchased 1981

P07436 [title not known] (1979)
CJπ:622x933:signed:Purchased 1981

P07437 [title not known] (1979)
CJπ:500x745:signed:Purchased 1981

P07438 [title not known] (1979)
CJπ:622x933:signed:Purchased 1981

P07439 [title not known] (1979)
CJπ:622x933:signed:Purchased 1981

P07440 [title not known] (1979)
CJπ:622x933:signed:Purchased 1981

P07441 [title not known] (1979)
CJπ:622x933:signed:Purchased 1981

P07442 [title not known] (1979)
CJπ:622x933:signed:Purchased 1981

VLAMINCK, Maurice de 1876-1958
Modern Collection
Tate Gallery Archive holds material concerning this artist

T01254 View near Martigues (1913)
Oc:651x819:signed:Bequeathed by Sir Robert Hart 1970

VOLLON, Antoine 1833-1900
Modern Collection

N04212 Harbour at Marseilles (circa 1882)
Oc:606x733:signed:Presented by T.W. Bacon 1926

VON GRAEVENITZ, Gerhard - see GRAEVENITZ, Gerhard von

VON HERKOMER, Sir Hubert 1849-1914
British Collection

N01575 Found (1884-5)
Oc:1372x2305:signed:Presented by the Trustees of the Chantrey Bequest 1879

N02481 The Council of the Royal Academy (1908)
Oc:2972x6223:signed:Presented by the artist 1909

N03517 Sir Henry Tate (1897)
Oc:1422x1118:signed:Bequeathed by Amy, Lady Tate 1920

VON HOLST, Theodore 1810-1844
British Collection

T01518 The Fairy Lovers (circa 1840)
Oc:413x311:Purchased 1972

VON MOTESICZKY, Marie-Louise born 1906
Modern Collection
Tate Gallery Archive holds material concerning this artist

T04849 View from the Window, Vienna (1925)
Oc:625x310:Presented by the artist 1986

T04850 Still Life with Sheep (1938)
Oc:400x805:Purchased 1986

T04851 From the Night into Day (1975)
Oc:838x1166:Purchased 1986

VORDEMBERGE-GILDEWART, Friedrich
1899-1962
Modern Collection

T01474 Composition No. 15 (1925)
Oc:1499x1251:Purchased 1971

VUILLARD, Edouard 1868-1940
Modern Collection

N04436 Girl in an Interior (circa 1910)
Jeune femme dans un intérieur
Ob:730x641:signed:Presented by the Contemporary Art
Society 1929

N04612 Landscape - House on the Left (1900)
Paysage - Maison à gauche
Ob:508x416:signed:Purchased 1931

N05145 The Laden Table (circa 1908)
La Table encombrée
GPπ:470x546:signed:Bequeathed by Montague
Shearman through the Contemporary Art Society 1940

T01075 Sunlit Interior (circa 1920)
Intérieur ensoleillé
Gπ:832x638:signed:Bequeathed by the Hon. Mrs A.E.
Pleydell-Bouverie through the Friends of the Tate Gallery
1968

VUONG, Ha van born 1914
Modern Collection

P06645 Itinerant Singer (1975)
CLπ:638x483:signed:Presented by Curwen Studio 1976

WADE, Thomas 1828-1891
British Collection

N01713 An Old Mill (1879)
Wπ:533x552:signed:Presented by the Trustees of the Chantrey Bequest 1879

WADSWORTH, Edward 1889-1949
Modern Collection
Tate Gallery Archive holds material concerning this artist

N04935 The Beached Margin (1937)
Tf:711x1016:signed:Purchased 1938

N05147 Still Life (circa 1926)
TDb:356x251:signed:Bequeathed by Montague Shearman through the Contemporary Art Society 1940

N05380 Bronze Ballet (1940)
Tf:635x762:Presented by the artist 1942

N05988 Granite Quarries, Darby Hill, Oldbury (1919)
Dπ:254x362:signed:Purchased 1951

N06029 Signals (1942)
Tf:1016x711:signed:Presented by the Trustees of the Chantrey Bequest 1951

T00109 Abstract Composition (1915)
GDπ:419x343:signed:Purchased 1956

T00497 Seaport (1923)
Tf:635x889:signed:Presented by the Trustees of the Chantrey Bequest 1962

T01124 Dux et Comes I (1932)
Tc:508x610:signed:Presented by the Trustees of the Chantrey Bequest 1969

T01904 Landscape (1913)
GDπ:276x295:Purchased 1974

T03398 Regalia (1928)
TOcw:763x917:signed:Purchased with assistance from the Friends of the Tate Gallery 1982

P07118 Bedford: View of a Town (circa 1918)
CJπ:175x127:Purchased 1970

P07119 The Port (circa 1915)
CJπ:187x127:Purchased 1970

P07120 The Open Window (circa 1915)
CJπ:184x133:Purchased 1970

WAINWRIGHT, John active 1859-1869
British Collection

T03378 Flower-piece (1867)
Oc:662x559:signed:Bequeathed by Mrs Bessie Gornall 1982

WALKER, Arthur G. 1861-1939
British Collection

N04101 Christ at the Whipping Post (exhibited 1925)
Sis:584x229x178:Presented by the Trustees of the Chantrey Bequest 1925

WALKER, Dame Ethel 1861-1951
British Collection
Tate Gallery Archive holds material concerning this artist

N03685 Miss Buchanan (circa 1922)
Oc:762x368:signed:Purchased 1922

N03874 Two Figures, Study for 'The Excursion of Nausicaa' (circa 1919)
DWπ:400x229:Purchased 1924

N03885 Decoration: The Excursion of Nausicaa (1920)
Oc:1835x3670:signed:Purchased 1924

N04669 Miss Jean Werner Laurie (1927-8)
Oc:610x508:Presented by the Trustees of the Chantrey Bequest 1931

N04944 The Hon. Mrs Adams (circa 1901)
Oc:902x743:Purchased 1938

N05038 Vanessa (1937)
Oc:610x508:Presented by the Contemporary Art Society 1939

N05332 Seascape: Autumn Morning (circa 1935)
Oc:641x889:Presented by the Trustees of the Chantrey Bequest 1940

N05668 The Zone of Love: Decoration (circa 1930-2)
Oc:2451x2464:signed:Presented by the artist 1946

N05669 The Zone of Hate: Decoration (1914-15)
Oc:2476x2464:signed:Presented by the artist 1946

N05855 The Bathers (circa 1910-20)
WDπ:679x1086:signed:Purchased 1948

N06006 Self-Portrait (?exhibited 1930)
Oc:635x765:Presented by Major E.O. Kay 1951

N06028 The Artist's Stepmother, Mrs Arthur Walker (circa 1899)
Oc:1118x864:Bequeathed by the artist 1951

T00128 Flowers in a Jug (circa 1935-6)
Oc:610x508:signed:Bequeathed by Miss Grace English 1957

T00131 Lilith (?exhibited 1916)
WDπ:508x324:Bequeathed by Miss Grace English 1957

WALKER, Frederick 1840-1875
British Collection

N01209 The Vagrants (1868)
Oc:832x1264:signed:Purchased 1886

N01391 The Harbour of Refuge (1872)
Oc:1168x1975:Presented by Sir William Agnew Bt 1893

N02080 The Woman in White (1871)
Gπ:2172x1289:signed:Presented by Sir Claude Phillips in memory of his sister Eugenie Phillips 1906

N02687 Refreshment (exhibited 1864)
Gπ:248x308:signed:Presented by Alfred A. de Pass 1910

N02688 Study for Marlow Ferry (1861)
Gπ:302x403:Presented by Alfred A. de Pass 1910

N02762 Study for 'The Harbour of Refuge' (circa 1872)
Wπ:248x454:Bequeathed by Sir William Agnew Bt 1911

N03158 The Plough (exhibited 1870)
Oc:1435x2127:Presented by Lady Wernher through the National Art Collections Fund 1917

N03514 The Old Gate (exhibited 1869)
Oc:1346x1683:signed:Bequeathed by Amy, Lady Tate 1900

N03515 Philip in Church (circa 1862)
WGπ:457x368:signed:Bequeathed by Amy, Lady Tate 1920

N03516 The Chaplain's Daughter (circa 1868)
WGπ:137x203:signed:Bequeathed by Amy, Lady Tate 1920

N03525 The Old Gate (1874-5)
Wπ:260x322:signed:Bequeathed by R.H. Prance 1920

N03526 The Housewife (1871)
Wπ:178x254:signed:Bequeathed by R.H. Prance 1920

N03972 Autumn Days, engraved by the Brothers Dalziel (published 1882)
Jπ:159x121:Purchased 1924

N04026 Spring Days, engraved by the Brothers Dalziel
(published 1866)
Jπ:162x121:Presented by Gilbert Dalziel 1924

N04027 Rain, engraved by the Brothers Dalziel (published 1867)
Jπ:165x133:Presented by Gilbert Dalziel 1924

N04059 Philip in Church, engraved by Swain (published 1862)
Jπ:175x121:Presented by Harold Hartley 1925

WALKER, John born 1939

Modern Collection
Tate Gallery Archive holds material concerning this artist

T01093 Lesson I (1968)
Ac:2667x6147:Purchased 1968

T01579 Study (1965)
Ac:2210x3073:Purchased 1972

T01936 Untitled (1974)
ADπ:1003x708:signed:Purchased 1974

T01937 Untitled (1974)
ADπ:1006x711:signed:Purchased 1974

T03071 Labyrinth III (1979-80)
OTc:2457x2988:signed:Purchased 1980

T03314 Drawing 1981 (1981)
DWπ:1581x2222:Purchased 1981

P01666 Untitled (1970)
CNπ:686x997:signed:Presented by the Institute of
Contemporary Prints 1975

P01667 Untitled (1970)
CNπ:689x1003:signed:Presented by the Institute of
Contemporary Prints 1975

P07262 Untitled (1972)
CLπ:277x220:signed:Purchased 1979

P07263 Untitled (1972)
CLπ:270x210:signed:Purchased 1979

P07264 Untitled (1972)
CLπ:270x210:signed:Purchased 1979

P07265 Untitled (1972)
CLπ:235x235:signed:Purchased 1979

P07266 Untitled (1972)
CLπ:275x220:signed:Purchased 1979

The Blackboard Suite (P07267-P07278; complete group)

P07267 I (1973)
MLπ:1030x702:signed:Purchased 1979

P07268 II (1973)
MLπ:1033x705:signed:Purchased 1979

P07269 III (1973)
MLπ:1025x705:signed:Purchased 1979

P07270 IV (1973)
MLπ:1030x705:signed:Purchased 1979

P07271 V (1973)
MLπ:1030x705:signed:Purchased 1979

P07272 VI (1973)
MLπ:1025x705:signed:Purchased 1979

P07273 VII (1973)
MLπ:1025x700:signed:Purchased 1979

P07274 VIII (1973)
MLπ:1025x705:signed:Purchased 1979

P07275 IX (1973)
MLπ:1032x705:signed:Purchased 1979

P07276 X (1973)
MLπ:1030x705:signed:Purchased 1979

P07277 XI (1973)
MLπ:1025x705:signed:Purchased 1979

P07278 XII (1973)
MLπ:1025x705:signed:Purchased 1979

Tank Suite (P07279-P07281; incomplete group)

P07279 Tank III (1973)
CNπ:1040x750:signed:Purchased 1979

P07280 Tank IV (1973)
CNπ:1040x750:signed:Purchased 1979

P07281 Tank V (1973)
CNπ:1040x750:signed:Purchased 1979

Ten Large Silk Screens (P07282-P07291; complete
group)

P07282 [no title] (1973)
CNπ:1570x1168:signed:Purchased 1979

P07283 [no title] (1973)
CNπ:1570x1168:signed:Purchased 1979

P07284 [no title] (1973)
CNπ:1570x1168:signed:Purchased 1979

P07285 [no title] (1973)
CNπ:1570x1168:signed:Purchased 1979

P07286 [no title] (1973)
CNπ:1570x1168:signed:Purchased 1979

P07287 [no title] (1973)
CNπ:1570x1168:signed:Purchased 1979

P07288 [no title] (1973)
CNπ:1570x1168:signed:Purchased 1979

P07289 [no title] (1973)
CNπ:1570x1168:signed:Purchased 1979

P07290 [no title] (1973)
CNπ:1570x1168:signed:Purchased 1979

P07291 [no title] (1973)
CNπ:1570x1168:signed:Purchased 1979

P07292 Untitled (1973)
:940x640:signed:Purchased 1979

P07293 Untitled (1973)
:765x595:signed:Purchased 1979

P07294 Untitled (1973)
:943x640:signed:Purchased 1979

P07295 Untitled (1973)
:943x637:signed:Purchased 1979

P07296 Untitled (1973)
:720x1040:signed:Purchased 1979

Five Red Linocuts (P07297-P07301; complete group)

P07297 Untitled (1974)
CJπ:177x127:signed:Purchased 1979

P07298 Untitled (1974)
CJπ:180x130:signed:Purchased 1979

P07299 Untitled (1974)
CJπ:178x127:signed:Purchased 1979

P07300 Untitled (1974)
CJπ:178x127:signed:Purchased 1979

P07301 Untitled (1974)
CJπ:178x127:signed:Purchased 1979

P07302 Juggernaut (1974)
CNπ:864x1448:signed:Purchased 1979

P07303 Untitled (1974)
MNπ:845x686:signed:Purchased 1979

P07304 Untitled (1974)
MIπ:102x149:signed:Purchased 1979

P07305 Untitled (1974)
MIπ:95x152:Purchased 1979

P07306 Untitled (1974)
MIπ:95x152:Purchased 1979

P07307 Untitled (1975)
CNπ:1753x2591:signed:Purchased 1979

P07308 Untitled (1975)
CNπ:1753x2591:signed:Purchased 1979

P07309 Untitled (1975)
::signed:Purchased 1979

P07310 Untitled (1975)
::signed:Purchased 1979

P07311 Untitled (1975)
::signed:Purchased 1979

P07312 Untitled
::signed:Purchased 1979

P07313 Untitled (1976)
CIπ:1010x816:signed:Purchased 1979

P07314 Newhaven 5 (1976)
MIπ:302x451:signed:Purchased 1979

P07315 Newhaven 2 (1976-7)
MIπ:216x184:signed:Purchased 1979

P07316 Newhaven 7 (1976-7)
MIπ:216x184:signed:Purchased 1979

P07317 Newhaven 10 (1976-7)
MIπ:216x184:signed:Purchased 1979

P07318 Newhaven 11 (1976-7)
MIπ:216x184:signed:Purchased 1979

P07319 Newhaven 15 (1977)
MIπ:175x149:Purchased 1979

P07320 Newhaven 16 (1977)
MIπ:175x149:signed:Purchased 1979

P07321 Newhaven 13 (1977)
MIπ:384x899:signed:Purchased 1979

P07499 Conservatory I (1979)
CNπ:1273x1054:Purchased 1981

P07500 Conservatory II (1979)
CNπ:1448x1267:Purchased 1981

The Prahran Etchings (P07749-P07753; incomplete group)

P07749 Prahan 3 (1981)
MIπ:450x298:signed:Purchased 1982

P07750 Prahan 5 (1981)
MIπ:445x600:signed:Purchased 1982

P07751 Prahan 8 (1981)
MIπ:250x200:signed:Purchased 1982

P07752 Prahan 12 (1981)
MIπ:125x115:signed:Purchased 1982

P07753 Prahan 17 (1981)
MIπ:118x120:signed:Purchased 1982

P11051 Pacifica (1982)
CNπ:1550x1190:signed:Presented by the Contemporary Art Society to commemorate Nancy Balfour's retirement 1982

P11200 Form at Salsipuedes (1987)
Jπ:2160x3555:signed:Presented by Garner H. Tullis and Pamela Auchincloss 1988

P11215 Untitled (1988)
Jπ:662x540:Presented by Garner H. Tullis and Pamela Auchincloss 1989

P11216 Untitled (1988)
Jπ:356x254:Presented by Garner H. Tullis and Pamela Auchincloss 1989

P11273 [no title] (1989)
Jπ:1016x760:signed:Presented by Garner H. Tullis and Pamela Auchincloss 1990

P11274 [no title] (1989)
Jπ:1015x1526:signed:Presented by Garner H. Tullis and Pamela Auchincloss 1990

P77128 Untitled (1984)
MJπ:1846x2943:signed:Purchased 1985

WALL, Brian born 1931
Modern Collection
Tate Gallery Archive holds material concerning this artist

T00835 Three Circles II (1966)
Sm:1295x1092x660:Purchased 1966

WALLER, Samuel 1850-1903
British Collection

N01551 Success! (1881)
Oc:1346x2134:signed:Presented by Sir Henry Tate 1894

N01552 Sweethearts and Wives (1882)
Oc:1448x2019:signed:Presented by Sir Henry Tate 1894

WALLIS, Alfred 1855-1942
British Collection
Tate Gallery Archive holds material concerning this artist

T00219 Schooner under the Moon (?circa 1935-6)
Ob:292x292:Purchased 1958

T00220 Voyage to Labrador (?circa 1935-6)
Ow:368x387:Purchased 1958

T00239 Houses at St Ives, Cornwall (?circa 1928-42)
Ob:267x318:Purchased 1959

T00291 The Blue Ship (?circa 1934)
Ob:438x559:Presented by H.S. Ede 1959

T00881 St Ives (circa 1928)
ODb:257x384:Presented by Ben Nicholson 1966

T01087 'The Hold House Port Mear Square Island Port Mear Beach' (?circa 1932)
Oπ:305x387:signed:Presented by Dame Barbara Hepworth 1968

T01967 Two-Masted Ship (circa 1928)
Oπ:302x591:Bequeathed by Mrs Doris Sealy 1975

T01968 String of Boats (circa 1928)
Ob:117x403:Bequeathed by Mrs Doris Sealy 1975

T01969 P.Z. 11 (circa 1928)
Ow:359x460:Bequeathed by Mrs Doris Sealy 1975

T01970 Two Boats (circa 1928)
Ob:213x305:Bequeathed by Mrs Doris Sealy 1975

WALLIS, Henry 1830-1916
British Collection

N01685 Chatterton (1856)
Oc:622x933:signed:Bequeathed by Charles Gent Clement 1899

T00042 The Room in Which Shakespeare Was Born (1853)
Ow:292x419:Purchased 1955

T01721 Study for 'Chatterton' (circa 1856)
Dπ:194x254:Purchased 1973

T01722 Study for 'Chatterton' (circa 1856)
Dπ:273x445:Purchased 1973

T01723 Study of a Girl Sitting in a Chair
Dπ:400x295:Purchased 1973

T01724 Landscape Study
Dπ:476x610:Purchased 1973

WALMSLEY, William born 1931
Modern Collection

P06601 Ding Dong Daddy Dog Biscuits 2 (1974-5)
CLπ:632x511:signed:Presented by Curwen Studio
through the Institute of Contemporary Prints 1975

WALTON, Edward Arthur 1860-1922
British Collection
Tate Gallery Archive holds material concerning this artist

T03447 Berwickshire Field-workers (1886)
Oc:914x609:signed:Purchased 1982

WALTON, Henry 1746-1813
British Collection

N02870 Plucking the Turkey (exhibited 1776)
Oc:762x635:Purchased 1912

WARD, David - see McLEAN, Bruce and WARD, David

WARD, Edward Matthew 1816-1879
British Collection

N00430 Doctor Johnson in the Ante-Room of Lord Chesterfield
Waiting for an Audience, 1748 (1845)
Oc:1060x1394:Presented by Robert Vernon 1847

N00431 Sketch for 'The Disgrace of Lord Clarendon, after his
Last Interview with the King, Whitehall Palace' (1846)
Oc:533x737:Presented by Robert Vernon 1847

N00432 The South Sea Bubble: A Scene in Change Alley in 1720
(1847)
Oc:1295x1880:Presented by Robert Vernon 1847

N00616 James II in his Palace of Whitehall, Receiving the News
of the Landing of the Prince of Orange, in 1688
(exhibited 1850)
Oc:1206x1822:Bequeathed by Jacob Bell 1859

N04697 Scene from 'David Garrick'
Oc:749x957:Purchased 1933

WARD, James 1769-1859
British Collection

N00385 Lake and Tower in de Tabley Park (1814)
Oc:940x1359:Presented by Robert Vernon 1847

N00688 Landscape with Cattle (1820-2)
Oc:3289x4851:signed:Purchased 1862

N01043 Gordale Scar (A View of Gordale, in the Manor of East
Malham in Craven, Yorkshire, the Property of Lord
Ribblesdale) (?1812-14, exhibited 1815)
Oc:3327x4216:Purchased 1878

N01158 Harlech Castle (1808)
Ow:1313x2159:signed:Purchased 1884

N01175 Cattle-Piece, ? Marylebone Park (1807)
Oc:743x1175:signed:Bequeathed by Mrs Elizabeth
Vaughan 1885

N02142 Sketch for 'Gordale Scar' (circa 1811)
Oπ:318x429:Purchased 1907

N03702 Studies of a Man's Head
Ow:219x302:signed:Purchased 1922

N03703 Sketch for 'Gordale Scar' (circa 1811)
DWπ:314x425:Purchased 1922

N03704 A Man in a Smock
Dπ:267x184:signed:Purchased 1922

N04937 L'Amour de Cheval (1827)
Oc:1448x2126:signed:Presented by Francis Howard 1938

N04985 Sketch for 'Daniel in the Lion's Den' (circa 1841 or circa
1852)
Ow:171x235:Purchased 1939

N04986 Study for 'Daniel in the Lion's Den' (circa 1841 or circa
1852)
Dπ:86x127:Purchased 1939

N04987 Dying Swan (circa 1817)
Dπ:244x333:signed:Purchased 1939

N05161 Fighting Stags, Study for 'Gordale Scar' (circa 1811-15)
Dπ:187x260:signed:Presented by Sir Robert Witt through
the National Art Collections Fund 1940

N05318 Beef (circa 1805-15)
Oc:441x318:Purchased 1942

N05410 Study of Sheeps' Heads (1836)
Oc:495x768:signed:Presented by the National Art
Collections Fund 1943

N05926 A Spaniel Frightening Ducks (1821)
Oc:1216x1819:signed:Purchased 1950

N05940 The Black Horse (1824)
Ow:806x1121:signed:Presented by Mrs H. Arthurton in
memory of her husband 1950

N05972 The Deer Stealer (exhibited 1823)
Oc:2289x3664:Presented by F. Howard 1950

T02377 Portraits of Blackthorn, a Broodmare, with Old Jack, a
Favourite Pony, the Property of E. Mundy, Esq. (1812)
Ow:705x918:signed:Presented by Paul Mellon through
the British Sporting Art Trust 1979

T03440 The Moment (1831)
Ow:367x466:signed:Purchased 1982

T03577 First Compositional Study for 'Gordale Scar' (1811)
Dπ:273x364:signed:Purchased 1983

T03578 Study for 'Gordale Scar': Details of Rocks near Waterfall
(1811)
Dπ:279x394:signed:Purchased 1983

WARDLE, Arthur 1864-1949
British Collection

N01947 Fate (1904)
Oc:946x1480:signed:Presented by the Trustees of the
Chantrey Bequest 1904

WARHOL, Andy 1928-1987
Modern Collection
Tate Gallery Archive holds material concerning this artist

T01288 Self-Portrait (1967)
ACc:1832x1832:Purchased 1971

T03093 Marilyn Diptych (1962)
2 ANc:2054x1448:signed:Purchased 1980

T05495 Untitled (Beauty Products) (1960)
GDπ:736x580:Purchased 1988

Marilyn (P07121-P07130; complete group)
P07121 [no title] (1967)
CNπ:910x910:signed:Purchased 1971

P07122 [no title] (1967)
CNπ:910x910:signed:Purchased 1971

P07123 [no title] (1967)
CNπ:910x910:signed:Purchased 1971

P07124 [no title] (1967)
CNπ:910x910:signed:Purchased 1971

P07125 [no title] (1967)
CNπ:910x910:signed:Purchased 1971

P07126 [no title] (1967)
CNπ:910x910:signed:Purchased 1971

P07127 [no title] (1967)
CNπ:910x910:signed:Purchased 1971

P07128 [no title] (1967)
CNπ:910x910:signed:Purchased 1971

P07129 [no title] (1967)
CNπ:910x910:signed:Purchased 1971

P07130 [no title] (1967)
CNπ:910x910:signed:Purchased 1971

P07242 Black Bean (from Soup Can Series I) (1968)
CNπ:889x587:signed:Purchased 1978

Electric Chairs (P07725-P07734; complete group)

P07725 [no title] (1971)
CNπ:900x1216:signed:Purchased 1982

P07726 [no title] (1971)
CNπ:900x1216:signed:Purchased 1982

P07727 [no title] (1971)
CNπ:900x1216:signed:Purchased 1982

P07728 [no title] (1971)
CNπ:900x1216:signed:Purchased 1982

P07729 [no title] (1971)
CNπ:900x1216:signed:Purchased 1982

P07730 [no title] (1971)
CNπ:900x1216:signed:Purchased 1982

P07731 [no title] (1971)
CNπ:900x1216:signed:Purchased 1982

P07732 [no title] (1971)
CNπ:900x1216:signed:Purchased 1982

P07733 [no title] (1971)
CNπ:900x1216:signed:Purchased 1982

P07734 [no title] (1971)
CNπ:900x1216:signed:Purchased 1982

Mao Tse-Tung (P77073-P77082; complete group)

P77073 [no title] (1972)
CNπ:914x914:signed:Purchased 1984

P77074 [no title] (1972)
CNπ:914x914:signed:Purchased 1984

P77075 [no title] (1972)
CNπ:914x914:signed:Purchased 1984

P77076 [no title] (1972)
CNπ:914x914:signed:Purchased 1984

P77077 [no title] (1972)
CNπ:914x914:signed:Purchased 1984

P77078 [no title] (1972)
CNπ:914x914:signed:Purchased 1984

P77079 [no title] (1972)
CNπ:914x914:signed:Purchased 1984

P77080 [no title] (1972)
CNπ:914x914:signed:Purchased 1984

P77081 [no title] (1972)
CNπ:914x914:signed:Purchased 1984

P77082 [no title] (1972)
CNπ:914x914:signed:Purchased 1984

WARREN, Michael born 1938
Modern Collection

P06602 Lapwing (1973)
CLπ:508x257:signed:Presented by Curwen Studio
through the Institute of Contemporary Prints 1975

P06603 Crested Grebe (1974-5)
CLπ:521x384:signed:Presented by Curwen Studio
through the Institute of Contemporary Prints 1975

WATERFORD, Louisa Anne, Marchioness of 1818-1891
British Collection

N03222 Christ Raising the Dead
Wπ:286x368:Bequeathed by Adelaide, Lady Brownlow 1917

N03223 Sleeping Disciples
Wπ:127x391:Bequeathed by Adelaide, Lady Brownlow 1917

N03224 A Funeral
Dπ:121x222:Bequeathed by Adelaide, Lady Brownlow 1917

WATERHOUSE, John William 1849-1917
British Collection

N01541 Consulting the Oracle (1884)
Oc:1194x1981:signed:Presented by Sir Henry Tate 1894

N01542 Saint Eulalia (exhibited 1885)
Oc:1886x1175:signed:Presented by Sir Henry Tate 1894

N01543 The Lady of Shalott (1888)
Oc:1530x2000:signed:Presented by Sir Henry Tate 1894

N01572 The Magic Circle (1886)
Oc:1829x1270:signed:Presented by the Trustees of the Chantrey Bequest 1886

T02106 Study for 'Consulting the Oracle' Verso: Studies of (i) Same Composition (ii) Priestess on a Tripod Throne (circa 1884)
Dπ:124x244:Purchased 1977

T02107 Study for 'Saint Eulalia' (circa 1885)
DWπ:127x76:Purchased 1977

WATERLOW, Sir Ernest Albert 1850-1919
British Collection

N01596 Galway Gossips (exhibited 1887)
Oc:762x1276:signed:Presented by the Trustees of the Chantrey Bequest 1887

WATSON, Harry 1871-1936
British Collection

N02938 Across the River (circa 1913)
Wπ:445x546:Presented by the Trustees of the Chantrey Bequest 1913

WATSON, Lyall born 1908
Modern Collection

Four Book Pages (P06819-P06820; complete group)

P06819 [no title] (1978)
CLπ:559x762:signed:Presented by Curwen Studio 1978

P06820 [no title] (1978)
CLπ:559x762:signed:Presented by Curwen Studio 1978

WATSON, Spencer 1869-1934
British Collection
Tate Gallery Archive holds material concerning this artist

N04806 A Lady in Black (1922)
Oc:1270x1022:signed:Presented by the Trustees of the Chantrey Bequest 1935

WATT, George Fiddes 1873-1960
British Collection

N04541 The Artist's Mother (1910)
Oc:1054x800:signed:Presented by the Trustees of the Chantrey Bequest 1930

WATTS, Frederick Waters 1800-1870
British Collection

T01707 Two Sketches of a Cornfield with Harvesters (circa 1829)
Ob:114x175:Presented by Mrs M. Bernard 1973

T01708 Sketch of a Harvest Wagon (circa 1829)
Ob:117x175:Presented by Mrs M. Bernard 1973

WATTS, George Frederic 1817-1904
British Collection
Tate Gallery Archive holds material concerning this artist

N01561 Self-Portrait (1864)
Oc:648x521:signed:Bequeathed by Sir William Bowman Bt 1898

N01585 Psyche (1880)
Oc:1886x597:Presented by the Trustees of the Chantrey Bequest 1882

N01630 Mammon (1884-5)
Oc:1829x1060:Presented by the artist 1897

N01631 The Dweller in the Innermost (circa 1885-6)
Oc:1060x698:Presented by the artist 1897

N01632 'For he had great possessions' (1894)
Oc:1397x584:signed:Presented by the artist 1897

N01633 Dray Horses (circa 1863-75)
Oc:3023x4051:Presented by the artist 1897

N01634 The Minotaur (1885)
Oc:1181x945:Presented by the artist 1897

N01635 Death Crowning Innocence (1886-7)
Oc:1283x800:Presented by the artist 1897

N01636 Jonah (1894)
Oc:1537x889:Presented by the artist 1897

N01637 The Spirit of Christianity (1873-5)
Oc:2730x1524:Presented by the artist 1897

N01638 Sic Transit (1891-2)
Oc:1029x2045:signed:Presented by the artist 1897

N01639 Faith (circa 1890-6)
Oc:2138x927:signed:Presented by the artist 1897

N01641 Love and Life (circa 1884-5)
Oc:2222x1219:Presented by the artist 1897

N01642 She Shall Be Called Woman (circa 1875-92)
Oc:2578x1168:signed:Presented by the artist 1897

N01643 Eve Tempted (exhibited 1884)
Oc:2578x1168:signed:Presented by the artist 1897

N01644 Eve Repentant (circa 1865-97)
Oc:2591x1194:Presented by the artist 1897

N01645 Love and Death (circa 1885-7)
Oc:2476x1168:Presented by the artist 1897

N01646 The Messenger (circa 1884-5)
Oc:2743x1505:Presented by the artist 1897

N01654 Russell Gurney (circa 1875-8)
Oc:635x508:Presented by the Rev. Alfred Gurney 1898

N01687 The All-Pervading (1887-90)
Oc:1626x1092:Presented by the artist 1899

N01692 Love Triumphant (1899-1900)
Oc:2965x1702:signed:Presented by the artist 1900

N01693 Time, Death and Judgement (1900)
Oc:2337x1676:Presented by the artist 1900

N01768 Clytie (circa 1868-78)
Sz:711x597x419:Presented by the artist 1900

N01913 A Story from Boccaccio (circa 1844-7)
Oc:3658x8915:Purchased with assistance from members of the Cosmopolitan Club 1902

N01920 Life's Illusions (1849)
Oc:2445x1835:Presented by Mrs Alfred Seymour 1902

N01983 Echo (1844-6)
Oc:3886x1981:Presented by Mrs George Frederic Watts 1903

N02682 Eustace Smith (circa 1870-80)
Oc:610x508:Presented by Eustace Smith 1910

N04223 Dorothy Tennant, Later Lady Stanley
Ow:635x533:Presented by Henry Curtis in memory of Dorothy Tennant, Lady Stanley 1926

N04449 Mrs Arthur Sassoon (1882)
Oc:660x533:signed:Presented by Mr and Mrs Arthur Sassoon 1929

N04555 Ruth and Boaz (circa 1835-7)
Ow:305x254:Presented by Miss Lucy Jarvis 1930

N04556 The Golden Age (circa 1840)
Oc:298x349:signed:Presented by Miss Lucy Jarvis 1930

N04557 Nymphs and Satyrs (circa 1840)
Oc:298x349:signed:Presented by Miss Lucy Jarvis 1930

N05116 Eveleen Tennant, later Mrs F.W.H. Myers (exhibited 1880)
Oc:1003x711:Presented by Mrs Richard Blennerhassett 1940

N05806 Mrs George Augustus Frederick Cavendish-Bentinck and her Children (exhibited 1860)
Oc:1270x1016:Presented by W.G.F. Cavendish-Bentinck 1948

N06026 Study of Clouds (circa 1890-1900)
Oc:762x635:Purchased 1951

N06083 Augusta, Lady Castletown (circa 1846)
Oc:2083x1435:Bequeathed by Maj. W.R.D. Mackenzie 1952

N06084 Miss Mary Kirkpatrick Brunton (1841)
Oc:603x400:signed:Purchased 1952

T00012 Daphne (circa 1879-82)
Ss:711x610x381:Presented by the executors of Francis Howard 1955

WATTS, George Frederic with assistants 1817-1904
British Collection

N01640 Hope (1886)
Oc:1422x1118:Presented by George Frederic Watts 1897

N01647 Chaos (circa 1875-82)
Oc:1067x3048:Presented by George Frederic Watts 1897

N01894 The Court of Death (circa 1870-1902)
Oc:4242x2743:Presented by George Frederic Watts 1902

WEAVER, Thomas 1774 or 5 - 1843
British Collection

T01586 Foxgloves and Brambles, with a Hawk Confronting an Adder (1814)
Oc:1118x943:signed:Purchased 1972

T03438 Ram-Letting from Robert Bakewell's Breed at Dishley, near Loughborough, Leicestershire (1810)
Oc:1028x1286:signed:Bequeathed by Mrs F. Ambrose Clark through the British Sporting Art Trust 1982

WEBB, Boyd born 1947
Modern Collection

T04120 Scott's Tent (1984)
CFπ:1220x1523:signed:Purchased 1985

WEBB, James circa 1825-1895
British Collection

N01684 Mont St Michel, Normandy (?exhibited 1857 or 1866)
Oc:1511x2429:signed:Bequeathed by Rev. M. Davison 1899

WEBB, Philip 1831-1915
British Collection

N05170 The Bull and the Lion
Wπ:660x991:Purchased 1940

A01016 Study for Heraldic Glass (1893)
Wπ:165x157:Bequeathed by J.R. Holliday 1927

A01017 Study for Heraldic Glass (1893)
Dπ:267x279:Bequeathed by J.R. Holliday 1927

A01018 Emblems of Saints Luke and John (1863)
Dπ:346x492:Bequeathed by J.R. Holliday 1927

A01019 Emblems of Saints Matthew and Mark (1863)
Dπ:356x530:Bequeathed by J.R. Holliday 1927

WEBSTER, Thomas 1800-1886
British Collection
Tate Gallery Archive holds material concerning this artist

N00426 Going into School or the Truant (1834)
Ow:432x368:signed:Presented by Robert Vernon 1847

N00427 A Dame's School (1845)
Ow:622x1219:signed:Presented by Robert Vernon 1847

N01225 The Artist's Father and Mother (exhibited 1844)
Ow:298x241:signed:Bequeathed by the artist 1887

T00046 A Letter from the Colonies (1852)
Ow:413x521:Purchased 1955

T04145 Study for 'A Letter from the Colonies' (circa 1852)
Ob:116x122:Presented by J.G. Milner 1986

WEEKES, Henry 1807-1877
British Collection

N01769 John Flaxman
Ss:2165x1016x851:Bequeathed by Henry Vaughan 1900

N02075 Thomas Stothard (1868)
Ss:768x610x368:signed:Presented by subscribers 1868

N02076 William Mulready (1866)
Ss:876x679x406:signed:Presented by subscribers 1868

WEGNER, Nicholas born 1948
Modern Collection
Tate Gallery Archive holds material concerning this artist

P06604 Map / Girls's Head (1972)
2 MLπ:775x575, 775x575:signed:Presented by Curwen Studio through the Institute of Contemporary Prints 1975

P06605 Aerial View / Figures with Motor Bike (1972)
2 MLπ:775x575, 775x575:signed:Presented by Curwen Studio through the Institute of Contemporary Prints 1975

P06606 Love Making / Aerial City (1972)
2 MLπ:775x575, 775x575:signed:Presented by Curwen Studio through the Institute of Contemporary Prints 1975

P06607 Girl's Head / Man, Head and Shoulders (1972)
2 MLπ:775x575, 775x575:signed:Presented by Curwen Studio through the Institute of Contemporary Prints 1975

P06608 Back View of a Girl / Girl Standing (1972)
2 MLπ:775x575, 775x575:signed:Presented by Curwen Studio through the Institute of Contemporary Prints 1975

P06609 Girl Lying on a Decorated Bed / Two Men (1972)
2 MLπ:775x575, 775x575:signed:Presented by Curwen Studio through the Institute of Contemporary Prints 1975

P06610 Girl Lying Down (1972)
MLπ:775x575:signed:Presented by Curwen Studio through the Institute of Contemporary Prints 1975

P06611 Back View of Standing Girl (1972)
MLπ:775x575:signed:Presented by Curwen Studio through the Institute of Contemporary Prints 1975

P06612 Aerial View of a City (1972)
MLπ:775x575:signed:Presented by Curwen Studio through the Institute of Contemporary Prints 1975

P06613 Guitarist (1972)
MLπ:775x575:signed:Presented by Curwen Studio through the Institute of Contemporary Prints 1975

WEGNER, Nicholas - see GALLERY, LONDON, The

WEIGHT, Carel born 1908
Modern Collection
Tate Gallery Archive holds material concerning this artist

N06177 The Rendezvous (1953)
Oc:864x1118:signed:Presented by the Trustees of the Chantrey Bequest 1953

T00095 The Dogs (1955-6)
Ob:1226x2438:signed:Presented by the Trustees of the Chantrey Bequest 1956

T00139 Miss Orovida Pissarro (1956)
Oc:914x711:signed:Presented by the Trustees of the Chantrey Bequest 1957

T00593 Sienese Landscape (1960-3)
Oc:762x635:signed:Presented by the Trustees of the Chantrey Bequest 1963

T01063 The Friends (1968)
Oc:1524x2080:signed:Presented by the Trustees of the Chantrey Bequest 1968

T02325 Clapham Junction (1978)
Oc:708x908:signed:Presented by the Trustees of the Chantrey Bequest 1978

WELCH, Denton 1915-1948
Modern Collection

T04946 Harvest (circa 1931-5)
Ob:910x1222:Presented by Betty Swanwick 1987

WELLINGTON, Hubert L. 1879-1967
British Collection
Tate Gallery Archive holds material concerning this artist

T00448 The Big Barn, Frampton Mansell (1915)
Oc:508x616:signed:Presented by the Trustees of the
Chantrey Bequest 1961

WELLS, Henry Tanworth 1828-1903
British Collection

N01919 Victoria Regina (1880)
Oc:2451x1918:signed:Presented by the artist's daughter
1903

WELLS, Joanna Mary 1831-1861
British Collection

N03814 Gretchen (1861)
Oc:730x437:Presented by the artist's daughters 1923

WELLS, John born 1907
Modern Collection
Tate Gallery Archive holds material concerning this artist

T00370 Brimstone Moth Variation (1960)
Ob:1219x762:signed:Purchased 1960

T00682 Painting (1962)
Ob:762x152:signed:Purchased 1964

T01759 Relief Construction (1941)
GDVab:321x422x35:signed:Purchased 1973

T02229 Microcosm (1957-9)
Ow:406x254:signed:Bequeathed by Miss E.M. Hodgkins
1977

T02230 Sea Bird Forms (1951)
Ob:432x495:signed:Bequeathed by Miss E.M. Hodgkins
1977

T02231 Aspiring Forms (1950)
Ob:1067x724:signed:Bequeathed by Miss E.M. Hodgkins
1977

T02232 Profiles (1949)
ODw:279x368:signed:Bequeathed by Miss E.M.
Hodgkins 1977

T02233 Untitled Drawing (1952)
DPWπ:289x235:signed:Bequeathed by Miss E.M.
Hodgkins 1977

T02234 Painting (1957)
Ob:302x279:signed:Bequeathed by Miss E.M. Hodgkins
1977

T03957 Painting (1956)
Ob:915x1220:Presented by Ken Powell 1985

P77129 Personage (1950)
MIπ:168x118:signed:Purchased 1985

P77130 Topsail (1950)
MIπ:140x115:signed:Purchased 1985

P77131 Abstraction (1950)
MIπ:67x115:signed:Purchased 1985

P77132 Cliff Figure (1950)
MIπ:117x144:signed:Purchased 1985

P77177 Abstract (1958)
Lπ:320x405:signed:Purchased 1986

WEMAERE, Pierre born 1913
Modern Collection

For Jorn (P03241-P03255; complete group; mixed group)
Pour Jorn
P03254 [no title] (1975-6)
CLπ:505x657:signed:Presented by the Asger Jorn
Foundation 1978

WENTWORTH, Richard born 1947
Modern Collection
Tate Gallery Archive holds material concerning this artist

T03924 Shower (1984)
SVv:890x1100x880:Purchased 1984

Jam Press Phase One (P08006-P08014; complete group;
mixed group)
P08015 1. 12 (1973-4)
MLπ:441x559:Transferred from the Library 1977

WESCHKE, Karl born 1925
Modern Collection
Tate Gallery Archive holds material concerning this artist

T03287 Body on a Beach (1977)
Oc:1730x1299:signed:Purchased 1981

P77178 Brown and Black (1958)
Lπ:465x334:signed:Purchased 1986

WESSELMANN, Tom born 1931
Modern Collection

P07760 Seascape Dropout (1982)
CJπ:556x635:signed:Purchased 1982

WEST, Benjamin 1738-1820
British Collection

N00121 Cleombrotus Ordered into Banishment by Leonidas II,
King of Sparta (1768)
Oc:1384x1854:signed:Presented by W. Wilkins 1827

N00126 Pylades and Orestes Brought as Victims before Iphigenia
(1766)
Oc:1003x1264:signed:Presented by Sir George Beaumont
Bt 1826

N00132 The Last Supper (1784)
Oc:1835x2769:Presented by King George IV 1828

N00315 The Installation of the Order of the Garter (circa 1790)
Oc:406x559:Presented by Robert Vernon 1847

N00799 Mrs Worrell as Hebe (circa 1770)
Oc:1270x1003:Bequeathed by Miss Harriet Worrell 1869

N05264 Sir Thomas Beauchamp-Proctor, Bt (1777)
Oc:1264x1003:Presented by the daughters of Maj-Gen.
G.E.H. Beauchamp through the National Art Collections
Fund 1941

N05265 Lady Beauchamp-Proctor (1778)
Oc:1264x1003:Presented by the daughters of Maj-Gen.
G.E.H. Beauchamp through the National Art Collections
Fund 1941

N05310 View from the Terrace at Windsor (1792)
Oc:283x371:signed:Purchased 1941

N05620 A View of Windsor from Snow Hill, Windsor Great Park
(1799-1803)
Oπ:610x851:Purchased 1945

N05621 Sketch for 'The Ascension' (circa 1782)
Oc:1264x711:Presented by the National Art Collections
Fund 1945

N05622 Sketch for 'St Paul Shaking off the Viper' (1786)
Oc:1295x724:signed:Presented by the National Art
Collections Fund 1945

T00945 The Golden Age (1776)
Oc:654x765:signed:Purchased with assistance from the
Friends of the Tate Gallery and The National Art
Collections Fund 1967

T01900 The Bard (1778)
Ow:292x229:signed:Purchased 1974

WEST, Walter 1860-1933
British Collection

N02934 Sunshine, Breeze, and Blossom: Lake Como (exhibited
1913)
Oc:1016x1283:Presented by the Trustees of the Chantrey
Bequest 1983

WESTALL, Richard 1765-1836
British Collection

N01414 Philip Sansom, Jun., as a Child
Oc:1257x1016:Bequeathed by Miss Ellen Sansom 1894

T00088 The Reconciliation of Helen and Paris after his Defeat by
Menelaus (exhibited 1805)
Ow:1270x1010:Purchased 1956

WESTALL, William 1781-1850
British Collection

N01877 The Commencement of the Deluge (exhibited 1848)
Oc:1270x1930:Purchased 1956

after
WESTALL, William 1781-1850
British Collection

Picturesque Views on the Southern Coast of England
(T05218-T05463; complete group; mixed group)
T05320 Netley Abbey, Hampshire (1816)
Iπ:138x214:Purchased 1988

T05321 Netley Abbey, Hampshire (1816)
Iπ:139x216:Purchased 1988

T05322 Southampton, Hampshire (1814)
Iπ:141x215:Purchased 1988

T05323 Southampton, Hampshire (1814)
Iπ:142x216:Purchased 1988

WHEATLEY, Francis 1747-1801
British Collection

N03678 A Family Group in a Landscape (circa 1775)
Oc:1016x1270:Bequeathed by W. Asch 1922

N04654 Man with a Dog (circa 1775)
Oc:978x737:Purchased 1932

WHEATLEY, Grace 1888-1970
Modern Collection

N03642 Seated Woman (1913)
DWπ:356x254:Purchased 1922

WHEATLEY, John 1892-1955
Modern Collection

N03851 Mother and Child (1915)
Dπ:559x445:signed:Purchased 1924

WHEELER, Sir Charles 1892-1974
Modern Collection
Tate Gallery Archive holds material concerning this artist

N03959 The Infant Christ (1920-4)
Sz:343x216x133:Presented by the Trustees of the
Chantrey Bequest 1924

N04548 Spring (1929-30)
Sz:1626x1308x648:Presented by the Trustees of the
Chantrey Bequest 1930

N05559 Aphrodite II (1943)
Ss:1314x384x267:Presented by the Trustees of the
Chantrey Bequest 1944

WHISHAW, Anthony born 1930
Modern Collection

T03926 Drawing (Landscape) (1983)
AVπ:810x1930:signed:Purchased 1984

WHISTLER, James Abbot McNeil 1834-1903
British Collection
Tate Gallery Archive holds material concerning this artist

N01959 Nocturne in Blue and Gold: Old Battersea Bridge (circa
1872-5)
Oc:679x508:Presented by the National Art Collections
Fund 1905

N02426 Black Lion Wharf, Wapping (1859)
Iπ:143x225:Presented by Ernest Marsh 1909

N03418 The Little White Girl: Symphony in White, No. 2 (1864)
Oc:765x511:signed:Bequeathed by Arthur Studd 1919

N03419 Nocturne in Black and Gold: The Fire Wheel (1875)
Oc:543x762:Bequeathed by Arthur Studd 1919

N03420 Nocturne in Blue and Silver: Cremorne Lights (1872)
Oc:502x743:signed:Bequeathed by Arthur Studd 1919

N04060 Count Burckhardt (published 1862)
Jπ:159x102:Presented by Harold Hartley 1925

N04622 Miss Cicely Alexander: Harmony in Grey and Green
(1872)
Oc:1899x978:signed:Bequeathed by W.C. Alexander 1932

N05065 Crepuscule in Flesh Colour and Green: Valparaiso
(1866)
Oc:584x754:signed:Presented by W. Graham Robertson
1940

N05964 Miss Agnes Mary Alexander (circa 1873)
Oc:1924x1016:Bequeathed by W.C. Alexander 1950

N05971 Three Figures: Pink and Grey (1868-78)
Oc:1391x1854:Purchased with the aid of contributions
from the International Society of Sculptors, Painters and
Gravers as a Memorial to Whistler, and from Francis
Howard 1950

T01571 Nocturne in Blue-Green (1871)
Ow:502x591:signed:Bequeathed by Miss Rachel and Miss
Jean Alexander 1972

WHISTLER, Rex 1905-1944
Modern Collection
Tate Gallery Archive holds material concerning this artist

N05865 Self-Portrait (circa 1933)
Oc:406x368:Bequeathed by Miss Edith Olivier 1948

N05881 Illustrations to 'Königsmark' (1940-1)
DWπ:337x254:signed:Bequeathed by A.E.W. Mason 1949

WHITCOMBE, Thomas active 1783-1824
British Collection

N01659 The Battle of Camperdown (1798)
Oc:1219x1829:signed:Bequeathed by Mrs Fisher 1898

WHITE, Ethelbert 1891-1972
Modern Collection
Tate Gallery Archive holds material concerning this artist

N03848 Under the Hills (1923)
Oc:406x368:signed:Presented by the Contemporary Art Society 1924

T02390 Under the Hills (1923)
DWπ:197x251:Presented by the executors of the artist's estate 1979

WHITEFORD, Kate born 1952
Modern Collection

T05739 Shadows - Spiral (1987)
Dπ:1306x1126:Purchased 1990

T05740 Shadows - Fish (1987)
Dπ:1310x1126:Purchased 1990

P11268 Double Chevron and Spiral (1989)
Nπ:1225x968:signed:Presented by the King Edward's Hospital Fund 1989

P77283 Untitled (1988)
Nπ:270x217:Purchased 1989

WHITELEY, Brett born 1939
Modern Collection

T00433 Untitled Red Painting (1960)
OVc:1327x1861:signed:Purchased 1961

T00670 Woman in a Bath II (1963)
OTVb:1829x1880:signed:Purchased 1964

Towards Sculpture, Eight Studies of the Nude
(P03289-P03296; complete group)
P03289 1 (1977)
CLπ:760x508:signed:Presented by Ganymed Press 1979
P03290 2 (1977)
CLπ:760x482:signed:Presented by Ganymed Press 1979
P03291 3 (1977)
CLπ:775x510:signed:Presented by Ganymed Press 1979
P03292 4 (1977)
CLπ:760x516:signed:Presented by Ganymed Press 1979
P03293 5 (1977)
CLπ:775x470:signed:Presented by Ganymed Press 1979
P03294 6 (1977)
CLπ:690x490:signed:Presented by Ganymed Press 1979
P03295 7 (1977)
CLπ:775x456:signed:Presented by Ganymed Press 1979
P03296 8 (1977)
CLπ:725x395:signed:Presented by Ganymed Press 1979

My Relationship between Screenprinting and Regent's Park Zoo between June and August 1965
(P05290-P05295; complete group)
P05290 1. Swinging Monkey (1965)
CNπ:760x558:signed:Presented by Rose and Chris Prater through the Institute of Contemporary Prints 1975
P05291 2. Swinging Monkey (1965)
CNπ:762x560:signed:Presented by Rose and Chris Prater through the Institute of Contemporary Prints 1975

P05292 3. Swinging Monkey (1965)
CNπ:762x557:signed:Presented by Rose and Chris Prater through the Institute of Contemporary Prints 1975
P05293 4. Drawing About Drawing (1965)
CNπ:762x560:signed:Presented by Rose and Chris Prater through the Institute of Contemporary Prints 1975
P05294 5. Giraffe (1965)
CNπ:760x557:signed:Presented by Rose and Chris Prater through the Institute of Contemporary Prints 1975
P05295 6. Hyena (1965)
CNπ:764x601:signed:Presented by Rose and Chris Prater through the Institute of Contemporary Prints 1975
P05296 10 Rillington Place W11 (1965)
CNπ:594x559:signed:Presented by Rose and Chris Prater through the Institute of Contemporary Prints 1975
P06614 Seated Nude (1973)
MLπ:749x552:signed:Presented by Curwen Studio through the Institute of Contemporary Prints 1975

WHITNEY-SMITH, Edwin 1880-1952
Modern Collection

N05113 The Irishman (?circa 1900-10)
Sz:267x190x165:Presented by the Trustees of the Chantrey Bequest 1940

WIENER, Martin born 1913
Modern Collection
Tate Gallery Archive holds material concerning this artist

The Hands of the People who are Building Israel
(P06615-P06758; complete group)
P06615 1. Golda Meir (1972-3)
CLπ:694x495:signed:Presented by Curwen Studio through the Institute of Contemporary Prints 1975
P06616 2. David Ben Gurion (1972-3)
CLπ:714x515:signed:Presented by Curwen Studio through the Institute of Contemporary Prints 1975
P06755 3. Kibbutz Palmach Tzuba (1972-3)
CLπ:554x759:signed:Presented by Curwen Studio 1976
P06756 4. Three Arabs and a Sabra (1972-3)
CLπ:547x752:signed:Presented by Curwen Studio 1976
P06757 5. Nahal Settlement Ein Sivan (1972-3)
CLπ:800x705:signed:Presented by Curwen Studio 1976
P06758 6. Children in the Panto Family Kindergarten (1972-3)
CLπ:498x703:signed:Presented by Curwen Studio 1976

WIENS, Stephen M. 1871-1956
British Collection

N02141 Girl and Lizard (1906)
Sz:140x502x241:signed:Presented by the Trustees of the Chantrey Bequest 1907

WILDE, Gerald 1905-1986
Modern Collection

T00413 Red Composition (1952)
Oπ:813x559:signed:Presented by P.A. Cook 1961

T03892 Fata Morgana (1949)
Oc:1036x902:signed:Purchased 1984

T03893 The Marriage of Heaven and Hell (1971-72)
PGπ:1530x2123:signed:Purchased 1984

WILDING, Alison born 1948
Modern Collection
Tate Gallery Archive holds material concerning this artist

T04912 Airing Light (1985-6)
SOm:2450x617x900:Presented by the Patrons of New Art through the Friends of the Tate Gallery 1987

WILKIE, Sir David 1785-1841
British Collection
Tate Gallery Archive holds material concerning this artist

N00099 The Blind Fiddler (1806)
Ow:578x794:signed:Presented by Sir George Beaumont Bt 1826

N00122 The Village Holiday (1809-11)
Oc:940x1276:signed:Purchased 1824

N00231 Thomas Daniell, R.A. (1838)
Oc:749x629:signed:Bequeathed by Miss Mary Ann Fuller 1853

N00241 The Parish Beadle (1820-1823)
Ow:597x895:signed:Bequeathed by Lord Colborne 1854

N00328 The First Ear-Ring (1835)
Ow:743x603:signed:Presented by Robert Vernon 1847

N00329 The Bag-Piper (1813)
Of:254x200:Presented by Robert Vernon 1847

N00330 A Woody Landscape (1822)
Ow:241x241:signed:Presented by Robert Vernon 1847

N00331 Newsmongers (1821)
Ow:437x361:signed:Presented by Robert Vernon 1847

N00332 The Peep-o'-Day Boys' Cabin, in the West of Ireland (1835-6)
Oc:1257x1753:Presented by Robert Vernon 1847

N00894 The Preaching of Knox before the Lords of the Congregation, 10th June 1559 (1832)
Ow:1226x1651:signed:Purchased 1871

N00921 Study for 'Blind Man's Buff' (1811)
Ow:302x457:Bequeathed by Miss Harriet Bredel 1875

N01187 Study for 'The Village Holiday' (circa 1809-11)
Dπ:92x114:Bequeathed by Mrs Elizabeth Vaughan 1885

N01727 Mrs Elizabeth Young in Eastern Costume (1841)
WDπ:495x337:signed:Bequeathed by Mrs Elizabeth Young 1900

N01739 ?Sir Willoughby. Gordon and his Daughter Julia, Cooking on a Griddle at Puckaster, near Niton, Isle of Wight (1822)
DWπ:251x267:signed:Presented by Miss Julia Emily Gordon 1888

N01740 Miss Julia Emily Gordon (1833)
WDπ:311x235:signed:Bequeathed by Miss Julia Emily Gordon 1896

N01942 Study for a Portrait of William IV and Queen Adelaide (circa 1832-4)
WDπ:362x229:Presented by J.H.P. Bright 1904

N02131 A Picnic (?1822)
Ow:184x260:Presented by Sir J.C. Robinson through the National Art Collections Fund 1907

N02271 Head of an Elderly Man
Lπ:73x44:Presented by Sir J.C. Robinson through the National Art Collections Fund 1908

N02272 Lady at a Window (two states)
Lπ:83x41:Presented by Sir J.C. Robinson through the National Art Collections Fund 1908

N02273 Three Boys
Lπ:73x44:Presented by Sir J.C. Robinson through the National Art Collections Fund 1908

N02274 The Sedan Chair
Lπ:124x83:Presented by Sir J.C. Robinson through the National Art Collections Fund 1908

N02275 The Cottage Door (two states)
Lπ:124x83:Presented by Sir J.C. Robinson through the National Art Collections Fund 1908

N02276 Reading the Will (three states) (1819)
Lπ:92x127:Presented by Sir J.C. Robinson through the National Art Collections Fund 1908

N02277 The Lost Receipt
Lπ:146x159:Presented by Sir J.C. Robinson through the National Art Collections Fund 1908

N02278 Mother and Child (two states) (1820)
Lπ:222x184:Presented by Sir J.C. Robinson through the National Art Collections Fund 1908

N03603 Study of a Head for 'The Rabbit on the Wall' (circa 1815)
Ow:197x162:Purchased 1921

N03695 Sketch of a Cottage Interior with Figures
DWπ:610x508:signed:Purchased 1922

N04276 His Highness Muhemed Ali, Pacha of Egypt (1841)
Ob:610x508:signed:Bequeathed by the Earl of Effingham 1927

N04830 Study for 'The First Ear-Ring' (1834)
WDπ:521x368:signed:Presented by the National Art Collections Fund 1936

T03821 Five Preliminary Studies for Figures in 'The Village Holiday'. Verso: Two Preliminary Studies for Parts of Figures in 'The Village Holiday' (1809-10)
Dπ:184x278:Purchased 1984

A01020 After Rembrandt (1822)
DWπ:102x83:Bequeathed by Miss Julia Emily Gordon 1896

A01021 Archers
DWπ:92x105:Bequeathed by Miss Julia Emily Gordon 1896

A01022 Head and Shoulders of a Woman and Another Head
DWπ:121x83:Bequeathed by Miss Julia Emily Gordon 1896

A01023 Head and Shoulders of a Woman
DWπ:89x38:Bequeathed by Miss Julia Emily Gordon 1896

A01024 Julia Emily Gordon in a Fez (1830)
DWπ:98x102:Bequeathed by Miss Julia Emily Gordon 1896

A01025 Head and Shoulders of a Woman (1833)
DWπ:86x79:Bequeathed by Miss Julia Emily Gordon 1896

WILLATS, Stephen born 1943
Modern Collection
Tate Gallery Archive holds material concerning this artist

T03296 Living with Practical Realities (1978)
Fb:1099x768:Purchased 1981

T03795 Are you Good Enough for the Cha Cha Cha? (1982)
RVwπ:2540x4700x70:Purchased 1983

T04106 Organic Exercise No. 3, Series No. 2 (Tower Block Drawing) (1962)
Dc:554x764:signed:Purchased 1985

T04107 Drawing for Construction (1963)
Dπ:206x291:signed:Purchased 1985

T04108 Drawing for a Project No. 12 (1965)
DGπ:492x558:signed:Purchased 1985

P07947 Wall Print (1980)
MLπ:203x152:signed:Purchased 1983

WILLCOCK, George Burrell 1811-1852
British Collection

N01389 Chelston Lane, Torquay (1851)
Oc:616x514:signed:Purchased 1893

WILLIAMS, Edward 1782-1855
British Collection

N00123 Landscape with Figures by Moonlight (?exhibited 1826)
Ow:603x813:Bequeathed by Lieut. Col. J.H. Ollney 1837

T00788 A Village Forge: Moonlight (?exhibited 1845 or 1847)
Oc:308x457:signed:Presented by Edward Croft-Murray 1965

WILLIAMS, Glynn born 1939
Modern Collection

T05216 Morning (1987-8)
Ss:458x965x2235:Purchased 1988

WILLIAMS, Hugh William 1773-1829
British Collection

N03042 View of Perth
WDπ:200x346:Presented by Miss Gertrude Toynbee 1915

WILLIAMS, Kyffin born 1918
Modern Collection
Tate Gallery Archive holds material concerning this artist

P06617 Pontlyfni in Snow (1974)
CLπ:397x733:signed:Presented by Curwen Studio through the Institute of Contemporary Prints 1975

WILLIAMS, Penry 1798-1885
British Collection

N00433 Italian Girl with Tambourine (1837)
Oc:508x406:signed:Presented by Robert Vernon 1847

N00434 Pilgrims Reposing at a Cross (?1835)
Oc:508x406:signed:Presented by Robert Vernon 1847

N00662 Neapolitan Peasants at a Fountain (1859)
Oc:1067x1530:signed:Bequeathed by Mrs Huskinsson 1860

WILLIAMS, Terrick 1860-1936
British Collection

N04858 Quiet Twilight, Honfleur (exhibited 1922)
Oc:921x1270:signed:Presented by Evelyn E. Barron 1937

WILLIAMS, William active 1758-1797
British Collection

T00519 Thunderstorm with the Death of Amelia (1784)
Oc:635x1019:signed:Purchased 1962

WILLING, Victor 1928-1988
Modern Collection
Tate Gallery Archive holds material concerning this artist

T03186 Place with a Red Thing (1980)
Oc:2000x2502:Purchased 1980

T03187 Rien (1980)
Oc:2000x1829:Purchased 1980

WILLSON, Terry born 1948
Modern Collection

P01668 Afternoon Tea Party (1975)
MLπ:492x657:signed:Presented by Susan Loppert through the Institute of Contemporary Prints 1975

WILSON, Richard 1713-1782
British Collection

N00108 Distant View of Maecenas' Villa, Tivoli (circa 1756-7)
Oc:1219x1702:signed:Presented by Sir George Beaumont Bt 1823

N00267 Lake Avernus
Oc:229x292:Bequeathed by Richard and Catherine Garnons 1854

N00301 Strada Nomentana (circa 1765-70)
Oc:571x762:Presented by Robert Vernon 1847

N00302 Hadrian's Villa (circa 1765)
Oc:356x254:Presented by Robert Vernon 1847

N00303 Maecenas' Villa, Tivoli (circa 1765)
Oc:361x254:Presented by Robert Vernon 1847

N00304 Lake Avernus and the Island of Capri (circa 1760)
Oc:470x724:Presented by Robert Vernon 1847

N01097 Ariccia (circa 1752-7)
Oc:489x635:Presented by T. Hollis 1861

N01290 Landscape with Bathers, Cattle and Ruin (circa 1770-5)
Oc:584x749:Bequeathed by John Staniforth Beckett 1889

N01880 George III and the Duke of York (?1749)
Oc:1016x1270:Bequeathed by Richard and Catherine Garnons 1854

N01889 A View of the Thames
Oc:610x762:Bequeathed by Richard and Catherine Garnons 1854

N02438 The Castle of St Angelo, Rome (1752-6)
Dπ:241x394:Presented by J. Bowyer Nichols through the National Art Collections Fund 1909

N02646 Baths of Ischia, near Naples
Oc:445x546:Bequeathed by George Salting 1910

N02984 The Inner Temple after the Fire of 4 January 1737 (1737)
Oc:648x952:signed:Bequeathed by Richard and Catherine Garnons 1854

N02989 View near the Loggerheads, Denbigh (circa 1765-70)
Oc:419x521:Bequeathed by Richard and Catherine Garnons 1854

N03136 The Cock Tavern, Cheam, Surrey (circa 1745)
Oc:730x436:Bequeathed by Rev. A. Stopford Brooke 1916

N03727 Francesco Zuccarelli (1751)
Oc:495x419:signed:Purchased 1923

N04458 On Hounslow Heath (?exhibited 1770)
Oc:425x527:Presented by R.E.A. Wilson and M. Oliver 1929

N04874 The Thames near Marble Hill, Twickenham (circa 1762)
Oc:464x730:signed:Purchased 1937

N05551 Apollo and the Seasons
Oc:914x1194:Presented by Miss Eileen Brenton 1944

N05596 Llyn-y-Cau, Cader Idris (?exhibited 1774)
Oc:511x730:Presented by Sir Edward Marsh 1945

N05842 Hounslow Heath
Oc:438x540:Bequeathed by Mrs Arthur James 1948

N06267 Lake, Ruin and Pine Trees (circa 1765-70)
Oc:686x889:Bequeathed by Lady Sassoon 1956

T01706 Tivoli; Temple of the Sibyl and the Campagna (circa 1765-70)
Oc:1003x1257:Accepted by the Commissioners of Inland Revenue in lieu of tax and allocated 1973

T01873 Rome: St Peter's and the Vatican from the Janiculum (circa 1753)
Oc:1003x1391:Purchased with assistance from the National Art Collections Fund and an anonymous donor 1974

T03026 Ponte Nomentana (1754)
Dπ:287x422:signed:Purchased 1980

T03366 Meleager and Atalanta (circa 1770)
Oc:1045x1295:Purchased 1982

T03665 Westminster Bridge under Construction (1744)
Oc:725x1460:signed:Purchased with assistance from the National Heritage Memorial Fund 1983

attributed to
WILSON, Richard 1713-1782
British Collection

N05560 View of Carlton House, with a Royal Party in the Grounds (circa 1732-6)
Oc:635x756:Bequeathed by Richard and Catherine Garnons 1854

studio of
WILSON, Richard 1713-1782
British Collection

N01064 On the Wye
Oc:254x311:Purchased 1879

N01890 Valley with a Bridge over a River
Oc:1010x1365:Bequeathed by Richard and Catherine Garnons 1854 or J.M.W. Turner 1856

N01891 Niagara Falls
Oc:1003x1365:Bequeathed by Richard and Catherine Garnons 1854

N02647 River View, on the Arno (?)
Oc:445x546:Bequeathed by George Salting 1910

N04511 Strada Nomentana
Dπ:279x387:Presented by Mrs F. Evans in memory of Judge Evans 1930

N04745 Landscape with Castle
Oc:362x527:Presented by Gosta Stenman 1933

N05538 Tivoli
Oc:737x965:Bequeathed by J.M.W. Turner 1856

after
WILSON, Richard 1713-1782
British Collection

N05565 Lake Nemi with Figures Bathing
Oc:464x730:Presented by Miss M.H. Turner 1944

WILSON, Scottie 1889-1972
Modern Collection
Tate Gallery Archive holds material concerning this artist

T00288 The Tree of Life (1958-9)
Dπ:521x641:signed:Presented by Charles Aukin 1959

T00289 The Bowl of Life (1958-9)
Dπ:648x521:signed:Presented by Charles Aukin 1959

WINDUS, William Lindsay 1822-1907
British Collection

N03597 Too Late (1858)
Oc:952x762:signed:Presented by Andrew Bain 1921

N03598 The Second Duchess (before 1866)
Ob:152x229:Presented by Andrew Bain 1921

N03599 The Flight of Henry VI from Towton (circa 1860-70)
Wb:130x267:Presented by Andrew Bain 1921

N04885 Study of a Dead Child, the Artist's Son (1860)
Oc:149x159:Presented by P.L. Teed 1937

N04886 Mrs Teed, the Artist's Daughter (circa 1880)
Oc:546x457:Presented by P.L. Teed 1937

WINES, James born 1932
Modern Collection

T00760 Homage to Léger (1965)
Sv:470x610x571:Presented by Mr and Mrs H.J. Heinz II through the American Federation of Arts 1965

WINNER, Gerd born 1936
Modern Collection
Tate Gallery Archive holds material concerning this artist

P01669 St John's Wharf (1971)
CNπ:660x667:signed:Presented by the artist through the Institute of Contemporary Prints 1975

P01670 Telephone Box (1971-2)
CNπ:705x549:signed:Presented by the artist through the Institute of Contemporary Prints 1975

P01671 Free Trade Wharf (1972)
CNπ:610x1026:signed:Presented by the artist through the Institute of Contemporary Prints 1975

P01672 Slow - First Version (1972)
CNπ:629x622:signed:Presented by the artist through the Institute of Contemporary Prints 1975

P01673 Slow - Fog I (1973)
CNπ:625x692:signed:Presented by the artist through the Institute of Contemporary Prints 1975

P01674 Untitled (New York) (1974)
CNπ:943x540:signed:Presented by the artist through the Institute of Contemporary Prints 1975

P02337 Untitled (1972)
CNπ:905x695:signed:Presented by the artist 1976

Lorry I (P05297-P05302; complete group)
P05297 [title page] (1969)
CNπ:744x600:signed:Presented by Rose and Chris Prater through the Institute of Contemporary Prints 1975

P05298 [no title] (1969)
CNπ:743x670:signed:Presented by Rose and Chris Prater through the Institute of Contemporary Prints 1975

P05299 [no title] (1969)
CNπ:783x610:signed:Presented by Rose and Chris Prater through the Institute of Contemporary Prints 1975

P05300 [no title] (1969)
CNπ:770x683:signed:Presented by Rose and Chris Prater through the Institute of Contemporary Prints 1975

P05301 [no title] (1969)
CNπ:754x647:signed:Presented by Rose and Chris Prater through the Institute of Contemporary Prints 1975

P05302 [no title] (1969)
CNπ:700x681:signed:Presented by Rose and Chris Prater through the Institute of Contemporary Prints 1975

Blueprints (P05303-P05307; complete group)

P05303 [title page] (1970)
CNπ:882x711:signed:Presented by Rose and Chris Prater through the Institute of Contemporary Prints 1975

P05304 [no title] (1970)
CNπ:1015x762:signed:Presented by Rose and Chris Prater through the Institute of Contemporary Prints 1975

P05305 [no title] (1970)
CNπ:1015x763:signed:Presented by Rose and Chris Prater through the Institute of Contemporary Prints 1975

P05306 [no title] (1970)
CNπ:1017x763:signed:Presented by Rose and Chris Prater through the Institute of Contemporary Prints 1975

P05307 [no title] (1970)
CNπ:713x713:signed:Presented by Rose and Chris Prater through the Institute of Contemporary Prints 1975

P05308 Container [blue] (1970)
CNπ:710x740:signed:Presented by Rose and Chris Prater through the Institute of Contemporary Prints 1975

P05309 Container [orange] (1970)
CNπ:710x740:signed:Presented by Rose and Chris Prater through the Institute of Contemporary Prints 1975

P05310 Container [red] (1970)
CNπ:709x740:signed:Presented by Rose and Chris Prater through the Institute of Contemporary Prints 1975

P05311 Container [silver] (1970)
CNπ:710x740:signed:Presented by Rose and Chris Prater through the Institute of Contemporary Prints 1975

P05312 Container [yellow] (1970)
CNπ:710x740:signed:Presented by Rose and Chris Prater through the Institute of Contemporary Prints 1975

London Docks: St Katharine's Way (P05313-P05319; complete group)

P05313 [title page]
CNπ:1014x764:signed:Presented by Rose and Chris Prater through the Institute of Contemporary Prints 1975

P05314 [no title]
CNπ:864x713:signed:Presented by Rose and Chris Prater through the Institute of Contemporary Prints 1975

P05315 [no title]
CNπ:864x714:signed:Presented by Rose and Chris Prater through the Institute of Contemporary Prints 1975

P05316 [no title]
CNπ:872x710:signed:Presented by Rose and Chris Prater through the Institute of Contemporary Prints 1975

P05317 [no title]
CNπ:923x711:signed:Presented by Rose and Chris Prater through the Institute of Contemporary Prints 1975

P05318 [no title]
CNπ:874x711:signed:Presented by Rose and Chris Prater through the Institute of Contemporary Prints 1975

P05319 [no title]
CNπ:934x711:signed:Presented by Rose and Chris Prater through the Institute of Contemporary Prints 1975

London Transport (P05320-P05326; complete group)

P05320 [title page] (1970)
CNπ:1041x790:signed:Presented by Rose and Chris Prater through the Institute of Contemporary Prints 1975

P05321 Dust-Cart (1970)
CNπ:1042x790:signed:Presented by Rose and Chris Prater through the Institute of Contemporary Prints 1975

P05322 Green Line Bus (1970)
CNπ:1042x790:signed:Presented by Rose and Chris Prater through the Institute of Contemporary Prints 1975

P05323 'Pollock' Long Distance Lorry (1970)
CNπ:1042x790:signed:Presented by Rose and Chris Prater through the Institute of Contemporary Prints 1975

P05324 Red Arrow Bus (1970)
CNπ:1042x790:signed:Presented by Rose and Chris Prater through the Institute of Contemporary Prints 1975

P05325 Suburban Train (1970)
CNπ:1042x790:signed:Presented by Rose and Chris Prater through the Institute of Contemporary Prints 1975

P05326 Tube Train (1970)
CNπ:1042x790:signed:Presented by Rose and Chris Prater through the Institute of Contemporary Prints 1975

Berlin Suite (P05327-P05332; complete group)

P05327 Victoire [title page] (1970-1)
CNπ:916x703:signed:Presented by Rose and Chris Prater through the Institute of Contemporary Prints 1975

P05328 Back-yard, Kreuzberg (1970-1)
CNπ:962x711:signed:Presented by Rose and Chris Prater through the Institute of Contemporary Prints 1975

P05329 Hotel Metro (1970-1)
CNπ:1010x764:signed:Presented by Rose and Chris Prater through the Institute of Contemporary Prints 1975

P05330 Marcus (1970-1)
CNπ:925x704:signed:Presented by Rose and Chris Prater through the Institute of Contemporary Prints 1975

P05331 Urinal (1970-1)
CNπ:1015x766:signed:Presented by Rose and Chris Prater through the Institute of Contemporary Prints 1975

P05332 Underground Station Hallesches Tor (1970-1)
CNπ:867x707:signed:Presented by Rose and Chris Prater through the Institute of Contemporary Prints 1975

P05333 Clink Wharf (1971)
CNπ:660x908:signed:Presented by Rose and Chris Prater through the Institute of Contemporary Prints 1975

P05334 London Docks: Warehouse (1971)
CNπ:959x660:signed:Presented by Rose and Chris Prater through the Institute of Contemporary Prints 1975

P05335 London Docks II: Metropolitan Wharf (1971)
CNπ:660x959:signed:Presented by Rose and Chris Prater through the Institute of Contemporary Prints 1975

P05336 Waterloo Station (1971)
CNπ:664x940:signed:Presented by Rose and Chris Prater through the Institute of Contemporary Prints 1975

P05337 Bull Wharf (1972)
CNπ:657x918:signed:Presented by Rose and Chris Prater through the Institute of Contemporary Prints 1975

P05338 Dockland I (1972)
CNπ:628x946:signed:Presented by Rose and Chris Prater through the Institute of Contemporary Prints 1975

P05339 Dockland II (1972)
CNπ:626x931:signed:Presented by Rose and Chris Prater through the Institute of Contemporary Prints 1975

P05340 Dockland III (1972)
CNπ:624x853:signed:Presented by Rose and Chris Prater through the Institute of Contemporary Prints 1975

P05341 Harrison Wharf (1972)
CNπ:1911x686:signed:Presented by Rose and Chris Prater through the Institute of Contemporary Prints 1975

P05342 Nile Street (1972)
CNπ:664x635:signed:Presented by Rose and Chris Prater through the Institute of Contemporary Prints 1975

P05343 19 Aberdeen Road I (1972)
CNπ:927x638:signed:Presented by Rose and Chris Prater
through the Institute of Contemporary Prints 1975

P05344 19 Aberdeen Road II (1972)
CNπ:698x518:signed:Presented by Rose and Chris Prater
through the Institute of Contemporary Prints 1975

P05345 Slow (1972)
CNπ:629x619:signed:Presented by Rose and Chris Prater
through the Institute of Contemporary Prints 1975

P05346 Sunday Afternoon I (1972)
CNπ:972x662:signed:Presented by Rose and Chris Prater
through the Institute of Contemporary Prints 1975

P05347 Sunday Afternoon II (1972)
CNπ:959x658:signed:Presented by Rose and Chris Prater
through the Institute of Contemporary Prints 1975

P05348 Sunday Afternoon III (1972)
CNπ:960x665:signed:Presented by Rose and Chris Prater
through the Institute of Contemporary Prints 1975

P05349 Underground Old Street (1972)
CNπ:635x927:signed:Presented by Rose and Chris Prater
through the Institute of Contemporary Prints 1975

P05350 Colonial Wharves (1973)
CNπ:476x991:signed:Presented by Rose and Chris Prater
through the Institute of Contemporary Prints 1975

P05351 Hatfields (1972)
CNπ:629x984:signed:Presented by Rose and Chris Prater
through the Institute of Contemporary Prints 1975

P05352 Hoboken Ferry (1973)
CNπ:571x987:signed:Presented by Rose and Chris Prater
through the Institute of Contemporary Prints 1975

P05353 Isle of Dogs II (1973)
CNπ:946x635:signed:Presented by Rose and Chris Prater
through the Institute of Contemporary Prints 1975

P05354 New York Canyon (1972)
CNπ:991x616:signed:Presented by Rose and Chris Prater
through the Institute of Contemporary Prints 1975

P05355 Off Broadway (1973)
CNπ:733x606:signed:Presented by Rose and Chris Prater
through the Institute of Contemporary Prints 1975

P05356 Pennsylvania R.R. (1973)
CNπ:559x991:signed:Presented by Rose and Chris Prater
through the Institute of Contemporary Prints 1975

P05357 Window (1972)
CNπ:702x1029:signed:Presented by Rose and Chris
Prater through the Institute of Contemporary Prints 1975

P05358 Brooktorkai (1974)
CNπ:883x603:signed:Presented by Rose and Chris Prater
through the Institute of Contemporary Prints 1975

P05359 Kaffeeborse (1974)
CNπ:664x606:signed:Presented by Rose and Chris Prater
through the Institute of Contemporary Prints 1975

P05384 Thomas More Street (1972)
CNπ:635x648:signed:Presented by Rose and Chris Prater
1976

P05385 Underground Highbury and Islington (1972)
CNπ:632x635:signed:Presented by Rose and Chris Prater
1976

P05386 Underground Holborn (1972)
CNπ:635x638:signed:Presented by Rose and Chris Prater
1976

P05387 Bankside (1973)
CNπ:606x838:signed:Presented by Rose and Chris Prater
1976

Making a Print (P05388-P05397; incomplete group)

P05388 4. Artist's Notes (1973-5)
CNπ:687x692:signed:Presented by Rose and Chris Prater
1976

P05389 5. Colour Separations (1973-5)
CNπ:611x602:signed:Presented by Rose and Chris Prater
1976

P05390 6. Sheet A (1973-5)
CNπ:603x604:signed:Presented by Rose and Chris Prater
1976

P05391 7. Transparent Overlay Sheet (1973-5)
CNπ:686x685:signed:Presented by Rose and Chris Prater
1976

P05392 8. Sheet B (1973-5)
CNπ:603x603:signed:Presented by Rose and Chris Prater
1976

P05393 9. Printing 6 (1973-5)
CNπ:573x603:signed:Presented by Rose and Chris Prater
1976

P05394 10. Sheet C (1973-5)
CNπ:602x602:signed:Presented by Rose and Chris Prater
1976

P05395 11. Sheet D (1973-5)
CNπ:603x603:signed:Presented by Rose and Chris Prater
1976

P05396 12. Sheet E (1973-5)
CNπ:602x603:signed:Presented by Rose and Chris Prater
1976

P05397 13. Completed Print (1973-5)
CNπ:602x603:signed:Presented by Rose and Chris Prater
1976

P05398 D & C Trucking (1975)
CNπ:695x746:signed:Presented by Rose and Chris Prater
1976

P05399 West Embankment Warehouse (1975)
CNπ:1003x752:signed:Presented by Rose and Chris
Prater 1976

P05493 Amalien Project (1978)
CNπ:857x603:signed:Presented by Rose and Chris Prater
1979

P05494 Emergency (1978)
CNπ:625x930:signed:Presented by Rose and Chris Prater
1979

P05495 Gasteig Window (1978)
CNπ:625x848:signed:Presented by Rose and Chris Prater
1979

P05496 Britannia Walk (1978)
CNπ:857x648:signed:Presented by Rose and Chris Prater
1979

P05497 New York Wall (1978)
CNπ:845x948:signed:Presented by Rose and Chris Prater
1979

P05498 Mince Wall (1978)
CNπ:813x641:signed:Presented by Rose and Chris Prater
1979

P05540 American Transport (1979)
CNπ:616x927:signed:Presented by Rose and Chris Prater
1979

P05541 Inside Outside 1 (1979)
CNπ:580x905:signed:Presented by Rose and Chris Prater
1979

P05542 Inside Outside 2 (1979)
CNπ:580x905:signed:Presented by Rose and Chris Prater
1979

P05543 Inside Outside 3 (1979)
CNπ:635x850:signed:Presented by Rose and Chris Prater 1979

P05544 New York Canyon II (1979)
CNπ:841x619:signed:Presented by Rose and Chris Prater 1979

Catfish Row (P05555-P05559; complete group)

P05555 Catfish Row, New York 1 (1979)
CIπ:688x545:signed:Presented by Rose and Chris Prater 1980

P05556 Catfish Row, New York 2 (1979)
CIπ:688x545:signed:Presented by Rose and Chris Prater 1980

P05557 Catfish Row, New York 3 (1979)
CIπ:688x545:signed:Presented by Rose and Chris Prater 1980

P05558 Catfish Row, New York 4 (1979)
CIπ:688x545:signed:Presented by Rose and Chris Prater 1980

P05559 Catfish Row, New York 5 (1979)
CIπ:688x545:signed:Presented by Rose and Chris Prater 1980

P05566 Autumn in New York (1980)
CNπ:752x600:signed:Presented by Rose and Chris Prater 1980

P07366 East One (1978)
CNπ:502x698:signed:Purchased 1980

WINT, Peter de - see DE WINT, Peter

WINTERS, Terry born 1949
Modern Collection

T04928 Untitled (1986)
DWπ:1213x804:signed:Purchased 1987

T05076 Monkey Puzzle (1987)
Oc:2750x3664:signed:Purchased with assistance from the Eli Broad Family Foundation 1988

P77061 Morula I (1983-4)
CLπ:1073x812:signed:Purchased 1984

P77062 Morula II (1983-4)
CLπ:1092x825:signed:Purchased 1984

P77063 Morula III (1983-4)
CLπ:1089x825:signed:Purchased 1984

WISE-CIOBOTARU, Gillian born 1936
Modern Collection

T00568 Brown, Black and White Relief with Prisms (1962)
AVb:610x610x83:signed:Purchased 1963

T01965 Looped Network Suspended in Pictorial Space (1974)
Aa:1626x1219:signed:Presented by the Contemporary Art Society 1975

T01966 Study for 'Looped Network Suspended in Pictorial Space' (1974)
WDπ:508x381:Purchased 1975

T03776 Relief Constructed from Unicursal Curve No. 2 (1977)
Ramw:813x813x41:Transferred from the Victoria & Albert Museum 1983

P07430 Rational Concepts (1977)
CNπ:600x600:signed:Purchased 1981

WISEMAN, Albany born 1930
Modern Collection

P06618 French Engine (1972)
CLπ:416x581:signed:Presented by Curwen Studio through the Institute of Contemporary Prints 1975

P06619 Charlotte Place (1974)
CLπ:406x518:signed:Presented by Curwen Studio through the Institute of Contemporary Prints 1975

P06620 Fitzroy Square (1974)
CLπ:422x591:signed:Presented by Curwen Studio through the Institute of Contemporary Prints 1975

The Soho Suite (P06621-P06626; complete group)

P06621 Berwick Market (1974)
CLπ:585x471:signed:Presented by Curwen Studio through the Institute of Contemporary Prints 1975

P06622 Meard Street (1974)
CLπ:420x587:signed:Presented by Curwen Studio through the Institute of Contemporary Prints 1975

P06623 Mitchell's Yard (1974)
CLπ:515x419:signed:Presented by Curwen Studio through the Institute of Contemporary Prints 1975

P06624 Romilly Street (1974)
CLπ:531x414:signed:Presented by Curwen Studio through the Institute of Contemporary Prints 1975

P06625 Soho Shop Fronts (1974)
CLπ:536x586:signed:Presented by Curwen Studio through the Institute of Contemporary Prints 1975

P06626 Soho Square (1974)
CLπ:442x543:signed:Presented by Curwen Studio through the Institute of Contemporary Prints 1975

P06697 The Phoenician (1975)
CLπ:584x403:Presented by Curwen Studio 1976

WISZNIEWSKI, Adrian born 1958
Modern Collection

T04131 Kasmin and Kappo (1985)
Oc:2443x2768:signed:Purchased 1985

P77194 Chez Nous (1987)
Jπ:2335x1773:signed:Purchased 1987

P77195 The Sculptor's Nightmare (1986)
Iπ:607x910:signed:Purchased 1987

WITHERINGTON, William Frederick 1785-1865
British Collection

N00420 Stepping Stones on the Machno, North Wales (exhibited 1844)
Oc:635x762:signed:Presented by Robert Vernon 1847

N00421 The Hop Garland (exhibited 1843)
Ow:445x356:signed:Presented by Robert Vernon 1847

A01026 The Broken Pitcher (circa 1814)
Ob:117x92:Bequeathed by Miss Julia Emily Gordon 1896

A01027 Going to School (circa 1817)
Ob:117x92:Bequeathed by Miss Julia Emily Gordon 1896

A01028 The Gleaners
Ob:117x92:Bequeathed by Miss Julia Emily Gordon 1896

WITKIN, Isaac born 1936
Modern Collection

T01025 Angola I (1966)
OSm:1937x2419x851:Purchased 1968

T01392 Alter-Ego (1963)
SAwa:1664x705x470:Presented by Alistair McAlpine
(later Lord McAlpine of West Green) 1970

T01393 Vermont I (1965)
SAm:927x2588x1714:Presented by Alistair McAlpine
(later Lord McAlpine of West Green) 1970

T01394 Shogun (1968)
Sm:1711x3080x2591:Presented by Alistair McAlpine
(later Lord McAlpine of West Green) 1970

T01395 Baalbec (1968)
SAm:2505x2629x1448:Presented by Alistair McAlpine
(later Lord McAlpine of West Green) 1970

WITT, Jan Le - see LE WITT, Jan

WOLFE, Edward 1897-1982
Modern Collection
Tate Gallery Archive holds material concerning this artist

N04997 Laugharne Castle (circa 1937-8)
Oc:777x1124:Presented by Mrs Jameson 1939

T03228 P.C. 77 (circa 1927)
Oc:1076x781:Presented by the Trustees of the Chantrey
Bequest 1981

WOLFE, Robert born 1930
Modern Collection
Tate Gallery Archive holds material concerning this artist

Homage to Albert Dumouchel (P03166-P03178;
complete group; mixed group)
Hommage à Albert Dumouchel

P03178 Untitled (1971)
CNπ:679x460:Presented by the University of Quebec
1976

WOLFF, Robert Jay born 1905
Modern Collection

T01530 Woodville (1967)
Oc:1981x1016:signed:Presented by Thomas P. Whitney
through the American Federation of Arts 1972

WOLMARK, Alfred 1877-1961
British Collection
Tate Gallery Archive holds material concerning this artist

T00030 Fisher Girl of Concarneau (1911)
Oc:762x648:signed:Presented by Cyril J. Ross 1955

T01241 Decorative Still Life (circa 1911)
Oc:622x762:signed:Purchased 1970

WOLS (Alfred Otto Wolfgang Schulze) 1913-1951
Modern Collection

T04845 Untitled (circa 1944-5)
DWGπ:92x135:signed:Purchased 1986

Complete set of Wols etchings (P07948-P07980;
complete group)

P07948 [no title] (circa 1937-50)
MIπ:64x102:Purchased 1983

P07949 [no title] (circa 1937-50)
MIπ:102x124:Purchased 1983

P07950 [no title] (circa 1937-50)
MIπ:105x73:Purchased 1983

P07951 [no title] (circa 1937-50)
MIπ:130x80:Purchased 1983

P07952 [no title] (circa 1937-50)
MIπ:187x102:Purchased 1983

P07953 [no title] (circa 1937-50)
MIπ:248x168:Purchased 1983

P07954 [no title] (circa 1937-50)
MIπ:149x102:Purchased 1983

P07955 [no title] (circa 1937-50)
MIπ:203x120:Purchased 1983

P07956 [no title] (circa 1937-50)
MIπ:130x79:Purchased 1983

P07957 [no title] (circa 1937-50)
MIπ:124x98:Purchased 1983

P07958 [no title] (circa 1937-50)
MIπ:140x89:Purchased 1983

P07959 [no title] (circa 1937-50)
MIπ:140x86:Purchased 1983

P07960 [no title] (circa 1937-50)
MIπ:83x79:Purchased 1983

P07961 [no title] (circa 1937-50)
MIπ:200x146:Purchased 1983

P07962 [no title] (circa 1937-50)
MIπ:60x98:Purchased 1983

P07963 [no title] (circa 1937-50)
MIπ:124x98:Purchased 1983

P07964 [no title] (circa 1937-50)
MIπ:124x98:Purchased 1983

P07965 [no title] (circa 1937-50)
MIπ:204x118:Purchased 1983

P07966 [no title] (circa 1937-50)
MIπ:105x98:Purchased 1983

P07967 [no title] (circa 1937-50)
MIπ:197x149:Purchased 1983

P07968 [no title] (circa 1937-50)
MIπ:102x120:Purchased 1983

P07969 [no title] (circa 1937-50)
MIπ:118x95:Purchased 1983

P07970 [no title] (circa 1937-50)
MIπ:140x79:Purchased 1983

P07971 [no title] (circa 1937-50)
MIπ:124x95:Purchased 1983

P07972 [no title] (circa 1937-50)
MIπ:105x73:Purchased 1983

P07973 [no title] (circa 1937-50)
MIπ:121x102:Purchased 1983

P07974 [no title] (circa 1937-50)
MIπ:121x92:Purchased 1983

P07975 [no title] (circa 1937-50)
MIπ:124x98:Purchased 1983

P07976 [no title] (circa 1937-50)
MIπ:124x98:Purchased 1983

P07977 [no title] (circa 1937-50)
MIπ:124x98:Purchased 1983

P07978 [no title] (circa 1937-50)
MIπ:102x70:Purchased 1983

P07979 [no title] (circa 1937-50)
MIπ:105x70:Purchased 1983

P07980 [no title] (circa 1937-50)
MIπ:324x248:Purchased 1983

WONG, Judy born 1949
Modern Collection
Tate Gallery Archive holds material concerning this artist

P06821　Four Figures (1978)
CLπ:1000x698:signed:Presented by Curwen Studio 1978

WONNACOTT, John born 1940
Modern Collection

T03928　The Norwich School of Art (1982-4)
Oc:1935x2648:Presented by the Trustees of the Chantrey Bequest 1984

WOOD, Christopher 1901-1930
Modern Collection
Tate Gallery Archive holds material concerning this artist

N04552　Church at Tréboul (1930)
Ob:730x914:Presented by Dr and Mrs Lucius Wood, the artist's parents, through the Contemporary Art Society 1930

T00489　Boat in Harbour, Brittany (1929)
Ob:794x1086:Presented by Mrs Lucy Carrington Wertheim 1962

T00545　Douarnenez, Brittany (1930)
Ob:330x457:Bequeathed by Alberta, Countess of Sandwich 1962

T01085　Study for 'Church at Tréboul' (circa 1929-30)
Dπ:305x378:Purchased 1968

WOOD, F. Derwent 1871-1926
British Collection
Tate Gallery Archive holds material concerning this artist

N02976　Henry James (1913)
Ss:413x298x241:signed:Presented by the Trustees of the Chantrey Bequest 1914

N03451　Psyche (circa 1908 and 1919)
Ss:1753x521x400:Presented by the Trustees of the Chantrey Bequest 1919

N03602　Colonel T.E. Lawrence (1919)
Sz:362x178x229:Presented by the artist 1921

N04195　Bess Norriss (1921-2)
Sz:343x267x254:Presented by the Trustees of the Chantrey Bequest 1926

Studies for a statue of Sir Joshua Reynolds (N05647-N05654; complete group)
N05647　[title not known] (1916)
Sz:250x103x90:Presented by Mrs Derwent Wood 1946

N05648　[title not known] (1916)
Sz:210x78x78:Presented by Mrs Derwent Wood 1946

N05649　[title not known] (1916)
Sz:255x105x95:Presented by Mrs Derwent Wood 1946

N05650　[title not known] (1916)
Sz:245x93x93:Presented by Mrs Derwent Wood 1946

N05651　[title not known] (1916)
Sz:245x98x88:Presented by Mrs Derwent Wood 1946

N05652　[title not known] (1916)
Sz:235x110x120:Presented by Mrs Derwent Wood 1946

N05653　[title not known] (1916)
Sz:303x163x158:Presented by Mrs Derwent Wood 1946

N05654　[title not known] (1916)
Sz:255x103x100:Presented by Mrs Derwent Wood 1946

T03777　Torso of a Girl (1903)
Sp:1080x216x312:signed:Transferred from the Victoria & Albert Museum 1983

WOODFORDE, Samuel 1763-1817
British Collection

T02207　The Bennett Family (exhibited 1803)
Oc:3023x3632:Presented by the Rev. Gerald C. Streatfeild 1977

T05535　Study for 'The Bennett Family' (circa 1803)
Dπ:155x187:Presented by W. Drummond through the Patrons of British Art 1989

T05536　Study of Two Children in 'The Bennett Family'
Dπ:155x187:Presented by W. Drummond through the Patrons of British Art 1989

WOODHAM, Derrick born 1940
Modern Collection

T01491　Assume, Concede (1964/5)
SAWa:737x1346x584:Purchased 1971

WOODROW, Bill born 1948
Modern Collection
Tate Gallery Archive holds material concerning this artist

T03354　Twin-Tub with Guitar (1981)
Sv:889x762x660:Purchased 1982

T03355　Car Door, Ironing Board and Twin-Tub with North American Indian Head-Dress (1981)
Sv::Purchased 1982

T05009　English Heritage - Humpty Fucking Dumpty (1987)
Sv:2390x3276x1067:Purchased 1987

WOODS, Henry 1846-1921
British Collection

N01531　Cupid's Spell (1885)
Ow:1187x749:Presented by Sir Henry Tate 1894

WOODVILLE, Richard Caton 1856-1927
British Collection

N05202　Napoleon Crossing the Bridge to Lobau Island (1912)
Ow:356x251:signed:Presented by Robert Vernon 1847

N05203　General Wolfe Climbing the Heights of Abraham on the Morning of the Battle of Quebec (1906)
WGDπ:432x686:signed:Presented by Robert Vernon 1847

N05204　Marshal Ney at Eylau (1913)
Ow:356x251:signed:Presented by Robert Vernon 1847

N05205　Poniatowski's Last Charge at Leipzig (1912)
Ow:356x251:signed:Presented by Robert Vernon 1847

WOODWARD, Thomas 1801-1852
British Collection

N01379　The Rat-Catcher and his Dogs (exhibited 1824)
Ow:432x540:signed:Bequeathed by Edward Archer 1892

N05426　Horses Surprised by Wolves (1842)
Oc:733x1372:signed:Presented by the National Art Collections Fund 1943

WOOLNER, Thomas 1825-1892
British Collection

T05515　Alfred Tennyson (1856)
Rp:260x260:Purchased 1988

WOOTTON, John ?1682-1764
British Collection

N04679 George Henry Lee, 3rd Earl of Litchfield, and his Uncle the Hon. Robert Lee, Subsequently 4th Earl of Litchfield, Shooting in 'True Blue' Frock Coats (1744) Oc:2038x2451:signed:Purchased 1933

T02378 Lady Mary Churchill at the Death of the Hare (1748) Oc:1060x1556:signed:Presented by Paul Mellon through the British Sporting Art Trust 1979

T02379 Muff, a Black and White Dog (circa 1740-50) Oc:1251x1016:signed:Presented by Paul Mellon through the British Sporting Art Trust 1979

WOTRUBA, Fritz 1907-1975
Modern Collection

N06013 Standing Figure (1949-50) Sz:362x111x117:Purchased 1951

WRAGG, John born 1937
Modern Collection

T00635 Funeral Group (1963) Sm:597x546x381:Purchased 1964

T00857 Opus (1965) Sm:1962x502x686:Presented by Mr and Mrs Jack Steinberg through the Friends of the Tate Gallery 1966

WRIGHT, John Michael 1617-1694
British Collection

T00132 Sir Neil O'Neill (1680) Oc:2327x1632:signed:Purchased with assistance from the National Art Collections Fund 1957

WRIGHT, Joseph, of Derby 1734-1797
British Collection

N04132 Sir Brooke Boothby (1781) Oc:1486x2076:signed:Bequeathed by Miss Agnes Ann Best 1925

N05882 A Moonlight with a Lighthouse, Coast of Tuscany (?exhibited 1789) Oc:1016x1276:Purchased 1949

T00794 Thomas Staniforth of Darnall, Co. York (1769) Oc:930x775:Presented by the Friends of the Tate Gallery 1965

T01278 A View of Catania with Mount Etna in the Distance (circa 1775) Oc:660x886:Purchased 1971

WUNDERLICH, Paul born 1927
Modern Collection
Tate Gallery Archive holds material concerning this artist

P08180 [title not known: from the book 'Paul Wunderlich' by Jens Christian Jensen] (circa 1980) CLπ:143x114:signed:Transferred from the Library 1981

WYATT, Henry 1794-1840
British Collection

N00383 Vigilance (1835) Oc:349x298:signed:Presented by Robert Vernon 1847

N00384 Archimedes (?exhibited 1832) Oc:759x625:Presented by Robert Vernon 1847

follower of
WYCK, Jan 1652-1700
British Collection

N02986 Italianate Landscape with Town and Waterfall Oc:889x914:Bequeathed by Richard and Catherine Garnons 1854

WYCKAERT, Maurice born 1923
Modern Collection

For Jorn (P03241-P03255; complete group; mixed group) Pour Jorn
P03255 [no title] (1975-6) CLπ:546x467:signed:Presented by the Asger Jorn Foundation 1978

WYLLIE, Charles William 1853-1923
British Collection

N01594 Digging for Bait (1877) Oc:6670x1270:signed:Presented by the Trustees of the Chantrey Bequest 1877

WYLLIE, William Lionel 1851-1931
British Collection

N01580 Toil, Glitter, Grime and Wealth on a Flowing Tide (1883) Oc:1156x1651:signed:Presented by the Trustees of the Chantrey Bequest 1883

N01697 The Battle of the Nile (1899) Oc:1524x2743:signed:Presented by the Trustees of the Chantrey Bequest 1899

WYNNE, David born 1926
Modern Collection

T00791 Oskar Kokoschka (1965) Sz:368x254x279:signed:Presented by Sir Edward Beddington-Behrens 1965

WYNTER, Bryan 1915-1975
Modern Collection
Tate Gallery Archive holds material concerning this artist

T00558 Seedtime (1958-9) Oc:1422x1118:Purchased 1962

T00765 Imoos VI (1965) KGVπ:1092x1010x1168:Purchased 1965

T03289 Mars Ascending (1956) Oc:1527x1013:signed:Presented by Fello Atkinson 1981

T03362 Saja (1969) OAc:2130x1685:signed:Purchased 1982

T03363 Green Confluence (1974) Oc:1825x1215:Purchased 1982

P77361 Path Through Wood (1950) Jπ:375x292:signed:Purchased 1990

YALE, Brian born 1936
Modern Collection
Tate Gallery Archive holds material concerning this artist

P01769 Monsters of the City I (1969-71)
CNπ:597x502:Presented by John Berry 1976

P01770 Monsters of the City 2 (1969-71)
CNπ:591x505:Presented by John Berry 1976

P01771 Nativity (1969-71)
CNπ:597x498:Presented by John Berry 1976

P01772 Plan of Progress (1970)
CNπ:600x502:signed:Presented by John Berry 1976

P01773 Untitled (1969-71)
CNπ:603x498:Presented by John Berry 1976

YEAMES, William Frederick 1835-1918
British Collection

N01609 Amy Robsart (exhibited 1877)
Oc:2819x1880:Presented by the Trustees of the Chantrey
Bequest 1877

YEATS, Jack Butler 1871-1957
British Collection
Tate Gallery Archive holds material concerning this artist

N04076 Back from the Races (1925)
Ow:241x356:signed:Purchased 1925

N05660 The Two Travellers (1942)
Ow:921x1226:signed:Purchased 1946

N05836 The Death of Diarmuid, the Last Handful of Water
(1945)
Oc:610x914:signed:Purchased 1948

T00693 Morning after Rain (1912-3)
Oc:610x914:signed:Presented by the Friends of the Tate
Gallery 1964

YHAP, Laetitia born 1941
Modern Collection

T03930 Michael Balling Up Old Net (1984)
Ob:1205x1496:signed:Presented by the Trustees of the
Chantrey Bequest 1984

YOUNG, Kathleen Hilton - see KENNET, Lady

YOUNG, Robert born 1938
Modern Collection

P01675 Sounds Inside (1973)
CNπ:556x683:signed:Presented by Christie's
Contemporary Art through the Institute of
Contemporary Prints 1975

YOUNG-HUNTER, John 1874-1955
British Collection

N01698 My Lady's Garden (1899)
Oc:1067x1822:signed:Presented by the Trustees of the
Chantrey Bequest 1899

YUON, Konstantin 1875-1958
Modern Collection

T00653 The Monastery at Zagorsk (circa 1911)
Ow:327x403:signed:Bequeathed by Peter Provatoroff
1964

YVARAL, Jean-Pierre born 1934
Modern Collection

T00716 Kinetic Relief - Optical Acceleration (1963)
Relief cinétique - Accélération optique
Rv:1010x991x108:Purchased 1964

ZACK, Leon born 1892
Modern Collection

T00321 Painting (1952)
Peinture
Oc:965x1295:signed:Purchased 1959

ZADKINE, Ossip 1890-1967
Modern Collection
Tate Gallery Archive holds material concerning this artist

N06226 Venus (circa 1922-4)
Vénus
Sw:1918x533x464:signed:Presented by F.H. Mayor as
executor of the late Richard Wyndham 1954

T05705 The Maenads (1935)
Les Ménades
Sz:760x380x520:Bequeathed by Miss Elizabeth Watt 1989

P06627 Acrobat (1964)
MLπ:559x451:signed:Presented by Curwen Studio
through the Institute of Contemporary Prints 1975

P06628 Figure with Guitar (1964)
MLπ:533x244:signed:Presented by Curwen Studio
through the Institute of Contemporary Prints 1975

P06629 Figure with Guitar (1964)
MLπ:537x343:signed:Presented by Curwen Studio
through the Institute of Contemporary Prints 1975

P06630 Daphne - Treeform (1964)
Daphné - La Forme de l'arbre
MLπ:625x464:signed:Presented by Curwen Studio
through the Institute of Contemporary Prints 1975

ZAO WOU-KI born 1921
Modern Collection

T00182 Before the Storm (1955)
Avant l'orage
Oc:724x537:signed:Purchased 1958

ZOFFANY, Johan 1733-1810
British Collection

N01487 Thomas Gainsborough (circa 1772)
Oc:197x171:Presented by the family of Richard J. Lane
1896

N04434 Stephen Rimbault (1764)
Oc:889x711:Bequeathed by Mrs Aslett 1929

N06005 Charles Macklin as Shylock (circa 1768)
Oc:1162x1511:Presented by the National Art Collections
Fund 1951

N06261 The Bradshaw Family (exhibited 1769)
Oc:1621x1753:Bequeathed by Ernest E. Cook through
the National Art Collections Fund 1955

T00054 A Florentine Fruit Stall (circa 1777)
Oc:578x492:Purchased 1955

T01895 Mr and Mrs Dalton and their Niece Mary de Heulle
(circa 1765-8)
Oc:908x711:Bequeathed by Alan Evans 1974

T02217 Mrs Woodhull (circa 1770)
Oc:2438x1651:Presented by Dr D.M. McDonald 1977

ZOX, Larry born 1936
Modern Collection

T01080 Orange Time (1965)
Ac:2235x2489:signed:Purchased 1968

ZUCCARELLI, Francesco 1702-1788
British Collection

T04121 A Landscape with the Story of Cadmus Killing the
Dragon (exhibited 1765)
Oc:1264x1572:Purchased 1985

ZULOAGA, Ignacio 1870-1945
Modern Collection

N01357 View of the Escorial (?circa 1905)
Oc:292x406:signed:Presented by T.W. Bacon through the
National Art Collections Fund 1923

ZYW, Aleksander born 1905
Modern Collection

T00534 Light (1957)
Oc:914x648:signed:Presented by Lady Alice Egerton
through the Friends of the Tate Gallery 1962

LOANS TO THE TATE GALLERY

ALKEN, Henry Thomas 1785-1851
British Collection

L00353 Sittingbourne with S. Rogers and West Australian with F. Butler
Oc:295x397:Lent by the Executors of Victor Morley-Lawson through the British Sporting Art Trust 1979

AUERBACH, Frank born 1931
Modern Collection
Tate Gallery Archive holds material concerning this artist

L01022 Head of E.O.W. V (1961)
Ob:610x510:Lent from a private collection 1984

BALTHUS (Balthasar Klossowski de Rola) born 1908
Modern Collection

L00642 The First Communicants (1925)
Les Premières Communiantes
Oc:565x540:signed:Lent from a private collection 1981

BLAKE, William 1757-1827
British Collection
Tate Gallery Archive holds material concerning this artist

L00866 The Penance of Jane Shore (circa 1779)
WDπ:133x184:Lent from a private collection 1983

BOMBERG, David 1890-1957
Modern Collection
Tate Gallery Archive holds material concerning this artist

L01097 'Hear O Israel' (1955)
Ob:917x712:signed:Lent by Miss Cecily Deidre Bomberg, the artist's niece 1986

BOYCE, George Price 1826-1897
British Collection
Tate Gallery Archive holds material concerning this artist

L01404 Venice: Near the Public Gardens (1854)
Wπ:190x273:Lent from a private collection 1987

BRANCUSI, Constantin 1876-1957
Modern Collection
Tate Gallery Archive holds material concerning this artist

L00624 Nude Study for a Fresco
Gπ:651x460:signed:Lent from a private collection 1981

BRAQUE, Georges 1882-1963
Modern Collection
Tate Gallery Archive holds material concerning this artist

L01457 Helios (1948)
Lπ:559x467:signed:Lent from a private collection 1974

BUTLER, Reg 1913-1981
Modern Collection
Tate Gallery Archive holds material concerning this artist

L01102 Final Maquette for 'The Unknown Political Prisoner' (1951-2)
Smzp:445x205x165:Lent by Mrs Rosemary Butler, the artist's widow 1986

COLDSTREAM, Sir William 1908-1987
Modern Collection
Tate Gallery Archive holds material concerning this artist

L01441 Standing Nude (1936)
Oc:457x356:signed:Lent by Sir Lawrence Gowing 1989

GAINSBOROUGH, Thomas 1727-1788
British Collection
Tate Gallery Archive holds material concerning this artist

L01438 Sir Henry Bate-Dudley (circa 1780)
Oc:2235x1499:Lent by Lord Burton 1989

L01439 Lady Bate-Dudley (circa 1787)
Oc:2210x1450:Lent by Lord Burton 1989

GREENHAM, Peter born 1909
Modern Collection

L01089 Lady Bonham-Carter (1978)
Oc:914x711:signed:Lent by the estate of Charlotte, Lady Bonham-Carter 1985

GRIMSHAW, Atkinson 1836-1893
British Collection

L00957 Nab Scar (1864)
Ob:406x508:Lent from a private collection 1983

GRIS, Juan 1887-1927
Modern Collection
Tate Gallery Archive holds material concerning this artist

L01118 The Bay (1921)
La Baie
Oc:686x975:signed:Lent from a private collection 1974

L01452 Bottle of Rum and Newspaper (1914)
Bouteille de rhum et journal
Oc:470x380:signed:Lent from a private collection 1974

L01453 Bowl of Fruit (1924)
Compotier
Gπ:171x216:signed:Lent from a private collection 1974

L01454 Pipe and Domino (1924)
Pipe et domino
Gπ:155x187:signed:Lent from a private collection 1974

L01455 Pierrot (1920)
Dπ:313x255:signed:Lent from a private collection 1974

L01456 Guitar and Music Book (1923)
Guitare et cahier de musique
Dπ:146x229:signed:Lent from a private collection 1974

GUTTUSO, Renato 1912-1987
Modern Collection
Tate Gallery Archive holds material concerning this artist

L01465 Sicilian Landscape (1956)
Oc:640x780:signed:Lent from a private collection 1974

L01466 Nude (1959)
Pπ:740x510:signed:Lent from a private collection 1974

HEPWORTH, Dame Barbara 1903-1975
Modern Collection
Tate Gallery Archive holds material concerning this artist

L00020 Sculpture with Profiles (1932)
Ss:224x239x139:Lent by the estate of F.L.S. Murray 1973

L00935 Ascending Form (Gloria) (1958)
Sz:1945x600x505:Lent by the Trustees of the Barbara
Hepworth Museum 1983

L00936 Spring (1966)
Sz:850x570x530:Lent by the Trustees of the Barbara
Hepworth Museum 1983

L00937 Four-Square Walk Through (1966)
Sz:4290x1990x2295:Lent by the Trustees of the Barbara
Hepworth Museum 1983

L00939 River Form (1965)
Sz:870x1930x688:Lent by the Trustees of the Barbara
Hepworth Museum 1983

L00940 Corymb (1959)
Sz:276x330x240:Lent by the Trustees of the Barbara
Hepworth Museum 1983

L00941 Shaft and Circle (1973)
Sz:1220x470x305:Lent by the Trustees of the Barbara
Hepworth Museum 1983

L00942 Single Form (1937-8)
Spw:1500x284x310:Lent by the Trustees of the Barbara
Hepworth Museum 1983

L00943 Oval Sculpture (1943)
Sp:340x410x300:Lent by the Trustees of the Barbara
Hepworth Museum 1983

L00944 Landscape Sculpture (1944)
Sw::Lent by the Trustees of the Barbara Hepworth
Museum 1983

L00945 Apollo (1951)
Sm:1735x1050x860:Lent by the Trustees of the Barbara
Hepworth Museum 1983

L00946 Image (1951-2)
Ss:1590x510x460:Lent by the Trustees of the Barbara
Hepworth Museum 1983

L00947 Stone Sculpture (Fugue II) (1956)
Ss:1350x525x415:Lent by the Trustees of the Barbara
Hepworth Museum 1983

Projects for Waterloo Bridge (L00948-L00950; complete
group)

L00948 I (1949)
Dπ:464x590:Lent by the Trustees of the Barbara
Hepworth Museum 1983

L00949 II (1949)
Dπ:464x590:Lent by the Trustees of the Barbara
Hepworth Museum 1983

L00950 III (1949)
Dπ:464x590:Lent by the Trustees of the Barbara
Hepworth Museum 1983

L00951 Seated Nude with Clasped Hands (1949)
ODπ:470x355:Lent by the Trustees of the Barbara
Hepworth Museum 1983

L00952 Reclining Figure, St Remy (1955)
Oc:650x1240:Lent by the Trustees of the Barbara
Hepworth Museum 1983

L00953 Spring (1957)
Ob:265x457:Lent by the Trustees of the Barbara
Hepworth Museum 1983

HERRING, John Frederick 1795-1865
British Collection

L00350 Mr Greville's Preserve
Oc:520x630:Lent by the Executors of Victor
Morley-Lawson through the British Sporting Art Trust
1979

attributed to
HILLIARD, Nicholas active 1547-1619
British Collection

L00128 Queen Elizabeth I (circa 1575)
Ow:787x610:Lent by the National Portrait Gallery 1965

KLEE, Paul 1879-1940
Modern Collection
Tate Gallery Archive holds material concerning this artist

L01461 Seaside Resort in the South of France (1927)
Süedfranzöesisches Seebad
Wπ:230x300:signed:Lent from a private collection 1974

L01462 The Protector (1926)
Der Beschützer
Dπ:86x220:signed:Lent from a private collection 1974

KOKOSCHKA, Oskar 1886-1980
Modern Collection
Tate Gallery Archive holds material concerning this artist

L00868 Self-Portrait (1969)
Oc:905x704:signed:Lent from a private collection 1983

L01029 Arab Women and Child (1929)
Oc:885x1280:signed:Lent from a private collection 1984

LAURENS, Henri 1885-1954
Modern Collection
Tate Gallery Archive holds material concerning this artist

L01467 Head of a Young Girl (1920)
Tête de jeune fille
Ss:390x165x110:signed:Lent from a private collection
1974

L01468 Still Life with Bottle (1917)
Nature morte - Bouteille
Wπ:377x285:signed:Lent from a private collection 1974

LE CORBUSIER (Charles-Edouard Jeanneret) 1887-1965
Modern Collection

L00752 Purist Composition (1926)
Oc:1000x805:signed:Lent from a private collection 1982

LÉGER, Fernand 1881-1955
Modern Collection
Tate Gallery Archive holds material concerning this artist

L01458 Three Bottles (1954)
Les Trois Bouteilles
Oc:330x460:signed:Lent from a private collection 1974

L01459 ABC (1927)
Gπ:192x279:signed:Lent from a private collection 1974

L01460 Mechanical Elements (1926)
Elements mécanique
Wπ:225x242:signed:Lent from a private collection 1974

LOUIS, Morris 1912-1962
Modern Collection

L00627 Beth Kuf (1958)
Ac:2324x3391:signed:Lent by Mrs Abner Brenner, the
artist's widow 1981

L00628 Phi (1960-1)
Ac:2650x3620:signed:Lent by Mrs Abner Brenner, the
artist's widow 1981

MASSON, André 1896-1987

Modern Collection
Tate Gallery Archive holds material concerning this artist

L01463 Riez (1953)
Oc:654x810:signed:Lent from a private collection 1974

L01464 Cooking (1961)
La Cuisine
Oc:505x610:signed:Lent from a private collection 1974

MESTROVIC, Ivan 1883-1962

Modern Collection
Tate Gallery Archive holds material concerning this artist

L00635 Torso of Banovic Strahinia (circa 1907-8)
Ss:1333x775x635:Lent by the Victoria & Albert Museum 1970

MILLAIS, Sir John Everett, Bt 1829-1896

British Collection
Tate Gallery Archive holds material concerning this artist

L01026 James Wyatt and his Grand-daughter (1849)
Ow:356x451:Lent from a private collection 1984

MONDRIAN, Piet 1872-1944

Modern Collection
Tate Gallery Archive holds material concerning this artist

L00097 Composition with Red and Blue (1935)
Oc:560x552:signed:Lent from a private collection 1981

MOORE, Henry, OM, CH 1898-1986

Modern Collection
Tate Gallery Archive holds material concerning this artist

L01450 Maquette for Fallen Warrior (1957)
Sz:134x155x265:Lent from a private collection 1974

L01451 Seated Nude (1954)
Dπ:552x375:signed:Lent from a private collection 1974

PALMER, Samuel 1805-1881

British Collection
Tate Gallery Archive holds material concerning this artist

L01094 Sheep Shearers (circa 1833-4)
OTw:514x711:Lent from a private collection 1985

L01095 The Golden Valley (circa 1833-4)
WGπ:127x165:Lent from a private collection 1985

PICASSO, Pablo 1881-1973

Modern Collection
Tate Gallery Archive holds material concerning this artist

L01225 The Studio (1955)
L'Atelier
Oc:803x636:signed:Lent from a private collection 1987

L01445 The Peak (Bull Fight) (1960)
La Picque (Corrida)
Wπ:480x616:signed:Lent from a private collection 1974

L01446 Faun Unveils a Woman (1936)
Faune devoilant une femme
Lπ:312x415:signed:Lent from a private collection 1974

L01447 Woman in an Armchair (The Polish Cloak) (1949)
Femme au fauteuil (Le manteau polonais)
Lπ:690x545:signed:Lent from a private collection 1974

L01448 Studio Scene (1963)
Scene d'Atelier
Lπ:419x571:signed:Lent from a private collection 1974

L01449 Woman by a Window (1952)
Femme à la fenêtre
Lπ:830x475:signed:Lent from a private collection 1974

RAEBURN, Sir Henry 1756-1823

British Collection

L00645 The Allen Brothers (circa 1800)
Oc:1525x1180:Lent from a private collection 1981

RODIN, Auguste 1840-1917

Modern Collection
Tate Gallery Archive holds material concerning this artist

L00514 The Muse (circa 1896-7)
La Muse
Sz:1460x768x571:signed:Lent by the Victoria & Albert Museum 1969

L00516 Torso (circa 1900-5)
Torse
Sz:622x362x229:signed:Lent by the Victoria & Albert Museum 1969

L00519 Large Head of Iris (1890-1, cast ?before 1913)
Grosse tête d'Iris
Sz:584x318x425:signed:Lent by the Victoria & Albert Museum 1969

SCHWITTERS, Kurt 1887-1948

Modern Collection
Tate Gallery Archive holds material concerning this artist

L01103 Peg Sculpture (circa 1945-7)
Sv:82x280x137:Lent by Mrs Edith Thomas 1986

L01104 Mother and Egg (circa 1945-7)
Sv:112x193x105:Lent by Mrs Edith Thomas 1986

L01105 Chicken and Egg (1946)
Sv:445x240x185:signed:Lent by Mrs Edith Thomas 1986

L01106 (Togetherness) (circa 1945-7)
Sv:219x75x70:Lent by Mrs Edith Thomas 1986

L01107 Painted Plaster and Wood Form (circa 1945-7)
Sv:223x160x160:Lent by Mrs Edith Thomas 1986

L01108 Stone (1945-7)
Sos:50x95x82:Lent by Mrs Edith Thomas 1986

L01109 White Miniature (1945-7)
Sv:126x109x109:Lent by Mrs Edith Thomas 1986

L01110 (The Clown) (circa 1945-7)
Sv:195x152x60:Lent by Mrs Edith Thomas 1986

L01113 Painted Stone (1945-7)
Sos:35x80x313:Lent by Mrs Edith Thomas 1986

SMITH, David 1906-1965

Modern Collection
Tate Gallery Archive holds material concerning this artist

L01023 Agricola IX (1952)
Sm:930x1450x50:signed:Lent from the collection of Candida and Rebecca Smith 1984

L01024 The Five Spring (1956)
Sm:915x375x1970:signed:Lent from the collection of Candida and Rebecca Smith 1984

L01025 Home of the Welder (1945)
Sm:533x438x356:signed:Lent from the collection of Candida and Rebecca Smith 1984

SOEST, Gerard circa 1600-1681
British Collection

L00099 Portrait of a Lady as a Shepherdess (circa 1670)
Oc:1213x997:Lent by the National Portrait Gallery 1958

L00131 Double Portrait (circa 1645-8)
Oc:1391x1746:Lent by the National Portrait Gallery 1976

SPENCER, Sir Stanley 1891-1959
Modern Collection
Tate Gallery Archive holds material concerning this artist

L00629 Portrait of Hilda (1931)
Dπ:788x628:signed:Lent by Mrs Richard Carline, the
artist's sister-in-law 1984

STUBBS, George 1724-1806
British Collection

L00100 A Horse Frightened by a Lion (?exhibited 1763)
Oc:705x1038:Lent from a private collection 1973

SUTHERLAND, Graham, OM 1903-1980
Modern Collection
Tate Gallery Archive holds material concerning this artist

L01140 Portrait of Sir Charles Clore (1965-75)
Oc:1080x940:Lent by Sears plc 1987

THOMSON, Henry 1773-1843
British Collection

L00077 The Raising of Jairus' Daughter (exhibited 1820)
Oc:2388x2997:signed:Lent by the Friends of the Tate
Gallery

WRIGHT, Joseph, of Derby 1734-1797
British Collection

L01407 Richard Cheslyn (1777)
Oc:1270x1016:Lent from a private collection 1987

after
ZOFFANY, Johan 1733-1810
British Collection

L00681 Portrait of Mrs Woodhull, engraved by R. Houston
(published 1772)
Lπ:343x241:Lent by the Witt Library 1982

WORKS OF ART FORMING PART OF THE FABRIC OF THE TATE GALLERY'S MILLBANK BUILDING

ANREP, Boris 1883-1969
Modern Collection

Blake's Proverbs
Mosaic pavement

BOSSANYI, Ervin 1891-1975
Modern Collection

The Angel Blesses the Women Washing Clothes
Stained glass window

WHISTLER, Rex 1905-1944
Modern Collection
Tate Gallery Archive holds material concerning this artist

The Expedition in Pursuit of Rare Meats (1926-7)
Restaurant mural

MIXED GROUPS: CONTRIBUTING ARTISTS

Approval Stamp Offer
GREAVES, Derrick
PHILLIPS, Tom
PINKNEY, Richard
TYSON, Ian

Centennial Suite
BATES, Maxwell
BAXTER, Iain
BINNING, Bertram
BREEZE, Claude
CAPEL-DORAY, Audrey
FISHER, Brian
KORNER, John
MORRIS, Michael
ONLEY, Toni
SHADBOLT, Jack
SMITH, Gordon
SMITH, Joel
TANABE, Takao

Europaeische Graphik VII
GREAVES, Derrick
HOCKNEY, David
HODGKIN, Howard
JONES, Allen
JONES, Stanley
SCHMIDT, Peter

Follies
BAWDEN, Richard
BEER, Richard
JONES, Barbara
ROSOMAN, Leonard
THIRSK, John

For John Constable
ABRAHAMS, Ivor
BLAKE, Peter
BRANDT, Bill
CAULFIELD, Patrick
DENNY, Robyn
FLANAGAN, Barry
GRANT, Duncan
GROSS, Anthony
HITCHENS, Ivon
HOCKNEY, David
HODGKIN, Howard
HOLLWEG, Alexander
HOYLAND, John
MILLINGTON, Terence
SANDLE, Michael
SMITH, Richard
STEVENS, Norman
TILLYER, William

For Jorn
ALECHINSKY, Pierre
APPEL, Karel
BAJ, Enrico

CONSTANT (Constant A. Nieuwenhuys)
CORNEILLE, Guillaume
DOTREMONT, Christian
LAM, Wifredo
MATTA (Roberto Matta Echaurren)
MICHAUX, Henri
SAURA, Antonio
TING, Walasse
VELDE, Bram van
WEMAERE, Pierre
WYCKAERT, Maurice

Homage to Albert Dumouchel
AYOT, Pierre
BEAMENT, Tib
BOISVERT, Gilles
CAISERMAN-ROTH, Ghitta
CHARBONNEAU, Monique
DAGLISH, Peter
FRENKEL, Vera
LANGLOIS, Denis
MONTPETIT, Guy
PICHET, Roland
TOUSIGNANT, Serge
TREMBLAY, Gerard
WOLFE, Robert

IAA Portfolio
ADAMS, Robert
BLOW, Sandra
DANIELS, Harvey
FROST, Terry
HERMES, Gertrude
HOUSE, Gordon
HUGHES-STANTON, Blair
KESTLEMAN, Morris
MEDLEY, Robert
ROTHENSTEIN, Michael

Jam Press Phase One
BIRD, John
BLAKE, John
DOWNSBROUGH, Peter
GALLERY, LONDON, The (GRYLLS, Vaughan and WEGNER, Nicholas)
GRAYSON, Roy
HERRING, Ed
MURPHY, John
PARK, Alistair
STEZAKER, John
WENTWORTH, Richard

Penwith Portfolio
ADAMS, Robert
DAVIE, Alan
EVANS, Merlyn O.
GRANT, Duncan
HEPWORTH, Dame Barbara
LANYON, Peter

LEACH, Bernard
MOORE, Henry, OM, CH
McWILLIAM, F.E.
NICHOLSON, Ben, OM
ROTHENSTEIN, Michael

Picturesque Views on the Southern Coast of England

after ALEXANDER, William
after BLORE, Edward
after CLENNELL, Luke
after COLLINS, William
after CRISTALL, Joshua
after DE WINT, Peter
after EDRIDGE, Henry
after FRANCIA, François Louis Thomas
after HAKEWILL, James
after HAVELL, William
after OWEN, Samuel
after PROUT, Samuel
after TURNER, Joseph Mallord William
after WESTALL, William

School Prints

BRAQUE, Georges
CARR, Thomas
COOPER, Gerald
COUDERC, G.
DEHN, Adolf
DUFY, Raoul
FEIBUSCH, Hans
GENTLEMAN, Tom
GINGER, Phyllis
HUTTON, Clarke
JONES, Barbara
KELLY, Felix
LA DELL, Edwin
LOWRY, L.S.
LÉGER, Fernand
MATISSE, Henri
MOORE, Henry, OM, CH
MOZELEY, Charles
NASH, John
PICASSO, Pablo
REEVE, Russell
ROTHENSTEIN, Michael
ROWNTREE, Kenneth
SKEAPING, John
TISDALL, Hans
TOPOLSKI, Feliks
TREVELYAN, Julian
TUNNARD, John
ULREICH, Buk

Tetrad Pamphlets Vol. I Nos. I-X

GREAVES, Derrick
PHILLIPS, Tom
PINKNEY, Richard
TYSON, Ian

The Institute of Contemporary Arts Portfolio

AYRES, Gillian
BLAKE, Peter
BOSHIER, Derek
CAULFIELD, Patrick
COHEN, Bernard
COHEN, Harold
DENNY, Robyn
HAMILTON, Richard
HEATH, Adrian
HOCKNEY, David
HODGKIN, Howard
HOUSE, Gordon
HUGHES, Patrick
IRWIN, Gwyther
JONES, Allen
KITAJ, R.B.
MUNDY, Henry
PAOLOZZI, Sir Eduardo
PHILLIPS, Peter
SMITH, Richard
TILSON, Joe
TURNBULL, William

Artists contibuting to a mixed 'supergroup'

The Great War: Britain's Efforts and Ideas

BONE, Sir Muirhead
CLAUSEN, Sir George
BRANGWYN, Sir Frank
KENNINGTON, Eric
PEARS, Charles
HARTRICK, Archibald Standish

CONCORDANCE OF FORMER NATIONAL GALLERY NUMBERS TO TATE GALLERY NUMBERS

ARDIZZONE, Edward
5085   A01029-A01033

AUERBACH, Frank
451   A01034-A01037

BEERBOHM, Sir Max
5391   A01038-A01060

BLAKE, Robert
3694   A00001-A00004

BLAKE, William
3371   A00005-A00011
3372   A00012-A00032
3694   A00033-A00050
3866   A00111-A00127

BRITISH SCHOOL
2234   A00051-A00056

BURNE-JONES, Sir Edward Coley, Bt
3143   A00057-A00058
3144   A00059-A00060
3146   A00061-A00062
3147   A00063-A00064
3148   A00065-A00067
3985   A00068-A00069
4112   A00070-A00071
4338   A00072-A00073
4339   A00074-A00077
4341   A00078-A00079
4345   A00080-A00082
4346   A00083-A00089
4347   A00090-A00096
4348   A00097-A00104
4349A   A00105-A00106
4351   A00107-A00110, A01160
4352   A01161-A01162
4353   A01163-A01164
4354   A00128, A01165-A01176
4355   A00129-A00130

BUTLER, Reg
103   A01061-A01063

CALLOW, William
2886   A00131-A00156

CALVERT, Edward
2885   A00157-A00167

CLARKE HALL, Lady Edna
5425   A01064-A01073

COX, David
4309   A00168-A00176
4314   A00177-A00189

GAINSBOROUGH, Thomas
2722A   A00190

GRECO, Emilio
381   A01074-A01079
382   A01080-A01081

GRANT, Duncan
T1744   A01111

HAYDON, Benjamin Robert
2445   A00191-A00192

HILLS, Robert
4324   A00193-A00196

HOUGHTON, Arthur Boyd
3615   A00197-A00200
4126   A00201-A00210

HUGHES, Arthur
4147   A00211-A00213

HUNT, William Henry
4315   A00217-A00218

JACOVLEFF, Alexandre
4994   A01082-A01088

JONES, Thomas
5996   A00219-A00701

LANDSEER, Sir Edwin Henry
410   A00702-A00703

LEGROS, Alphonse
2899   A00704-A00729

LEIGHTON, Frederic, Lord
4012   A00730-A00738

LESLIE, Charles Robert
1794   A00739-A00741

LINNELL, John
3867   A00742-A00791

MILLAIS, Sir John Everett, Bt
4011   A00792-A00811
5902   A00812-A00814

MORRIS, William
4287   A00815-A00818

attributed to MORRIS, William
5220   A00819-A00820

MÜLLER, William James
2373   A00821-A00824

POTTER, Helen Beatrix
5746   A01089-A01110

POYNTER, Sir Edward
3950   A00825-A00836

REYNOLDS, Sir Joshua
78A   A00837

RICHMOND, George
3694   A00838

ROOKE, Thomas Mathews
1624   A00839-A00841

ROSSETTI, Dante Gabriel
3965   A00842-A00844
4286   A00845-A00846

SANDYS, Frederick
4291   A00847-A00849

SARGENT, John Singer
5913   A00850-A00851

SMIRKE, Robert
761   A00852-A00863

SMITH, Sydney Robert James
1742   A00864-A00865

STEPHENS, Frederic George
2012A   A00866

STOTHARD, Thomas
2232   A00867-A00878

TOWNROE, Reuben
2851   A00879-A00908

TURNER, Joseph Mallord William
561   A00909
561A   A00910
2941   A01112-A01159
4094   A00911-A01015

WEBB, Philip
4288   A01016-A01017
4340   A01018-A01019

WILKIE, Sir David
1741   A01020-A01025

WITHERINGTON, William Frederick
1873   A01026-A01028

SOURCES OF REFERENCE FOR THE COLLECTION

All works acquired since April 1953 are fully catalogued in *The Tate Gallery Reports*, published annually until 1968 and then biennially. Since 1974-6, the *Illustrated Catalogue of Acquisitions* has been published as a separate volume.

In 1981, the Tate Gallery and Sotheby's published the extensive *Catalogue of The Tate Gallery's Collection of Modern Art, other than works by British Artists* written by Ronald Alley. This volume lists all unique works of art by non-British artists acquired up to November 1978.

Now out of print, but available in many libraries, is *Modern British Paintings, Drawings and Sculpture*, a two-volume work published in 1964 written by Mary Chamot, Dennis Farr and Martin Butlin. The volumes catalogue all work by British artists born in or after 1850 acquired by the Tate Gallery before 1963.

A separate volume, published in 1980, the *Catalogue of the Print Collection*, lists in concise form all the holdings of the Gallery's Print Collection up to March 1980. After 1980, all prints acquired by the Gallery are published in the consecutive Reports and Illustrated Catalogues.

There are no general catalogues relating to the British Collection, although a multi-volume series cataloguing the entire British School is now in preparation. The first, *The Age of Hogarth*, devoted to Hogarth and his contemporaries, was published in 1988, the second, *William Blake*, in 1990.

Works in the Tate Gallery by J.M.W. Turner and John Constable have been fully catalogued in *The Paintings of J.M.W. Turner*, by Martin Butlin and Evelyn Joll, 1977, and *The Tate Gallery Constable Collection*, by Leslie Parris, 1981. Two facsimiles of Turner sketchbooks have been published by the Tate Gallery, as part of a series of publications of the sketchbooks, *The 'Ideas of Folkestone' Sketchbook* by David Blayney Brown, 1987; and *The 'Wilson' Sketchbook* by Andrew Wilton, 1988. Cataloguing is in progress on the Turner works on paper from the Turner Bequest transferred from the British Museum in 1987, and a complete concise catalogue for these will be published in due course.

The Gallery has also published numerous catalogues for exhibitions and displays which may be useful to researchers. Further information is available from the Tate Gallery Library.

BORROWING FROM THE COLLECTION - CONDITIONS FOR LOAN

1. LOANS POLICY

The Tate Gallery lends several hundred works each year to temporary exhibitions both domestic and abroad. All loans are administered through the Tate Gallery, London, including any works currently on display at the Tate Gallery Liverpool. To enable the Gallery to operate a consistent loans policy, the Trustees have decided that loans from the Gallery should normally be limited to three general categories:

a) important one-person exhibitions,

b) exhibitions devoted to a particular movement or school that will make a contribution to art-historical knowledge,

c) exhibitions introducing a school or period to a new audience.

Organisers should make a full case for the importance and relevance of the exhibition and why the requested works are wanted. The loan of works required primarily as illustrations will not normally be considered. Occasionally, the Trustees will approve loans to exhibitions which do not fall into the three categories, but this is only if the Gallery can accommodate the additional work involved.

Works in fragile, poor, or unstable condition making them unsuitable for display or transport will not be lent.

Some works of art are permanently on display in the Gallery and are of such importance that the public expect to see them when they visit. Such works will not normally be available for loan.

The display of works of art at the Tate Gallery in London and Liverpool, and the Barbara Hepworth Museum, St Ives, will be given higher priority than the loan of works.

1.1 TOURING EXHIBITIONS

Only in exceptional circumstances will works of art be loaned for touring exhibitions consisting of more than three venues: it has been the Gallery's experience that extensive tours increases the incidence of damage and deterioration.

1.2 LONG LOANS

To enable the Gallery to concentrate upon loans for exhibitions, the Trustees have decided that long loans from the Collections will be strictly limited. They will be considered for regional museums only where there is a clear purpose or context for the loan of a particular work, or for public buildings with a strongly justifiable case for a particular work.

2. INITIAL PROCEDURE

Initial requests for loan should be made in writing to the Director of the Gallery (see item 6 below for addresses) at least six months before the work is required. Requests are considered at regular meetings, and recommendations are made to the Trustees of the Tate Gallery, for their approval. The Trustees meet six times a year (normally January, March, May, July, September and November).

ALL LOANS FROM THE GALLERY ARE AGREED SUBJECT TO THE FOLLOWING CONDITIONS

3. CONDITIONS GOVERNING THE LOAN OF WORKS OF ART FROM THE COLLECTIONS

3.1 NOTICE

Requests must be submitted at least six months before the exhibition opens. This is to allow sufficient time for the request to be fully considered by the Trustees, any necessary conservation treatment and preparation to be carried out, security and environmental checks at the loan venue made, as well as accommodating other loan commitments and the Gallery's own needs. Only in exceptional circumstances will the Trustees consider any loan request which does not allow enough time for the processing and preparation of the works of art.

3.2 COSTS

The Gallery does not normally charge for loans from the Permanent Collections, or for staff time spent on loans administration. It does, however, expect borrowers to pay for the following: insurance; additional materials required for preparing works for loan (for example, acrylic glazing); frames for unframed items and bases for sculpture; the provision of packing cases; all transport costs, including the expenses of couriers from the Tate Gallery; photographs and colour transparencies supplied by the Tate Gallery Publications Department. Borrowers will also be charged if installation by Tate technical staff has been made a condition of loan and they are required to work beyond their normal working hours at the loan venue. The Gallery will always endeavour to inform borrowers of any additional costs as early as possible.

3.3 SECURITY

The Gallery submits details of all loans to the National Museums Security Adviser, based at the Museums and Galleries Commission in London. Loan will only proceed if the Adviser is able to approve the security and fire prevention arrangements at the loan venue. If the existing arrangements are not sufficient, recommendations to improve them will normally be made.

Twenty-four hour invigilation is normally required, although intruder-detector alarm systems for use during closed hours may be considered acceptable under certain circumstances.

Confidentiality about security arrangements is maintained by both the National Museums Security Adviser and the Gallery.

3.4 INSURANCE

All works lent by the Tate Gallery must be insured against 'all risks' and 'nail-to-nail'. In the case of a touring exhibition, a single policy must usually cover all journeys and exhibition venues.

A copy of the insurance certificate must be deposited with the Gallery at least two weeks before the works are to be collected. Works from the Collection cannot be released without proof of adequate insurance cover.

DOMESTIC LOANS

The Gallery will accept cover provided by commercial insurance companies in the form of a copy of their certificate, or a letter addressed directly to the Gallery from their brokers, or, in the case of local authorities, letters of confirmation from the City Treasurer. In both instances, cover must be against 'all risks' and 'nail-to-nail', the Gallery and the works of art with their agreed valuations, must be named.

INTERNATIONAL LOANS

The Gallery will accept indemnities offered by the government of the borrowing institution, provided that details of the indemnity are lodged with the Gallery well in advance of the release of the works, for approval.

Where an indemnity is not available, commercial cover will be taken out by the Gallery, at the borrower's expense, with a London based broker nominated by the Tate Gallery. The Trustees do not accept international commercial insurance cover.

GOVERNMENT INDEMNITY

The Tate Gallery is empowered to grant an indemnity on behalf of the Office of Arts and Libraries to those institutions which qualify under the Government Indemnity Scheme, as set out in the 1980 National Heritage Act. Applications for government indemnity should be made to the Registrar, the Tate Gallery.

3.5 VALUATIONS

Valuations for loaned works will be supplied by the Tate Gallery prior to loan. The Gallery reserves the right to increase the value of any work at any time, to take into account changes in the market value of works of art.

3.6 CANCELLATION OF LOAN

The Gallery recognises that a loan may be cancelled for valid reasons, but reserves the right to charge the borrower for any conservation or other costs which may have been incurred.

3.7 REPRODUCTION AND PHOTOGRAPHY

The borrower may reproduce official Tate Gallery photographs and/or colour transparencies of loaned works only in exhibition catalogues and publicity related to the exhibition. The credit line designated by the Tate Gallery must be used.

Permission for the reproduction of images from the Collections can be obtained from the Copyright Controller, Tate Gallery Publications Department. A fee is normally charged for this service. Queries relating to reproduction rights, fees, photographs, transparencies and slides should be made directly to the Copyright Controller (Appendix 2).

Works of art on loan from the Tate Gallery may not be filmed, photographed, video recorded or televised without the prior permission of the Tate Gallery. Requests should be made to the Registrar. Where permission is granted, the Tate Gallery Filming and Photography Regulations must be adhered to and the operation supervised by a member of the Tate Gallery staff (at the borrower's expense) or agreed appointee.

3.8 PACKING

DOMESTIC LOANS

All works of art leaving the Tate Gallery for loan will be prepared by Tate staff prior to departure. For most domestic loans, paintings will be fitted with a transit frame or cornered and wrapped, but a packing case may be required for loans to touring exhibitions, or for works particularly vulnerable to changes in environmental conditions (e.g. panels). Any journey requiring overnight travel, sea or air journeys will require a packing case. All cases will be commissioned by the Gallery and built to Tate Gallery specifications, at the borrower's expense.

Sculptures are normally packed in special crates provided by the Gallery, although occasionally a packing case may have to be especially constructed, at the borrower's expense.

INTERNATIONAL LOANS

A packing case will always be required for international loans, and the Gallery will arrange for construction of a case to its own specifications, at the borrowing institution's expense. The initial packing and preparation of the work will be carried out by Tate Gallery staff.

Packing cases and materials must be stored by the borrowing institution in good conditions to prevent deterioration.

3.9 COLLECTION

At least three weeks' notice must be given of the intended date for collection, to allow sufficient time for the preparation of the work of art and for the approval of the transport arrangements.

3.10 TRANSPORT ARRANGEMENTS

Transport arrangements must be approved by the Tate Gallery before any work of art will be released for loan. Transportation must be carried out by accredited agents. If new or unknown companies are proposed, they will be investigated before endorsed. The Tate Gallery reserves the right to veto any companies which do not comply with its conditions for the transportation of works of art.

3.11 COURIERS

For loans of works which present particular problems in terms of their condition or handling, or are of very high value, the Gallery may wish to send a courier. Couriers are responsible for the supervision of all handling and may also be required to supervise the installation of Tate Gallery works. The courier is the official representative of the Gallery and has the authority to withdraw items from display where the stipulated requirements have not been met, whether for reasons of security or conservation. All travel expenses, as defined by the Tate Gallery, and associated costs incurred by the courier are the responsibility of the borrowing institution.

3.12 CUSTOMS

Customs formalities are the responsibility of the borrower; loaned works must not be unpacked for customs inspection en route. Customs inspections must take place either at the borrowing institution or at the Tate Gallery (or both). In the event of a work being unpacked by Customs whilst in transit, the Tate Gallery must be informed **immediately**.

3.13 RETURNING WORKS OF ART

The borrowing institution should contact the Tate Gallery at least one week before the close of the loan exhibition to discuss the arrangements for the return of loaned works.

A loaned work should be repacked in the custom-made packing case in which it travelled, using the original packing materials and methods. Works which travelled uncased, should be wrapped by a method similar to that used for the original journey.

The return shipment will be by the same method and carrier as the outward journey, unless the Gallery specifies otherwise. Any changes must be agreed between the Tate Gallery and the borrowing institution.

3.14 ENVIRONMENTAL CONDITIONS

All works of art require particular conditions for display, and the Gallery's Collections include many objects with complex or unusual display and/or environmental requirements. Every prospective borrowing institution is required to complete a Tate Gallery Facilities Report, which asks for information about existing facilities at the loan venue. In the case of a touring exhibition all venues will be asked to complete a Facilities Report.

All prospective borrowers are expected to be equipped to continuously record temperature and relative humidity for each separate exhibition space, and should also possess an illuminance meter. Full records of the temperature, relative humidity and illuminance during the relevant period of previous years will be required.

The borrower will be notified of any specific conditions for individual works of art, and will be required to submit to the Tate Gallery details of how it is proposed to meet these requirements **before** loan may proceed.

The Tate Gallery reserves the right to install automatic monitoring equipment in the display space where Tate works are being displayed and to receive copies of environmental records at the end of the loan period.

Air conditioning systems should be in operation 24 hours a day and should not be turned off until the works concerned have left the conditioned area - even if the works have been cased.

STANDARD ENVIRONMENTAL REQUIREMENTS
The following notes are provided as a guide to the standard environmental requirements for certain classes of works of art. Sometimes more stringent requirements may have to be imposed but very often the Gallery is prepared to accept lesser standards of environmental control, especially when the borrowing institution can demonstrate by submitted records that its environmental conditions are known.

(i) LIGHTING

Daylight
Daylight may be used for the illumination of most classes of works of art in the Gallery's Collection, provided that it is controlled by curtains, blinds or other sunscreens so that the average illuminance is no more than 200 lux per hour of public display. Curtains or blinds should be closed when the exhibition is closed to the public. Direct sunlight must always be excluded from the display zone and preferably from the exhibition rooms as a whole (because of the adverse effect on room temperature and humidity). The more vulnerable classes of object, such as works on paper, photographs and unprotected textiles (such as unprimed canvas) are best displayed under artificial light at no more than 50 lux (see below): daylight should be excluded.

Artificial light
When works of art are artificially lit an illuminance of no more than 200 lux is allowed. Watercolours, drawings, prints, photographs and all other works on paper, exposed canvas, or other materials particularly vulnerable to damage by light may only be illuminated at 50 lux. For all categories, a maximum illuminance of no more than 10 lux is allowed during closed periods, except for short periods for cleaning and similar routine activities.

Photographic, film and TV lighting

The Tate Gallery does not allow loans to be photographed, filmed or televised. The Tate Gallery's works of art must be protected from the intense lights used for these purposes when other neighbouring works of art in the exhibition are photographed or filmed.

Ultra violet light

UV radiation is a damaging and unnecessary component of daylight and of light from fluorescent and other discharge lamps. Filters should be used to reduce it to the following standard: the component of the radiation of wavelength shorter than 400 nanometres (i.e. ultraviolet radiation) must be less than 75 microwatts per lumen of total visible radiation.

(ii) CLIMATE

Temperature control

A maximum temperature of 25 degrees Celsius is permitted. Temperature should not vary by more than four degrees Celsius in any twenty-four hour period.

Relative humidity

Relative humidity is to be maintained between 45% and 65%. It should not vary by more than 10% in any 24 hour period or by more than 15% during the course of the loan.

Atmospheric pollution

Works of art should not be exposed to concentrations of sulphur dioxide in excess of ten micrograms per cubic metre, of nitrogen oxides in excess of ten micrograms per cubic metre, or ozone in excess of two micrograms per cubic metre. In areas of heavy pollution, active measures must be taken to exclude or reduce levels of gaseous pollution. A high standard of dust filtration is required when a mechanical ventilation system is employed.

General

Works of art must never be placed in close proximity to sources of heat, cold or strong air-currents (radiators, fireplaces, dehumidifiers, air-conditioning outlets or intakes).

3.15 DISPLAY

Normally all pictures on loan from the Tate Gallery will be glazed with perspex, prior to leaving the Gallery. Occasionally, a work will remain fitted with glass, or if there is no provision for glazing, will travel unglazed. Works must not be unglazed or removed from their display frames **under any circumstances** without prior consultation and permission from the Director of the Tate Gallery.

Framed works of art must be securely fastened to the wall, using mirrorplates and security screws. Small objects should be displayed in locked showcases or, under fixed glass or acrylic covers, as specified by the Gallery. Larger sculptures may require plinths and barriers. Unglazed paintings must also be displayed behind a barrier. Works which are difficult to install or particularly fragile may have to be installed by Tate Gallery staff as a condition of loan, at the borrower's expense.

In the case of heavy, large, awkward objects, or works demanding special handling requirements, the Gallery will require information about handling equipment, floor loadings, access routes and their dimensions and availability of trained staff.

3.16 CARE AND TREATMENT OF WORKS OF ART

Except for packing and installation, works of art may not be handled. Works should only be handled by trained gallery/museum staff and recognised fine art packers and shippers.

Unframed works or paintings with decorative and vulnerable frames may be fitted into a transit frame before departure from the Gallery. They should not be removed from the transit frame, other than for installation.

Works may not be unframed or have their backboards or glazing removed without permission from the Tate Gallery.

Works of art may not be subjected to any form of scientific examination, neither may any conservation treatment be undertaken nor any alteration to the glazing or framing be made without permission from the Registrar, Tate Gallery.

3.17 CREDIT

Loans from the Tate Gallery must be credited 'Tate Gallery' followed by the mode and date of acquisition (details will be provided by the Gallery).

3.18 GENERAL

The Trustees of the Tate Gallery reserve the right to withdraw or cancel a loan at any time.

In the event of any dispute in any translation of these Loan Regulations, the English text must be final.

4. REPORTING DAMAGE OR LOSS OF LOANED WORK

In the event of a work of art being lost or damaged, the borrower must inform the Tate Gallery **immediately** after the accident has occurred or as soon as the loss is noticed.

5. ADDRESSES AND TELEPHONE NUMBERS

5.1 REQUESTS

All loan requests should be addressed to the Director in the first instance:

Nicholas Serota
Director
Tate Gallery
Millbank
LONDON
SW1P 4RG
England

5.2 ADMINISTRATION

Subsequent correspondence should be addressed to the member of the Registrars Department administering the loan, or:

The Registrar
Tate Gallery
Millbank
LONDON
SW1P 4RG
England

5.3 PHOTOGRAPHIC MATERIAL AND COPYRIGHT

All queries relating to copyright, reproduction rights, fees, photographs, transparencies and slides:

The Copyright Controller
Tate Gallery Publications
Tate Gallery
Millbank
LONDON
SW1P 4RG
England

5.4 TELEPHONE, FACSIMILE AND TELEX NUMBERS

Tate Gallery: (44) 071-821 1313

Tate Gallery Publications: (44) 071-834 5651/2

Tate Gallery facsimile:
for Director: (44) 071-931 7512
for Registrar: (44) 071-821 9329
general: (44) 071-931 0440

Tate Gallery telex: 944010 TATGAL G